A TEXTBOOK OF
GENERAL PHYSIOLOGY

A TEXTBOOK

OF

GENERAL PHYSIOLOGY

by

HUGH DAVSON, D.Sc. (Lond.)

Scientific Staff, Medical Research Council;
Honorary Research Associate, University College, London

WITH 288 ILLUSTRATIONS

LONDON
J. & A. CHURCHILL LTD.
104 GLOUCESTER PLACE, W.1
1951

To

Sir Charles Lovatt Evans, F.R.S.
Emeritus Professor of Physiology in the University of London

Printed in Great Britain

PREFACE

In the 'twenties of this century, two great textbooks, both published from University College London, occupied a prominent position in the physiological literature, and graced the shelves of most teachers and students of physiology ; I need hardly say that their titles were *Principles of Human Physiology* and *Principles of General Physiology* by Starling and Bayliss respectively. To-day, Starling's *Physiology* still occupies its dignified station, thanks to the labours of Lovatt Evans. Bayliss' *General Physiology* has had a less fortunate history ;[1] in 1924 a revised edition was brought out by a group of Bayliss's colleagues, but since then it has remained out of print and become progressively out of date. In speculating on possible causes for the different fates of these books, it has occurred to me that a factor is the growing tendency to drop the distinction between mammalian or human physiology, on the one hand, and general physiology, on the other. Claude Bernard, who first introduced the term, described " general physiology " as " the study of phenomena common to animals and plants," whilst Bayliss, in the introduction to his *Principles*, adopted the definition of his teacher, Burdon-Sanderson, namely, " the study of the endowments of living material " ; and, although this definition is so wide as to include all biological research within its compass, in practice it has meant, so far as I have gathered from the scope of his *Principles*, the study of those aspects of living material that show some immediate prospect of being described in terms of the known laws of physics and chemistry.

The behaviour of living matter in its highest development, namely in mammals, is so complex that the general physiologist has usually turned to other forms for study, leaving the elucidation of those phenomena depending on the *organisation* of living material—rather than its " endowments "—to others, who have therefore been commonly described as " mammalian physiologists," since these organisational, or integrative, characteristics have been most commonly studied in this class. Nevertheless, the distinction between the two types of physiologist is not based on a difference of experimental material ; the difference between them is essentially one of attitude. The general physiologist, because he has had a thorough training in mathematics, physics, or chemistry, seeks to provide explanations in terms of concepts already familiar to him ; consequently, if nervous activity interests him, he will be concerned in interpreting the origin of the resting and action potentials, and the special problems involved in synaptic transmission ; in his search for suitable material he may range widely over the animal and vegetable kingdoms ; and it has frequently happened, as the following pages will testify, that the most revealing experimental material has been from cold-blooded and invertebrate sources. The mammalian physiologist, with a primarily biological training, will accept the action potential at its face value and utilise the power of recording it to elucidate the more complex aspects of animal behaviour ; he, also, should be liberal in his choice of experimental material, and the wide use of the mammal has been occasioned more by the accident of its

---

[1] That is, up to the moment of writing (June, 1951); my colleague, Dr. L. E. Bayliss, tells me that he is busy preparing a new edition of his father's book—a courageous enterprise, in the execution of which all general physiologists will wish him God speed.

close relationship to man, and the desire of so many physiologists to relate their work to human pathology, than by its greater value as an experimental object.

With the progress of the science, the fields of the general and mammalian physiologists have tended to overlap, and nowhere is this better illustrated than in the study of synaptic function, so that in many instances it would be hard and profitless to distinguish the contributors to this branch of the physiological literature in terms of their attitude to the problem. In this field, therefore, the mammalian physiologist, by simplifying his concepts, and the general physiologist, by extending the application of physico-chemical principles, have met on common ground ; and ultimately it is the hope of all physiologists that such a state of affairs will pertain over the whole field of biological research.

A rigid segregation of general and mammalian physiologists, whereby they tended to work in different departments and to belong to different learned societies, would be a harmful development ; and it might, therefore, be considered that the publication of a new textbook of general physiology would be a retrograde step, emphasising as it does the existence of a distinction which must eventually, with the growth of the science, vanish. This would be a just consideration, if it were not for a very important point, namely that, in Britain, the teaching of physiology, and to a very large extent the research work, are becoming progressively restricted to the field covered by the mammalian physiologist. So long as the learning of anatomy occupies the lion's share of the medical student's time, it is only reasonable that the teaching of physiology to these students be confined to those aspects that have a fairly immediate bearing on medicine, and that general physiology, with its more remote usefulness and greater difficulty in understanding, should be squeezed out of the curricula. As a result of this tendency, a number of fields of physiological research are slipping beyond the ken of the mammalian physiologist, and the very meaning of the word " physiology," as currently used in this country, is contracting rather than expanding.

In the present book, therefore, I have attempted to gather together the results of modern research carried out by workers with the viewpoint of the general physiologist, namely that of the investigator who attempts to explain living phenomena in terms of concepts familiar in the basic sciences of physics and chemistry. Regarding the distinction between the two forms of physiology as one of outlook rather than of subject for investigation, I have roamed a wide field and have necessarily covered a great deal of ground regularly trodden by the mammalian physiologist ; in these regions of overlap the more detailed treatment provided in this book may amplify, and make more intelligible, the sometimes scanty treatments of the same subjects afforded by the ordinary physiological texts.

This, then, is my justification to potential readers in this country for writing a new textbook of general physiology. In the United States of America, the flourishing of the *Journal of General Physiology* alongside the *American Journal of Physiology*, the existence in some of the large universities of chairs of both mammalian and general physiology, and the currency of several textbooks of general physiology, relieve me of the duty of apologising for writing this book ; furthermore, the fact that it is an intruder, competing with others of established worth, needs no special apology or justification in a field where viewpoints change rapidly, and where the selection of material gives such scope for individuality.

In writing this book I have been guided by the requirements of several types of reader. First, there is the degree student in physiology and related subjects—zoology, botany, etc.—for whom the ordinary textbooks of physiology are generally inadequate ; such a student requires, besides a lucid explanation of a given subject, references to the literature that will permit him to dig deeper ; generally, references to monographs and review articles are sufficient for his purpose. Secondly, there is the medical student who is genuinely fond of physiology, and who is willing to absorb rather more than the quantum considered necessary for a medical education. Such a student would be well advised not to attempt a systematic reading, but to browse and to skip with agility when the going becomes heavy. With some diffidence, I have considered the research worker in physiology and related fields ; generally, for the specific purposes of his research, a textbook, however well documented, is unnecessary to the experienced research worker. To the beginner, on the other hand, still uncertain as to the real direction in which his interests lie, I feel that a textbook of this character can be of real value, and to that end I have made every effort, consistent with the difficulties of publishing in this country, to make my accounts up-to-date, and to document them with reasonable care. At the same time I have desired to avoid prolixity, and the overburdening of the text with names and dates, that are the necessary corollaries of exhaustiveness ; prolixity has been partly avoided by the generous use of footnotes, whilst the text has been relieved of dates by the simple expedient of quoting the titles of the published papers and monographs in the bibliographies. Since, with few exceptions, I have only quoted the papers that I have read, the number of references at the end of any chapter is not so large as to make it inconvenient, where necessary, to read through them in search of the required title. The progress of physiology depends on the recruitment of adequate numbers of research workers who have already qualified in one of the more exact sciences ; bearing these in mind, too, I have been at pains to make the matter intelligible to readers without a biological training. Finally, there is the mammalian physiologist who wishes to understand what his general physiologist colleagues are doing, both for his own interest and for the purposes of teaching. To such a reader I can offer this book with some confidence that it will be useful, however much it may fall short of its great predecessor in this country, Bayliss's *Principles*. One serious defect, which will be evident at a glance, is the restricted scope of the book ; this, however, is a failing occasioned by the necessity to keep its size within bounds imposed by the extraordinary increase in publishing costs since the war. In spite of the generous allowance of space that Messrs. Churchill have made me, chapters on electrical activity in smooth muscle, on the aqueous humour and synovial fluid, and on phototropic phenomena, which I had already written, had to be removed before going to press, and a chapter on the comparative physiology of respiration and circulation died at conception.

Most, if not all, textbooks of general physiology begin with a synopsis of the principles of physical chemistry which may be as long as the part devoted to physiology. It has always seemed to me that this is a wrong procedure, for several reasons which I need not detail ; and in writing the present book I have assumed that the reader has some knowledge of the principles of physics and chemistry, so that I have only introduced simple accounts of the more advanced aspects in the contexts to which they are appropriate.

In writing a textbook covering a wide field, a modern author must necessarily expound matters with which he, himself, has had no first-hand experience ; in doing so, he is in continual danger of committing solecisms occasioned by his ignorance or defective comprehension ; this book doubtless contains many such errors, but far fewer than would have been the case had I not been fortunate enough to have three such critical proof-readers as my colleagues Dr. R. D. Harkness, Dr. E. J. Harris, and Dr. Bernhard Katz ; I am sincerely grateful to them for the conscientious manner in which they carried out what must have been a tiresome—but not a thankless—task.

When its need has to be proved by experience, the production of a new book is an uncertain venture for a publisher, and I must therefore take this opportunity of thanking Mr. J. Rivers, the managing director of Messrs. J. & A. Churchill Ltd., for taking up my suggestion of writing this book, and for accepting a manuscript very much larger than he had been led to anticipate.

In dedicating this book to my former chief, Sir Charles Lovatt Evans, F.R.S., I wish to express something more than my appreciation for help and encouragement, manifested in numerous ways since I first entered his department at University College, I wish to emphasise also, on the occasion of his retirement from the Jodrell chair, the great contribution to the progress of physiology that his enlightened direction of the department has made. From his successor, Prof. G. L. Brown, F.R.S., I have already acquired a heavy, but pleasing, burden of indebtedness ; especially for the hospitality that has permitted me to return to what I must be permitted to call my true academic home, the Department of Physiology, University College, London. I must also express my thanks to my employers, the Medical Research Council—personified for me by two courteous gentlemen, Dr. H. P. Himsworth and Dr. A. Landsborough Thomson—who have silently acquiesced in the theft of so many hours, devoted to this book, which might, perhaps, have been better employed in original research.

This partial recital of my indebtedness—the account is completed on page IX— would oppress me with my inability to repay it, were I not able, like Don Quixote, to lay the flattering unction to my soul, that " if I have not been able to repay the good deeds I receive with other deeds, I put in their place the desire to do them, and if that be not sufficient, I make them public ; for he that tells and proclaims the kindnesses he receives would repay them if he could."

HUGH DAVSON.

University College London.
June, 1951.

ACKNOWLEDGMENTS

THE labours of writing a book may be lightened considerably by the courtesy and willingness of librarians, and it is a pleasure to begin this catalogue of indebtedness by recording my thanks to Mr. C. F. A. Marmoy, of the Thane Library, and Messrs. H. W. Callaghan and G. G. Rideout of the Foster Court Library, of University College ; in addition, Miss J. Taylor, librarian of the Medical Research Council, Mill Hill, and Mr. T. C. Hunt of the Royal Society of Medicine, together with their assistants, have been of great help. In the preparation of a manuscript for press an author generally depends heavily on his secretary, his illustrators and his publishers' representative in charge of production ; the manuscript of this book has proved no exception to the rule, and my heartfelt thanks are due to Miss Mollie Kirk, my secretary ; to Messrs. C. A. Evans, N. Y. Jeffreys, T. R. Tarrant and R. Lunnon, who have assisted me, by their skill in photography, in my depredations from the original literature ; to Miss Marjorie Heath, Miss P. A. Matchett, Miss B. P. Matchett and Mr. C. A. Purvis, who executed the original illustrations ; and to an old acquaintance on the staff of Messrs. Churchill, Mr. A. Knightley.

In a work of this kind an author has to rely largely upon published material, and this is naturally reflected to a great extent in the collection of suitable illustrations. The present author is under a great debt to the writers of scientific books and papers, all of whom have readily given their consent to the reproduction of illustrations from their work.

The granting of permission to reproduce illustrations, by author and publisher, is a courtesy so universally extended as to be taken as a matter of course and acknowledged perfunctorily ; on the other hand, the provision of original micro-photographs is more than a courtesy—it is an act of kindness for which an author must be sincerely grateful ; on this account, therefore, my thanks are due to W. T. Astbury ; R. Barer ; John T. Bucholz ; G. Causey ; A. Claude ; K. S. Cole ; A. Couceiro ; V. M. Emmel ; H. Fernández-Morán ; S. Granick ; C. E. Hall ; E. J. Harris ; A. L. Houwink ; Hans Jenny ; K. Mühlethaler ; F. H. Pratt ; R. D. Preston ; R. Reed ; Hans Ris ; K. M. Rudall ; F. O. Schmitt ; Homer W. Smith ; F. S. Sjöstrand ; H. H. Ussing ; R. W. G. Wyckoff.

Moreover, my colleague Mr. K. C. Richardson and his assistant, Mr. F. J. Pittock, were kind enough to prepare two original micro-photographs for this book.

While it is indeed hoped that the credits given individually in the captions to borrowed illustrations are both exhaustive and correct, it is a pleasure to acknowledge the co-operation of the editors, publishers, and official bodies similarly concerned, in making available copyright illustrations. They comprise the following impressive list.

Acta Physiologica Scandinavica : (*American Journal of Physiology.*) ; *American Jl. of Botany* ; *Biochimica et Biophysica Acta* ; *Biochemical Journal* ; *Biological Reviews* ; *Biological Symposia* ; Butterworth Scientific Publications Ltd. ; Cambridge University Press ; Carnegie Institute of Washington ; Jacques Cattell Press ; *Chronica Botanica* ; Clarendon Press, Oxford ; *Cold Spring Harbor Symposia* ; Elsevier Publishing Co. Inc. ; *Federaion Proceedings* ; *Gastroenterology* ; Grune & Stratton Inc. ; *Harvey Lectures* ; Interscience Publishers, N.Y. ; *Jl. of Clinical Investigation* ; *Jl. of Experimental Biology* ; *Jl. of Experimental Medicine* ; *Jl. of the Franklin Institute* ; *Jl. of Physiology* ; H. K. Lewis & Co. Ltd. ; Longmans Green & Co. Ltd. ; Macmillan & Co. (*Nature*) ; Oxford University Press ; *Protoplasma* ; The Royal Society (*Proceedings*) ; Rockefeller Inst. for Medical Research (*J. Gen. Physiol.*) ; *Science ;* Chas. C. Thomas (*Jl. of Neurophysiology*), University of Chicago Press ; University of Pennsylvania Press ; The Wistar Institute of Anatomy & Biology (various periodicals) ; and Year Book Publishers, Chicago.

Finally, it is a great pleasure to acknowledge the assistance of my former colleague, Sir Jack Drummond, F.R.S., for advice on a number of biochemical points.

CONTENTS

1.—*The Structural Basis of Living Matter*

2.—*Transformations of Energy in Living Systems*

3.—*The Transport of Water and Solutes*

CHAPTER I

THE INDIVIDUAL CELL

ALTHOUGH all the cells of a given organism are ultimately derived from a single fertilised ovum, such specialisation to meet particular needs has taken place during development that, when we contemplate the erythrocyte, the long fibre-like cells of nerve and muscle, and the syncytial cells of the heart, it is indeed difficult to conceive of a " typical " cell. In the following discussion, therefore, it must be borne clearly in mind that the characteristics that are being described are essentially those of the given cell in which they are observed. In view, however, of the common origin of the cells of an organism, it is very likely that any given feature of a cell has an analogue in other and functionally remote cells. For example, the power of conduction of an impulse is associated in our minds primarily with the nerve cell, yet there is reason to believe that numerous other cells likewise possess this feature though not in so highly a developed form ; in fact, the propagation of a disturbance from one part of a cell surface to another may be a universal characteristic of all living cells, however primitive or specialised.

Experimental studies on single living cells from the complex organism are by no means easy ; and, although the comparatively recent development of the technique of tissue culture has provided useful information on the behaviour of certain types of cell, we are still largely dependent, for information regarding the essential characteristics of the cell, on the results of researches on protozoa such as *Amœba*, the eggs of certain marine animals such as the sea-urchin, *Arbacia punctulata*, and various plant cells ; it is therefore useful to employ these as our reference point.

Experimental Methods

Light-Microscope. Before entering into a detailed description of the cell, it is worth reviewing the modes of study available to the modern cytologist. The classical light-microscope depends for its power of exhibiting structural detail on a difference in absorption of light between the parts to be differentiated. Most cells reveal little detail when viewed in the living state through the light-microscope ; and this is due mainly to the absence of sufficiently great differences in absorption of light by the structural components ; it is also due to the fact that many of these elements are too small to be resolved by the microscope. Thus true images of particles smaller than the wavelength of the light employed cannot be formed, a limitation that excludes particles of less than about 0.4μ (4,000A) ; by the use of ultra-violet light and photographing the image, even greater magnification is possible, but even here the limit is in the region of 1,000A. With differential staining techniques, the presence of various elements in the cell, previously unsuspected, can be made evident ; these techniques generally involve the killing of the cell by " fixation " procedures which coagulate the protoplasm, so that for a long time the real existence in the living cell of many of the structures brought to light by the classical staining methods was called into question.

The use of differential staining techniques, as a result of which certain structures in the cell take up dye-stuffs preferentially, is still largely empirical, but under the form of *histochemistry* the rationale is rapidly becoming clearer ; histochemical techniques rely on the production of certain chemical reactions in localised regions of the cell ; thus if a cell is known to decompose organic phosphate, incubation of the cell with a solution of glycerophosphate and calcium should result in the deposition of insoluble calcium phosphate in those regions where the reaction occurred. By subsequent treatment of the cell with a cobaltous salt and ammonium sulphide a black precipitate is formed where the calcium was deposited. As we shall see, the Golgi apparatus of the cell was for long considered as an artefact, but by treating the cell in the above manner a black structure appears, identical in situation and general contour with the bodies originally identified by ordinary staining techniques. In this example the histochemical technique has exhibited a structure by virtue of its power of catalysing a chemical reaction (*i.e.*, by virtue of the presence of the enzyme *phosphatase*) ; simple staining reactions, on the other hand, rely on a chemical reaction between the dye and the structure to be stained ; thus the common stains fall into two main classes, acidic and basic, and the structures in the cell are classed as *acidophilic* or *basophilic* in accordance with their power of combining with an acid or basic dye. The main chemical reaction resulting in staining is thus a simple salt formation ; for example, the marked power of the cell nucleus to take up basic stains is due to the presence in it of nucleic acid which, even though it is itself probably united to protein, retains sufficient acidity to combine with basic dyes. The observation, moreover, that the nature of a staining reaction frequently depends on the technique of fixation is consistent with this explanation, since certain fixing reagents, such as the heavy metals, by combining with the acidic groups of proteins, tend to make the latter more basic and so favour their combination with acid dyes ; formic acid, on the other hand, makes a structure basophilic. The presence of fatty materials is generally demonstrated by their power of behaving as reducing agents ; thus osmic acid, which may be applied as a vapour, is reduced to give a black precipitate by fatty structures ; the value of osmic acid is further increased by its power of fixing the tissue at the same time as it behaves as a stain. To return to the more recent developments of histochemistry, we may note that the presence of certain materials within a cell may be verified frequently by the simple process of removing them by appropriate reagents which either decompose them or dissolve them out. Various enzymes, which specifically attack certain substances, have been applied to thin sections of tissues, and the consequent disappearance of structures has been observed ; for example, the nucleic acids associated with certain particles in the cytoplasm may be removed with the enzyme *ribonuclease*, with the result that the particles lose their basophilia ; again, by simply soaking the section in various concentrations of NaCl, Bensley & Hoerr were able to dissolve out different structures from the cell one by one. The technique of *radioautography* may be regarded as a development of histochemistry. If an animal is injected with the radioactive isotope (p. 177) of iodine, for example, the material will accumulate in the cells of the thyroid gland ; and it may be exactly localised by covering a histological section with a layer of photographic emulsion and subsequent development, fixation, and staining ; the radiations emitted by the I^{131} causing localised blackening of the emulsion. For example, Leblond found that I^{131} is concentrated after a time in the colloid of the thyroid vesicles ; in a similar manner P^{32} has been used in a variety of studies, such as the demonstration of the movement of phosphate in the transpiration stream of plants, in studies of bone, and so on. Fig. 127 (p. 268) by Causey & Harris is a radioautograph, showing the accumulation of P^{32} at the surface of the muscle fibres.

Ultra-Violet Microscope. The light-microscope depends, as we have seen, predominantly on the preferential absorption of light of certain

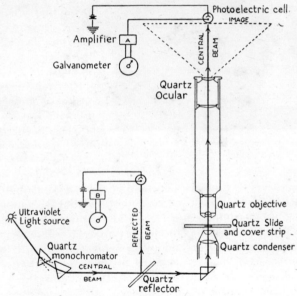

Fig. 1. Illustrating the ultra-violet microscope modified to permit measurement of absorption spectra of very small objects. (Gersh & Bodian. *Biol. Symp.*)

wavelengths by the structures thus made visible ; the same principle may be extended to the absorption of light beyond the visible spectrum. Thus the ultra-violet absorption microscope, devised by Kohler, and later refined by Caspersson, relies on the fact that certain substances within the cell, notably nucleic acid and proteins, absorb ultra-violet light in a sufficiently characteristic way to enable one to identify them *in situ* ; thus nucleic acid absorbs most intensely at 2,600A, whilst proteins generally absorb most intensely in the region of 2,800A. Ultra-violet light is concentrated on the section of tissue to be examined and, after passing through a quartz microscope, falls on a photographic plate to give an ultra-violet picture of the tissue ; alternatively, the emerging light may be caused to fall on a photoelectric cell and the amount of absorption by very small particles (as small as 4,000A) may be determined ; by varying the wavelength of ultra-violet light, the degree of absorption at different wavelengths may be measured, to give an ultra-violet absorption spectrum of the particle observed. The general scheme of the apparatus is indicated in Fig. 1. By applying this technique Caspersson has made valuable contributions to our knowledge of the structure of the cell nucleus.[1]

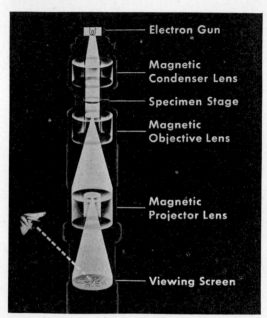

FIG. 2. Schematic representation of the principle of the electron-microscope. (R.C.A. Photophone, Ltd.)

Electron Gun

Magnetic Condenser Lens

Specimen Stage

Magnetic Objective Lens

Magnetic Projector Lens

Viewing Screen

Electron-Microscope. The *electron-microscope* depends primarily on the scattering of a beam of electrons which may be regarded as rays of extremely short wavelength (less than 1A, which compares with the 4,000 to 7,600A of visible light) ; theoretically, therefore, if an apparatus could be designed to form a picture with electrons as the source of illumination, details of less than 1A, *i.e.*, of atomic dimensions, should be resolvable.[2] Electron rays may be made to deviate in a regular manner by the application of electric and magnetic fields, consequently it is possible to construct " electron lenses " capable of bringing a bundle of electron rays to a focus, and thus to construct an electron-microscope. The general principles of this apparatus are illustrated in Figs. 2 and 3 ; the electrons

[1] The reflecting microscope, with a mirror optical system, has an important application to ultra-violet microscopy ; this instrument does not suffer from chromatic aberration and therefore the focussing is independent of the wavelength of light used. Consequently an object may be focussed with visible light and subsequently photographed in ultra-violet light without the tiresome re-focussing necessary with the ordinary compound microscope which can only be done by trial-and-error. A simple description of the instrument is that of Barer.

[2] The smallest detail that can be resolved, d, is given by the following formula :—

$$d = \frac{0 \cdot 5\lambda}{n \sin \alpha}$$

where α is the angular aperture of the lens, λ is the wavelength of the radiation employed and n the refractive index of the medium surrounding the object ; with values of 4,000A for λ, 1·7 for the maximum index of refraction, the smallest distance distinguishable is emerging from the refracting system impinge on a fluorescent screen and give a visible picture of the structure through which they have passed. In general, the scattering of electrons depends on the mass of the atoms in their path, so that regions of high density, in which atoms of large weight are aggregated, will appear black in contrast with regions of lower density.

Contrast may be brought out artificially by the use of " electron stains," containing elements of high atomic number which react preferentially with certain parts of the structure ; for example the classical osmic acid or bichromate fixatives have been employed with great profit in " staining " individual cells for the electron-microscope. So far it has not been possible, for technical reasons, to attain the magnifications that would permit resolution on the basis of atomic detail, nevertheless in some pictures details as fine as 30A

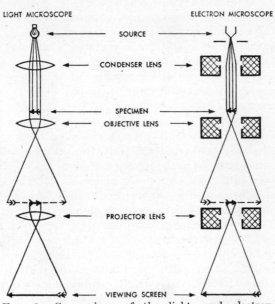

FIG. 3. Comparison of the light- and electron-microscopes. (R.C.A. Photophone, Ltd.)

have been resolved, that is between 50 and 100 times smaller than can be resolved by the light-microscope. Because electrons are strongly absorbed and scattered by the molecules of the air, the whole electron-microscope must be evacuated, so that only dried specimens of biological material are suitable for study ; they must, moreover, be very thin (0.1μ is the limit of thickness for currently employed instruments), and it is quite impossible to use as a support for the preparation an ordinary glass slide. The preparation is therefore mounted on a very thin film of cellulose, about 100A thick, which itself is mounted on a fine wire mesh. It is not possible here to describe in detail the various devices employed by the electron-microscopist in the study of biological material ; two important aids must, however, be mentioned. By the *replica* technique the surface of a body, too thick to be studied directly, may be made visible ;

about 1,200A when sin α is given its maximum value of unity. The wavelength of an electron varies with its velocity, and is given by :—

$$\lambda = \sqrt{\frac{150}{V}} \text{ Angström Units.}$$

where V is the electron velocity in volts ; with a value of V of 60,000 volts this gives an effective wavelength of 0·05A. In the electron-microscope the angular aperture has to be very restricted (1 to 2 thousandths of a radian), so that a figure of 10 to 20A may be taken as the limiting size for resolution.

a thin film of some plastic material, *e.g.*, methyl-cellulose (Formvar) is allowed to dry on the surface and then stripped off and mounted on the grid. By *shadowcasting*, the contours of a structure are emphasised ; this technique, introduced by H. O. Muller in 1942, has been extensively developed by Williams and Wyckoff ; the specimen is exposed to a stream of evaporated heavy-metal atoms (Cr, Ni, Pd, Au and U have all been used with success), impinging at oblique incidence on the supporting plane ; surface irregularities are accentuated, since they screen the surface from deposition of metal for a distance depending on their height ; these " shadows " transmit electrons, whilst other regions are opaque ; on the fluorescent screen of the instrument they appear bright, but dark in the negative of the electron-micrograph. The extent of the shadow gives a measure of the height of a projection, *e.g.*, the size of a protein molecule, if the angle of incidence of the stream of atoms is known. A combination of these two methods gives a *shadowed replica*, the actual replica having been shadowed ; alternatively the material may be shadowed first and then submitted to the replica technique, in which case the metal film comes away on the replica-forming material. Besides its value in multiplying the magnification of the light-microscope by a factor of 50 to 100, the electron-microscope provides a marked increase in the resolving power, when used at less extreme magnifications, over that given by the light-microscope, so that details in the structure of a whole cell may be made out. Fig. 4, Pl. I, for example, is a composite electron-micrograph of a whole embryonic cell grown in tissue-culture by Claude ; the cell was sufficiently thin to permit a direct study. The detail exhibited is beyond anything observable in the ordinary light-microscope, but to what extent many of the structures in the electron-microphotograph are artefacts, resulting from the drying of the cell, cannot be decided ; this necessity for drying is indeed a severe limitation on the applicability of the electron-microscope and attempts are being made to enclose the specimen in an impervious coating before introducing it into the apparatus.

Phase-Contrast Microscope. For studies on unfixed preparations the recently developed *phase-contrast microscope* has proved useful in identifying structures, within the cell, which before had only been seen in fixed and stained preparations. The ordinary light-microscope gives contrast by profiting from differences of opacity in the specimen, and since these are normally small, this necessitates staining. The phase-contrast microscope profits by differences of refractive index in the structure ; these differences are such as to cause diffraction of the light passing through, similar to that taking place at the classical diffraction-grating. Diffracted rays from regions of one refractive index will be out of phase with rays from regions of different refractive index, because of their path differences, consequently, in the image, differences of refractive index of the parts of the structure will be reflected in differences of phase of the light. The problem was to convert these differences of phase, which cannot be appreciated by the eye, into differences of intensity, which can. The problem was solved by allowing the undiffracted light to pass through a " phase strip," a device for increasing the effective path of the rays by a

PLATE I

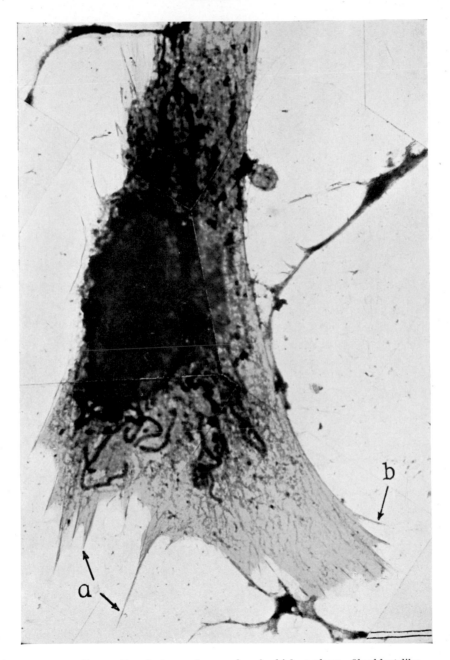

FIG. 4. Composite electron-micrograph of chick embryo fibroblast-like cell grown in tissue culture. The extended cytoplasm is thin enough to allow the differential penetration of electrons. Mitochondria are clearly outlined, and a delicate cytoplasmic network is revealed. The centre of the cell, especially the nucleus, remains too thick. *a*, so-called "jagged points"; *b*, "finger-like processes." Three nerve cells may be seen. × 1,600. (Claude. *Harvey Lectures*.)

[*To face p.* 6.

definite amount ; this undiffracted light provided a background for the diffracted rays. If these were retarded by the same amount, *i.e.*, if their effective path length was the same, the waves would add and the point from which they emanated would appear bright ; if, on the other hand, the diffracted waves were half-a-wavelength out of phase with the background, the point would appear dark. Thus differences of phase of the light, caused by variations in the refractive index of the object, are transformed into differences of light intensity.

These, then, are the methods available to the cytologist to make visible the differentiated parts of the individual cell ; other but less direct methods are those of X-ray diffraction and polarisation microscopy which will be described later ; first we must review some of the outstanding facts made evident by these " visualising " techniques, taken in conjunction with other experimental procedures.

Structure of the Cell

In Fig. 5 is shown a diagrammatic representation of the more outstanding parts of the normal resting sea-urchin egg, parts which have been differen-

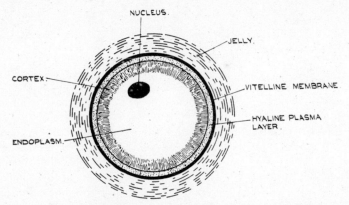

FIG. 5. Diagrammatic representation of *Arbacia* egg. Thicknesses of the various layers are not drawn to scale.

tiated by a variety of means. From without inwards there are an outermost *jelly*, some 23μ thick ; a thin *vitelline membrane* bounding the *hyaline plasma layer*, the latter only becoming prominent in the fertilised egg ; the *plasma membrane* which is too thin to be resolved microscopically, and, within this, the *cytoplasm*, divided into an outer, more solid, *cortex* or *plasmagel*—which may be about 5μ thick in the *Arbacia* egg—and a more fluid interior, the *endoplasm* or *plasmasol*. Within the cytoplasm is the *nucleus* which is bounded by a nuclear membrane and contains within it one or more small spherical bodies, the *nucleoli*. Scattered throughout the cytoplasm are various granules or *inclusions*. In Fig. 6 the typical appearance of *Amœba proteus* is shown and it is clear that in this cell the inclusions dominate the appearance, whereas in a number of other cells the cytoplasm is relatively free from these bodies. It will be noted also in

Fig. 6 that the cytoplasm contains *vacuoles* which appear to be regions of the cytoplasm " screened off " from the rest by a membrane ; they change in size, appear, and disappear, in accordance with the activity of the cell and seem to be related to the occurrence of localised chemical reactions, such as the absorption of ingested particles, and so on. In the plant cell,

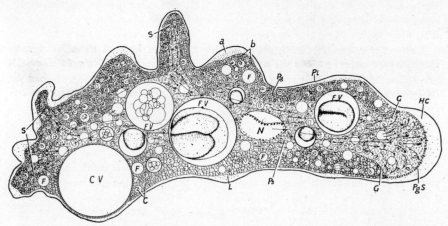

Fig. 6.   *Camera lucida* sketch of horizontal optical section of *Amœba proteus*. HC, hyaline cap ; PgS, plasmagel sheet ; G, region of gelation ; S, region of solation ; CV, contractile vacuole ; FV, food vacuole ; Pg, plasmagel ; Ps, plasmasol ; L, liquid layer ; Pl, plasmalemma ; *a*, alpha granules ; *b*, beta granules ; *c*, crystals in vacuoles. (Mast. *J. Morph.*)

the existence of a large central vacuole (Fig. 60, p. 91) dominates the appearance.

Jelly Layer. Viewed directly under the microscope, the outermost jelly layer is not visible, but its presence becomes obvious as soon as India ink is added to the sea-water surrounding the egg ; the ink does not penetrate the jelly which appears as a transparent ring against a dark background ; the jelly may be removed by shaking the eggs, and is not essential to life. In the eggs of *Nereis limbata* the jelly of the resting, *i.e.*, unfertilised, egg is *within* the vitelline membrane and is only extruded as a result of fertilisation ; in this case the egg contains granules—the so-called " jelly precursor granules "—which provide the material for the greatly increased quantity of jelly that is required to form a thick layer round the fertilised egg. Chemical evidence on the nature of these external jellies is very meagre ; in *Arbacia* and *Arenicola* it probably consists of a polysaccharide belonging to the class of hyaluronic acid, whilst in *Mnemiopsis* the jelly is a nucleoprotein. Hyaluronic acid may be decomposed by an enzyme, *hyaluronidase.* Fertilisation of the egg requires that the sperm should penetrate the jelly layer ; according to Monroy & Ruffo, extracts of sperm contain a principle that rapidly liquefies the jelly of *Arbacia pustulosa.*

Vitelline Membrane. The vitelline membrane, or *plasmalemma,* is an elastic structure (as shown by the fact that it can be drawn out into threads by a micro-needle which recoil on being released), which fits closely to the underlying protoplasm in most cells ; when the egg shrinks as a result of the osmotic withdrawal of water (Chapter VII), this membrane contracts, so that shrinkage is not associated with a separation of this membrane from its underlying structure ; in many other cells, however, the analogue of this membrane is a much tougher structure, for example in the protozoan *Paramœcium*. In plant cells—where the tough cellulose coat is thought to be analogous with the vitelline membrane—the osmotic withdrawal of water results in the retraction of the underlying protoplasm from the cellulose wall, *plasmolysis* (Fig. 95, p. 168). The vitelline membrane may be removed by chemical reagents, for example by washing the egg in KCl solution, or by micro-dissection needles, and it is found that, as with the jelly layer, the egg remains intact in spite of this loss ; nevertheless the "naked" egg is much more susceptible to injury.

Plasma Membrane. If a naked egg is injured by a cut with a micro-dissection needle, the cytoplasm flows out through the cut portion ; it is quite clear, therefore, that the cytoplasm is separated from its surrounding medium by some barrier besides the layer of jelly and vitelline membrane ; this barrier, which may be only one or two hundred Angström units thick, *i.e.*, too thin to be resolved microscopically, is called the plasma membrane and its structure, so far as it has been determined by essentially inferential methods, will be dealt with in Chapter VIII.

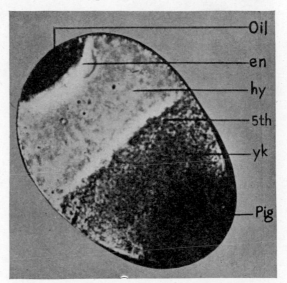

FIG. 7.   Centrifuged *Arbacia* egg.   *Oil*, oil cap ; *en*, egg nucleus ; *hy*, hyaline zone ; *pig*, pigment layer ; *yk*, yolk layer ; *5th.*, so-called fifth layer. (Moser, *J. exp. Zool.*)

Cytoplasm. Within the plasma membrane is the cytoplasm, a large part of which, the endoplasm, is thought to be liquid ; thus if the *Arbacia* egg is submitted to a high centrifugal force the granules may be seen to move towards the centrifugal pole of the egg whilst the fat droplets and the nucleus move towards the centripetal pole, so that after a time the egg becomes stratified (Fig. 7) ; Heilbrunn and other workers have calculated the viscosity of the fluid through which the particles pass under the influence of this centrifugal force ; the values so computed have turned out to be of the order of some two to ten times that of water. Table I shows the viscosities of the vacuolar sap and cytoplasm of various cells together with that of several common oils ; it will be seen that the bulk of the cytoplasm through which the granules move is certainly not highly viscous but whether, on this account, we are to deny the endoplasm any submicroscopic structure, which would impart some rigidity, is a matter for future discussion. That the cytoplasm is essentially aqueous in nature is revealed by the fact that injection of water into the cell does not result in the formation of any separate phase, whereas the injection of oil does.

TABLE I

Relative Viscosities of Sap, Cytoplasm and some Oils.
(*After Frey-Wyssling*, 1948)

	η
Water	1
Cell Sap :	
Stem Parenchyma of the *Vicia Faba* germ.	1·9
Protonema of *Leptobryum piriforme*	1·9
Epidermic cells of the *Allium Cepa* bulb .	2
Terminal vacuole of *Closterium*	2·5
Cytoplasm :	
Amœba	6
Red cell of man .	30
Glycerol .	87
Paraffin oil	92
Castor oil .	1,250

An interesting experiment of Seifriz was the following. By means of a micro-needle he inserted a nickel particle into the cytoplasm of an egg of the sand-dollar, *Echinarachnius*. The pole of an electromagnet was brought close to the egg and the current switched on ; the particle moved rapidly towards the surface of the egg but was brought to a halt before reaching it ; on switching off the current, the particle remained in its final position, *i.e.*, the absence of observable elastic recoil indicated that the cytoplasm in which the egg remained was essentially fluid. If the particle was placed in the layer of cytoplasm just under the surface (*i.e.*, in the cortical layer), it moved towards the pole of the magnet, as before, but this time on switching off the current there was sufficient elastic recoil to deform the surface of the egg, an observation suggesting that the cortical layer was solid. More recently Crick and Hughes have applied the same technique to the chick fibroblast ; they, too, observed elastic phenomena, and noted that particles could frequently be made to move more easily after repeated backward and forward movements, as though a path had to be cut through a semisolid structure. These and many other experiments indicate that within the plasma membrane there are normally two components ; an apparently liquid phase with a viscosity about 2 to 10 times that of water, in which solid particles may be seen to be in Brownian movement, and may be easily displaced in comparatively weak centrifugal fields ; immediately under the plasma membrane, however, there is a cortical layer which is characterised by elasticity and in which Brownian movement, if observed at all, is very restricted ; as we shall see, it may be classed as a solid gel. The solid nature of this cortical layer is best revealed by experiments with the ultra-centrifuge ; thus in the eggs of *Arbacia punctulata* it was shown by Brown and by Costello that the pigment granules located in the cortex required much higher centrifugal forces to displace them than those in the endoplasm. In *Arbacia pustulosa* eggs, where the granules are almost entirely confined to the cortical region, it was found that a centrifugal force of over 18,000 times gravity gave practically no displacement.

In *Paramœcium* the cortex is an elastic jelly-like wall ; on tearing this with micro-needles the fluid interior of the cell pours out and the torn edges of the cortex turn in, the entire cell shrinking in size ; if the torn edges meet, they unite so that further outflow is brought to an end, but in no instance has any regeneration of cortical material been observed. Again, the fluid interior of an *Arbacia* egg can be extruded experimentally ; as a result, the cortex is left behind and the extruded endoplasm rounds up into a sphere. It is found that, although the endoplasmic fragment is apparently a stable system, it cannot be fertilised and caused to divide, whereas the cortical layer can. This experiment demonstrates the functional differentiation of the cortical layer from the rest of the proto-plasmic interior, and the difficulty, or rather impossibility in this case, of converting fluid endoplasm into solid cortex.

Functional Changes in Cytoplasm

The liquid condition of the interior cytoplasm is, nevertheless, by no means a permanent and immutable characteristic ; severe damage to a cell with chemical reagents such as ether, or mechanically caused by a micro-dissection needle, can result in a complete solidification of the whole cell, whereby the formerly liquid cytoplasm becomes of jelly-like consistency. In many instances severe damage is unnecessary to produce this change ; thus Seifriz found that merely compressing a *Rhizopus*, with just sufficient pressure to make a hypha close, caused it to solidify ; removal of the pressure allowed it to return to its liquid state. Similarly, it has been shown that by forcing a marine egg through a tube, smaller in diameter than that of the egg, the deformation is sufficient to solidify it, so that on emerging from the tube it retains its abnormal shape.

Pseudopod Formation. The most striking example of the apparent interconvertibility of cortex and endoplasm is shown by the phenomena of pseudopod formation and locomotion in *Amœba*. Fig. 6 (p. 8) is a general-ised picture of the structure of *Amœba proteus* as given by Mast, showing the outer plasmalemma, an elastic pellicle about 0.25μ thick ; a region of cortex of varying thickness in which Brownian movement of the granules is very restricted ; and the liquid endoplasm. In the form shown in Fig. 6 the *Amœba* is said to be *monopodal, i.e.*, instead of having numerous processes, or pseudopods, extending in different directions, there is only one process, making the cell somewhat cylindrical in form. The careful microscopical investigations of numerous investigators, in particular those of Mast, have shown that pseudopod formation in *Amœba* results from the following series of changes. First, at the region where the pseudopod is about to form, the plasmagel or cortex liquefies ; as a result of this localised weakening of the cortical wall, liquid endoplasm is forced into this region causing a bulge, the force behind this flow being either the result of an active contraction of the posterior cortex or merely the expression of a normal turgor in the cell. The streaming endoplasm, as it reaches the weakened region, solidifies above and below, apparently as soon as it comes into contact with the cortex, so that a tube of solid cortex is gradually built up ; the liquid endoplasm flowing into and extending this tube is derived from the more posterior regions of the cell, and necessitates a liquefaction of the posterior cortex. The general scheme is illustrated in Fig. 8. It will ·be seen that pseudopod formation consists, not of the elastic drawing out of a portion of the cell, but of a re-modelling of the cell made possible by the interconvertibility of endoplasm and cortex. In Fig. 8, A the granular endoplasm is shown flowing forward as far as the plasmalemma before solidifying ; very frequently, however, the tip of the advancing pseudopod consists of a hyaline cap, free from granules and apparently solid (Fig. 8, B) ; this sheet of gel often persists for long periods, being built up by gelation as rapidly as it is broken down by stretching ; at other times breaks occur which permit granules to reach the plasmalemma (Fig. 8, c). Why this particular region should remain free of granules is not well understood ; certainly the general problem of the migration of granules merits further study ; thus, on fertilisation of an *Arbacia* egg, there

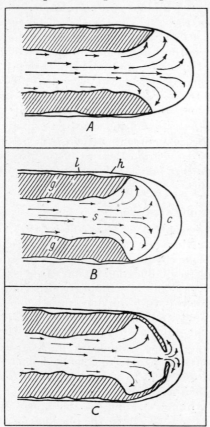

Fig. 8. Illustrating the growth of a pseudopod. Shaded region represents gelled cytoplasm. In A the flowing endoplasm reaches the plasmalemma at the tip of the advancing pseudopod ; in B there is a well-defined hyaline cap, c ; in C the hyaline cap has broken. s, plasmasol ; g, plasmagel ; l, plasmalemma ; h, hyaline layer. (Mast. *Protoplasma.*) .

is a migration of the granules from endoplasm to cortex within a few minutes. The importance of the pressure within and without the *Amœba* for pseudopod formation is well brought out by an experiment described by Mast ; an *Amœba* was drawn into a fine capillary tube as in Fig. 9 ; in the cylindrical form it may be regarded as a single large pseudopod, any extension of this pseudopod resulting in an obvious translatory movement of the whole cell ; in A the cell is moving to the right, a hyaline cap has appeared on the anterior (right) end, and endoplasm streams from left to right. On applying a gentle pressure from the right, as in B, the hyaline cap disappears, streaming reverses its direction and

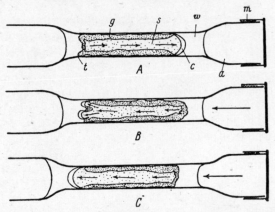

Fig. 9. Sketches illustrating the effect of pressure against the anterior end of an *Amœba* moving in water in a capillary tube. *t*, capillary tube ; *m*, adjustable metal cap ; *w*, water ; *a*, air ; *s*, plasmasol ; *g*, plasmagel ; *c*, hyaline cap. A, before pressure is applied ; B, a very short time after ; C, a few moments later. Small arrows, direction of streaming ; large arrows, direction of pressure. When pressure is applied to the anterior end, the direction of streaming is reversed and a new anterior end is formed. (Mast. *Protoplasma*.)

eventually a hyaline cap forms at what was formerly the posterior end ; and locomotion is reversed in direction. In this connection it is worth mentioning that Holtfreter has observed rhythmical undulations in the vitelline membrane during locomotion, and he considers that the changes in local pressure induced in this manner contribute just as much as the alternate liquefaction and solidification of the cortex to the phenomenon.

Pseudopod formation is the basis of locomotion, as the above example

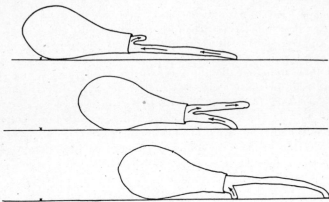

Fig. 10. Sketches illustrating locomotion in *Difflugia*. Arrows, direction of streaming. As the attached pseudopod contracts, pulling the shell along, the free pseudopod extends and the substance in the one flows into the other. (Mast. *J. Morph*.)

has shown ; the actual form the motion takes depends, with a given species, on whether the plasmalemma attaches itself to a substrate or not ; for example, if the *Amœba* depicted in Fig. 6 is attached to the surface on which it is resting, the extension of a pseudopod to the right (associated of course with a contraction of the posterior end), produces a bodily movement to the right ; since the plasmalemma is fixed at the base, extension of the pseudopod is associated with a sliding of the upper plasmalemma over the cortex, which results in a " rolling " movement until the attachment is broken. If the plasmalemma is not attached anywhere, movement is quite smooth, the membrane being stretched evenly over the advancing pseudopod. If the tip of the advancing pseudopod becomes attached after it has extended, and then contracts, the rest of the *Amœba* is drawn forward ; if, simultaneously with the contraction of the first pseudopod, a new one is formed which itself attaches farther forward, we get an interesting " walking " movement illustrated in Fig. 10, for the case of a shelled rhizopod, *Difflugia*. Here the first formed pseudopod is clearly behaving as the posterior end of an *Amœba*, liquefaction of this pseudopod providing the material for the newly advancing one.

Protoplasmic Streaming. The streaming of protoplasm is observed in its most active state in the slime mould ; the plasmodium of *Physarum polycephalus* is a non-cellular protoplasmic mass in which active flow may be seen continuously, the channels of flow shifting frequently. Kamiya grew small pieces of plasmodia on

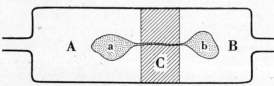

FIG. 11. Experimental arrangement for measuring pressure required to prevent protoplasmic streaming. *a* and *b* are two blobs of protoplasm connected by a thin strand. The pressures in compartments A and B may be varied independently. (Kamiya. *Science.*)

a cover-glass coated with agar ; and these soon spread into fine sheets which later developed protoplasmic strands ; with these strands he was able to make up forms illustrated in Fig. 11, obtained by causing two blobs of protoplasm to fuse with the two ends of a strand. A regular ebb and flow from one body to the other took place ; and, by applying a uniform pressure over one body, he was able to measure the pressure necessary to prevent flow into it ; on the average it was of the order of 20 cm. H_2O. By recording the pressures developed in the protoplasmic bodies he was able to demonstrate the existence of quite a complex rhythm of pressure changes. According to Seifriz we must view the flow as resulting from an actual contraction of the wall of the protoplasm, so that the streaming may be said to result from a " muscular contraction " of a very primitive type. As we shall see, the flow in this case is also associated with a reversible conversion of solid cortex to fluid endoplasm.

Mitotic Division. When a cell undergoes mitotic division the nucleus and cytoplasm undergo an interesting cycle of changes which may now be described. The first stage of mitotic division, called *prophase*, is characterised by the appearance of two small areas on the surface of the nucleus which pass to opposite poles of the cell ; these are the *centrosomes*.

The nucleus elongates along the polar axis and, with the loss of its membrane which disappears from view, the nucleus loses its apparent homogeneity, fibre-like bodies, the *chromosomes*, appearing in it. At the beginning of the next stage, *metaphase*, the outline of the nucleus disappears and the chromosomes are seen lying as an irregular group

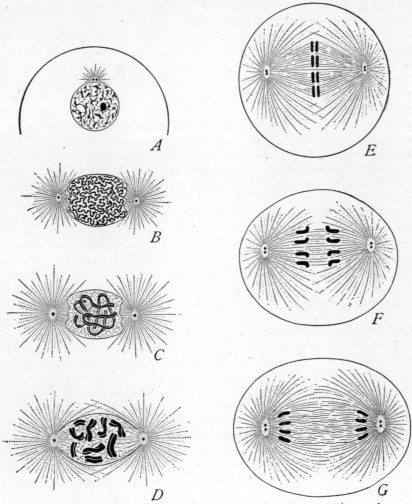

Fig. 12. Diagrammatic figures of typical mitosis. *A*, vegetative nucleus; *B*, fine spireme; *C*, coarse spireme; *D*, late prophase; *E*, metaphase; *F* and *G*, early and late anaphases. (Gray, from Wilson. *Experimental Cytology*, C.U.P.)

midway between the centrosomes; and the area formerly outlined by the nucleus is occupied by a series of fibrils, the *spindle*, converging on each centrosome. At the end of metaphase, the chromosomes are organised in a plane across the equator of the spindle; each chromosome, during the ensuing *anaphase*, splits longitudinally into two halves which then move to the opposite poles of the egg; the cycle is completed by the mergence of the chromosomes with each other to give two new, apparently homogeneous, nuclei. The changes described above are illustrated diagrammatically in Fig. 12 ; they have been brought to light by the application of classical fixing and staining techniques ; that the broad outlines of the process of mitosis thus revealed are not the result of artefacts is shown by many recent studies—especially with the phase microscope. Moreover, by insertion of a micro-needle into an egg during the process of nuclear division, Chambers was able to catch hold of the chromosomes, which proved to be markedly elastic bodies in contrast with the apparently homogeneous fluid from which they emerged. In a similar manner the spindle, separating the chromosomes, and along which they migrate, was shown to be a partially rigid body. The result of these changes is obviously to ensure a division of the nucleus into two halves, so that when cleavage of the cell into two daughter cells takes place these shall have nuclei. Further details of the structure of the nucleus and chromosomes will be given later ; for the moment we may note that they are apparently the structures, belonging to the cell, that contain the *genes*, *i.e.*, those factors postulated by the geneticist as necessary for the transmission of hereditary characteristics. The longitudinal splitting of the chromosomes before migration to the poles of the mitotic spindle ensures their incorporation in the daughter cells.

The centrosomes, mentioned above, which act as poles for the dividing nucleus, may be surrounded by rays, the *asters*, which enter the cytoplasm. In echinoderm eggs the rays are often marked out by the radial arrangement of the granules. As the intervening spindle increases in size, the centrosomes grow (they are then called *centrospheres*), and the rays of the aster project farther and farther into the cytoplasm of the cell (Fig. 13). Associated with the development of the asters is an elongation of the cell along the mitotic axis followed, eventually, by cleavage into two daughter cells in such a way that each cell has a nucleus and an aster. The asters soon fade away after cleavage and re-appear when the next mitotic cycle is under way. As with the spindle, the aster is probably a solidification of originally liquid cell material, and there is reason to believe that the formation of the asters is a primary cause of cell division. Any experimental change that causes the asters to disappear, such as treatment with ether, immediately inhibits cell cleavage even though it may have gone to the extent of the appearance of a well defined cleavage furrow. Conversely, in a normal resting cell, any change that causes the appearance of two asters will lead to division of the cell ; alternatively, if a new aster is formed, in a cell undergoing cleavage, the process is drastically modified.

The mitotic division of the cell may consequently be divided into two functionally separate processes ; one associated with the division of the nucleus and the other with the division of the cytoplasm ; it would appear that these processes are in large measure independent. Thus it has been found that fragments of mature eggs, without nuclei, can divide if aster formation is induced by a suitable agent ; and, conversely, if aster formation is inhibited by cold, fat solvents, or hypotonic and hypertonic solutions, the cytoplasmic division is inhibited without that of the

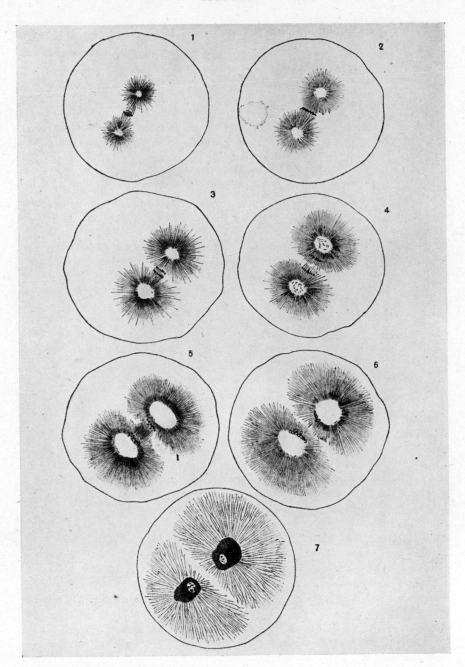

FIG. 13. *Camera lucida* drawings of developing asters from sections of *Echinus* eggs fixed in corrosive sublimate. Note change in shape of the asters after the anaphase stage is reached ; also loss of definition of astral rays with increase in size of asters. (Gray. *Experimental Cytology*, C.U.P.)

nucleus being necessarily affected ; as a result, a cell with two nuclei is formed.

The Mitotic Spindle. During the metaphase of mitotic division, the nucleus becomes elongated, the nuclear membrane disappears from view, and the chromosomes arrange themselves in the equator of the fibrillar arrangement called the spindle. The micro-dissection studies of Chambers indicate that the spindle is not an artefact of fixation ; thus it may be removed bodily from the insect spermatocyte, retaining its shape as a fusiform body; after several minutes, however, the substance of the spindle goes into solution and the chromosomes lose their orientation. On inserting a needle into a cell undergoing mitotic division, it is found that it may readily be moved through the substance of the spindle without disturbing the chromosomes, and no appreciable resistance to the movement of the needle is met until the granular cytoplasm in immediate contact with the spindle is reached. Thus micro-dissection studies, whilst they suggest that the spindle is a characteristic portion of the protoplasmic interior of the cell, leave us in some doubt as to whether it has a continuous solid structure all the way through, or is essentially liquid and surrounded by a jellied layer of cytoplasm. The phase-contrast microscope, as also the polarising microscope (p. 42), both indicate the presence of fibrils, however.[1]

The Asters. The characteristic cytoplasmic feature of cell division is the appearance and growth, within the cytoplasm, of two asters ; these normally appear in association with the nucleus, and their relative positions determine the site of the cleavage furrow, but they may appear, chiefly under abnormal conditions, far removed from the nucleus, in which case they are called *cytasters*. Nevertheless, in spite of their abnormal position or origin, cytasters are equally capable of determining the mode of cleavage ; thus the development of a third aster in a cell causes multiple cleavage. The aster may often be observed in the living, unstained, cell, its rays being outlined by the pigment granules which accumulate at its surface. It is consequently no artefact and, in view of its frequent association with cell division, there is little reason to doubt that its appearance is a prime factor in this process. On inserting a needle gently into an egg undergoing division, Chambers found that the aster could be rolled and pushed about ; on pushing the needle through the aster, a definite distortion of its structure was produced. Numerous micro-dissection experiments of this nature suggest that the aster consists of strands of solid granular cytoplasm, with fluid hyaline rays in between. The reversible nature of this solidification is shown firstly by the normal disappearance of the asters in the two daughter blastomeres, and secondly by their disappearance by merely agitating the egg, by cold, or by drugs such as ether. The disappearance of the asters is invariably associated with a suppression of cleavage ; on returning the egg to its normal environment, the asters reappear and cleavage proceeds.

[1] The importance of the length of the spindle in determining the relative sizes of the blastomeres is emphasised by recent work of Carlson & Hollaender ; treatment of the grasshopper neuroblasts with ultra-violet light during late metaphase and anaphase caused a shortening which made the cell divide equally, whereas normal division is into two unequal daughter cells. Dan & Dan attribute a dominant role to the lengthening of the spindle in pushing the asters apart.

The Cleavage Furrow. Although the appearance of the solid asters seems to be a necessary prerequisite for cleavage, it is not the only one ; whatever the ultimate mechanism of cytoplasmic cleavage may be, there is no doubt that a process of primary importance is the development of the cleavage furrow. The comparatively recent studies of Chambers, of Schectman and of Marsland join in illustrating the analogy between the growth of the furrow and that of a pseudopod. If the two blastomeres of a dividing egg are to have the same morphology as that of the parent egg, new solid cortex must clearly be formed in places that were originally liquid, *i.e.*, in the equator of the egg as illustrated in Fig. 14. If the analogy between pseudopod formation and the development of the cleavage furrow is apt, this new cortical material will be formed at the expense of the fluid endoplasm. According to Schectman's analysis of the division

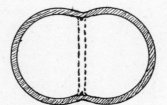

Fig. 14. Illustrating the necessity for the production of new cortical material during growth of the cleavage furrow.

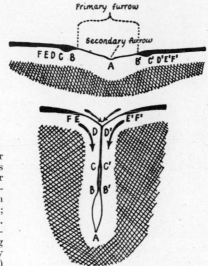

Fig. 15. Diagram illustrating the manner of cortical growth. Cortical pigment is shown as a solid black line ; remainder of the cortex white ; subcortical cytoplasm cross-hatched. The top sketch represents an early stage of cleavage ; the lower one a more advanced stage. Arrows indicate direction and approximate site of growth. Corresponding portions of the cortex are indicated by letters A, A', etc. (Schectman. *Science*.)

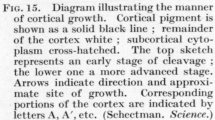

of the egg of the newt, *Triturus torosus*, based on following the migration of stained portions of cortex during division, the first sign of cleavage is a localised contraction of the cortex to give a primary furrow, BB' of Fig. 15 ; this is followed by the development of a secondary furrow, A, and the growth of the cortex in the region of the furrow as indicated by Fig. 15, where the black region represents pigmented cortex, the white region unpigmented, and the cross-hatched region the fluid endoplasm. The growth of the cortex is thought to take place between the points C and E so that, in effect, the solid cortex is *pushed* into the furrow by the interpolation of new material in this region.[1] Certainly protoplasmic streaming is observable, consisting of a vortical flow sweeping round the

---

[1] It is difficult to decide, from purely microscopical observations, what contribution a stretch of the existing cortex makes to the development of the furrow ; according to Dan & Dan (1940) there is a considerable stretching of the superficial layers, and it is only some time after division that they reacquire their former thickness.

asters from the polar regions towards the wall of the furrow at the equator. The development of a comparatively rigid wall of cortex in the furrow, as postulated above, has been confirmed by a number of micro-dissection experiments of Chambers, one of which may be cited. In this, the polar surface of a dividing egg was torn before the furrow had completed its advance ; the potential blastomere involved in the injury disintegrated, but the other maintained its form whilst the furrow actually continued to advance ; meanwhile, however, the liquid endoplasm in the intact blastomere escaped through the connecting stalk and eventually it disintegrated, but there was nothing to indicate that the floor of the advancing furrow, the dotted region in Fig. 14, was weaker than elsewhere, in fact it was the last portion of the egg to disintegrate (Fig. 16). That there is some force behind the furrow is indicated by the fact that an oil drop introduced into the egg in the region of the equator is split into two by the advancing furrow. (In this connection it may be mentioned that Chambers and Kopac estimated the thickness of the cortical wall to be 4 to 5μ from a study of the distance of the external wall of the furrow from an oil drop before the latter was deformed.)

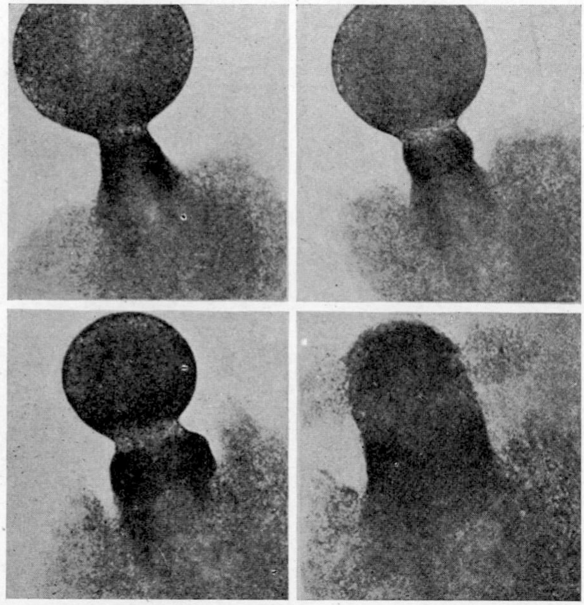

FIG. 16.   Effect of tearing polar end of one of two incipient blastomeres of a naked *Arbacia* egg in KCl solution. The outflow through open connection causes the other blastomere to shrink. Note especially in bottom left-hand photo the persistence of the wall at the original floor of the furrow. (Chambers.   *J. cell. & comp. Physiol.*)

The Effects of Pressure. The formation of the cleavage furrow, the aster, and the pseudopod, and the phenomenon of streaming in the plasmodium, all seem to have the common characteristic of requiring a change of solid cortex into liquid endoplasm simultaneously with a change of liquid endoplasm into solid cortex in a different region. We may expect, therefore, any change in the environment, that modifies the conditions of transformation of the one to the other, to influence these various phenomena. Early studies on *Amœba* showed that soaking the cell in an alkaline medium, which makes the protoplasm more liquid, caused the pseudopods formed under these conditions to be much more lobate than normal, a fact suggesting a delayed solidification of the cortex during formation. In an acid medium, on the other hand, the pseudopods were much longer and narrower. More recently the work of Brown and Marsland has shown that high pressures, of the order of 400 atmospheres, liquefy the formerly solid cortex ; thus in the ultra-centrifuge the speed necessary to move the granules in the cortex was determined ; on applying a uniform hydrostatic pressure, in the region of 400 atmospheres, to the eggs the

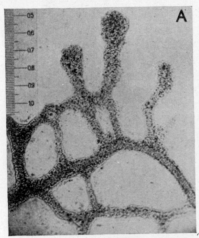
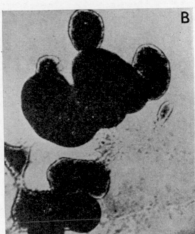
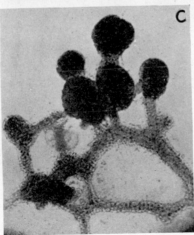

Fig. 17. Effects of pressure on plasmodium. A, normal. B, 5 min. after application of pressure of 6000 lb./in.² C, 35 min. after release of pressure. (Pease. *J. cell. & comp. Physiol.*)

centrifugal force necessary to sediment the granules was considerably reduced, in fact a curve, showing the variation of the apparent viscosity of the cortex with pressure, could be constructed, a change of 68 atmospheres causing a change of about 25 per cent. in the viscosity. Similar studies were made on a variety of cells, for example *Amœba* and the leaves of *Elodea ;* they concurred in exhibiting a marked decrease in apparent viscosity of the cortex on applying pressure, *i.e.*, the pressure caused a reversible liquefaction of the cortex.

On applying these high pressures to cells undergoing . cleavage, to *Amœbæ* forming pseudopods, or to streaming cytoplasm, as in the slime moulds, the effects observed are all perfectly consistent with those we should expect on the basis of an active reversal of the solid cortex to fluid endoplasm. Thus on rapidly raising the pressure surrounding an *Amœba* to 440 atmospheres, pseudopods already formed retract rapidly to leave

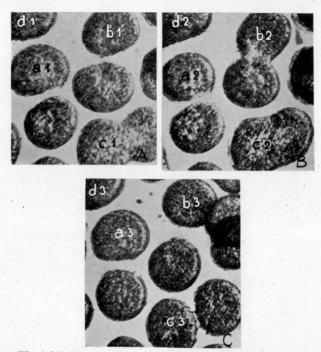

Fig. 18. The inhibition and recession (A and B) of the cleavage furrow at a compression of 450 atmospheres, and (C) the re-formation of the furrow after decompression. A, 10 seconds after applying the pressure ; B, 2 minutes later ; C, 2 minutes after decompression which occurred immediately after B was taken. Note (b_1 and b_2) that recession occurred even though the " blastomeres " were connected by a mere strand of protoplasm at the time the pressure was applied. Apparently pressure has a liquefying action upon the hyaline plasma layer as well as upon the cortex proper, as may be seen in d_1 to d_2 and in c_2. Under pressure, this material shows a greater tendency to form beads, which project out or become detached from the general surface. Under pressure this layer also fails later to shrink and pull the blastomeres tightly together. The blastomeres remain apart (as in a_2) when pressure is applied and maintained at this stage. (Marsland. *J. cell. & comp. Physiol.*)

mere " terminal spheres " on the main body ; if the pressure is maintained for some time the *Amœba* becomes spherical. Fig. 17 shows the effects of high pressure on the slime mould plasmodium ; it will be seen that the walls of the channel appear to break down with the formation of reservoirs ; release of the pressure allows the channels to re-form. At about 270 atmospheres streaming ceases, a pressure similar to that necessary to inhibit pseudopod formation in *Amœba*. Changes in the cortical zone of the egg of *Arbacia*, resulting from fertilisation, are well brought out by Brown's technique ; in the fertilised egg the pigment granules migrate to the cortex within about ten minutes of fertilisation ; any sedimentation of the granules by centrifuging is then due to migration through the cortex. Application of a high pressure (408 atmospheres) increases the sedimentation rate, as with unfertilised eggs, but only within some thirty-three minutes of fertilisation ; after this, the highest pressures and the highest centrifugal forces barely allow the particles to move, a fact showing a large increase in the solidity of the cortex, a change necessary, as we have seen, for the development of the cleavage furrow. Direct studies of the cleavage process by Marsland have shown, however, that pressures above 350 atmospheres have sufficient effect on the solidification process to prevent the progress of the furrow (Fig. 18). The effects of pressure are not confined to cytoplasmic structures ; Pease has shown that the spindle of certain pollen cells can be liquefied by a pressure of 340 atmospheres ; in consequence, the movement of the chromosomes ceases ; with release of the pressure the spindle re-forms and movement is resumed. Pease concluded from these studies that the migration of the chromosomes was really due to a movement of the spindle to which they were attached ; this movement is envisaged as being similar to pseudopod formation—*i.e.*, sol-gel changes—but in this case circular or elliptical in its progression, like that of a conveyer-belt.

The interpretation of these striking effects of pressure on the physical state of the protoplasm will be deferred till later ; here we may point to the justifiable conclusion that physical factors which apparently liquefy the cortical regions inhibit those changes that are dependent on a reversible transformation of the solid cortex to liquid endoplasm, and *vice versâ*. The actual causes leading to the initiation of the furrow and the formation of asters are quite unknown ; it is interesting that Beams and King were able to suppress the cleavage of *Ascaris* eggs by centrifuging at 150,000 times gravity ; as Marsland showed, the pressures developed in the egg due to this centrifugal force were not sufficient to cause any cortical liquefaction, so that the effect is doubtless due to the sedimentation of some material important for the cleavage process ; eggs so treated showed a " bubbling," or emission of pseudopodia, suggesting that a surface-active material was concentrated in the surface as a result of the centrifugal force.

The Outer Layers of the Cell

The Plasma Membrane. We may now pass to the consideration of some phenomena associated with the more superficial structures of the cell ; here the technique of micro-dissection has provided most useful information. We have already seen that the outermost jelly, and the vitelline membrane lying under this, may be removed from the *Arbacia* egg, leaving the latter intact, clearly differentiated from its environment, and capable of undergoing fertilisation and cleavage. If a needle is inserted into the egg, and a sudden and extensive tear is made, the contents flow out and the cell disintegrates ; if, on the other hand, the cell is torn gradually and not too extensively, a certain " healing " process takes place which allows the cell to maintain its integrity. The decisive factor in the destruction of a cell by a tear is undoubtedly the injury to the plasma membrane ; the healing process probably represents the formation of a new plasma membrane capable of preventing the outflow of cytoplasm. If this new film is punctured, it disintegrates in a wave up to the edges of the torn cortex between which it initially stretched ; at this point disintegration of the surface layer ceases, and it would seem that normally the cortical layer of protoplasm acts as a support for the plasma membrane, significant damage to the latter being only possible by a mechanical tearing away of the cortex. Tearing away a piece of the cortex, in this manner, exposes the contents of the egg to disruptive contact with its environment ; if a new film is formed in time, disintegration of the cell is prevented and the two ends of the cortex may eventually join up ; failure of the film to form in time leads to the destruction of the cell.

During the disintegration of a cell whose wall has been suddenly torn, surface films appear to sweep around masses of the disorganised areas (*i.e.*, areas in which the granules have swollen and burst), converting them into spherical fragments of varying size ; these, however, subsequently swell up and burst. Sometimes, on the other hand, a film sweeps round a part of the cytoplasm that has not yet become disorganised, thereby converting it to a fragment of apparently healthy cytoplasm. As a result of cell injury, then, a protective mechanism comes into play which insulates the cytoplasm from too intimate contact with its environment by the formation of a film which probably becomes continuous with the original undamaged plasma membrane on the cortex. In *Amœba* this process has been observed to occur naturally in the event of a part of its surface sticking to the substratum ; when the cell moves away a piece of its cortex may come away in a strand, but the damaged plasma membrane is healed by the formation of a new film. If an egg is torn in sea-water from which the Ca^{++} has been removed, film formation does not occur and disintegration inevitably follows ; thus the formation of a membrane is dependent on the presence of Ca^{++} in the surrounding medium and Heilbrunn has described results which suggest that the formation is dependent on a chemical reaction involving a substance, *ovothrombin*, formed from some precursor in the egg in the presence of Ca^{++}, in rather the same way as blood clotting depends on a reaction involving thrombin, which is likewise formed from a precursor in the presence of Ca^{++}.

The liquid nature of the newly formed plasma membrane is indicated by gently pressing an egg which has been damaged ; a bulge is formed at the part covered by the newly formed film, and granules from the cytoplasm can be seen flowing in the surface. In a similar way, the plasma membrane on a naked but otherwise normal egg (*i.e.*, one with the vitelline membrane removed) can be shown to be liquid by placing a small cap of oil on its surface ; by appropriate micro-manipulation the oil cap can be made to move over the surface of the egg, causing flowing movements in the surface.

If the naked egg is bounded by an apparently liquid fatty membrane it may be asked why, when two eggs are approximated closely, either artificially, or naturally in the case of two blastomeres, the membranes do not fuse. An answer to this question is not possible, but some suggestive observations of Chambers can be quoted. When certain eggs cleave, the furrow advances in a knife-like manner, leaving behind the separated halves tightly pressed against each other, but nevertheless separate. At the head of both of the furrows, however, there is a rounded space, as in Fig. 19 ; and the exertion of high pressures fails to bring the surfaces of the blastomeres in contact in this region ; the advance of the furrow is brought about by the movement of the rounded spaces towards each other, leaving behind the flattened surfaces of the parts of the blastomeres already separated. Thus the *new surfaces* are formed initially in the loop and are held apart for a definite time before being allowed to come into contact ; during this time, presumably some change in the surface of the blastomeres takes place which makes them non-coalescent. The fact that oil droplets, which normally coalesce when brought into apposition, will not do so when they have been contaminated with cytoplasmic debris, suggests that the non-coalescence of the cell's surface is achieved by the diffusion of some substance from the cytoplasm to the newly formed surface.

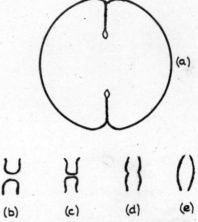

Fertilisation Membrane and Hyaline Plasma Layer. The changes in the cell during cleavage, namely mitosis and aster formation, have been described ; with the mature egg, cleavage is normally initiated by fertilisation, a process which is associated with a profound alteration in the vitelline membrane. A short time after the penetration of the spermatozoon (about eighteen seconds in the case of *Arbacia*), the vitelline membrane

FIG. 19. Illustrating the growth of the cleavage furrow. Note rounded space at head of each furrow, keeping the newly-formed surfaces apart (*a*). (*b*)— (*e*) illustrate gradual mergence of the heads of the furrows. (Chambers. *Cowdry's General Cytology*, Univ. of Chicago Press.)

separates from the surface of the egg, and subsequent cleavage takes place within this elevated membrane, which is now tough and elastic and quite different from the original structure ; in this state it is referred to as the *fertilisation membrane*. Loeb found that proteins, added to the sea-water, prevented the lifting of the fertilisation membrane ; and it would seem that the separation is an osmotic effect of the penetration of sea-water between the vitelline membrane and the subjacent hyaline plasma layer, due possibly to the secretion of osmotically active substances incapable of diffusing through the vitelline membrane (*see* Chapter VII). Moser has studied the behaviour of the cortical granules during the elevation, both as a result of normal fertilisation and of various artificial stimuli such as treatment with saponin, toluol, ultra-violet irradiation, etc. The elevation progresses as a wave round the egg and, as it proceeds, the cortical granules appear to dissolve. Whether the granules provide the osmotically active material supposed to be necessary for elevation, or contribute material for the hardening of the vitelline, is not known. Following the lifting of the fertilisation membrane, the hyaline plasma layer becomes prominent, presumably as a result of the secretion of fresh

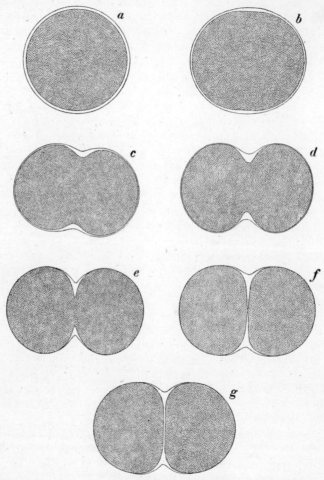

FIG. 20. Normal cleavage of egg of *Echinus esculentus*. Note gradual flow of hyaloplasm (white) from the poles of the egg to the equator. In (*f*) note that the cytoplasm is almost completely divided. In (*g*) the hyaloplasm has joined in the centre and the two masses of cytoplasm are completely divided off from each other, but are completely surrounded by hyaloplasm. (Gray. *Experimental Cytology*, C.U.P.)

material from the underlying cortex; it is this material that actually binds the blastomeres together. The various changes that take place in the distribution of the hyaline plasma layer during cleavage of the egg of *Echinus esculentus* are shown in Fig. 20, and it will be noted that the two blastomeres are held together closely and are thereby deformed from a spherical shape ; if the hyaline layer is removed, the blastomeres separate and become spherical. The chemical nature of the hyaline plasma layer is a matter of speculation ; it is considered to be a mucopolysaccharide ; according to Chambers (1949), sperm extracts do not cause a disintegration of the material, in that the blastomeres of a developing egg do not separate on treatment with the extracts. Naturally occurring mucopolysaccharides are several in number (p. 103), and there are probably specific enzymes capable of disintegrating them. The intercellular cement of a complex tissue, such as the endothelium of a capillary, is, presumably, the analogue of the hyaline plasma layer binding the blastomeres, and it is therefore of interest that hyaluronidase has no apparent effect on the integrity of the capillary proper (p. 219).

Coalescence with Oil Droplets. If a small drop of oil, say 50μ in diameter, is placed close to an *Arbacia* egg, whose outermost jelly layer has been removed, one of two things may happen ; the oil may either form a cap on the surface of the egg as in Fig. 21*a*, or it may coalesce with the egg as in Fig. 21*b*. The tendency for an oil drop to coalesce with an egg is measured quantitatively by esti- mating the surface energies of the system egg-oil before and after coalescence ; if we concentrate attention on the oil droplet, its surface energy when it is outside the egg is measured by its area and the surface tension between it and the surrounding sea-water ; when inside the egg, by its area and the surface tension between it and the inside of the egg. If the energy is the smaller when the oil is in the egg, there is a tendency for the oil to penetrate ; in actual fact the surface tension of oil droplets in the egg is always very much less than that of the same droplets outside, owing to the

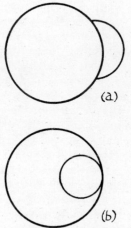

FIG. 21. Illustrating behaviour of an oil drop brought up to the surface of an egg. (*a*) cap formation ; (*b*) coalescence.

presence of proteins in the egg, which are adsorbed on to the surface of the oil and lower its interfacial tension ; thus an oil with a tension of 10 dynes/cm. in sea-water will have a tension of only a fraction of a dyne in the egg (Danielli). Consequently, in general, oil droplets will have a tendency to coalesce with cells, and the reason why all of them do not do so resides in the resistance of the cell surface to rupture during the process of penetration ; if the surface layers are strongly resistant, an oil with a high surface tension is required to achieve penetration, and *vice versâ*. Besides the surface tension of the drop, its diameter is also important, the greater the size of the droplet the greater the tendency to coalesce. The study of the coalescence of cells with oil droplets of various sizes and surface tensions thus provides a useful quantitative method of studying the nature of cell surfaces, a method that has been exploited with valuable results by Chambers and Kopac.

The normal *Arbacia* egg, complete with its jelly layer, will not coalesce with any oil droplets, however high their tension ; apparently the jelly prevents an intimate contact between the oil and the true protoplasmic surface of the egg. The vitelline membrane offers the most serious resistance to coalescence when the jelly has been removed ; thus an immediate increase in the coalescency may be achieved by mechanical removal of this membrane ; similarly, the gradual erosion of the vitelline, which takes place when eggs are allowed to age in sea-water, is associated with a marked increase in coalescency which may amount to a hundred-fold after twenty hours. Corresponding with the increase in coalescency there is a diminished resistance of the cell as a whole to mechanical stresses ; for example, on centrifuging an egg at high speed it elongates and, if the centrifugal force is great enough, it breaks into two spherical fragments ; in the absence of the vitelline membrane the centrifugal force required to fragment the egg is considerably reduced. By micro-dissection methods it can be shown that the eggs of different species have vitelline membranes of differing strength ; that of the *Asterias* egg is stronger than that of *Echinarachnius* which is stronger than that of *Arbacia*, and correspondingly the coalescences of the different species of egg vary in the inverse order, the mature *Asterias* egg not coalescing with any oil droplet however great its diameter or surface tension. In a similar way the fundamental change in the vitelline membrane due to fertilisation, referred to above, is reflected in the reduced coalescency of the egg, coalescence being prevented within a few minutes after fertilisation.

The secretion of the hyaline plasma layer on the surface of the fertilised egg may be followed by the same experimental technique ; fertilised eggs in sea-water, with their fertilisation membranes removed, show a rapid decrease in coalescence, so that after fifteen minutes oil drops fail to enter the cell ; on placing the eggs in KCl solution, a treatment which dissolves the hyaline plasma layer, the coalescence rapidly returns and reaches very high values, appropriate to the fact that the egg surface is now completely denuded of surface coats, only the fatty plasma membrane being left.

To review the knowledge presented here on the outer layers of the cell, we may divide them into a group of " extraneous coats " and an inner protoplasmic layer ; the former are not essential to the life or reproduction of the cell and consist, in the case of *Arbacia*, of a secreted jelly which may be removed by shaking ; a pellicle, called the vitelline membrane, which on fertilisation is lifted from its underlying stratum and becomes a tough protective outer shell within which the embryo develops ; and a hyaline plasma layer, secreted by the underlying cortex after the lifting of the fertilisation membrane. The two first mentioned layers are protective in function—the tougher the vitelline the more resistant is the cell to mechanical damage—whereas the hyaline plasma layer exerts its function as a cement when the egg divides, holding the blastomeres together in a definite pattern. The inner layer is made up of the plasma membrane and the cortex ; damage to these by tearing or chemical agents, unless rapidly repaired, leads to the destruction of the cell ; the plasma membrane probably represents the true barrier which separates the interior of the cell from its external medium, one of the functions of the cortex being to act as a support for this membrane.

Cytoplasmic Inclusions

Solid particles or liquid droplets within the cytoplasm of cells are given the generic name of *inclusion bodies ;* in many eggs these are most prominent as pigment granules, but probably the most important physiologically are the *mitochondria* (or *chondriosomes*) and *Golgi apparatus* —both microscopically visible—and sub-microscopic particles recently described by Claude, the *microsomes*. The cell is the seat of numerous chemical reactions ; a simple homogeneous medium would be quite inadequate for the ordered progress of these diverse chemical processes, so that the inclusion bodies may be regarded as separate phases, distinct from the cytoplasm, in which, or at the boundary of which, some reactions may proceed without interference from others. In addition, it is quite likely that the material of which the inclusion bodies are composed enters into the composition of certain products elaborated by the cell for special purposes ; thus in primitive nucleated red blood cells the mitochondria decrease in number as the amount of hæmoglobin in the cells increases ; or, again, the formation of fat in some cells appears to take place at the expense of the mitochondria. Finally, some inclusion bodies, such as granules of glycogen in the liver cell, represent storage depots resulting from intra-cellular synthesis.

Mitochondria and Microsomes. Mitochondria are seen in all cells (probably not in bacteria however), and are either filaments or granules ; the range of size is roughly 0.5 to 1.5μ ; they may be seen quite clearly, in constant movement, in tissue-culture cells under dark field illumination, so that they are not artefacts of fixation as has been sometimes suggested. Fig. 22, Pl. II, illustrates an electron-micrograph of a mitochondrion, whilst in Fig. 4, Pl. I, the long filamentous mitochondria of a cultured cell are clearly distinguishable. The movements of mitochondria are of two sorts ; a definite translation from one point to another, and a wriggling motion. The motion is inhibited by the metabolic poison, cyanide, and thus would appear to be due to currents occasioned by osmotic differences created by chemical reactions in their immediate neighbourhood.

One of the most valuable stimuli to research in cytology has been provided by the development of methods of separation of the morphological constituents of the cell in bulk, pioneered by Bensley. The methods were worked out by observation of the effects of various solutions on microscopic sections of frozen-dried tissue ; when the most suitable medium for preserving the desired element intact had been discovered, it was then employed in a large-scale extraction of the cells. In their classical extraction of the mitochondria from liver cells, Bensley & Hoerr ground up the tissue mechanically in order to destroy as many cells as possible ; the large pieces of debris were then removed by centrifuging at low speed (about $1{,}000\ g$). The supernatant fluid was then centrifuged at higher speeds ($3{,}000\ g$) to give a sediment which was purified by re-suspending in aqueous NaCl and centrifuging, the process being repeated several times. The mitochondria thus prepared are typically yellowish and contain a high percentage of water (possibly as high as 80 per cent.) ; the dry material has been analysed and been shown to contain mainly protein and fats, the latter representing some 35 per cent. and consisting to a great extent of phospholipids such as lecithin. At least a proportion of the protein belongs to the class of nucleoproteins (p. 73). More recently Claude has shown that, beisdes the mitochondria, all cells so far studied contain sub-microscopical particles ranging from 50 to 300mμ in diameter ; the technique followed in their isolation was essentially that of Bensley & Hoerr for mitochondria, but much greater centrifugal forces had to be applied to sediment the microsomes (18,000 g). Chemical analysis of the sedimented material, which was cherry-red in colour, indicated the presence of nucleoprotein and lipids. That the microsomes probably corresponded to definite entities within the cell was indicated by high-speed centrifuga-tion of a portion of liver tissue ; as Fig. 23, Pl. II, shows, the individual cells are stratified, the glycogen being at the centrifugal pole, the nucleus and mitochondria in the next layer, whilst above this there is a layer giving a basophilic reaction probably constituting the microsomes, and, finally, a clear hyaline layer.

The relation of the particulate matter of the cytoplasm—the mitochondria and microsomes—to the function of the cell is still largely a matter of speculation. The digestive functions of mitochondria in the unicellular organism are suggested by the observation of Horning that when an *Amœba* engulfs a piece of food the latter circulates in the cytoplasm and, in the process, comes in contact with mitochondria which adhere to it. A vacuole is secreted round the particle with its adhering mitochondria, whilst other mitochondria aggregate outside ; as digestion of the particle proceeds, it breaks up and at the same time the mitochondria become smaller and smaller, gradually passing into solution. Claude has suggested an intimate relationship between the microsomes and the *secretory granules* of the cells of glands and of the liver. By applying the methods of differential centrifugation he was able to isolate the secretory granules of the liver—solid or semi-solid globular particles distributed in the cytoplasm ; their chemical composition in terms of N, P, C and H was remarkably similar to that of the microsomes isolated from the same tissue. From the purely secretory cells of a tissue like the pancreas, *zymogen granules* were likewise isolated and proved to be similar chemically to the secretory granules of the liver. A similar relationship between the mitochondria and secretory granules has been postulated by Noël who states that filamentous mitochondria in the liver may transform gradually into mature secretory granules. Whatever the exact function of these particulates may be, it is worth noting that their composition is mainly made up of lipids and nucleoprotein ; both these substances probably exist normally as aggregates of large molecules (p. 76) in contrast to the corpuscular proteins, such as the globulins, which form true solutions ; they are thus ideally suited as a structural basis for discrete particles ; moreover it would seem that all the nucleoprotein and most, if not all, of the lipids of the cytoplasm are present in these particulates. Consequently, besides acting as separate phases for specific chemical reactions (thus

PLATE II

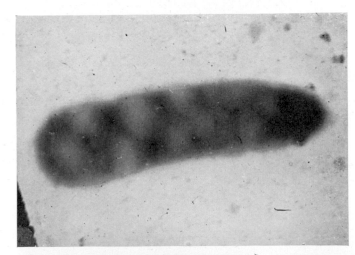

Fig. 22. Electron-micrograph of mitochondrion from pollen mother cell of maize. (Bucholz. *Amer. J. Bot.*)

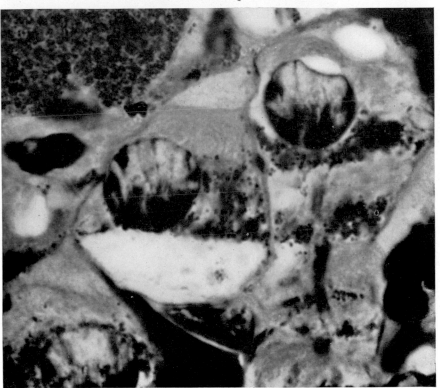

Fig. 23. Intracellular segregation of the morphological constituents of the hepatic cells of *Amphiuma* liver by sixty minutes' centrifugation at 18,000 g. The unstained layer at the base—centrifugal pole—of the large cell in the centre of the field consists of glycogen ; above it are the nucleus and mitochondria ; above these, the microsomes, whilst at the very tip—the centripetal pole—are fat globules or Golgi bodies. × 1,500. (Claude. *Harvey Lectures.*)

[To face p. 30.

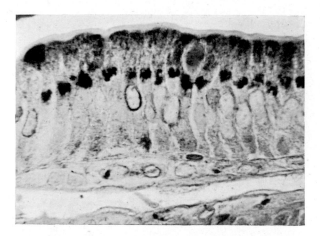

FIG. 24. Above : Mouse small intestine ; osmic acid staining. Below :
Mouse small intestine treated by Gomori method, the alkaline phosphatase
being sharply localised, appearing as a discrete body in the supra-
nuclear region of each cell and corresponding to the Golgi apparatus made
evident by osmic acid staining. × 800. (Emmel. *Anat. Rec.*)

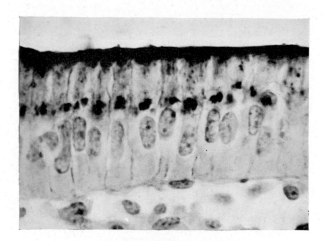

FIG. 25. Electron-micrograph of *Rickettsia prowazeki*. × 15,000, *ca.* (Ris
& Fox. *J. exp. Med.*)

certain enzymes [1] are definitely associated with the particulates, *e.g.*, succinoxidase, cytochrome oxidase, phosphatase, etc.), it is possible that they act as reservoirs of lipids and nucleoprotein, both of which are vitally important for certain cell structures (lipids for the plasma membrane ; nucleoproteins for the chromosomes of the nucleus and possibly also for the ground-structure of the cytoplasm (p. 64).

Golgi Apparatus. The Golgi apparatus is a dense network situated near the nucleus, which is blackened on fixation of the cell with osmic acid ; it was discovered first in the nerve cells of the barn-owl and the cat. The existence of this apparatus in the normal living cell has frequently been called into question but as a result of recent studies its existence cannot now be seriously denied. Thus it has been detected in unfixed tissue-culture cells, stained with methylene blue and viewed under dark-field illumination; moreover, as a result of a high concentration of the organic phosphate-splitting enzyme, alkaline phosphatase, in the apparatus, an excellent microphotograph showing its outline may be obtained by treating the cell with calcium glycerophosphate and subsequently precipitating cobalt sulphide (p. 2) as in Fig. 24, Pl. II. Perhaps the most convincing proof of the existence of the Golgi apparatus rests on its behaviour under different physiological and pathological conditions. This is so characteristic and reproducible that there should be no doubt of the reality of the structure exhibiting it. Moreover, by centrifuging with a force of 400,000 times gravity, the apparatus may be removed from its normal position. In general, it may be stated that the Golgi apparatus is present in all invertebrate and vertebrate cells, in protozoa but not in algæ, fungi, or bacteria ; its extreme variability in form suggests that it is in more or less constant movement. The Golgi apparatus seems to be intimately connected with the vital activities of the cell ; thus, in cells whose function it is to synthesise certain products and eliminate them as secretions, it is claimed that during activity droplets of secretion appear in the interstices of the apparatus and, as they grow in number, so the apparatus hypertrophies and finally, when the cell carries its full load of secretion, the apparatus appears to break up and small pieces become attached to some of the secretory granules. The Golgi apparatus, as with the mitochondria and microsomes, thus represents a separate phase in the cytoplasm at whose interface metabolic processes take place ; alternatively, these inclusion bodies may be what are called " condensation membranes," interfaces at which the products of metabolism may be accumulated. According to Ludford, the mitochondria-cytoplasm interface is the site of the synthesis of cellular enzymes ; these products diffuse into the cytoplasm and at the Golgi-cytoplasm interface they are concentrated into droplets, preliminary to their elimination from the cell as secretion.

[1] Harman (1950) has shown that the mitochondria contain a complex group of enzymes, given the collective name of *cyclophorase*, which catalyse the complete oxidation of pyruvic acid, fatty acids, and certain amino-acids by way of what is known as the *citric-acid cycle*. This finding indicates that mitochondria must be regarded as highly specialised morphological units and not mere chance aggregates of cellular material ; dispersion of the structure of the mitochondria destroyed the cyclophorase activity.

Virus and Rickettsia. Pathological types of inclusion bodies are provided by the *viruses* and *Rickettsiæ* which deserve mention if only because they exhibit types of living organisms that can only grow and multiply in the cells of another and higher type. Most viruses lead to the formation of " atypical bodies " and granulations within the cells of the infected host ; these bodies may be removed by microdissection techniques, for example by Woodruff in the case of the Bollinger inclusions of fowl pox and by Sheffield in the case of the mosaic virus of plants ; a single body inoculated into a normal host was capable of producing a typical lesion. The bodies are of microscopic size whilst the typical units of which they are made, and which constitute the actual virus, are either just above or below the limits of resolution by the light-microscope ; the yellow fever virus, for example, having a diameter of only 220A and that of the small-pox being 1,750A. In some cases, as with yellow fever, the virus proliferates in the nucleus, whilst in others, as with rabies, it grows in the cytoplasm.

The Rickettsiæ are bacterium-like organisms, usually less than 0.5μ in diameter, found intra-cellularly in arthropods such as the louse ; they are transmitted to the human host when the louse bites, and exist almost entirely intra-cellularly in their human hosts ; they are found in both nucleus and cytoplasm and are the causative agents in typhus, trench-fever, Rocky Mountain fever, and heart water of cattle. Fig. 25, Pl. II, is an electron micrograph of a strain of the epidemic typhus Rickettsia (*Rickettsia prowazeki*) made by Ris & Fox ; the dark bodies in the cytoplasm are equivalent to nuclei in higher organisms.

The viruses and Rickettsiæ, besides providing examples of living bodies inside the cells of another organism, are an interesting example of extremely " low " forms of life, forms which have carried parasitism to the most extreme degree in that they not only utilise the sources of chemical energy of their host, but they likewise make use of the host's specialised intra-cellular environment. Bacteria may be grown on inanimate culture media and maintain a suitable intra-cellular composition appropriate to the metabolic tasks necessary for growth and life. The virus, on the other hand, cannot live and multiply on an inanimate culture medium. It would appear to be, as we shall see, little more than a high molecular-weight nucleoprotein, and it requires to be within a living organism in order to be able to show that quality by which it is distinguished from dead matter, namely the power of reproduction. This reproduction requires energy which is derived from the chemical reactions in the host cell ; and it is possible that its injurious action resides in this robbing of the host cell of its metabolic energy. It is clear that we have in the virus a substance that is hovering on the border-line between living and dead matter, it is, in fact, a manifestation of life that promises to confound the distinction between animate and inanimate matter.[1]

---

[1] Some idea of the relative sizes of the organisms and structures discussed above will be given by the following :—
Arbacia egg, 1,000,000A ; *B. prodigiosum*, 7,500A ; small-pox virus, 1,750A ; yellow fever virus, 220A ; horse hæmoglobin, 55A.

References

BARER, R. (1948). " The Reflecting Microscope." *Brit. Sci. News*, 1, (6), 66.

BARER, R. (1948). " Phase-Contrast Microscopy." *Brit. Sci. News*, 1, (9), 10.

BARER, R. (1949). " The Reflecting Microscope." *Lancet*, p. 533.

BARER, R. (1950). " Ultra-Violet and Infra-Red Photomicrography." *Photo. J.*, 90B, 83.

BARER, R., HOLIDAY, E. R. & JOPE, E. M. (1950). " Technique of Ultra-Violet Spectroscopy with the Burch Reflecting Microscope." *Biochim. Biophys. Acta*, 6, 123.

BEAMS, H. W. (1943). " Ultracentrifugal Studies on Cytoplasmic Components and Inclusions." *Biol. Symp.*, 10, 71.

BEAMS, H. W. & KING, R. L. (1937). " Suppression of Cleavage in *Ascaris* Eggs by Centrifuging." *Biol. Bull.*, 73, 99.

BEAMS, H. W. & KING, R. L. (1940). " The Air-Driven Centrifuge, its Application in Biology, etc." *J. Roy. Micr. Soc.*, 60, 240.

BENSLEY, R. R. & HOERR, N. L. (1934). " Preparation and Properties of Mitochondria." *Anat. Rec.*, 64, 449.

BROWN, D. E. S. (1934). " The Pressure Coefficient of ' Viscosity ' in the Eggs of *Arbacia Punctulata*." *J. cell. & comp. Physiol.*, 5, 335.

BROWN, D. E. S. & MARSLAND, A. (1936). " Viscosity of *Amœba* at High Hydrostatic Pressure." *J. cell. & comp. Physiol.*, 8, 159.

BOURNE, G. (1942). Ed. " Cytology and Cell Physiology." Oxford. O.U.P.

BOURNE, G. (1942). Mitochondria and Golgi Apparatus. *loc. cit.*

BUCHOLZ, J. T. (1947). " Preparation of Chromosomes and Other Parts of Cells for Examination With an Electron Microscope." *Amer. J. Bot.*, 34, 445.

CARLSON, J. G. & HOLLAENDER, A. (1948). " Mitotic Effects of U.V. Radiation with Special Reference to the Spindle Cleavage." *J. cell. & comp. Physiol.*, 31, 149.

CASPERSSON, T. (1936). " U.d. Chemischen Aufbau der Strukturen des Zellkerns." *Scand. Arch. Physiol.*, 73, Suppl. 8.

CASPERSSON, T. (1940). " Methods for the Determination of the Absorption Spectra of Cell Structures." *J. Roy. Micr. Soc.*, 60, 8.

CHAMBERS, R. (1924). The Physical Structure of Protoplasm as Determined by Micro-Dissection and Injection. Cowdry's " General Cytology," p. 237.

CHAMBERS, R. (1940). " Recent Developments of the Micro-Manipulative Technique and its Application." *J. Roy. Micr. Soc.*, 60, 113.

CHAMBERS, R. (1940). " The Physical Properties of the Extraneous Coats of Living Cells." *C.S.H. Symp.*, 8, 144.

CHAMBERS, R. (1943). " Electrolyte Solutions Compatible with the Maintenance of Protoplasmic Structure." *Biol. Symp.*, 10, 91.

CHAMBERS, R. (1949). " Micrurgical Studies on Protoplasm." *Biol. Rev.*, 24, 246.

CHAMBERS, R. & KOPAC, M. J. (1937). " The Coalescence of Living Cells with Oil Drops." *J. cell. & comp. Physiol.*, 9, 331.

CLAUDE, A. (1943). " Distribution of Nucleic Acids in the Cell and the Morphological Constitution of Cytoplasm." *Biol. Symp.*, 10, 111.

CLAUDE, A. (1944). " Constitution of Mitochondria and Microsomes and the Distribution of Nucleic Acid in the Cytoplasm of a Leukæmic Cell." *J. exp. Med.*, 80, 19.

CLAUDE, A. (1947–8). " Studies on Cells : Morphology, Chemical Constitution and Distribution of Biochemical Functions." *Harvey Lectures*, 43, 121.

CLAUDE, A. & FULLAM, E. F. (1945). " Electron Microscope Study of Isolated Mitochondria." *J. exp. Med.*, 81, 51, 61.

COSTELLO, D. P. (1934). " The Effects of Temperature on the Viscosity of *Arbacia* Egg Protoplasm." *J. cell. & comp. Physiol.*, 4, 421.

COSTELLO, D. P. (1949). " The Relations of the Plasma Membrane, Vitelline Membrane and Jelly in the Egg of *Nereis Limbata*." *J. gen. Physiol.*, 32, 351.

CRICK, F. H. C. & HUGHES, A. F. W. (1950). " Physical Properties of Cytoplasm. A Study by Means of the Magnetic Particle." *Exp. Cell. Res.*, 1, 37.

DAN, K. & DAN, J. C. (1940). " Behaviour of the Cell Surface During Cleavage." *Biol. Bull.*, 78, 486.

DAN, K. & DAN, J. C. (1947). " Division Mechanism of Cells with Excentric Nuclei." *Biol. Bull.*, 93, 139.

DANIELLI, J. F. (1942). The Cell Surface and Cell Physiology. " Cytology and Cell Physiology." Ed. Bourne. Oxford. O.U.P.

DANIELLI, J. F. (1942). Physical and Physicochemical Studies of Cells. *loc. cit.*

DANIELLI, J. F. (1945). Some Reflections on the Forms of Simpler Cells. "Essays on Growth and Form." p. 255. Ed. Le Gros Clark & Medawar. Oxford.

DANIELLI, J. F. (1950). "Cell Physiology and Pharmacology." New York and Amsterdam. Elsevier.

DANIELLI, J. F. & HARVEY, E. N. (1935). "Tension at Surface of Mackerel Egg Oil, etc." *J. cell. & comp. Physiol.*, **5**, 483.

DEMPSEY, E. W. & WISLOCKI, G. B. (1946). "Histochemical Contributions to Physiology." *Physiol. Rev.*, **26**, 1.

DRUMMOND, D. G. (1950). Ed. "The Practice of Electron-Microscopy." *J. Roy. Micr. Soc.*, **70**, 1.

EMMEL, V. M. (1945). "Alkaline Phosphatase in the Golgi Zone of Absorbing Cells of the Small Intestine." *Anat. Rec.*, **91**, 39.

EVANS, T. C. (1948). "Selection of Radioautographic Technique for Problems in Biology." *Nucleonics*, **2**, (3), 52.

FREY-WYSSLING, A. (1948). "Submicroscopic Morphology of Protoplasm and its Derivatives." New York and Amsterdam. Elsevier.

GERSH, I. & BODIAN, D. (1943). "Histochemical Analysis of Changes in *Rhesus* Motoneurones after Root Section." *Biol. Symp.*, **10**, 163.

GOMORI, G. (1939). "Microchemical Demonstrations of Phosphatase in Tissue Sections." *P.S.E.B.M.*, **42**, 23.

GORBMAN, A. (1948). "Radioautography in Biological Research." *Nucleonics*, **2**, (6), 30.

GROSS, J. & LEBLOND, C. P. (1946). "Histological Localisation of Radioactive Elements." *McGill Med. J.*, **15**, 399.

HARMAN, J. W. (1950). "Association of Cyclophorase with Mitochondria." *Exp. Cell. Res.*, **1**, 382.

HARMAN, J. W. (1950). "Structure of Mitochondria in Relation to Enzymatic Activity." *Exp. Cell. Res.*, **1**, 394.

HARVEY, E. N. & DANIELLI, J. F. (1938). "Properties of the Cell Surface." *Biol. Rev.*, **13**, 319.

HEILBRUNN, L. V. (1929). "Absolute Viscosity of *Amœba* Protoplasm." *Protoplasma*, **8**, 65.

HEILBRUNN, L. V. (1943). "An Outline of General Physiology." Philadelphia. Saunders.

HEILBRUNN, L. V. & WILSON, W. L. (1948). "Protoplasmic Viscosity Changes during Mitosis in the Egg of *Chœtopterus*." *Biol. Bull.*, **95**, 57.

HOERR, N. L. (1943). "Methods of Isolation of Morphological Constituents of the Liver Cell." *Biol. Symp.*, **10**, 185.

HOGEBLOOM, G. H., CLAUDE, A. & HOTCHKISS, R. D. (1946). "Distribution of Cytochrome Oxidase and Succinoxidase in the Cytoplasm of the Mammalian Liver Cell." *J. biol. Chem.*, **165**, 615.

HOGEBLOOM, G. H., SCHNEIDER, W. C. & PALLADE, G. E. (1948). "Isolation of Intact Mitochondria from Rat Liver, etc." *J. biol. Chem.*, **172**, 619.

HOLTFRETER, J. (1947). "Phenomena Relating to the Cell Membrane in Embryonic Processes." *Proc. Int. Congr. Cyt.*, p. 497.

HORNING, E. S. (1926). "Observations on Mitochondria." *Austr. J. exp. Biol. Med.*, **3**, 149.

KAMIYA, N. (1940). "The Control of Protoplasmic Streaming." *Science*, **92**, 462.

KITCHING, J. A. & PIRENNE, M. H. (1940). "Influence of Low Tensions of O_2 on Protoplasmic Streaming." *J. cell. & comp. Physiol.*, **16**, 13.

KOPAC, M. J. (1940). "Physical Properties of the Extraneous Coats of Living Cells." *C.S.H. Symp.*, **8**, 154.

KOPAC, M. J. & CHAMBERS, R. (1937). "Coalescence of Living Cells with Oil Drops." *J. cell. & comp. Physiol.*, **9**, 345.

LAZAROW, A. (1943). "Chemical Structure of Cytoplasm, etc." *Biol. Symp.*, **10**, 9.

LEWIS, W. H. (1942). "Relation of Viscosity Changes of Protoplasm to Amœboid Locomotion and Cell Division." *Structure of Protoplasm*. Ed. Seifriz. Ames, Iowa.

LUDFORD, R. J. (1942). Pathological Aspects of Cytology. "Cytology and Cell Physiology." Ed. Bourne. Oxford. O.U.P.

MARSLAND, D. A. (1938) "Effects of High Hydrostatic Pressure on Cell Division in *Arbacia* Eggs." *J. cell. & comp. Physiol.*, **12**, 57.

MARSLAND, D. A. (1939). "Hydrostatic Pressure Effects on Dividing Egg Cells." *J. cell. & comp. Physiol.*, **13**, 15.

MARSLAND, D. A. (1939). "Effects of High Hydrostatic Pressure on Cyclosis in *Elodea Canadensis*." *J. cell. & comp. Physiol.*, **13**, 23.

MARSLAND, D. A. & BROWN, D. E. S. (1936). "Amœboid Movement at High Hydrostatic Pressure." *J. cell. & comp. Physiol.*, **8**, 167.

MARSLAND, D. A. & BROWN, D. E. S. (1942). "Effects of Pressure on Sol-Gel Equilibria with Special Reference to Myosin and Other Protoplasmic Gels." *J. cell. & comp. Physiol.*, **20**, 295.

MARSLAND, D. A. & JAFFEE, O. (1949). "Effects of Pressure on the Cleaving Eggs of the Frog." *J. cell. & comp. Physiol.*, **34**, 439.

MARTIN, L. C. (1947). "Phase-Contrast Methods in Microscopy." *Nature*, **159**, 827.

MAST, S. O. (1926). "Structure, Movement, Locomotion and Stimulation in *Amœba*." *J. Morph.*, **41**, 347.

MAST, S. O. (1931). "Locomotion in *Amœba*." *Protoplasma*, **14**, 321.

MAST, S. O. & PROSSER, C. L. (1932). "Effect of Temperature, Salts and pH on Rupture of the Plasmagel Sheet, Rate of Locomotion and Gel/Sol Ratio in *Amœba Proteus*." *J. cell. & comp. Physiol.*, **1**, 333.

MEYER, K. (1947). "The Biological Significance of Hyaluronic Acid and Hyaluronidase." *Physiol. Rev.*, **27**, 335.

MONROY, A. (1947). "Formation of the Fertilisation Membrane in the Sea Urchin." *Proc. Int. Congr. Cyt.*, p. 525.

MONROY, A. (1947). "Fine Structure of the Cortical Layer of Unfertilised and Fertilised Sea Urchin Eggs." *J. cell. & comp. Physiol.*, **30**, 105.

MONROY, A. & RUFFO, A. (1947). "Hyaluronidase in Sea-Urchin Sperm." *Nature*, **159**, 603.

MOSER, F. (1939). "Studies on a Cortical Layer Response to Stimulating Agents in the *Arbacia* Egg." *J. exp. Zool.*, **80**, 423, 447.

NOËL, R. (1923). "Recherches histo-physiologiques sur la cellule hépatique des mammifères." *Arch. d'Anat. Micr.*, **19**, 1.

NORRIS, C. H. (1940). "Elasticity Studies on the Myxomycete *Physarum Polycephalum*." *J. cell. & comp. Physiol.*, **16**, 313.

PAYNE, B. O. (1947). "Image Formation in Phase-Contrast Microscopy." *J. sci. Instr.*, **24**, 163.

PEASE, D. C. (1940). "Hydrostatic Pressure Effects on Protoplasmic Streaming in *Plasmodium*." *J. cell. & comp. Physiol.*, **16**, 361.

PEASE, D. C. (1946). "Hydrostatic Pressure Effects on Spindle Figure and Chromosome Movement." *Biol. Bull.*, **91**, 145.

PEASE, D. C. & MARSLAND, D. A. (1939). "Cleavage of *Ascaris* Eggs Under Exceptionally High Pressure." *J. cell. & comp. Physiol.*, **14**, 407.

PORTER, K. R., CLAUDE, A. & FULLAM, E. F. (1945). "Study of Tissue Culture Cells by Electron Microscopy." *J. exp. Med.*, **81**, 233.

RIS, H. & FOX, J. P. (1949). "Cytology of Rickettsiæ." *J. exp. Med.*, **89**, 681.

RUNNSTRÖM, J., MONNÉ, L. & BROMAN, L. (1944). "Some Properties of the Surface Layers in the Sea-Urchin Egg and Their Changes on Activation." *Arch. f. Zool.*, **35**A, No. 3.

SCHECTMAN, A. M. (1937). "Localised Cortical Growth as the Immediate Cause of Cell Division." *Science*, **85**, 222.

SCHNEIDER, W. C., CLAUDE, A. & HOGEBLOOM, G. H. (1948). "Distribution of Cytochrome-*c* and Succinoxidase Activity in Rat Liver Fractions." *J. biol. Chem.*, **172**, 451.

SCHULMAN, J. H. (1942). Physical and Physicochemical Studies of Cells. "Cytology and Cell Physiology." Ed. Bourne. Oxford. O.U.P.

SEIFRIZ, W. S. (1924). "Structure of Protoplasm and of Inorganic Gels : an Analogy." *J. exp. Biol.*, **1**, 431.

SEIFRIZ, W. S. (1942) Ed. "The Structure of Protoplasm." Ames, Iowa. Iowa State College Press.

SEIFRIZ, W. S. (1942). Some Physical Properties of Protoplasm and Their Bearing on Structure. *loc. cit.*, p. 245.

SHEFFIELD, F. M. L. (1939). "Micrurgical Studies on Virus-Infected Plants." *Proc. Roy. Soc.*, B, **126**, 529.

SOSA, J. M. (1947). "Morphological, Chemical and Physico-Chemical Significance of the Golgi Apparatus." *Proc. Int. Congr. Cyt.*, p. 402.

STEINBACH, H. B. & MOOG, F. (1945). "Localisation of Adenylpyrophosphatase in Cytoplasmic Granules." *J. cell. & comp. Physiol.*, **26**, 175.

WILLIAMS, R. C. & WYCKOFF, R. W. G. (1945). "Applications of Metallic Shadow-Casting to Microscopy." *J. app. Phys.*, **17**, 23.

WOODRUFF, C. E. & GOODPASTURE, E. W. (1925). "Infectivity of Isolated Inclusion Bodies of Fowl-Pox." *Amer. J. Path.*, **5**, 1.

CHAPTER II

THE SUBMICROSCOPIC STRUCTURE OF THE CELL

HAVING reviewed in some detail those structures of the cell that have been made visible, we may now delve further into the submicroscopic structure of its parts ; to this end two other weapons, besides the electron-microscope, have been applied, namely the *polarising microscope* and the *X-ray diffraction* apparatus. These methods of analysis depend on the fact that most solid bodies are, in effect, crystalline, *i.e.*, that their constituent atoms or molecules are packed together in a definite regular three-dimensional pattern. With certain obviously crystalline substances, such as copper sulphate, this orderly arrangement can be inferred from the appearance and mode of growth of the crystals ; with substances commonly called amorphous, on the other hand, the regular spacings of the atoms or molecules have been deduced from the more refined methods now to be described.

Polarisation Microscopy

Polarisation optical methods depend on the *anisotropy* of crystalline matter ; by anisotropy is meant the variation in some characteristic of the material with directions within it ; thus its magnetic susceptibility, or its coefficient of linear expansion, may vary according to the direction along which it is measured. This anisotropy follows from the ordered packing of its constituent elements or "units." Thus Fig. 26 represents a section through a crystal built up by a regular arrangement of a group of three atoms, and of one atom ; it will be seen that the order in which the various atoms are encountered varies with the direction, so that

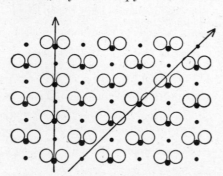

FIG. 26. Crystal properties vary with direction. (Bunn. *Chemical Crystallography*. Clarendon Press, Oxford.)

light travelling in different directions may be differently affected. In an isotropic medium, on the other hand, owing to the random distribution of atoms or structural units, on the average one direction through the solid will be equivalent to any other.

Polarisation and Double Refraction. Light may be regarded as vibrations in planes containing the direction of propagation ; in ordinary light the vibrations may be thought of as taking place in all possible planes ; moreover, a vibration in any one of these planes may be resolved into components in any two planes at right-angles ; for example the vertical and horizontal. With a vibration at 45° to the vertical plane, for example, half of the energy of the vibration may be said to be in the vertical plane and half in the horizontal ; if the vibration is in the vertical plane all its energy is in this plane and none in the horizontal. In plane *polarised* light the vibration is confined to a certain plane, that is, the vector describing its vibration is in a given plane. In planes inclined to this plane of vibration there will be components of vibration-energy, as indicated above, except for the case of the plane at right-angles ; thus light polarised in the vertical plane has no vibration-energy in the horizontal plane. If, therefore, it were possible to find a material which would exclude certain vibrations in virtue of their plane of vibration, it should be possible to *extinguish* light, polarised in an appropriate plane, on passing it through this substance ; moreover such a substance would polarise ordinary light. For example, if the substance excludes vibrations in the horizontal plane, vertically polarised light will pass through unaffected in intensity because its vibrations are in the vertical plane entirely ; with horizontally polarised light, on the other hand, the light will be completely extinguished since all the vibration-energy of the light was in this plane. Light polarised at 45°, on the other hand, will be partially transmitted, since the vertical vibrations have a component in the 45° plane, and it will only be the component in the horizontal plane that is excluded ; the intensity will in fact be cut down by one half.[1] It is because an anisotropic substance has the power of polarising light that it is possible to analyse its structure with the polarising microscope.

When light passes from air into a crystal its velocity decreases, and this manifests itself as a bending of the rays of light, *refraction*, the ratio of the sines of the angles of incidence and refraction being called the *refractive index ;* alternatively it may be shown that the ratio of the velocities of light in the air and the crystal is a measure of the refractive index. In an isotropic medium, such as glass, the velocity of light is independent of the direction of vibration of the light, *i.e.,* there are no " preferred " directions in which it is easier for vibration to take place than others ; consequently the velocity of light is independent of direction and the refractive index is invariable. In an anisotropic medium, on the other hand, we may generally expect the velocity to be different for different directions of vibration ; by choice of the angle of incidence, the ray of light is split into two components, travelling with unequal velocities and polarised in planes at right-angles ; these are known as the *ordinary* and *extraordinary rays*. The two phenomena, namely of polarisation and double refraction, are both manifestations of the same cause, namely the existence within the crystal of an orderly arrangement of units built up on such a plan that only the resolved components of the vibrations in two mutually perpendicular planes are transmitted.[2] With a certain direction of propagation, however, ordinary light will not be polarised, or

[1] The intensity in any plane inclined at an angle θ to the plane of the vector will be given by $I \cos^2\theta$.

[2] To explain *why* this should result in the rays taking different directions is beyond the scope of this book, but it follows simply from the application of Huygens' principle.

doubly refracted, because all directions at right-angles to the direction of propagation are equivalent ; this direction of propagation is called an *optic axis* of the crystal, and corresponds to a symmetry axis ; some crystals have several such directions, or optic axes (*e.g.*, the cubic crystal of sodium chloride with three), but a great many have only one and are called *uniaxial*. Thus let us consider a crystal built up of long molecules as in Fig. 29 (p. 41) ; the optic axis corresponds with a direction parallel to the long axes of the molecules, since a section at right-angles to this axis gives an arrangement of units that are completely symmetrical about the axis; *i.e.*, vibration, which must occur at right-angles to the direction of propagation, will be just as easy in any direction at right-angles to the axis, so that no double-refraction occurs when the direction of propagation is along the axis. When the light is incident at an angle to the axis, however, all directions of vibration are not equivalent, and the vibrations will be

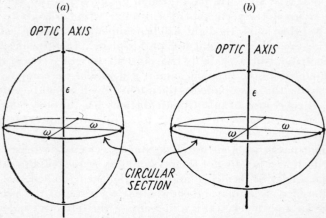

(*a*)   (*b*)

Fig. 27.   Left : positive uniaxial indicatrix, n_e being greater than n_o (n_ω) ; right : negative uniaxial indicatrix, n_e being less than n_o (n_ω).   (Bunn. *Chemical Crystallography*.   Clarendon Press, Oxford.)

resolved into components along the optic axis and at right-angles to this, giving rise to two sets of vibrations in mutually perpendicular planes, *i.e.*, two rays of polarised light which emerge in different directions. The two rays, as we have seen, exhibit different refractive indices ; the *ordinary ray*, *i.e.*, that which gives a refractive index, n_o, independent of the angle of incidence and thus obeys Snell's Law ; and the extraordinary ray showing a refractive index varying with the direction of propagation, being equal to that of the ordinary ray when the direction of propagation is along the optic axis and at a minimum, or maximum, n_e, when at right-angles to the optic axis. It is common to represent the refractive indices of a crystalline material by the so-called *indicatrix* ; thus starting from a point within a crystal we may draw lines in all directions with lengths corresponding to the refractive index of light vibrating along these lines ; the ends of these lines fall on the surface of an ellipsoid, a solid figure all sections passing through the centre of which are ellipses. For a uniaxial crystal this takes the form of an ellipsoid of revolution, obtained by rotating an ellipse about one of its principal axes ; it will thus have a circular section at right-angles to the optic axis, indicating that the refractive index is the same for all directions of vibration at right-angles to the axis, and equal to n_o, the refractive index shown by the ordinary ray (Fig. 27). When the refractive index for the vibration-direction along the axis, n_e, is greater than that for vibration at right-angles to the axis, n_o, the crystal is said to be *uniaxial positive*, the indicatrix taking the form of Fig. 27a ; in the uniaxial negative crystal n_o is greater than n_e (Fig. 27b).

Polarisation Optical Analysis of Structure. The analysis of the structure of a crystalline body by polarisation optics is essentially an analysis of the direction of the optic axis (or axes) ; since the optic axis corresponds to a principal symmetry direction, it is a valuable aid in identification ; in biological work, as we shall see, the determination of this axis provides considerable information regarding the build-up of a variety of structures.

The Nicol prism, used in the analysis of structure, is a body built up of a

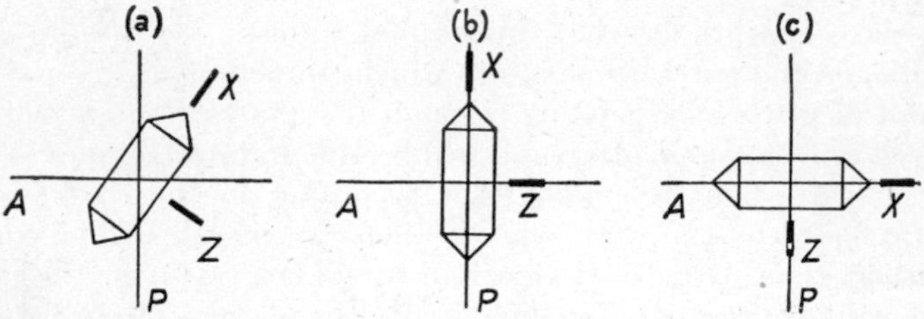

Fig. 28. Crystals of monammonium phosphate between crossed Nicols. The polarising Nicol transmits light vibrating in a vertical plane through P ; X and Z are the vibration-planes of the crystal. (a) Light is transmitted through the crossed Nicols because vibrations in plane P have components in X and Z, which will not be extinguished by the analyser. (b) and (c) Light is not transmitted because light emerging from the crystal remains polarised in the plane, P, of the analyser which is at right-angles to A. (Bunn. *Chemical Crystallography*. Clarendon Press, Oxford.)

doubly refracting material (calcite) in such a way that the ordinary refracted ray is lost and only the extraordinary ray is passed [1]; thus a beam of light passing through a Nicol prism is single, and polarised in the vibration plane of the prism. Let us suppose that this is vertical. If now this beam is passed through another Nicol prism with its optic axis at right-angles to that of the first—*polarising*—prism, the light is completely extinguished, since the vibrations are in the vertical plane with no component in the horizontal plane. The first Nicol is called the *polariser* and the second the *analyser*, and the arrangement is described as " crossed Nicols." On placing a birefringent (doubly refracting) material between the crossed Nicols, however, the resulting appearance will depend on the orientation of the material in respect to the Nicols. With a certain position the light will be extinguished, whilst at others it will be visible. On rotating the material it will be extinguished four times per revolution. The explanation of the phenomenon is as follows : If the first, polarising, Nicol transmits

[1] The ordinary ray passes out at the side of the crystal and is absorbed by the blackened side of the tube in which it is mounted.

light vibrating in the vertical plane, P, of Fig. 28 (*i.e.*, a plane through the line P perpendicular to the plane of the paper), the vibrations are resolved into the vibration-planes of the crystal, X and Z. This light, on passing through the second, analysing, Nicol is resolved into the plane A, at right-angles to P. Thus light is transmitted through the crossed Nicols. When the vibration-planes of the crystal correspond with the vibration-planes of the Nicols, on the other hand, as in (*b*) and (*c*) no light is transmitted ; for example, in (*b*), the light from the first Nicol passes through the crystal unchanged in its vibration-direction so that it is still vibrating in the plane P, at right-angles to the plane A of the analyser, and so has no component in this latter plane.

The polarising microscope permits also a determination of the magnitude of the birefringence, *i.e.*, the value of $n_e - n_o$; the method is based on a determination of the *retardation* of the extraordinary ray in respect to the ordinary ray, measured by $\gamma\lambda$, where γ is the *phase-difference* and λ the wavelength of the light ; thus $n_e - n_o = \gamma\lambda/d$, where d is the thickness of the material. Essentially what this implies is that a ray of light gives rise to an ordinary and extraordinary ray which, travelling at different speeds, will be out of phase ; on passing through the analyser the vibrations will be resolved into the same plane and will be able to interfere and so produce colours, if white light is employed. According to the thickness of the crystal traversed by the light, one or other wavelength will be completely extinguished, thus giving rise to a colour by subtraction (*e.g.*, the extinction of yellow will give rise to a blue light). By the use of a birefringent quartz wedge (*i.e.*, a quartz crystal of continuously increasing thickness), and sliding this gradually over the material between the crossed Nicols, it is possible to extinguish the light coming through the analyser, *i.e.*, to neutralise the birefringence of the material being examined. By then observing the colour obtained with the wedge in this position in the absence of the material, the retardation of the wedge may be read off from a chart ; since this just compensates that due to the material being examined, it is equal to the retardation of the latter.

Wiener Mixed Body. The double refraction of crystals built up of atoms or small molecules is generally small, whereas when the units of structure are large, for example in a body made up of long rod-like particles as in Fig. 29, the double refraction is large ; the polarising microscope is thus most useful in the analysis of the structure of bodies in terms of the arrangement of comparatively large structural units. In biological systems it frequently happens that the structure can be resolved into a fairly regular array of large *micelles* or *crystallites* (large on an atomic scale but submicroscopic) ; these micelles generally themselves possess a crystalline structure, so that the observed birefringence of the body as a whole is due to both the orientation of the large micelles as units in a crystalline or semi-crystalline structure (*form birefringence*). and the birefringence due to the crystalline arrangement of the atoms or molecules in the micelles (*micellar birefringence*). A material made up in this way is called a *Wiener mixed body* after O. Wiener who analysed the relationship between the two components of birefringence. Fig. 29 represents two typical cases of mixed bodies ; in general, we may note that the total birefringence will disappear when the large units are randomly orientated since in this case there is no form birefringence, and the micellar birefringence, whilst still present in so far as any individual micelle is concerned, will be effectively cancelled out. According to Wiener's treatment, moreover, when the refractive index of the material between the micelles is the same as that of the micelles, the form birefringence becomes zero, so that the observed birefringence is entirely micellar. Consequently on soaking a tissue in

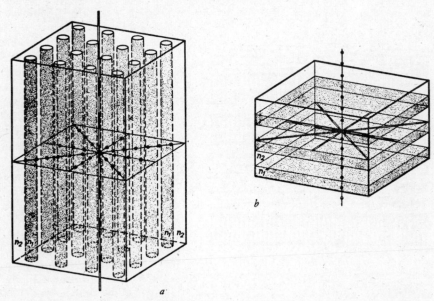

FIG. 29. Wiener composite bodies. n_1 and n_2 are the refractive indices of particles and medium respectively. (*a*) The optic axis is parallel to the rods; vibrations parallel to the rods have the higher refractive index, n_e, so that the form birefringence is positive. (*b*) The optic axis is at right-angles to the laminæ ; vibrations parallel to the laminæ—*i.e.*, at right-angles to the optic axis—have the higher refractive index ; n_o is therefore greater than n_e and the form birefringence is negative. (Frey-Wyssling. *Submicroscopic Morphology of Protoplasm and its Derivatives*. Elsevier. N.Y.)

media of increasing refractive index, if it is due to a Wiener mixed body, the birefringence will pass through a minimum.

With long particles or molecules, the refractive index for light vibrating in the direction of the long axis of the molecule is greater than for light vibrating across this axis ; consequently for a crystal made up of long molecules we may state that the *birefringence is positive*, the optic axis lying in the direction of the long axes of the molecules, and light vibrating parallel to the optic axis, *i.e.*, giving rise to the extraordinary ray, showing the greater refractive index (n_e greater than n_o). The indicatrix is an ellipse with its major axis parallel to the optic axis. Flat molecules, or lamellæ, on the other hand, show a greater refractivity for light vibrating in the plane of the molecules ; the optic axis is perpendicular to the plane of the flat molecule (Fig. 29) so that the ellipse lies with its major axis at right-angles to the optic axis and the *birefringence is negative*. According to the way the molecules in the micelles are built up, and according to the orientation of the optic axes of the micelles in the larger structure, we may get several types of double refraction in composite bodies. Fig. 30 illustrates an example provided by W. J. Schmidt ; here we have a structure made up of orientated layers of lipids—long-chain molecules with their long axes at right-angles to the surface ; beneath this is a layer of water which separates the upper lipid layer from a lower one built up on the same pattern. Beneath this is a layer of protein, thought to consist of lamellæ on top of each other. The indicatrix for each component of the structure is indicated in the diagram, both for form and micellar birefringence. Thus the optic axis is perpendicular to the surface for all types of bire-fringence except the micellar birefringence of the protein lamellæ ; each layer of lipid may be regarded as a crystal with a refractive index for vibrations parallel to the optic axis greater than that at right-angles, so that the micellar birefringence of this layer is positive. The protein lamellæ consist, as we shall see, of long chains running parallel to the surface, so that their micellar double refraction is also posi-tive. The form birefringence is negative for both lipids and protein since the structure is one of lamellæ piled on top of each other.[1]

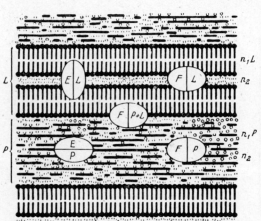

FIG. 30. Ultra-structure and polarisation-optics of a layer system made up of protein laminæ (P) and bimolecular lipoid laminæ (L). EP, FP, micellar and form birefringence of protein respectively ; EL, FL, the same for lipids. F P + L is the form birefringence of the protein-lipid layer body. n_1P and n_1L are refractive indices of protein and lipid micelles respec-tively ; n_2 is the refractive index of the inter-micellar medium. (Slightly modified from W. J. Schmidt. *Ergebn. d. Physiol.*)

Birefringence of Protoplasm. A study of normal resting cytoplasm of, for example, the *Arbacia* egg or *Amœba* with the polarising microscope

---

[1] Birefringence is frequently referred to the axis of the biological structure, as opposed to the true optic axis, a practice leading to confusion. Thus the sheath of a myelinated nerve (p. 378) is made up of long lipoid molecules orientated radially (Fig. 165) ; the birefringence due to these molecules is positive, the optic axis being radial (along the molecules) and n_e, the refractive index for vibrations parallel to the optic axis, is greater than n_o the refractive index at right-angles to the axis. The birefringence of the nerve is however, described as negative (*e.g.*, by F. O. Schmitt), the axis of reference being the long axis of the nerve, which is at right-angles to the true optic axis, *i.e.*, the refractive index for vibrations parallel to the *axis of the nerve* is less than that for vibrations at right-angles, so that the birefringence is said to be negative. Where biological systems are concerned, it is most satisfactory to indicate the position of the index ellipse in the cell ; if the long axis of this is parallel to the axis of the cell the birefringence is positive in relation to this axis.

gives little evidence of submicroscopic structure ; this is due most probably to the effectively random orientation of the micellar elements within it. When, however, the cytoplasm is active, as in the formation of rhizopods in *Miliola*, definite birefringence is observable (Fig. 31, Pl. III), indicating the presence of long micelles with their axes orientated in the direction of flow. Again, the mitotic spindle is birefringent, positive in relation to the spindle axis, suggesting once again orientated protein fibrils (Fig. 32, Pl. III) ; the asters, moreover, show double refraction, positive in relation to the radius of the rays. In *Amœba* the surface layers, probably both the plasmalemma and the cortex, are negatively birefringent, with the optic axis perpendicular to the surface, *i.e.*, the material seems to be a laminated and probably protein structure ; similar findings are reported for the fertilisation membrane of eggs, the birefringence being very strong, in marked contrast to the weakly birefringent or isotropic vitelline membrane.

These studies, and a variety of others carried out by Ambronn, W. J. Schmidt, Frey-Wyssling, F. O. Schmitt, Runnström, and Monné, provide evidence that the cytoplasm consists of large (although submicroscopic) units which, under the influence of stresses or certain physiological changes, acquire an orientation that permits their identification by polarisation microscopy. For a long time there was a tendency to dismiss the fibrillar structures appearing in fixed specimens as artefacts ; and the demonstration, by polarisation microscopy, of formed elements capable of providing some sort of solid structure in the cytoplasm may be regarded as one of the most fundamental contributions to cytology. This tendency to ignore the significance of structures appearing in fixed specimens, whilst it indicates a healthy scientific caution, has certainly been a handicap to the advance of the theory of cytoplasmic structure ; thus the presence of fibrils in the nerve axoplasm (p. 377), observed in fixed specimens, was generally doubted for the living tissue ; however Bear, Schmitt & Young have shown that the nerve axoplasm is positively birefringent, indicating the presence of submicroscopic fibrils lying parallel with the axis of the nerve. Other examples of the value of the polarisation microscope will be given in succeeding chapters ; it is sufficient to note that the application of this method has revealed the presence of submicroscopic units, or micelles, in the cytoplasm capable of providing the basis for a submicroscopic structure. By the use of X-rays some knowledge of the fine structure of these micellar units has been acquired ; we may therefore pass to a consideration of the principles of the technique and some of the results of its application.

X-Ray Diffraction Studies

Diffraction of X-Rays. Visible light may be *diffracted* by a grating consisting of a series of parallel microscopically thin lines ruled on a glass plate ; the diffraction consists of the reflection of the light from each line, associated with interference between the reflected beams, so that the light from a slit, falling on a screen after diffraction by the grating, consists of a series of lines. An analysis of the spacing of these lines enables us to deduce the spacing of the lines on the glass plate, provided the wavelength of the light is known. X-rays have such a small wavelength (of the order of 1A), that the spacings of regular arrays of atoms in a crystal have the same relation to the wavelength as those of the classical ruled grating bear to the wavelength of visible light ; thus the diffraction of X-rays by a crystal reveals the spacing of the atoms, or rather layers of atoms, in this crystal (Fig. 33). It is not sufficient that the atoms in a crystal should form a single reflecting plane ; in order that the resulting diffraction pattern should have some definiteness it is necessary that the atoms should be so arranged throughout the bulk of the crystal as to present a *series of planes* to the X-rays. The crystals of gold, aluminium, copper, etc., are built up of a " lattice " of atoms which consists essentially of the indefinite

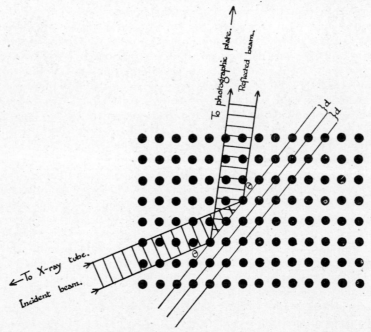

FIG. 33.   Illustrating the reflections of an X-ray beam by a layer of molecules in the body of a crystal. (Astbury. *Fundamentals of Fibre Structure.* O.U.P.)

repetition of a *face-centred cube*, *i.e.*, a cube made up of atoms at its eight corners and one at the centre of each face (Fig. 34). Iron, at ordinary temperatures, is made up of a *body-centred cube*, *i.e.*, with the eight atoms at the corners and one in the centre of the cube. Building up one cube on top of another, in all dimensions, will clearly give rise to an ordered arrangement of atoms in planes at definite distances from each other. The spacings of these planes will be unique for the particular arrangement, and so the structure may be deduced from the X-ray diffraction pattern.[1] The

---

[1] To define the repeating unit of the gold crystal, for example, it s not necessary to describe the complete cube ; thus the whole crystal lattice could be built up by repeats of the atoms A B C D in the directions AB, AC, AD ; the figure ABCD is therefore the repeat-unit. In many structures the lines along which the atoms or molecules repeat

PLATE III

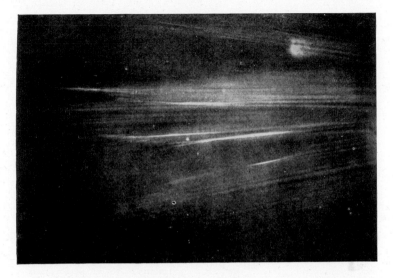

FIG. 31. *Miliola* rhizopods between crossed Nicols. × 165. (W. J. Schmidt. *Ergebn. d. Physiol.*)

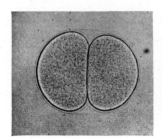 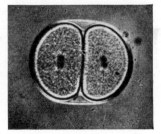

FIG. 32. Left : Egg of *Psammechinus miliaris* in normal light. Right : The same, between crossed Nicols, showing birefringence of recently divided nuclear spindle. × 185. (W. J. Schmidt. *Ergebn. d. Physiol.*)

[To face p. 44.

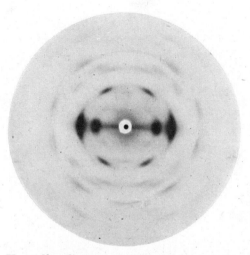

FIG. 37. X-ray fibre diagram of native cellulose, ramie. (Astbury.)

diffracted beam of X-rays, after passing through a crystal, may be made to impinge on a photographic plate to give a series of spots, the *Laue photograph* (Fig. 35); if, during the passage of the beam, the crystal is

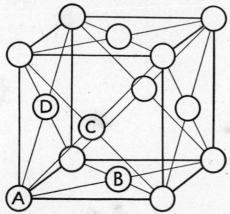

FIG. 34. Face-centred cube. The atoms A, B, C, D make up the repeat-unit of a face-centred cubic lattice. (After Astbury. *Fundamentals of Fibre Structure.* O.U.P.)

rotated about an axis perpendicular to the X-ray beam, all the reflecting planes come round into position where they may be reflected without interference, and the result is an X-ray *rotation photograph*, with spots

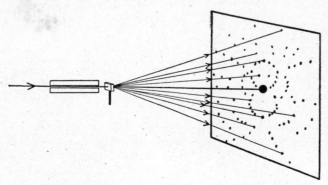

FIG .35. Illustrating the formation of a Laue photograph. (Astbury. *Fundamentals of Fibre Structure.* O.U.P.)

arranged along hyperbolæ symmetrical with respect to a line parallel with the axis of rotation and another perpendicular to this axis (Fig. 36). A similar type of photograph is obtained with a fibre, consisting of a bundle of what are essentially long crystals; if the individual crystals are

are not all at right-angles to each other, nor are the periods along each line the same ; hence the complete definition of a perfect crystal demands a knowledge of the three distances, a, b, c, and the three angles α, β, γ, made by the planes of the repeating units with each other. In the fibrous systems with which we shall be concerned here, the b-axis is the fibre-axis.

sufficiently numerous, and if their axes are more or less parallel, the bundle behaves in the X-ray beam as a single crystal rotated as above, because there is a good chance, with a bundle, that every reflecting plane will make the appropriate angle with the incident beam to give the necessary reflection without interference (Fig. 37, Pl. III). If a body is made up of minute crystals arranged at random, the X-ray photograph is a series of rings which really consist of dots so close together as not to be resolvable ; if the crystals in a fibre are not perfectly orientated with their axes parallel, the dots tend to be drawn out into arcs.

These principles may be illustrated in the case of rubber ; in its unstretched state rubber gives a typical *powder photograph, i.e.,* a series of rings. On stretching, the appearance becomes one of a fibre-photograph with the spots drawn out into arcs, indicating that the long crystallites, of which rubber is composed, have been drawn out of their purely random distribution but have not acquired the perfect alignment necessary to give

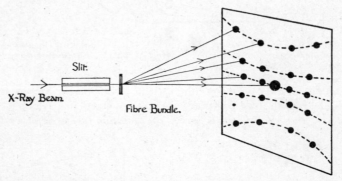

FIG. 36.   The formation of an X-ray fibre photograph, or of a single crystal rotation photograph. (Astbury. *Fundamentals of Fibre Structure.* O.U.P.)

a true crystal-rotation photograph. A study of the distance between successive hyperbolæ, containing the spots of a fibre-photograph, gives the molecular or atomic " repeat " along the fibre axis, whilst the spacings of the spots along the hyperbolæ indicate the repeats in a direction at right-angles to the axis. Thus, if the fibres consist of bundles of long chains of atoms arranged in a regular sequence, the X-ray photograph enables us to measure the sequences in which different atoms are repeated along the chains, and also the lattice spacing between the chains. The shape of the spots tells us, as we have seen, something about the perfection with which the chains are orientated, whilst the size, or diffuseness, of the spots is some indication of the size of the individual long crystals.

The Carbon-Carbon Linkage. Organic matter is made up of carbon-containing materials in which many atoms of carbon are frequently linked together ; it is therefore of primary importance to understand the nature of the C–C linkage, especially from a spatial point of view. Before considering the results of the X-ray analysis of biological structures, it would be useful to find out first what X-rays can tell us about this linkage in simpler material. The diamond is a perfect crystal built up of C-atoms, held together by valency forces ; the arrangement of the C-atoms in this material should therefore provide evidence of the way in which the same atoms are linked together in organic materials. Fig. 38 shows the result of an X-ray analysis of the diamond ; the plan consists in an arrangement such that every C-atom is surrounded by four others, *i.e.*, the four valencies are satisfied by mutual combination ; the angle between any pair of bonds is 109°·28′—the tetrahedral angle of stereochemistry—and the centres of the atoms are separated by a distance of 1·54A ; as a result of this angle between the bonds, the atoms may be considered to be arranged in a zig-zag chain as Fig. 40*a* illustrates. In graphite the C-atoms combine with each

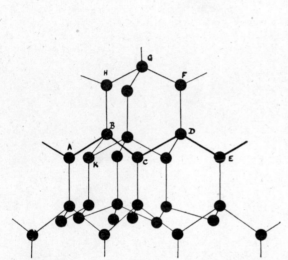

Fig. 38. Arrangement of C-atoms in the structure of diamond. For the sake of clearness, each atom is represented by a small black circle ; in reality we must consider them as actually touching each other.

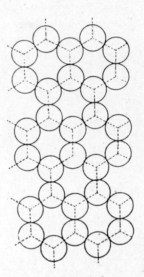

Fig. 39. The flat sheets of C-atoms in the structure of graphite. (Astbury. *Fundamentals of Fibre Structure.* O.U.P.)

other to build a flat pattern, consisting of hexagons with an angle between the valencies of 120° (Fig. 39) ; it is evident here that in any plane each C-atom uses three of its valencies, whilst the fourth is used to hold successive planes together.[1] This arrangement is typical of the ring structure of the aromatic compounds in which the fourth valency is considered to differ radically from the other three ; the diamond type of linkage, on the other hand, is typical of the aliphatic compounds.

The zig-zag pattern of the carbon linkages in diamond is typical of many chain compounds in organic chemistry ; the paraffins are the simplest of such chains, the two valencies of each C-atom in the chain remaining free

[1] The distance between C-atoms in any plane is rather smaller, 1·45A, indicating a stronger bonding. The distance between C-atoms in successive planes is large, 3·41A, showing the weaker bonding ; hence the tendency of graphite to split along definite cleavage planes parallel to the planes of the rings.

to combine with hydrogen (Fig. 40*a*) ; owing to the zig-zag arrangement, each new C-atom incorporated into the chain increases the length by only 1·27A ; moreover, the intra-molecular periodicity of the chain is the distance between every other carbon atom, *i.e.*, 2·54A (Fig. 40*a*). The long chains of the higher paraffins may be packed together as in Fig. 40*b*, to give a so-called rhombic lattice ; the linkages between the chains are loose, however, since all the main valencies are used up and the cohesion between chains is due only to residual or van der Waals forces. When the molecules are small they can be arranged with a high degree of symmetry, a circumstance that leads to cleavage planes where the ends of the molecules come into juxtaposition (Fig. 40*b*) ; with very long chains such an ordered arrangement becomes more difficult, the end-groups of the

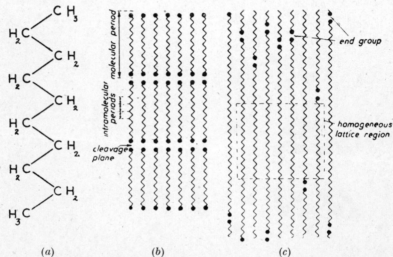

Fig. 40.   (*a*) The zig-zag arrangement of C-atoms in the aliphatic chain.   (*b*) Crystal structure of short-chain paraffins.   (*c*) The less regular arrangement of long-chain paraffins.   (After Frey-Wyssling. *Submicroscopic Morphology of Protoplasm and its Derivatives.* Elsevier.)

chains having a random distribution along the axis ; cleavage planes at right-angles to the chains will therefore be absent.   If the end-to-end unions are the weak points of the structure, we may expect a greater tensile strength with a long-chain system since, to separate any chain from its neighbours, lateral adhesions must be overcome (Fig. 40*c*).   The fibre structures of organic matter are, however, not made up on quite such a simple basis as that provided by the paraffin chains ; they consist of two main classes, the *polysaccharides*, such as cellulose, and the *proteins*, such as silk fibroin.

Cellulose.   Of the polysaccharides occurring in nature, and of interest from a structural viewpoint, we may single out for immediate discussion cellulose, the principal component of the fibrous scaffolding of plant cells and tissues.   Other polysaccharides, such as pectin, chitin, hyaluronic acid (the probable constituent of the jellies and other extraneous coats of many

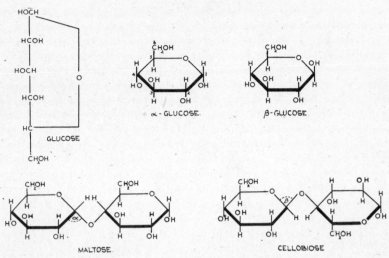

Fig. 41. Formulæ of some sugars.

cells) will be considered later. Starch and glycogen are not of interest from a structural point of view since they act as reservoirs of carbohydrate material in the cytoplasm. On hydrolysis, cellulose can be broken down to its fundamental structural unit, *cellobiose*, which can be further broken down into two molecules of *glucose*. Projected on to a plane, the carbon atoms of glucose may be represented as a heterocyclic structure consisting of a six membered pyranose ring (Fig. 41). Two molecules of glucose may unite with the elimination of water in two different ways, according to the

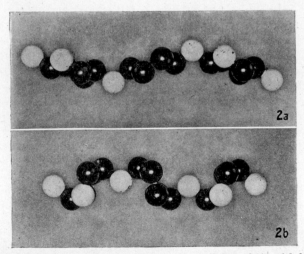

Fig. 42. (*a*) Side view of a short length of the cellulose chain with hydroxyl-groups omitted. (*b*) Corresponding view of the alginic acid chain. Black balls represent carbon atoms and white balls oxygen atoms. Astbury. (*Growth and Form.* Clarendon Press, Oxford.)

positions of the H- and OH-groups on the 1-C-atom, to give an α-disaccharide, *maltose*, or a β-disaccharide, cellobiose as in Fig. 41.[1]

Polysaccharide chains can clearly be built up by the successive linking together of maltose or cellobiose units, with the elimination of one molecule of water with each linkage. X-ray studies of natural fibres reveal that cellulose is built up on a crystalline pattern with a well defined unit cell (Fig. 43) ; the fibre-period, *i.e.*, the distance between successive cellobiose molecules along the chain, being 10·3A ; these almost flat chains are packed to give a three-dimensional pattern, the distance between the chains laterally being 8·35A in the plane of the rings and 7·9A in the direction perpendicular to these planes. The fact that the spots on the X-ray diffraction photo, due to reflections by planes of atoms parallel with the fibre, are more diffuse than those due to reflections at right-angles to this direction indicates that the crystallinity of cellulose is not perfect in all dimensions. It has therefore been concluded that the chains are collected together in parallel bundles, *i.e.*, micelles or crystallites, and it is the discontinuities between the bundles that cause the diffuseness of the spots, the number of regularly repeating planes being necessarily smaller in a direction at right-angles to the fibre-axis than along it. On the basis of arguments of this nature, applied to the X-ray diffraction photos, it has been stated that the probable length of chains is not less than 600A, whilst the width is about 50A. Birefringence studies, moreover, suggest a micellar structure, since there is evidence that a part of the birefringence is due to the rod- or form-type, *i.e.*, to rod-shaped particles small in comparison with the wavelength of light but thicker than a single cellulose chain. The evidence for a long-chain structure of cellulose is overwhelming ; however, the task of assigning a definite length—if such exists—to the chains is difficult. Haworth, on the basis of chemical studies [2] estimated a length of 200 glucose units, corresponding to 1,030A (200 × 5·15), whilst Staudinger, on the basis of an empirical equation relating molecular length to viscosity, computed a figure of 1,000 glucose

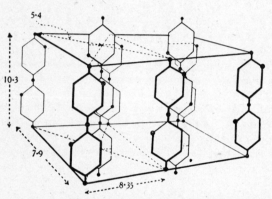

FIG. 43.   Space-lattice of cellulose derived by Meyer & Mark. (Preston. *Biol. Rev.*)

---

[1] The atoms making up the six-membered ring are not co-planar ; a profile view of a chain of glucose units, as in cellulose, is shown in Fig. 42, where black balls represent C-atoms and white balls O-atoms.

[2] Haworth's argument was that the terminal glucoses of a chain should form tetramethyl glucose derivatives since they have an extra free OH-group ; tetramethyl glucose was isolated and from its amount, relative to the amount of cellulose treated, the length of the chain was computed.

residues for purified ramie and 750 for cotton cellulose. Whatever figure we accept, there seems little doubt that the chains are limited in length ; this is made particularly evident by Preston's calculation of the theoretical tensile strength of a polysaccharide chain. Thus it requires 3.10^{-10} kg. to rupture a C—C linkage ; if the cross-sectional area of a chain is $30A^2$, an area of 1 mm.^{2} of fibre will contain 3.10^{12} chains and the rupturing force required for a strand of 1 mm.^{2} cross-section will be 900 kg., if rupture implies the breakage of a C—C linkage in each chain. Actually the tensile strength of cotton hairs is some 20 kg./mm.^{2}, so that rupture is not a matter of breaking C—C linkages, but rather of separating the large crystallites held together laterally by relatively weak bonding forces.

Proteins. Chains built up by the elimination of water from amino-acids, the so-called *polypeptide chains*, represent the basis of the proteins ; in the fibrous proteins such as collagen, fibrinogen, keratin, fibroin, etc., the chains are stretched out, whilst in the *corpuscular proteins* these chains are apparently folded up tightly in definite patterns to give large molecules which may be approximately spheres, as with egg albumin, or elongated, as with zein, whose molecules are about twenty times as long as they are thick. Under special conditions, *e.g.*, after denaturation or when the protein spreads itself at an air-water interface, the corpuscular proteins unfold. The natural amino-acids contain an NH_2- group on the α-C-atom ; they may be written :—

$$NH_2$$
$$|$$
$$R—CH . COOH$$

where R indicates a side-chain which may be only a hydrogen atom in the case of glycine, or the more complex $-CH_2 . CH_2 . CH_2 . NH . C \big\langle \begin{smallmatrix} NH \\ NH_2 \end{smallmatrix}$ in the case of arginine, for example. The condensation of two amino-acids with the elimination of water leads to a dipeptide :—

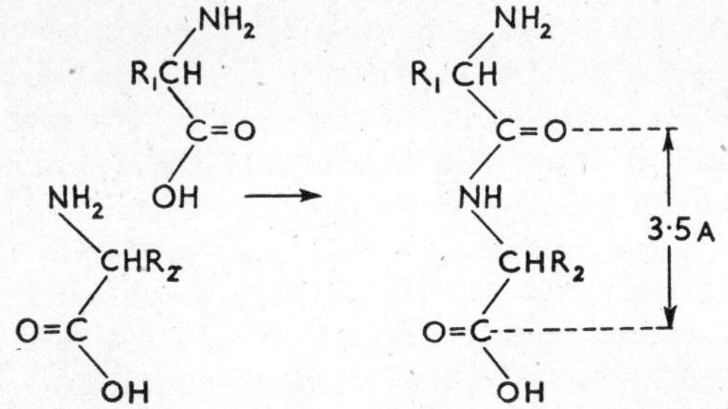

and it is evident that chains of indefinite length may be built up on this basis.

X-ray analysis of silk fibroin, the protein of natural silk, indicates a grid structure of this type ; the main repeating unit along the chain length will clearly be the distance between successive identical atoms in the chain, *e.g.*, the two O-atoms ; this may be calculated from the known bond lengths to be 3·5A, a figure agreeing well with the main spacing of the fibroin chain.   These chains are piled together in three dimensions, *i.e.*, side by side in the plane of the paper, and one above the other perpendicular to this plane.   The side-by-side, or *backbone*, spacing is 4·5A (Fig. 44). The spacing perpendicular to the plane of the paper will be determined in large measure by the lengths of the side-chains, R, which point alternately up and down out of the plane of the paper ; in silk fibroin the amino-acids are mainly glycine and alanine, but others are undoubtedly present (*e.g.*, tyrosine), and it is possible that, owing to the different lengths of the

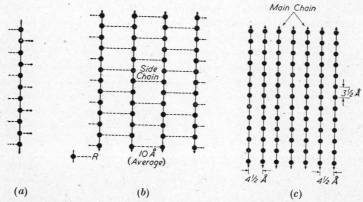

FIG. 44.   (*a*) Single polypeptide chain.   (*b*) Polypeptide grid.   (*c*) Polypeptide crystallite ; the side-chains project out of the plane of the paper, and the distance between chains in the plane of the paper (the back-bone spacing) is 4·5A. (Rudall after Astbury.   *Advances in Biophysics.* Butterworth-Springer.)

side-chains, there is no great regularity in the packing of the grids in this dimension.   Estimates are of a spacing roughly equal to 10A.

Keratin is the structural protein of mammalian hair, horn, and nails ; like fibroin it is a typical fibrous protein, but its repeat-period along the chains is not 3·5A but 5·1A.   On stretching in water, keratin exhibits a striking long-range reversible elasticity ; when stretched to the limit it gives a new type of X-ray photo, with a spacing of 3·38A, *i.e.*, quite close to that of fibroin.   Astbury concluded from these observations that the polypeptide chains of keratin, in its normal unstretched state, are folded in the so-called α-configuration in such a way that three amino-acid residues occupy only 5·1A of the length of the chain (Fig. 45) ;   on stretching, these chains will be drawn out to a fully-extended form, the so-called β-configuration, in which a single amino-acid residue occupies 3·38A, a change permitting an increase in length of some 100 per cent.   A study with models by Astbury & Bell showed that a fold in the chain to give a repeating unit of 5·1A was just about the shortest distance at which it was possible to fold the chain so as to leave the side-chains projecting alternately from one side and the other of the fold, as indicated in Fig. 46. This results in a grouping of side-chains in close-packed columns first on one side of the fold and then on the other. The regular packing of the side-chains brings out the importance of the chemical groupings in these regions, in so far as cohesion between the chains is concerned. As with silk fibroin, the α-protein grids are probably packed together to form tablet-shaped bodies, micelles or crystallites. The folding of the polypeptide chains in keratin is doubtless due to interaction between the side-chains ; thus the long-range elasticity is only manifest in the presence of a polar solvent like water which, by surrounding the reactive groups, weakens their interaction ; if the stretched fibre is allowed to dry in its extended state,

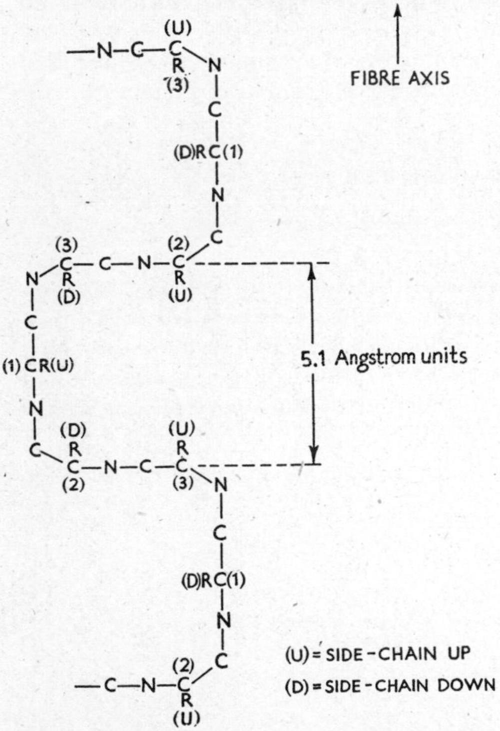

FIBRE AXIS

5.1 Angstrom units

(U)= SIDE-CHAIN UP
(D)= SIDE-CHAIN DOWN

Fig. 45. Basis of the intramolecular fold in α-keratin and α-myosin. (Astbury & Bell. *Nature*.)

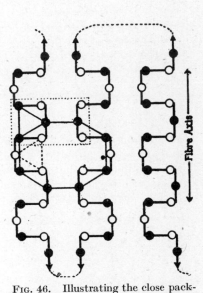

Fig. 46. Illustrating the close packing of side-chains in the α-fold of keratin and myosin. — represents the direction of the main chain ; ● represents a side-chain pointing up from the plane of the diagram ; O represents a side-chain pointing down from the plane of the diagram. (Astbury & Bell. *Nature*.)

it remains " set " in this condition ; moreover, if the moist fibre is maintained for some thirty minutes in this condition, it fails to contract on release ; under these conditions it is presumed that new bonds have been formed between the side-chains, thereby making permanent the extended β-configuration of the chains. As we shall see, keratin is not the only protein to exhibit the α-pattern ; *myosin*, the predominant protein in muscle, *fibrinogen*, the protein responsible for the clotting of blood, and the proteins of mammalian epidermal tissue, are all built up on the same general plan, although the nature of their constituent amino-acids varies greatly ; these proteins are referred to as the *k-m-e-f group* by Astbury. The keratin of sea-gull quill gives a β-pattern with a period some

7 per cent. shorter than that of fully-stretched mammalian keratin, a fact suggesting a slight " crumpling " of the chains ; it is referred to by Astbury as "*feather keratin*" to distinguish it from the more common α-type ; it shows only a limited elasticity, as we should expect from the extended nature of the chains.

The essential substance of tendon and such supporting structures as the cornea and sclera of the eye, is collagen ; the X-ray photograph of this substance is not entirely unambiguous ; it reveals a fibre structure which has been confirmed by electron-microscopy.   However, the distance between the repeating units of the chain is not 3·5A, as with fibroin, but 2·86A ;   it would appear that the chains are not fully elongated, but occupy a somewhat crumpled position ; it was originally suggested that this crumpling resulted from a tautomeric chemical change in the polypeptide chain as follows :—

$$N-CHR \qquad CHR-C[OH] \quad C[OH]=N$$
$$-C[OH] \quad C[OH]=N \qquad N-CHR \qquad CHR-C[OH]$$

the $C = N$ double-bonds imposing a so-called alternating *cis-trans* orientation, such that three amino-acid residues occupy some 8·55A, *i.e.*, giving a repeat-period for a single residue of 2·85A. This view is probably wrong in detail in that the lactam-lactim tautomerisation is unlikely, but it may well be that the presence of numerous proline and hydroxy-proline residues in the chain is sufficient in itself to impose this crumpled form :—

$$N-CH \qquad CH_2 \quad NH \qquad N-CH$$
$$-CO \qquad CO-NH \quad CO \quad CH-CO \qquad CO-$$
$$R$$
$$\longmapsto \quad 8\cdot55A \quad \longrightarrow$$

thus a chain built up of alternating proline, glycine, and a third amino-acid with a side-chain R, satisfies the stereochemical requirements, as models have shown. Collagen is not highly elastic so that there is doubtless a resistance to extension of the chain in this *cis*-configuration ; experiments with models indicate that as soon as the chain is stretched the side-chain, R, swings over to the same side as the proline residues, causing the chain to fall into loops.

Supercontraction and Hydration. Collagen has two striking properties ; in dilute acids or alkalis it swells up enormously by some 4,500 per cent., due of course to the incorporation of water in its structure ; in pure water the swelling is less, but still considerable, the fibres increasing by about 50 per cent. in thickness. Secondly, on placing in hot water (at 60–70° C.), the collagen fibres shrink suddenly to a quarter, or less, of their original length. The disappearance of the X-ray picture associated with this shrinkage, together with the large change in length of the fibres, indicates that the chains have in some way curled up strongly, but in a random manner so as to leave no regularity in structure. Collagen in this " supercontracted state," if kept hot, shows a long-range elasticity indicating that the chains will unfold again under tension, and return to their folded state when the tension is released ; this is in strong contrast to normal collagen, or fibroin, fibres which allow of only a small degree of reversible extension, with tensions beyond a certain limit the fibre extending irreversibly or breaking.[1]

The great swelling of collagen is in marked contrast to the limited (but not insignificant) ability of silk, cotton or wool fibres to absorb water. The absorption of water by wool fibres, for instance, has been studied in detail by Speakman ; a wool fibre, if given enough time, will absorb water to the extent of some 33 per cent. of its dry weight ; this absorption does not modify the X-ray photograph appreciably and can best be accounted for on the assumption that the individual crystallites (*i.e.*, bundles of polypeptide chains) adsorb water molecules on their surfaces ; if these are long and thin, moreover, they will have a relatively large surface and thus a thin layer of water will correspond to a large total absorption of water by the whole fibre. Because the length of the crystallite is so much greater than its width, the percentage change in width must greatly exceed the percentage change in length ; thus a wool fibre becomes as much as 18 per cent. wider, but only 1 per cent. longer, when soaked in water. A detailed study of the water-uptake of wool has led Speakman to conclude that the units of the wool fibre, responsible for adsorption, are only 200A thick, a figure in agreement with that deduced from the size of the X-ray spots. Collagen fibres, on the other hand, can become 50 per cent. thicker in water, and many hundred per cent. in acid or alkali ; this effect must be due to the penetration of water *between* the individual chains of the crystal lattice ; this increases the spacings between the chains but does not affect the fibre period, as Kuntzel and Prakke have shown. The great increase of hydration in dilute acids is due, doubtless, to the breaking of bonds which normally hold the polypeptide chains together, with the result that the crystal lattice is far more seriously disturbed.

The Gel State

The two phenomena exhibited in such a marked degree by collagen— namely of contraction and swelling—lead us to some further considerations on the organisation of living matter. The fundamental unit in the protein and carbohydrate has appeared as a molecule, capable of linking together with others to form chains. The chains are bound together to form long crystallites, or micelles, by chemical linkages or residual molecular forces ; the crystallites themselves are also bound together but generally by weaker forces than those operating to keep the chains together. With keratin and

---

[1] This irreversible extension is probably due to a slipping of the submicroscopic bundles of chains—the crystallites—along their length ; these crystallites are probably linked to each other laterally so that the first effect of a stress on a normal collagen fibre is a stretch of these linkages, but later, as the stress increases, the linkages break and, if the force is not too great, the crystallites slide into new relative positions and establish new bonds. The fibre remains set in the stretched state ; the stretch is irreversible.

cellulose fibres, water is taken up to only a limited extent, but the forcing of the chains apart in collagen, resulting from a less pronounced attraction of the polypeptide chains or grids, leads to a structure which combines the properties of a liquid with those of a solid, it gives the *gel* condition consisting, in the system envisaged here at least, of a structural framework of submicroscopic fibres holding together comparatively large quantities of water.

Side-Chains. The amount of water held together by a given amount of fibrous protein depends primarily on the hydrophilic properties of the protein, and these depend on the nature of the side-chains, the reaction of the medium, and the concentration of ions in this medium. Thus we have seen that the proteins are built up of grids with side-chains projecting outwards in a plane at right-angles to the chain axis ; these side-chains vary considerably in quality, depending on the amino-acid residue incorporated at a given point ; several side-chains are indicated below :—

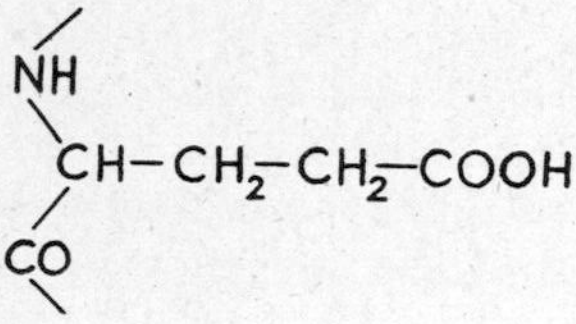

$$\begin{array}{l} NH \\ | \\ CH-CH_2-CH_2-COOH \\ | \\ CO \end{array}$$

Glutamic Acid

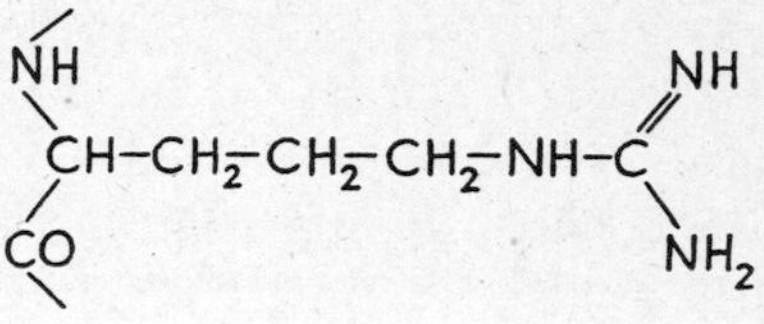

$$\begin{array}{l} NH \\ | \\ CH-CH_2-CH_2-CH_2-NH-C \\ | \qquad\qquad\qquad\qquad\quad NH_2 \\ CO \end{array}$$

Arginine

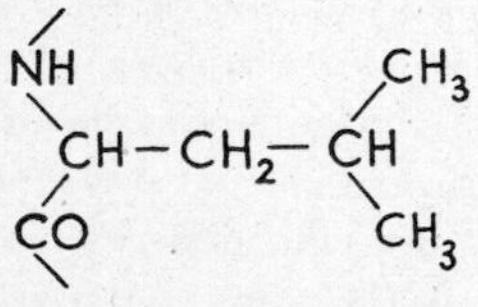

$$\begin{array}{l} NH \\ | \qquad\qquad CH_3 \\ CH-CH_2-CH \\ | \qquad\qquad CH_3 \\ CO \end{array}$$

Leucine

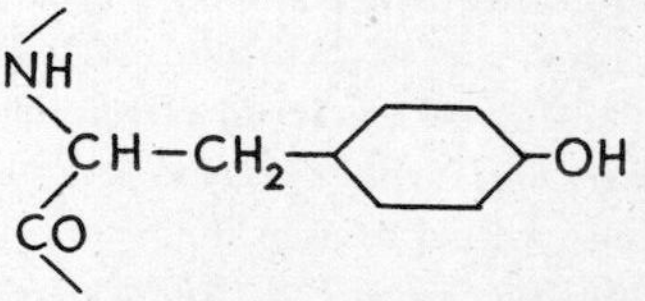

$$\begin{array}{l} NH \\ | \\ CH-CH_2- \bigcirc -OH \\ | \\ CO \end{array}$$

Tyrosine

$$\begin{array}{l} NH \\ | \\ CH-CH_2-SH \\ | \\ CO \end{array}$$

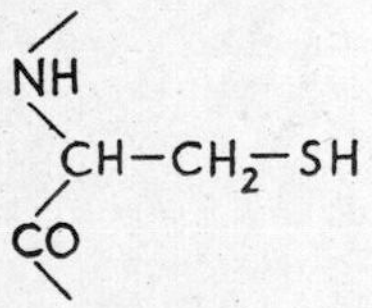

Cysteine

Side-chains with such strongly polar groups as —SH, —OH, and —NH₂ are called *hydrophilic*, since they attract a thick layer of water molecules ; whilst the absence of these groups on the hydrocarbon side-chain imparts a *hydrophobic* character to the chains. From the point of view of lateral linkages between the grids, the side-chains containing the polar groups are of great importance (*a*) because of their reactivity which favours the production of strong links between neighbouring side-chains, and (*b*) because they attract water.

Let us consider first the linking of chains ; inspection of the glutamic acid and arginine side-chains shows us that they are acidic and basic respectively. A link between two grids could therefore be quite simply achieved by salt formation :—

$$—COOH + HOH_3N— \rightarrow —COOH_3N—$$

provided that conditions are suitable ; binding of this sort is clearly only possible when the neighbouring carboxyl- and amino-groups are oppositely charged, *i.e.*, as $—COO^-$ and $—NH_3^+$, or undissociated : $—COOH$ and $—NH_3OH$. At the isoelectric state this condition prevails on the average, *i.e.*, the numbers of negative and positive charges are equal, so that this type of bonding finds its most favourable condition in this state. Consequently changing the pH of the medium, for example by adding dilute acid, may break down or strengthen this binding. A very important type of bond is the homopolar valency type in which, for example, two SH-groups of cysteine residues react to form a disulphide :—

$$—SH + —SH \rightarrow —S—S—$$

This is a powerful linkage and is not sensitive to moderate changes in pH.[1] The *hydrogen bond* is something mid-way berween the covalent (homopolar) link and the salt bridge, the hydrogen in the NH_2^- or OH-groups (including that of water) is able to act as a link with a similar group. We may regard it as a special case of the interaction of dipoles. Thus if, with a covalent link between two atoms, one atom tends to attract the shared electrons more strongly than another (it is said to be more electronegative) the result is an uneven distribution of electric charge to give a dipole. For example, the C=O-group is dipolar ; similarly the OH- and NH_2-groups ; the water molecule has two dipoles :—

Polar molecules containing these and other similar groups will be attracted towards each other in virtue of their electric charges ; this accounts for the tendency for water to be attracted to the hydrophilic groups discussed above. However, it is thought that, in the case where the polar group contains a hydrogen-atom, the latter tends to be shared between the two electronegative atoms ; thus water molecules tend to be linked fairly strongly together by a hydrogen bridge or *hydrogen bond*, as it is called. Similarly an OH- and NH_2-group can be linked together.

Besides the interaction of permanent dipoles to give attractive forces between molecules, there are other modes depending on the occurrence of transient changes in the distribution of charge in the molecules ; they are called dispersion forces and give rise to the van der Waals forces between

[1] It may be broken by dilute alkali ; for example keratin passes into a " super-contracted state " with this reagent ; the chains no longer maintain their regular folds but curl up more strongly.

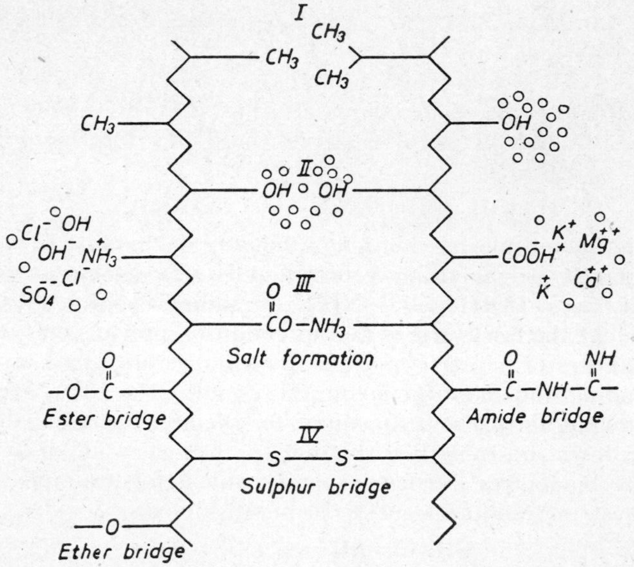

FIG. 47.   Schematic representation of possible linkages between polypeptide chains.   o = water molecule.   (Frey-Wyssling.   *Submicroscopic Morphology of Protoplasm and its Derivatives.*   Elsevier.)

non-polar molecules.   The various linkages are indicated schematically in Fig. 47.

Swelling.   This study of the bridges between side-chains indicates to some extent how they may be broken down ; the most powerful factor will clearly be the presence of water which, by surrounding the various points of attraction, weakens the force between polar groups ; if this action of water is reinforced by other steps taken to break down bridges (*e.g.,* dilute alkali will break down the S—S linkages in keratin) we can see that the disorganisation may go to the extent of a complete breakdown of any structural scaffolding.   Such a state of affairs may be observed with gelatin, and with the polysaccharide, agar-agar, which at high temperatures pass from the swollen gel state to one in which the micelles have independent movement, *i.e.,* the gel passes into the *sol* form.   On cooling, however, the sol may set into a gel, the long particles forming new linkages when the kinetic energy is sufficiently reduced.   Under any set of conditions, we may think of a swelling maximum attained by a solid fibrous protein ; for example, on placing dried collagen into water it will incorporate a certain fixed number of water molecules, depending on the acidity of the medium, the salt concentration and temperature, the remainder of the water remaining outside the gel as a separate phase.   A change in the conditions, leading for example to an increased ionisation of acid or basic groups, or to the breaking of side-chain bonds, causes more water to be attracted until a new equilibrium is attained.   So long as the protein framework remains intact, *i.e.,* so long as all intermicellar linkages are not disrupted, the system will have structural rigidity and so be classed as a gel ; it may be classed, moreover, as an *equilibrium gel* because as much water as possible has been taken up under these particular conditions. If, on the other hand, the conditions are such as to allow the complete breakdown of the structure, this leads to the formation of a sol, provided enough water is present ; if insufficient water is present it is all incorporated into the structure which may then be classed as a non-equilibrium type of gel. In biological systems some very dilute equilibrium gels may be found ; thus the *vitreous body* of the eye is a gel containing only about 0·02 per cent. of a fibrous type of protein similar to collagen ; as we shall see, the apparently liquid endoplasm is probably best regarded as a very dilute gel. The formation of gels is by no means confined to the fibrous proteins ; thus, by choosing the physical conditions suitably, gels may be formed from a large variety of inorganic and organic materials ; it is sufficient that the atoms or molecules build up into aggregates of such a size that, by immobilising the solvent, they impart a rigidity to the system ; this immobilisation can be achieved by a fibrous honeycomb structure consisting of long branching micelles, in which case the fibrous type of material, such as cellulose or collagen, provides the most suitable basis. The water may also be immobilised by being bound as thick hydration sheaths round micelles, which may be spherical or rod shaped ; finally, a certain proportion of the water in a gel may be intra-micellar, as occurs when collagen is treated with dilute acids, the water entering between the long polypeptide chains.

Sol-Gel Transformation. The conversion of a sol to a gel may be regarded as a partial precipitation of the solid material which, formerly existing as free particles, is aggregated, but not to the extent of complete precipitation to give a separate solid phase ; conditions favouring the transformation are thus an increased tendency to bond-formation between the solid particles, and a decreased hydration of the particles. The conversion of a sol to a gel is typically seen in the clotting of blood plasma ; here the substance responsible for clotting is *fibrinogen*, an α-type protein ; as a result of a chemical reaction catalysed by an enzyme, *thrombin*, the fibrinogen micelles are altered so as to favour an end-to-end aggregation to give much longer particles, which provide the scaffolding for the gel structure. Thus X-ray analysis of both fibrinogen and fibrin reveals essentially the same identity period along the chains (Bailey, Astbury and Rudall), so that the change from the one to the other does not, apparently, involve a serious intra-molecular alteration.

The case cited above showed the formation of a gel by the chemical transformation of the protein, fibrinogen ; most of the gels studied by the colloid chemist are formed by a simple change of physical conditions ; perhaps the most striking gel-sol and sol-gel transformation is given by the *thixotropic* class ; here it is sufficient to shake the gel in the test-tube to convert it into a sol which solidifies again when the agitation ceases. Although practically all colloidal solutions exhibit thixotropy if the conditions are chosen correctly, a rod-shaped micelle is considered favourable ; presumably the rod-shaped particles are able to link up to give a honeycomb structure, the links being, however, so weak as to be unable to withstand the stresses imposed by mechanical agitation.

Folding of Polypeptide Chains. We may turn now to the second characteristic of the collagen fibre mentioned earlier, namely its contractility on placing in hot water. Its interest lies, as Astbury has emphasised, in the phenomenon of the folding up of the polypeptide chains. In the case of collagen this occurs with such vigour, and to such an extent, that no regular pattern is produced from the point of view of X-ray analysis. A more regular folding is found in the k-m-e-f group of proteins. As we shall see, this folding can, in the case of muscle and keratin, be increased even further in a reversible manner. Now the great majority of proteins are not fibrous, but what we may call *corpuscular* ; although they are built up of amino-acids which must be linked together to form chains, they exist in solution and, often, in perfect crystals, as corpuscular units which may be nearly isodiametric in some cases. With molecular weights varying from 30,000 to over 200,000 they must contain 300 to 1,700 amino-acid residues which would give them a chain length of some 1,000–8,000A ; since the diameters of these corpuscular proteins are only of the order of 30–50A, the chains must be folded to a great extent. The nature of the folding must remain a matter of speculation since the interpretation of the X-ray analysis of protein crystals is by no means unambiguous. These proteins are very susceptible to what is called *denaturation* ; for example, it is usually sufficient to leave a protein sol at room temperature for the protein to become less soluble ; if the protein is made isoelectric at the same time, this loss of solubility results in a more or less complete coagulation. It would seem that denaturation consists essentially in an unfolding of the polypeptide chains, presumably as a result of the breakdown of side-chain linkages which normally maintain this folded state ; thus Mirsky has shown that the number of free SH-groups increases during denaturation, and it is generally believed that an important linkage between side-chains is given by the reaction of cysteine and methionine residues to give S—S linkages (p. 57). Moreover Astbury has been able to make fibres from a typical corpuscular protein—edestin from cotton seed—by denaturing it. This denatured material, after being spun, gave a typical X-ray fibre photograph although the crystal lattice was by no means perfect. Finally we may note that when a thin film of protein is formed at an air-water interface, studies of its thickness reveal that it has unfolded itself on the surface, the polypeptide grids lying in the surface with the side-chains orientated out of it.

The corpuscular proteins, because of their comparatively symmetrical shape, probably do not participate to any great extent in the fundamental scaffolding of protoplasm ; they are present as large molecules in free solution, capable of migrating from one part of the cytoplasm to another ; the same is probably true of the reserve polysaccharides such as starch and glycogen although they may be coagulated into granules.[1]

[1] Thus Lazarow has separated submicroscopic glycogen particles from the guinea-pig cell by differential centrifugation ; he suggests that the general level of sugar in the blood is regulated by the precipitation of glycogen from the liver cytoplasm, thereby shifting the equilibrium between dissolved glycogen and glucose :—

$$\text{Glucose-1-Phosphate} \longrightarrow \text{Glycogen} + \text{Phosphate}$$

If, as he suggests, the granules result from the formation of a complex of glycogen with a protein, the amount of glycogen stored may be regulated by varying the amount of this protein available to combine with the glycogen.

Cytoplasmic Structure

For a long time it was thought that the endoplasm of the cell was a simple sol with the power of alternating, at least in certain regions, between this state and that of a gel. Against this conception there are serious theoretical arguments ; thus the complexity of the chemical reactions taking place within the cell demands the presence of localised regions in which the individual reactions may be catalysed ; these will be provided in part by the cytoplasmic inclusions, such as the mitochondria and the chloroplasts of plant cells, but it has been questioned whether these would be sufficient. Moreover, the *polarity* exhibited by many eggs, as a result of which a certain region gives rise to a blastomere with a very different developmental fate from that formed from the rest of the egg, would suggest that there is a differentiation of the cytoplasm, and it is difficult to conceive of such a differentiation in a quite fluid medium. We have seen that particles may certainly move through the endoplasm under the influence of centrifugal force, and during streaming ; in a similar way the polarity of the egg may be changed ; thus Whitaker has described experiments on the eggs of *Fucus*, a marine brown alga. In normal development the egg, after fertilisation, forms a bulging protuberance and at the first division the cell plate cuts across the base of the protuberance to give two very differently shaped blastomeres with very different developmental fates. By centrifuging at 50,000–200,000 g, the egg is stratified, as with other cells, and it is found that the protuberance always forms at the centrifugal pole (in normal sea-water at pH 8) ; consequently the polarity of the egg may be altered by changing the distribution of some constituent or constituents of the cytoplasm. This would suggest, but of course does not prove, that polarity is determined by the localisation of certain material within the cell, and if this is the case this would demand some sort of cytoplasmic structure. Whether or not this could be provided by the cortical layer remains to be proved.[1]

With regard to the direct evidence for a cytoplasmic structure, this is by no means conclusive but it is certainly strongly suggestive. The cytoplasm is, indeed, optically empty in the microscope and ultramicroscope, but, as Frey-Wyssling has pointed out, this does not exclude the existence of ultra-microscopic fibrils, since they may easily be too thin to show up in the dark-field microscope in spite of possessing considerable length. The polarising microscope, too, reveals little evidence of structure in the resting cell's fluid endoplasm,[2] but it will be remembered that, in order that the presence of rod-like particles be demonstrated by this technique, these must be regularly orientated ; a honeycomb structure built up of long fibrils would be *statistically isotropic*, the anisotropic particles cancelling out their individual micellar birefringences. Thus Pfeiffer centrifuged frog's eggs at high speeds in an ultra-centrifuge

---

[1] It should be noted that the protuberance forms at the centripetal end of the egg if the medium is made acid.

[2] The cortical gel of the sea-urchin egg is certainly birefringent, positive in respect to the radius which coincides with the optic axis ; it is thought that this is due to orientated lipids (Monroy, 1947 ; Runnström, Monné & Broman, 1944).

designed to permit observation with a polarising microscope during centrifugation ; in the normal egg he found no evidence of orientation, whereas at 20,000 r.p.m. some birefringence was observed at the centrifugal pole, indicating the presence of fibrils with their axes parallel to the centrifugal force. On stopping the centrifugation the statistical isotropy reasserted itself. In active cytoplasm, as we have seen, there is indisputable evidence of the presence of fibrils, and it is reasonable to suppose that they are pre-formed ; the asters, for example, may be regarded as resulting primarily from an orientation of pre-existing fibrils. We may therefore accept, in its general outlines, the picture of cytoplasmic structure put forward by Seifriz, by Meyer & Mark, and by Frey-Wyssling. The cytoplasm is regarded as a very dilute gel, containing some 70 to 80 per cent. of water, with no permanent scaffolding, it is true, but nevertheless with a system of very fine [1] sub-microscopic fibrils capable of forming labile bonds between them which may be easily broken down and as easily re-established. The framework is thus dynamic, perhaps being intact in one region and " liquefied " in another, and in this way provides a basis for the protean characteristics of the cytoplasm. Frey-Wyssling's scheme is represented in Fig. 48, consisting of a series of interlacing fibrils capable of bonds of varying degrees of strength ; these fibrils need not be simple rods, as for example in the vanadium pentoxide gels ; the long chains of amino-acid residues will probably be grouped into bundles, but one chain may belong to several bundles as indicated in Fig. 48. In certain regions the ordering of these pseudo-rods may be almost crystalline, thereby giving rise to birefringence, whilst in other regions there will be statistical isotropy. The supposed lability of the bonds provides the possibility of an apparently fluid system, so that a large particle, such as the nickel particle studied by Seifriz, may move continuously by breaking down the structure as it proceeds. A small particle, under a smaller force, would move discontinuously and exhibit the anomalous, or structural, viscosity reported by so many investigators. That is, a viscosity varying with the speed of the particle, or " shearing force " ; thus Scarth has observed that particles, moving through the plant cytoplasm, progress like " hail-shot through a brush-heap," again and again the particles seem to meet invisible

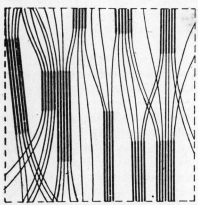

Fig. 48.   Local formation of a crystal lattice in a gel framework. (Frey-Wyssling. *Submicroscopic Morphology of Protoplasm and its Derivatives.* Elsevier.)

---

[1] Not, however, single polypeptide chains, as Frey-Wyssling has proposed ; as Rudall (1950) and Crick & Hughes (1950) have pointed out, this is most unlikely. A single chain would fold on itself, and it is only by forming bundles that the chains may remain extended.

strands and change their direction. Finally, the power of bond-formation between the fibrils would enable the cytoplasm to become definitely more solid in localised portions, if this power were locally increased. We have referred to the clotting of fibrinogen sols ; this results from a chemical change permitting of a bonding between the comparatively short fibrinogen fibrils to allow the growth of very long fibrin chains ; and it may well be that similar transformations occur in the cytoplasm during the formation of asters and pseudopods. On the scheme proposed above, the interlacing fibrils enclose in their spaces relatively large volumes of water ; this water belongs, in a sense, to the protein fibrillæ, part of it being bound to the lyophilic groupings on their surface, but the great majority being held by much weaker forces which will be discussed in dealing with the properties of certain viruses. A more rigid building of the fibrillæ would be expected to close up the meshes and make some of the water superflous, so that we may envisage the setting out of a rigid gel, the aster, floating in an excess of the superfluous fluid. The complete setting of the whole endoplasm, as observed on passing an *Arbacia* egg through a capillary tube, might result from a more general change leading to a stabilisation of the labile bonds throughout the cytoplasm. In this connection we may return to a consideration of the striking effects of pressure on egg cleavage, pseudopod formation, and streaming, described by Brown and by Marsland. If, during the conversion of a sol to a gel there is an increase in volume of the whole system, we must expect a rise in pressure to inhibit gelation or convert a gel into a sol. With many gels, *e.g.*, gelatin, however, the reverse phenomenon takes place, a rise in pressure tending to favour gelation ; methyl cellulose, on the other hand, is solated by increase in pressure. With the fibrous protein from muscle, myosin (p. 521), Marsland & Brown (1942) have shown that the gel, like that of methyl cellulose, can be rapidly converted into a sol by high pressures, so that if, as seems possible, the scaffolding protein of cytoplasm is a fibrous protein similar to myosin, the effects of pressure on streaming, cleavage, and the formation of pseudopods become intelligible, being due to a reversible solation of the plasmagel or an inhibition of the sol-gel transformation. Gelation of the " Type II " systems, typified by methyl cellulose, is also inhibited by a decrease in temperature, and it is therefore of added interest that Marsland, in some recent work, has shown that the inhibition of the cleavage furrow caused by low temperatures is similar to that caused by high pressures.

Structural Protein of Cytoplasm. There have been frequent attempts to isolate a protein from cytoplasm to which may be attributed the property of maintaining the scaffolding, or " cytoskeleton " as Peters calls it. Bensley applied the techniques, developed for extracting the cell particulates (p. 29), to this problem ; on removing all the globulins, the mitochondria, and nuclear chromatin (p. 73), from the cells of a sectioned liver by soaking in appropriate solutions, the cells retained their original structure, so that the presence of some material still capable of holding the remains of the cell together was postulated. Extraction of the section with 0·1 N ammonia gave a ropy solution from which a fibrous protein could be precipitated, which they called *ellipsin*. Subsequent separative procedures suggested the presence of two proteins ; one, extracted with 10 per cent. NaCl, called *plasmosin*, and the remainder, soluble in alkali, to which the original name of ellipsin was applied. Plasmosin is by no means the only material isolated from cells to which the function of cytoskeleton has been ascribed ; for example Szent-Györgyi and his collaborators have isolated from a variety of cells protein material showing, in solution, a high birefringence of flow,[1] high viscosity, and the ability to form thixotropic gels ; to the material from the kidney, for example, Banga & Szent-Györgyi gave the name *renosin*. The materials thus isolated appear to be nucleoproteins (p. 77) ; since, however, plasmosin was shown to be of the desoxyribose-type (p. 76), which has never been identified before outside the nucleus, Mirsky & Pollister argue that Bensley's preparation comes, not from the cytoplasm, but from the nucleus. Brachet & Jeener take the same view ; they have shown that the solution used by Szent-Györgyi to extract the cells definitely causes the loss of nucleic acids from the nucleus ; moreover, the reactions of renosin are precisely those of thymonucleohistone (p. 77), and the amount of material extractable from a given type of cell depends on the prominence of the nucleus ; for example rabbit erythrocytes, with no nuclei, gave no " cytoplasmic protein " whilst the nucleated goose erythrocytes gave large quantities. Further work is clearly required for the identification of the protein, or other material, associated with the maintenance of cytoplasmic structure.

After fertilisation of an egg, there is a great increase in the rigidity of the cortical cytoplasm (p. 23) ; Mirsky extracted proteins with 1 M KCl from the eggs of *Arbacia* and *Strongylocentrotus*, and found that the amount of extractable material decreased on fertilisation. He suggested that fertilisation was accompanied by a partial denaturation of the cytoplasmic proteins. This denaturation may be the result of a more rigid bonding of the fibrous protein micelles, decreasing the solubility. The protein actually extracted could be precipitated with ammonium sulphate, to give, on redissolving, highly viscous solutions which showed birefringence of flow, thus indicating a protein of the fibrous type.

In reviewing the evidence on the structure of cytoplasm we may conclude, tentatively at least, that the only picture that can be held to be consistent with the variety of phenomena taking place within it is one of a fibrous scaffolding, holding within its meshes large quantities of water ; the lability of the bonds holding the scaffolding together is such as to impart a remarkable fluidity which allows the migration of particles within the endoplasm, whilst the capacity of these bonds to strengthen under appropriate influences permits a ready change to a more rigidly gelated structure.

---

[1] A sol containing long crystalline particles will not usually show birefringence, owing to the random orientation of the particles ; when the solution is made to flow, however, the particles orientate themselves with their axes parallel to the lines of flow, and thus the statistical isotropy gives way to anisotropy of flow.

References

ASTBURY, W. T. (1933). " The Fundamentals of Fibre Structure." Oxford. O.U.P.

ASTBURY, W. T. (1940). " The Molecular Structure of the Fibres of the Collagen Group." *J. Int. Soc. Leather Trades' Chem.*, 24, 69.

ASTBURY, W. T. (1943). " X-Rays and the Stoichiometry of the Proteins." *Advances in Enzym.*, 3, 63.

ASTBURY, W. T. (1945). The Forms of Biological Molecules. " Essays on Growth and Form," p. 309. Ed. Le Gros Clark & Medawar. Oxford. Clarendon Press.

ASTBURY, W. T. & BELL, F. O. (1938). " Some Recent Developments in the X-Ray Study of Proteins and Related Structures." *C.S.H. Symp.*, 6, 109.

ASTBURY, W. T. & BELL, F. O. (1941). " Nature of the Intramolecular Fold in Alpha-Keratin and Alpha-Myosin." *Nature*, 147, 696.

ASTBURY, W. T. & DICKINSON, S. (1940). " X-Ray Studies of the Molecular Structure of Myosin." *Proc. Roy. Soc.*, B, 129, 307.

ASTBURY, W. T., DICKINSON, S. & BAILEY, K. (1935). " The X-Ray Interpretation of Denaturation and the Structure of the Seed Globulins." *Biochem. J.*, 29, 2351.

BAILEY, K., ASTBURY, W. T. & RUDALL, K. M. (1943). " Fibrinogen and Fibrin as Members of the Keratin-Myosin Group." *Nature*, 151, 716.

BANGA, I. & SZENT-GYÖRGYI, A. (1940–41). "Strukturproteine." *Enzym.*, 9, 111.

BEAMS, H. W. (1943). " Ultracentrifugal Studies on Cytoplasmic Components and Inclusions." *Biol. Symp.*, 10, 71.

BEAR, R. S. (1942). " The Large Fibre-Axis Period of Collagen." *J.A.C.S.*, 64, 1297.

BEAR, R. S. (1942). " Feather Rachis, Porcupine Quill Tip and Clam Muscle." *J.A.C.S.*, 64, 2043.

BEAR, R. S., SCHMITT, F. O. & YOUNG, J. Z. (1937). " The Ultra-Structure of Nerve Axoplasm." *Proc. Roy. Soc.*, B, 123, 505.

BENSLEY, R. R. (1938). " Plasmosin. The Gel and Fibre-Forming Constituent of the Protoplasm of the Hepatic Cell." *Anat. Rec.*, 72, 351.

BENSLEY, R. R. (1943). " The Chemistry of Cytoplasm." *Biol. Symp.*, 10, 323.

BERNAL, J. D. (1947). " The Structure and Interaction of Protein Molecules." *Proc. Int. Congr. Cyt.*, p. 15.

BRACHET, J. & JEENER, R. (1947). Protéines de structure de Szent-Györgyi et thymonucléohistone. *Biochim. Biophys. Acta*, 1, 13.

BUNN, C. W. (1945). " Chemical Crystallography." Oxford. Clarendon Press.

CHAMBERS, R. (1943). " Electrolyte Solutions Compatible with the Maintenance of Protoplasmic Structure." *Biol. Symp.*, 10, 91.

CROWFOOT, D. (1948). " X-Ray Crystallographic Studies of Compounds of Biochemical Interest." *Ann. Rev. Biochem.*, 17, 115.

FREY-WYSSLING, A. (1948). " Submicroscopic Morphology of Protoplasm and its Derivatives." New York and Amsterdam. Elsevier.

HALL, C. E., JAKUS, M. A. & SCHMITT, F. O. (1945). " The Structure of Certain Muscle Fibrils as Revealed by the use of Electron Stains." *J. App. Phys.*, 16, 459.

KUNTZEL, A. & PRAKKE, F. (1933). " Morphologie u. Feinbau der kollagenen Faser." *Biochem. Z.*, 267, 243.

LAZAROW, A. (1942). " Particulate Glycogen : a Submicroscopic Component of the Liver Cell ; its Significance in Glycogen Storage and the Regulation of the Blood Sugar." *Anat. Rec.*, 84, 31.

LAZAROW, A. (1943). " Chemical Structure of Cytoplasm." *Biol. Symp.*, 10, 9.

MARSLAND, D. A. (1950). " Temperature-Pressure Experiments on the Cleaving Eggs of Arbacia." *J. cell. & comp. Physiol.*, 36, 205.

MARSLAND, D. A. & BROWN, D. E. S. (1942). " The Effects of Pressure on Sol-Gel Equilibria with Special Reference to Myosin and Other Protoplasmic Gels." *J. cell. & comp. Physiol.*, 20, 295.

MEYER, K. H. (1942). Proteins and Protoplasmic Structure. " Structure of Protoplasm." Ed. Seifriz. Ames, Iowa. Iowa State College Press.

MIRSKY, A. E. (1936). " Protein Coagulation as a Result of Fertilisation." *Science*, 84, 333.

MIRSKY, A. E. & POLLISTER, A. W. (1943). " Fibrous Nucleoproteins of Chromatin." *Biol. Symp.*, 10, 247.

PICKEN, L. E. R. (1940). " The Fine Structure of Biological Systems." *Biol. Rev.*, 15, 133.

PFEIFFER, H. H. (1940). "Rheologische, polarisationsoptische und beugungs-polarisatorische Untersuchungen an Protoplasmatropfen, etc." *Protoplasma*, 34, 347.

PRESTON, R. D. (1939). " The Molecular Chain Structure of Cellulose and its Biological Significance." *Biol. Rev.*, 14, 281.

RUDALL, K. M. (1950). Fundamental Structures in Biological Systems. " Progress in Biophysics." Ed. Butler & Randall. London. Butterworth-Springer.

SCARTH, G. W. (1942). Structural Differentiation in Protoplasm. " Structure of Protoplasm." Ed. Seifriz. Ames, Iowa. Iowa State College Press.

SCHMIDT, W. J. (1941). " Die Doppelbrechung des Protoplasmas und ihre Bedeutung fur die Erforschung seines submikropischen Baues." *Ergebn. d. Physiol.*, 44, 27.

SCHMITT, F. O. (1939). " The Ultrastructure of Protoplasmic Constituents." *Physiol. Rev.*, 19, 270.

SCHMITT, F. O. (1944–45). " Ultrastructure and the Problems of Cellular Organisation." *Harvey Lectures*, 40, 249.

SCHMITT, F. O., HALL, C. E. & JAKUS, M.A. (1943). " The Ultrastructure of Protoplasmic Fibrils." *Biol. Symp.*, 10, 261.

SEIFRIZ, W. (1942). Some Physical Properties of Protoplasm and their Bearing on Structure. " Structure of Protoplasm." Ed. Seifriz. Ames, Iowa. Iowa State College Press.

SPEAKMAN, J. B. (1931). " The Micelle Structure of the Wool Fibre." *Proc. Roy. Soc.*, A, 132, 167.

SPONSLER, O. L. & BATH, J. D. (1942). Molecular Structure in Protoplasm. "Structure of Protoplasm." Ed. Seifriz. Ames, Iowa. Iowa State College Press.

WHITAKER, D. M. (1940). " Effects of Ultracentrifuging and of pH on the Development of *Fucus* Eggs." *J. cell. & comp. Physiol.*, 15, 173.

CHAPTER III

THE NUCLEOPROTEIN STRUCTURES

The Tobacco Mosaic Virus

THE virus has been classed with the mitochondria, chloroplasts, microsomes, etc., as an inclusion body ; this classification is probably just, in so far as all these bodies contain large quantities of nucleic acid, and have the power of self-reduplication. The study of the virus is therefore of great interest from the point of view of reproduction in its simplest form ; moreover, some of the results of such studies, particularly those of Bernal & Fankuchen with X-rays and the polarisation microscope, illustrate and extend many of the concepts already developed in relation to cytoplasmic structure.

Top- and Bottom-Layer Solutions. The infective agent of plants suffering from mosaic disease was extracted as a crystalline protein by Stanley in 1935 ; later Bawden & Pirie reported the results of an extensive series of investigations in which they extracted a material which, in solution, spontaneously separated into two layers, the so-called *top-* and *bottom-layers*. The top-layer showed positive birefringence of flow indicating a solution of long particles which became orientated with their long axes parallel with the direction of flow. The bottom-layer, although liquid, exhibited strong birefringence without flow, suggesting a crystalline or ordered state of the particles. The variation of the birefringence in the different parts of the solution indicated, however, that ordinarily various regions were differently orientated with respect to others, so that the polarisation-microscopical appearance was that of a mass of crystals. On causing the bottom-layer to flow, it behaved as a perfect single crystal with the long particles orientated in the direction of flow ; having been orientated, moreover, they remained so after flow ceased, in contrast to the top-layer solutions which reassumed their isotropy. On drying the bottom-layer solution, a thin skin could be obtained which was referred to as a *dry gel*, still, however, containing some water ; on placing this dry gel in varying amounts of water, wet gels of different concentrations could be obtained. X-ray studies of the bottom-layer solution, and of these gels of different concentration, revealed essentially the same picture, namely that of a crystalline structure built up of long thin particles in a hexagonal packing, the lateral spacing varying from 150A, in the dry gel, to as much as 500A in the dilute gels and orientated bottom-layer solutions ; Fig. 49 illustrates this result. The absence of an observable intermolecular reflection from planes not parallel to the axis of birefringence indicated a minimum length of about 1,500A for the particles. The transition from the dry gel, through wet gels and bottom-layer solutions of decreasing concentration, to the minimum concentration compatible with a crystalline structure (1·8 per cent.) was continuous, in that there was no change in the intra-molecular pattern, but only in the lateral spacing of the molecules ; one may therefore speak of these forms as representing a continuous phase, equivalent to the crystalline structure of a solid. The top-layer solution, on the other hand, represents another separate phase equivalent to a saturated liquid in contact with a solid. The spontaneous separation of a bottom-layer solution (of concentration greater than 1·8 per cent. of the purified material) is therefore equivalent to the separation of solid from a super-saturated solution, but in this case the separated " solid " is still liquid, in so far as it flows. The maintenance of this crystalline state by the bottom-layer solutions raises an important point regarding the effectiveness of intermolecular forces ; the thermal energy of the molecules must tend to disturb any orientation, so that, unless there are sufficiently large forces to withstand this disorientating effect, the crystalline structure cannot be maintained ; in top-layer solutions, as we have seen, the thermal energy is sufficient to disorientate the particles after they have been orientated by flow ; when the intermolecular distance is of the order of 500A, however, the forces of attraction between the molecules seem to be large enough to prevent significant disorientation. Van der Waals forces and the simple electrostatic forces of attraction between dipoles and fixed ions are not sufficient, since they fall off rapidly with distance and would have negligible values at 500A. The problem has been attacked theoretically by Levine and by Langmuir. According to Levine's calculations, the interaction of ionic atmospheres surrounding the particles is sufficient to create such an electrical field in the region

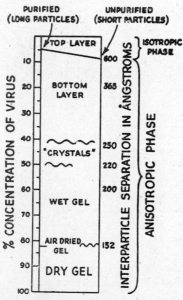

Fig. 49. Illustrating the variation of interparticle distance with concentration of tobacco mosaic virus. (Bernal & Fankuchen. *J. gen. Physiol.*)

of two particles that there is a definite separation at which their mutual energy is a minimum ; in other words a particle at the bottom of this potential energy trough (*i.e.*, at this fixed distance from another particle) will be repelled back to this position whether it moves towards the other particle or away from it ; thus the disrupting effects of thermal energy will be prevented, provided of course that the depth of the trough of potential energy is greater than kT, the thermal energy. With most spherical particles, however, the depth of the energy-minimum is much less than the thermal energy of the particles, so that a molecule will be continually separated from its partners and thus give a random distribution of orientations. On the other hand, with long rod-shaped particles the position is different, effective cohesive forces operating over 500A or more being quite feasible ;

moreover, it may be calculated that the interparticle distance at which the potential energy is a minimum (and thus the distance which the particles will adopt if left to themselves) decreases with increasing concentration of salt in the medium in a simple manner ; on increasing the salt concentration of a bottom-layer solution, therefore, we may expect the X-ray photograph to show a decreasing interparticle distance. This has been confirmed by Bernal & Fankuchen, the curve showing this variation with concentration following closely that predicted on the basis of Levine's theory. In this connection we may note that modification of the conditions of a top- and bottom-layer system, in such a way as to decrease the interparticle distance, will shift the equilibrium between the two so as to cause the bottom-layer to increase at the expense of the upper ; thus increasing the concentration of salt has just this effect, a phenomenon that has its counterpart in the " salting-out " of protein solutions, *i.e.*, the precipitation of solid protein from a sol by the addition of salt.

FIG. 50. Tactoids. *Top :* negative ; *middle :* positive ; *bottom :* positive tactoid between crossed Nicols. (Bernal & Fankuchen. *J. gen. Physiol.*)

Tactoids. During the separation of the top- and bottom-layers, for example after shaking them together, characteristic spindle-shaped bodies are observed ; they are of two types, and a study of their behaviour under the polarising microscope indicates that one type, the *positive tactoid*, consists of bottom-layer in top-layer, whilst the other, the *negative tactoid*, consists of top-layer in bottom-layer, as in Fig. 50 ; they are toroidal in shape and represent an equilibrium form between the conditions of surface energy tending to produce a spherical shape and those of orientation tending to keep the particles parallel ; after mechanical distortion they recover their shape spontaneously. Tactoids are formed under conditions favouring a reduced interparticle distance, *i.e.*, by adding acid or salt to a top-layer solution, and are simply to be regarded as pieces of bottom-layer (in the case of positive tactoids), with the constituent molecules orientated in a more perfect crystalline fashion ; thus the " crystals " described by Stanley, and obtained by acidifying a virus solution, are essentially positive tactoids. According to Bernal & Fankuchen, the formation of tactoids may be regarded as a fundamental step in the formation of many gels ; for example, it is possible to form a gel from a virus solution made up of tactoids by simply shaking. Presumably the tactoids, on shaking, tend to fuse together and so entrap the surrounding water to give a very dilute gel (Fig. 51). It is profitable to consider the water in such a gel as made up of two parts ; the water held between the individual particles, determining the interparticle distance, and *trapped water* belonging to a separate phase and depending in amount on the conditions under which the gel was formed.

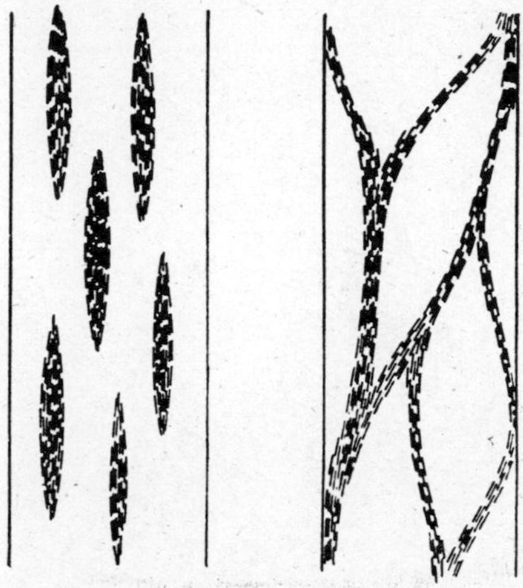

The tactoid may be regarded, as we have seen, as a balance struck between surface forces, tending to make the system curved, and interparticle attractions tending to make it flat ; if this is true the tactoid should be much flatter when the concentration of salts is high, since here the interparticle distance is small ; this prediction is borne out by experiment, the radius of curvature changing from 0·07 mm. in a salt-free solution to 0·12 mm. in 0·1N salt solution ; when the interparticle distance becomes much smaller, *e.g.*, by the addition of acid, the tactoid becomes a fibre, the orientation of the particles being perfect.

Fig. 51. Illustrating the fusion of tactoids to give a gel framework with trapped water. (Bernal & Fankuchen. *J. gen. Physiol.*)

Particle Size and Structure. According to Bernal & Fankuchen, the

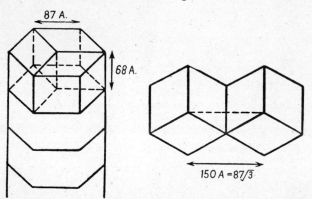

Fig. 52. Structure of the tobacco mosaic virus derived from X-ray crystallographic data. (Schramm, after Bernal & Fankuchen. *Z. Naturf.*)

lengths of the particles must be greater than 1,000A ; early electron-microscopical studies of Kauschke indicated a varying length, multiples of 1,500A. The most recent studies (Ruska, quoted by Schramm & Bergold), suggest a length of 2,500A ; the average thickness of a particle

PLATE IV

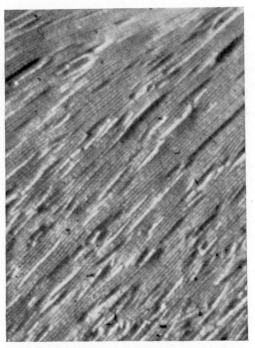

FIG. 53.   Electron-micrograph of tobacco mosaic virus.   × 43,000.   (Wyckoff.
Biochim. Biophys. Acta.)

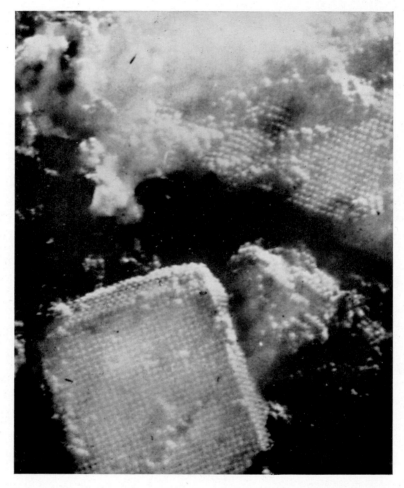

FIG. 55.   An electron-micrograph of a single crystal of a tobacco necrosis
virus.   × c. 40,000.   (Markham, Smith and Wyckoff.   *Nature.*)

(the minimum inter-particle distance) is 150A, so that with a specific gravity of 1·37 this corresponds to a molecular weight of some 40.10^6. In the ultra-centrifuge [1] Schramm & Bergold found a value of $40·7.10^6$.

Bernal & Fankuchen did not rest with a study of the inter-particle relationships of the virus; their X-ray analysis was extended to the intramolecular arrangement, and they concluded that the large particles are made up of small units, 11 × 11 × 11A, arranged in a hexagonal lattice with a period along the rod-axis of 68A, and one at right-angles of 87A; thus the structure could be considered to be built up of packed units, 87 × 87 × 68A, three of these giving a cross-sectional diameter of 150A (Fig. 52); a group of three of these units would have a molecular weight of about 1,110,000. With a molecular weight for the whole particle of some 40,000,000 this would mean a chain of thirty-six of these groups, about 2,500A long. Fig. 53, Pl. IV, from Wyckoff illustrates the electron-microscopical appearance of a frozen-dried solution of the virus; the tendency for the particles to arrange in sheaves is striking. There is some evidence, however, that aggregation of units takes place, in an end-to-end manner, during purification of the virus preparations; so that it may well be that in the plant the particles are smaller than 2,500A; in the plant itself, definite crystals have been observed, and this would suggest a shorter length in relation to breadth.[2] Strong evidence for the breakdown of the large units has been provided recently by Schramm & Bergold, who found

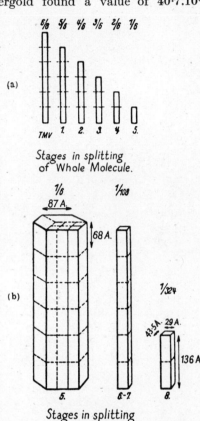

Stages in splitting of Whole Molecule.

Stages in splitting $\frac{1}{6}$th of Molecule.

FIG. 54. Illustrating the splitting of the tobacco mosaic virus molecule. (After Schramm. *Z. Naturf.*)

---

[1] Svedberg developed a method for determining the molecular weights of large particles by measuring their rate of sedimentation in a high-speed centrifuge—the "ultra-centrifuge." The molecular weight is given by :—

$$M = \frac{RTs}{(1 - Vd)D}$$

where s is the experimentally determined "sedimentation constant" calculated from the rate of sedimentation and the centrifugal force; V is the specific volume of the particles; D is the diffusion constant, and d the density of the solvent.

[2] A well ordered three-dimensional arrangement of molecules is more easily built up if these are spherical rather than unsymmetrical; the discovery by Bailey (p. 522) that the highly asymmetrical tropomyosin gives good crystals, however, must give us pause in any interpretation of the tendency of particles to form crystals.

that in an alkaline medium the particles of a purified preparation, with a molecular weight of $40 \cdot 7.10^6$, broke down to smaller units some of which could be separated ultra-centrifugally as definite fractions, whilst the presence of others was inferred from the sedimentation diagrams. Altogether some seven particle-sizes were identified, the smallest with a molecular weight of 120,000. The breakdown seemed to occur in regular steps, corresponding, during the early stages, to the loss of 1/6th of the molecule, *i.e.*, groups of 18 of the $87 \times 87 \times 68A$ units of Bernal & Fankuchen (Fig. 54*a*), so that it would seem that the long molecules break transversely. Further breakdown is probably associated with a longitudinal splitting of these " sixths," as in Fig. 54*b*, to give 108ths with a molecular weight of 360,000 , finally, a transverse break of these into three parts gives the smallest particles of 120,000 molecular weight. Two fractions of molecular weight 360,000 were obtained, one with nucleic acid and the other without ; the latter was inactive as a virus although all the other, nucleic acid-containing, fractions multiplied vigorously. On re-acidifying the solution, the small units built up to larger aggregates, with the result that compounds of the original molecular weight of the virus could be recovered ; the rebuilding was regular only to a limited extent ; for example the 120,000 units gave homodisperse solutions containing 360,000 units, but subsequent aggregation gave molecules of irregular weight ; again, the 7,000,000 units gave double-molecules but, after this, polydispersion occurred. None of the synthetic polymers showed any virus activity.[1]

So far as other plant viruses are concerned the measurements, both X-ray and electron-microscopical, indicate a corpuscular type of molecule ; thus the bushy stunt virus of tomatoes forms crystals built up of units estimated by Bernal & Fankuchen to have a diameter of 276A ; Price, Williams & Wyckoff have studied the growth of these crystals in the electron microscope [2] ; units of about 250–270A in diameter could be seen packed in a regular hexagonal array ; where it was possible to see several layers, there was evidence of a body-centred cubical packing. The tobacco necrosis virus, with a molecular weight of some 1,850,000, is crystalline and has been examined by X-rays in this state by Crowfoot & Schmidt ; they compute a minimum radius of 80A, for the units in the crystals, whilst electron-microscopical studies of Markham, Smith & Wyckoff suggest molecular arrays some 275A apart (Fig. 55, Pl. IV).

Hence it appears that the striking characteristics of the tobacco mosaic virus, depending as they do on the rod-shape of its molecule, are not shared by the other plant viruses ; it may well be, moreover, that many of these properties result from an artificial elongation of the protein molecules by an end-to-end growth during purification ; nevertheless the

[1] Oster found an average length of about 2,800A in the electron-microscope ; on treatment of the preparation with sonic vibrations the particles decreased progressively in size, first into halves and later into quarters. Associated with the fragmentation there was a progressive decrease in biological activity. The inactivation of the virus by ribonuclease, described by Loring, is not due to a splitting of the molecule ; apparently a complex is formed with the enzyme.

[2] That is, they have made replicas of the surface during growth of the crystal, and studied these in the electron-microscope.

study of these properties has clarified markedly our notions of the morphological possibilities of the fibrous type of protein. Thus the fundamental importance of the interparticle distance has been emphasised ; when it is beyond a certain limiting value, orientation is impossible and the solution is a true sol ; on decreasing the distance below this limiting value we may progress through various crystalline conditions, in which the solid characteristics increase, until we obtain the tactoids and later the fibre and dry gel. The interparticle distance is modified by changes in salt concentration and acidity of the medium, whilst the particle length may be critically determined by enzymic chemical reactions, so that we have in the tobacco mosaic virus a system capable of striking changes in physical properties in accordance with the chemical reactions and composition of the medium, *i.e.*, it contains within it many of the potentialities that we require for the ground substance of the cytoplasm.

The Nucleoproteins

Nucleus and Chromosomes. The general outline of the mitotic process involved in nuclear division has been given earlier (p. 14) ; it will be recalled that the chromosomes appear from an apparently homogeneous medium, they grow larger to achieve a maximum size in metaphase and subsequently are lost to view in telophase. Although the resting nucleus has been described by some workers as a homogeneous liquid with a viscosity of about twice that of water, separated from the cytoplasm by a membrane, the great bulk of the evidence suggests that at least a part of the nucleus is a solid phase. Thus the whole science of genetics has been built up on the basis of the essential permanence of the chromosomes which, as we have seen, become obvious during cell division. These chromosomes are thought to be built up of smaller elements, the genes, the presence of which in an orderly array in the chromosome determines the pattern of heredity. The complete dissolution of these formed elements at any stage in the life of the nucleus would be an insuperable difficulty in the way of interpreting genetic phenomena,

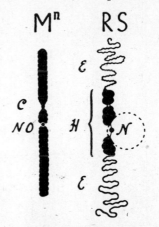

FIG. 56. Diagram of a chromosome of *Drosophila* at metaphase (M^n) and in resting stage (RS). C, centromere ; NO, nucleolar organiser ; H, heterochromatin ; E, euchromatin ; N, nucleolus. (Darlington. *Nature*.)

so that, as Wilson has said, we must treat the chromosomes as if they were persistent individuals which grow and divide and hand on their specific type of organisation to their descendants. On the modern view, amply substantiated by cytochemical studies, the resting nucleus contains formed elements, the chromosomes, which, because of their small content of stainable material, are not easily visible ; mitosis is accompanied by the synthesis of stainable material, *chromatin*, associated with a strong coiling of the chromosomes, so that they attain the rod-like form in metaphase illustrated in Fig. 56.   On the chromosome we can distinguish four parts : (*a*) the *centromere*, which controls the movements of the chromosome on the spindle ; (*b*) *heterochromatin*, stainable material persisting during the resting phase of the nucleus and genetically inert, which distinguishes it from (*c*) the *euchromatin* ; (*d*) the *nucleolar organisers*, characteristic regions of the chromosome which appear to control the formation of the *nucleoli*, small organelles which disappear during mitosis and reappear in the daughter nuclei.

Nuclei for chemical analysis may be obtained in large quantities from fish sperm, since these consist of little else than nucleus. From other cells, the nuclei may be obtained by breaking up the tissue in a mincer and suspending it in 1 per cent. citric acid. The suspension is centrifuged at low speed first, to remove the heavy fragments of cells, and then at about 2,400 r.p.m. for ten minutes when the nuclei are found at the bottom ; they are resuspended in citric acid solution and centrifuged down about six times, after which treatment they are free from cytoplasmic debris. The pioneering studies of Miescher, and all later studies (*e.g.*, those of Pollister & Mirsky), indicate that the main constituent of the nucleus is a nucleoprotein ; thus Mirsky estimates that 91 per cent. of the trout sperm is a nucleoprotamine consisting of a complex of nucleic acid and a strongly basic protein called a *protamine*, whilst most other nuclei contain nucleic acid combined with another type of

Yeast Nucleic Acid

(Adenine)

(Cytidine)

(Guanine)

(Uridine)

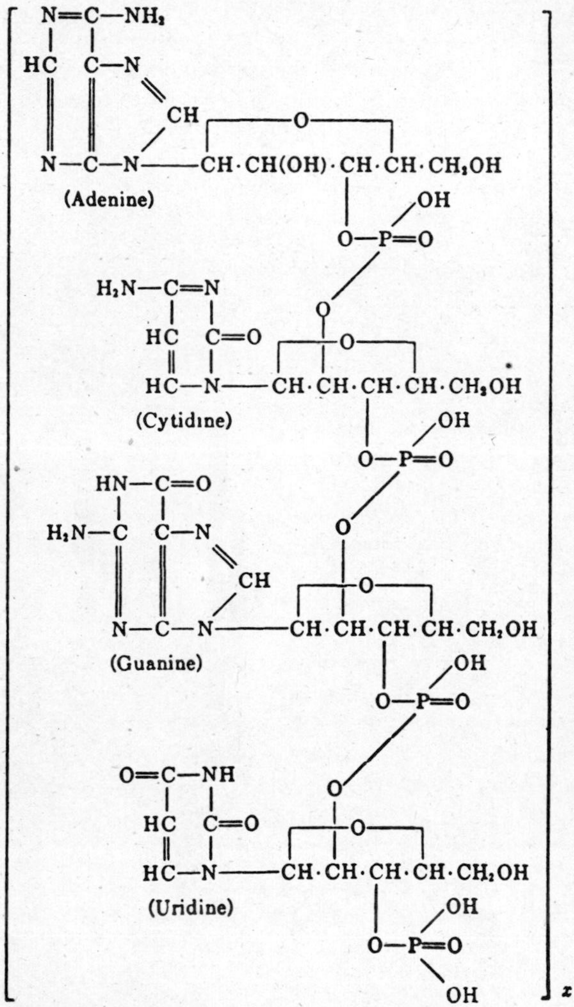

Fig. 57. (*a*) Yeast tetranucleotide.

basic protein, *histone*. Before discussing the chemical constitution further we may enter briefly into the structure of this important substance, nucleic acid.

Nucleic Acid. This term describes a class of substances, some, at least, having a very high molecular weight (of the order of 600,000–1,000,000),

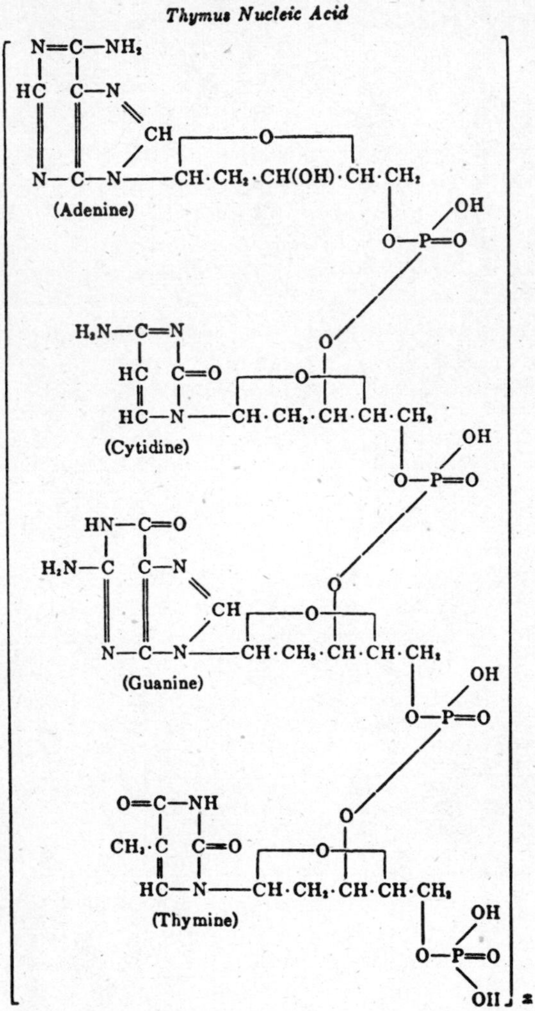

Thymus Nucleic Acid

FIG. 57. (*b*) Thymus tetranucleotide.

built up by the condensation of smaller units, the *nucleotides*. A typical nucleotide is *cytidylic acid*, consisting of a pyrimidine derivative, *cytosine*, linked to a pentose, *ribose*, which is linked to phosphoric acid. The nucleic acids are formed by the linkage of successive nucleotides through the phosphoric acid residues as in Fig. 57, *a, b*, which illustrates the structures of tetranucleotides obtained from yeast and thymus nucleic acids. The nucleic acids found in nature are classed as *ribose-nucleic acids* and *desoxyribose-nucleic acids* according as the pentose they contain is d-ribose or d-2-ribodesose (desoxyribose) :—

d-ribose d-2-ribodesose

Thus most of the nucleic acids obtained from nuclei are of the desoxy-class whilst all found in the cytoplasm belong to the ribose-class.[1] Since the cytosine in cytidylic acid may be replaced by a variety of pyrimidine and purine derivatives, the number of different nucleotides found in nature is large ; moreover the number of possibilities for variation in the structure of the nucleic acids, by the incorporation of different nucleotides in differing orders, is very great indeed.

It is probably incorrect to speak of a molecular weight for the nucleic acids, since this appears to vary considerably with the mode of preparation ; some estimates are shown in Table II compiled by Greenstein ; undoubtedly

TABLE II

Molecular Weight and Shape of Nucleic Acids (Greenstein)

Substance	Molecular weight	Length	Width
Na Thymonucleate	200,000	—	—
,,	500,000–1,000,000	—	—
,,	500,000	—	16A
,,	580,000	5,200A	13A
,,	430,000	2,720A	16A
,,	450,000	3,000A	15A
,,	1,200,000	—	—
,,	1,235,000	4,580A	22A
Thymonucleic Acid	4,800	42A	14A
Yeast Nucleic Acid	17,000	—	—
Ribonucleic Acid from Tobacco Mosaic Virus	200,000	700A	—
,, ,, ,,	290,000	—	—

the mode of preparation influences the degree of end-to-end aggregation of smaller units. This characteristic is important biologically since it indicates the ease with which the molecule can change its size. Moreover an enzyme, *ribonuclease*, which specifically attacks the ribose-type of nucleic acid, has been isolated in the crystalline form by Kunitz from tissue extracts ; the enzyme does not attack the desoxy-form, whereas another enzyme, *desoxyribonuclease*, recently purified by McCarty and Kunitz, does. These enzymes appear to be widely distributed and therefore probably play an important role in the nucleic acid economy of the cell.[2]

---

[1] Since ribose-nucleic acid was first isolated from yeast, substances belonging to this class are often called *yeast nucleic acids*, whilst the desoxy-type is called *thymonucleic acid*.

[2] The terminology respecting the nucleases is confusing because of the tendency to attach an enzyme-name to a type of reaction instead of to a definitely isolated enzyme. If we follow the treatment of Greenstein, Carter & Chalkley, we may distinguish four

Sodium thymonucleate, prepared from thymus gland nuclei, is soluble in all proportions in water to form viscous solutions which can be spun into threads ; the solutions are highly doubly refracting on streaming, the double refraction being negative in contrast to other fibrous systems. It is considered, on the basis of studies of birefringence, that the units in solution are some 300 times longer than they are broad. X-ray studies by Astbury have revealed a strongly marked period of 3·34A, along the fibre-axis, which probably corresponds to the spacing between successive nucleotides. Consequently, if the nucleotides are built up in a chain, they will give the appearance of a tall column of discs, linked together with a rod down one side, this linking rod consisting of the successive phosphoric acid residues. Such a structure would probably show negative micellar birefringence.

Nucleoproteins. The striking fact discovered by Astbury in regard to thymonucleic acid is its fibre-period of 3·34A, which corresponds very closely with that of a fully extended polypeptide chain as in β-keratin ; union between nucleic acid and a protein might therefore be expected to take place with a minimum of steric hindrance by the two chains lying alongside each other.[1] It seems very likely, moreover, that nucleic acids in the nucleus and elsewhere are associated with protein. In the nuclei the proteins are relatively simple, the strongly basic *protamines* of certain fish sperm, *e.g.*, salmon, and the *histones* of other nuclei. Thus Pollister & Mirsky, by extracting the nuclei carefully with 1 M NaCl, obtained a viscous solution which on dialysis lost a protamine, the latter passing through the collodion dialysis membrane ; its molecular weight was consequently very small (clupein, a protamine, has a molecular weight of only 4,000–4,100) ; the loss of this protein caused no loss of viscosity, indicating that the nucleic acid was responsible for this characteristic of the nucleoprotein complex. The complex is very loosely bound since the use of 1 M NaCl is sufficient to break it down ; it is probably for this reason that the nucleoprotein is soluble in this concentration of salt ; if 0·14 M NaCl is used as extractant the complex is not dissolved ; this is interesting since the concentration of salts within the cell is about 0·16 M and thus the chromosomes, which are mainly nucleoproteins, remain stable structures.

The solution of the problem of the association of nucleic acid with protein is fundamental to any interpretation of the complex events involved in nuclear and cytoplasmic phenomena, in particular the synthesis of proteins

types of reaction : (*a*) depolymerisation of the micelle to give polynucleotides previously held together by hydrogen-bond forces (Gulland), the appropriate enzyme being a *nucleodepolymerase ;* (*b*) the rupture of the phosphate link holding successive nucleotides together, to give the individual nucleotides, the enzyme being a *polynucleotidase ;* (*c*) dephosphorylation of a nucleotide to give a nucleoside (the base-sugar combination), the enzyme being called a *nucleotidase ;* (*d*) the breakdown of the nucleoside to base and sugar by a *nucleosidase.* Since Kunitz' crystalline ribonuclease and desoxyribonuclease break down the intact nucleic acid to individual nucleotides, they must be classed both as depolymerases and polynucleotidases.

[1] Astbury has shown that the protamine, clupein, combines with thymonucleic acid to give a compound with an X-ray fibre photograph similar to that of nucleic acid ; moreover, the combination of nucleic acid with edestin, a globular protein, also gives a fibre photograph, so that it would seem that the edestin molecule unrolls, the polypeptide chain fitting along the nucleic acid skeleton.

necessarily associated with growth and division. The native nucleic acids are birefringent, indicating the presence of large symmetrical units, yet some of the nucleoproteins from which they are derived are not flow-birefringent, for example the nucleohistone of the thymus gland. That this means that there is a fundamental difference in shape of the particle of nucleic acid when it combines with protein, is indicated by the profound decrease in viscosity,[1] which is observed as a result of the combination. Thus purified serum proteins, of the corpuscular type with low viscosity, when added to highly birefringent and structurally viscous nucleic acid solutions, cause a sudden diminution in these characteristics. When a denatured protein is added, however, there appears to be no interaction. We must assume, especially from the ease with which the linkage is affected by the salt concentration of the medium, that the linkage between the basic protein and the acidic nucleic acid is one of salt formation ; whether or not the nucleic acid is depolymerised during combination, so as to enable the parts to react separately with the protein and allow the resulting complex to retain its symmetrical shape, is not clear ; and the possibility of a spiral winding of the long chain cannot be excluded. The fact that denaturation of a protein prevents the formation of a complex (and splits it if it is already formed), is of great interest ; denaturation consists, as we have seen (p. 60), in the partial unfolding of the polypeptide grids, presumably allowing of new linkages between side-chains as a result. It may be, therefore, that reactive groups, formerly available to the nucleic acid, are withdrawn. Since denaturation may be reversible, we are presented with the possibility of a reversible linkage and release of nucleic acids in various parts of the cell.

The inclusion bodies extracted from infected plants and cells—the viruses—represent more complex bodies than the nucleoprotamines and nucleohistones ; the nucleic acid is, moreover, much more strongly bound. Generally the percentage of nucleic acid in the complex is smaller ; thus thymus nucleohistone contains 50 per cent. of nucleic acid, whereas the tobacco mosaic virus contains only 5 per cent., the alfalfa mosaic 15 per cent., and the tobacco ringspot virus 40 per cent. It is worth remarking that estimates of the lengths of the nucleic acid and protein of the tobacco mosaic virus indicate that there is room for eight molecules of nucleic acid

---

[1] The high viscosities shown by some protein and polysaccharide solutions are due to the rod-like particles ; the presence of these particles frequently gives rise to anomalous viscous effects, the so-called structural viscosity, the latter varying with the pressure employed to cause flow ; bottom-layer solutions exhibit it in a marked degree. An estimate of the asymmetry of the molecules may be obtained from measurements of viscosity with the aid of Kuhn's formula :—

$$\frac{\eta}{\eta_0} - 1 = g \left\{ 2 \cdot 5 + \frac{1}{16} \left(\frac{b}{a}\right)^2 \right\}$$

where η and η_0 are the viscosities of the solution and solvent respectively, g is the concentration in volume per cent., and b/a is the ratio of the long-axis to the short axis of the particle, the *asymmetry ratio*. The diffusion coefficient will similarly reflect the asymmetry of the molecule ; thus if D is the actual diffusion coefficient, and D_0 that of a sphere of the same mass and volume, calculated from the Einstein equation : $D_0 = \dfrac{kT}{6\pi\eta r}$, the ratio D_0/D is related to the asymmetry ratio, b/a. D_0/D is the same as Svedberg's " frictional ratio," f/f_0. Cohn & Edsall provide a table relating f/f_0 to b/a.

to lie along one molecule of virus protein ; it will be remembered that the tobacco mosaic virus is strongly birefringent. The particulates isolated by Bensley and by Claude from a variety of animal cells are nucleoproteins of the more complex type containing 16 per cent. of the total weight as nucleic acid. The animal viruses are doubtless more complex than the simple plant viruses, containing lipids and possibly some enzymes within the complex. The percentage of nucleic acid varies from 4 per cent. in the equine encephalomyelitis virus to 10 per cent. in the chicken sarcoma virus. As we have indicated earlier, the ribose-type of nucleic acid is found in practically all non-nuclear material ; however the influenza, vaccinia and rabbit papilloma viruses contain the desoxyribose form.[1]

Chromosome Structure

Gross analysis can yield little information regarding the location and function of nucleoprotein in the nucleus and cytoplasm ; fortunately, however, three important methods of study *in situ* have been developed. The first is the *Feulgen nucleal reaction* which relies on the production of an aldehyde after hydrolysis ; it is specific for desoxyribose and, as a result of its application, it has been shown that this class of nucleic acid is found only in the nucleus of animal and plant cells, although the nucleolus was not stained. Secondly, and even more important, since the tissue may be examined directly and without injurious chemical treatment, is Caspersson's technique based on the ultra-violet absorption of nucleic acid (p. 3) ; with his instrument the presence of as little as 10^{-11} mg. of nucleic acid may be determined. This method does not differentiate between the two types of nucleic acid, but when the results are compared with those given by the Feulgen technique it is possible to deduce the presence or absence of the ribose-nucleic acid. Thus the nucleoli absorb strongly at 2,600A, and therefore contain a high concentration of nucleic acid ; since they are Feulgen-negative, the acid must be of the ribose variety. In a similar manner the cytoplasmic granules of many cells have been shown to contain ribose-nucleic acid. Caspersson has shown that the ultra-violet absorption spectrum can distinguish not only the presence of nucleic acid but also that of certain types of protein. For instance, the tyrosine and tryptophane residues absorb strongly at 2,750 and 2,800A respectively, whilst the aliphatic types have no specific absorption in the ultra-violet. Finally, by the use of the specific enzymes, *ribonuclease* and *desoxyribonuclease*, nucleic acids may be digested from a tissue section.[2]

The chromosomes become microscopically visible largely as a result of the basophilia that they develop, *i.e.*, in virtue of their nucleic acid content. The fact that this detail only becomes evident during certain phases in the life of the nucleus suggests that, during these phases, nucleic acid is

---

[1] In bacteria certain bodies, thought to be the equivalent of nuclei, were shown to contain this nucleic acid.

[2] Thus Gersh & Bodian have shown that the changes in the Nissl granules of nerve-cell bodies (which are accumulations of ribose nucleic acid), following section of the axons may be simulated by applying ribonuclease. Apparently the highly polymerised nucleic acid of the granules must be depolymerised before being mobilised for the synthetic activities associated with regeneration of the nerve fibres.

actively synthesised. This viewpoint is confirmed by the investigations of Caspersson with the ultra-violet microscope on cells undergoing *meiosis*. By meiosis is meant the nuclear events in certain germ cells, equivalent to the mitotic division of other (somatic) cells. A *primary spermatocyte* undergoes division to give two daughter cells, *secondary spermatocytes ;* during this division the chromosomes do not split, so that half go to each daughter cell ; this is the first meiotic division resulting in cells with the *haploid* (as opposed to the *diploid*), number of chromosomes. The secondary spermatocytes divide again, the chromosomes this time splitting, so that the haploid number is retained. The following stages in the first meiotic division are distinguished : *Leptotene* consisting of the appearance of the fibres, or chromatin threads, which conjugate two by two to give the haploid number of bivalent chromosomes : *Pachytene* in which the filaments become shorter and thicker : *Diplotene* in which the chromosomes show a split, *i.e.*, indicate that they are made up of two side by side. The resting nucleus shows little absorption of light at 2,650A, a fact indicating a low nucleic acid content ; in the first stage of meiosis, the leptotene stage, small granules appear to draw together to appear finally as the *chromomeres* of the classical cytologists, the chromosome thus emerging as a chain of discrete units. The whole process of meiosis, during which the tetrad chromosomes are built up, is revealed very clearly in the ultra-violet microscope, the large tetrads absorbing very strongly indeed. Finally the telophase, in which the chromosomes of the daughter nuclei tend to fade from sight, is associated with a decrease in the nucleic acid content. By digesting the chromosomes with an enzyme, trypsin (which attacks the proteins but not the nucleic acid), in the presence of a lanthanum salt (which precipitates the liberated nucleic acid *in situ*), Caspersson was able to show that the densely absorbing chromosomes were still built up on a chromomere basis, so that it seems likely that in all stages of the life of a chromosome this fundamental structure is maintained.[1] By applying more selective enzymes, Mazia showed that the chromosome structure could be considered to be made up of a matrix of " complex protein," *i.e.*, of the non-histone or -protamine type ; removal of this matrix (by treatment with pepsin which does not attack the simpler histones and protamines appreciably), caused the chromosome to shrink strongly but otherwise to retain its shape. Treatment with trypsin caused a more or less complete disintegration, as Caspersson had found. Since pepsin does not attack protamines, Mazia thought that the fundamental fibrous structure of the chromosome was maintained by nucleoprotamine. Treatment with a phosphatase, which removed the nucleic acid by breaking down the phosphate linkages with the protein, left the chromosome intact and Feulgen-negative. Evidently the nucleic acid is not structurally indispensable material. The phosphatase used by Mazia was effective on the relatively depolymerised forms of nucleic acid ; the fact that the nucleic acid in the chromosome was attacked suggests that the acid in this

---

[1] Ris denies the existence of the chromomere as a unit of structure ; he interprets the banded appearance of chromosomes as being due to local spiralisation of the chromonemata.

structure is not highly polymerised, *i.e.*, its molecules cannot be regarded as long fibrous units running for thousands of Angstrom units along the chromosome. This viewpoint seems to be confirmed by Caspersson's studies of the behaviour of chromosomes in polarised light ; the birefringence and dichroism [1] are so small that such a picture must be ruled out, and we must think, instead, of localised accumulations of short nucleic acid molecules (of molecular weight of the order of 20,000 or less).

According to Caspersson, therefore, the appearance of a chromosome from the previously optically homogeneous nucleus may be considered to result primarily from the synthesis and aggregation of nucleic acid and protein on a pre-existing fibre which, because of its thinness, is not resolvable by microscopic methods. As a result of fission, the fibres are generally double and are called *chromonemata* or *chromatids*. Thus a chromosome consists of one or more fibres or chromonemata each resembling a string of beads, the chromomeres, united at the centromere. The geneticist, studying the variations in hereditary characteristics of living organisms, has not only convinced himself that the chromosomes are responsible for the transmission of these characteristics, but that each hereditary characteristic is associated with a discrete unit on the chromosome, the *gene*. The geneticist's picture is thus that of a series of discrete bodies linked together by internodes ; this implies a considerable length and it is interesting that the chromosomes are, in effect, coiled structures and not simple cylinders as originally thought ; moreover the coiling takes place during the period of maximal synthesis of new material, namely in metaphase.

The true nature, and structural significance, of the proteins in the chromosomes is still a matter of dispute. Caspersson concluded that the fundamental fibrous basis was due to a histone, the type of protein which was apparently common to all parts of the chromosome. Mirsky & Ris have concluded, on the other hand, that the basic structure is made up of a non-histone type of protein. They base this conclusion on their studies of isolated chromosomes. When the nucleus is treated with 1 M NaCl under the microscope it is observed to swell and at one stage to resemble the early prophase nucleus, containing numerous fibres ; when the nucleus bursts (after swelling to twelve-fold its size), there is left a tangled mass of threads, presumably the remains of the chromosomes after losing most of their nucleoprotein. The threads are thin and have a helicoid structure, and probably represent the individual fibrous units of which the chromosomes are thought to consist, the chromonemata. Mirsky & Ris isolated the chromosomes from a large number of nuclei and showed that the protein responsible for maintaining their structure intact was a nucleoprotein of the complex type (containing tryptophane) ; thus 1 M NaCl extracted some 90 per cent. of the chromosome material (nucleohistone), but left the essential fibrous structure intact ; this residue appeared to be chiefly a ribose-type of nucleoprotein, suggesting that some of this form of nucleic acid is present in the nucleus. Stedman & Stedman had come to a rather

---

[1] *Dichroism*, or more generally *pleochroism*, results from varying degrees of absorption of the different wavelengths of light according to the vibration-direction.

similar conclusion, in so far as they stated that the structural basis of the chromosomes was not nucleohistone (or nucleoprotamine in the case of salmon and herring sperm which does not contain histone), but a protein they called *chromosomin*.   These authors actually deny that nucleic acid belongs to the chromosomes, arguing that coloured material, resulting from the Feulgen reaction with nucleic acid, is adsorbed on to the chromosomes *after* the reaction.   According to Stedman & Stedman, therefore, the chromosome consists of a protein, chromosomin, whilst the nucleic acid and histone belong to the matrix in which this is embedded. The final conclusion of Stedman & Stedman, to the effect that nucleic acid is not a fundamental element in the structure of the chromosome, has been repudiated by most workers in this field.[1]

The actual state of the chromosomes in the resting (interphase) nucleus has been discussed by Ris & Mirsky (1949).   It will be recalled that these authors isolated chromosomes from the resting nucleus ; double, tightly spiralled threads.   The question still remains as to whether these are artefacts of the experimental technique, and why they are not visible in the intact cell.   Nuclei teased out of the cell into saline solution show the presence of chromosomes, whereas in sucrose solution they appear optically homogeneous, as in the living cell.   It looks, therefore, as though the appearance of these filaments is a result of the experimental procedure ; and the experiments of Ris & Mirsky strongly suggest that the appearance of chromosomes in the resting nucleus is due to the reversible condensation of chromosome material—histone, desoxyribose nucleic acid, etc.   In the normal resting condition, therefore, the chromosomes are greatly swollen, occupying the whole body of the nucleus ; as a result of injury, be it teasing into saline solution, treatment with certain fixatives, or even observation by ultra-violet light, the material condenses to give the typical chromosomal appearance.

The chromosomes of certain nuclei divide repeatedly, without an associated division of the nucleus, thereby giving rise to *polyploidy*, the presence of more than the characteristic number of chromosomes (the *diploid* number), in the nucleus.   In the nuclei of the salivary glands of certain Diptera, *e.g.*, the fruit-fly *Drosophila*, this multiplication goes on to an enormous extent ; moreover, the resulting chromatids fail to separate, thus giving rise to the " giant salivary chromosomes " some 100 times the size of ordinary chromosomes.   These appear banded on staining, indicating the presence of localised concentrations of nucleic acid a few tenths of a micron thick ; if the salivary chromosome were really just a magnified ordinary chromosome, the darkly staining bands would be the chromomeres.   That the bands are definitely composed of nucleic acid is confirmed by the ultra-violet studies of Caspersson ; thus Fig. 58, Pl. V (*a*), shows an ultra-violet photograph of a portion of a *Chironomus* salivary chromosome treated with lanthanum acetate to localise the nucleic acid, and (*b*) a phase-contrast microphotograph of the same type of chromosome neither fixed nor stained.   Digestion experiments showed that the light

[1] By Brachet (1946), Callan (1943) and Caspersson (1944). Stedman & Stedman have recently (1950) reaffirmed their position, quoting new evidence.

PLATE V

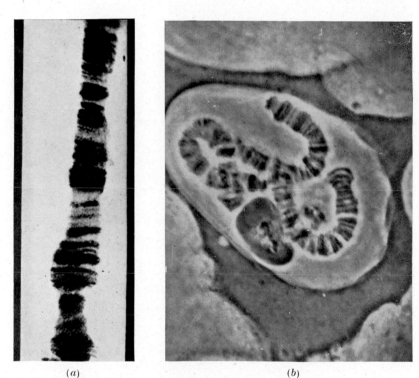

(a)   (b)

FIG. 58. *Chironomus* salivary chromosomes. (a) Ultra-violet micrograph
of material fixed with lanthanum acetate. × 930. (Caspersson. *Scand.
Arch. Physiol.*) (b) Phase-contrast microphotograph on unfixed and
unstained tissue. × 700. (Barer. *Brit. Sci. News.*)

[*To face p.* 82.

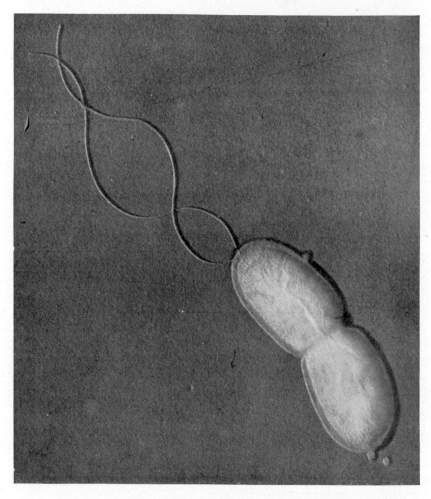

FIG. 59. Electron-micrograph of *Pseudomonas fluorescens.* × 32,000.
(Houwink & Van Iterson, Delft. *Biochim. Biophys. Acta.*)

bands were of protein, which was also present in the dark bands, *i.e.*, that the nucleic acid was present as a nucleoprotein. A rough calculation shows that if the giant chromosome is really no more than an enlarged ordinary chromosome, the size of the bands in the latter would correspond to the size of a protein molecule, *i.e.*, the gene, supposing it to be identical with the chromomere, would be little else than a nucleoprotein.

In the electron-microscope, Bucholz reports that the chromosomes appeared as threads—varying in width from 500 to 1,000A—with attached granules which varied greatly in size, shape, and density to electrons ; for example, the spherical granules had diameters varying from 750 to 1,650A. These granules are presumably the chromomeres of the classical cytologist, but whether they will be resolvable into smaller units, or not, remains to be seen.

Nucleic Acid-Protein Inter-Relationships

Although the desoxy-type of nucleic acid seems to be confined to the nucleus, it appears that ribose-nucleic acid, generally associated with the cytoplasm, is present in the nucleus, too ; certainly in the nucleolus and possibly in heterochromatin (Brachet). The relationships between the four loci of nucleic acid, namely the euchromatin, the heterochromatin, the nucleoli and the cytoplasmic nucleic acid, is the theme of most modern studies of nuclear cytology and viruses, but it is frequently difficult to separate experimental facts from mere speculation. Cytoplasmic nucleic acid seems to be largely associated with the " inclusion bodies " or particulates discussed earlier ; it will be recalled that Claude classifies them as large particles $(0 \cdot 5-1 \cdot 5\mu)$, corresponding to the mitochondria of the histologist, and small particles $(50-300\text{m}\mu)$, or microsomes. They differ fundamentally in composition, such enzymes as have been studied being concentrated in the large particles whilst the nucleic acids are predominantly associated with the small particles. The large particles may be fragmented by osmotic means, in which case small particles of diameter about $0 \cdot 1\mu$ may be separated, containing most of the nucleic acid originally associated with the large particles. The question thus arises as to whether the large particles are really built up of small particles with a loss of nucleic acid during the process ; this viewpoint is supported by Jeener and by Chantrenne, the latter having shown that the cytoplasmic particles vary almost continuously in size from the smallest to the largest ; the smallest (separated by centrifuging for sixty minutes at 100,000 g.), contained, per unit of weight, ten times more ribonucleic acid than the largest. Jeener found that the amount of nucleic acid extractable from the particles varied inversely with their size, and suggested that the smallest particles acted as " nuclei " in the organisation of the larger ones, the nucleic acid in them being necessary for protein synthesis.

The importance of nucleic acid for the synthesis of protein seems now to be generally recognised ; thus Caspersson and his colleagues have established a sound correlation between the size of the nucleolus and the degree of cytoplasmic protein synthesis (see for example Hydén, 1947, and Thorell, 1947) ; moreover the division of chromosomes involves, besides

the synthesis of nucleic acid, that of protein too ; again, the viruses
stimulate the cells to intense protein synthesis, and these bodies are
nucleoproteins. Whether or not Astbury's suggestion that nucleic acid
behaves as a template for synthesis is true, the identity of their repeat
periods is certainly of great interest ; it may be, however, as Spiegelman
& Kamen have suggested, that the acid controls the metabolic energy in
some way so as to funnel it into protein synthesis at critical stages in the
cell's development.

The relationship between nuclear and cytoplasmic nucleic acids is also
one that has provoked speculation ; Caspersson has suggested that the
nucleolus acts as intermediary between the two systems ; thus he thinks
that the nucleolus is built up by the heterochromatic regions of the
chromosome, *i.e.*, that the desoxy-type of nucleic acid is converted to the
ribose-type,[1] whence it is carried to the nuclear membrane and diffuses
out into the cytoplasm to form cytoplasmic nucleoproteins. In support
of this notion Painter, from a study of the glandular cells of the honey-bee,
concludes that desoxyribose-nucleic acid is first synthesised on or about
heterochromatic regions of the chromosomes and then, through the
agency of the nucleoli, is converted into products which yield nucleic acid
in the cytoplasm. Painter interprets the endomitotic growth—which
leads to the formation of giant chromosomes in certain secretory cells—as
the mechanism whereby heterochromatic centres and nucleolar organisers
are increased in quantity, thereby making it possible for a single cell to
secrete large amounts of protein. Finally, Sparrow & Hammond state
that Feulgen-positive bodies may be found in the cytoplasm in certain
phases of meiosis in plant cells. A reverse relationship, whereby the
cytoplasm supplies the nucleus, is suggested by the work of Brachet who
found a reciprocal relationship between the ribose- and the desoxy-types
of nucleic acid in the developing sea-urchin embryo. In general, when
the predominant activity is cell division [2] the cytoplasmic basophilia
decreases to provide nucleic acids (of the desoxy-type of course), for the
multiplying nuclei ; when rapid cell division gives way to cell differentiation, *i.e.*, in the period of cytoplasmic protein synthesis, then the
ribose-nucleic acids show striking increases ; and, since the total nucleic
acid content of the embryo increases, this must be due to the formation of
new material. Some recent quantitative studies of Caldwell &
Hinshelwood are in agreement with this viewpoint ; these authors found
that, whereas the desoxyribose-nucleic acid content of *B. lactis œrogenes*
remained tolerably constant when the organisms were grown under a

---

[1] A direct interconversion is chemically unlikely, *vide* Gulland.

[2] In an embryo, the cytoplasm of cells actually dividing is always less basophilic than
that of neighbouring, resting, cells, a fact suggesting the conversion of ribose- to
desoxyribose-nucleic acid. This conclusion of Brachet has been disputed by Schmidt,
Hecht & Thannhauser who, by the application of modern methods of separation and
estimation of the nucleic acids, have shown that a decrease in the ribose-acid does *not*
take place during the phase of rapid increase of desoxy-acid. Marshak has isolated a
fraction from liver nuclei which he believes to be a precursor to both types of nucleic
acid ; thus injected P^{32} is rapidly taken up into the nuclei in this precursor form ; if the
cells are mitotic, it passes into the desoxy-acid, but in resting cells it goes rapidly into
the cytoplasm as ribonucleic acid.

variety of conditions, the ribose-nucleic acid content was variable and proportional to the rate at which the bacteria were growing. The fact that, during the phase of logarithmic growth, very little of the organic phosphorus exchanged with P^{32} in the medium suggested that the ribose-nucleic acid remained polymerised during protein synthesis.

It would seem, therefore, that the two types of nucleic acid are inter-convertible ; moreover their associated protein-types also change. Thus there seems little doubt of the truth of Kossel's suggestion that the rapid synthesis of protamine by the spawning salmon is carried out at the expense of the complex muscle proteins, which are consequently broken down to relatively simple units. In the chromosomes there is probably, if Caspersson's analysis of the ultra-violet absorption spectra is justified, a cycle of changes in the protein composition. At metaphase the proteins are exclusively of the histone type whilst in prophase the predominant type is " complex protein." In the resting nucleus the sap shows the presence of complex protein, presumably derived from the histones of the chromosomes, whilst the surviving formed elements, namely the heterochromatin and nucleoli, contain mainly histone.

Finally we may note that the virus is a nucleoprotein which utilises the host's cellular environment in the synthesis of itself, *i.e.*, as Cohen has emphasised, it forces the cell to re-duplicate it (the virus). Studies on bacteriophages—viruses that live in bacteria—show that the phage apparently interrupts the normal synthetic activities of its host, thereby inhibiting its growth, and side-tracks them to the synthesis of large amounts of protein, *i.e.*, to re-duplicate the phage. It is perhaps significant that the more primitive types of virus are ribo-nucleoproteins ; where the virus shows evidence of some sort of organisation it contains the desoxy-type ; it has therefore been suggested that the reduplication of highly organised structures requires the desoxy-type of nucleic acid ; where relatively unorganised blocks of material are to be synthesised, on the other hand—as in the cytoplasmic particles, simple viruses, and possibly the material synthesised by heterochromatin—it seems that the ribose-type is sufficient.

Bacteria. The bacterial cell consists of a wall, which, being apparently rigid, is responsible for the permanent shape of the organism ; a plasma membrane beneath this is probably present, and beneath this the cytoplasm may be differentiated into a cortical layer and endoplasm. A number of bodies are present within the cell which are Feulgen-positive and which divide longitudinally during cell division ; these may therefore be likened to primitive nuclei, or possibly to individual chromosomes on which genes may be distributed. The cytoplasm contains large amounts of ribonucleic acid which, according to Boivin, Vendrely & Tulasne, may amount to 20 per cent. of the dry weight of the organism ; this high concentration is doubtless connected with the amazing ability of the bacteria to multiply, since Malmgren & Hydén have shown that the amount of this nucleic acid increases by five-fold as the cells pass from the " lag-phase " to the phase of " logarithmic multiplication." The outermost layers of the bacteria are necessarily those that have come in for most study, since it is this region that is probably responsible for their specific staining reactions and antigenic properties.[1]   Dubos, and other authorities on bacterial cytology, differentiate the true *wall* of the bacteria, responsible for their shape and integrity, from an outermost layer which may be regarded as an extraneous coat secreted by the cell.   This secretion takes the form of a slime which may be sufficiently compact to be described as a *capsule* ; the material of this may be protein—in which case it may be digested away with trypsin— or a polysaccharide of the mucin type, of which hyaluronic acid is an example.   The extraneous nature of this capsule is made evident by the fact that its artificial removal leaves the morphology, and often the physiology, of the organism unaffected.   The capsule, or slime, is neverthe- less of fundamental importance for the antigenic properties of the bacteria since antibodies can be developed that are specific for the particular type of polysaccharide present in it ; moreover, in the case of pneumococci, virulence is associated with encapsulation ; thus a non-virulent R-strain may appear as a variant of the virulent S-strain, the R-variant being non- encapsulated whilst the S-strain is.   It is of great interest, moreover, that the transformation from the non-encapsulated to the encapsulated form can be induced experimentally ; Griffith showed that on injecting R together with heat-killed S into a mouse, the animal succumbed, the living R-strain being converted into fully encapsulated virulent cells. Later workers showed that the same transformation could be brought about *in vitro* with extracts of the encapsulated organisms, and finally Avery, MacLeod & McCarty showed that the principle in these extracts was desoxyribose-nucleic acid.   The transformation was permanent in the sense that successive cultures continued to develop capsules, so that the action is equivalent to a mutation in higher organisms and serves to emphasise the importance of desoxyribose-nucleic acid in this type of phenomenon.   The chemical nature of the bacterial wall is not by any means clear, in fact it would be quite unsafe to generalise on this point since, as Dubos remarks, its constitution doubtless varies widely from one group of organisms to another.   That polysaccharides are present as an integral part of the structure of some organisms is made likely by Fleming's observation that the substance lysozyme, found in tears, could destroy certain bacteria ; lysozyme seems to be identical with the enzyme, *hyaluronidase*, which specifically attacks hyaluronic acid.   The Gram- positivity of bacteria is associated with the presence of magnesium ribonucleate, but whether this is present as a thin layer on the surface, or belongs to the deeper structures, is not yet clear.   Motility in bacteria may be achieved (according to Pijper) by wave-like spiral contractions of the cytoplasm which are communicated to the cell wall, or by the presence of definite flagella (Fig. 59, Pl. V), which arise in the cytoplasm and pass through the cell wall (Mudd ; Houwink & Van Iterson).

[1] On a purely empirical basis bacteriologists have divided bacteria into three classes ; if bacteria are stained with methyl violet and mordanted with iodine, then washed with alcohol and counterstained with a dye of contrasting colour, the cells retaining the original dye are said to be *Gram-positive*, whereas those that lose this and take the counterstain are *Gram-negative*.   With the Ziehl-Neelsen technique basic fuchsin is taken up, and retained under acid conditions, by a third group called *acid-fast bacteria*. Bacteria behave as *antigens* in that they stimulate their host to produce *antibodies* which destroy or agglutinate them.

References

ASTBURY, W. T. (1943). " X-Rays and the Stoichiometry of the Proteins." *Adv. in Enzym.*, **3**, 63.

ASTBURY, W. T. (1947). " X-Ray Studies of Nucleic Acids." *Symp. Soc. Exp. Biol.*, **1**, 66.

ASTBURY, W. T. & BELL, F. O. (1938). " Some Recent Developments in the X-Ray Study of Proteins and Related Structures." *C.S.H. Symp.*, **6**, 109.

AVERY, O. T., MACLEOD, C. M. & MCCARTY, M. (1944). " Induction of Transformation of Pneumococcal Types by a Desoxyribonucleic Acid Fraction from Pneumococcus Type III." *J. exp. Med.*, **79**, 137.

BARER, R. (1948). " Phase-Contrast Microscopy." *Brit. Sci. News*, **1**, (9), 10.

BAWDEN, F. C. (1950). " Plant Viruses and Virus Diseases." Waltham, Mass. Chronica Bot. Co.

BAWDEN, F. C. & PIRIE, N. W. (1937). " Isolation and Some Properties of Liquid Crystalline Substances from Solanaceous Plants Infected with Three Strains of Tobacco Mosaic Virus." *Proc. Roy. Soc.*, *B*, **123**, 274.

BERNAL, J. D. & FANKUCHEN, I. (1941). " X-Ray Crystallographic Studies of Plant Virus Preparations." I–III. *J. gen. Physiol.*, **25**, 111.

BOIVIN, A., VENDRELY, R. & TULASNE, R. (1947). " Le Rôle des Deux Acides Nucléiques dans la Constitution et dans la vie Bactérienne." *Proc. Int. Congr. Cyt.*, p. 208.

BRACHET, J. (1933). " Synthèse de l'Acide Thymonucléique Pendant le Développement de l'Œuf d'Oursin." *Arch. Biol.*, **44**, 519.

BRACHET, J. (1942). " La Localisation des Acides Pentosenucleiques dans les Tissus Animaux et les Œufs d'Amphibiens en voie de Développement." *Arch. Biol.*, **53**, 207.

BRACHET, J. (1947). " Metabolism of Nucleic Acids During Embryonic Development." *C.S.H. Symp.*, **12**, 18.

BRACHET, J. (1947). " Nucleic Acids in the Cell and Embryo." *Symp. Soc. Exp. Biol.*, **1**, 66.

BRUES, A. M., TRACY, M. M. & COHN, W. E. (1944). " Nucleic Acids of Rat Liver and Hepatoma : Their Metabolic Turnover in Relation to Growth." *J. biol. Chem.*, **155**, 619.

BUCHOLZ, J. T. (1947). " Methods in the Preparation of Chromosomes and Other Parts of Cells for Examination With an Electron Microscope." *Amer. J. Bot.*, **34**, 445.

BUCHOLZ, J. T. (1947). " Chromosome Structure Under the Electron Microscope." *Science*, **105**, 607.

CALDWELL, P. C. & HINSHELWOOD, C. (1950). " Some Considerations on Autosynthesis in Bacteria." *J. Chem. Soc.*, 3156.

CALDWELL, P. C., MACKOR, E. L. & HINSHELWOOD, C. (1950). " Ribose Nucleic Acid Content and Cell Growth of *B. Lactis Aerogenes*." *J. Chem. Soc.*, 3151.

CALLAN, H. G. (1943). " Distribution of Nucleic Acid in the Cell." *Nature*, **152**, 503.

CASPERSSON, T. (1936). " U.d. Chemischen Aufbau der Strukturen des Zellkerns." *Scand. Arch. Physiol.*, **73**, Suppl. 8.

CASPERSSON, T. (1943). " 'Chromosomin' and Nucleic Acids." *Nature*, **153**, 499.

CASPERSSON, T. (1947). " Relations Between Nucleic Acid and Protein Synthesis." *Symp. Soc. Exp. Biol.*, **1**, 66.

CASPERSSON, T. & SCHULTZ, J. (1939). " Pentose Nucleotides in the Cytoplasm of Growing Tissues." *Nature*, **143**, 602.

CASPERSSON, T. & SCHULTZ, J. (1940). " Ribonucleic Acids in both Nucleus and Cytoplasm and the Function of the Nucleolus." *Proc. Nat. Acad. Sci. U.S.*, **26**, 507.

CATCHESIDE, D. G. & HOLMES, B. (1947). " Action of Enzymes on Chromosomes." *Symp. Soc. Exp. Biol.*, **1**, 225.

CHANTRENNE, H. (1947). " Hétérogenéité des Granules Cytoplasmiques du Foie de Souris." *Biochim. Biophys. Acta*, **1**, 437.

CLAUDE, A. (1943). " Distribution of Nucleic Acids in the Cell and the Morphological Constituents of Cytoplasm." *Biol. Symp.*, **10**, 111.

CLAUDE, A. (1944). " Constitution of Mitochondria and Microsomes and the Distribution of Nucleic Acid in the Cytoplasm of a Leukemic Cell." *J. exp. Med.*, **80**, 19

CLAUDE, A. (1947/8). " Studies on Cells : Morphology, Chemical Constitution and Distribution of Biochemical Functions." *Harvey Lectures*, **43**, 121.

CLAUDE, A. & POTTER, J. S. (1943). " Isolation of Chromatin Threads from the Resting Nucleus of Leukemic Cells." *J. exp. Med.*, **77**, 345.

COHEN, S. S. (1947). " Synthesis of Bacterial Viruses in Infected Cells." *C.S.H. Symp.*, 12, 35.

COHN, E. J. & EDSALL, J. T. (1943). " Proteins, Amino Acids and Peptides as Ions and Dipolar Ions." N.Y. Reinhold.

CROWFOOT, D. & SCHMIDT, G. M. J. (1945). " X-Ray Crystallographic Measurements on a Single Crystal of Tobacco Necrosis Virus." *Nature*, 155, 504.

DANIELLI, J. F. " Study of Techniques for the Cytochemical Demonstration of Nucleic Acids and Some Components of Proteins." *Symp. Soc. Exp. Biol.*, 1, 101.

DARLINGTON, C. D. (1942). " Chromosome Chemistry and Gene Action." *Nature*, 149, 66.

DARLINGTON, C. D. (1947). " Nucleic Acid and the Chromosomes." *Symp. Soc. Exp. Biol.*, 1, 252.

DUBOS, R. J. (1947). " The Nature and Properties of the Membranes of Bacterial Cells." *Proc. Int. Congr. Cyt.*, p. 192.

FREY-WYSSLING, A. (1948). " Submicroscopic Morphology of Protoplasm and its Derivatives." New York and Amsterdam. Elsevier.

GERSH, I. & BODIAN, D. (1943). " Histochemical Analysis of Changes in Rhesus Motoneurones After Root Section." *Biol. Symp.*, 10, 163.

GREENSTEIN, J. P. (1944). " Nucleoproteins." *Adv. in Protein Chem.*, 1, 209.

GREENSTEIN, J. P., CARTER, C. E. & CHALKLEY, H. W. (1947). " Enzymatic Degradation of Ribosenucleic and Desoxyribosenucleic Acids." *C.S.H. Symp.*, 12, 64.

GRIFFITH, F. (1928). " The Significance of Pneumococcal Types." *J. Hyg.*, 27, 113.

GULLAND, J. M. (1947). " The Structures of Nucleic Acids." *C.S.H. Symp.*, 12, 95.

HOUWINK, A. L. & VAN ITERSON, W. (1950). " Electron Microscopical Observations on Bacterial Cytology. II. A Study in Flagellation." *Biochim. Biophys. Acta*, 5, 10.

HYDÉN, H. (1943). " Protein Metabolism in the Nerve Cell during Growth and Function." *Acta. Physiol. Scand.*, 6, Suppl. 17.

HYDÉN, H. (1947). " Protein and Nucleotide Metabolism in the Nerve Cell under Different Functional Conditions." *Symp. Soc. Exp. Biol.*, 1, 152.

HYDÉN, H. (1947). " The Nucleoproteins in Virus Reproduction." *C.S.H. Symp.*, 12, 104.

JEENER, R. (1948). " L'Hétérogenéité des Granules Cytoplasmiques." *Biochim. Biophys. Acta*, 2, 633.

KAUSCHE, G. A., PFANKUCH, E. & RUSKA, H. (1939). " Die Sichtbarmachung von Pflanzlichem Virus im Ubermikroskop." *Naturwiss*, 27, 292.

KNIGHT, C. A. (1947). " Nucleoproteins and Virus Activity." *C.S.H. Symp.*, 12, 115.

KOLLER, P. C. (1947). " Integration of Nuclear and Cytoplasmic Activities in the Cell." *Proc. Int. Congr. Cyt.*, p. 85.

KUNITZ, M. (1940). " Crystalline Ribonuclease." *J. gen. Physiol.*, 24, 15.

KUNITZ, M. (1950). " Crystalline Desoxyribonuclease." *J. gen. Physiol.*, 33, 349.

LORING, H. S. (1942). " Reversible Inactivation of Tobacco Mosaic Virus by Crystalline Ribonuclease." *J. gen. Physiol.*, 25, 497.

LORING, H. S. & CARPENTER, F. H. (1943). " Isolation of Mononucleotides after Hydrolysis of Ribonucleic Acid by Crystalline Ribonuclease." *J. biol. Chem.*, 150, 381.

MALMGREN, B. & HYDÉN, H. (1947). " Some Aspects of Nucleotide Metabolism and Variations of Volumes in Bacteria." *Proc. Int. Cong. Cyt.*, p. 214.

MARKHAM, R., SMITH, K. M. & WYCKOFF, R. W. G. (1947). " Electron Microscopy of Tobacco Necrosis Virus Crystals." *Nature*, 159, 574.

MARSHAK, A. (1941). " P^{32} Uptake by Nuclei." *J. gen. Physiol.*, 25, 275.

MARSHAK, A. (1948). " Evidence for a Nuclear Precursor of Ribo- and Desoxyribonucleic Acid." *J. cell. & comp. Physiol.*, 32, 381.

MARSHAK, A. & CALVET, F. (1949). " Specific Activity of P^{32} in Cell Constituents of Rabbit Liver." *J. cell. & comp. Physiol.*, 34, 451.

MAZIA, D. (1941). " Enzyme Studies on Chromosomes." *C.S.H. Symp.*, 9, 40.

MCCARTY, M. (1946). " Purification and Properties of Desoxyribonuclease Isolated from Beef Pancreas." *J. gen. Physiol.*, 29, 123.

MIRSKY, A. E. (1943). " Chromosomes and Nucleoproteins." *Adv. in Enzym.*, 3, 1.

MIRSKY, A. E. (1947). " Chemical Properties of Isolated Chromosomes." *C.S.H. Symp.*, 12, 143.

MIRSKY, A. E. & POLLISTER, A. W. (1943). " Fibrous Nucleoproteins of Chromatin." *Biol. Symp.*, 10, 247.

MIRSKY, A. E. & POLLISTER, A. W. (1946). " Chromosin, a Desoxyribose Nucleoprotein Complex of the Cell Nucleus." *J. gen. Physiol.*, 30, 117.

MIRSKY, A. E. & RIS, H. " Isolated Chromosomes." *J. gen. Physiol.*, 31, 1, 7.

MORGAN, W. T. J. (1944). " Transformation of Pneumococcal Types." *Nature*, **153**, 763.

MUDD, S. (1947). " Submicroscopic Structure of the Bacterial Cell as shown by the Electron Microscope." *Proc. Int. Congr. Cyt.*, p. 217.

OSTER, G. (1947). " Sonic Treatment of Tobacco Mosaic Virus." *J. gen. Physiol.*, **31**, 89.

PAINTER, R. S. (1945). " Nuclear Phenomena Associated with Secretion in Certain Gland Cells with Special Reference to the Origin of Cytoplasmic Nucleic Acid." *J. exp. Zool.*, **100**, 523.

PEASE, D. C. (1946). " Hydrostatic Pressure Effects on the Spindle Figure and Chromosome Movement." *Biol. Bull.*, **91**, 145.

PIJPER, A. (1946). " Shape and Motility of Bacteria." *J. Path. Bact.*, **58**, 325.

POLLISTER, A. W. & MIRSKY, A. E. (1946). " The Nucleoprotamine of Trout Sperm." *J. gen. Physiol.*, **30**, 161.

PRICE, W. C. & WYCKOFF, R. W. G. (1946). " Electron Micrographs of Molecules on the Face of a Crystal." *Nature*, **157**, 764.

PRICE, W. C., WILLIAMS, R. C. & WYCKOFF, R. W. G. (1946). " Electron Micrographs of Crystalline Plant Viruses." *Arch. Biochem.*, **9**, 175.

RAWLINS, T. E., ROBERTS, O. & UTECH, N. M. (1946). " An Electron Microscope Study of Tobacco Mosaic Virus at Different Stages of Infection." *Amer. J. Bot.*, **33**, 356.

RIS, H. (1945). " Structure of Meiotic Chromosomes in the Grasshopper and its Bearing on the Nature of ' Chromomeres ' and ' Lamp-Brush Chromosomes '." *Biol. Bull.*, **89**, 242.

RIS, H. & MIRSKY, A. E. (1949). " State of the Chromosomes in the Interphase Nucleus." *J. gen. Physiol.*, **32**, 489.

ROBINOW, C. F. (1947). " Cytological Observations on Bacteria." *Proc. Int. Congr. Cyt.*, p. 204.

RUDALL, K. M. (1950). Fundamental Structures in Biological Systems. " Progress in Biophysics." Ed. Butler & Randall. London. Butterworth-Springer.

SCHMIDT, G. & LEVENE, P. A. (1938). " Ribonucleodepolymerase (the Jones-Dubos Enzyme)." *J. biol. Chem.*, **126**, 423.

SCHMIDT, G., HECHT, L. & THANNHAUSER, S. J. (1947). " Behaviour of the Nucleic Acids during the Early Development of the Sea-Urchin Egg." *J. gen. Physiol.*, **31**, 203.

SCHMITT, F. O. (1944/5). " Ultrastructure and the Problem of Cell Organisation." *Harvey Lectures*, **40**, 249.

SCHMITT, F. O., HALL, C. E. & JAKUS, M. A. (1943). " The Ultrastructure of Protoplasmic Fibrils." *Biol. Symp.*, **10**, 261.

SCHRAMM, G. (1947). " Spaltung des Tabakmosaikvirus und die Wiedervereinigung der Spaltstücke." *Z. Naturf.*, **2b**, 249.

SCHRAMM, G. & BERGOLD, G. (1947). " Molekulärgewicht des Tabakmosaikvirus." *Z. Naturf.*, **2b**, 108.

SCHULTZ, J., CASPERSSON, T. & AQUILINIUS, L. (1940). " The Genetic Control of Nuclear Composition." *Proc. Nat. Acad. Sci. U.S.*, **26**, 515.

SCOTT, J. F. (1948). " Electron Micrograph Studies on Sodium Desoxyribose Nucleate." *Biochim. Biophys. Acta*, **2**, 1.

SHEFFIELD, F. M. L. (1947). " The Virus in the Plant Cell." *Proc. Int. Congr. Cyt.*, p. 178.

SPARROW, A. H. & HAMMOND, M. R. (1947). " Cytological Evidence for the Transfer of Desoxyribose Nucleic Acid from Nucleus to Cytoplasm in Certain Plant Cells." *Amer. J. Bot.*, **34**, 439.

SPIEGELMAN, S. & KAMEN, M. D. (1947). " Some Basic Problems in the Relation of Nucleic Acid Turnover to Protein Synthesis." *C.S.H. Symp.*, **12**, 115.

STACEY, M. (1947). " Bacterial Nucleic Acids and Nucleoproteins." *Symp. Soc. Exp. Biol.*, **1**, 86.

STANLEY, W. M. (1935). " Isolation of a Crystalline Protein Possessing the Properties of Tobacco-Mosaic Virus." *Science*, **81**, 644.

STEDMAN, E. & STEDMAN, E. (1943). " Chromosomin, a Protein Constituent of Chromosomes." *Nature*, **152**, 267.

STEDMAN, E. & STEDMAN, E. (1947). " Function of Desoxyribose-Nucleic Acid in the Cell Nucleus." *Symp. Soc. Exp. Biol.*, **1**, 232.

STEDMAN, E. & STEDMAN, E. (1947). " Chemical Nature and Functions of the Components of the Cell Nucleus." *C.S.H. Symp.*, **12**, 224.

STEDMAN, E. & STEDMAN, E. (1950). " Cytological Interpretation of the Feulgen Reaction." *Biochem. J.*, **47**, 508.

TAYLOR, A. R. (1944).   " Chemical Analysis of the Influenza Viruses A (PR8 strain) and B (Lee strain), and the Swine Influenza Virus."   *J. biol. Chem.*, 153, 675.

THORELL, B. (1947).   " Relation of Nucleic Acids to the Formation and Differentiation of Cellular Proteins."   *C.S.H. Symp.*, 12, 247.

VILLEE, C. A., LOWENS, M., LEONARD, E. & RICH, A. (1949).   " Incorporation of P^{32} into the Nucleoproteins and Phosphoproteins of the Developing Sea-Urchin Embryo."   *J. cell. & comp. Physiol.*, 33, 93.

WEIBULL, C. (1948).   " Some Chemical and Physico-Chemical Properties of the Flagella of *Proteus Vulgaris*."   *Biochim. Biophys. Acta*, 2, 351.

WHITE, M. J. D. (1942).   Nucleus, Chromosomes, and Genes.   " Cytology and Cell Physiology."   Ed. Bourne, Oxford.   O.U.P.

WYCKOFF, R. W. G. (1947).   " Electron Micrographs from Concentrated Solutions of the Tobacco Mosaic Virus Protein."   *Biochim. Biophys. Acta*, 1, 143.

CHAPTER IV

EXTERNAL STRUCTURES

WE may conclude this account of the structural features of the cell with a short description of the organisation of certain external protective structures, namely the wall of plant cells, the arthropod and annelid cuticles, and the vertebrate epidermis.

Plant Cell Wall

The plant cell possesses all the essential features of the animal cell discussed above ; two characteristics, namely the dense outer coating or cellulose wall, and the large, fluid-filled vacuole in the mature cell,

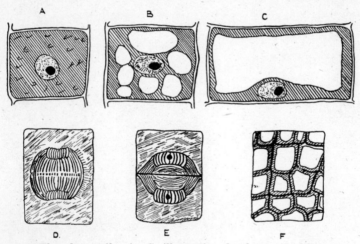

FIG. 60. The plant cell. A—C, illustrating development of large vacuole from smaller ones. D—E, illustrating formation of middle lamella from cell plate. F, the primary and secondary walls.

distinguish it from the latter type (Fig. 60, c). A newly formed cell is full of protoplasm ; in the course of development vacuoles appear which fuse, to give, finally, a large sap-filled space. The tough cellulose wall is peculiar to the fully grown plant cell ; cells in active division and growth (*meristematic*) have only a thin membrane, the thickening occurring later by secretion from the cytoplasm. Thus when a cell divides, the wall of separation between the daughter cells is a very thin, non-cellulosic, membrane formed during mitosis and is probably to be identified as the *cell plate* (Fig. 60, D, E). The daughter cells sooner or later secrete on this plate a thin layer, the *primary wall*, which is sufficiently thin and plastic to allow of continued growth ; finally, when growth has almost ceased, the relatively thick *secondary wall* is laid down. Consequently the initial layer of separation between the two cells is sandwiched between two double-layers, and is therefore called the *middle-lamella* (Fig. 60, F).

As we have indicated earlier, cellulose is the predominant structural material of the plant cell wall; in a few instances, *e.g.*, the cotton fibre, this is virtually the only constituent besides water,[1] but in most cases the walls contain other materials whose chemical constitution is by no means well understood, for example, *hemicelluloses, pectic substances, suberin* and *lignin*, besides many others; whether these materials merely act as impregnating substances in a fundamental framework of cellulose, or whether they are intimately related structurally to cellulose, is not yet clear, although the recent electron-microscopical observations of Mühlethaler on woody, or *lignified*, walls favours the impregnation hypothesis. In general, pectic substances are highly concentrated in the middle lamella and primary wall; lignin, as just indicated, is found only in woody tissues in the secondary wall, whilst suberin is the name given to the waxy material that accumulates in the wall during " suberisation," *i.e.*, water-proofing; it is typically present in the cell walls of cork and in the cuticle of the leaf, preventing excessive evaporation.

Pectin and Lignin. The structure of cellulose has been discussed earlier (p. 48); here we need only refer to the substances pectin and lignin; they are likewise built up of small repeat-units, α-d-galacturonic acid, in the case of pectin, and various derivatives of phenylpropane in the case of lignin :—

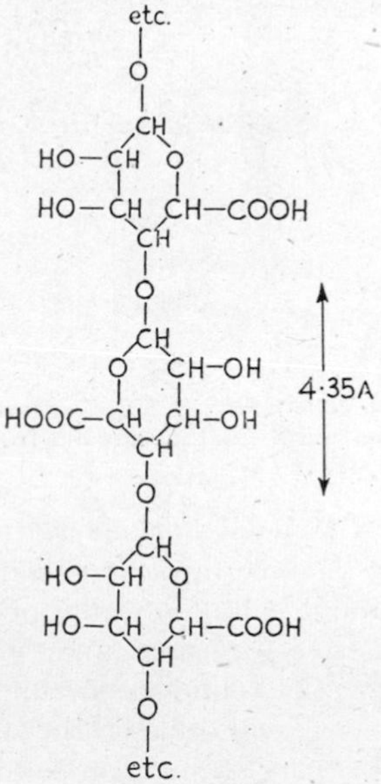

Alginic Acid or Pectin

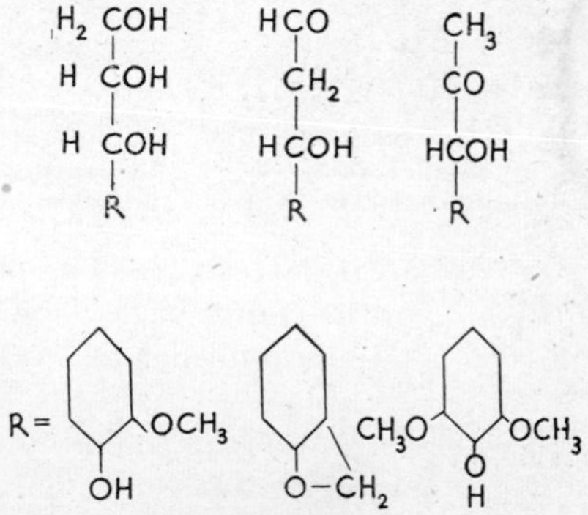

Lignin

It will be noted that the repeat-unit of pectin is 4·35A, compared with 5·15A for the glucose residue of cellulose; this difference is considered by

[1] Ninety-one per cent. of the cotton fibre is cellulose.

Astbury to be due to a folding of the ring structure so that, if this opinion is correct, profile views of the chains will be as in Fig. 61.[1]

Cotton Fibre. The cotton fibre is one that has been studied most exhaustively, from the structural viewpoint, owing to its economic importance ; it is an ideal object for the study of the secondary wall since, in its fully developed condition, it consists of little else than this. The X-ray diffraction photo of the stretched fibre is a typical fibre-photo of chains orientated along the fibre-axis. In the walls of the native cotton fibre, however, the orientation is more complex. The fibre originates as a tubular outgrowth from an epidermal cell of the seed coat ; this increases in length for fifteen to twenty days ; further growth, after this, results only in an increase in thickness. During the period of increase in length, the fibre has only the primary wall enclosing the protoplasm. In this wall, the cellulose probably consists of a network of criss-crossing strands, within the meshes of which are large quantities of wax and pectic materials. In contrast to the relatively unorientated arrangement of the cellulose in the

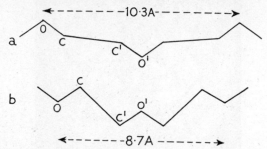

Fig. 61. *Above :* profile of cellulose chain. *Below :* profile of alginic acid chain. (*cf.* Fig. 42.) (Astbury. *Essays on Growth and Form.* Clarendon Press, Oxford.)

primary wall, the secondary wall is a more ordered structure, built up of successively deposited layers made up of parallel chains which run a spiral course, the direction of the spiral frequently reversing.

Algæ. The wall of *Valonia* is another excellent object for study ; *Valonia* is an alga characterised by bubble-like cells which may achieve a diameter of 2 cm. The wall is laid down with microscopically visible layers ; in general, there is a total of 30–40 of these with the remarkable feature that the cellulose chains are laid down in fundamentally different patterns in successive layers, as Preston & Astbury have shown from an analysis of the X-ray diffraction photos. In one layer the chains run as a spiral, as illustrated by the model of Fig. 62, whilst in the next they run as meridians from one pole of the cell to the other. This X-ray analysis of a complex structure is in itself a remarkable achievement, and it is therefore all the more satisfactory that the conclusions have been confirmed by Preston and his co-workers with the aid of the electron-microscope ; thus Fig. 63, Pl. VI, illustrates surface replicas of the

---

[1] The chains actually shown are those of cellulose and alginic acid ; the latter is made up of β-*d*-mannuronic acid units, *i.e.*, isomeric with galacturonic acid.

wall of *Valonia* ; it will be seen that the fibres run parallel in any one lamella, and that in successive lamellæ they make an angle, generally rather less than 90°, with each other. The fibrils are some 300A in diameter, and are of indefinite length (greater than 100,000A), and thus consist of bundles of cellulose chains, *i.e.*, crystallites of indefinite length.[1] In a filamentous alga, *Cladiphora*, Preston & Astbury demonstrated a similar alternation in the direction of cellulose chains. In successive laminæ, the chains made an average angle of 83° ; they ran in spirals ; in one lamina the spiral was flat, the chain direction being thus nearly transverse, and in the next the spiral was steep. The angles of the spirals changed with

Fig. 62.   Model of the *Valonia* wall, as deduced from X-ray diffraction analysis.   (Preston & Astbury.   *Proc. Roy. Soc.*)

position on the cell, but both flat and steep spirals appeared to maintain a more or less fixed relationship with each other, so that the angle between chains in successive laminæ was always nearly a right-angle. In many other plant walls, *e.g.*, the conifer tracheid (a long cylindrical cell that makes up the xylem system, (p. 278) a spiral arrangement has been proved by Preston.

Electron-microscopical Studies.   The most exhaustive electron-microscopical study of plant cell walls is that of Mühlethaler ; of particular interest are his studies of the development of the primary and secondary walls, and of the development of an extraneous cellulose " membrane " by

---

[1] Farr has claimed that the cellulose wall is laid down by the deposition of ellipsoidal particles, some $1·5 \times 1·1$ μ, formed in special plastids during growth. This theory is based on the changes in the polarisation-microscopical appearance of *Aspergillus*. As Castle has pointed out, however, the wall of this fungus is made of chitin, not cellulose ; moreover, the primary wall at the growing tip of a conidiophore may be only $0·5\mu$ thick, *i.e.*, thinner than one of Farr's postulated units. Finally, electron-microscope studies, *e.g.*, those of Mühlethaler, have failed to reveal the existence of these units.

PLATE VI

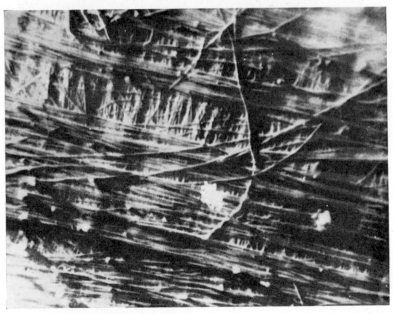

FIG. 63. Surface replicas of wall of *Valonia*. (Preston, Nicolai, Reed & Millard. Courtesy W. T. Astbury. *Nature*.)

[*To face p.* 94.

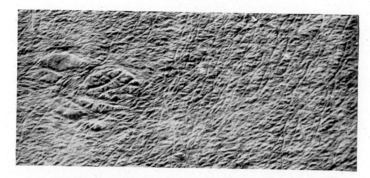

FIG. 64. Primary wall of a parenchymatic cell in oat coleoptile. × 18,000.
(Mühlethaler. *Biochim. Biophys. Acta.*)

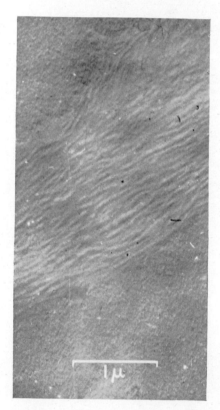

FIG. 65. Electron-micrograph of bacterial
cellulose. Strands of cellulose can be
seen forming in the slime. × 22,000.
(Mühlethaler. *Biochim. Biophys. Acta.*)

FIG. 66. Electron-micrograph of bacterial
cellulose in a later stage of development.
× 17,000. (Mühlethaler. *Biochim.
Biophys. Acta.*)

certain bacteria. In growing maize and oat coleoptiles, the newly deposited primary wall consists of interlacing fibres with no order ; it may be seen to develop from amorphous material, possibly consisting of very small cellulose units which subsequently build up, by end-to-end aggregation, into long fibrils. Growth is associated with an increase in the number of fibrils, so that, when completed, the wall appears as a dense meshwork (Fig. 64, Pl. VI). The secondary wall actually begins to form before the cell has finished growing ; the fibres are at first in considerable disarray, but later-formed layers exhibit the regular arrangement described earlier by Preston.[1]

The bacterium, *Acetobacter xylinium*, secretes a slime which eventually becomes a tough membrane on the surface of the culture medium ; under the electron-microscope, the first step in the organisation of this membrane was the emergence from the slime of a few fibres of diameter about 250A ; as time progressed the number of fibres increased and a parallel orientation became manifest (Fig. 65, Pl. VI). As will be seen from Fig. 66, Pl. VI, the finished product does not exhibit the regularity of the secondary wall of plants, and this is not surprising since the membrane is built up at a distance from the secreting cells. In the plant cell, on the other hand, each layer is formed in close contact with the cytoplasm by which it is secreted ; the factors determining the direction of the chains in any given layer must therefore be sought in the cytoplasm itself ; the alternation in the steepness of the spirals demands, moreover, a periodicity in the behaviour of the cytoplasm. Astbury tentatively suggests that the cellulose chains are built up in association with cytoplasmic protein chains ; and, if this is true, it is no accident that the period of a cellobiose unit (10·3A), is approximately equal to two periods of an α-protein grid (10·2A). Thus the protein would act as a template for the synthesis, casting off the finished cellulose chains and, in some manner, imposing a new orientation of the chains as each layer was formed.

The Arthropod Cuticle

Histological Studies. The outer coat of insects (and crustacea) is called the *cuticle*, which is a complex structure secreted by an epidermal layer of cells (often called the hypodermis), resting on a basement membrane. The cuticle is an important structure from the point of view of maintaining the water-balance of the insect ; here, however, we shall only be concerned with its function as an important structural element in the organism, enabling the insect to withstand external stresses and, in localised places, acting as an insertion for muscles—in fact behaving as an *exoskeleton*. In the adult insect we may distinguish three general regions in the cuticle ; the *endocuticle*, a soft, generally colourless, layer next to the hypodermis and usually built up on a laminated plan of microscopical dimensions ; above this is the brittle, pigmented, *exocuticle*, and most superficial of all, the *epicuticle*, a tough thin membrane, only a few micra across. The

---

[1] Mühlethaler's electron-microscope studies revealed the minute pits in the primary wall associated with the presence of protoplasmic bridges between meristematic cells ; as the secondary walls develop, the pits are gradually covered over with cellulose fibrils.

exocuticle results from a hardening—the so-called *chitinisation* [1]—of the endocuticle ; since the exocuticle may be absent, as in larvæ or in soft regions of the adult cuticle, it is best to think of the cuticle as being made up primarily of two layers, endocuticle and epicuticle (Fig. 67). The rigidity of the cuticle requires that growth should be associated with repeated moults involving the casting off of the old, and secretion of a new, cuticle by the hypodermal cells ; by careful microscopic observation of the moulting process, it is therefore possible to describe the mode of formation of the new cuticle, as was done recently by Wigglesworth. The epicuticle is secreted first over the hypodermal cells and under the old cuticle ; this is followed by the formation of endocuticle associated with a partial

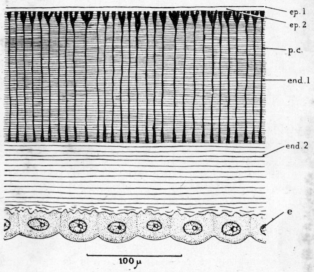

Fig. 67. Cuticle of the mature larva. *ep.* 1, outer epicuticle ; *ep.* 2, inner epicuticle ; *p.c.*, pore canal ; *end.* 1, outer endocuticle ; *end.* 2, inner endocuticle ; *e*, hypodermis. (Dennell. *Proc. Roy. Soc.*)

reabsorption of the material of the old cuticle ; thus when the old cuticle is cast, the insect or larva is already equipped with a new, but soft, cuticle. Of particular interest is the transformation of the larva into the pupa, since here we may observe with some ease the hardening process actually taking place ; from the structural aspect, therefore, we may profitably concentrate attention on the larval and pupal cuticles ; for this purpose the recent histochemical description of their structure by Dennell will suffice. Fig. 67 is a section through the cuticle of the mature blow-fly larva (*Sarcophaga falculata*) ; the outer layer of the endocuticle, destined to become the exocuticle in the hardened puparium, is traversed by very fine *pore canals* which apparently terminate under the epicuticle. The epicuticle is not simple but consists, according to the histochemical studies of Dennell and the electron-microscopical studies of Richards & Anderson,

[1] This is a misnomer (p. 98).

of two layers ; the inner layer seems to consist of hardened or " tanned " protein and is often indistinguishable from the hardened exocuticle beneath it ; the outer epicuticle is also made up of protein, but is apparently impregnated with lipids. The remainder of the cuticle consists of a mixture of chitin and protein.

Chitin. Chitin is a polysaccharide, differing from cellulose in that its chains consist of acetyl-glucosamine, instead of glucose, residues.

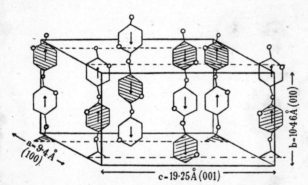

$$\begin{array}{cc}
\text{Cellulose} & \text{Chitin}
\end{array}$$

According to the X-ray studies of Meyer & Pankow, the chitin crystallographic unit has the dimensions indicated in Fig. 68, the crystallites consisting, as with cellulose, of long particles built up from these units. Polarisation-microscopical studies on many insects have

FIG. 68. Crystal lattice of chitin, according to Meyer and Pankow. (Fraenkel & Rudall. *Proc. Roy. Soc.*)

shown that the endocuticle is generally birefringent ; the hardened exocuticle is not, however, unless the pigmented protein material is removed, in which case the birefringence becomes as strong as that in the endocuticle ; this suggests that the birefringence is a form birefringence, normally obscured in the hardened exocuticle by the presence of material between the chitin rodlets of about the same refractive index (p. 41).

Hardening of the Cuticle. An instructive study of the changes taking place during hardening of the endocuticle (to form the exocuticle) is that of Fraenkel & Rudall ; at a certain stage in its development, the larva of the blow-fly becomes sluggish and gradually broadens and shortens to become barrel-shaped (Fig. 69) ; in this stage it is called a *pupa* but its cuticle is still white and soft like that of the larva ; this *white pupa* stage only lasts a few minutes, after which the cuticle becomes darker and harder. The change of length amounts to some 40 per cent. whilst the diameter increases by about 12 per cent. ; associated with the contraction, a regular circular striation appears at right-angles to the long axis of the larva. X-ray studies showed that in the larval cuticle the chitin crystallites were arranged in planes parallel to the surface, but without any regular orientation ; during the hardening process, however, the crystallites became orientated with the long axes transversely (*i.e.*, at right-angles to the long axis of the puparium). This arrangement is doubtless the sub-microscopical basis for the visible striations ; moreover, it permits a decrease in length and increase in diameter of the larva during its transition to the pupa. It would seem that this stage is brought about by muscular contraction. The actual hardening process appeared to be associated with a decrease in the crystalline character of the chitin along the *a*- and *c*-axes, whilst the regularity of the repeats along the *b*-axis, *i.e.*, along the chains, was unaffected. This suggested the formation, during hardening, of a protein-chitin complex. In company with this change in the X-ray pattern, there was a progressive decrease in the solubility of the proteins in the puparium and a decrease in the percentage of water held by this structure, so that, in contrast to what was thought earlier, the hardening of the cuticle would not be viewed as an incrustation process but rather as a change in the physical and chemical state of the material already present. This material, as we have indicated, is predominantly a mixture of a

a   *b*

Fig. 69. (*a*) Larva of *Sarcophaga* in an extended condition. (*b*) Puparium formed by a larva of the same size. (Fraenkel & Rudall. *Proc. Roy. Soc.*)

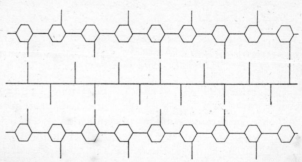

Fig. 70. Beta-protein layer between chitin layers. (Fraenkel & Rudall. *Proc. Roy. Soc.*)

protein—called by Fraenkel & Rudall, *arthropodin*—and chitin ; in the soft condition of the cuticle the protein is water-soluble, is not coagulated in hot water, and is soluble in hot 30 per cent. alcohol. A later study of the X-ray diffraction of the soft larval cuticle forced Fraenkel & Rudall to revise their earlier views on the arrangement of the chitin ; they concluded that the main regularity was confined to the *b*-axis, *i.e.*, along the chitin chains ; in other directions the crystalline pattern, previously found, was due to artefacts of preparation ; in other words, chitin is not in a highly crystalline condition in the larval cuticle but acquires this regularity under conditions that lead to a removal of the protein. Consequently the protein is intimately related to the chitin, and a further analysis of the X-ray pattern suggested that the two substances lie in planes consisting of parallel rows of orientated chains as in Fig. 70 ; thus the 10·3A repeat-unit of chitobiose would fit well with three amino-acid residues in the extended *β*-configuration. Such an arrangement would be consistent with the observed deterioration of the X-ray pattern of chitin along the *a*- and *c*-axes ; it demands, moreover, a proportion of 55 parts of chitin by weight to 45 parts of protein, which approximates to the ratios found in cuticles from many species.[1]

Removal of protein from the soft larval cuticle leads, as we have indicated, to a regular orientation of the chitin chains ; this is manifest in a marked increase in toughness of the cuticle ; and we may consider that the normal state of the cuticle is critically determined by the chitin-protein proportions. A loss of protein, however, is not the cause of hardening in the transition from larva to puparium. The X-ray evidence suggests that the laminar arrangement of protein and chitin is not significantly changed, a pronounced spacing at 33A, perpendicular to the planes, remaining unaltered ; presumably, therefore, the hardening consists of a rigid lateral binding of the protein chains by the formation of powerful cross-linkages. That such a " tanning " process does indeed take place has been made very probable by the work of Pryor. His pioneering work was carried out on a non-chitinous structure, the *öotheca* of the cockroach, which is built up predominantly of a protein, and which hardens in a manner similar to the hardening of the cuticle. The öotheca is a body some 8 mm. long secreted by the female ; it is shaped like a carpet-bag and contains twelve eggs. It is carried by the female in the genital pouch until complete, the end projecting farther and farther out as more is secreted until it is finally dropped. In the early stages, the end projecting is white and opaque, but in three to four hours it becomes transparent and its colour changes to pink and then to reddish chestnut. After being laid it darkens further and in about three weeks it is almost black ; in the white condition the öotheca is soft, and pigmentation is associated with hardening. The öotheca is secreted conjointly by two glands ; the secretion of the left gland is a water-soluble protein whilst that of the right gland is a solution of dihydroxyphenols ; by studying the effects of mixing the two glands Pryor showed that the hardening and pigmentation were essentially a

---

[1] Fraenkel & Rudall make the interesting suggestion that chitin is actually synthesised on the protein chains, and that the stable lattice obtained by a laminated protein-chitin complex leads to the retention of the synthesised chitin in association with its protein ; in the case of cellulose, where very little protein is found in structural association, it may be that the protein-cellulose lattice is unstable, so that the synthesised cellulose moves away from its protein " former " and a new chain is produced ; thus in the chitin system a lot of protein is necessary to synthesise a given amount of chitin, whilst in the cellulose system a little protein produces a lot of cellulose.

tanning reaction brought about by the combination of an oxidation product of the phenolic compound, which is probably 3 : 4-dihydroxyphenyl acetic acid, with the protein, the combination being such as to bind either the main chains of the polypeptides or the side-chains :—

The oxidation product was presumably a quinone and required the presence of an enzyme, *polyphenol oxidase ;* the effects of the right gland secretion could be imitated to a large extent, moreover, by benzoquinone and other quinonoid substances. In a later study the substance responsible for the tanning reaction was shown to be 3 : 4-dihydroxybenzoic acid (protocatechuic acid).

Extension of this work to the insect cuticle revealed an essentially similar mechanism, not only in the hardening of the exocuticle but also in the formation of the epicuticle, which is secreted first as a protein layer and is subsequently tanned by a polyphenolic compound ; later, according to Pryor, lipids are secreted on to this tanned " *sclerotin* " layer and become incorporated in it. On extraction of the cuticles of *Calliphora* (puparium), and *Tenebrio* (adult), protocatechuic acid was found in the former and 3 : 4-dihydroxyphenyl-acetic and 3 : 4-dihydroxyphenyl lactic acids, in the latter ; all these compounds may be regarded as degradation products of tyrosine, which, according to Fraenkel & Rudall, is present

3 : 4-dihydroxy-   3 : 4-dihydroxy-   Tyrosine   3 : 4-dihydroxyphenyl
  benzoic acid   phenyl lactic acid   alanine

in a markedly decreased concentration in the blood during formation of the puparium.

The remarkable feature of hardening of the exocuticle is that it takes place from without inwards ; this is due, as Dennell has shown, to the fact that the polyphenol oxidase, required to convert the protocatechuic acid to a quinone, is located in the epicuticle ; the acid diffuses unchanged through the inner endocuticle, which thus remains soft, and is oxidised at the epicuticle where it tans the outer layer of endocuticle ; moreover, on diffusing back, the quinone probably itself oxidises more phenolic compound, and thus a large region of the endocuticle is hardened. Why a definite region of endocuticle remains immune to hardening is not clear, but it may be associated with the strong reducing characteristics of this region which prevent the oxidised form from accumulating. Thus the general picture is one of a steady rise in the blood tyrosine content before pupation ; as a result of some hormonal stimulus the tyrosine is abruptly converted, by the action of tyrosinase—also circulating in the blood, but until then inhibited—to 3 : 4-dihydroxyphenyl alanine (*dopa*) which is subsequently converted to protocatechuic acid by the hypodermal cells. The protocatechuic acid is oxidised to a quinone at the boundary of the

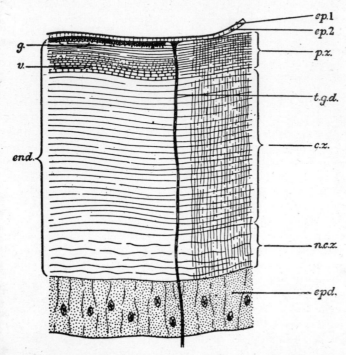

Fig. 71. Structure of the fully formed crustacean (decapod) cuticle. The pore-canals are illustrated only on the right of the figure and the vacuolisation of the pigmented zone only on the left. *c.z.*, calcified zone ; *end.*, endocuticle ; *epd.*, epidermis ; *ep.* 1, outer epicuticle ; *ep.* 2, inner epicuticle ; *g*, granules ; *n.c.z.*, non-calcified zone ; *p.z.*, pigmented zone ; *t.g.d.*, duct of tegumental gland ; *v*, region of pigmented zone apparently vacuolated. (Dennell. *Proc. Roy. Soc.*)

epicuticle and outer endocuticle, either diffusing there or being transported by way of the pore canals. The reaction of the quinone with the protein seems to be the well known tanning process, as typified by the action of similar agents on collagen, which cause a rigid binding of the polypeptide chains. The associated pigmentation is probably a result of the combination, although it is possible that specific materials are also elaborated.

Crustacean Cuticle. Space will not permit a detailed study of the crustacean cuticle ; the recent studies of Pryor and Dennell serve to emphasise the fundamental similarities in the insect and crustacean cuticles (Fig. 71). The epicuticle may be differentiated into an outer, lipid-containing, and an inner protein layer, both free from chitin ; beneath this is the endocuticle which may be differentiated into three regions, a pigmented zone ; a calcified zone, and a non-calcified zone resting on the epidermis. The pigmented zone has a canal system, analogous to that in the outer endocuticle of insects. When the crab moults, the new cuticle is at first soft and consists only of epicuticle and the pigmented zone of the endocuticle ; according to Dennell, polyphenol oxidases are concentrated in the epicuticle and these bring about a tanning of the new cuticle after the moult ; this, however, is an insignificant feature in the hardening process which consists mainly of the deposition of calcium salts in the growing endocuticle.

The Earthworm Cuticle

The cuticle of the earthworm differs from that of arthropods in that it is built up on a basis of collagen fibrils [1] ; it may be removed quite easily from the worm, and has been subjected to X-ray and electron-microscopic analysis. The collagen has the same wide-angle diffractions as those given by collagen from mammalian sources, but differs from the latter in its physico-chemical behaviour and electron-microscopic appearance. Thus the fibrils fail to reveal the banding, so typical of mammalian collagen (Fig. 72, Pl. VII), and the material dissolves in water at 40–50° C. and does not yield a gel on cooling. So far as the electron-microscope studies have gone (Reed & Rudall), they reveal a structure built up of layers of large parallel fibrils in alternate layers running at right-angles ; the fibrils are embedded in a protein matrix. They are themselves composed of apparently spiral-wound micro-fibrils about 200A thick. Fig. 73, Pl. VII illustrates an electron-micrograph of the torn lower surface, showing three laminæ ; the lowest, revealed in the top left-hand corner, consists of a flat ground substance with ridges and barely distinguishable fibrils running at right-angles to these ridges ; in the upper right-hand region the layer above is seen, consisting of well-defined fibrils running at right-angles to the ridges beneath ; the lower region is occupied by the third layer consisting of large fibrils running at right-angles to the lower fibrils, but parallel to the ridges of the lowest layer.

Mucopolysaccharides. Cellulose, as we have seen, is formed in association

[1] Collagen is the structural protein of connective tissue and tendons in the vertebrates ; a material with an essentially similar X-ray diffraction photo has been isolated by Marks, Bear & Blake from a number of invertebrate sources. Thus the fibrous skeleton of sponges is made of spongin ; coelenterates such as the jelly-fish have a gelatinous mesoglea between their inner and outer layers ; whilst sea-urchins and star-fish have a layer of mesodermal connective tissue, just beneath the outermost thin epithelial layer, acting as a matrix for the calcareous plates so characteristic of this class. The protein extracted from all these sources gave the typical repeat of 2·8–2·9A along the fibre-axis ; in addition, the large repeat of about 640A, found for mammalian collagen, was also present (650–675A). This does not mean, of course, that the proteins from all sources are certainly not ; it does indicate a certain over-riding similarity in the build-up of the amino-acid residues. Thus, as Bear and his colleagues point out, the value of the X-ray method of classifying proteins lies in the fact that it is insensitive to small changes in chemical structure (*i.e.*, amino-acid composition), and is able to detect an underlying unity of pattern.

PLATE VII

FIG. 72.   Collagen fibrils from beef tendon.   Shadow-cast with Pt.   × 63,000.
(C. E. Hall.)

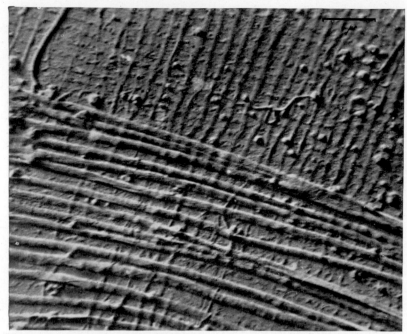

FIG. 73. Electron-micrograph of earthworm cuticle prepared by layer-stripping technique. Three layers are discernible ; the outermost is made up of large fibrils running nearly horizontally ; beneath this is a layer of fibrils running at right-angles, whilst the lowest layer is a series of ridges running at right-angles to the second layer of fibrils, and best seen in the top left-hand portion of the field. (Reed & Rudall. *Biochim. Biophys. Acta.*)

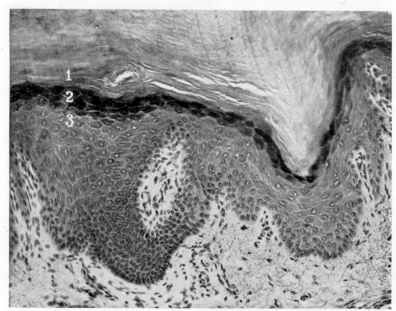

FIG. 74. Photomicrograph of human epidermis. 1, *Stratum corneum* ; 2, *Stratum granulosum* ; 3, *Stratum germinativum.* × 200. (Photo by F. J. Pittock, F.R.P.S., from preparation of K. C. Richardson.)

with certain impregnating materials, lignin, pectin, suberin, etc. ; chitin
is accompanied by a protein which may function similarly as an impregnating substance. It is of interest in this connection, therefore, that collagen
in connective tissue, and in such transparent structures as the cornea,
vitreous body, and the jelly of the umbilical cord, is found in association
with mucoid substances which may act as a matrix for the collagen fibres.
The terminology relating to these substances is complex (Meyer), and
need not be entered into in detail ; by a *mucoid* is understood a firm
combination of a high-polymer polysaccharide—a *mucopolysaccharide*—

Hyaluronic acid

with a protein. The best understood of the polysaccharides is hyaluronic
acid, built up of N-acetylglucosamine and glucuronic acid units as
above, the linkage being of the β-type (Meyer & Fellig, 1950). Other
polysaccharides are *mucoitin sulphate* built up with the same units in which
sulphate groups are incorporated, and *chondroitin sulphate* with the
glucosamine replaced by *chondrosamine* (2 : amino-galactose). It may well
be, as Day has emphasised, that many of the physical characteristics of
collagenous structures are partly determined by the presence of mucoids ;
the importance of these substances as bacterial antigens has already been
indicated (p. 86).

The Vertebrate Skin

This is a complex structure which is divided into an avascular *epidermis*
and a vascular *derma ;* the epidermis may be regarded as the protective
coat of the animal but, unlike the cuticle of lower forms, is entirely cellular
being made up typically of an outer, horny, *stratum corneum* and an inner
stratum germinativum or *Malpighian layer* (Fig. 74, Pl. VII) ; between them
is a layer of granular cells, the *stratum granulosum.* The outermost layer
consists of much flattened, closely packed, cells derived from the layers
beneath ; these cells are continually shed and are replaced from below, so
that there is a more or less continuous transformation of cells of the
stratum germinativum into " keratinised " cells of the stratum corneum,
the cells of the stratum granulosum occupying a stage intermediate
between the one and the other. The protein material synthesised by the
epidermis is of the keratin type ; histologists describe the granules in the
granular cells as *keratohyalin,* and the change from the granular to the
translucent type of cell as due to the conversion of this substance to *eleidin*
which is finally converted to *para-eleidin* or keratin. The keratin classically
studied is derived from hair or nails ; since these tissues consist of cells
derived from the epidermis, it would not be surprising if the protein
present in the stratum corneum were of the α-type. Recently Rudall has

made an X-ray study of the epidermis from a number of classes ; in mammals the protein is definitely of the α-type, with the difference from hair keratin that the temperature required for supercontraction is much lower (70–80° C.). On moderate stretching of the epidermis a well orientated α-pattern is observed ; on further stretching in warm water a more or less complete α- to β-transformation takes place. If the tension is released in hot water the fibres supercontract ; the temperature necessary varies with the layer of the *stratum corneum* studied, the innermost layer requiring only 60–70° C. whilst the outermost layer requires 80–90° C. Supercontraction may be regarded as the consequence of a rupture of linkages—presumably cystine S-S bridges—which permits the chains to curl up ; thus the progressive " keratinisation " of the cells of the stratum corneum may be regarded as a progressive "vulcanisation" of the keratin molecule, more and more S-S linkages being incorporated into the chains thereby increasing the temperature necessary for supercontraction. In the supercontracted state, the chains of epidermal keratin are in the β-form, with the difference from ordinary stretched keratin that the chains appear to run transversely to the fibre-axis ; a similar " cross-β " pattern was found by Astbury, Dickinson & Bailey in stretched boiled egg-white and may be the result of a tight buckling of the chains as in Fig. 75, such that the polypeptide grids run transversely to the fibre-axis during most of their course.

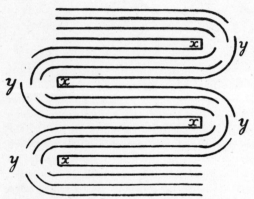

FIG. 75. Illustrating the possible buckling of polypeptide chains in supercontraction of epidermal protein to give the cross-β pattern with chains running at right-angles to the fibre-axis. At localised regions, indicated by *x*, the alpha-configuration is retained whilst in the remaining regions the chains have extended to the beta-configuration. At the regions indicated by *y* a certain amount of chain breakage has occurred. (Rudall. *Symp. on Fibrous Proteins.*)

On prolonged treatment of supercontracted epidermal keratin with a saturated solution of urea the α-pattern returns ; since this solution loosens hydrogen-bonds, it would seem that the supercontracted state is maintained by this type of linkage.

In conclusion, we may draw attention to the relatively inextensible β-type of keratin called by Astbury " feather keratin," since it was first discovered in sea-gull quill ; its repeat-period of 3·1A indicates a somewhat crumpled polypeptide chain capable of reversible extension by some 7 per cent. Rudall (1947), has recently published an account of the distribution of the α- and feather-type keratins in a number of animal classes ; in reptiles and birds the feather-keratin is found in the hard parts of the keratinous structures, *i.e.*, in the feathers, beak, and scales ; in softer regions, *e.g.*, the epidermis between the scales of reptiles or between the toes and on the gripping under-surface of the feet of birds, the α-type predominates, so that in these classes it appears that Nature disposes of two substances (apparently synthesised by different types of cell) in the building of the epidermal structures. This is especially manifest in the scales of snakes, the outermost horny part of the scale being of the feather-type whilst the inner layer is made up of α-keratin.

Final Remarks on the Structural Proteins

In this discussion of the structural features of the cell the protein molecule has emerged as clearly the most significant unit ; moreover, of the large variety of protein molecules known, it seems to be those that Astbury has classified as " fibrous," in contrast to the " corpuscular," proteins that contribute primarily to the living framework. Whether this rather rigid distinction between the two types is justified in the light of the most recent evidence is beginning to appear doubtful ; thus Astbury's studies have been largely confined to the " wide-angle " diffraction pattern, revealing order on a small scale ; the more recent narrow-angle studies, particularly those of Bear and of Bernal, coupled with electron-microscopical studies, have revealed large periods along the fibre-axis of many proteins, *e.g.*, 198A for porcupine quill, 95A for feather keratin, 640A for collagen, and so on. It may well be that these large periods represent localised aggregations of protein material, *i.e.*, small corpuscular units, so that the true picture of a fibrous protein may consist of units, either strung together on extended polypeptide chains or else packed together tightly with a cement of these polypeptide chains between them. Then the wide-angle pattern might show the presence of these chains, whilst the narrow-angle pattern would bring out the larger repeat-units of the corpuscular elements. The corpuscular elements themselves would be built up of strongly coiled polypeptide chains, as Astbury suggested ; and the final picture would be, as Bernal has expressed it, of fibres within corpuscles and corpuscles within fibres.[1]

---

[1] As we shall see, the muscle protein, F-actin, is definitely built up of corpuscular units ; Mercer's electron-microscopical studies of wool keratin have revealed the existence of corpuscular units in this typically fibrous protein ; conversely the typically corpuscular protein, insulin, may be converted into fibres by aggregation (Waugh). The realisation that fibrous proteins may be built up of corpuscular units has brought into prominence the interpretation of the large repeat-units revealed by the narrow-angle diffractions. An analogy may make the subject clearer. A striped wall-paper, with the stripes 3 in. apart, exhibits a fundamental repeat of 3 in., whilst 2nd., 3rd., etc., orders of this repeat will be given by every second, every third, etc., line ; thus a repeat-unit of 90 in. could be the 30th order of the fundamental 3 in. unit. However, if the wall were only partially covered with strips of the same wall-paper, each strip say 89 in. apart, a repeat unit of 89 in. would be observed in the " diffraction pattern " as well as the fundamental 3 in. repeat. The repeat of 89 in. would not be an order of the 3 in. repeat but would represent a larger scale pattern, although the nearness of its value to the 30th order of the fundamental 3 in. spacing might lead the investigator into assuming that this is what it was indeed. The corpuscular units of a fibrous protein, repeating at intervals of perhaps hundreds of Angstrom units, will exhibit a pattern on a large scale which is not to be interpreted as an order of the polypeptide spacing, *e.g.*, 5·1A of an α-protein.

References

ASTBURY, W. T. (1943). "X-Rays and the Stoichiometry of Proteins." *Adv. in Enzym.*, **3**, 63.

ASTBURY, W. T. (1945). The Forms of Biological Molecules. "Growth and Form." Oxford, Clarendon Press.

ASTBURY, W. T. (1945). "Structure of Alginic Acid." *Nature*, **155**, 667.

ASTBURY, W. T. & BELL, F. O. (1938). "Some Recent Developments in the X-Ray Study of Proteins and Related Substances." *C.S.H. Symp.*, **6**, 109.

ASTBURY, W. T. & PRESTON, R. D. (1940). "Structure of the Cell Wall in some Species of Filamentous Green Alga *Cladophora*." *Proc. Roy. Soc.*, B, **129**, 54.

BAILEY, I. W. (1938). "Cell Wall Structure of Higher Plants." *Ind. Eng. Chem.*, **30**, 40.

BEAR, R. S. (1942). "Long X-Ray Diffraction Spacings of Collagen." *J.A.C.S.*, **64**, 727.

BEAR, R. S. (1942). "Large Fibre-Axis Period of Collagen." *loc. cit.*, p. 1297.

BEAR, R. S. (1942). "Feather Rachis, Porcupine Quill Tip and Clam Muscle." *loc. cit.*, p. 2043.

BERNAL, J. D. (1943). "Structure and Interaction of Protein Molecules." *Proc. Int. Congr. Cyt.*, p. 15.

CASTLE, E. S. (1945). "Structure of the Cell Walls of *Aspergillus* and the Theory of Cellulose Particles." *Amer. J. Bot.*, **32**, 148.

CROWFOOT, D. (1948). "X-Ray Crystallographic Studies of Compounds of Biochemical Interest." *Ann. Rev. Biochem.*, **17**, 115.

DAY, T. D. (1949). "Mode of Reaction of Interstitial Connective Tissue with Water." *J. Physiol.*, **109**, 380.

DENNELL, R. A. (1946). "A Study of an Insect Cuticle : the Larval Cuticle of *Sarcophaga Falculata*." *Proc. Roy. Soc.*, B, **133**, 348.

DENNELL, R. A. (1947). "A Study of an Insect Cuticle : the Formation of the Puparium of *Sarcophaga Falculata*." *Proc. Roy. Soc.*, B, **134**, 79.

DENNELL, R. A. (1947). "Occurrence and Significance of Phenolic Hardening in the Newly Formed Cuticle of Crustacea Decapoda." *Proc. Roy. Soc.*, B, **134**, 485.

FLINT, E. A. (1950). "Structure and Development of the Cotton Fibre." *Biol. Rev.*, **25**, 414.

FRAENKEL, G. & RUDALL, K. M. (1940). "A Study of the Physical and Chemical Properties of the Insect Cuticle." *Proc. Roy. Soc.*, B, **129**, 1.

FRAENKEL, G. & RUDALL, K. M. (1947). "The Structure of Insect Cuticles." *Proc. Roy. Soc.*, B, **134**, 111.

FREUDENBERG, K. (1939). "Polysaccharides and Lignin." *Ann. Rev. Biochem.*, **8**, 81.

FREY-WYSSLING, A. (1948). "Submicroscopic Morphology of Protoplasm and its Derivatives." Elsevier, New York and Amsterdam.

HALL, C. E., JAKUS, M. A. & SCHMITT, F. O. (1945). "The Structure of Certain Muscle Fibrils as Revealed by the Use of Electron Stains." *J. App. Physics*, **16**, 459.

HOCK, C. W. (1942). Microscopic Structure of the Cell Wall. "Structure of Protoplasm." Ed. Seifriz, Iowa State College Press.

MARKS, M. H., BEAR, R. S. & BLAKE, C. H. (1949). "X-Ray Diffraction Evidence of Collagen-type Protein Fibres in the Echinodermata, Coelenterata and Porifera." *J. exp. Zool.*, **111**, 55.

MERCER, E. H. (1947). "Electron Microscopic Study of Wool." *Proc. Int. Congr. Cyt.*, p. 60.

MEYER, K. H. (1947). "Biological Significance of Hyaluronic Acid and Hyaluronidase." *Physiol. Rev.*, **27**, 335.

MEYER, K. H. & FELLIG, J. (1950). "La Constitution de l'Acide Hyaluronique." *Experientia*, **6**, 186.

MORGAN, W. T. J. (1947). "Mucoids as Components of the Human Erythrocyte Surface." *Proc. Int. Congr. Cyt.*, p. 228.

MÜHLETHALER, K. (1949). "Electron Micrographs of Plant Fibres." *Biochim. Biophys. Acta*, **3**, 15.

MÜHLETHALER, K. (1949). "Structure of Bacterial Cellulose." *loc. cit.*, p. 527.

MÜHLETHALER, K. (1950). "Electron Microscopy of the Developing Plant Wall." *Biochim. Biophys. Acta*, **5**, 1.

PICKEN, L. E. R. (1940). "Fine Structure of Biological Systems." *Biol. Rev.*, **15**, 133.

PRESTON, R. D. (1939). "Molecular Chain Structure of Cellulose and its Botanical Significance." *Biol. Rev.*, **14**, 281.

PRESTON, R. D. (1946 ; 1947). "Fine Structure of the Wall of the Conifer Tracheid." *Proc. Roy. Soc.*, B, **133**, 327 ; **134**, 202.

PRESTON, R. D. (1948). "Spiral Growth and Spiral Structure." *Biochim. Biophys. Acta*, **2**, 155.

PRESTON, R. D. & ASTBURY, W. T. (1937). " Structure of the Wall of the Green Alga, *Valonia Ventricosa.*" *Proc. Roy. Soc.*, B, **122**, 76.

PRESTON, R. D., NICOLAI, E., REED, R. & MILLARD, A. (1948). " Electron Microscope Study of Cellulose in the Wall of *Valonia.*" *Nature*, **162**, 665.

PRYOR, M. G. M. (1940). " On the Hardening of the Ōotheca of *Blatta Orientalis.*" *Proc. Roy. Soc.*, B, **128**, 378.

PRYOR, M. G. M. (1940). " On the Hardening of the Cuticle of Insects." *loc. cit.*, p. 393.

PRYOR, M. G. M., RUSSELL, P. B., & TODD, A. R. (1946). " Protocatechuic Acid, the Substance Responsible for the Hardening of the Cockroach Ōotheca." *Biochem. J.*, **40**, 627.

PRYOR, M. G. M., RUSSELL, P. B. & TODD, A. R. (1947). " Phenolic Substances Concerned in Hardening the Insect Cuticle." *Nature*, **159**, 399.

REED, R. & RUDALL, K. M. (1948). " Electron Microscope Studies on the Structure of the Earthworm Cuticle." *Biochim. Biophys. Acta*, **2**, 7.

RICHARDS, A. G. & ANDERSON, T. F. (1942). " Electron Microscope Studies of Insect Cuticle." *J. Morph.*, **71**, 135.

ROELOFSEN, P. A. (1951). " Cell Wall Structure in the Growth Zone of *Phycomyces* Sporangiophores. II. Double Refraction and Electron Microscopy." *Biochim. Biophys. Acta*, **6**, 357.

RUDALL, K. M. (1946). " The Structure of Epidermal Protein " in " Symp. on Fibrous Proteins." Bradford, Soc. Dyers & Colourists.

RUDALL, K. M. (1947). " X-Ray Studies on the Distribution of Protein Chain Types in the Vertebrate Epidermis." *Biochim. Biophys. Acta*, **1**, 549.

RUDALL, K. M. (1950). Fundamental Structure in Biological Systems. " Progress in Biophysics." Ed. Butler & Randall. London, Butterworth-Springer.

SCHMITT, F. O. (1944/5). " Ultrastructure and the Problems of Cellular Organisation." *Harvey Lectures*, **40**, 249.

SCHMITT, F. O., HALL, C. E. & JAKUS, M. A. (1942). " Electron Microscope Investigations of the Structure of Collagen." *J. cell. & comp. Physiol.*, **20**, 11.

SCHMITT, F. O., HALL, C. E. & JAKUS, M. A. (1943). " The Ultrastructure of Protoplasmic Fibrils." *Biol. Symp.*, **10**, 261.

SEN, M. K. & WOODS, H. J. (1949). " Structure of Jute. I. The Twofold Function of Lignin." *Biochim. Biophys. Acta*, **3**, 510.

WAUGH, D. F. (1944). " Linkage of Corpuscular Protein Molecules. I. A Fibrous Modification of Insulin." *J.A.C.S.*, **66**, 663.

WIGGLESWORTH, V. B. (1948). " The Insect Cuticle." *Biol. Rev.*, **23**, 408.

CHAPTER V

UTILISATION OF CHEMICAL ENERGY

IT is not our purpose here to analyse rigorously the difference between living and dead matter ; in the previous section we have seen that the viruses pose an interesting problem in this respect, being structurally similar to what we are accustomed to consider as inanimate matter, but, in their powers of reproduction, and the chemical synthetic activity that this reproduction implies, being unmistakably alive. We will not go far wrong if we characterise living matter by its continuous activity or, more precisely, its continuous performance of work or transformation of energy. In many organisms activity, and its cessation with death, are obvious ; the respiratory movements of the fish and the land animal ; the beating of the heart ; the constant lashing of the flagella, and so on. In other organisms this activity is not obvious, so that we must use special methods to demonstrate the performance of work, or the transformation of energy from one form to another.

Potential Energy Status

An organism alive may be said to be in a state of higher *potential energy* than when it is dead ; and, in order to maintain this state—to prevent it from running down—energy must continually be supplied. We may understand, without going into rigorous thermodynamic definitions, what we mean by these statements if we consider a warm-blooded animal. Alive, it normally maintains a higher temperature than that of its environment ; because of the loss of heat resulting from this gradient of temperature, the animal must continually generate heat. Here, then, the gradient of temperature between the organism and its environment indicates the high potential energy of the former ; and the heat production, inferred from the fact that the gradient of temperature is maintained in spite of heat loss, represents the energy transformation necessary for maintaining the high potential energy in the face of the tendency of the condition to " run down." The heat production may be said to be the sign of an energy transformation; *i.e.*, the conversion of some of the chemical energy of certain molecules of carbohydrate, fat or protein, into heat as a result of their decomposition into substances with a smaller chemical energy, such as CO_2, H_2O, etc.

The maintenance of a temperature gradient is an obvious symptom of energy transformations going on in the organism, but it is by no means the only one, in fact, as we shall see, the heat production necessary for this gradient is essentially a by-product of transformations of energy associated with these other vital activities. The cold-blooded organisms do not maintain temperatures significantly above that of their environment, but they are in a state of higher potential energy than when they are dead ;

in succeeding chapters we shall be concerned with some of the ways in which this state of high potential energy is manifested ; here we need only note that it may take various forms such as gradients of concentration, and the maintenance of structures which, but for the supply of energy, would break down. Thus cells maintain higher concentrations of certain ions than are found in the medium surrounding them ; when the cells die these ions diffuse out of the cell in accordance with the general tendency for a system to pass from a condition of higher to one of lower free energy. In the living cell these concentration gradients are established and maintained by the continual performance of work—*osmotic work* we may call it—or, in other words, chemical energy is transformed into osmotic or concentration energy. In a complex organism, therefore, every cell, if it is alive, requires to expend energy to maintain its *status quo*—its state of potential energy characteristic of being alive. The energy is furnished by chemical reactions, so that the organism must be provided with means of supplying the cells with the metabolites necessary for these reactions, and for clearing away their decomposition products. The highly developed organism therefore requires a circulatory system to effect this transport ; this circulatory system requires the continual performance of mechanical work, mediated by the contractions of the ventricles of the heart ; again, oxygen must be supplied to this blood through lungs, or gills, which must be mechanically ventilated, another process involving mechanical work. This mechanical work represents another demand on the energy transformations of the organism, besides those less obvious demands we have already considered. Thus the animal, completely at rest, must continuously transform chemical energy to maintain what we may call its *potential energy status ;* it is this transformation of energy that we may describe as *vegetative* or *basal metabolism*, to distinguish it from the extra metabolism that is necessary when the animal does more than maintain this status, for example when it runs, climbs a tree, etc.

We have treated the high temperature of the warm-blooded animal as one respect in which it maintains a high potential energy ; and we have regarded the continuous utilisation of chemical energy as a necessary mechanism for making good the lost heat. By analogy the system would appear similar to the burning of coal in a boiler, to maintain the temperature of a radiator. It will become increasingly evident, however, that this is altogether a too naïve, in fact a misleading, point of view. According to the *Second Law of Thermodynamics*, the liberation of heat is a necessary accompaniment of any transformation of energy of whatever sort, even when carried out at maximum efficiency, so that all the varied transformations of energy, which constitute the vegetative metabolism of the organism, are accompanied by the liberation of heat. The more inefficiently these processes are carried out, in a thermodynamic sense, the more heat appears as a by-product. It is possible to compute, by a study of their functions, the work carried out by certain organs, *e.g.*, the mechanical work of the heart, the osmotic work performed by the kidney, and so on. Since we also know the fundamental chemical reactions from which the organs derive their energy, and can find out how much of the chemicals have been used up in the processes, it is possible to find out how much energy is made available to the organ. The *efficiency* of the organ may then be expressed as a percentage as follows :—

$$\frac{\text{Energy Theoretically Necessary}}{\text{Energy Made Available}} \times 100$$

Probably the most efficient process in the higher organisms is the contraction of skeletal muscle, yet even in this case some 80 per cent. of the liberated chemical energy appears as heat—*i.e.*, the efficiency is 20 per cent. The heat production of the organism, viewed as a by-product of the performance of mechanical, osmotic and other forms of work, is therefore likely to be considerable.

The First Law of Thermodynamics and the Basal Heat Production. Heat production, as we have seen, is an essential by-product of the energy transformations of the organism ; if the *First Law of Thermodynamics*, or the *Law of Conservation of Energy*—which tells us that in physical processes there is no loss of energy on converting from one form to another—applies to living matter, we may expect that the energy made available by the chemical reactions taking place within it, or at its surface, will appear in the form of work and heat ; *i.e.*

$$E = W + H$$

Thus a steam-engine, on dragging a train up a hill, burns a certain amount of coal which provides an amount of energy which may be computed by the methods of thermodynamics. During the process of transforming this chemical energy into kinetic energy, heat is liberated because of the limitations imposed on the transformation by the Second Law, and because of the inefficiency of the engine. Arrived at the top of the hill the train stops ; the kinetic energy is zero and has been converted into heat as a result of friction. Thus of the energy made available a great deal, by far the larger portion, has appeared as heat ; and the remainder is in the form of potential energy, since the train is at the top of a hill and can roll down. We may say that the train has raised its potential energy status by climbing the hill, and that this has involved a much larger expenditure of energy, the bulk of which has appeared as heat. If the train rolls down the hill and comes to a stop at its starting place, it is now in the same energy status as it had at the beginning of the cycle of events, the potential energy it possessed at the top of the hill being transformed into kinetic energy, which was then dissipated by friction into heat. Thus the whole of the energy made available in this cyclical transformation appears as heat ; and if the First Law applies to living matter we may expect that, during any period in which the potential energy status of an organism remains unchanged, all the energy liberated by its chemical reactions should appear as heat. This thesis, so fundamental to an understanding of the phenomena of basal metabolism, may be made clearer—if this is necessary —by a consideration of the circulation of blood. Contraction of the ventricle of the heart raises the blood pressure, so that at this precise moment a part of the chemical energy made available in the heart is transformed into pressure energy ; this energy is at once transformed into kinetic energy of flow. The blood moves faster, but as a result of friction, the rate of flow subsides to its former rate until a new contraction occurs. The extra kinetic energy, due to the contraction of the heart, is thus finally transformed into heat ; and, at the end of a cycle, the organism, from the aspect of blood flow, is in the same potential energy status as it had before the ventricle contracted. Thus all the chemical energy liberated in the contraction of the heart during any period must appear as heat. The same may be said of other vital activities ; the cells of the body continually tend to lose their concentration gradients, and osmotic work must be performed in re-establishing them ; their structures are continually breaking down and requiring new syntheses for their repair ; and so on. Consequently, although the living organism at rest is constantly carrying out work of varying sorts, the energy made available appears just as surely and quantitatively as heat as if the energy-producing chemical reactions had been carried out in a test-tube. We must remember the proviso, however ; namely, that the potential energy status of the organism is unchanged. In an adult man, containing millions of cells, it is statistically probable that, during rest, his potential energy status will remain constant for several hours at least ; with a single-celled organism, on the other hand, such a condition would be rare. Bacteria, for example, multiply with enormous rapidity under favourable conditions. A given suspension of these organisms must therefore increase its potential energy status as a result of the synthetic activity involved in building the new structures ; and it would be quite incorrect to expect its heat production to be equated to its energy utilisation.

Indirect Calorimetry

In order to be able to test the applicability of the First Law of Thermodynamics to living matter, we must be able to determine not only the heat produced by an animal, or tissue, during a given period but also the amount of energy made available by its metabolic processes. Then, if the animal does not alter its potential energy status during this period, the First Law demands that the energy, made available by metabolism, be equal to the heat production. The determination of the energy made available by chemical reactions is thus an important step in the study of the thermodynamics of living processes ; moreover, once the truth of the First Law has been established in this connection, the energy made available by chemical reactions can be equated to the heat production, provided, of course, that the organism remains in the same potential energy status. By *indirect calorimetry* is meant the assessment of the heat production from the nature and amount of chemical reactions taking place within the organism. To calculate this energy we must know the essential energy-giving chemical reactions taking place within the organism, or at its surface. Thus the vast majority of living organisms utilise carbohydrate, *e.g.*, glucose ; this may undergo oxidation to CO_2 and H_2O in accordance with the equation :—

$$C_6H_{12}O_6 + 6\,O_2 \rightarrow 6\,CO_2 + 6\,H_2O$$

The actual energy available for work of all sorts—osmotic, mechanical, etc.—is called the free energy of the chemical reaction [1] ; whilst the total amount of energy set free (including heat), is the heat of reaction, *i.e.*, the heat that would be liberated were the glucose converted directly to CO_2 and H_2O in a calorimeter. According to Hess' Law, this is true whether the reaction proceeds in one step or by a multitude of stages, so long as the end-products are the same, and in the same physical state. The heat of combustion of glucose has been determined experimentally to be 673 Calories [2] per gramme-molecule (mole), or 3·74 Calories per g., so that although the oxidation of glucose in the organism is not carried out in the simple way indicated by the above equation, but rather step-wise through a variety of intermediate products, the energy made available is given by this quantity, 3·74 Cal./g. Under basal conditions, *i.e.*, those in which the animal maintains its potential energy status unchanged, the energy made available must appear as heat ; we may therefore compute the heat production from the quantity of glucose utilised. In the complex organism, such as man, energy from three general types of chemical reaction is utilised —the oxidation of carbohydrate, of fat and of protein. To assess the energy made available in any period we must know the extents to which all three reactions have taken place, and the heats of reaction of these oxidations.

Tri-olein, a typical fat, has the formula $C_{57}H_{104}O_6$; it reacts with oxygen in the body to give, as final products, H_2O and CO_2 in accordance with the equation :—

$$C_{57}H_{104}O_6 + 80\ O_2 \rightarrow 57\ CO_2 + 52\ H_2O$$

ca. 7,900 Calories being liberated when one mole reacts. Thus 1 g. of tri-olein liberates 9·3 Calories, a value that may be taken as typical for fat metabolism.

Protein presents a more complex problem, since it is not completely oxidised in the body ; the heat of combustion, as measured in a calorimeter, is, therefore, not equivalent to the energy made available in the organism. Nevertheless, a knowledge of the final products of its metabolic reactions permits an accurate estimate of the energy made available. Calculations show that 1 g. of protein should liberate some 4·1 Calories. Man utilises energy from all three sources simultaneously, so that we must know, not only the amount of material consumed during a given period, but the relative amounts of the three types—carbohydrate, fat, and protein—if we are to assess the amount of energy made available. To obtain the relative proportions, use is made of the fact that the proportions of liberated CO_2 to consumed O_2 are different according to the material metabolised ; thus from the equation describing the combustion of carbohydrate the ratio, known as the *respiratory quotient* (R.Q.), is :—

$$\frac{6 \text{ vols. } CO_2}{6 \text{ vols. } O_2} = 1.$$

---

[1] The change in free energy of a reaction is to be distinguished from the change in total heat, or heat of reaction. The free energy change indicates the total amount of energy available for work whilst the heat of reaction measures the total amount of energy liberated.

[2] A Calorie, spelt with a capital C, is the amount of heat required to raise 1 kg. of water through 1° C.

For fat it is :—

$$\frac{57 \text{ vols. } CO_2}{80 \text{ vols. } O_2} = 0.71.$$

For protein, it may be calculated that the R.Q. is 0·80. Thus the R.Q. of an animal utilising all three sources of energy should lie between 1 and 0·71 ; under ordinary basal conditions, in man, it is in the region of 0·85. If only two of these general classes of reaction took place within the organism, instead of three, it would be an easy matter to compute, from the observed R.Q., the proportions of the two utilised. With all three classes of reaction taking place we must first estimate the amount of protein utilised, by an analysis of the amount of urea in the urine, since urea is an end-product of the metabolism of protein in most mammals. Having made allowance for the O_2 utilised in the combustion of protein, and the CO_2 liberated in the reaction, we may compute a *non-protein R.Q.*, the ratio of the CO_2 liberated to the O_2 consumed in the combustion of carbohydrate and fat. From this non-protein R.Q. the proportions of these two materials utilised by the organism may be deduced.

A knowledge of the energy available to the complex organism thus demands, besides the total weight of material consumed, a knowledge of the respiratory exchange—the O_2 consumed and the CO_2 liberated. We may now show that quite an accurate estimate may be derived from the respiratory exchange alone. Thus, from the stoichiometric equation describing the oxidation of glucose, it can be deduced that the consumption of 1 litre of O_2 in the utilisation of carbohydrate is equivalent to the liberation of 5·05 Calories ; in the utilisation of fat it is on the average 4·69 Calories, and in that of protein 4·25 Calories. For various non-protein R.Q.'s the *calorific value* of 1 litre of O_2 is thus :—

R.Q. (Non-protein)	Cal./l.O_2
0·71	4·69
0·80	4·80
0·85	4·86
0·90	4·92
0·95	4·98
1·00	5·05

The contribution of protein to the energy available to the organism is not large, especially under basal conditions ; and since the calorific value of O_2 for the combustion of protein is only some 12 per cent. less than that for the combustion of carbohydrate and fat in the proportions to give an R.Q. of 0·85, no great error is introduced by adopting an overall figure for the calorific value of the O_2 consumed, independently of the actual amount of protein utilised.

Thus if provision is made for the analysis of the air entering and leaving a chamber in which the heat production of an animal is being measured (a calorimeter), both the actual heat liberated by the animal and the heat that *ought to be liberated* as a result of the chemical energy made available can be determined. The results of the classical experiments of Rubner, using this type of respiration calorimeter, showed that these two quantities differed only by about 1 per cent.

Rubner's results may be interpreted as showing either that the First Law applies to the energy transformations in living matter or, since there is no *a priori* reason why this law should not apply, that the accuracy of the computation of heat production from a study of the gaseous exchanges is remarkably good.

O_2-Consumption of Cells

Over a given period, then, the O_2-consumption, instead of the directly measured heat production, may be taken as a measure of the basal energy transformations necessary for the continued existence of an organism. The human erythrocyte, whose main function is simply a passive one of transporting the respiratory gases, has an O_2-consumption of 8.10^{-10} mm.^{3}/hr., involving the liberation of some 4.10^{-15} Cal./hr. This energy consumption is doubtless mainly concerned with the maintenance of a concentration gradient of K^+ between the contents of the cell and the surrounding plasma (p. 248); it is interesting, moreover, that when the cell is treated with saponin, an agent that attacks its plasma membrane, the oxygen consumption increases rapidly, as though the cell were attempting to maintain its structure in the face of a harmful attack.

The leucocyte, another blood cell, has more varied activities; it has the power of independent movement which the erythrocyte lacks, and it can ingest foreign materials and organisms (*phagocytosis*). Appropriate to its more varied activities we find that its O_2-consumption is greater than that of the erythrocyte, being 5.10^{-7} mm.^{3}/hr.

The egg of the sea-urchin, *Arbacia punctulata*, is an interesting example of a cell, since it can be studied in a passive, or resting, state and in an active one; these states being those of the unfertilised and fertilised eggs respectively. An unfertilised egg has an oxygen consumption of about $3 \cdot 5.10^{-5}$ mm.^{3}/hr.; even allowing for the fact that the egg is some ten times larger than an erythrocyte, this rate of oxygen consumption betokens a considerably more intense form of vital activity; on fertilisation the oxygen consumption is increased four- to five-fold.

Autotrophic Bacteria

Before passing on to consider the heat production of animals, it would be instructive to consider the metabolism of some of the lowest forms of life, the autotrophic bacteria. We have so far considered the source of energy available to the organism as that derived from the oxidation of organic matter, in particular of carbohydrate; this is true of practically all members of the animal kingdom, including the majority of bacteria, but the *autotrophic bacteria* derive their energy, in the first place, from reactions involving the oxidation of inorganic materials; in fact, the *obligatory autotrophs* cannot live in a medium containing organic matter, and it was only by using silica-gel that Winogradsky was able to culture them satisfactorily. These bacteria, however, in common with all living matter, are made up of carbon-containing compounds, so that their chemical reactions must involve the synthesis of these complex organic molecules—starch, protein and lipid—the necessary carbon being obtained from CO_2 and the nitrogen generally from NH_3. To convert CO_2 and H_2O into carbohydrate, energy must be supplied to the system ; in the plant this energy is obtained by the absorption of light by the pigment chlorophyll, the energy so absorbed being transferred, in some way by no means clearly understood, to the CO_2 and H_2O molecules, which can then react to give carbohydrate or some intermediary organic compound (p. 552). The obligatory autotroph makes use, instead, of the energy obtainable by the oxidation of inorganic material. Thus the sulphur bacterium, *Th. thioparus*, isolated from the soil by Nathansohn, will grow on thiosulphate solutions, obtaining energy from the reaction :—

$$2\ Na_2S_2O_3 + O_2 \rightarrow 2\ Na_2SO_4 + 2S$$

Again, the bacterium *Th. thio-oxidans*, found in soils in the neighbourhood of sulphur deposits, produces large quantities of sulphuric acid, in accordance with the reaction :—

$$2\ S + 3\ O_2 + 2\ H_2O \rightarrow 2\ H_2SO_4$$

The anaerobic *Th. denitrificans* does not make use of atmospheric oxygen, in fact it can only be grown under conditions in which oxygen is rigidly excluded (*anaerobic*) ; it obtains the oxygen necessary for the oxidation of thiosulphate from KNO_3. The fundamental energy-producing reaction is :—

$$5\ Na_2S_2O_3 + 8\ KNO_3 + 2NaHCO_3 \rightarrow 6\ Na_2SO_4 + 4\ K_2SO_4 + 4N_2$$
$$+ 2CO_2 + H_2O$$

The morphologically more complex sulphur bacteria, such as *Beggiatoa*, contain globules of sulphur within their cells ; they are obligatory autotrophs which require H_2S for their growth, the H_2S being oxidised in two stages, first to sulphur and then to sulphate ; as long as H_2S is available, the cell contains globules of free sulphur, but as soon as the supply fails the globules are oxidised. Other sulphur bacteria, such as the purple *Thiocystis*, obtain their energy from a photochemical reaction, the purple pigment, which is a mixture of a green chlorophyll-like pigment and a red carotenoid, absorbing light. The fundamental reaction here is :—

$$nCO_2 + 2nH_2S + \text{Light Energy} \rightarrow n(CH_2O) + nH_2O + 2nS$$
$$\text{(carbohydrate)}$$

It must be appreciated that these simple inorganic chemical reactions do not by any means represent the sum total of the autotrophic bacterium's metabolic activities ; these reactions, *e.g.*, the oxidation of sulphur, are the original sources of energy for the organism, but in order that the energy so liberated may be utilised for vital activities it must be transferred, by means of further chemical reactions, to other products. The red cell and the leucocyte utilise the energy available in the glucose dissolved in the blood plasma ; *i.e.*, the cell maintains its potential energy status by utilising the energy derived from the breakdown of glucose into simpler products with a smaller free energy content. The energy-giving material is thus already available to the cell. The autotroph, on the other hand, is more independent ; whilst it needs carbohydrate as a source of energy for its vital activities, in much the same way as the leucocyte does, it synthesises its own carbohydrates from substances of lower free energy content, the necessary energy for these syntheses being provided by the fundamental inorganic chemical reaction. Since a given weight of bacteria increases rapidly in weight by the process of multiplication and growth, and since multiplication and growth imply a continual synthesis of organic matter necessary for structure and metabolism, a suspension of bacteria may be regarded as a system continually increasing its potential energy status, the increase in free energy coming from the fundamental chemical reaction.

Synthetic Efficiency. Some estimate of the efficiency of the autotrophs in synthesising carbohydrates is possible with a knowledge of the changes in free energy involved in their chemical reactions.

Thus the synthesis of carbohydrate from CO_2 requires an increase of free energy of 118 Calories for every gramme-molecule of CO_2 utilised, or $118/12 = 9.85$ Calories per gramme of carbon. It is found experimentally that the *Nitromonas* bacteria, which derive their energy from the reaction :—

$$NH_4^+ + \tfrac{3}{2} O_2 \rightarrow NO_2^- + H_2O + 2 H^+$$

assimilate 1 g. of carbon for every 35 g. of nitrogen oxidised, the assimilated carbon being in the form of carbohydrate. Under the conditions in which the reaction takes place, the oxidation of each gramme-ion of ammonium makes available 66.5 Calories of free energy. Consequently the oxidation of 35 g. of nitrogen provides $66.5/14 \times 35 = 166$ Calories.

The efficiency of the synthetic process will be given by the amount of energy required for the synthesis divided by the amount of energy actually made available, *i.e.*, by :—

$$\frac{9.85}{166} = 0.059$$

or 5.9 per cent.

We may thus expect about 94 per cent. of the energy, made available by the oxidation of ammonia, to appear as heat. Meyerhof actually measured the heat production of these organisms and calculated the heat that should have been produced had there been no synthetic activity. The difference gave the amount of energy actually utilised ; it ranged from 2.5 to 9 per cent. A more recent study by Hutchens and his collaborators on the heterotroph *Chilomonas paramœcium*, which grows on culture media containing acetate and ammonia, may also be cited. Here the energy-producing reaction for the synthesis of carbohydrate, protein and fat is the oxidation of acetate :—

$$CH_3COOH + 2 O_2 \rightarrow 2 CO_2 + 2 H_2O$$

This reaction involves a decrease in free energy of 208 Calories per mole of acetate, *i.e.*, this amount of energy is made available for synthetic activity. The synthesis of carbohydrate from acetate, according to the stoichiometric equation :—

$$3\ CH_3COOH \rightarrow C_6H_{12}O_6$$

requires the supply of 29·3 Calories per mole of acetate used. Consequently the oxidation of one mole of acetate provides the energy for the incorporation of $\dfrac{208}{29\cdot3} = 7\cdot1$ moles of acetate.

It is found experimentally that, for every mole oxidised, 1·22 moles of acetate are assimilated, *i.e.*, that the energy which, ideally, would be adequate for the synthesis of 7·1 moles of acetate is used to synthesise only 1·22 moles. The efficiency is therefore :—

$$\frac{1\cdot22}{7\cdot1} = 0\cdot17$$

or 17 per cent., considerably greater than that shown by the autotrophic bacteria. In contrast to this low *energy efficiency*, we may note a remarkable economy in the use of carbon. Thus 10^6 cells synthesise, per hour, 22 g. of starch, 21 g. of protein and 6 g. of fat, containing carbon that corresponds to 42 per cent. of the acetate disappearing in the same time ; since the metabolic studies indicate that only 55 per cent. of the acetate disappearing is used in synthesis, it means that some $\dfrac{42}{55} \times 100 = 76\cdot5$ per cent. of the acetate, available for synthesis, is utilised.

These examples of energy transformations are instructive in so far as they emphasise that the synthetic, or anabolic, activities of the organism represent a building up of free energy in the living organism ; this building up, in accordance with the requirements of the Second Law, necessitates the supply of energy which, in the case of autotrophs, is obtained from inorganic chemical reactions. Synthesis is not the whole, although it is doubtless the principal, activity of the organism ; concentration gradients must be established and maintained ; and these processes require energy, which is obtained from the oxidative degradation of the organic synthetic products, presumably chiefly carbohydrate. Hetertrophic bacteria and higher organisms require organic material as the source of energy both for their synthetic power and for their basal energetic requirements ; thus the evolution of higher forms has been associated with a loss of synthetic power, in the sense that the organism has become more and more dependent on highly complex organic molecules for its fundamental energy requirements. Amongst the bacteria we find that this loss of synthetic power has been gradual and Knight has classified them on this basis as follows :—

1. Organisms which derive their carbon from CO_2 and their nitrogen from inorganic sources, their energy being derived from inorganic chemical reactions—in the case of the chemosynthetic autotrophs—and from light, in the case of the photosynthetic autotrophs,

2. Organisms deriving their carbon *and their energy* from organic compounds, and their nitrogen from inorganic compounds.

3. Organisms deriving their carbon and energy from organic compounds and their nitrogen from amino-acids ; in many cases there are certain amino-acids that cannot be dispensed with, *e.g.*, tryptophane.

4. Organisms which derive their carbon and energy from organic compounds and their nitrogen from amino-acids, of which a considerable number are required. One or more " growth factors," *e.g.*, *p*-amino-benzoic acid, are also required.

The viruses, as we have seen, are parasitic and have lost the synthetic powers necessary to build up their own requirements, in the sense that they stimulate their host to do the synthesis for them.

References

BAAS-BECKING, L. G. M., & PARKS, G. S. (1927). " Energy Relations in the Metabolism of Autotrophic Bacteria." *Physiol. Rev.*, **7**, 85.

BALLENTINE, R. (1940). " Analysis of the Changes in Respiratory Activity Accompanying Fertilisation of Marine Eggs." *J. cell. & comp. Physiol.*, **15**, 217.

BRODY, A. (1945). " Bioenergetics and Growth." Reinhold, N.Y.

DuBois, E. F. (1927). " Basal Metabolism in Health and Disease." Lea & Febiger, Philadelphia.

HARVEY, E. N. (1932). " Physical and Chemical Constants of the Egg of the Sea-Urchin, *Arbacia Punctulata*." *Biol. Bull.*, **62**, 141.

HUTCHENS, J. O., PODOLSKY, B. & MORALES, M. F. (1948). " Studies on the Kinetics and Energetics of C and N Metabolism of *Chilomonas Paramœcium*." *J. cell. & comp. Physiol.*, **32**, 117.

KNIGHT, B. C. J. G. (1936). " Bacterial Nutrition." Med. Res. Council. Sp. Rept., Ser. 210.

PONDER, E. (1949). " Hæmolysis and Related Phenomena." Grune & Stratton, N.Y.

SHAPIRO, H. (1939). " Some Functional Correlatives of Cellular Metabolism." *C.S.H. Symp.*, **7**, 406.

SMITH, A. H. & KLEIBER, M. (1950). " Size and O_2-Consumption in Fertilised Eggs." *J. cell. & comp. Physiol.*, **35**, 131.

STEPHENSON, M. (1939). " Bacterial Metabolism." Longmans Green, London.

VAN NIEL, C. B. (1943). " Biochemical Problems of the Chemo-Autotrophic Bacteria." *Physiol. Rev.*, **23**, 338.

CHAPTER VI

HEAT PRODUCTION AND HEAT LOSS OF ANIMALS

Homoiothermy and Poikilothermy

The Body Temperature. Mammals and birds maintain a temperature above that of their normal environment, and are thus described as " warm-blooded " to distinguish them from the greater part of the animal kingdom whose members have a temperature slightly below that of the environment, the so-called " cold-blooded " animals. The blood, or rectal, temperatures of a number of species of warm-blooded animals are shown in Table III ; an " average temperature " for the warm-blooded animal may therefore be said to be in the region of 37° C. although, in general, birds have rather higher temperatures, and fluctuations of 2° may be considered normal in any given species. The most striking feature of the warm-blooded animal, however, is not the actual value of its blood temperature,[1] but the relative constancy of this temperature under a variety of conditions. The " *lower*

TABLE III
The Rectal Temperatures of Various Species of Homoiotherm.

Species	Rectal Temperature °C.
Albino Mouse	36–39
Elephant	36
Marmot	37
Macaque	37
Rat	37
Man	37 (Normal Range : 36–38)
Pig	39
Cow	38
Rabbit	39–40
Goat	39
Sheep	39
Goose	41
Chicken	42·5
Ornithorhynchus	32
Echidna	29
Sloth	32
Armadillo	34
Brown Opossum	34

[1] The " cold-blooded " fish *Leuciscus thermalis*, living in the hot springs of Ceylon at a temperature of 50° C., has this temperature and therefore one considerably greater than that of the " warm-blooded " animals.

TABLE IV

*Lower Critical Temperatures below which the Animal cannot maintain
its Normal Body Temperature during One Hour's Exposure.* (Giaja,
1938.)

Sparrow	− 30° C.
Hen	− 50° C.
Rabbit	− 45° C.
Dog	− 100° C.

critical temperature" of an animal is defined as the environmental
temperature that may be withstood for an hour without a serious fall in the
temperature of the blood, and the figures above are given by Giaja
(Table IV). Thus the dog, normally living at an environmental temperature

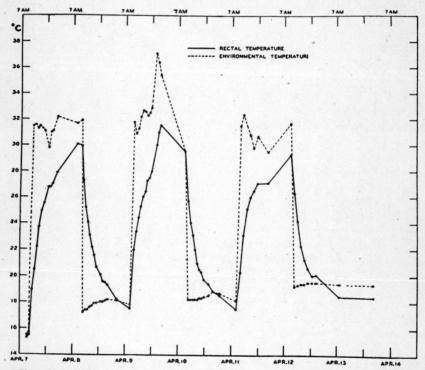

FIG. 76. Influence of changes in environmental temperature upon rectal
temperature of snake. (Benedict. *Carnegie Inst. Wash., Rept. No. 425.*)

of 20° C., can maintain its blood-temperature at 37° C. for an hour, although
subjected to an environmental temperature of − 100° C. Again, the
warm-blooded animal may maintain its blood-temperature at 37° C.
in the face of environmental temperatures not only considerably above
the average temperate value, but also above that of the blood. For these
reasons the warm-blooded animal is more aptly described as a

" *homoiotherm* "—an animal that maintains a constant temperature—in contrast to the " *poikilotherm*," an animal whose temperature varies passively with that of the environment. The contrast between the poikilotherm and the homoiotherm is brought out by the curves of Fig. 76 showing the variation in rectal temperature of the snake with changing environmental temperature ; the corresponding curve for a homoiotherm would be approximately a straight line parallel with the abscissæ.

Homoiothermy is a characteristic of the highest forms of life—the mammals and birds—and the survival value of such an attribute need not be laboured ; suffice it to say that the maintenance of a constant internal environment is of fundamental importance to the life of the organism, and the temperature of this environment, namely that of the circulating blood, must be considered to be just as important a factor as its chemical composition and pH. One has only to compare the active dog and the torpid snake in winter to be convinced of the value of a constant and high value of the blood temperature under a variety of conditions.

The condition of homoiothermy must involve a delicate balance between the two factors of *heat production* and *heat loss* ; it is quite clear that the rate of loss of heat by an animal may vary between wide limits according to the prevailing physical conditions ; similarly the heat production must, at least when the animal is exercising, vary too. It is reasonable to suppose that the balance between heat loss and heat production is achieved by independent variations in both these quantities to meet the demands of any situation. The polar fox, for example, normally existing at a temperature some 60° C. below that of its blood, can live in a temperate climate where the temperature differential may be less than 20° C. ; clearly this adaptation to a changed environmental temperature would be more efficient if the animal could modify both its heat production and its heat loss, and this, as we shall see, is generally true of all homoiotherms although the relative importance of the two factors, *chemical regulation* of heat production and *physical regulation* of heat loss, varies with different species.

We cannot enter into a detailed discussion of the *optimum temperature* of the animal, but we may consider a few of the factors concerned. The higher the temperature the more rapidly the vital chemical and physical processes, essential to life, will occur—other things being equal. Thus nerve conduction in the cold-blooded frog occurs at about 30m./sec. whereas in the mammal it is about 120 m./sec. A high temperature thus favours a more intense form of existence. A temperature higher than that of the environment is an important factor in heat loss, since it may be dissipated by convection and radiation ; hence a resting animal has a better chance of maintaining a constant temperature if this is above that of the environment ; the heat production, and therefore the potential of metabolic activity, may also be higher because of the more efficient method of heat dissipation. With a temperature above that of the environment, moreover, the heat loss may be regulated with considerable precision by the diversion of blood into the peripheral regions which must necessarily have a lower temperature—*the skin temperature*. The higher the normal temperature of the blood the more adequate will this supplementary mode of heat loss be. The importance of this physical regulation becomes evident when we consider that the heat production of a man indulging in vigorous exercise may increase twenty-fold without his blood-temperature rising by as much as a degree. A high blood-temperature is thus of value in maintaining a high potential of vital activity, and in permitting the regulation of heat loss ; a limit to the height of the useful blood-temperature is probably imposed by the requirements of heat production, which necessitates the expenditure of chemical energy in the form of foodstuffs, so that a balance must be struck between the demand for a high temperature in the interests of temperature regulation and vital activity, and a low temperature in the interests of economy in the utilisation of energy. For example, owing to the inefficiency of its digestive processes, the elephant maintains its normal heat production only by continuous eating and searching for food ; a higher body temperature would therefore be out of the question with this species.

Let us take it, therefore, that the optimum temperature is in the region of 36–37° C. It is worth noting in this connection that some of the more primitive mammals studied by Wardlaw, and by Martin, in Australia have defective temperature regulating mechanisms ; as Table III shows, the normal rectal temperatures of these species are considerably below the value of 37°, which we may take as characteristic of the perfected homoiotherm. These primitive species may therefore be considered to be defective because they have not achieved the necessary high level of heat production to permit the maintenance of a constant temperature ; in conformity with this we find that the basal heat production (p. 128) is only about a half that of the perfect homoiotherm of the same size, being in the region of 300 Calories per square metre of body surface, per 24 hr. *Echidna*, one of the primitive mammals studied, has, in fact, a temperature regulating mechanism only when its body-temperature lies between 27·6° and 32·6° ; outside these limits it behaves as a poikilotherm.[1]

Heat Production at Different Environmental Temperatures

Chemical Regulation. If our postulate regarding thermal regulation is true—namely that the homoiotherm responds to a lowering of its environmental temperature by an increase in its heat production—we may expect considerable variations in the recorded heat production according to the temperature at which the measurement is made. In Fig. 77 the heat production of two species of birds, the goose and *Melopsittacus* (budgerigar), has been plotted against ambient temperature and it may be seen that, as we proceed from a moderate to a low temperature, the heat production

[1] Newly-born and young white rats are much less resistant to cold than older ones, the age of maximal resistance being 61–300 days. Associated with the improvement in homoiothermy, there is a rise in the body temperature from 36·5° C. at 18 days to 38° C. at 30 days (Hill, 1947). The central American mammals studied by Morrison (the spiny rat and two species of opossum), showed poor temperature regulation, in that raising the environmental temperature above 30° C., or decreasing it below 17° C., caused considerable changes in body temperature. Two of the three species had low body temperatures under normal environmental conditions.

increases ; this reaction to cold has been termed *chemical regulation*. It will be noted that the reaction of the goose is much less pronounced than that of *Melopsittacus*, a decrease of 10° causing a 100 per cent. increase in heat production in the latter animal, but only a 40–50 per cent. change in the goose. This is understandable if the difference in the featherings of the two birds is taken into account. The goose is well protected by its down against heat loss so that a decrease of 20° in its environmental temperature has only a small influence on the heat lost by convection and radiation, whereas *Melopsittacus* is poorly provided with insulation and so must rely more heavily on chemical regulation for maintaining a constant

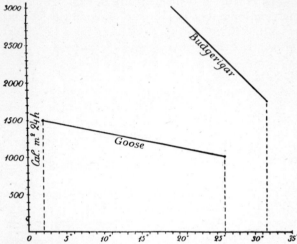

FIG. 77. The responses of the goose and budgerigar to decreased environmental temperature. Note the greater response of the poorly-feathered
budgerigar, *i.e.*, the steep *slope of thermogenesis*. (Giaja. *Thermo-
régulation. Hermann.*)

blood-temperature.[1] With any given animal it is found that, on varying the environmental temperature over a wide range, a curve of heat production plotted against ambient temperature takes the general form shown in Fig. 78. As the temperature is reduced a point is reached, the *lower critical temperature*, at which, in spite of the greatly increased heat production, the animal can no longer maintain its normal rectal temperature and the *zone of hypothermia* is entered. Further lowering of the temperature leads to a lowered rectal temperature and, if this is too great or too prolonged, to death. In general, many homoiotherms may recover from a hypothermia of 20° if it is not too prolonged. Newly-born animals survive considerable degrees of hypothermia ; Ware, Hill & Schultz have shown that a one-day-old rat will survive a rectal temperature of 5° C. ; at thirty days it survives a temperature of 8° ; at sixty days of 11° ; above

[1] The changes in body-temperature of poikilotherms, as a result of exercise, are often striking ; the heat production of butterflies may rise 50–200-fold during flight, and many insects cannot fly until, as a result of vibrating their wings, they have raised their body-temperature above 30° C. The bat raises its body-temperature to that of a homoiotherm during flight.

eighty days old it survives a rectal temperature of 15° C. According to Haterius & Maison, adult dogs survive rectal temperatures of 14—16° C., the rectal temperature being below 24° C. for as long as 110 minutes. Simpson & Herring state that a rectal temperature of less than 16° C. is lethal for cats. The heat production at the lower critical temperature is described as the *peak metabolism (métabolisme du sommet)*, and the ratio of the peak metabolism over the basal metabolic rate (p. 128) is called the *metabolic quotient*, being used to define the power of any species to adapt itself to a low environmental temperature by chemical regulation. It should be appreciated, however, that the lower critical temperature is an arbitrarily chosen condition defined by the lowest temperature at which the animal may maintain its normal rectal temperature *for one hour* ; very

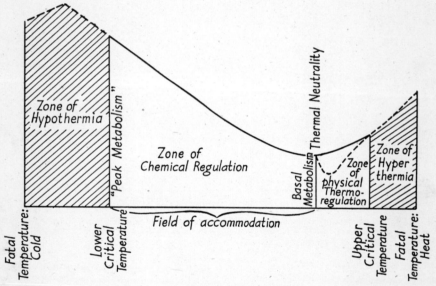

FIG. 78. Scheme of thermoregulation in homoiotherms. (Giaja. *Thermo-régulation. Hermann.*)

soon a fatigue of the thermoregulatory process sets in and hypothermia ensues.

At the other end of the temperature scale there is the zone of hyperthermia, the surrounding temperature being too high to permit of adequate heat loss ; the rectal temperature of the animal rises, a hyperthermia of 5° C. being, in general, fatal. The true course of the curve for the heat production as we pass from a condition in which the animal is producing heat to compete against the cold, say 16° C., to the condition in which the animal is fighting against hyperthermia, by invoking special mechanisms for heat dissipation such as sweating or hyperventilation of the lungs—say at 35° C.—is a matter of some dispute, but in general it would seem that there is a region of *minimum heat production*, the *zone of thermal neutrality*, in which the animal may be said to be neither fighting against cold nor against heat, the rise in heat production on the warm side of this zone being due, presumably, to the secretory and muscular activities of sweating and hyperpnœa. The heat production in this zone may therefore be correctly regarded as the *basal heat production*, or *basal metabolism*, *i.e.*, the minimum energy requirements of the animal when completely at rest. The zone of thermal neutrality may be quite wide, as in man, or may be limited to a degree or two, as with the rat. On theoretical grounds we may expect that, if an animal is well protected against heat loss, its zone of thermal neutrality will be wider than if it is badly protected ; thus the sheep has a wide zone, extending from 0° to

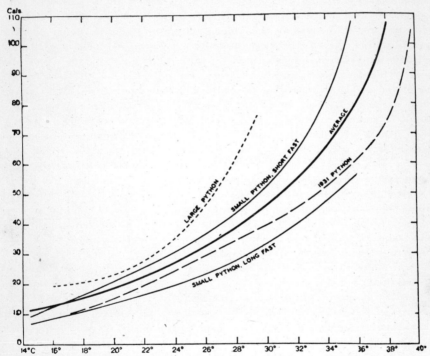

Fig. 79.   Standard heat production of pythons, per sq. metre of body-surface, per 24 hr., referred to temperature. (Benedict. *Carnegie Inst. Wash., Rept. No. 425.*)

28° C., whilst the hairless mouse is restricted to only a degree, between 34° and 35° C. ; the comparatively wide zone of thermal neutrality shown by man (between about 18° and 40° C.) is due entirely to his highly developed powers of regulating his heat loss (p. 144).

We may think of chemical regulation, then, as a purposive adaptation to increased heat loss [1] ; the primitive mammals discussed earlier show this

[1] Herrington (1940) studied the chemical regulation of mice, rats and guinea-pigs ; he showed that the increases in heat production per degree fall of ambient temperature were 46·3, 43·2 and 26·1 Calories respectively, *i.e.*, in the order of the ratios of surface area to weight, which were in the order : 2·81 : 1·23 : 1·0. Chemical regulation is thus adapted to the rate at which the animal loses heat.

power in a marked degree, whereas the other response to heat loss, physical regulation, is defective ; and this accounts for their deficient homoiothermy; at the other end of the phylogenetic scale we find that physical regulation is most highly developed in man, whilst chemical regulation contributes so little that its existence has been called into question. The acquisition of the power of chemical regulation may therefore be regarded as the first stage in the transition from poikilothermy to homoiothermy ; and it is in this respect that the difference between the two great classes is so striking. Thus the heat production of the snake decreases progressively as we pass from a high to a low ambient temperature, as Fig. 79 shows ; the response of the poikilotherm to a varying ambient temperature is therefore very similar to that of a simple chemical reaction. In general, a rise in temperature, by increasing the kinetic energy of the reacting molecules, ncreases the rate of a chemical reaction. Because of the logarithmic relationship between temperature and the rate of reaction, the effect of a rise in temperature is most conveniently indicated by the *temperature coefficient*, or Q_{10}, the ratio of the rates at two temperatures 10° C. apart. Over a range of about 30° C. this quantity is reasonably constant for a simple chemical reaction, and generally has a value between 2 and 3. It is commonly stated in the literature that the heat production of poikilotherms obeys the " Q_{10} *Law*," implying that the ratio of the heat productions at two temperatures 10° C. apart is fairly constant over the temperature range at which it is possible to study the animal. As Krogh has emphasised, this is not by any means true ; whereas the Q_{10}, computed from the heat production of poikilotherms at different temperatures, frequently has a value between 2 and 3, it is by no means constant over a wide range of temperature. Thus the Q_{10} for a small poikilotherm studied by Krogh varied between 10·9 and 2·2 between 0° and 27·5° C. With normal homoiotherms, at ambient temperatures within their field of accommodation, the response to a change of temperature is entirely different, because physiological mechanisms are brought into play adapting the heat production to the heat loss ; in animals robbed of their physiological mechanisms, by the surgical procedure of destroying their heat-regulating centre in the hypothalamic region of the brain, it was found that the heat production varied with ambient temperature in essentially the same manner as that shown by the poikilotherm. Moreover, with man in fever it is said that the Q_{10}, computed from his heat production in the febrile and normal states, has the same value as that of the dog with its heat regulating mechanism destroyed.

The Nature of Chemical Regulation. Chemical regulation, the increase in heat production in response to cold, has been recognised since the work of Lavoisier [1] ; the assumption generally implied in its definition is that the extra heat production is not associated with muscular activity, such as

---

[1] It is worth preserving the description of these experiments. " *Il résulte des expériences auxquelles M. Séguin s'est soumis, qu'un homme à jeun et dans un état de repos, et dans une température de 26 degrés de thermomètre à mercure divisé en 80 partis, consomme par heure* 1·210 *pouces d'air vital ; que cette consommation augmente par le froid, et que le même homme, également à jeun et en repos, mais dans une température de 12 degrés seulement, consomme par heure* 1·344 *pouces d'air vital.*

shivering, and in recent years there has been a tendency to question this. There is no *a priori* reason why the animal should not respond by a general increase in the basal metabolism of all its cells in response to an environmental change ; certainly the phenomena of long-term adaptation to environmental temperature indicate this possibility. For example, the basal heat production of rats, exposed successively for several weeks to diverse temperatures, showed considerable differences according as the adapting temperature was high or low, even though the actual measurements of heat production were carried out at the neutral temperature of the rat. In so far, however, as the metabolism of the musculature of any animal must represent a very large proportion of the whole, the problem essentially resolves itself into finding the mechanism whereby the muscle fibres increase their metabolism above the resting level. Recent studies of Burton & Bronk suggest that it is by contraction that the muscle fibres increase their heat production. Thus, when the body temperature of a cat was reduced below a critical level, there was a rise in the activity of the voluntary muscles, shown by their action currents (p. 382), due to an unco-ordinated asynchronous twitching of the individual fibres ; the onset of the action currents coincided with the onset of chemical regulation. Only at a later stage did this type of activity pass into the co-ordinated firing of fibres that shows itself in the gross tremor of shivering. More recently Hemingway & Hathaway have applied similar criteria for muscular activity during the cooling of dogs ; they have come to the conclusion that only a 7 per cent. increase in heat production occurs before the onset of shivering (in which the heat production rose by 30 per cent.). They argue that the pre-shivering chemical regulation would be quite inadequate to combat significant heat losses, and suggest that chemical regulation, as such, is only a long-term adaptation (of which there can be little doubt), whilst the more immediate response is a nervous one of shivering and muscular activity generally.[1]

It would seem that chemical regulation differs only in degree from the increased heat production due to shivering, and this, in turn, from the voluntary bodily activity, such as stamping the feet, indulged in by man as a temporary defence against cold. Biologically speaking, chemical regulation is, by itself, an inefficient means of combating cold over a long period. A vigorous man trained to cold, placed suddenly in a bath at 4° C., shows an eighteen-fold increase in heat production over a period of twelve minutes. Thus his increase in heat production to combat cold is of the same order as that involved in maximal physical exercise. As an immediate response to a crisis it serves its purpose of preventing the fatal effects of hypothermia, but as a means of protection over a long period, it would represent an extravagant expenditure of energy In general, when heat loss is great, fatigue of the chemical regulation mechanism sets in and

[1] Against this view we have the observation of Horvath that a rat maintained at 4° C. increases its metabolism by 22 per cent., and that this occurs when the actual measurement of heat production is made at 29° C. ; moreover, the increase is independent of the time during which the rats are maintained at 4° C. between four and 48 hours. Unilateral adrenalectomy, furthermore, reduces the chemical regulation to only 7 per cent.

the animal eventually succumbs to hypothermia ; it is found that even though an animal may maintain a heat production at double its basal value for indefinite periods, it seeks whenever possible to reduce its heat loss to such a level that the basal heat production alone is sufficient. Physical regulation is therefore exploited to the maximum extent to reduce the drain on the metabolic resources. Where even this fails, as in the case of the marmot in spite of its thick fur and layer of fat, hypothermia of a striking degree is suffered rather than the extravagant use of energy in chemical regulation, so that the animal abandons homoiothermy and becomes essentially a poikilotherm (p. 139). The same considerations apply to physical exercise ; as a means of keeping warm for a short period it is excellent, but over a long period the exhaustion that sets in is far greater than if the work had been carried out at a higher temperature. Thus Giaja has shown that of two rats in the cold, one at rest and the other working on a treadmill, it was the latter that succumbed first to hypothermia.[1]

Basal Metabolism of Homoiotherms

The *basal metabolism* is a somewhat artificial quantity and is essentially an ideal—the expenditure of energy necessary for the organism to maintain its potential energy status ; and, as we have seen, it may be measured by the total heat production in a given period (generally taken as 24 hours, although the actual duration of the measurement is usually much shorter). To obtain a reliable estimate of the animal's basal heat production many precautions must be observed ; thus a temperature must be chosen such that the animal is neither fighting against cold nor against hyperthermia, *i.e.*, the temperature must be within the zone of thermal neutrality. Moreover, recent studies have indicated that the most reliable results are obtained only when the animal is properly adapted to the temperature at which the measurement is made. The importance of making measurements in the zone of thermal neutrality is shown by the comparative heat productions of three species measured at 17° C. and at thermal neutrality as follows :—

Species	Heat Production (Cal./m.²/24 hr.) 17° C.	Thermal Neutrality
Goldfinch . . .	3,369	1,485
Dove	2,069	809
Quail	1,822	1,140

At 17° C. the birds are fighting against cold—the dove to a greater extent than the others—so that a different order of " basal metabolic rates " is obtained at 17° C. than that at thermal neutrality. Again, the animal

[1] As a result of the interplay of these two factors—chemical and physical regulation—the body-temperature remains tolerably constant. According to Herrington (1940), however, a fall in the rectal temperature need not necessarily indicate a defective adaptation to cold, in fact it must be treated as one of the factors in adaptation. Herrington argues that a regulative mechanism, so perfect that in a cold environment it would actually maintain the skin at some ideal temperature, would produce undesirably high internal body-temperatures ; whilst a mechanism that maintained an ideal internal temperature would allow the surface to become too cool. Thus the response to a cold environment is a moderate fall in rectal temperature.

must be relaxed and in a post-absorptive condition, since the act of digestion involves an extra heat production. It will be readily appreciated that this ideal is impossible of attainment with many species ; for example, the elephant is a restless animal continually moving its ears, tail, and trunk ; moreover, its digestion is so inefficient that it must eat almost continuously ; consequently a post-absorptive condition is well-nigh impossible of achievement if, at the same time, the animal is to be quiescent. The most extensive experiments on the basal metabolism of different species are undoubtedly those of Benedict and his colleagues at the Carnegie Institute in Washington, and of Giaja and Gelineo in Belgrade ; and the present description is taken largely from their work.

An animal may be regarded, from a thermodynamic viewpoint, as a

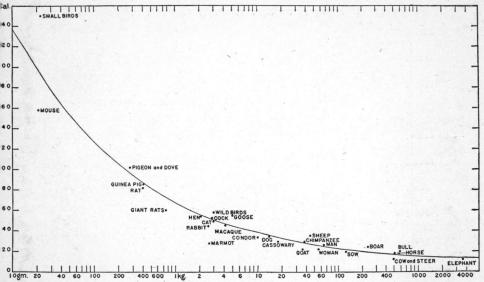

Fig. 80. Semi-logarithmic graph showing the trend of the average heat production, per kilogram, of each species of animal referred to the average body-weight. (Benedict. *Carnegie Inst. Wash., Rept. No. 503.*)

conglomeration of cells, each producing heat ; it is therefore a truism to say that the larger the animal of any given species the greater will be its heat production ; in actual fact, when animals of the same species are compared, the heat production appears to increase linearly with the increase in weight. We might therefore expect that the heat production per unit weight of the animal would be fairly characteristic of a species, and that the basal metabolism of different species could best be compared on this basis. This, however, is to take too simple a view of the matter, since it is found that, with any species, the larger the animal the smaller is its heat production *per kilogramme of weight.* Thus a 600 g. rat has a heat production of 75 Calories/kg., whilst a rat weighing 150 g. has a value of 113 Calories/kg. However, if we take the mean heat production of the species, and divide it by the mean weight of the animals used in the investigation, we get a figure which should be reasonably characteristic of the basal metabolism of the species. If these figures are plotted against the mean weight of the species, we get the curve shown in Fig. 80. This curve brings out two important points ; first, that there are unmistakable differences in the basal metabolic rates of different species, ranging from 13 Calories/kg. for the elephant to over 250 Calories/kg. for small birds ; and secondly that, just as with the individuals of a given species, the basal metabolism per unit of body-weight is highest with the smallest animals.

Surface-Area Law. The classical studies on the basal metabolism of animals were carried out by Rubner ; the impressive decrease in basal metabolism, per kilogramme of body-weight, with increasing size of the animal led him to the hypothesis that the basal heat production of any

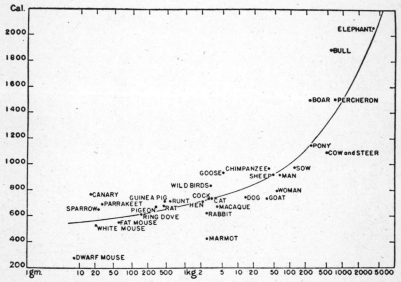

Fig. 81. Semi-logarithmic chart showing trend of the average heat production, per sq. metre of surface-area, per 24 hr., of each animal species referred to the average body-weight. (Benedict. *Carnegie Inst. Wash., Rept. No.* 503.)

animal was adjusted to its rate of loss of heat. The loss of heat, particularly by radiation and convection, depends on the *surface-area* of the animal ; and, since the surface-area in relation to the body-weight decreases with increasing size of the animal, the loss of heat per kilogramme of body-weight will be greater with a small animal than with a larger. If this is true, he argued, we may expect that the heat production *per square metre of body-surface* will be constant for the animals of any given species, and possibly also for the animals of different species. Rubner's experiments on dogs and other mammals indicated a value of 1,000 Calories per sq. metre per 24 hours, at 16° C., as the basal metabolic rate characteristic of warm-blooded animals. As a result of the much more rigorous experiments of Benedict, it would appear that this " Surface-Area Law " is of only limited application as Fig. 81 shows, where the heat production per sq. metre of body-surface is plotted against the mean body-weight of different animals. It will be seen that although the basal metabolism of a group of fifteen species falls within the limits of 600–800 Calories per sq. metre, and therefore gives some plausibility to the hypothesis, the total range extends from 278 Cal./m.^{2} for the dwarf mouse to 2,060 Cal./m.^{2} for the elephant ; there is, moreover, a consistent trend towards an increased heat production per unit area with increasing size of the animal.

The essential implication in the " Surface-Area Law " is that the basal metabolism of the animal is adjusted precisely to its heat loss which, in turn, depends on the surface-area. If the implication is true, we may expect that the heat production, expressed on a basis of body-surface, will be a much less variable quantity than when expressed on a body-weight basis. We have seen that this main conclusion is true, the heat production per kilogramme of body-weight varying by a factor of more than twelve, on passing from small mammals and birds to the elephant, whilst on a surface-area basis the factor is only some three to four. Nevertheless, this implication is probably not altogether true ; the basal heat production of the animal is primarily determined by the number and organisation of the cells of which it is built up ; the heat production is the fundamental and inescapable concomitant of its maintenance at a proper level of potential energy. As a given animal grows, or as we pass from one species to another of larger average weight, the total heat production must increase, but the *extent* to which it will increase, *i.e.*, whether the increase will follow the increase in weight in a linear or more complex fashion, will depend on the laws of growth.

Let us assume that the heat production varies with the weight in accordance with the simple formula :—

$$\text{Heat Production} = k \times \text{Weight}^n \quad \cdots \quad (1)$$

If the heat production were to double with a doubled weight, the law of heat production would take the simpler form :—

$$\text{Heat Production} = k \times \text{Weight}$$

or

$$\text{Heat Production/Weight} = \text{Constant}$$

Now we have seen that the heat production, divided by the weight of the animal, is not constant but decreases with increasing size of the animal, so that we must rule this simple linear law out of court.

Let us suppose that the law takes the form of Equation 1 and that n is $\frac{2}{3}$. We get :—

$$\text{Heat Production} = k \times \text{Wt.}^{\frac{2}{3}}$$

i.e., if the weight is doubled, the heat production increases by a factor of only 1·59. Now the most probable value for the surface-area of an animal is given by the equation [1] :—

$$\text{Area} = 10 \times \text{Wt.}^{\frac{2}{3}}$$

[1] That is, if the area is in sq. cm. and the weight in grammes.

Hence we may expect, if this " Two-Thirds Power Law " holds, that the heat production, divided by the area of the animal, will be constant. The curve of Fig. 81 shows us, however, that the heat production per unit area (or rather the heat production divided by ten times the weight raised to the two-thirds power), is not constant. This means, essentially, that the fundamental equation defining the heat production as a function of the weight of the animal is in error. Let us return to our original equation :—

$$\text{Heat Production} = k \times \text{Weight}^n$$

If we take logarithms of both sides we get :—

$$\text{Log Heat Production} = \text{Log } k + n \text{ log Weight}$$

By plotting the logarithm of the heat production against the logarithm of the weight we should get a straight line, if the law of heat production with

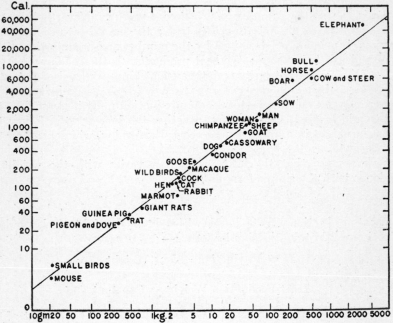

FIG. 82.   Logarithmic plot of heat production against mean body-weight of each species. (Benedict. *Carnegie Inst. Wash., Rept. No. 503.*)

increasing size, exemplified by Equation 1, holds. If this is done, as in Fig. 82, we see that the result is indeed a straight line. It has been shown by Brody that the best fit is obtained if n in Equation 1 is taken as 0·73 ; *i.e.*, the heat production, divided by the weight raised to the power of 0·73, is a characteristic of the animal, independent of its size and species, being on the average some 70 Cal./24 hr. If the surface-area of an animal were to be proved to vary as the 0·73 power of its body-weight, the Surface-Area Law could be said to apply strictly, but even then the assumption implicit in the law—to the effect that, as an animal increases in area, its basal heat production is adjusted exactly to the heat loss involved in this increase in area—still remains to be proven. As an animal increases in size, a number of problems are presented ; an increase in size involves an increase in the amount of metabolising tissue and therefore of heat production, unless the heat production per unit weight is modified ; the surface-area per unit weight will decrease unless there is a suitable change of *form* of the animal, and therefore the area available for dissipation of heat is relatively decreased. As the size increases, the problem of supporting the animal becomes important, since the weight increases as the cube of the height whilst the strength of the supporting structures as the square ; the proportion of supporting tissues must therefore be modified. Thus it may be shown that an increase in size means a readjustment of very many factors, no one of which can be varied to any extent independently of the others ; the growth of an animal must therefore follow certain " laws " ; as a result, certain fairly definite relationships between the sizes of individual organs, for example, and body-weight are found. It is unwise to single out two characteristics of the animal, the heat production and surface-area, and try to prove that these are carefully adjusted to each other ; all we know is that one of the restraints imposed on the modification of weight is that the heat production must be equal to the dissipation of heat. For this reason a spherical animal, for example, cannot increase in size indefinitely without a corresponding reduction in heat production per unit weight, so that a point will come when its metabolic activities must be so low as to imperil its survival. The heat dissipation under fixed environmental conditions is a function of *two main variables*, the surface-area and the conductance of the tissues ; if the surface-area is not modified appropriately, when the animal increases in size, the conductance must be adjusted in order that the increased heat production may be dealt with. It seems most reasonable to assume, therefore, that the animal maintains homoiothermy as a result of the interplay of all three variables : weight, surface-area, and conductance ; as Burton says, to decide whether the heat production is adjusted to the heat loss, or whether the heat loss is adjusted to the heat production, is more a problem for the philosopher than for the physiologist. As we shall see, the poikilotherm's heat production obeys the " Surface-Area Law " rather more regularly than that of the homoiotherm ; here heat dissipation is not an urgent problem, so that we are led to the conclusion that the special relationship between heat production and body-weight, implied in this " Law," is essentially a manifestation of the general laws of growth which impose certain restrictions on heat production and weight.

Finally, it should be pointed out that the basal heat production is measured at thermal neutrality, a temperature generally in the region of 30° C. ; if the animals were studied at the temperatures prevailing in their normal habitats, entirely different values would frequently be obtained, and it is interesting that Rubner made his comparisons at 14° C., a temperature at which many animals exhibit chemical regulation, and thus produce heat more rapidly than at thermal neutrality. The fact that the surface-area law appears to hold moderately well with many animals at thermal neutrality suggests that the basal heat production is mainly determined by certain fixed laws of growth ; to meet and restrict the heavy losses of heat that would occur in very cold climates, the factor of thermal regulation is mainly invoked ; this may take the form of a steep slope of thermogenesis, whereby the heat production is increased markedly in response to a low environmental temperature, or in the restriction of heat loss by the development of a thick fur, or by other mechanisms.

Basal Metabolism and the O_2-Consumption of Excised Tissues. If the O_2-consumption of an excised tissue gives a true picture of its O_2-consumption *in vivo*, we may expect the O_2-consumption per unit weight (Q_{O_2}) of homologous tissues, from animals of increasing size, to show a progressive decrease. Thus the mouse produces heat at the rate of about 160 Cal./kg./24 hr., whereas the elephant produces only about 16 Cal./kg.; consequently a gramme of excised mouse muscle might be expected to consume O_2 at about ten times the rate of that of a gramme of elephant muscle. There have been a number of experimental investigations of this point with conflicting results. It is sufficient to mention only the most recent work, namely that of Krebs who has summarised critically the earlier experiments and their interpretations. Krebs devoted a great deal of attention to establishing a suitable medium, and standardised procedure, for the measurement of the Q_{O_2} of isolated tissues ; having achieved something approaching a " standard Q_{O_2}," he compared the values obtained with tissues from animals of varying weight, as in Table V. The results certainly indicate a progressive decline in Q_{O_2} with increasing weight, but

TABLE V

Average Q_{O_2} of 5 tissues of 9 mammalian species compared with average basal heat production (Krebs, 1950)

Species	Mean Body Weight (kg.)	Q_{O_2}					Basal Heat Production/kg. Body-weight in 24 hrs. (Cal.)
		Brain Cortex	Kidney Cortex	Liver	Spleen	Lung	
Mouse .	0·021	− 32·9	− 46·1	− 23·1	− 16·9	− 12·0	158
Rat .	0·21	− 26·3	− 38·2	− 17·2	− 12·7	− 8·6	100
Guinea Pig .	0·51	− 27·3	− 31·8	− 13·0	− 11·6	− 8·5	82
Rabbit .	1·05	− 28·2	− 34·5	− 11·6	− 14·2	− 8·0	60
Cat .	2·75	− 26·9	− 22·7	− 13·2	− 8·4	− 3·9	50
Dog .	15·9	− 21·2	− 27·0	− 11·7	− 6·6	− 4·9	34
Sheep .	49	− 19·7	− 27·5	− 8·5	− 6·9	− 5·4	25
Cattle .	420	− 17·2	− 23·5	− 8·2	− 4·4	− 4·3	20
Horse .	725	− 15·7	− 21·5	− 5·4	− 4·2	− 4·4	17

the correlations exhibited here and in many other experiments were by no means perfect. In general, Krebs concluded that it is unlikely that the metabolism of the organs, studied by him, would be adjusted to the thermal requirements of the animal. The voluntary musculature exerts the dominant influence on the total production of heat by the animal ; since the heat production of the musculature *in vivo* is highly variable, it would be profitless to study its Q_{O_2} in the excised state,[1] and this gives an atmosphere of unreality to the whole discussion. If it is realised that the curarised animal (*i.e.*, one in which muscular activity is abolished), loses its power of chemical regulation, it may be concluded that it is the voluntary musculature that is primarily responsible for the general level of heat production ; variations in heat production, per unit weight, from one species to another will therefore be due mainly to variations in the heat production of the voluntary musculature, although there is an unmistakable trend in the Q_{O_2} of other tissues in the direction of a decrease with increasing size.

The Basal Metabolism of Man. Because of its clinical value, and because of the ideal nature of man as an experimental subject in comparison with animals, the basal metabolism of man has been extensively studied. The " Surface-Area Law " appears to apply to man with great precision in spite of wide variations in height, weight and shape, so that the basal heat production can be predicted with considerable accuracy if his surface-area is known. In order to establish this relationship between body-surface and basal metabolism it was necessary to compute very accurately the surface-area of any given man ; this measurement is a tiresome process, however carried out. For instance DuBois' method consisted of dressing the subject in tightly-fitting underwear and sticking paper over the whole so as to make a flexible mould. The area of this mould was estimated by cutting it into pieces and laying these on a large piece of weighed photographic paper. After exposure to light, the blackened pieces of photographic paper were cut away and weighed, and the weight of the unexposed portion obtained by difference ; from this weight the area of the mould was directly computed. Having made measurements of this sort on several subjects, DuBois showed that the surface area, in square metres, could be computed from the height and weight by substitution in the " Linear Formula " :—

$$\text{Area} = W^{0.425} \times H^{0.725} \times 71.8$$

where W and H are the weight in kg. and height in cm. respectively. The results of thousands of measurements of basal heat production were then plotted against the surface area, computed from the height and weight, to give the curve shown in Fig. 83. It will be seen from this curve that the young child has a much higher basal metabolic rate per unit area than the

---

[1] That the O_2-consumption of the excised tissues is not the same as that *in vivo* has been shown by several workers ; for example Field, Belding & Martin (1939) found that the summated O_2-consumption for all the tissues of the rat amounted to only 65.8 per cent. of the O_2-consumption of the intact animal. After making allowance for the minimal amount of muscular activity that occurs with a living animal at rest, the summated O_2-consumption amounted to 89 per cent. of the basal metabolic rate. According to Fedorov & Shur, the liver may contribute appreciably to thermo-regulation ; they recorded a six-fold increase in heat production by this organ, *in vivo*, on cooling an animal. It is interesting that Kleiber (1941) found an excellent parallelism between the Q_{O_2} of liver slices and the basal heat production of animals of varying size. According to Kleiber the Q_{O_2} is inversely proportional to the fourth root of the weight, *i.e.*, $Q_{O_2} \propto W^{-\frac{1}{4}}$. The metabolic rates of the animals are proportional to $W^{\frac{3}{4}}$; the metabolic rates per unit weight of animal are therefore proportional to $W^{\frac{3}{4}} \div W = W^{-\frac{1}{4}}$.

adult ; Burton has shown that this must correspond with an increased conduction of heat to the periphery. Secondly it will be seen that women have a basal metabolic rate some 6–10 per cent. less than that of men ; the cause of this difference is apparently *not* to be found in the layer of subcutaneous fat in women since the basal metabolic rate of a fat man is no smaller than that of a thin one ; moreover it is not due to the greater

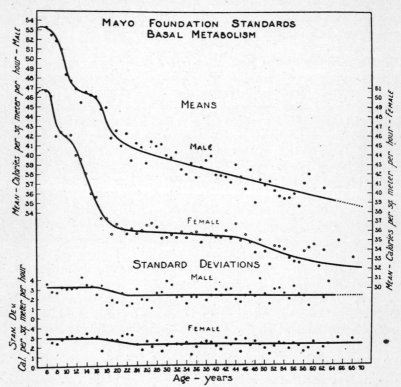

Fig. 83. Basal heat production of humans, in Calories, per sq. metre, per hour, plotted against age. (Boothby, Berkson & Dunn. *Amer. J. Physiol.*)

muscular development in man since the B.M.R. of trained athletes falls within the average for all men.

The Heat Production of Poikilotherms

Standard Metabolism. The important characteristic of the metabolism of the poikilotherm has been brought out earlier, namely that the heat production varies with the ambient temperature in rough accordance with the laws governing the response of a chemical reaction. The term " basal metabolism," applying as it does to the heat production of the resting homoiotherm at its thermal neutrality, cannot very well be applied to the poikilotherm, hence one speaks, instead, of the *standard metabolism*, measured under conditions approximating as closely as possible to those laid down for measurements on homoiotherms. The poikilotherm's heat production over any period must balance the heat loss, since the rectal and skin temperatures are generally maintained slightly below that of the environment ; the loss of heat must, moreover, be achieved entirely by insensible perspiration, *i.e.*, by the evaporation of water from the surface of the body and the respiratory organs. With muscular exercise, however, the heat production increases, so that temporarily we may expect the poikilotherm to have a higher temperature than that of the environment and to lose heat by convection and radiation besides by evaporation. In estimating the standard metabolism of the poikilotherm we must therefore

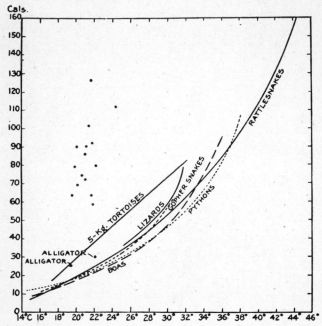

Fig. 84. Comparison of standard heat production, per sq. metre of body surface per 24 hr., with reference to environmental temperature amongst different species. Plotted points are for giant tortoises. (Benedict. *Carnegie Inst. Wash., Rept. No. 425.*)

take great care to ensure that the animal is at rest. Moreover, the temperature at which the measurement is made must be rigidly specified, in fact the results are ideally expressed in the form of a curve showing the standard metabolism as a function of rectal temperature.

In Fig. 84 the heat production of a variety of large cold-blooded animals, studied by Benedict, has been plotted against ambient temperature. The heat production has been expressed in terms of Calories per square metre of body surface and it is found (at any rate in so far as snakes ranging in weight from the 32 kg. python to the 2·4 kg. gopher snake) that the curves for the different species approximate each other much more closely than do similar curves in which heat production is expressed on a weight basis. In other words, it would seem that the " Surface-Area Law " applies at least as well to the poikilotherm as to the homoiotherm.

Comparison of Cold-Blooded and Warm-Blooded Animals

In any comparison of the basal metabolism of the homoiotherms and the standard metabolism of the poikilotherms it seems only fair to compare them at the same rectal temperature. This may be done either by inducing a state of hypothermia in the warm-blooded animal (by the use of curare or some surgical procedure), or, preferably, by raising the temperature of the poikilotherm to 37° C. This latter procedure is not always possible, however, since this temperature is fatal to many poikilotherms, *e.g.*, most fishes can survive 20° C. but 30° C. is generally fatal. Snakes, on the other hand, seem to thrive best at 30° C., whether they come from tropical or temperate climates, and it is possible to study rattle-snakes and the python at 37° C. with no hint of any damage, either at the time of measurement or subsequently. When it is not feasible to study the cold-blooded animal at 37° C., a careful study of the variation of heat production with temperature *i.e.*, the determination of the Q_{10}, permits a reasonable estimate of the probable heat production at higher temperatures. Finally, in comparing the basal metabolism of different species of homoiotherm, the most satisfactory comparison is that between animals of the same weight.

First, then, we may compare poikilotherms at 37° C. (either measured directly or inferred from the Q_{10}) with homoiotherms of similar weight, as in Table VI. The Table leaves no doubt as to the greater rate of heat

TABLE VI

Heat Production of Poikilotherms and Homoiotherms of Approximately the same Weight, at 37° C. (Benedict, 1932.)

Poikilotherm			Wt. (kg.)	Cal./24 hr.	Homoio-therms	Wt. (kg.)	Cal./24 hr.
Python	.	.	32	189	Man	32·2	997
Alligator	.	.	53	408	Man	53	1,470
Tortoise.	.	.	117	876	Man	109	2,559
			(Flesh)				
Boa	.	.	10	55	Dog	11·5	389

production of the homoiotherm when the comparison is made on this basis. If the curves obtained by plotting the heat production of individual poikilotherms against temperature are combined, we may extrapolate the mean curve to 37° C. and obtain an average value of about 100 Cal./m.²/ 24 hr. for the standard metabolism of poikilotherms of all sizes ; the mean basal metabolism of homoiotherms may be taken as about 800 Calories, so that on this basis, too, the basal heat production of the homoiotherm is considerably greater than that of the poikilotherm. If the comparison is made between the hypothermic homoiotherm and the poikilotherm at 25° or 30° C., an essentially similar result is obtained. Krogh's curarised dog cooled to 23° C., and Velten's rabbit at 26° C., had heat productions in the region of 325 Calories, whilst the cold-blooded animals at 25° C. average only 25 Calories. At 30° C. the warm-blooded animals gave a heat production of 470 Calories and the cold-blooded only 60 Calories.

We may conclude, therefore, that the transition from poikilothermy to homoiothermy is achieved by a fundamental change in the metabolic rate of the tissues, quite apart from any steps taken to restrict the loss of heat —physical thermoregulation—or to increase the heat production in response to cold—chemical thermoregulation. Benedict has argued that the hibernant is to be regarded as an intermediate stage between poikilothermy and homoiothermy ; certainly the basal metabolism of the marmot is less than that of other, normal, homoiotherms (Fig. 81), but, as we shall see, this is not by any means true of all hibernants and it is probably better to regard the hibernant as a perfect homoiotherm which adapts itself to poikilothermy during the winter months to save the caloric expenditure associated with maintaining a high body-temperature when food is scarce.

Hibernants

Certain species, notably the wood-chuck or marmot (*Arctomys monax*), the squirrel, dormouse, hamster, etc., spend the winter in a state of what may be described as suspended animation. For several months they become torpid, and live entirely on their reserves of fat ; such a lengthy fast could not be maintained if the basal metabolism under these conditions were the same as that in their waking state. Thus a 3 kg. marmot in the waking state produces about 90 Calories per 24 hours, equivalent to the oxidation of about 10 g. of fat. In 100 days it would therefore lose 1 kg. in weight, *i.e.*, a third of its body-weight. It is therefore not surprising to find that the heat production sinks to very low values under these conditions, so low that the hibernating animal becomes very similar to, but not identical with, the poikilotherm, its body-temperature falling precipitately, but not generally to the environmental level.

In the cold weather, after food has become scarce, the marmot burrows underground below the " frost line " ; there it enters its state of torpor and may remain, with one or two awakenings for the purpose of micturition, etc., until the Spring. Laboratory studies show that the torpid condition, with low rectal temperature, is not achieved at once, but may take days. The animal may become lethargic one day with a rectal temperature of perhaps 25° C., only to recover its activity and temperature for a period of hours ; this process may be repeated several times until the true condition of hibernation sets in, when the rectal temperature falls consistently until it is only 1–3° C. above that of the environment. The changes in heat production are just as striking ; at an environmental temperature of, say, 10° C. the resting heat production of the non-hibernating marmot is high, as a result of chemical regulation—of the order of 1,500 Cal./m.^{2}/24 hr. During the process of hibernating, the heat production falls continuously to reach a level which may be as low as 17 Cal./m.^{2}/24 hr. ; this is a minimum value and the average is of the order of 27 Calories. In extreme cases, therefore, the heat production may fall by a factor of 70 or more. In the hibernating state, therefore, the marmot is a cold-blooded animal, but it differs in several respects from the true poikilotherm. In the first place its rectal temperature is always 1–3° C. above that of the environment. Secondly, the heat production, whether computed on a weight or surface-area basis, is considerably higher. For example, the snake, with a rectal temperature of 9° C., has a heat production of 8 Calories/m.², whereas that of the marmot lies between 25 and 30 Calories. Finally, whilst the poikilotherm's rectal temperature passively follows that of the environment, there is some evidence that the marmot, even in its torpid condition, shows some chemical regulation, a physiological mechanism called into play to prevent freezing. Thus at an environmental temperature of 0·9° C. the heat production of a marmot was 130 Calories ; on raising the temperature to 3·0° C. the heat production fell to 70 Calories.

The process of awakening from hibernation is rapid. The stimulus applied in the laboratory was generally to raise the environmental temperature to 28° C., or to apply an electric shock to the animal. The rectal temperature may increase by nearly 20° C. in an hour ; corresponding with this rapid rise in temperature there is an explosive outburst of heat production which may reach 3,000 Cal./m.²/24 hr. This peak metabolism may be maintained for half-an-hour, after which the animal subsides gradually into its basal rate.

The marmot is the only hibernant whose heat production, during all phases of its annual cycle, has been studied at all thoroughly ; the heat production during the non-hibernating phase of a number of other species has been investigated by Kayser. The results on the hamster, hedgehog, ground squirrel, and dormouse, among others, show the same general picture—namely the essentially homoiothermal character of the hibernant in the waking state. As with the marmot, however, the rectal temperature

TABLE VII

Basal Metabolic Rates of Various Hibernants Measured at 27–29·5° C.
(Kayser, 1939.)

Species	Marmot	Hedge-hog	Hamster	Squirrel	Dormouse (Loir)	Dormouse (Lérot)	Dormouse (Muscardine)	Bat
Cal./m.²/24 hr.	392	740	684	660	527	696	832	167

was not so stable as that of the non-hibernating species ; thus fluctuations of as much as 5° C. were recorded with the hamster. A point brought out by Kayser's studies was the steep slope of thermogenesis (p. 123) of the waking hibernants, *i.e.*, the comparatively large increases in heat production brought about by lowering the environmental temperature. One must conclude, therefore, that the hibernants in the waking state consume energy at an extravagant rate in the cold, presumably as a result of defective physical regulation. We have computed that the marmot should lose 1 kg. of weight in 100 days by living on its fat reserves ; this calculation, however, was made on the basis of the *basal metabolism* at thermal neutrality ; at an environmental temperature of 5° C. the heat production would be at least four times this, making an impossible demand on the fat reserves.

The basal heat productions of some hibernants in the waking state are shown in Table VII ; it will be seen that, with the exception of the marmot and bat, they fall within the normal range for non-hibernants.

The hibernants so far described are imperfect homoiotherms in the waking state ; the bat, on the other hand, can be described as essentially a poikilotherm all the year round, in the sense that its rectal temperature at rest follows the environmental temperature fairly closely, the response to a fall in the latter being, as with the poikilotherm, a fall in heat production. At a temperature of 27° C., the heat production is, on the average, 162 Cal./m.^{2}/24 hr., a figure only about a quarter of that given by Chevillard for the white mouse of comparable weight, but considerably above that for a true poikilotherm like the frog (41 Calories) ; the bat, moreover, can increase, by activity, its heat production so as to be comparable with a homoiotherm of equal weight, a figure of 728 Calories having been recorded at an environmental temperature of 5° C. on one occasion ; the same animal, at the same temperature, gave a heat production of only 12 Calories on another day.

General Remarks on Hibernation. The high level of vital activity characteristic of the homoiotherm requires a correspondingly high level of energy transformation which, as we have seen, leads to a necessarily high heat production ; this, in turn, permits the maintenance of the high and relatively constant temperature necessary for the rapid vital processes. The high level of energy transformation requires, of course, a suitable supply of metabolic material, so that the homoiotherm requires a much larger supply than the poikilotherm ; this becomes especially manifest at low environmental temperatures. The poikilotherm is thus better off in this one respect, but the disadvantage imposed by the torpid condition that follows from a low environmental temperature more than offsets this advantage. The hibernant is best regarded, therefore, as a type that has realised the advantages of homoiothermy and has developed the means for maintaining a constant blood-temperature in the face of very cold conditions if necessary. The difficulty of providing food for the winter, however,—the main problem for the homoiotherm—is overcome by the simple expedient of reducing the energy requirements by abandoning homoiothermy. In its hibernating state, nevertheless, the animal is by no means a perfect poikilotherm—except perhaps the bat ; the body is allowed to cool, but chemical regulation is called into play to prevent complete freezing ; and, although the hibernating animal is described as torpid and stiff, it differs from a snake in similar circumstances in that it can rapidly resume its high temperature by setting off an explosive burst of heat production. This may be brought about by an electrical stimulus, and recent studies suggest that even a noise is adequate to arouse the hibernating marmot. The exact physiological mechanisms involved in the transition from homoiothermy to the hibernating condition have aroused considerable speculation but they are still a mystery ; it is beyond the province of this section to discuss the various findings and we may simply emphasise the most striking characteristic of the hibernant, which is its ability to withstand degrees of hypothermia that would be fatal to other warm-blooded animals. Whether this is a characteristic of its individual tissues, or of their organisation, cannot yet be stated with confidence. The fact that the torpid marmot responds to sounds might suggest a difference in the characteristics of its nerves ; and this seems to be borne out by the recent investigations of Chatfield *et al.* who showed that, whereas the rat's isolated nerve failed to conduct at 9° C., that of the hamster failed at 3·4° C., *i.e.*, the body-temperature at which the hamster initiates chemical regulation to prevent any further cooling.

Physical Thermoregulation

In considering chemical thermoregulation the emphasis has naturally been on *heat production* ; by physical thermoregulation we mean the mechanisms available to the animal for modifying the *heat loss*. In general, heat may be lost by radiation, convection and the evaporation of water ; not all these avenues of heat loss will necessarily be open under any set of environmental conditions. Over any given period the heat produced by metabolism (M), will be equal to the heat lost by radiation (R), convection (C), and evaporative processes (E), provided that the total heat content of the animal remains the same. This proviso is by no means always fulfilled during changes in environmental conditions, so that we may introduce a *heat storage* term (S), which represents the balance of heat gains and losses, and is a measure of the hypo- or hyperthermia of the animal. Conventionally a negative value of S means a net gain of heat. The First Law may therefore be expressed thus :—

$$M \pm S - E \pm R \pm C = O, \text{ where M is always positive.}$$

If we regard an animal merely as a hot body, without any specially developed physiological mechanisms for dissipating or retaining heat, we can see that the loss of heat will be to some extent regulated by environmental and internal conditions. The animal continually produces heat at such a rate that the body-temperature is normally above that of the ambient air ; heat is lost from the surface, so that the skin-temperature is less than the blood-temperature ; and there is thus a gradient of temperature between the deeper parts and the surface ; the depth over which this gradient extends varies with different parts of the body and is about 25 mm. on the average. Between the surface of the skin and the bulk of the ambient air there is a layer of comparatively still air, so that the drop in temperature on passing from skin to the outer air is not abrupt. By a temperature gradient we mean the difference in temperature divided by the distance over which this takes place ; since the rate of loss of heat by conduction through a medium depends on the magnitude of the *temperature gradient*, the smaller the gradient the less the rate of loss of heat by this method ; an increase in the thickness of this layer of air will therefore tend to restrict heat losses ; consequently a hairy or feathery skin, in so far as it maintains a thick layer of comparatively motionless air, is a factor favouring the retention of heat.

An increase in heat production must raise the body-temperature and this, in turn, means a rise in skin-temperature ; the loss of heat by convection and radiation from the surface is given by Newton's Equation :—

$$\text{Rate of Heat Loss} = K_o (T_s - T_o)$$

where T_s is the skin-temperature and T_o the temperature of the surroundings, assuming that the ambient air has the same temperature as that of the various objects in the environment. A rise of skin-temperature must therefore increase the rate of loss of heat by these mechanisms. Furthermore, an increase in skin-temperature must increase the evaporation from the surface of the body—the insensible perspiration—and therefore facilitate the dissipation of heat. Increased heat production, as in exercise, therefore carries with it, to some extent at least, the means for dissipating it. An increase in environmental temperature, on the other hand, tends to decrease the heat lost by radiation and convection ; the consequent rise in skin-temperature, however, tends to modify the temperature gradient and compensate in some measure for the less favourable conditions of heat dissipation ; moreover, the raised skin-temperature increases the rate of evaporation and so permits a more efficient neutralisation of the hyperthermia. When the environmental temperature becomes equal to the body-temperature, the skin-temperature becomes equal to that of the body, too, and there is no gradient between body and ambient air. Heat loss in this case is therefore entirely by evaporation ; this factor thus becomes of more and more importance as the environmental temperature increases.

Physiological Mechanisms. We may now ask how physiological mechanisms may operate to increase or decrease the heat loss. First we may consider the thermal gradient between the skin and the deeper tissues ; if this gradient is steep, *i.e.*, if the depth of tissue over which the fall in temperature occurs is small, the rate of loss will be more rapid than if the gradient is shallow. Physiologically the gradient may be altered by a modification in the flow of blood through the peripheral tissues ; an increased flow tends to bring the region, at which body-temperature prevails, closer to the skin, and thus steepens the gradient. In general, the characteristic of the peripheral tissues that permits them to lose heat through the surface of the skin is described as the *skin conductance* ; and it is found that it varies under different conditions according as the body must lose or retain heat to maintain thermal equilibrium. Theoretically the conductance is made up of two parts ; the flow of blood through the skin, f, and conductance through the flesh along the gradient between the body- and skin-temperatures. We may speak of the specific conductance, c, of the tissue through which the heat must pass as a fairly definite quantity, depending on the nature of the tissue ; it is essentially a characteristic of the dead animal and is not considered to vary considerably with the skin-temperature. The total conductance is given by :—

$$f + c/d = \text{Total Conductance, where } d \text{ is the depth of the gradient.}$$

A special instance of the development of this power to shunt blood from the central to the peripheral regions is given by the large ears of the rabbit ; it is thought, also, that the externalisation of the testes is a development facilitating thermoregulation on similar lines.

In animals with hairy or feathered coats another mode of physical regulation consists in modifying the insulating layer of air in contact with the skin. By fluffing up the hair or feathers the depth of the temperature gradient between skin and ambient air is increased, and the rate of loss of heat reduced. Baldwin & Kendleigh, by preventing a bird from fluffing its feathers, caused it to go into hypothermia at an environmental temperature of 10° C., whereas it normally supported much lower temperatures ; again, Giaja showed that the pigeon, similarly restricted, increased its heat production by 3·2 per cent. per degree drop in environmental temperature as against 2·2 per cent. normally, *i.e.*, more chemical regulation was required to combat the cold when its means of physical regulation were confined. The nude human can make little use of this mechanism, but of course in everyday life the donning of more clothes in winter is essentially a matter of increasing the depth of the external temperature gradient.

The importance of loss of heat by evaporation has already been stressed ; in the human subject this must vary passively with the skin-temperature ; and we have seen how the latter may be varied by alterations in the flow of blood to the skin. Two other physiological mechanisms are available, moreover ; first by increasing the contribution of the lungs and respiratory passages, as exemplified by the panting of a dog or chicken —according to Shelley & Hemingway the heat lost by evaporation may be increased by a factor of 8–10 through panting—and secondly by the increase in the water available for evaporation from the surface of the body, namely sweating, as typically seen in man and the horse. Besides utilising these main physiological mechanisms, the animal may reduce its total effective area by curling itself up ; the different postures of a cat asleep on a hot and a cold day exhibit this tendency.

Studies on Man. Physical regulation is most suitably studied in the reactions of the nude human to changed external conditions of temperature and humidity. Winslow, Herrington & Gagge and Hardy, Milhorat & DuBois have made exhaustive studies on these lines. The former group developed the technique of *partitional calorimetry*, by which they could analyse the contributions of radiation, convection and evaporation to the exchanges of heat with the environment ; they then proceeded to develop the concept of *standard operative temperature*, a fictitious environmental temperature which makes allowance for a difference between the temperatures of the ambient air and surrounding objects.[1] Fig. 85 shows

---

[1] The rate of loss of heat is given by the Newton Equation : Rate = $K_o (T_s - T_a)$, where T_s is the skin-temperature and T_a the temperature of the ambient air. If the walls of the room have a temperature different from T_a this equation does not necessarily apply, but the rate of cooling is given by an equation of the same form with T_a replaced by a fictitious temperature, T_o, the *standard operative temperature*. T_o is a measure of the thermal demands of the environment, and the constant, K_o, the *environmental constant*, may be computed from the skin-temperature and the radiation

the result of an experiment ; here heat production, heat storage (a positive value means cooling), heat lost by evaporation, and the interchanges of heat by radiation and convection, are plotted against operative temperature. We may note first the striking constancy of the metabolic rate, in spite of a wide variation in the operative temperature ; thus, below about 28° C., the heat storage was positive, *i.e.*, the subject was chilling yet there was no increase in heat production to make up for it. At operative temperatures above about 35° C., heat is gained by the subject

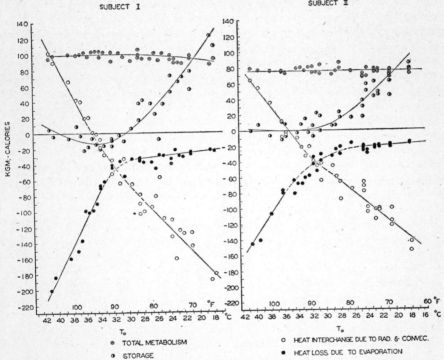

Fɪɢ. 85. Heat interchange for stout (1) and slender (2) subject, at varying operative temperatures (T_o). (Winslow, Herrington & Gagge. *Amer. J. Physiol.*)

from his environment, and we may note a steep rise in the rate of evaporative heat loss in this region, the absence of significant heat storage in this zone showing how well the evaporative heat loss is adjusted to the thermal demands of the subject.

At the lower operative temperatures, the body loses heat by three paths, and the evaporative loss tends to a minimum value of 31 Cal./m.²/hr. Studies of the skin-temperature show that it is essentially the fall in this quantity that permits the reduction of evaporative loss ; the skin-temperature, indeed, follows the operative temperature fairly closely in

and convection constants of the subject. By the radiation constant is meant the constant in the Stefan Equation : Rate of Loss by Radiation = $k_R A_R (T_s{}^4 - T_w{}^4)$ where A_R is the effective radiation area and T_w is the wall-temperature. The convection constant is given by the equation : Rate of Loss by Convection = $k_C V (T_s - T_a)$, where V is the velocity of air-movement.

the lower temperature regions, a differential of about 4° C. being maintained. When the skin-temperature reaches about 31–32° C., however, sweating begins ; and the rapid rise in evaporative heat loss, so occasioned, permits the skin-temperature to remain more or less constant at this value. On plotting the conductance of the peripheral tissues against skin-temperature, a steep rise is observed between 34° and 36° C., which corresponds fairly closely with the steep rise in evaporative heat loss. It would certainly appear that the rise in skin-temperature is the stimulus for the secretion of sweat and, presumably, also for the change in peripheral blood flow that causes the increased conductance of the skin.

The loss of heat at high environmental temperatures depends mainly on evaporation and consequently on the relative humidity. Thus with a relative humidity of 0 per cent., man at rest can withstand a temperature of 45·3° C. or 113·5° F. ; at 100 per cent. humidity this limit falls to 32·5° C. or 90·1° F. Whilst carrying out work, when the heat production may be increased several-fold, the powers to withstand climatic extremes are considerably reduced ; nevertheless the same physical regulatory processes are brought into play with equal nicety so that the skin-temperature remains remarkably constant. Secretion of sweat begins at a much lower skin-temperature, 20° C. instead of 30° C., and in summer the " trigger mechanism " is set off at even lower temperatures—about 16° C. In general, the rectal temperature shows an increase of 1° C., being 37·6° C. compared with 36·6–36·9° C. at rest.

In the laboratory of the Russell-Sage Institute, DuBois and his collaborators have made essentially similar studies, on nude human subjects, to those of Winslow, Herrington & Gagge. The basal metabolism of the men remained constant at 35 Cal./m.^{2}/hr. over a range of temperature extending from 22–35° C., a result confirming the absence of chemical regulation. With women, on the other hand, there was a definite fall in heat production—from 35 to 30·9 Calories—as the environmental temperature rose from 27 to 31° C., indicating an unmistakable chemical regulation, taking the form of a reduced heat production to combat the high environmental temperature. As with men, however, there was no evidence of chemical regulation at low environmental temperatures ; basal metabolism remained constant until the actual onset of chill with shivering.

References

BALDWIN & KENDLEIGH (1932). Sci. Pub. Cleveland Mus. Nat. Hist. III. (Quoted by Giaja.)

BENEDICT, F. G. (1932). " Physiology of Large Reptiles." Carneg. Inst. Wash., Rept. 425.

BENEDICT, F. G. (1936). " Physiology of the Elephant." Carneg. Inst. Wash., Rept. 474.

BENEDICT, F. G. (1938). " Vital Energetics." Carneg. Inst. Wash., Rept. 503.

BENEDICT, F. G. & LEE, R. C. (1937). " Hibernation and Marmot Physiology." Carneg. Inst. Wash., Rept. 497.

BOOTHBY, W. M., BERKSON, J. & DUNN, H. L. (1936). " A Standard for Basal Metabolism, with a Nomogram for Clinical Applications." *Amer. J. Physiol.*, 116, 468.

BRODY, S. (1945). " Bioenergetics and Growth." N.Y., Reinhold.

BURTON, A. C. (1934). "Application of the Theory of Heat Flow to the Study of Energy Metabolism." *J. Nutr.*, 7, 497.

BURTON, A. C. (1939). "Temperature Regulation." *Ann. Rev. Physiol.*, 1, 109.

BURTON, A. C. & BRONK, D. W. (1937). "Motor Mechanism of Shivering and of Thermal Muscular Tone." *Amer. J. Physiol.*, 119, 284.

CHATFIELD, P. O., BATTISTA, A. F., LYMAN, C. P. & GARCIN, J. P. (1948). "Effect of Cooling on Nerve Conduction in a Hibernator and Non-Hibernator." *Amer. J. Physiol.*, 155, 179.

DuBOIS, D. & DuBOIS, E. F. (1915). "Clinical Calorimetry." V. *Arch. int. Med.*, 15, 868.

DuBOIS, E. F. (1927). "Basal Metabolism in Health and Disease." Philadelphia Lea & Febiger,.

DuBOIS, E. F. (1948). "Fever and the Regulation of Body Temperature." Publ. No. 13. American Lecture Series, Illinois.

FEDOROV, N. A. & SHUR, E. I. (1942). "Role of the Viscera in Regulating the Temperature, etc." *Amer. J. Physiol.*, 137, 30.

FIELD, J., BELDING, H. S. & MARTIN, A. W. (1939). "Analysis of the Relation between Basal Metabolism and Summated Tissue Respiration in the Rat." *J. cell. & comp. Physiol.*, 14, 143.

GAGGE, A. P. (1937). "A New Physiological Variable Associated with Sensible and Insensible Perspiration." *Amer. J. Physiol.*, 120, 133.

GAGGE, A. P. (1940). "Standard Operative Temperature, a Generalised Temperature Scale, Applicable to Direct and Partitional Calorimetry." *Amer. J. Physiol.*, 131, 93.

GIAJA, J. (1938). "L'Homéothermie." Actualités Scientifiques et Industrielles. Paris, Hermann.

GIAJA, J. (1938). "La Thermorégulation." Actualités Scientifiques et Industrielles. Paris., Hermann.

GRAFE, E., REINWEIN, H. & SINGER (1925). "Die Atmung der Überlebenden Warmblüterorgane."

HARDY, J. D., MILHORAT, A. T. & DuBOIS, E. F. (1941). "Basal Metabolism and Heat Loss of Young Women at Temperatures from 22° to 35° C." *J. Nutr.*, 21, 383.

HARDY, J. D. & SODERSTROM, G. F. (1938). "Heat Loss from the Nude Body and Peripheral Blood Flow at Temperatures of 22° C. to 35° C." *J. Nutr.*, 16, 493.

HATERIUS, H. O. & MAISON, G. I. (1948). "Recovery after Severe Reduction in Body Temperature." *Amer. J. Physiol.*, 152, 225.

HEMINGWAY, A. & HATHAWAY, S. R. (1941). "An Investigation of Chemical Temperature Regulation." *Amer. J. Physiol.*, 134, 596.

HERRINGTON, L. P. (1940). "Heat Regulation of Small Laboratory Animals at Various Environmental Temperatures." *Amer. J. Physiol.*, 129, 123.

HILL, R. M. (1947). "Control of Body Temperature in White Rats." *Amer. J. Physiol.*, 149, 650.

HORVATH, S. M., HITCHCOCK, F. A. & HARTMAN, F. A. (1938). "Response to Cold after Reduction of Adrenal Tissue." *Amer. J. Physiol.*, 121, 178.

KAYSER, C. (1939). "Hibernating and Non-Hibernating Animals. Basal Metabolic Rate and Temperature Changes." *Ann. Physiol. Physico-chim. Biol.*, 15, 1087.

KENDEIGH, S. C. (1939). "Relation of Metabolism to Development of Temperature Regulation in Birds." *J. exp. Zool.*, 82, 419.

KENDEIGH, S. C. (1944). "Effect of Air Temperature on Rate of Energy Metabolism in the English Sparrow." *J. exp. Zool.*, 96, 1.

KLEIBER, M. (1941). "Body Size and Metabolism of Liver Slices *In Vitro*." *P.S.E.B.M.*, 48, 419.

KLEIBER, M. (1947). "Body Size and Metabolic Rate." *Physiol. Rev.*, 27, 511.

KREBS, H. A. (1950). "Body Size and Tissue Respiration." *Biochim. Biophys. Acta*, 4, 249.

KROGH, A. (1914). "Quantitative Relation between Temperature and Standard Metabolism in Animals." *Int. Z. f. physiol.-chem. Biol.*, 1, 491.

LAVOISIER & SÉGUIN (1920). "Mémoires sur la Respiration et la Transpiration des Animaux." (Quoted by Giaja.)

LEE, R. C. (1942). "Heat Production of the Rabbit at 28° C. as Affected by Previous Adaptation to Temperatures between 10° and 31° C." *J. Nutr.*, 23, 83.

LEE, R. C., COLOVOS, N. F. & RITZMAN, E. G. (1941). "Skin Temperatures of the Pig, Goat and Sheep under Winter Conditions." *J. Nutr.* 21, 321.

LYMAN, C. P. (1948). "O_2-Consumption and Temperature Regulation of Hibernating Hamsters." *J. exp. Zool.*, 109, 55.

MARTIN, C. J. (1903). "Thermal Adjustments and Respiratory Exchange in Monotremes and Marsupials." *Phil. Trans.*, 195, 1.

MARTIN, C. J. (1930). "Thermal Adjustments of Man and Animals to External Conditions." *Lancet*, 1930 (2), 561, 617, 673.

McGLONE, B. & BAZETT, H. C. (1927). "Temperature Gradients in the Tissues in Man." *Amer. J. Physiol.*, 82, 415.

McGLONE, B. & BAZETT, H. C. (1927). "Temperature of the Air in Contact with the Skin." *Amer. J. Physiol.*, 82, 452.

MEEH, K. (1879). "Oberflächenmessungen des Menschlichen Körpers." *Z. Biol.*, 15, 425.

MORRISON, P. R. (1946). "Temperature Regulation in Three Central American Mammals." *J. cell. & comp. Physiol.*, 27, 125.

MORRISON, P. R. (1948). "O_2-Consumption in Several Mammals under Basal Conditions." *J. cell. & comp. Physiol.*, 31, 281.

ODUM, E. P. (1942). "Muscle Tremors and the Development of Temperature Regulation in Birds." *Amer. J. Physiol.*, 136, 618.

RANDALL, W. C. & HIESTAND, W. A. (1939). "Panting and Temperature Regulation in the Chicken." *Amer. J. Physiol.*, 127, 761.

ROBINSON, S., TURRELL, E. S. & GERKING, S. D. (1945). "Physiologically Equivalent Conditions of Air Temperature and Humidity." *Amer. J. Physiol.*, 143, 21.

SHELLEY, W. B. & HEMINGWAY, A. (1940). "Effects of Thermal Polypnœa on the Energy Metabolism, RQ, and Water Loss of Dogs." *Amer. J. Physiol.*, 129, 623.

SIMPSON, S. & HERRING, P. T. (1905). "Effect of Cold Narcosis on Reflex Action in Warm-Blooded Animals." *J. Physiol.*, 32, 305.

TERROINE, E. F. & ROCHE, J. (1925). "Production Calorique des Homéothermes et Intensité de la Respiration *In Vitro* des Tissus Homologues." *Arch. int. Physiol.*, 24, 356.

VELTEN, W. (1880). "Uber Oxydation im Warmblüter bei Subnormalen Temperaturen." *Pflüg. Arch.*, 21, 361.

WARDLAW, H. S. H. (1918). "Note on the Temperature of *Echidna Aculeata*." *Proc. Linn. Soc. N.S.W.*, 43, 844.

WARE, A. G., HILL, R. M. & SCHULTZ, F. H. (1947). "Effect of Interference with Respiration in the Control of Body Temperature in White Rats and New Zealand Rabbits." *Amer. J. Physiol.*, 149, 657.

WINSLOW, C. E. A. & GAGGE, A. P. (1941). "Influence of Physical Work on Physiological Reactions to the Thermal Environment." *Amer. J. Physiol.*, 134, 664.

WINSLOW, C. E. A. & HERRINGTON, L. P. (1949). "Temperature and Human Life." Princeton Univ. Press.

WINSLOW, C. E. A., HERRINGTON, L. P. & GAGGE, A. P. (1936). "A New Method of Partitional Calorimetry." *Amer. J. Physiol.*, 116, 641.

WINSLOW, C. E. A., HERRINGTON, L. P. & GAGGE, A. P. (1936). "Determination of Radiation and Convection Exchanges by Partitional Calorimetry." *Amer. J. Physiol.*, 116, 669.

WINSLOW, C. E. A., HERRINGTON, L. P. & GAGGE, A. P. (1937). "Physiological Reactions of the Human Body to Varying Environmental Temperatures." *Amer. J. Physiol.*, 120, 1.

WINSLOW, C. E. A., HERRINGTON, L. P. & GAGGE, A. P. (1937). "Physiological Reactions of the Human Body to Various Atmospheric Humidities." *Amer. J. Physiol.*, 120, 288.

CHAPTER VII

SIMPLE EQUILIBRIA

FROM a structural point of view we have regarded the cell as the fundamental unit ; this viewpoint is borne out by the chemical analysis of a variety of cells, and tissues made up of aggregations of similar cells, which reveals that the internal composition is fundamentally different from that of the medium surrounding them (*see, e.g.*, Table XVIII). Thus the *Arbacia* egg differs from its surrounding sea-water in containing a much higher concentration of K^+ and a lower concentration of Na^+ ; and in containing numerous organic compounds absent from the sea-water. The erythrocyte contains a protein, hæmoglobin, absent from the surrounding plasma, and so on. The existence of these two fundamentally different media, the *internal* and the *external environments* of the cell, implies the existence of a separating membrane, since the media are both aqueous and would otherwise mix. Moreover, the cell, being the seat of chemical reactions which derive their energy, in the last analysis, from oxidative chemical reactions, this membrane must permit the transport of materials from external to internal environment and *vice versâ*. At the same time, in order to maintain this fundamentally different internal environment, this membrane must exhibit a certain selectivity, in the sense that the passage of some molecules must be favoured in preference to that of others. In the present section we shall consider the general problems involved in the transport of materials in the organism. In the unicellular protozöon this transport implies only the passage across the limiting membranes ; in the more complex organism it implies, besides this, the transport of material from one part of it to another, a process that is achieved by the circulation of fluid—blood—through some sort of vascular system ; where the circulating fluid is enclosed within vessels, transport implies the migration of material out of these vessels and thence, by way of an interstitial fluid, into the cells. Alternatively, we shall also have to consider the absorption of material from the external environment, the absorbed material passing first through cells and then being passed on to the blood stream.

The general problem of transport is therefore of very wide scope so that, to bring its discussion within the compass of this book, we must confine it to certain specific aspects. We shall therefore consider first some simple equilibria between the cell and its environment, since it is only by understanding the equilibrium state of affairs adequately that we can hope to interpret the phenomena of transport which involve adjustments of a system to a disturbance of equilibrium. We may next pass to the mechanism whereby materials pass across membranes, and attempt to deduce the nature of the membrane capable of imposing the observed restraints ; having considered this aspect, we may return to some more complex equilibria involving the Gibbs-Donnan distribution, such as the formation and circulation of the interstitial fluid ; this will take us to a consideration of a more specialised tissue fluid—the cerebro-spinal fluid —and we will thus be led to the problem of *secretion,* or *active transport.* Since this form of transport is predominantly associated with the migration of ions, we shall have to consider some salt equilibria in relation to electrical potentials, and we will then be in a position to analyse the significance of the phenomena of secretion of ions by the erythrocyte, muscle, and nerve. More general aspects of secretion involved in the function of the intestine, gastric mucosa and kidney may then be entered into ; and, finally, the general problem of osmotic regulation in certain animals may be briefly discussed. Before entering into the simple physico-chemical theory of equilibrium, we may conveniently take a brief glance at some of the biological phenomena we wish to explain.

Simple Osmotic Phenomena

If a drop of blood, which consists predominantly of a suspension of erythrocytes in a clear fluid—the plasma—is mixed with about 10 ml. of water, the resultant mixture is clear and transparent, and on examining it microscopically no cells are observed. It is clear that the water has, in some way " dissolved," or destroyed, the erythrocytes. If, on the other hand, a drop of blood is added to a 1 per cent. NaCl solution, the resulting mixture is not clear but turbid, and under the microscope the cells are clearly visible. The opacity of the mixture is obviously due to the scattering of light by the individual cells. If the blood is placed in rather more dilute solutions of NaCl, *e.g.,* 0·9 per cent., 0·8 per cent., 0·7 per cent., etc., it is found that in the region of 0·5 per cent. the opacity of the mixture is definitely less than with the 1 per cent. solution ; and with a still more dilute solution, say 0·4 per cent., the effect is the same as with distilled water, *i.e.,* a clear solution is obtained with no cells observable microscopically. If the concentration of NaCl is increased above 1 per cent. the cells remain intact but tend to become " crenated " and shrunken. This experiment shows that there is a definite concentration of NaCl below which erythrocytes are unstable when added to it. If, instead of NaCl, a solution of glucose is used, the same phenomena are observed, but this time the limit of concentration below which destruction, or *hæmolysis,* of the cells takes place is much higher, about 2·6 per cent. ; with sucrose the limiting concentration is about twice this. If, however, glycerol is taken as the dissolved substance we observe a new phenomenon ; on adding the blood to a 3 per cent. solution of this substance the resulting mixture is opaque, but after a minute or so—in the case of human blood and much later in the case of beef blood—it is noticed that the mixture rapidly becomes less opaque and eventually becomes as clear as though the blood had been added to distilled water. If the concentration of glycerol is increased, to say 6 per cent., it is found that the period during which the mixture remains opaque is increased but that the same ultimate result is achieved, namely complete hæmolysis ; further increases in the concentration of glycerol merely lengthen the period of opacity but do not alter the final state of the mixture. If ethylene glycol or urea is used instead of glycerol, the same phenomena are observed but the periods of opacity are much shorter, being, in the case of human blood, a matter of five or six seconds. On microscopical observation of the blood suspension, obtained immediately after mixing a drop of blood with 3 per cent. glycerol solution, individual cells are seen to disappear from view until finally none are left.

Substances may thus be placed in two classes in respect to the behaviour of their aqueous solutions to erythrocytes ; Class I, those which, in concentrations above a certain value, allow the cells to retain their existence, *e.g.*, NaCl, glucose, etc., and Class II, those which, whatever their concentration, cause hæmolysis with greater or less delay, *e.g.*, glycerol, urea, etc.

The blood contains a small proportion of cells other than the erythrocytes, the *leucocytes* ; in an ordinary blood suspension these are difficult to detect, and for experimental purposes it is convenient to obtain them in larger quantities, free from red cells, by injecting into the peritoneal cavity of a rabbit about one litre of 1 per cent. NaCl solution. On withdrawing what remains of this fluid some twenty-four hours later, it is found to be milky in appearance and to contain large numbers of leucocytes, mainly polymorphs. If we carry out the same experiments on these cells, essentially the same phenomena are manifest. On observing them, in 0·4 per cent. NaCl under the microscope, they are seen to increase in diameter as time progresses until they suddenly become indistinct ; the same swelling is seen to happen in ethylene glycol solution, although more slowly ; and it would seem that the destruction of the cells, caused by distilled water, very weak NaCl, or by ethylene glycol solution, is due to a swelling in the same way that a balloon bursts on too great distention. In the erythrocytes, no such swelling was observable under the microscope, but the strong similarity in behaviour in these solutions suggests that the same cause was in operation ; in actuality it may easily be proved that the destruction of the erythrocyte in distilled water, or in glycerol solution, is preceded by a considerable engorgement, but this swelling is not observable under the microscope owing to the disk-like shape of this cell (p. 161) ; the leucocyte, being a sphere, shows up changes in its volume by changes in its diameter, and thus allows the swelling to be seen microscopically.

By carefully measuring the diameters of a number of leucocytes with an ocular micrometer, an average size of the cells may be obtained ; if, now, drops of the milky white cell suspension are added to different concentrations of NaCl, say 2·0 per cent., 1·8 per cent., 1·6 per cent., etc., it is found that the average diameters of the cells in the different suspensions are progressively larger ; at one definite concentration, in the region of 0·9 per cent., they have the same average diameter as that of the cells in the original suspension. On placing a drop of this original suspension in the rabbit's own blood plasma, obtained by centrifuging away the cells, it is found that the average diameter is the same once again. The concentration of NaCl that gives no change in volume of the cell, from that pertaining normally, is often defined as the *isotonic concentration*, but, as we shall see later, this definition must be modified. Concentrations below and above the isotonic concentration are called *hypotonic* and *hypertonic* respectively.

Another subject, widely used in the study of osmotic exchanges, is the sea-urchin egg. If, during the breeding season, a female sea-urchin, *e.g.*, *Arbacia punctulata*, is cut open by an equatorial incision, the ovaries are seen to be engorged with eggs ; on scraping these gently into sea-water, allowing to stand,. and filtering through muslin, a concentrated suspension of the eggs in sea-water may be obtained. Under the microscope they appear perfect spheres with a diameter of about 75μ. Essentially similar phenomena may be demonstrated with these eggs as with the leucocyte ; the swelling which takes place in distilled water is slower but it leads to the destruction of the cell ; with NaCl solutions of different concentrations, varying degrees of swelling or shrinkage may be elicited. When the concentration of NaCl is about 3 per cent., *i.e.*, about three times greater than in the case of the leucocyte, the volume remains the same as in sea-water, the natural environment of the eggs ; hence, in this case, the isotonic concentration is about 3 per cent. of NaCl (ca. 0·5 M.).[1]

These are just a few, and perhaps the simplest, of the phenomena which an understanding of the general principles of diffusion and osmosis allows us to interpret ; other, and more complicated phenomena, will be discussed later in this and succeeding chapters.

Some Properties of Solutions

The Mixing of Solutions. Suppose we have two separate solutions of glucose, A and B, of different concentrations, 2M and 1M respectively, placed side by side and separated by a porous diaphragm which permits the ready exchange of water and dissolved substances through it. We know by experience that after the lapse of sufficient time the two solutions will have the same concentration, which will be intermediate between the two initial values, its actual value being dependent on the relative volumes of the two solutions.

This mixing is brought about simply as a result of the random motions of the individual molecules composing the two solutions. If the molecules had no independent motions the two solutions would retain their initial concentrations, just as, when two solids are placed together, no mixing occurs. If we look more closely into the exact mechanism of the mixing, we may separate it ideally into two parts, one due to the random motions of the solute (glucose) molecules, and one to the motions of the solvent (water) molecules. Both factors aid in the mixing, since the migration of water from the more dilute into the more concentrated solution dilutes the

---

[1] With fresh-water organisms, *e.g.*, the trout or salmon, where the natural environment of the shed egg is so dilute as almost to be equivalent to distilled water, it is found, as we might expect on biological grounds, that the eggs, taken from the ovary, do not swell up and burst in distilled water ; in fact trout and salmon eggs appear to be quite immune to changes in the salt content of their environment. This is due to the fact that water cannot penetrate the eggs.

latter and concentrates the former. This migration of water, or solvent, from a solution of low, to one of high, concentration is called *osmosis* ; the mechanism is not essentially different from that of diffusion of solute, but the osmotic process is generally more obvious, in that the movement of water causes an increase in volume of the aqueous solution to which it migrates, whereas the migration of solute molecules makes very little change.

Osmosis, Osmotic Pressure, Ultra-Filtration. In most calculations on the rate of diffusion of a solute, the effect of the second factor in the mixing process, viz., osmosis of solvent, is generally neglected and the process is formally considered as one of simple diffusion of solute alone ; nevertheless it must be remembered that osmosis is a factor, not very important perhaps when mixing can take place by diffusion of solute, but of supreme importance when a restraint is placed on the movement of solute molecules. Thus if, instead of separating the solutions A and B by a completely porous diaphragm, we interpose a membrane, permeable only to water molecules, between the two solutions, the mixing process will be limited now to the osmosis of water, but the end result will be very nearly the

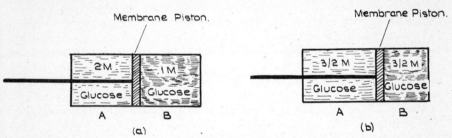

FIG. 86. Illustrating mixing by osmosis.

same, in the sense that equal concentrations of glucose in the two compartments will be achieved. However, since mixing is possible only by the transfer of water from B to A the volume of the latter will be increased at the expense of the former.

A simple arrangement by which the process of osmosis may be studied is to have the two solutions separated by a membrane in the form of a piston which can slide horizontally ; if this is done, the mixing occurs as in Fig. 86 ; as water penetrates compartment A, the membrane-piston moves to the right and comes to rest when sufficient water has entered A to cause both concentrations to become equal. If the piston is fixed, it is clear that compartment A cannot increase in volume, and hence that osmosis and mixing cannot take place ; nevertheless there is a tendency for this to occur, and if some pressure-measuring apparatus were inserted into compartment A it would be found that there was a pressure tending to drive water into it. This pressure, measured in atmospheres, kg. per sq. cm., or any other units, is called the *osmotic pressure* and may be indicated by the symbol π. Osmotic pressure, therefore, is the measurable tendency of two solutions to mix, when this mixing can only be achieved by osmosis. A simple way of measuring the osmotic pressure generated in the above system would be to exert a force along the piston which is just great enough to prevent water from entering compartment A. This force, divided by the cross-sectional area of the membrane, is equal to the osmotic pressure of the system. If a greater force is exerted on the piston, water will be driven out of compartment A into compartment B until a sufficiently high osmotic pressure has been created to prevent the mechanical force from driving out more water. If a smaller force is exerted, water will osmose into compartment A, thereby reducing the difference in concentration, until the final osmotic pressure is just equal to the mechanical pressure actually exerted.

The case in which a pressure, greater than the osmotic pressure, was exerted, causing the migration of water from a higher concentration in A to a lower one in B, represented a condition known as *ultra-filtration*. It can be seen from the example that ultra-filtration is the direct opposite of osmosis ; osmosis represents the migration of water from the lower to the higher concentration and is a *mixing* process ; ultra-filtration represents the migration of water from the higher to the lower concentration and is a *separation* process. As we shall see, ultra-filtration plays a significant part in the maintenance of the fluid balance of the complex organism.

The osmotic pressure generated by two solutions of unequal concentration is capable of performing mechanical work, and consequently a solution may be regarded as containing a supply of energy in virtue of its concentration of solute. On the other hand we can see that a mechanical source of energy is capable of performing " osmotic " work, *i.e.*, it can, by the process of ultra-filtration, cause a change in the relative concentrations of two solutions ; in this case we have the transformation of mechanical energy into osmotic, or concentration, energy.

Concentration, however, is not only an expression of energy but it is an intensive quantity, in the same sense that electrical potential and temperature are intensive quantities ; thus, under certain conditions, the temperature is a measure of the thermal energy of a substance, yet the temperatures of two bodies also tells us whether heat energy will pass from one to the other, or *vice versâ* ; whereas the total quantity of energy contained by each body does not. If we have two quantities of gas, say 1 g. and 1/1,000 g. ; if the 1 g. quantity has a temperature of 100° Absolute and the other a temperature of 1,000°, the total quantities of thermal energy in each will be proportional to 100 and 1 respectively, yet we know that heat will flow from the hotter body to the colder, in spite of the fact that in this case the hotter body contains less total thermal energy than the cooler. Thus it is the temperature, and not the total energy content, that determines the direction of flow of heat energy ; likewise the electrical potential determines the flow of electrical energy or current, and the concentration of solute determines the direction of flow of osmotic energy. Viewed in this light, the tendency of two solutions of unequal concentration to mix, either by the diffusion of solute from the more concentrated to the more dilute, or by osmosis in the reverse direction, is an expression of the much more general tendency for energy to flow from a state of high potential to one of low. If energy is to travel in the reverse direction, *i.e.*, if water is to pass from the more concentrated solution to the more dilute (ultra-filtration) or if solute is to pass from the more dilute to the more concentrated solution ("accumulation"), work must be done on the system, *i.e.*, an extraneous supply of energy must be provided. These qualifications regarding the transfer of energy are in effect a statement of the Second Law of Thermodynamics, a law which applies equally to living and dead matter. In living systems ultra-filtration and its counterpart, *accumulation*, are very frequently encountered ; in the former case the energy is provided by the mechanical contractions of the heart, and in the latter by the chemical energy of certain metabolic reactions.

Osmotic pressure arises from the fundamental tendency of two solutions to mix ; it may therefore be expected that the magnitude of this pressure will depend on the concentrations of the two solutions separated by the semi-permeable membrane. The approximate way in which this pressure depends on concentration is given by the Van't Hoff expression :

$$\pi = R.T. (C_1 - C_2) \quad . \quad . \quad . \quad . \quad . \quad . \quad (2)$$

where R is the Gas Constant, T the absolute temperature and C is the concentration. That is, the osmotic pressure is directly proportional to the difference in concentration of the two solutions.[1] R has the units of energy per degree per mole ; its value is 0.08 when the units of osmotic pressure and of concentration are atmospheres and moles/l. respectively ; in ergs it is $8.31.10^7$; in calories, 1.98. When one of the concentrations is zero, *e.g.*, when a solution is separated from pure water, the osmotic pressure is RTC, and this is what is meant by the *osmotic pressure of a single solution* ; two solutions of concentration C_1 and C_2 have each an osmotic pressure defined in this way, viz., RTC_1 and RTC_2 ; the pressure developed when they are separated by a membrane is, as Equation 2 shows, the difference in these values. Thus one speaks of a *difference of osmotic pressure* between two solutions, and this is synonymous with the osmotic pressure generated when they are separated by a semi-permeable membrane.

[1] In this, and succeeding chapters, we shall ignore the effects of ions or molecules on each other, which, in concentrated solutions, may produce quite serious modifications in their effective concentrations. To allow for these effects, many of which are predictable on physical principles, a quantity called the *activity* is substituted for the concentration. Thus the law relating osmotic pressure with concentration should be more accurately expressed :—

$$\pi = RTa$$

where a is the activity of the solute molecules. The activity is related to the concentration by a factor, f, the *activity coefficient* :—

$$fC = a$$

may be calculated from the equation :—

$$- \log f = 0.509 \, z^2 \sqrt{\mu}$$

where z is the valency of the ion and μ the *ionic strength* of the solution. The ionic strength is a measure of the intensity of the electrical field in the solution and is defined as half the sum of the terms obtained by multiplying the concentration of each ion by the square of its valency, *i.e.* :—

$$\mu = \tfrac{1}{2} \Sigma C z^2$$

Equation 2 tells us that the osmotic pressure depends only on the difference in concentration of the impermeable molecules on the two sides of the membrane, *i.e.*, the actual nature of the molecules is irrelevant ; thus solutions of 1 M urea and 1 M glucose, separated by a membrane impermeable to both solutes, are in osmotic equilibrium, the osmotic pressure being zero. They are not in diffusion equilibrium, as this can only be achieved by migration of solute molecules. If the molecule dissociates into ions the osmotic pressure will be determined by the concentration of these ; thus 1 M glucose would be osmotically equivalent to about 0·5 M NaCl.

Osmotic Behaviour of Arbacia Egg

When a membrane separates two solutions of different composition the changes in the system as it approaches equilibrium will depend on the permeability of the membrane to the different solutes ; where it is impermeable to all the solutes the change will be confined to osmosis ;

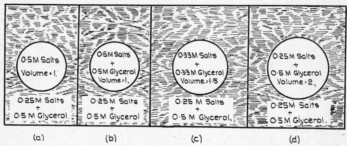

Fig. 87.   Swelling of *Arbacia* egg resulting from dilution of the external salt solution with an equal volume of isotonic glycerol.

where one or more of the solutes can pass through the membrane the changes may be quite complex. Thus let us consider what happens when a sea-urchin egg is placed in sea-water which has been diluted with an equal volume of a glycerol solution of the same osmotic concentration.[1] The membrane is impermeable to salts,[2] but permeable to water and glycerol ; the initial condition can be represented by Fig. 87 (*a*). The system is in osmotic equilibrium, but not in diffusion equilibrium since glycerol may enter the cell. Let us suppose that glycerol does so until it achieves equal concentrations inside and outside as in (*b*) ; the passage of glycerol has created a difference of osmotic pressure which must be levelled out by osmosis (*c*) ; this reduces the concentration of glycerol which penetrates, and so on. The equilibrium position is given by (*d*) with equal concentrations of glycerol and salts inside and outside the cell, and the volume of the latter twice its initial size. (In this example it has been

---

[1] Sea-water contains chiefly NaCl and may be expressed as osmotically equivalent to 0·5 M NaCl, or 0·5 M " salts." Since NaCl gives two ions, this solution is equivalent to 1 M non-electrolyte.

[2] We shall see that this statement requires modification ; any permeability to salts, however, is of such a low order compared with the permeability to water, glycerol, etc., that no great inaccuracy is introduced by this assumption.

assumed that the volume of the solution outside the cell is so large in comparison with that in the cell that the passage of glycerol and water from the former makes no difference to its concentration ; this assumption will be maintained in all succeeding biological examples since it coincides with experimental practice, the cells studied being generally so small as to justify this assumption. For simplicity, moreover, it has been assumed that the contents of the cell are entirely aqueous, so that a 100 per cent. increase in the water content produces a 100 per cent. increase in the volume. In the case of *Arbacia* some 10–12 per cent. of the volume is made up of solid matter so that a 100 per cent. increase in the water content

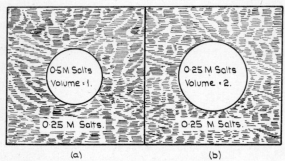

Fig. 88. Swelling of *Arbacia* egg resulting from dilution of the external salt solution with an equal volume of distilled water.

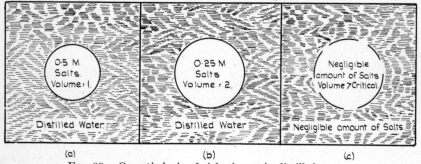

Fig. 89. Osmotic lysis of *Arbacia* egg in distilled water.

makes only a 90–88 per cent. increase in volume. The percentage of solids in the erythrocyte is much higher, about 30 per cent.)

If the egg is placed in sea-water diluted with an equal volume of distilled water, instead of the glycerol solution, equilibrium is achieved this time simply by the migration of water into the more concentrated solution within the egg, as in Fig. 88; the result is an egg swollen to twice its volume, *i.e.*, the same as with sea-water diluted with the glycerol solution. If the egg is placed in distilled water we can see that no equilibrium is possible and the egg swells until it bursts, *i.e.*, the lysis described in the earlier part of this chapter is an osmotic phenomenon (Fig. 89). Similarly, if the egg is placed in a pure solution of a penetrating substance, *e.g.*, glycerol, it will behave, so far as the final result is concerned, as though it were in distilled water; this is clear from Fig. 90 in which the processes are taken in steps. At first there is osmotic equality (*a*); glycerol, however, penetrates to give equal concentrations inside and out (*b*); this penetration causes a difference of osmotic pressure leading to the migration of water (*c*); the migration of water causes a reduction in the concentration of glycerol in the cell so that more enters, water follows, and at a definite stage the cell can contain no more water and bursts.[1] In a solution containing 0·5 M salts (*e.g.*, sea-water, 0·5 M NaCl, etc.) it is clear that the egg is in osmotic equilibrium with its environment, an equilibrium which cannot be disturbed by the penetration of solute, since the membrane is impermeable to salts; the volume of the egg, therefore, is unchanged on transferring it to 0·5 M NaCl, *i.e.*, 0·5 M NaCl is the *isotonic concentration*; on diluting the NaCl, say to 0·45 M, 0·40 M, and so on, equilibrium is achieved by the penetration of water until the salt concentrations are equal inside and out;

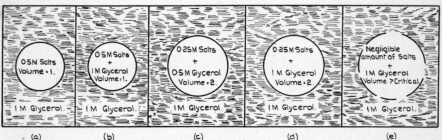

FIG. 90.   Osmotic lysis of *Arbacia* egg in an isotonic solution of a penetrating non-electrolyte (glycerol).

at a certain point in the dilution of NaCl (ca. 0·25 M), the cell can contain no more water and therefore concentrations below this cause lysis.

We are now in a position to understand the various phenomena discussed earlier. In NaCl solutions above a certain concentration the cell is stable because osmotic equilibrium can be maintained; when, however, the concentration of this salt is reduced to such an extent that the cell is unable to hold the water necessary to dilute its contents to the outside concentration, the cell is no longer stable. The changes in volume of the cell in hypertonic and hypotonic solutions of NaCl are thus due to the migration of water. In isotonic glycerol solution the cell is unstable because no osmotic equilibrium is possible; however, the difference of osmotic pressure, which drives water into the cell, depends in the first place on the penetration of glycerol; if this takes place slowly, the swelling and bursting of the cell will also be slow in comparison with the same process occurring in distilled water, since the difference of osmotic pressure is present initially in this case. In Fig. 90 the cell was considered to be in a solution of glycerol of the same osmotic pressure as that of sea-water (1 M); if the concentration were made much higher, the final effect—

[1] It should be noted that these "steps" are entirely artificial; glycerol and water penetrate the cell simultaneously.

namely lysis—would be observed just the same. Solutions of sucrose behave in the same way as solutions of NaCl because sucrose cannot penetrate the membrane ; urea and ethylene glycol, on the other hand, penetrate the membrane and therefore behave in the same way as glycerol. The mixture of glycerol and sea-water, or the pure glycerol solution, considered in Figs. 87 and 90, are referred to as isotonic solutions, although the egg does not maintain its initial volume in them. Hence an isotonic solution is one which maintains the cell at its normal value *only if it consists entirely of a solution of substances which do not penetrate the cell* ; a better definition is a solution with the same osmotic pressure (given by multiplying the concentration, in moles per litre, by R × T) as that of the contents of the cell. Thus for marine eggs the isotonic concentration will generally be approximately 0·5 M salts or 1 M non-electrolyte.

Temporary and Permanent Osmotic Changes. Conditions may arise, especially in experimental studies, in which a change in osmotic pressure can be equalled out by both diffusion of water, *i.e.*, osmosis, and by

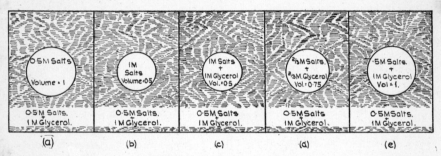

Fig. 91. Temporary shrinkage of *Arbacia* egg resulting from addition of glycerol to the external salt solution.

diffusion of solute in the opposite direction. In these circumstances the final volume of the cell will be the same as its initial volume, but during the course of the adaptation the volume may change considerably. Let us consider the sea-urchin egg in a large volume of sea-water. Suppose pure glycerol is added to the sea-water to make it 1 M with respect to this substance. The membrane is permeable to both water and glycerol, so that equality of osmotic pressure can be achieved either by glycerol diffusing into the egg or by water diffusing out. These two processes occur simultaneously, so that we have water moving out of the cell while glycerol enters it. The loss of water causes the cell to shrink, whilst the penetration of glycerol has no appreciable effect on cell volume. If we imagine the adaptation to proceed in stages we get the following as the first three steps (Fig. 91) : In stage (*b*) it is imagined that the water has diffused out to produce equal osmotic pressures, and the cell has shrunk ; in stage (*c*) that glycerol has diffused in and produced equal concentrations inside and out ; in stage (*d*) that water has penetrated the cell to level out the difference of osmotic pressure created by the entrance of glycerol ; and so the process goes on until the final equilibrium, given by (*e*) is attained. The successive stages shown in Fig. 91 are, of course, artificial ; and the actual course of events will be determined by the relative rates at which water can leave the cell and the solute can enter it ; if glycerol penetrates very slowly in comparison with water, there will be a rapid shrinking of the cell followed by a slow swelling as glycerol and water penetrate together ; if the opposite relationship holds, there will be only a slight shrinkage of the cells followed by a return to normal. The osmosis of water is, in this example, a temporary one, as opposed to the permanent one obtained by placing the cell in hypertonic or hypotonic NaCl ; it is temporary because the solute, used to make the medium hypertonic, can penetrate the cell.

Osmotic Behaviour of the Erythrocyte

The foregoing account of certain simple equilibria, and the responses of the system to changes in the salt concentration of the medium surrounding the cell, serves to bring out the elementary physico-chemical principles involved. As an accurate account of changes taking place in a particular cell they may be misleading, since some of the assumptions are not realised in practice. The osmotic behaviour of the erythrocyte has been studied in far greater detail than that of any other cell, so that a discussion of the responses of this cell will serve as a useful corrective to the over-simplification of our earlier treatment.

Structure of the Erythrocyte. The primary task performed by the erythrocyte is the carriage of O_2 in the blood-stream ; it is enabled to do this adequately in virtue of its content of hæmoglobin which reversibly combines with O_2. This cell, having no nucleus, is incapable of division, so that new cells can only be formed by the differentiation of more primitive types ; one may therefore observe the various stages in the development of the erythrocyte in the bone-marrow of the adult organism where this process takes place continuously.

The red bone-marrow of certain of the bones of the adult mammal is the site of origin of the erythrocytes ; the marrow owes its red colour to the presence of numerous vessels, the *sinusoids*, in which it is believed that the cells develop and mature ; these sinusoids are lined with a layer of large endothelial cells which are capable of dividing to form free cells, called *megaloblasts* ; these are large nucleated colourless cells which themselves divide to form *erythroblasts*. In the marrow, erythroblasts are observed in various stages of development, characterised by the increasing quantities of hæmoglobin contained in them ; the cell in the next stage of maturation is called the *normoblast*, in which the nucleus is pyknotic (*i.e.*, is shrunken) ; up to this point the cells—megaloblasts, early and late erythroblasts and normoblasts—are capable of division ; and the normal process of multiplication of red cells, for replacement in the blood-stream, is through the division of the later erythroblasts and normoblasts. The normoblast, during further maturation, loses its nucleus to become a *reticulocyte*, distinguishable only from the mature erythrocyte into which it develops by possessing a fine reticulum throughout its cytoplasm.[1]

---

[1] According to Plum the erythrocyte is formed by a pinching off of cytoplasm from the erythroblast.

The development from the normoblast to the reticulocyte and erythrocyte is accompanied by a very significant change in shape, namely from a sphere to a bi-concave disk ; in Fig. 92 a diagrammatic end-on view of a human erythrocyte, constructed from his own measurements by Ponder, is shown. The biological value of this change in shape was pointed out by Hartridge who showed that it was essentially an adaptation of the cell to its physiological functions as a carrier of O_2. In order that O_2 should reach the centre simultaneously from all points on the surface (*i.e.*, to ensure an even distribution of the gas throughout the whole cell), the cell should be either a sphere or an infinitely thin disk ; if it were a sphere the available surface area for a given volume would be at a minimum and this would necessarily entail a minimum rate of penetration of O_2 ; if the cell were a flat disk of measurable thickness the area per unit volume would be large, but O_2 would reach the centre more rapidly from the periphery of the disk than from elsewhere. Moreover, a simple disk shape would present grave structural difficulties. The form of the erythrocyte is, in effect, a compromise between a sphere and a disk, its greater thickness at the periphery compensating for the greater ease with which O_2 can penetrate to the centre from there. As a result, O_2 reaches the central region of the cell more or less simultaneously from all parts of its surface, and an even uptake of gas is assured. Ponder in 1925 computed the shape of surface consistent with the requirement that molecules, started off simultaneously and allowed to diffuse inward, would all reach a central ring at the

Fig. 92. Outline of human erythrocyte. (Ponder. *Hæ-molysis and Related Pheno-mena*. Grune & Stratton, N.Y.)

same moment ; the surface so calculated agreed remarkably well (but not perfectly) with the actual surface of the erythrocyte. The advantage of the disk shape over the sphere, from the viewpoint of *rapidity* of diffusion of O_2, is evident if it is realised that nine times as many spherical erythrocytes, each with one-ninth of the volume of the disk, would be necessary to provide so efficient a transport system.

Disk-Sphere Transformation. The forces which are brought into play when the spherical normoblast is converted into a bi-concave disk are by no means understood, but experiments show that the mechanism whereby the disk shape is maintained is a delicately balanced one ; thus, on transferring the erythrocyte from its normal plasma environment to a solution of NaCl and observing it between slide and coverslip, the cell is found to have lost its disk form and become a sphere ; if, on the other hand, the coverslip is not placed on the slide the cell retains its normal shape. The addition of small quantities of blood plasma to the salt solution prevents the " slide-and-coverslip " change, or, if the change has already taken place, addition of plasma immediately converts the cells to their disk shape, although this time they are not entirely normal since they tend to adhere to each other to a much greater extent than before. For a long time it was thought that the mechanical or electrical forces exerted by the coverslip were the cause of the change of shape, but recently it has been shown by Furchgott that the effect of the coverslip is due to the alkaline glass of which it is made ; the amount of alkali dissolved from the glass is sufficient to remove from the surface of the cell a layer of adsorbed albumin whose presence is apparently essential to the maintenance of the disk structure. This *anti-sphering factor*, as Furchgott calls it, may be isolated as the crystalbumin fraction of plasma, and consequently the effect of the plasma in inhibiting the disk-sphere transformation is explained ; this interpretation is also consonant with earlier observations that acid buffer solutions, or the waxing of the slide and coverslip, prevented the disk-sphere transformation. It is evident that the shape of the erythrocyte is maintained, in the first place, by the presence of a layer of protein on the surface ; the amount of anti-sphering factor extracted from cells indicates that it can be only about 45–60A thick.

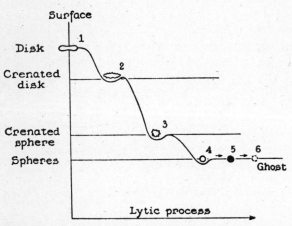

Fig. 93. Diagrammatic representation of the shape changes, from disk to sphere, which occur during the action of a typical lysin. 1, disk ; 2, crenated disk ; 3, crenated sphere ; 4, sphere ; 5, prolytic sphere ; 6, ghost. The descending levels indicate that the cell surface decreases as one form passes into the other ; the stepwise shape of the curve is to indicate that each form is, to some extent, a stable one. (Ponder. *Hæmolysis and Related Phenomena.* Grune & Stratton, N.Y.)

The plasma membrane of the erythrocyte may be ruptured in a variety of ways ; as a result, the hæmoglobin escapes, leaving behind the cell residue or " ghost " ; by carefully washing large quantities of these ghosts free of hæmoglobin, a white residue is obtained which may be submitted to chemical analysis ; the principal constituents have been shown to be a protein called *stromatin* (by Jorpes), and fatty material—lecithin, cephalin, cholesterol, etc., there being about four to five times as much protein as lipid.[1] It is likely that the lipids are concentrated in the surface of the cell and make up the plasma membrane ; it is probable, but not certain, that the stromatin is distributed throughout the bulk of the cell in the form of a fine meshwork of fibres (Boehm). As Ponder has shown, the ghost adopts the bi-concave shape and can exhibit the disk-sphere transformation ; the presence of hæmoglobin within the cell is therefore not a prerequisite of the disk shape, although there is some evidence that the amount of hæmoglobin remaining in a ghost can influence the form adopted by it under various conditions.

[1] The surface of the erythrocyte contains certain specific group substances responsible for the agglutination phenomena observed when " incompatible " bloods are mixed. These factors remain on the ghosts after hæmolysis. Morgan has recently reviewed their chemical nature ; it would seem that they are polysaccharide complexes similar to hyaluronic acid-containing mucins.

We have pointed out earlier that the surface-area of a bi-concave disk is considerably greater than that of a sphere of equal volume ; what then happens when the normal erythrocyte becomes a sphere ? Careful measurements have shown that there is no increase in volume of the cell during the slide-and-coverslip transformation ; clearly, then, unless the surface membrane shrinks, it is more than adequate to cover the spherical cell. Studies of the process of disk-sphere transformation show that the cells adopt intermediate forms before becoming spheres ; in these so-called " thorn-apple " forms, the surface is finely crenated ; when the spherical form has been reached, however, no crenations can be seen, but it is possible that the surface does indeed possess minute folds too small to be resolved by the microscope. Crenation and the adoption of the spherical form are not peculiar to the slide-and-coverslip situation ; treatment of the erythrocyte with any substance that, in a sufficiently high concentration, causes hæmolysis (*i.e.*, rupture of the cell so that hæmoglobin escapes), brings about a series of changes rather similar to the slide-and-coverslip changes ; these are shown diagrammatically in Fig. 93 from Ponder.

Response to Hypotonicity. The chemical composition of the erythrocyte is shown in Table XVIII, p. 241 ; as we shall see, the permeability of the erythrocyte membrane to salts is of such a low order, in comparison with the rate of penetration of water, that we may assume, as a first approximation, that the erythrocyte conforms to the system discussed earlier in the case of the marine egg, namely that it consists of a solution primarily of salts— this time approximately 0·165 M—separated by a salt-impermeable and water-permeable membrane from an isotonic solution, also primarily made up of salts. The salts are different on the two sides of the membrane, being potassium salts in the cell and sodium salts outside, but this does not affect the main issue with which we are concerned here.

If the plasma surrounding the cells is steadily diluted (*i.e.*, made hypotonic), the latter increase in volume until they finally burst and allow the hæmoglobin within them to escape. This does not mean, however, that all the cells burst at the same tonicity ; on the contrary, if the percentage of cells hæmolysed is plotted against the tonicity, an S-shaped curve is obtained, as in Fig. 94, indicating that the individual cells of the population have different " resistances " to osmotic hæmolysis ; an analysis of the S-shaped curve shows that the resistances are normally distributed about a mean. So long as no hæmolysis occurs, the increase in total volume of the cells should follow the simple equation :

$$V = W\,(1/T - 1) + 100 \quad . \quad . \quad . \quad . \quad . \quad . \quad (3)$$

where the initial volume of the cells is put at 100, W is the percentage of cell-water initially present, and T is the *tonicity*—the ratio of the effective concentrations of salts in the diluted medium and in the original plasma. The assumption at the basis of this equation is simply that the difference of osmotic pressure, caused by placing the cells in a medium of tonicity T, is cancelled out by the migration of water into the cell (or out of it in a hypertonic medium) ; this implies that the cell offers no mechanical resistance to the penetration of water. The careful studies of Ponder have shown that the erythrocyte follows this equation only under certain experimental conditions ; under other conditions the volume attained in a hypotonic medium is less than that expected by the above equation, *i.e.*, the erythrocyte under these conditions is not a *perfect osmometer*, its behaviour being characterised by the modified equation :

$$V = RW (1/T - 1) + 100 \quad \ldots \ldots \quad (3^1)$$

If the cells are studied in heparinised plasma, or in defibrinated serum, they behave as nearly perfect osmometers, R being approximately unity ; in oxalated plasma, on the other hand, or in artificial salt solutions, the cells are imperfect osmometers with values of R which may be as low as

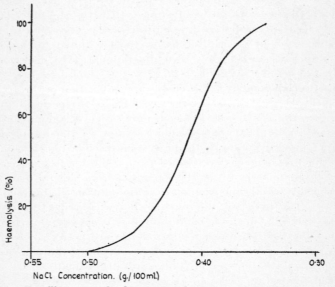

FIG. 94. Fragility curve for human erythrocytes. (After Hunter. *J. clin. Invest.*)

0·5 (*i.e.*, the volume achieved in a hypotonic oxalated plasma may be only half that predicted on the basis of Equation 3). The cause of these deviations from theory have been the subject of much speculation and some argument. Three general explanations have been put forward based on (*a*) an escape of salts from the cell during the manipulation ; (*b*) the presence of " bound water " in the cell, and (*c*) the existence of an appreciable mechanical resistance of the erythrocyte to changes in volume.

An escape of salts from the cell when placed in a hypotonic medium would certainly decrease the final volume achieved, since the difference of osmotic pressure would be diminished, and thus the amount of water that must penetrate the cell to neutralise this difference of osmotic pressure would be smaller. This possibility has been investigated in some detail and it would appear that, although the erythrocyte does indeed become " leaky " in hypotonic solutions, in the sense that there is a measurable loss of K+, the actual rate of loss is by no means sufficiently great to account for the osmotic effects, which are manifest within a few minutes or less.

The postulate of bound water implies that a proportion of the water is unavailable to act as solvent for the salts in the cell, so that the effective concentration within the cell is higher than indicated by the number of moles per litre of cell water. Thus the value of W in Equation 3 would have to be decreased by a factor indicating the fraction of bound water ; and R would indicate this fraction. For a long time it was thought that water could be " bound " in appreciable quantities within the cell but more recent studies, *e.g.*, those of Ørskov (1946) on the erythrocyte, have shown that this is very unlikely, the observed osmotic pressure of the contents of the cell being fairly close (within 2 or 3 per cent.) to that predicted from the concentration of osmotically active material.[1]

The existence of a mechanical resistance of the erythrocyte to a change in volume was for a long time thought impossible, largely because the cell was viewed simply as a sac composed of a thin membrane which would be quite incapable of withstanding the stresses created by even a small difference of osmotic pressure. Let us enquire more thoroughly into the morphological changes taking place when an erythrocyte undergoes hypotonic hæmolysis. Microscopical studies of erythrocytes in hypotonic solutions show that, when they swell, they do not increase in diameter measurably ; instead, the cell's shape changes continuously from that of a typical bi-concave disk, through intermediate forms, to a sphere—in rather the same way as a rubber ball with a leak in it, which has been flattened, resumes its spherical shape on allowing air to enter it. Such a change from a disk to a sphere involves no change in the surface-area, in spite of a considerable increase in volume ; thus a rabbit cell with an initial volume of $60\mu^3$ has an area of $105\mu^2$; a sphere with this area would have a volume of $100\mu^3$, so that the cell could absorb water until its volume increased to 167 per cent. of its initial value, without any necessity for expansion of its surface membrane. Beyond this point, however, the surface would have to increase with further increase in volume, and it is interesting that Ponder, and Castle & Daland, have shown that it is just at this point, namely when the cell has become a sphere, that further swelling results in the rupture of the cell. The *critical hæmolytic volume* of the cell is thus apparently determined by its shape, a large flat cell being able to take up far more water before bursting than a small and relatively thick cell. It seems fair to deduce, therefore, that the surface membrane of the erythrocyte differs from that of the sea-urchin egg in that it is incapable of any degree of expansion ; it is true that certain chemical reagents such as the urethanes, lysolecithin, etc., do increase the resistance to hæmolysis, presumably by allowing the membranes to stretch a little before bursting, but the effects are small and it is doubtful whether an increase of more than 10 per cent. of the area ever occurs. This finding,

---

[1] Blanchard (1940) has reviewed this vexed question. He concludes ". . . there is no certainty that even in the presence of lyophilic substances bound water has any real existence."

however, does not answer the question as to whether the cell offers any appreciable mechanical resistance to the osmotic force driving water into it ; if the strength of the cell resided only in its membrane it would be very unlikely that it offered any significant resistance, otherwise we should expect a discontinuity in its behaviour when the cell became a sphere. Up to this point there would be no strain on the membrane ; on further dilution of the plasma, however, the membrane would resist the penetration of water and so maintain the difference of osmotic pressure, and only when the tensile strength of the membrane had been exceeded would the cell rupture ; *i.e.*, if the membrane were capable of exerting a mechanical force of such a high order as to account for some of the anomalous behaviour described above, we should expect to have to dilute the plasma by an appreciable amount before the swollen spherical cell burst. No such discontinuity has been observed ; and, moreover, the tensile strength of the membrane required to resist a difference of osmotic pressure created by, say, a 10 per cent. change in tonicity, would be impossibly high. If the rigidity of the cell were determined by an internal structure—the stroma— the position would be different since this structure would be under strain as soon as the cell departed from its normal shape, and we could expect the resistance to expansion to be continuous with increasing volume. In heparinised plasma, however, the perfect osmometric behaviour of the erythrocyte would indicate that the stroma does not offer any appreciable resistance to the deformation of the cell ; furthermore, the ease with which the disk can become a crenated sphere under a variety of conditions precludes the existence of any great structural rigidity. On the other hand, if, under certain conditions, the hæmoglobin within the cell were to change its physical condition from a sol to an orientated crystalline gel, the change in mechanical properties of the cell as a whole might be drastic ; Teitel-Bernard observed that the coarse crenations, which develop spontaneously in cells in plasma or in acid media, were associated with an apparent crystallisation of the hæmoglobin within the cells, as indicated by polarisation microscopy. Moreover, such cells could be cut with a micro-dissection needle as though they were solid, whereas normal cells generally disintegrated when touched. The crenation under these conditions was thus due to a solidification of the contents of the cell, a change that imposed a new shape ; erythrocytes in oxalated plasma likewise showed these coarse crenations and it will be remembered that it is these cells that show the strong deviations from perfect osmometers ; Ponder (1944) has calculated the bulk modulus [1] of a cell such that it could resist differences of osmotic pressure of the order of those encountered in this anomalous osmometric behaviour, and has shown that it is not impossibly large.

A striking example of anomalous osmotic behaviour is given by the rat erythrocyte ; if these cells are kept in citrate solution for forty-eight hours at 4° C., it is found that their resistance to osmotic hæmolysis has increased to such an extent that very little swelling is observed even at a tonicity of 0·1, a tonicity that would cause complete hæmolysis in fresh rat cells.

---

[1] For an R value of 0·52 the bulk modulus would have to be $5 \cdot 10^6$ dynes/cm.^{2}, a value of the same order as that obtained with gelatin gels (Northrop, 1927).

Associated with this increase in resistance is the appearance of a marked birefringence of the cells, indicating a crystallisation of the hæmoglobin in the interior ; moreover the cells cannot now be converted to spheres by the usual methods (*e.g.*, between slide and cover-slip), and their whole behaviour suggests that they have become solid bodies of orientated hæmoglobin molecules. The effects are reversible, in that warming the cells destroys their birefringence and restores the possibility of disk-sphere transformations and osmotic hæmolysis. Thus, as Ponder has pointed out, the osmotic properties of the erythrocyte may vary from almost perfect behaviour, when the fresh cell is in its natural medium, through varying degrees of imperfection to a condition of complete osmotic inertia when the hæmoglobin has become orientated to such a rigid structure as to prevent any change of shape in spite of the large osmotic forces that must be generated on placing the cell in very dilute solutions.[1]

Fragility of Erythrocytes. Dilution of the plasma surrounding the erythrocyte beyond a certain point initiates hæmolysis as Fig. 94 shows ; the fact that the cells hæmolyse over a fairly wide range of concentrations may be described by saying that the cells of a suspension have varying resistances to hæmolysis ; the resistance of a given cell may thus be indicated by the reciprocal of the tonicity of the medium necessary for its osmotic bursting ; the tonicity itself could be described as a measure of the *fragility* of the cell. Individual erythrocytes, however, are not usually studied ; rather, a suspension containing many millions ; when we speak of the fragility of a sample of blood we should therefore mean the value of the average tonicity required to hæmolyse the cells ; to determine this would require, however, a complete curve similar to that of Fig. 94, and it is customary to choose the tonicity required to cause a fixed degree of hæmolysis, or more usually *incipient hæmolysis, i.e.*, the medium surrounding the cells is diluted until a trace of hæmoglobin appears in the medium after centrifuging the cells away. This is clearly an inadequate measure of the mean characteristics of the blood sample, since a change in fragility of quite a small percentage of the cells could produce the observed change ; however, such a test has been used for a long time both clinically and in experimental studies of hæmolysis. Probably the most important factor determining the fragility of the cells is their shape ; as we have seen, the extent to which a cell can take up water is determined by the difference in volume of the original disk-shape and that of the sphere obtained by " blowing out " the disk ; we may therefore expect that the erythrocytes of species showing a predominance of the relatively fat type of cell (*spherocyte*) will be more fragile than those having a predominance of the thin type (*platycyte*) ; that this is an important factor is shown by the finding that the fragility of the cells of the goat, cat, rabbit, dog, and man

---

[1] Ponder describes the condition of the rat cell as that in which the activity of K^+ is nearly zero ; this is an incorrect way of viewing the matter as it is very unlikely that anything like all the K^+ is bound in organic combination with the hæmoglobin under any conditions. We must assume that the K^+ salts are trapped in the aqueous medium in the meshes of a rigid protein gel or paracrystal ; so long as water can enter the cell, the difference of osmotic pressure will persist, and must be resisted by a structural rigidity if the cell is not to swell.

are in this order, the goat's being the most fragile. The order of the values of ratio of the diameter over greatest thickness is (Haden) :—

Man	Dog	Rabbit	Cat	Goat
4·2	4·2	3·6	3·2	2·1

Other factors in the fragility will be the extent to which the cells behave as perfect osmometers and, of course, the distribution of shapes throughout the sample ; thus a pathological increase in fragility may be due to a preponderance of spherocytes, in fact variations in the shape of the fragility curve of Fig. 94 are generally interpreted as due to changes in the distribution of shapes in the population.

The Plant Cell

We have seen that the erythrocyte and the marine egg adjust themselves to differences of osmotic pressure by taking in (or in hypertonic saline by

FIG. 95.   Plant cell in (*a*) hypotonic saline ; (*b*) hypertonic saline (plasmo-lysed). (Davson & Danielli. *Permeability of Natural Membranes.* Cambridge.)

losing) water, to give as a final state equal concentrations of salts on both sides of the membrane. The plant cell is surrounded by a tough cellulose membrane which is able to withstand considerable pressures, hence its adaptations to osmotic changes may be different. Fig. 95 (*a*) is a diagrammatic representation of a plant cell, consisting of a thin layer of protoplasm—the *protoplast*, surrounding a large vacuole full of sap. The protoplast is considered to be covered on both sides by a thin plasma membrane, permeable to water but impermeable to salts. The cellulose wall, on the other hand, is permeable to water and most dissolved substances. If this cell is surrounded with an external fluid, *e.g.*, a salt solution, diffusion of substances from this external fluid into the vacuole must occur by way of the protoplast, so that we may consider the latter to be a membrane which allows water to diffuse from the external medium to the vacuole, but prevents the migration of salts.[1] If the plant cell is placed in a hypotonic solution, there will be a difference of osmotic pressure driving water into the vacuole ; the volume of the vacuole, however, is limited by the tough cellulose wall, so that very little fluid can be accommodated. Hence the equilibrium position will be given by unequal

---

[1] The impermeability to salts is only relative.

concentrations of salts on the two sides of the membrane (protoplast), the difference of osmotic pressure being opposed by a structural resistance to the penetration of water. The system is similar to that shown in Fig. 86 where a force is exerted on the piston sufficient to prevent water from entering compartment A.

If the surrounding medium is made hypertonic, water leaves the cell, the vacuole shrinks and the protoplast detaches itself from the cellulose wall as in Fig. 95 (*b*). This phenomenon is known as *plasmolysis*. The adaptation consists, this time, in the concentrating of the fluid in the vacuole until the difference in osmotic pressure is levelled out. It may be noted that this simple view of the protoplast, as a selectively permeable membrane separating the vacuole from the external fluid, is useful ; but it can be misleading when the more complicated ionic equilibria are considered ; in actuality the protoplast is much more than a membrane, being virtually a cell on its own and the seat of metabolic activity.

References

BLANCHARD, K. C. (1940). " Water, Free and Bound." *C.S.H. Symp.*, **8**, 1.

BOEHM, G. (1935). " U.d. Form der Micellen des Stromaeiweisses." *Biochem. Z.*, **282**, 32.

CASTLE, W. B. & DALAND, G. A. (1937). " Susceptibility of Erythrocyte to Hypotonic Hæmolysis as a Function of Discoidal Form." *Amer. J. Physiol.*, **120**, 371.

DAVSON, H. (1937). " Loss of K^+ from the Erythrocyte in Hypotonic Saline." *J. cell. & comp. Physiol.*, **10**, 247.

DAVSON, H. & DANIELLI, J. F. (1943). " The Permeability of Natural Membranes." Cambridge, C. U. P.

FURCHGOTT, R. F. (1940). " Observations on the Structure of Red Cell Ghosts." *C.S.H. Symp.*, **8**, 224.

FURCHGOTT, R. F. (1940). " Disk-Sphere Transformation in Mammalian Red Cells." *J. exp. Biol.*, **17**, 30.

FURCHGOTT, R. F. & PONDER, E. (1940). " Nature of the Anti-Sphering Factor." *J. exp. Biol.*, **17**, 117.

HADEN, R. L. (1934). " Mechanism of the Increased Fragility of the Erythrocyte in Congenital Hæmolytic Jaundice." *Amer. J. med. Sci.*, **188**, 441.

HUNTER, F. T. (1940). " A Photoelectric Method for the Quantitative Determination of Erythrocyte Fragility." *J. clin. Invest.*, **19**, 691.

JACOBS, M. H. & PARPART, A. K. (1931). " Influence of pH, Temperature, and Oxygen Tension on Hæmolysis by Hypotonic Solutions." *Biol. Bull.*, **60**, 95.

JACOBS, M. H. & STEWART, D. R. (1947). " Ionic and Osmotic Equilibria with a Complex External Solution." *J. cell. & comp. Physiol.*, **30**, 79.

JORPES, E. (1932). " Protein Component of the Erythrocyte Membrane or Stroma." *Biochem. J.*, **26**, 1488.

MORGAN, W. T. J. (1947). " Mucoids as Components of the Human Erythrocyte Surface." *Proc. Int. Congr. Cyt.*, p. 228.

NORTHROP, J. H. (1927). " Swelling of Isoelectric Gelatin in Water." *J. gen. Physiol.*, **10**, 893.

ØRSCOV, S. L. (1946). " Solvent Water in the Human Erythrocyte." *Acta Physiol. Scand.*, **12**, 192.

PLUM, C. M. (1947). " The Production of Erythrocytes." *Proc. Int. Congr. Cyt.*, p. 399.

PONDER, E. (1925). " Shape of the Mammalian Erythrocyte and its Respiratory Function." *J. gen. Physiol.*, **9**, 197.

PONDER, E. (1937). " Changes in Surface Area in Disks and Spheres." *J. exp. Biol.*, **14**, 267.

PONDER, E. (1944). " The Osmotic Behaviour of Crenated Red Cells." *J. gen. Physiol.*, **27**, 273.

PONDER, E. (1945). " The Paracrystalline State of the Rat Red Blood Cell." *J. gen. Physiol.*, **29**, 89.

PONDER, E. (1948). " Hæmolysis and Related Phenomena." N.Y., Grune and Stratton ; London, Churchill.

TEITEL-BERNARD. (Quoted by Ponder, 1948.)

CHAPTER VIII

PERMEABILITY AND THE STRUCTURE OF THE PLASMA MEMBRANE

Mechanism of Diffusion

BEFORE entering into the measurement of permeability, and the results of these measurements, it would be profitable to consider in some detail the intimate mechanism of simple diffusion in an aqueous medium and to contrast this with the migration across a membrane. Diffusion consists in the migration of solute from a higher to a lower concentration, and is a result of the random motions of the solute molecules. In the measurement of diffusion we are therefore concerned with the amount of substance that passes from one region of the solution to another in a given time ; and this will clearly depend on the difference in concentration of the substance in the two regions considered. According to the theoretical treatment of Fick, the amount of substance diffusing through a cross-section of area, A, is directly proportional to the concentration gradient across this section ; expressed mathematically the law takes the form :

$$\frac{ds}{dt} = -\,DA\,\frac{dc}{dx} \quad \cdots \cdots \cdots (4)$$

The differential $\frac{ds}{dt}$ expresses the rate of transport, $i.e.$, the amount of substance, in moles, crossing in time dt ; the differential $\frac{dc}{dx}$ is the concentration gradient at the point considered. D is the diffusion coefficient, and represents the number of moles transported across unit area when the concentration-gradient is unity ; its units are therefore [1] :

$$\frac{Moles}{Area \times Time \times Concentration\ Gradient}$$

If a solution of concentration, C_o, is placed beneath pure water, the solute passes into the water as a result of diffusion ; at any given point, x, the concentration will vary continuously with time, and, therefore, the concentration-gradient ; to calculate the amount that has passed from the

---

[1] The unit of concentration is moles/cm.^{3}, that of concentration gradient is therefore moles/cm.^{4}. Thus the unit of diffusion is :—

$$\frac{Moles}{cm.^2 \times sec. \times \dfrac{Moles}{cm.^4}} = cm.^2/sec.$$

Results are frequently given as cm.^{2}/day in which case they must be divided by 86,400, to convert them to cm.^{2}/sec.

solution into the water at any period of time we must integrate Equation 4. This is, in general, a difficult mathematical procedure,[1] so that for the experimental determination of the constant, D, the conditions are generally simplified so as to permit of an easy solution.

We may note that a concentration gradient is necessary to demonstrate *chemically* the existence of diffusion. Owing to the random movements of the molecules in a solution, however, diffusion is continually taking place in a homogeneous solution ; but since, on the average, the flux in any one direction is equal to the flux in the opposite direction, this diffusion does not result in a measurable (chemically) change in concentration at any given point.

This treatment of diffusion has been superficial, in that we have only taken account of the bare fact that solute passes from a region of high concentration to one of low, and we have attributed this to the random movements of the solute molecules. In gases this random motion requires little further investigation ; the molecules are free to move and are subject to only small intermolecular forces ; since the kinetic energy of the molecules of a gas is represented by $\frac{1}{2}MN\bar{c}^2$, where N is the number of molecules, M their molecular weight, and $\bar{c}^2$ their mean square velocity, it is not surprising that the diffusion constants of different gases are inversely proportional to the square roots of their masses, *i.e.*, $DM^{\frac{1}{2}}$ is constant, a relationship found experimentally by Graham. (Thus with any pair of gases at the same temperature, the average energy of their molecules will be the same, $\frac{1}{2}NM_1\bar{c}_1^2$ and $\frac{1}{2}NM_2\bar{c}_2^2$ will therefore be equal, so that the average velocities of the molecules will be inversely proportional to the square roots of their masses ; the velocities will determine their speeds of diffusion.) In liquids, on the other hand, the molecules are close together, and within each others' spheres of mutual attraction ; consequently, for any given molecule to move a significant distance, it must break itself away from its surrounding molecules. Diffusion in liquids therefore occurs discontinuously, a molecule only moving when it has acquired sufficient energy, by collision, to break away from its neighbours and push aside other molecules. We may regard the diffusion coefficient of a solute in a liquid therefore as being related to the *viscosity*, or frictional resistance between the molecules of solute and solvent.[2] When the attractions between molecules are small, as for example with a homopolar solvent where the forces are mainly of the weak van der Waals type, we may expect diffusion to be rapid. On the other hand, with substances like glycerol diffusing in water, the forces of attraction between the OH-groups of glycerol and of water, and of the water molecules amongst each other, are very high owing to the formation of quasi-chemical linkages (the

---

[1] The most exhaustive review of the different solutions that have been employed in biological studies is that of Jacobs (1935). Carslaw & Jaeger describe the solutions of analogous problems in the conduction of heat.

[2] For a molecule large in comparison with the solvent molecules, *e.g.*, a spherical colloidal particle, the diffusion coefficient is given by the Einstein Equation :—

$$D = \frac{RT}{6\pi r\eta N},$$

where r is the radius of the diffusing molecule, N Avogadro's number, and η the viscosity.

hydrogen-bond, p. 57), so that we may expect the diffusion coefficients to be generally lower. The molecular weight will nevertheless be of importance, and it is interesting that even with diffusion in liquids the relationship :

$$DM^{\frac{1}{2}} = constant$$

is true under certain conditions. Danielli has applied the theory of temperature coefficients to the problem and has suggested a formula of rather wider scope than the simple $DM^{\frac{1}{2}} = constant$ relationship ; according to Danielli, the product

$$DM^{\frac{1}{2}}Q_{10}{}^{\left(\frac{T+10}{10}\right)}$$

should be constant, where Q_{10} is the temperature coefficient of diffusion, *i.e.*, the ratio of D for values of temperature, T and $T + 10°$. This formula was derived quite simply from kinetic theory on the assumption that the diffusing molecule made a series of jumps as indicated earlier, a jump requiring a certain critical *activation energy*. The temperature coefficient of such a process will vary with the amount of activation energy necessary for a jump. Thus if a high energy is required, at any moment there will be only a few molecules with the necessary energy to move ; raising the temperature will increase the number of molecules with this energy and have an appreciable effect on the net rate of diffusion. If, on the other hand, the activation energy is low, perhaps at any moment nearly every molecule will have this minimum energy, and so an increase in the temperature will not have a large effect on the net rate of movement.[1] Consequently, the higher the activation energy—*i.e.*, the higher the frictional resistance to be overcome—the greater will be the effect of a rise in temperature, and thus the larger the value of Q_{10}. When we are comparing molecules with largely varying frictional resistances we cannot expect the simple product $MD^{\frac{1}{2}}$ to be constant, the greater the resistance the smaller being the value of the product ; however, since Q_{10} increases with increasing resistance, the product of $DM^{\frac{1}{2}} Q_{10}{}^{\left(\frac{T+10}{10}\right)}$ should tend to be constant, and is indeed found to be so. If Q_{10} does not vary widely among the molecules studied, *i.e.*, if the frictional resistance is of the same order of magnitude, we may expect $DM^{\frac{1}{2}}$ to be tolerably constant.

Mechanism of Penetration of a Membrane

This view of the process of diffusion, developed by Danielli, permits of an understanding of the more complex process of penetration of a membrane. Diffusion into a cell is often very slow indeed, so that it may take place perhaps at one millionth or less of the rate that would be computed from a knowledge of the diffusion coefficient in water, if the membrane were supposed to be also aqueous. The membrane must therefore constitute a serious barrier to diffusion ; if it can be represented

---

[1] Thus we may think of a dual effect of temperature—increase in speed and increase in energy. The increase in speed means an increase in the rate of diffusion ; the effects of the increased energy depend on how much energy is required.

as a separate liquid or semi-liquid phase, separating internal and external environments of the cell, the penetration of this membrane must involve two main steps ; namely (a) the detachment of the penetrating molecule from its surrounding solvent molecules, and its entry, or jump, into the new phase, the membrane ; and (b) the detachment of the penetrating molecule from the molecules of the membrane and its jump into the solvent within the cell. Between these two steps there is of course the movement of the solute molecule within the membrane. Now the introduction of this complication into the transport process may modify profoundly its kinetics, since it may well be that the energy necessary to detach a molecule so completely from the water as to enable it to penetrate the membrane is so high that the number of molecules with this energy at ordinary temperatures is negligibly small ; in this case penetration into the cell is infinitely slow. Thus in simple diffusion, even with macromolecules of microscopically visible size, there is always a significant number of molecules with sufficient energy to make some translatory movement through the medium, as witnessed by the Brownian movement, so that within an extremely wide range of size and chemical structure transport by simple diffusion is possible. Where a membrane intervenes, on the other hand, we can expect, and do indeed find, a discontinuity in behaviour ; hence, for a given membrane, there are molecules that do not pass through at all, whilst others pass through at rates varying from the just measurable to those comparable with diffusion in water. In a similar way, the temperature coefficients of slow permeability processes are high (2–4), a fact that was known for a long time although it is comparatively recently that its true significance was appreciated (Danielli and Davson, 1935). The membrane considered so far is a hypothetical one, consisting essentially of a certain *phase*, different from the surrounding water ; and the difficulty in penetrating the membrane has been attributed to the difficulty the penetrating molecule experiences in separating itself from its surrounding water molecules and, later, from the membrane molecules. Certain artificial and natural membranes, however, are not continuous structures, but may be represented as a solid skeleton with pores, as for example the collodion or cellophane membranes so frequently studied. In an aqueous medium these pores will be filled with water, so that penetration of this membrane will be essentially a matter of diffusion through water ; thus so long as the pores are large enough to allow the molecules to pass through, we might expect the phenomena of penetration of collodion membranes to be little different from those of diffusion in aqueous solution.[1] We might therefore expect the product $PM^{\frac{1}{2}}$ to be tolerably constant, as with diffusion in aqueous solution, where this time P is the permeability constant. With certain large-pored membranes, this relationship holds over quite a wide range of molecules. When the average size of the pores is very small, however, considerable divergences from the constancy of this

---

[1] The absolute rate of penetration of the membrane would, however, be less than the rate computed on the assumption that the barrier consisted only of a layer of water of thickness equal to that of the membrane, because of the restriction on the area for diffusion, only the pores being available.

product are found.   In this case the larger molecules are unable to diffuse through the smaller pores, and the number passing across the membrane in unit time is smaller than in the case of the small molecules for *two* reasons ; first, because the average velocity is smaller, and secondly, because only certain pores can be used.   Thus we may expect, with a pore membrane, that the magnitude of the product $PM^{\frac{1}{2}}$ will fall off as the size of the penetrating molecule increases, until a point is reached when the number of pores permitting the passage of the molecule is negligible, the membrane being impermeable to molecules of this size and above.   In Table VIII some values of $PM^{\frac{1}{2}}$ are shown for a small-pored collodion membrane, and it is seen that $PM^{\frac{1}{2}}$ falls off considerably with increasing molecular size [1] of the penetrating substances.   A study of this product is therefore a valuable tool in the elucidation of the mechanism of permeability in certain natural membranes.

TABLE VIII

Values of $PM^{\frac{1}{2}}$ and MR_D for a Small Pored Collodion Membrane
(Davson & Danielli, 1943)

Substance	Methyl Alcohol	Ethyl Alcohol	Propyl Alcohol	Butyl Alcohol	Ethylene Glycol	Glycerol	Glucose
$PM^{\frac{1}{2}}$ . .	5·2	2·0	0·8	0·7	0·2	0·21	0·0
MR_D .	8·2	12·8	17·5	22·2	14·4	20·6	37·5

The Measurement of Permeability

The speed with which a substance diffuses in a homogeneous medium is indicated by its diffusion constant or coefficient.   As we have seen, this involves a solution of the Fick equation, and the substitution, in this solution, of experimentally determined values of the amount of substance diffusing a certain distance in a known time through unit cross section.   The experimental set-up in the measurement of diffusion, moreover, is designed to permit a simple solution of the Fick equation.   In permeability studies the equation can generally be simplified, because the concentration gradient across the membrane may be considered to be uniform and therefore the simple ratio :

$$\frac{C_{Out} - C_{In}}{\text{Membrane Thickness}}$$

may be substituted for the differential dc/dx in Equation 4.   Thus we get :

$$dS/dt = \frac{D}{\text{Membrane Thickness}} (C_{Out} - C_{In})$$

[1] The relative volumes of molecules are best indicated by the values of the *molar refraction* given by :—

$$MR_D = \frac{n^2 - 1}{n^2 + 2} \cdot \frac{M}{\rho}$$

where n is the refractive index of the substance (for light corresponding to the D line of sodium), M is the molecular weight, and ρ the density.   The molar refraction is an additive property of the constituent atoms, so that it is easy to calculate the value for any given molecule by adding the " refraction equivalents " of its constituent groups.

or, since S/V is equal to the concentration inside, C_{In},

$$\frac{dC_{In}}{dt} = k\frac{A}{V}\,(C_{Out} - C_{In}) \quad . \quad . \quad . \quad . \quad . \quad . \quad (5)$$

where k has been substituted for $\dfrac{D}{\text{Membrane Thickness}}$ and is called the *permeability constant*; its units are those of velocity,[1] *e.g.*, cm./sec.

This treatment may be justified as follows. Fig. 96 represents a cell surrounded by an aqueous solution of the penetrating substance ; now the main obstacle to penetration of the cell is the membrane, so that although the transport of substance from the bulk of the external solution up to the membrane depends on a diffusion process, the rate of diffusion in the external medium is so much faster than diffusion into and through the membrane, that the concentration outside the cell remains effectively uniform, any decrease in the region of the cell being rapidly made good by diffusion from more remote areas. The concentration outside the cell is

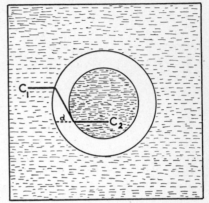

Fig. 96.

therefore C_{Out} ; within the cell the same state of affairs exists, a uniform concentration C_{In} at any moment being maintained throughout the cell contents. Across the membrane, therefore, the difference in concentration is $C_{Out} - C_{In}$. Since the membrane is very thin, even if the fall in concentration within the membrane is not uniform, the concentration gradient is given by $C_{Out} - C_{In}$, divided by the membrane thickness, without serious error. It is important to remember, however, that the fundamental assumption behind this simplification of the Fick diffusion equation is that the rate of penetration of the membrane is small compared with the rate of diffusion in the aqueous medium ; if this condition is not fulfilled—for example with very rapidly penetrating substances— the concentration is not uniform inside the cell, the concentration nearest the membrane being higher than in other regions ; consequently the effective concentration gradient across the membrane is smaller than $C_{Out} - C_{In}$ divided by the membrane thickness.

From Equation 5 we see that the rate of change in concentration within the cell depends on the ratio A/V, other things being equal ; the great rapidity with which many exchanges occur between cells and their environment is, in fact, largely determined by the high value of this ratio ; thus a spherical cell of radius 1 cm. has a value of A/V equal to 3, whereas an egg, of radius 50μ, would have a value equal to 600, that is, equilibrium would be achieved in one 200th of the time.

[1] Often, when the dimensions of the cell are not known, $\dfrac{kA}{V}$ is combined into a single constant, k' ; its units are 1/sec.(sec.$^{-1}$).

Experimentally it is often possible to maintain the external concentration of a penetrating substance constant, by use of a large volume of external medium in comparison with the volume of the cell or cells being studied. The solution of Equation 5 then becomes very simple, especially if the area and volume of the cell remain effectively constant ; it takes the form :

$$k = \frac{V}{At} \; ln \; \frac{C_{Out} - C_{In}}{C_{Out} - C'_{In}} \; \cdots \cdots \cdots \quad (6)$$

where C_{In} and C'_{In} are the concentrations in the cell before and after the interval of time, t.

Thus if, by chemical determination,[1] the amount of substance penetrating a cell is known, it is simply a matter of substitution in Equation 6 to find k, the permeability constant.

The force driving water into the cell may be represented as the difference of osmotic pressure, so that the equation describing the rate of penetration is written in the form :

$$\frac{dV}{dt} = k \, A \, (P_i - P_o) \; \cdots \cdots \cdots \quad (7)$$

where P_i and P_o are the osmotic pressures of the solution inside and outside the cell. It is customary to give the permeability constant as a certain *volume* of water penetrating unit area of the cell in unit time when the difference of osmotic pressure is one atmosphere ; however, to make the figures comparable with those for solute molecules, it is best to indicate the permeability in the same units, *i.e.*, cm./sec., and this involves expressing the amount of water in moles and the difference of osmotic pressure in terms of the difference in concentration of osmotically active material in moles per cubic centimetre of solvent.[2]

The details of the experimental measurement of permeability constants need not be entered into here ; it is sufficient to note that the evaluation of the constant requires a knowledge of how much material enters the cell, in a given time, and the area and volume of the cell. Often indirect measurements of the amount penetrating are possible ; for example, the penetration of water is associated with a swelling of the cell which may be measured optically (*e.g.*, Lucké, Larrabee & Hartline) ; the penetration of solute is frequently associated with a simultaneous penetration of water ; and if the permeability constant for the latter is known it is often possible

[1] Only in rare instances, as in the case of the large plant cells such as *Chara*, or *Valonia*, is it possible to analyse chemically the contents of a single cell ; with small cells, such as erythrocytes, a suspension may be added to a large volume of medium containing the penetrating substance ; at intervals samples may be withdrawn, centrifuged down, and the cells analysed chemically.

[2] The use of different units by different authors to describe permeability constants makes comparison very difficult ; the following conversion factors are therefore useful. If the constant is given as moles/sq. micron of surface/sec/mole. per litre concentration-difference, it must be multiplied by 10^{11} to convert to cm./sec. Permeability to water is almost invariably given as cubic micra of water crossing one square micron of surface in one second with a difference of osmotic pressure of one atmosphere between the inside and outside of the cell. A pressure-difference of one atmosphere, at 27° C., corresponds to a concentration-difference of 1/24,000 moles/cm.[3] ; the complete conversion factor is 0·13, to bring the units to cm./sec.

to deduce the permeability constant for the solute from the observed changes in volume (Jacobs & Stewart, 1932), and so on.

Radioactive Isotopes. The most important advance in the methodology has been provided in recent years by the use of radioactive isotopes. By bombardment of an element with neutrons in the cyclotron or atomic pile, new elements may be formed with unstable nuclei which are radioactive, and by the emission of a particle, *e.g.*, a positive or negative electron, are transformed to a new element. The unstable radioactive element is isotopic with an ordinary, non-radioactive, element, in the sense that its outer configuration of electrons is identical, so that chemically it behaves in exactly the same manner as its non-radioactive isotope ; *e.g.*, Cl^{38}, obtained by irradiating Cl^{37} with neutrons, has an atomic weight of 38 instead of 37 ; its chemical behaviour is identical with that of ordinary chlorine ; its nucleus is, however, unstable, so that by the emission of a negative electron it becomes argon. By the use of a Geiger counter the estimation of minute amounts of radioactive isotope is possible. The application of isotopes to permeability studies becomes clear if we consider an example. Suppose we wish to find the rate of penetration of Na^+ into a cell ; if, to the medium surrounding the cell, a small quantity of Na^{24} is added, this will cross the membrane and mix with the ordinary Na^{23} within the cell ; the rate at which the cell contents become radioactive thus measures the permeability of the membrane to Na^+. At equilibrium the proportions of radioactive to non-radioactive Na^+ will be the same within and outside the cell, consequently if the concentrations of Na^+ are the same inside and out, the radioactivity of the two media (generally indicated as so many counts per minute), will be the same. If the concentration of Na^{23} is normally greater outside, then, of course, at equilibrium the outside solution will be the more active ; but the *specific activities*, *i.e.*, the radioactivities divided by the concentrations of Na^{23}, will be equal. The importance of choosing a correct equation for describing permeability to radioactive isotopes cannot be overestimated ; often quite illusory results are obtained by measuring changes in activity, as opposed to specific activity.

Heavy Water. A water molecule containing one or two atoms of *deuterium*, the isotope of hydrogen with an atomic weight of two, is isotopic with ordinary water ; deuterium is not radioactive but its concentration may be measured accurately by taking account of its greater atomic weight which gives *heavy water* a greater density than that of ordinary water. Methods of estimating the specific gravity of small amounts of water to one part in ten million have been developed, so that it is possible to measure the rate of penetration of heavy water into a cell by placing the latter in its natural medium in which some of the ordinary water has been replaced by heavy water. The heavy water molecules exchange with ordinary water molecules, and the rate of penetration can be calculated from the changes in specific gravity of the water within the cell.

The main advantage of the isotopic method resides in the opportunity it provides for studying exchanges of matter when the cell is in an approximately normal environment. Thus, by the classical methods, in order to measure the rate of penetration of water, the cell was placed in a hypotonic medium, and its rate of swelling determined ; to obtain accurately measurable degrees of swelling the medium had to be considerably diluted, often to half its original strength, and since the behaviour of cell membranes may be considerably modified by a change in the composition of the external medium, it was impossible to say how normal the permeability to water was. Moreover, the penetration of water was associated with a swelling far beyond the normal limits, so that the membrane was stretched. As we shall see, the isotope technique has revolutionised the study of the permeability of cells to such ions as Na^+ and K^+ since their permeability constants are generally low, and large concentration gradients must be established to obtain a measurable rate of penetration ; this has involved, by the classical chemical techniques, making large changes in the concentrations of Na^+ and K^+ in the medium surrounding the cell, a procedure capable of profoundly modifying its normal behaviour.

Permeability to Non-Electrolytes

Lipoid-Solubility and Molecular Size. The classical studies of Overton, on plant cells, and of Hedin and Gryns on the erythrocyte, brought out the important fact that the rate of penetration of a substance into a cell was largely determined by its lipoid-solubility, or, as it is generally expressed to-day, by its oil-water partition coefficient.[1] Substances such as ethers, ketones, and aldehydes penetrated so rapidly that their actual rates could not be measured, whereas the more water-soluble glycerol, ethylene glycol and erythritol penetrated much more slowly. A great deal of the early work was carried out on dye-stuffs, since these were easy to estimate chemically, and in general it tended to confirm Overton's lipoid-solubility generalisation ; but attempts to establish an exact parallelism between the lipoid-solubility and rate of penetration were unsuccessful. However, dyestuffs are generally weak acids or bases and it was argued by Nierenstein that, if the reason why a lipoid-soluble substance tended to enter a cell rapidly was because it was able to concentrate in a fatty membrane, then the presence of acidic and basic groups in the membrane would also be of importance in enabling this accumulation to take place ; consequently, instead of measuring the olive-oil/water partition coefficient, the coefficient between water and olive-oil containing certain acids and bases was considered to be the more suitable standard for comparison. By this means Nierenstein was able to obtain better correlations between partition coefficient and ease of penetration, but it must be remembered that the measurements were generally crude and non-quantitative. We may take it, however, that the substances studied can be divided into two main

---

[1] The partition coefficient is given by :—

$$\frac{\text{Concentration in Oil}}{\text{Concentration in Water}}$$

A molecule may be said to be appreciably " lipoid-soluble " when its partition coefficient is greater than about 0·01.

classes : the strongly lipoid-soluble which penetrate rapidly, and the strongly water-soluble which penetrate slowly.

We may now pass to the accurate quantitative studies and see what further generalisations may be drawn from their results. The most extensive study comes from the Finnish school of Collander & Bärlund ; some of their results on the large unicellular alga, *Chara ceratophylla*, are shown in Fig. 97 where the permeability constant is plotted against partition coefficient. The general trend of the points confirms the lipoid-solubility rule, a substance such as ethyl alcohol, with a partition coefficient

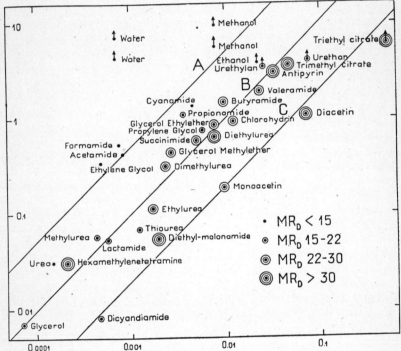

Fig. 97. Permeability of *Chara* cells plotted against oil/water partition coefficient. Ordinates : permeability in cm./hr. Abscissæ : oil/water partition coefficient. (Collander. *Physiol. Plant.*)

approaching unity, penetrating more than ten thousand times as rapidly as erythritol with a partition coefficient of less than 0·0001. As Collander & Bärlund point out, however, there is some evidence from these results that the size of the molecule plays a rôle in determining its ease of penetration, smaller molecules generally penetrating more rapidly than would otherwise be predicted from their partition coefficients. This effect of molecular size had been frequently observed before, particularly in the study of the sulphur bacteria, *Beggiatoa mirabilis,* and is well brought out by some results of Höber & Ørskov on the erythrocyte. In general, however, as Höber & Ørskov have pointed out, the rates of penetration are only proportional to the molecular size if groups of homologous compounds are considered, *e.g.*, the acid-amides ; thus if glycerol and propionamide are compared in the ox erythrocyte, propionamide is found to penetrate some 400 times as rapidly as glycerol, although their molecular sizes are about the same ; clearly the greater lipoid-solubility of propionamide is predominating here.

Further results on the effects of molecular size can be obtained from Jacobs' (1935) work on a series of alcohols ; in general, the rate of penetration decreases with increasing size, but a simple application of the test, indicated on p. 173, for establishing whether penetration is determined by passage through large water-filled pores, shows that no such simple mechanism is operative. Hence, if there is any molecular sieve effect, the pores must be of a size comparable with the penetrating molecules.

The general observation that the ease of penetration of a substance was some function of its lipoid-solubility and its molecular size led to the theory, particularly developed by Höber, that the membrane surrounding a cell could be considered as a mosaic containing lipoid regions and pore regions, the latter presumably being built up of some fibrous protein in a mesh-work. The relative preponderance of the lipoid-solubility and molecular volume effects would then be due to the relative areas of lipoid and protein material ; a small lipoid-soluble substance, on this basis, would be able to penetrate more rapidly than a large substance of the same oil-water partition coefficient because it would be restrained by the pores to a less extent. The behaviour of *Beggiatoa* in which molecular size apparently plays a predominant role would thus represent an extreme case in which the area of lipoid was minimal. Danielli's analysis of the mechanism of penetration, briefly entered into earlier, has shown, however, that the existence of the molecular volume effect may in many cases be illusory, in the sense that the increase in the number of groups in a molecule not only increases its size but also other characteristics which may be of paramount importance in determining its ease of penetration.

Danielli's Analysis. As we have seen, Danielli regards the process of penetration as first a detachment of the penetrating molecule from its surrounding water molecules. Next, the molecule travels through the fatty layer by simple diffusion ; this movement will not be continuous, however, but will occur in a succession of jumps ; finally the molecule must acquire sufficient energy to detach itself from the fatty material of the membrane and enter the water inside the cell. Now the important point brought out by Danielli is that, with substances containing polar groups, such as $-OH$, $-NH_2$, $-SO_3H$, etc., the energy necessary for detachment from surrounding water molecules is of a high order, because of the tendency for the polar groups to form chemical linkages (hydrogen-bonds) with water molecules. The subsequent steps are relatively easy for a compound of this nature, so that with a water-soluble substance the rate of penetration will be largely determined by its ease of passing from water to lipid.

The process of penetration can thus be represented by a simple potential energy diagram as in Fig. 98 ; the molecule, to enter the membrane, must make a potential energy-jump, of height μ_a (*i.e.*, it must wait until it gets this amount of energy before making the transition). Within the membrane it has a smaller potential energy than that necessary to enter, *i.e.*, it tends to adhere to the membrane molecules, and, to pass back into the aqueous phase, it must detach itself from these, *i.e.*, make the jump μ_b. In passing through the membrane, a succession of small jumps are made of height μ_e ; on leaving the membrane a jump of height μ_b must be made, μ_b being a measure of the attraction of the membrane molecules for the substance considered. The actual rate of penetration is therefore a function of a number of energy-jumps ; and if these can be determined, it should be possible to calculate the permeability constant. It should be noted that the potential jumps μ_a and μ_b determine the partition coefficient, the relative concentrations of a molecule in two layers of fat and oil being determined by the ease with which the molecules can pass from one layer to the other, in fact the partition coefficient is equal to the ratio a/b,

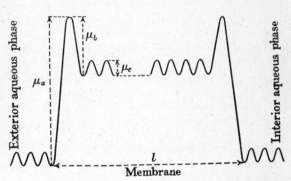

FIG. 98. Potential energy barrier representing the cell membrane. (Danielli. *Proc. VIth. Int. Congr. Cyt.*)

where a measures the rate of passage through the potential barrier μ_a, and b through the barrier μ_b. According to Danielli's mathematical analysis, P, the permeability constant, is given by :

$$P = \frac{ae}{nb + 2e} \quad \cdots \cdots \cdots \quad (8)$$

where a, b, and e are rates of diffusion across the potential energy jumps μ_a, μ_b, μ_e, and n is the average number of potential energy jumps within the membrane. This analysis is of great value in that it enables us to see under what conditions the partition coefficient will determine ease of penetration, and also the mathematical form of the relationship between permeability constant and partition coefficient. If a substance penetrates very slowly it can be shown that $2e$ is much greater than nb ; the equation then takes the form :—

$$P = a/2$$

i.e., the difficulty in detaching itself from the water phase overwhelmingly determines the rate of penetration of the molecule ; thus qualitatively we may expect that increasing the number of OH-groups in a homologous series of compounds, by successively increasing the formation of hydrogen-bond linkages with water, will decrease a and consequently the rate of penetration.

Moreover, it is possible to deduce the relationship between partition coefficient and permeability for slowly penetrating molecules, since B, the partition coefficient, is equal to a/b ; thus $P = \frac{1}{2}bB$, *i.e.*, a simple linear relationship between P and B is not to be expected.[1] When the rate of penetration of the molecule is rapid, on the other hand, the frictional resistance, indicated by μ_e, is large in comparison with the energy-jump necessary for the molecule to pass from membrane to water, consequently $2e$ may be negligible compared with nb, the equation then simplifies to :

$$P = a/b \times e/n$$

Since a/b is equal to the partition coefficient, and e, the rate of passage through the membrane probably does not vary much between rapidly penetrating molecules, we can say that $PM^{\frac{1}{2}} = $ const. $\times$ B (at constant temperature), *i.e.*, the permeability is determined by the partition coefficient and the mass of the penetrating molecule.

Danielli's quantitative analysis has thus been of great value in showing us what is to be broadly expected of a simple fatty membrane ; and it is of great interest that the experimental findings on *Chara* conform fairly well with expectation. Moreover, by making a number of approximations, it is possible to calculate the order of magnitude of the permeability constants for substances penetrating a layer of oil, and there is a fair parallelism between the absolute magnitudes, and also between the relative values, when such calculated figures are compared with the actual permeability constants obtained from a number of different cells.

TABLE IX

Permeability Constants, in cm./sec. (multiplied by 10^5), for Various Cells. B is Olive-Oil/Water Partition Coefficient. (After Davson & Danielli, 1943.)

	Ox Erythrocyte	Arbacia	Chara	Beggiatoa	B
Trimethylcitrate	—	—	6·7	—	0·047
Propionamide	—	2·3	3·6	—	0·0036
Acetamide	—	1·0	1·5	—	0·00083
Glycol	0·21	0·73	1·2	1·39	0·00049
Urea	7·8	—	0·11	1·58	0·00015
Malonamide	—	—	0·0039	—	0·00008
Diethylene glycol	0·075	0·43	—	—	0·005
Glycerol	0·0017	0·005	0·021	1·06	0·00007
Erythritol	—	—	0·0013	0·84	0·00003
Sucrose	—	—	0·0008	0·14	0·00003

Species Variability. This simple treatment, however, must not be allowed to obscure the fact that the permeability of different cells to the same substance may vary very widely indeed. This is indicated in Table

---

[1] The value of b is given by : $b = $ constant $\times M^{-\frac{1}{2}} exp\left(\dfrac{-\mu_b}{RT}\right)$. Thus P is related to the partition coefficient by the equation : $PM^{\frac{1}{2}} exp\left(\dfrac{\mu_b}{RT}\right) = B \times$ constant (at constant temperature). From a knowledge of the energies of adhesion between molecules an estimate of μ_b can be made so that the function on the left-hand side can be computed for different molecules. On plotting the values, so derived, against B, a straight line is obtained.

IX, and is brought out even more strongly by comparisons of the permeabilities of different species of erythrocytes. Thus it is found that the permeability of the ox erythrocyte to erythritol is less than one-hundredth that of the mouse erythrocyte ; an essentially similar result is obtained with glycerol ; in fact, the studies of Jacobs & Glassman have revealed some remarkable variations in permeability of the erythrocyte with the different species examined. Moreover, it is found that when a species of erythrocyte is encountered in which the permeability to glycerol, for example, is much higher than in many other species, this high rate is not associated with higher rates of penetration of all other comparable molecules, *e.g.*, ethylene glycol ; in other words, the high rate of penetration of glycerol in the rat erythrocyte is not necessarily an expression of the presence of a more " permeable " membrane. It would appear, rather, that the membrane is " specialised " in some way to permit the penetration of this unusually rapidly penetrating molecule.[1] We shall see later that cells are capable of transferring solutes against concentration gradients, *i.e.*, metabolic energy is converted into osmotic energy ; this process is given the name of *active transport*, but is not synonymous with the " special mechanism " of permeability considered here, although the two may be, and probably are, closely related. By " special mechanism " is simply meant that the membrane is differentiated in such a way as to permit rapid movement through the membrane in either direction ; only if it can be shown that metabolic energy is being supplied to the transport process can it be shown to be active. There is no conclusive evidence that energy is supplied to the transport of glycerol (*cf.* LeFevre, 1948). Apart from this " specialisation," however, large variations in rate occur when a variety of species are examined. This may be due to variations in the partition coefficient of a given substance from membrane to membrane ; the coefficient chosen as a standard of reference has been the olive-oil/water partition coefficient ; if the membranes of different cells do not have the same chemical constitutions it is clear that the partition coefficients for a given substance will be different ; consequently, other things being equal, the permeability constants will be different too.[2] Thus variations in the chemical nature of the membrane can play a large part in producing changes, not only in the absolute rates of penetration of a variety of molecules, but also in their relative rates. According to Danielli, when the

[1] This viewpoint is strengthened by Danielli's analysis of the permeability constants for a number of compounds ; thus he found that the product $PM^{\frac{1}{2}} Q_{10}^{\left(\frac{T + 10}{10}\right)}$ was reasonably constant for the molecules glycerol, dioxypropane, diethylene glycol and triethylene glycol, in the case of the ox erythrocyte, whereas in the case of the erythrocytes of man, the rat, and the rabbit the product for glycerol deviated strongly from that obtained with the other compounds, a result suggesting that a fraction of the membrane was specialised to permit rapid penetration of glycerol into the rabbit, human and rat erythrocytes, *i.e.*, those erythrocytes that showed a high rate of penetration of this substance.

[2] Collander (1947) has drawn attention to this matter ; he points out that butyramide and tricarballylic acid have equal partition coefficients between ether and water (0·06), whereas between olive oil and water they are widely different (0·009 and 0·0001 respectively). Collander has made a systematic study of the partition coefficients of many substances between water and several oils and his paper is a valuable source of information, with references to the appropriate literature.

possibilities—on passing from one cell to another—of variation in the partition coefficient, the frictional resistance, and the thickness of the membrane are taken into account, variations in permeability constant for the same substance within a range of 100,000- to 1,000,000-fold can be accounted for. It should be noted, however, that Dziemian's gross analyses of the lipids and proteins of different species of erythrocyte have failed to show any correlation between the rates of penetration of certain standard solutes and the chemical composition. Whether this is because the analytical methods are not sufficiently discriminating, or because variations in permeability from one species of erythrocyte to another depend more on the actual orientation of the lipid molecules than on their chemical nature, is an open question. According to Ballentine & Parpart, the lipid-splitting enzyme, lipase, accelerates the penetration of glycerol into the ox erythrocyte but decreases the rate in the case of the rabbit cell. Before leaving the discussion of the influence of lipoid-solubility on permeability, we may return to the problem of the " sieve effect." The results presented by Collander (Fig. 97) indicate a definite tendency for molecules of the same partition coefficient to penetrate more rapidly the smaller they are. According to Danielli's analysis, this need not reflect the presence of a molecular sieve, but Collander has recently (1949) drawn attention to the fact that water and methanol, at least, do indeed penetrate far more rapidly than can be accounted for on the basis of lipoid-solubility, even when Danielli's treatment is applied.

TABLE X

Permeability Constants, cm./sec., for Water. Values have been Multiplied by 100. (*Taken from Davson & Danielli,* 1943 ; *Value for* Nitella *taken from Osterhout,* 1950)

Arbacia egg	Zoothamnium	Onion Cell	Nitella	Ox Erythrocyte	Rabbit Leucocyte
2·1	2·6–5·3	6·3	1·8	5·2	6·3

Permeability to Water. The permeability of cells to water requires brief comment ; from the results shown in Table X it will be seen that water has a comparatively high permeability constant, although its rate of penetration of a cell is very much less than that of a layer of water ; thus the values in Table X range between 1·8 and $6·3.10^{-2}$ whereas penetration through water would give values about ten thousand times as large ; in comparison with urea, penetrating the ox erythrocyte—the most rapid substance for which accurate figures are available—the permeability constant for water is very high ; this may be due to the fairly high (comparatively speaking) partition coefficient of water in the membrane, and to an exceptionally low viscous resistance ; it would certainly seem that cells are adapted to permit the rapid exchanges of water across their membranes almost universally observed. Collander (1949) has drawn attention to the high permeability of plant cell membranes to water ; he quotes a value of 0·0007 for the oil-water partition coefficient and emphasises that water penetrates *Chara* cells at about the same rate as methanol, although the partition coefficient for the latter substance is much the higher (0·01 approx.).

TABLE XI

Relative Rates of Penetration of Different Sugars into Erythrocytes
(Wilbrandt, 1938)

	Arabinose	Xylose	Fructose	Sorbose	Galactose	Glucose	Mannose
Man . .	270	288	5·2	34	66	44	183
Dog . .	0·34	0·31	0·12	0·068	0·01	0	0
Rabbit .	0·97	1·34	0·45	0·42	0·13	0·15	0·10
Rat . .	1·09	1·24	0·38	0·57	0·21	0·061	0·07

Permeability to Sugars. The hexoses are highly important metabolically and, from a biological standpoint, should be able to penetrate a cell membrane with some ease. On the other hand, we may note that structurally the sugar molecule, with its large number of OH-groups, is most unsuited for penetrating a lipoid membrane ; and it would not be surprising to find a " special mechanism " operating in its transfer across cell membranes. It is unfortunate that quantitative studies on the permeability to sugars are not numerous ; Wilbrandt has measured the relative rates of penetration of a number of sugars into different species of erythrocyte. His results are given in Table XI ; he does not give absolute values of the permeability constants but estimates of these may be made from his curves. Thus for glucose penetrating into the human erythrocyte, the " half life " is about twenty-five seconds, corresponding to a constant of $1·5.10^{-6}$ cm./sec., *i.e.*, about 100 times greater than that of the smaller molecule glycerol penetrating the ox erythrocyte. In the rabbit, rat, and dog erythrocytes, however, permeability was very low, in fact so small that it was inadequate to account for the utilisation of sugar by the cell, so that it is possible that glucose is metabolised at the surface. Some evidence for the existence of an active transport of glucose is provided by the finding of Bang & Ørskov, subsequently confirmed by Wilbrandt, Guensberg & Lauener, that the permeability constant decreases with increasing concentration of sugar outside the cell. This would suggest that glucose enters the cell by combining with some group in the surface ; at the high concentrations this group would be saturated and so give a low overall rate of penetration ; similar saturation phenomena are found with absorption of glucose from the intestine and the renal tubule (pp. 303 and 338). In the case of muscle it would seem from the work of Sacks that the penetration of glucose involves a preliminary combination with a phosphate group.[1]

This quantitative study of the relative rates of penetration of non-electrolytes brings out the subtle nature of the barrier separating the contents of the cell from its environment ; a given cell is capable of

---

[1] Le Fevre (1948) has discussed the general problem of active transport of non-electrolytes by the red cells. Amino-acids have been studied by Ussing (1943) ; their penetration is apparently slow.

restraining the penetration of materials to varying degrees, ranging from complete exclusion, as in the case of sucrose in many cells, to the rapid exchanges found with water ; these characteristics are the properties that may be anticipated from an inert membrane consisting of a thin layer of fatty material ; nevertheless, we shall see that the stabilisation of the internal environment of the cell demands, not only a selective membrane, but also the supply of metabolic energy to fight against the continual losses to the external environment that must be occasioned by even very small degrees of permeability to substances important for the internal environment.

Permeability to Ions

Salts in aqueous solution dissociate into ions capable of independent movement, so that the permeability of a membrane to salts is the permeability of the membrane to the separate ions of which the salt is made up ; since a membrane can exhibit very different permeabilities to the separate

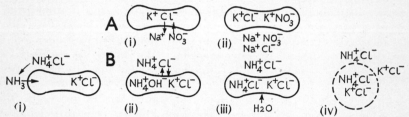

FIG. 99.   A. Exchange of Cl^- with NO_3^- across a cation-impermeable and anion-permeable membrane.   B. Illustrating the penetration of an ammonium salt. NH_4Cl hydrolyses to NH_3 which penetrates the cell ; the NH_4OH formed within the cell produces OH^--ions which exchange with external Cl^-.   The increased osmotic pressure, resulting from the penetration of NH_4Cl in this manner, leads to hæmolysis.

ions of a salt it will be quite unjustifiable to speak of the " permeability to a salt " ; the individual ions must be considered on their merits.   Moreover, where the salt contains a weak base or weak acid, one cannot be certain that any penetration that takes place is due to the migration of ions, since it may be that the undissociated weak acid or base penetrates.   These two points are illustrated in Fig. 99.   In (A) we may imagine a cell with a membrane permeable to Cl^- and NO_3^-, but not to K^+ and Na^+ ; the surrounding medium is $NaNO_3$, and NO_3^- exchanges with Cl^- to give, at equilibrium, a mixture of chloride and nitrate inside and outside the cell. In (B) the cell is permeable to Cl^-, as before, and impermeable to K^+ and NH_4^+ ; it is, however, permeable to the ammonia molecule, NH_3. The NH_4Cl hydrolyses to NH_4OH and HCl, and the NH_4OH breaks down to NH_3 and H_2O ; the NH_3 penetrates the cell and combines with water there to form NH_4OH ; the OH^--ion, so formed, leaves the cell to exchange with a Cl^--ion, so that, in effect, ammonium chloride has entered the cell. The rate of accumulation of ammonium chloride in the cell will depend not only on the rate of migration of NH_3, but also on the rate of exchange of Cl^- with OH^-.   Thus, placing the cell in a series of ammonium salts, NH_4Cl,

NH_4NO_3, NH_4 Acetate, etc., may be expected to give varying rates of entry of ammonium, according to the permeability of the cell to the different anions of the salts, provided that the determining factor is the rate of penetration of the ion rather than that of NH_3.

Since the transport of ions across natural membranes is almost invariably associated with secretory processes, and is also intimately connected with the potentials across the membrane, the exact quantitative studies on the permeability of membranes to ions will be described only after the problem of bioelectric potentials has been introduced, and in connection with secretory processes in general. For the present, therefore, we need only go into some qualitative aspects, paying particular attention to the effects of the cell's environment on ionic permeability.

Energetic Considerations. With few exceptions, it would seem that the penetration of ions is a slow process by comparison with many of the non-electrolytes considered above. The exceptions so far definitely proved are certain anions, such as Cl^- and HCO_3^- in the case of the erythrocyte, and probably H^+ and OH^- in the case of all cells.[1] A generally low order of permeability to ions could be predicted from a knowledge of the relative concentrations of these ions in the cell and its environment ; thus the salt composition of the erythrocyte's internal and external environments may be roughly represented as follows :—

Inside	Outside
K^+Hb	
K^+Cl^-	Na^+Cl^-
K^+HCO_3	$Na^+HCO_3^-$

If the membrane were permeable to all the ions of this system, the concentration of K^+ within the cell would fall, its rate of loss depending on the permeability coefficients for K^+ and Cl^- ; if the membrane were impermeable to Na^+ and K^+, but permeable to the anions, the system would be stable, but such a postulate begs the question as to how the K^+ got into the cell in the first place. If the membrane were impermeable to K^+, but permeable to Na^+ and anions, the system would be unstable since NaCl could diffuse into the cell, increasing its osmotic pressure and so eventually causing hæmolysis (p. 158) ; if the membrane were permeable to K^+ and anions, and impermeable to Na^+, K^+ would be lost from the cell. We must therefore conclude, granted that the membrane is permeable to anions, either that the membrane is impermeable to Na^+ and K^+, or that it *is* permeable to these cations, and that the continual loss of K^+, and gain of Na^+, are compensated by some " active transport " or secretory mechanism. Recent evidence indicates that this is indeed the case, so that the cell must perform osmotic work to draw in K^+ against a concentration gradient ; the rate at which this work is done must clearly depend on the rate of escape, a large rate of escape demanding a rapid performance of

---

[1] Certain species of bacteria, *e.g.*, the pathogenic mycobacteria, are able to withstand exposure to high concentrations of acid and alkali, concentrations that are normally destructive to cytoplasm ; it may be that these bacteria are impermeable to H^+ and OH^-.

work. The upper limit to the amount of work the cell is capable of doing is given by its O_2-consumption, assuming 100 per cent. efficiency ; in the case of the erythrocyte this amounts to about 40 cals./kg./hr. With a permeability constant for K^+ equal to that of urea ($7\cdot8.10^{-5}$ cm./sec.), for example, the work necessary would be about $1\cdot8.10^6$ cal./kg./hr., *i.e.*, far greater than that of which the cell is capable even supposing 100 per cent. efficiency. With a constant of 1.10^{-9} cm./sec., *i.e.*, with a very slow rate of penetration, the rate of work would be ca. 13 cals./kg./hr. and hence within the limits imposed by the O_2-consumption. In general, then, on economy grounds, any cell that maintains a high concentration gradient of salt across its membrane must show a low degree of permeability to at least some of the ions of its internal and external environments. So low is the permeability of the erythrocyte membrane to Na^+ and K^+, for example, that it was considered up till quite recently that, in its normal environment, the cell was actually impermeable to these ions ; and certainly the osmotic behaviour (studied, of course, over short periods of time) indicated that this assumption could be made without error.

Anions. The rapid penetration of anions such as Cl^- and HCO_3^- is, on

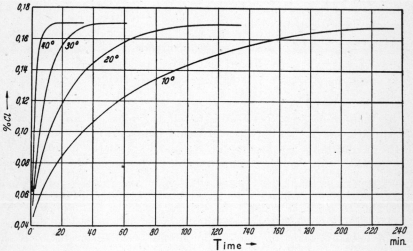

Fig. 100. Illustrating the exchange of Cl^- in the erythrocyte with SO_4^{--} outside. Ordinates : chloride in outside medium. Abscissæ : time in min. (Luckner. *Pflüg. Arch.*)

the other hand, well established ; thus Dirken and Mook found that complete exchange of Cl^- with HCO_3^- occurred within less than one second, and Luckner (1939) found a " half-life " for the exchange of $0\cdot14$ sec. at $24°$ C., indicating a permeability constant in the region of $2\cdot5.10^{-4}$ cm./sec. It will be appreciated that the rate of exchange depends on the permeabilities of the two ions, since in the interests of electrical neutrality, on the average, the loss of one Cl^-, for example, from the cell must be associated by the gain of one negative ion of the same valency from the medium. Where one ion penetrates very much more slowly, the rate of exchange is almost entirely dominated by the permeability of the slower ion ; thus the Cl^-—HCO_3^- exchange is too rapid to measure with the classical chemical techniques ; the exchange of Cl^- with SO_4^{--}, on the other hand, is sufficiently slow for this purpose ; Fig. 100 shows some results of Luckner on the exchange, from which one may deduce a permeability constant for SO_4^{--} of 4.10^{-8} cm./sec. Most of the work on the exchange of anions in the erythrocyte is only qualitative ; one may draw the following general conclusion from a variety of studies, namely that rate of penetration of inorganic anions follows the series :—

$$CNS^- > I^- > NO_3^- > Cl^- > SO_4^{--} > HPO_4^{--} > \text{Tartrate, Citrate}$$

the large divalent ions, with their high degree of hydration, penetrating the more slowly, so that an actual impermeability to the even larger anions, tartrate and citrate, has been claimed. With organic anions lipoid-solubility, *i.e.*, the predominance of non-polar groups in the ion, appears to favour penetration ; thus Höber found increasing rates of penetration on ascending the series of aliphatic acids from acetate (C_2) to caproate (C_6), whilst the more polar anions, such as succinate, tartrate, fumarate and citrate, apparently did not penetrate. Green's quantitative results on the human erythrocyte are as follows :—

Acid	C_1	C_2	C_3	C_4	C_5	C_6	C_7	C_8
k (cm./sec.)	3·6	10	90	96·5	167	102	35	41·5

where the figures have been multiplied by 10^7. It will be noted that the permeability constant increases up to C_5— valeric acid—and beyond this varies rather irregularly ; this irregularity may be due to the " narcotic " activity of the aliphatic fatty acids beyond C_5 (Davson, 1940). Studies on amino-acids—of great biological importance—are rare ; Ussing has recently shown that their rate of penetration into the erythrocyte is very slow, equilibrium being achieved in less than twenty-four hours so far as the mono-amino-mono-carboxylic acids are concerned ; the di-carboxylic acids, aspartic and glutamic, hardly penetrate the cell at all.

Salts of Weak Acids and Bases. The generally low order of permeability found with most ions, by comparison with many non-electrolytes, is unquestionably due to the electrical charge on the ion ; this results in the attraction of an atmosphere of water dipoles around it and makes the energy necessary for the molecule to penetrate the membrane of a high order. This is well brought out by the behaviour of acids that may exist as anions and in the undissociated form ; their rates of penetration are generally very much more rapid than those of comparable stronger acids, and is probably due to the fact that the penetration may take place as the undissociated acid. Thus with the Na^+ salt of a weak acid, NaA, owing to hydrolysis there is an appreciable amount of the weak acid HA present in solution :

$$NaA + H_2O \rightleftarrows NaOH + HA$$

If the HA penetrates the cell, the reaction goes to the right, causing more HA to be formed ; the acid accumulates within the cell whilst the medium becomes more alkaline ; however, the OH^--ions diffuse into the cell and Cl^--ions come out in exchange ; the OH^--ions react with HA to give H_2O and A^--ions, so that the final result is equivalent to the exchange of A^- with Cl^-. To what extent this is a significant factor in the penetration of anions of sodium salts is not clear ; in the case of the ammonium salts, on the other hand, where both basic and acidic radicles are weak, and consequently the amount of hydrolysis is much greater, weak acids, according to Jacobs, penetrate predominantly in the undissociated form. Thus the penetration of NH_4Cl into the erythrocyte goes according to the scheme indicated in Fig. 99, (B) ; NH_3 enters the erythrocyte and tends to make its contents alkaline ; the OH^--ions thus formed, diffuse out in exchange for Cl^-. The result is that NH_4Cl has, in effect, penetrated the cell. Ørskov observed that CO_2 accelerated the penetration of NH_4Cl into the erythrocyte.[1]   According to Jacobs

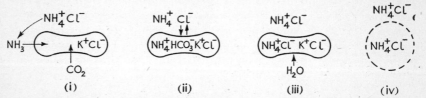

(i)   (ii)   (iii)   (iv)

FIG. 101. Jacobs' & Stewart's interpretation of the acceleration of the penetration of NH_4Cl into the erythrocyte by CO_2. CO_2 and NH_3 enter the cell to form NH_4HCO_3, and the HCO_3^--ions, so formed, exchange with Cl^--ions in the outside medium. (After Jacobs & Stewart. *J. gen. Physiol.*)

& Stewart (1942), the mechanism for this is illustrated by Fig. 101 ; as before, NH_3 penetrates the cell, but the presence of HCO_3^- in the latter, due to the addition of CO_2, provides adequate HCO_3^--ions to exchange for the Cl^--ions outside. If the HCO_3^--Cl^- exchange is more rapid than the OH^--Cl^- exchange, it follows that CO_2, by providing the necessary HCO_3^--ions, will accelerate the penetration of NH_4Cl. The formation of HCO_3^- from CO_2 and H_2O requires an enzyme, *carbonic anhydrase ;* this may be inhibited by sulphanilamide ; and the slowing of the penetration of NH_4Cl by this drug confirms the interpretation of Jacobs & Stewart. This is a remarkable finding since it suggests that HCO_3^- penetrates the erythrocyte membrane more rapidly than the much smaller ion, OH^-.

Cation Permeability in Erythrocytes. The erythrocyte seems to be a unique example of a cell with a very rapid exchange of anions, an exchange, moreover, not, apparently, complicated by secretory processes,[2] a feature that makes for ease in interpretation of the experimental data. The migration of cations in the erythrocyte, and the exchange of ions generally in other types of cell, are so closely linked with secretory or active transport

[1] In the normal plasma and cells, CO_2 and HCO_3^- are, of course, present ; under the experimental conditions usually employed for the measurement of penetration of ammonium salts, *i.e.*, the addition of a drop of blood to a large volume of the salt solution, the concentrations of CO_2 and HCO_3^- are very small.

[2] In the sense that the transport of anions is not dependent on metabolic activity.

processes that further discussion of normal ionic permeability will be deferred. Certain abnormal conditions in the erythrocyte may be briefly described, however, since they have a direct bearing on the nature of the plasma membrane. Erythrocytes placed in an isotonic NaCl medium lose their K^+ very slowly indeed, so that within an hour the loss is barely measurable. If the cells are caused to swell, by dilution of the medium, the loss of K^+ is accelerated ; a finding which suggests that a stretch, or deformation of the cell membrane, can modify its permeability. Another striking instance of an induced cation permeability is the rapid loss of K^+ that occurs from the erythrocytes of many species when they are placed in a non-electrolyte medium, for example, isotonic glucose. Addition of quite a small amount of salt reduces the rate of loss considerably, so that with a concentration of 0·09 M (the isotonic concentration is about 0·165 M) the cell is apparently normal (Fig. 102) ; Wilbrandt (1940), moreover, has shown that Ca^{++} salts are very much more effective in reducing this escape than Na^+ salts ; that the effect was in some way associated with the valency of the Ca^{++}-ion, was indicated by the observation that the ratio of the concentration of Na^+ over the square root of the concentration of Ca^{++}, required to produce the same effect, remained constant over a wide range of Na^+ and Ca^{++}

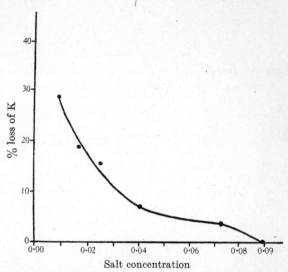

FIG. 102. Effect of added salt on the escape of K^+ from the human erythrocyte in isotonic sugar solution. Ordinates : per cent. loss of K^+ per 2 hr. Abscissæ : concentration of salt in the sugar solution. (Davson. *Biochem. J.*)

concentrations. This is by no means an isolated instance of an effect of the ionic concentrations in the medium on the normal physiological behaviour of a cell or tissue ; and it is now generally recognised that not only must the total salt concentration have at least a certain minimal value, but also the proportions of at least three important cations, Na^+, K^+, and Ca^{++}, must be maintained within certain limits if the cell is to be normal. To some extent a given ion may be replaced by another, *e.g.*, Na^+ by Li^+ ; K^+ by Rb^+ and Cs^+ ; and Ca^{++} by Sr^{++} and sometimes Ba^{++} ; and the effects are generally classed as *antagonistic phenomena*, the univalent ions tending to produce one effect, whilst the divalent ions produce the contrary. So far as permeability is concerned there is some evidence of a direct antagonism between Ca^{++} and univalent ions ; thus Lucké & McCutcheon found that the permeability of the *Arbacia* egg to water was increased by placing the cells in a non-electrolyte solution instead of sea-water (*i.e.*, the absence of electrolytes increased permeability just as with the erythrocyte) ; addition of Ca^{++} brought the permeability back to normal, whereas a mixture of univalent salts and Ca^{++} was less effective, although it contained the same amount of Ca^{++} ; the Na^+ salts were said to *antagonise* the action of Ca^{++}. Trivalent ions were even more effective than divalent ions. This is a straightforward case of antagonism, in which the effects of added Ca^{++} were reduced by addition of a univalent ion ; in the case of the erythrocyte's permeability to K^+, on the other hand, both Ca^{++} and Na^+ had the same effect in decreasing permeability, Na^+ merely being the less effective. Similarly Jacobs & Parpart have shown that Ca^{++} salts depress the permeability of the erythrocyte to water more effectively than Na^+ salts ; both salts have the same type of effect, however, so that there is no true antagonism.[1]

The Action of Narcotic Substances

Narcotics, such as the alcohols, urethanes, ether, and chloroform, depress the activity of the organism and, in appropriate concentration, kill it ; since exchanges across the membrane of the cell are of great importance to the metabolism taking place within it, it is of interest to see to what extent these substances affect permeability. In a high concentration a narcotic generally increases permeability and eventually, if the concentration is high enough, destroys the membrane. This destructive effect is manifest in the red cell by hæmolysis, *i.e.*, the membrane breaks down and allows the hæmoglobin molecules to escape. In lower concentrations, applied to the same cell, a rapid escape of K^+ (and often an increase in Na^+ concentration, Davson & Danielli, 1938 ; Ponder, 1947), takes place (Fig. 103). The effect is non-specific, in the sense that practically any fat-soluble, or surface-active, substance will cause this *pro-lytic* loss of

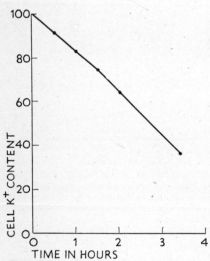

Fig. 103. Pro-lytic loss of K^+ from rabbit erythrocyte due to treatment with 0·8 per cent. *n*-butyl carbamate. (Davson. *J. cell. & comp. Physiol.*)

K^+, so that it would appear that the membrane is made unstable by the presence within it of foreign molecules in high concentration. In the case of non-electrolytes, penetrating the alga, *Chara*, Bärlund has shown that, whether the permeating substance is lipoid-soluble or

---

[1] Antagonism is thus used rather loosely ; Ca^{++} having the stronger effect than Na^+, presumably because of its higher valency, appears to antagonise the action of Na^+ but does not necessarily do so. A remarkable effect of Ca^{++} in preventing hæmolysis has been described by Lyman (p. 247).

-insoluble, the only effect of the narcotic, ether, is to cause a reversible increase in permeability ; similar effects are observed with the penetration of a variety of non-electrolytes into the erythrocyte of the ox, only an increase in permeability being found. In certain special cases of erythrocyte permeability, however, narcotics profoundly decrease the rate of penetration ; thus in the human erythrocyte the permeabilities of those substances that apparently show an unusually rapid rate of penetration, such as glycerol and erythritol, are greatly decreased by narcotics, whereas the penetration of thiourea into the same erythrocyte is increased. Similarly, it has been found that the permeability of the erythrocyte to anions is decreased by narcotics. It would seem—although more investigations are necessary to confirm the generalisation—that narcotics normally increase the permeability of a membrane ; the exceptions to this rule are shown by substances that appear to penetrate much more rapidly than might otherwise be deduced from their chemical nature. It may well be that this rapid penetration is made possible by the local differentiation of the membrane, which lowers the activation energy necessary for a given type of molecule or ion to penetrate, *i.e.*, it is possible that some sort of complex-formation between the membrane and penetrating solute takes place at the surface, which makes the transition from outside medium to the membrane an easy process. If it is this transition that is normally the main part of the barrier, such a complex-formation may very well increase permeability to a marked degree, and the action of the narcotic may be to block certain active groups in the membrane, preventing them from reacting with the penetrating substance. In the case of chemical reactions catalysed by enzymes (p. 546), it is generally recognised that the enzyme has special chemical groupings on its surface with which the reacting molecules can combine ; *e.g.*, the breakdown of a molecule AB to simpler molecules A and B is facilitated by a preliminary combination of AB with the enzyme. Enzyme-catalysed reactions are generally blocked by narcotics ; and it may be that certain permeability processes involve the formation of a complex with reactive groups of the membrane that are similarly sensitive to the action of narcotics.

Catalysed Permeability. This point of view finds confirmation in some studies on the permeability of the cat erythrocyte to both Na^+ and K^+ ; this cell differs from the erythrocytes of most species in containing mainly Na^+ as its cation, its internal composition is therefore little different from that of its external plasma. Placed in isotonic KCl, if the membrane is permeable to Na^+ and K^+, there will be a tendency for K^+ to enter and Na^+ to leave. The general results of numerous studies on ionic permeability have indicated that K^+, because of its smaller hydration, penetrates membranes more rapidly than Na^+, yet under these conditions it is found, as Fig. 104 shows, that Na^+ leaves the cells much more rapidly than K^+ enters ; in these circumstances, therefore, the Na^+ permeability is "unorthodox," so that one may reasonably postulate a "special mechanism" of penetration that enables the Na^+ ion to overcome the disabilities imposed by its greater degree of hydration. A study of the effects of temperature, and pH of the medium, supports this point of view ; thus the maximum permeability occurs at body temperature, 38° C., so that increasing the temperature above this point *decreases* the permeability to Na^+, whereas K^+ is quite orthodox in showing a continuous increase in permeability with increasing temperature.   Enzyme-catalysed reactions show a similar sensitivity to temperature.   If the pH of the medium is varied, we find an optimal permeability to Na^+ at pH 7·4, the body pH, whereas with the penetration of K^+ no striking effects of pH are observed. Once again, enzyme-catalysed reactions are strikingly sensitive to pH variations, and exhibit their maximum rate at the pH of their normal

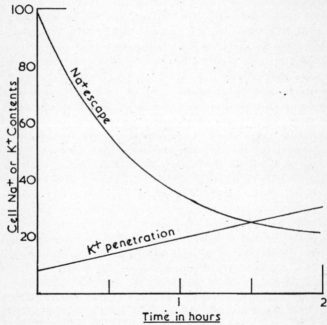

FIG. 104.   Variation in the concentrations of Na^+ and K^+ in the cat erythrocyte, with time of suspension in isotonic KCl.   Ordinates : millimoles of Na^+ or K^+ per kg. of cells.   Abscissæ : time in hours.   The intial concentration gradients are approximately the same for both Na^+ and K^+.   (Davson. *J. cell. & comp. Physiol.*)

medium.   Thus it may well be that a simple undifferentiated membrane is incapable of exhibiting the full selectivity required of it to fulfil its biological functions ; as a result, special groups are developed that permit some sort of complex-formation with certain " privileged " molecules, and enable them to pass through at much greater rates than would be expected for passage through a simple fatty layer.   It is in these cases that minor changes in the environment appear to produce profound effects on permeability.[1]   A final instance of an environmental change, in this

[1] The anion permeability of the erythrocyte may possibly be put in the same category ; rapid exchanges of Cl^- and HCO_3^- are of fundamental importance in the respiratory exchanges of the blood ; the exchange is affected by narcotics ; there is some evidence of an optimal pH (Parpart, 1940), and possibly an optimal temperature (Luckner, 1948).

connection, is provided by the heavy metals. Jacobs & Corson showed that traces of copper (10^{-5} M) are capable of slowing the rate of penetration of glycerol into the erythrocytes of man (and of those other species in which the permeability to glycerol is high—rabbit, cat, mouse, etc.) ; the same effect is shown by a large number of heavy metals such as Hg, Pb, etc. The effect of the heavy metal in this instance is similar to that of a narcotic, and the similarity is further brought out by the observations, first, that higher concentrations are generally destructive of cell membranes, secondly, that heavy metals cause K^+ to leak from the K^+-rich erythrocytes of the rabbit and man (Ørskov), and finally that heavy metals inhibit the penetration of Na^+ into the cat erythrocyte. The heavy metal thus seems capable of blocking the active groups of the membrane as effectively as narcotics, and the analogy with enzyme action is fortified by the fact that heavy metals are especially effective in inhibiting enzyme-catalysed reactions.

The environment of the cell in relation to its chemical composition and temperature is consequently important, so far as normal permeability is concerned ; nevertheless, it is apparently only in special cases that really profound changes in permeability can be induced by small environmental changes ; these special cases seem to be those in which a differentiation of the membrane has taken place to permit a more than " orthodox " rapidity of transfer. Since there is every reason to believe that these unorthodox rates are intimately connected with the metabolic needs of the cell, it would not be surprising that en-

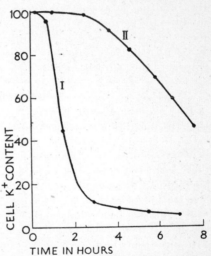

FIG. 105. Loss of K^+ from the rabbit erythrocyte in isotonic NaCl + 0·04 M Fluoride. Curve I, 38·5° C. ; Curve II, 23° C. (Davson. *J. cell. & comp. Physiol.*)

vironmental changes produced large effects on the function of the cell by modifying its permeability to these special solutes. We must beware, on the other hand, of taking too simple a view of this matter of environmental influences ; the transport of many substances, in particular of ions, is governed, not by the simple laws of diffusion, but by active transport, a process involving the supply of metabolic energy. Narcotics, by inhibiting the necessary metabolic reactions, will reduce the rate of this transport ; fortunately, however, there are substances such as cyanide, iodoacetate, and fluoride which may have quite specific effects on these metabolic reactions, so that if these substances block the transfer of a substance into the cell we may infer, fairly certainly, that energy is normally supplied in the process. Examples of this blockage will be discussed later, but the effects of fluoride on the normal permeability of the erythrocyte to K^+ deserve mention here, since, so far as can be ascertained, they are largely effects on membrane permeability. At body temperature fluoride causes a rapid escape of K^+, corresponding to a permeability constant of about $1.5.10^{-8}$ cm./sec. (Fig. 105) ; such a large permeability could not be normal, since the energy requirements to pump the K^+ back again would be beyond the energy available in the cell. We can conclude on these grounds, therefore, that fluoride, although it doubtless inhibits the cell's respiration, exerts its effect on the cell membrane. The fact that the effect is very much delayed at room temperature, however, indicates that it is not a simple action on the cell membrane ; this fact and others show that fluoride upsets the normal permeability of the cell membrane to K^+ by inhibiting glycolysis at a certain stage in the transition of glucose to lactic acid ; it is probably the resulting accumulation of an intermediate product in the cell that modifies the permeability to K^+ ; whether this is a direct action of the inter-mediate product on the cell membrane, or results from the combination of K^+ with this accumulated product—such a combination facilitating transport through the membrane—is not known.

Membrane Structure

The experiments of Kopac & Chambers, described earlier, indicated that the membrane, constituting the effective barrier to diffusion, is a fluid layer of oil on the surface of the naked *Arbacia* egg ; studies of the penetration of solutes through the membranes of a variety of cells indicate that, with certain possible exceptions such as that provided by the sulphur bacterium, *Beggiatoa*, permeability is broadly determined by the penetration of a thin layer of oil, perhaps only 50A thick. It is worth while collating here what further evidence has accrued as to the nature of the plasma membrane, and attempting to build up a picture of its molecular structure from the known characteristics of the lipids and proteins. Any accurate assessment of the thickness of a plasma membrane is of fundamental importance ; there have been various attempts to gauge this, but no one method, taken on its merits, is sufficiently reliable. Thus Fricke studied the behaviour of cell suspensions in an alternating current ; he established—what Höber had done many years before—that the interior of the cell had an electrical conductivity comparable with that of the outside medium, thereby proving that the salts within it were ionised, and not bound in some undissociated complex. The electrical characteristics were such, however, as to indicate a very high resistance to an alternating current passing across the cell membrane, thus confirming the fact, already established, that the membrane showed a low order of permeability to salts. The conclusion that interests us most here, was that the thickness of the non-conducting layer was of the order of 50A ; the main uncertainty in this estimate was caused by the necessity to assume a somewhat arbitrary figure for the dielectric constant of the membrane. Gorter & Grendel arrived at a similar figure by extracting the lipids from erythrocytes and showing that the amounts obtainable were only sufficient to provide a layer two molecules thick. More detailed analyses of the lipids obtained from cell residues have shown that they consist of mixtures of lecithin, sphingomyelin, cephalin and cholesterol with the following chemical formulæ :—

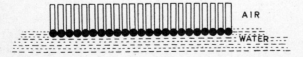

Cholesterol

Lecithin

Cephalin

Sphingomyelin

These substances possess the power of forming stable unimolecular films at an air-water interface, in which the individual molecules are orientated

Fig. 106.   Illustrating a lipoid film at an air-water interface.

in such a way as to have their water-soluble polar groups in the water, and their hydrophobic groups projecting out into the air, as in Fig. 106. It has therefore been suggested that a cell membrane could consist of just two layers of lipoid material, as in Fig. 107*a*, in which the membrane is represented as two layers of lipoid, with the polar groups pointing to the inside and outside of the membrane, and the non-polar ends held together by van der Waals adhesional forces. The stability of such a structure would depend greatly on the lateral adhesion between the non-polar long chains ; since proteins are also capable of spreading out in films, and may do this on an existing lipoid film, thereby contributing markedly to its stability, we may assume as a possible basic pattern of membrane structure a double layer of lipid and a layer of unfolded protein at each interface (Danielli ; Fig. 107*b*). Since the length of the lipoid molecules is of the order of 30A, the thickness of the lipoid layer would be 60A ; a protein film may have a thickness of about 10A, if the molecules unfold and spread

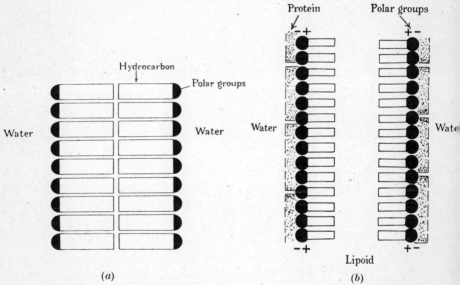

(*a*)   (*b*)

Fig. 107.   Hypothetical structure of the cell membrane.   (*a*) Gorter & Grendel; (*b*) Danielli.   (Davson & Danielli.   *Permeability of Natural Membranes.* Cambridge.)

out on the surface as is likely, so that the total thickness of the membrane would then be a minimum of 80A. The presence of a layer of protein is made very likely from measurements, by Danielli and Harvey among others, of the surface tension of eggs and other cells ; this is of a very low order, much lower than that of a simple lipoid surface, indicating the presence of surface-active material, such as protein.

A rather larger estimate of the total thickness of the membrane resulted from the development, by Waugh & Schmitt, of what they called the analytical leptoscope. This instrument measures the total thickness of the dried erythrocyte " ghost " (the residue of the cell after hæmolysis, when it has lost all its hæmoglobin), the method being based on comparing the intensity of light reflected from such a dried ghost, and from films of barium stearate of known thickness, the intensities of the reflected light being proportional to the thicknesses of the ghost and film. Double layers of barium stearate film may be piled on top of each other in successive units, by the simple process of dipping a glass slide repeatedly in a solution of the soap ; each dip and withdrawal adding a double layer. Photographs of the ghosts and films are taken side by side, and the film giving the same degree of blackening on the photographic plate as that of the ghosts is determined. The thickness so obtained is the thickness of two layers of membrane, and also of any stroma material remaining in the cell after hæmolysis. The maximum value of the thickness came out at 400A, giving a maximum value of 200A for the thickness of a single layer of membrane ; extraction of the lipids caused a reduction of about 200A in

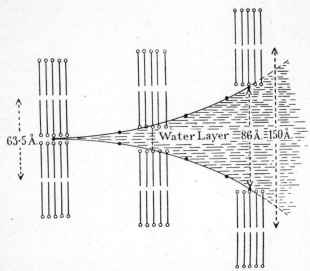

Fig. 108. Schematic representation of the thickness of the water layers between bimolecular leaflets of mixed lipids as a function of the relative amount of water with which the lipids were emulsified. Points represent values obtained when the water content was 0 (dry), 25, 50, 67 and 75 per cent. (Schmitt & Palmer. *Cold Spring Harbor Symp.*)

the thickness, so that the lipids of a single layer were about 100A thick, whilst the proteins also had this thickness, although it is very doubtful whether they were concentrated in the cell membrane.

It seems safe to conclude from these various attempts at measuring the thickness of the cell membrane, that the fatty component is not more than 100A thick, and would thus correspond to four molecules arranged as in Fig. 108. To what extent the molecules of lipid are rigidly held together as a solid film it is not easy to say, although some independence of movement can be inferred from *in vitro* studies of films of sterols and phospholipids. Protein, as we have indicated, may contribute greatly to the stability of such a system by unfolding, if it is normally corpuscular (p. 60) ; the non-polar side-chains being incorporated in the fat layer, and the polar groups orientated towards the aqueous phase. Finally, on top of this protein layer, large corpuscular protein molecules may be adsorbed without unfolding. The unfolded protein film, with its long polypeptide grids, might conceivably form a meshwork and so impart some sieve-like qualities to the membrane.

Some confirmation of this general picture of the cell membrane, as a series of radially orientated lipoid molecules with tangentially orientated protein molecules, is provided, first, by a polarisation-optical study of Schmitt and his collaborators which indicates the presence of radially orientated lipoid molecules, and secondly, by a detailed study of the myelin sheath of nerve, a very thick—by comparison with the plasma membrane— and predominantly lipoid covering to many nerve fibres (p. 378). Both polarisation-optical and X-ray studies of this sheath indicate the presence of radially orientated lipids and tangentially orientated proteins ; the X-ray evidence brings out the presence of an identity period of 63·5A, corresponding to a double layer of lipid ; a larger identity period of about 160A has been attributed to the presence of layers of protein, 25A thick, arranged between every two pairs of lipoid molecules. It is quite possible that this arrangement of four layers of lipid, and one of protein, represents a unit of membrane structure on the basis of which membranes of greater or less thickness may be built up, the plasma membrane of the erythrocyte, at least, being made up of only one unit. We must appreciate, however, that the thick myelin sheath exhibits no selective permeability characteristics, it is the plasma membrane beneath it that is the barrier between the nerve cell's internal and external environments ; the plasma membrane itself must therefore be a much tighter structure than the myelin sheath. The X-ray studies, however, were carried out on dried nerve, and studies on phospholipids show that in the wet condition a great deal of water is built into the fundamental structure, intercalated between the orientated polar groups of the lipoid molecules as in Fig. 108 ; thick layers of water would undoubtedly aid diffusion through such a structure, so that it may well be that the difference between the myelin sheath and the plasma membrane, apart from their thickness, resides in the amounts of water carried by the unit structure.

We may note that the plasma membranes of many cells may expand considerably when the cell swells in hypotonic media ; there is no evidence that under these conditions the membrane becomes thinner, so that it is possible that lipoid material from the interior of the cell enters the membrane under these conditions. At any rate, where such expansions occur, the membrane must have a considerable degree of fluidity, allowing of a fairly ready interchange of lipoid molecules ; and, if a thinning really occurs, an interchange between successive double layers. In this respect we may expect to find a difference between the lipoid components of erythrocytes, which exhibit a minimum alteration of their surface-area, and leucocytes, which, being spherical, undergo large increases of area on swelling. Some recent work of Burt & Rossiter confirms this expectation ; polymorphonuclear leucocytes contained large amounts of neutral fats by comparison with erythrocytes ; the two types of cell also differed markedly in the relative proportions of the lipoid fractions, for example cephalin was the predominant phospholipid in the erythrocyte whilst sphingomyelin predominated in the leucocyte.

Finally we may mention that Wolpers has studied the erythrocyte in the electron-microscope ; he concludes that the membrane consists of thin protein fibrils with fatty molecules interspersed between them.[1]

[1] For an excellent account of the electron- and phase-contrast microscopical appearances of the erythrocyte during and after lysis, and during its various changes in shape in the disk-sphere transformation, the reader is referred to a paper by Bessis & Bricka (1950).

References

ADAM, N. K. (1938). "The Physics and Chemistry of Surfaces." Oxford. Clarendon Press.

BALLENTINE, R. (1944). "Stromatin." *J. cell. & comp. Physiol.*, **23**, 21.

BALLENTINE, R. & PARPART, A. K. (1940). "The Action of Lipase on the Red Cell Surface." *J. cell. & comp. Physiol.*, **16**, 49.

BANG, O. & ØRSKOV, S. L. (1937). "Variations in the Permeability of the Red Blood Cell in Man, etc." *J. clin. Inv.*, **16**, 279.

BÄRLUND, H. (1938). "Einfluss des Äthyläthers auf die Permeabilität der *Chara*-Zellen." *Protoplasma*, **30**, 70.

BESSIS, M. & BRICKA, M. (1950). "Etudes au Microscope Électronique sur l'Hemolyse, l'Agglutination, la Forme et la Structure des Globules Rouges." *Rev. d'Hœmat.*, **5**, 396.

BOEHM, G. (1935). "Uber die Form der Micellen des Stromaeiweisses." *Biochem. Z.*, **282**, 32.

BURT, N. S. & ROSSITER, R. J. (1950). "Lipids of Rabbit Blood Cells. Data for Red Cells and Polymorphonuclear Leucocytes." *Biochem. J.*, **46**, 569.

CALLAN, H. G. (1947). "Some Physical Properties of the Nuclear Membrane." *Proc. Int. Congr. Cyt.*, p. 48.

COLLANDER, R. (1937). "Permeability of Plant Protoplasts to Non-Electrolytes." *Trans. Farad. Soc.*, **33**, 985.

COLLANDER, R. (1947). "On ' Lipoid Solubility '." *Acta Physiol. Scand.*, **13**, 363.

COLLANDER, R. (1949). "The Permeability of Plant Protoplasts to Small Molecules." *Physiol. Plant.*, **2**, 300.

COLLANDER, R. (1949). "Die Verteilung Organischer Verbindungen Zwischen Äther und Wasser." *Acta Chem. Scand.*, **3**, 717.

COLLANDER, R. (1950). "The Permeability of *Nitella* Cells to Rapidly Penetrating Non-Electrolytes." *Physiol. Plant.*, **3**, 45.

COLLANDER, R. & BÄRLUND, H. (1933). Permeabilitätsstudien an *chara ceratophylla*. II. Nicht elektrolyten. Acta bot. Fenn., *II*, p. 114.

DANIELLI, J. F. (1935). "The Thickness of the Wall of the Red Blood Corpuscle." *J. gen. Physiol.*, **19**, 19.

DANIELLI, J. F. (1943). Theory of Penetration of a Thin Membrane. Appendix. "Permeability of Natural Membranes." Davson & Danielli. Cambridge. C.U.P.

DANIELLI, J. F. (1947). "Activated Diffusion in Biology." *Proc. Int. Congr. Cyt.*, p. 312.

DANIELLI, J. F. & DAVSON, H. (1935). "A Contribution to the Theory of Permeability of Thin Films." *J. cell. & comp. Physiol.*, **5**, 495.

DANIELLI, J. F. & HARVEY, E. N. (1935). "The Tension at the Surface of Mackerel Egg Oil with Remarks on the Nature of the Cell Surface." *J. cell. & comp. Physiol.*, **5**, 483.

DAVSON, H. (1937). "Loss of K from Erythrocyte in Hypotonic Saline." *J. cell. & comp. Physiol.*, **10**, 247.

DAVSON, H. (1939). "Effect of Reducing the Salt Content of the Medium Surrounding the Cell." *Biochem. J.*, **33**, 389.

DAVSON, H. (1940). "Comparative Effects of Environmental Changes on the Permeability of the Cat Erythrocyte Membrane to Na and K." *J. cell. & comp. Physiol.*, **15**, 317.

DAVSON, H. (1940). "The Permeability of the Erythrocyte to Cations." *C.S.H. Symp.*, **8**, 255.

DAVSON, H. (1940). "Influence of the Lyotropic Series of Anions on Cation Permeability." *Biochem. J.*, **34**, 917.

DAVSON, H. (1941). "Effect of Some Metabolic Poisons on the Permeability of the Rabbit Erythrocyte to Potassium." *J. cell. & comp. Physiol.*, **18**, 173.

DAVSON, H. & DANIELLI, J. F. (1938). "Factors in Cation Permeability." *Biochem. J.*, **32**, 991.

DAVSON, H. & DANIELLI, J. F. (1943). "The Permeability of Natural Membranes." Cambridge. C.U.P.

DAVSON, H. & REINER, J. H. (1942). "Ionic Permeability: an Enzyme-like Factor Concerned in the Migration of Sodium Through the Cat Erythrocyte Membrane." *J. cell. & comp. Physiol.*, **20**, 325.

DIRKEN, M. N. J. & MOOK, H. W. (1931). "Rate of Gas Exchange between Blood Cells and Serum." *J. Physiol.*, **73**, 349.

DZIEMIAN, A. J. (1942). "The Permeability and the Lipid Content of Immature Red Cells." *J. cell. & comp. Physiol.*, **20**, 135.

ERICKSON, B. N. *et al.* (1938). "Lipid Distribution of Post-Hæmolytic Residue or Stroma of Erythrocytes." *J. biol. Chem.*, **122**, 515.

FRICKE, H. (1933). "The Electric Impedance of Suspensions of Biological Cells." *C.S.H. Symp.*, **1**, 1.

GORTER, E. & GRENDEL, F. (1925). "On Bimolecular Layers of Lipoids on the Chromocytes of the Blood." *J. exp. Med.*, **41**, 439.

GREEN, J. W. (1949). "The Relative Rates of Penetration of the Lower Saturated Monocarboxylic Acids into Mammalian Erythrocytes." *J. cell. & comp. Physiol.*, **33**, 247.

HEVESY, G. (1940). "Application of Radioactive Isotopes in Biology." *Ann. Rev. Biochem.*, **9**, 641.

HÖBER, R. (1936). "The Permeability of Red Blood Corpuscles to Organic Anions." *J. cell. & comp. Physiol.*, **7**, 367.

HÖBER, R. (1945). "Physical Chemistry of Cells and Tissues." Phila, Blakiston.

HÖBER, R. & ØRSKOV, S. L. (1933). "Permeiergeschwindigkeit von Anelektrolyten bei der röten Blutkörperchen verschiedener Tierarten." *Pflüg. Arch.*, **231**, 599.

JACOBS, M. H. (1935). "Diffusion Processes." *Ergebn. d. Biol.*, **12**, 1.

JACOBS, M. H. (1940). "Some Aspects of Cell Permeability to Weak Electrolytes." *C.S.H. Symp.*, **8**, 30.

JACOBS, M. H. & CORSON, S. A. (1934). "Influence of Minute Traces of Cu on Certain Hæmolytic Processes." *Biol. Bull.*, **67**, 325.

JACOBS, M. H. & GLASSMAN, H. N. (1937). "Further Comparative Studies on the Permeability of the Erythrocyte." *Biol. Bull.*, **73**, 387.

JACOBS, M. H., GLASSMAN, H. N. & PARPART, A. K. (1935). "Temperature Coefficients of Certain Hæmolytic Processes." *J. cell. & comp. Physiol.*, **7**, 197.

JACOBS, M. H. & PARPART, A. K. (1932). "Rate of Hæmolysis in Hypotonic Solutions of Electrolytes." *Biol. Bull.*, **63**, 224.

JACOBS, M. H. & PARPART, A. K. (1938). "On the Permeability of the Erythrocyte to Ammonia and the Ammonium Ion." *J. cell. & comp. Physiol.*, **11**, 175.

JACOBS, M. H. & STEWART, D. R. (1932). "Simple Method for the Quantitative Measurement of Permeability." *J. cell. & comp. Physiol.*, **1**, 71.

JACOBS, M. H. & STEWART, D. R. (1936). "The Distribution of Penetrating Ammonium Salts between Cells and their Surroundings." *J. cell. & comp. Physiol.*, **7**, 351.

JACOBS, M. H. & STEWART, D. R. (1942). "The Role of Carbonic Anhydrase in Certain Ionic Exchanges Involving the Erythrocyte." *J. gen. Physiol.*, **25**, 539.

JORPES, E. (1932). "The Protein Component of the Erythrocyte Membrane or Stroma." *Biochem. J.*, **26**, 1488.

KLINGHOFFER, K. A. (1935). "Permeability of the Red Cell Membrane to Glucose." *Amer. J. Physiol.*, **111**, 231.

LEFEVRE, P. G. (1948). "Evidence of Active Transfer of Certain Non-Electrolytes Across the Human Red Cell Membrane." *J. gen. Physiol.*, **31**, 505.

LUCKÉ, B., HARTLINE, H. K. & RICCA, R. A. (1939). "Comparative Permeability to Water and to Certain Solutes of the Egg Cells of Three Marine Invertebrates. *Arbacia, Cumingia & Chætopterus.*" *J. cell. & comp. Physiol.*, **14**, 237.

LUCKÉ, B., LARRABEE, M. G. & HARTLINE, H. K. (1935). "Studies on Osmotic Equilibria and on the Kinetics of Osmosis in Living Cells by the Diffraction Method." *J. gen. Physiol.*, **19**, 1.

LUCKÉ, B. & McCUTCHEON, M. (1928). "Effect of Valence of Ions on Cellular Permeability to Water." *J. gen. Physiol.*, **12**, 571.

LUCKÉ, B. & RICCA, R. A. (1941). "Osmotic Properties of the Egg of the Oyster." *J. gen. Physiol.*, **15**, 215.

LUCKNER, H. (1939). "Uber die Geschwindigkeit des Austausches der Atemgäse im Blut." *Pflüg. Arch.*, **241**, 753.

LUCKNER, H. (1948). " Die Temperaturabhängigkeit des Anionenaustausches röter Blutkörperchen." *Pflüg. Arch.*, **250**, 303.

ØRSKOV, S. L. (1934). " Weitere Untersuchungen u. d. Einfluss der Kohlensäure auf die Permeabilität der Ammoniumsalze." *Biochem. Z.*, **269**, 349.

OSTERHOUT, W. J. V. (1950). " Higher Permeability for Water than for Ethyl Alcohol in *Nitella*." *J. gen. Physiol.*, **33**, 275.

PARPART, A. K. (1935). " The Permeability of the Mammalian Erythrocyte to Deuterium Oxide." *J. cell. & comp. Physiol.*, **7**, 153.

PARPART, A. K. (1940). " Permeability of the Erythrocyte for Anions." *C.S.H. Symp.*, **8**, 25.

PONDER, E. (1947). " The Prolytic Loss of Potassium from Human Red Cells." *J. gen. Physiol.*, **30**, 235.

PONDER, E. (1947). " Potassium-Sodium Exchange Accompanying Prolytic Loss of Potassium from Human Red Cells." *J. gen. Physiol.*, **30**, 479.

SACKS, J. (1944). " P^{32} Studies on Hexosemonophosphate Metabolism in Resting Muscle." *Amer. J. Physiol.*, **142**, 145.

SCHMITT, F. O., BEAR, R. S. & PONDER, E. " The Red Cell Envelope Considered as a Mixed Wiener Body." *J. cell. & comp. Physiol.*, **11**, 309.

SCHMITT, F. O. & PALMER, K. J. (1940). " X-Ray Diffraction Studies of Lipide and Lipide-Protein Systems." *C.S.H. Symp.*, **8**, 94.

TING, T. P. & ZIRKLE, R. E. (1940). " Effects of X-Rays on the Permeability of Erythrocytes to Water and Certain Non-Electrolytes." *J. cell. & comp. Physiol.*, **16**, 269.

USSING, H. H. (1943). " The Nature of the Amino Nitrogen of Red Corpuscles." *Acta Physiol. Scand.*, **5**, 335.

WAUGH, D. F. & SCHMITT, F. O. (1940). " Investigations of the Thickness and Ultrastructure of Cellular Membranes by the Analytical Leptoscope." *C.S.H. Symp.*, **8**, 233.

WILBRANDT, W. (1938). " Die Permeabilität der röten Blutkörperchen für einfache Zucker." *Pflüg. Arch.*, **241**, 302.

WILBRANDT, W. (1938). " Die Permeabilität der Zelle." *Ergebn. d. Physiol.*, **40**, 204.

WILBRANDT, W. (1940). " Die abhängigkeit der Ionenpermeabilität der Erythrocyten von glykolytischen Stoffwechsel." *Pflüg. Arch.*, **243**, 519.

WILBRANDT, W. (1940). " Die Ionenpermeabilität der Erythrocyten in Nichtleiterlösungen." *Pflüg. Arch.*, **243**, 537.

WILBRANDT, W., GUENSBERG, E. & LAUENER, H. (1947). " Der Glukoseeintritt durch die Erythrocytenmembran." *Helv. Physiol. et Pharm. Acta*, **5**, C 20.

WOLPERS, C. (1941). " Zur Feinstruktur der Erythrocytenmembran." *Naturwiss*, **28**, 416.

CHAPTER IX

THE GIBBS-DONNAN EQUILIBRIUM AND THE PERMEABILITY OF CAPILLARIES

Capillary Structure

IN higher animals the exchanges of matter between the individual cells and the external environment are made possible by the existence of a circulating intermediary, the blood ; the larger parts of the circulatory system are concerned exclusively with the mechanical problem of

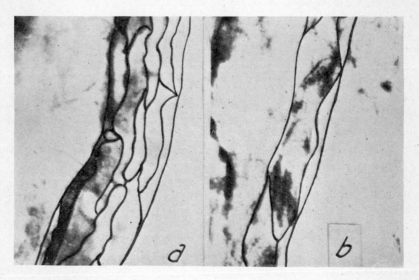

FIG. 109. Outlines of endothelial cells demonstrated by silver nitrate, sprayed on living capillary wall of the frog's mesentery with a micro-pipette. (*a*) is an *a–v* bridge ; (*b*) is a true capillary. (Zweifach. *Anat. Rec.*)

circulation, *e.g.*, the heart, arteries and veins ; the exchanges between blood and cells take place in the *capillaries*, very small vessels with a diameter of the order of 10μ ; these vessels are distinguished from the arterioles and venules, with which they are continuous, by the absence of a well-defined muscular coat, in fact they consist primarily of tubes built up of flattened endothelial cells, the *capillary endothelium*. With ordinary stains a capillary appears as a series of darkly staining nuclei, whilst, with the aid of $AgNO_3$, the boundaries of the endothelial cells may be made visible as in Fig. 109. Besides this fundamental morphology, various ancillary structures have been described, but there is still some doubt as to whether they belong to the capillary itself or to the structures with which the capillary is in relation ; thus a fine series of fibrils, the *perithelium*, staining with Ag, has been described by Loeschke & Loeschke ; embedded in the perithelium, or possibly attached to the surface of the endothelium, are certain branched cells, the *pericytes* or *Rouget cells*. It has been thought that these cells enable the capillary to contract, although Michels, among others, has denied vigorously that the Rouget cells bear any special relationship to the true capillaries ; he divides the small vessels into *arterioles, pre-capillary arterioles, true capillaries*—which are either arterial or venous in type—*pre-capillary venules*, and *venules* (Fig. 110) ; the pre-capillary arterioles contain muscular cells similar to those of the arterioles, and it is thought by Michels that these arterioles have been mistaken for

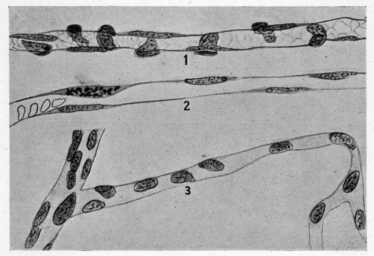

Fig. 110.   Camera lucida drawings of small vessels of rabbit.   Hortega-Globus-Penfield stain.
1. *Precapillary arteriole* with characteristic far-spread orientation of circular muscle cell nuclei ; interpreted by Krogh & Vimtrup as Rouget cells.   Reticulum of Volterra may be seen.
2. *Arterial capillary* consisting only of longitudinally disposed endothelial cells, one in mitosis.
3. *Venous capillary ;* the endothelial nuclei are bulkier, predominantly oval, more numerous and more closely packed.   (Michels.   *Anat. Rec.*)

capillaries, their muscular elements being described as Rouget cells. Various cells are certainly in close association with the true capillaries, but since they are only recognisable by their nuclei they are difficult to identify ; it would seem, for example, that the Remak nerve fibres, with their nuclei, may easily be mistaken for Rouget cells, and the same consideration applies to various wandering cells and nuclei sloughed off the endothelium.   In Michels' view the term Rouget cell should be dropped and the more general term *pericyte* adopted.

Zweifach, on the basis of direct observations on the intact circulation, has reached an essentially similar conclusion.   His general scheme of a unit in capillary circulation is indicated in Fig. 111.   According to this, there is a direct and permanent thoroughfare between arteriole and venule by way of a *metarteriole*, which eventually loses the muscular elements from its wall to become a capillary ; this leads to a pre-venule and thence into a venule.   The capillary region in this direct thoroughfare is called an *a-v-bridge*, in contrast to the so-called *true capillaries*, which are branches from it and from the metarteriole, arteriole, etc.   The *a-v*-bridges are capillaries, in the sense that there are no muscle cells on their walls, but they are larger than the true capillaries ; the latter are functionally distinguished from the former in that they may be open or closed in accordance with the vascular needs of the tissue and hence are concerned in regulating the local blood supply.   Thus in tissues that exhibit a very variable blood flow, *e.g.*, the muscles, the proportion of true capillaries to *a-v-bridges* is very high—in the region of 80–90 per cent.—whereas in the skin (of the frog or the mouse's ear) where blood-flow is fairly constant, the great majority of capillaries are of the *a-v*-type.   Generally the branch from the main thoroughfare channel is muscular in the first part of its course, and is described as the *pre-capillary sphincter* ; its muscular elements are responsible for the shunting of blood through or away from the true capillary.   On the basis of both Michels' and Zweifach's classifications, therefore, a capillary is a vessel without muscular elements in its wall ; the true capillaries certainly exhibit changes in tone, and may be completely open or completely closed ; this follows mainly, however, from the sphincter-like action of the pre-capillary portions.   A swelling of the endothelial cell nuclei, thereby .tending to obliterate the lumen (Kahn & Pollack), or a more genuine contractile process generated in the endo-

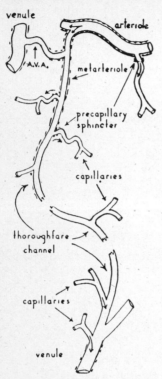

FIG. 111.   Diagram of a functional unit of the capillary bed, together with a metarteriolar-venular anastomosis (A.V.A) and a pre-capillary branching off directly from an arteriole. (Chambers & Zweifach. *Amer. J. Anat.*)

thelial cells themselves, or in the pericytes embedded in the perithelium, may also be concerned.   The functional studies of Chambers & Zweifach also confirm the existence of an outer sheath, which they call the *pericapillary sheath*.   A leucocyte, migrating through a capillary (*diapedesis*), does not pass directly through ; having squeezed between two endothelial cells it remains for some time flattened against the outside, as though it were compressed by this sheath.[1]

[1] An elaborate description of the phenomenon of diapedesis, and also of the extravasation of red cells, has been given by Baron & Chambers (1936).

Interstitial Fluid and Lymph

The capillaries do not lie directly on the cells they nourish but are separated by a space, the *interstitial* or *extracellular space*, which is filled with fluid, the *interstitial fluid* ; exchanges between blood and cells therefore take place by way of this fluid and it is consequently of great interest to study its mode of formation and circulation, as well as the dynamics of penetration of any given material from blood to tissue-cell by way of this intermediary. The volume of interstitial fluid varies with the tissue ; as we shall see, it constitutes in muscle about 11 per cent. of its weight, but since it is distributed as a very thin layer over all the cells it is difficult to analyse directly, and indirect methods are necessary both to determine its actual amount and its chemical composition. That the fluid is not stagnant is suggested by the existence of definite drainage channels for its removal, constituting the *lymphatic system*. The lymphatic capillaries are endothelial tubes closed at one end ; they form a ramifying system collecting eventually into large vessels, *lymphatic ducts*, which finally empty into a large blood vein, passing first, however, through a *lymph node* which serves to " filter " the fluid by bringing it into contact with a trabeculum of cells capable of phagocytosis (the ingestion of foreign particles) and which adds certain cells to this fluid—and thus to the blood—namely the *lymphocytes*. The larger vessels contain valves, so that flow tends to be uni-directional, from tissue to blood vessel ; in higher forms there is no lymph-heart, *i.e.*, a system for pumping the fluid continuously ; consequently flow is determined by localised compressions and expansions, resulting from contraction of the muscles. The *lymph capillaries*, with their thin endothelial lining, are the site of absorption of tissue fluid, since injection of a tissue with a dye is followed by the rapid appearance of the colour in the lymph duct ; moreover, the whole branching network of the lymphatic capillaries becomes microscopically visible following such an injection. As we shall see, however, the normal flow of lymph in a resting limb is of a very low order, so that a steady renewal of tissue fluid is brought about by a mechanism that does not require a continuous drainage by way of lymphatic channels. By cannulating a large lymphatic duct and massaging the limb, or submitting it to vigorous exercise; considerable quantities of lymph may be obtained and analysed. The chemical composition is indicated in Table XII, and its similarity to that of blood plasma will be immediately evident, the exception being the relatively low concentration of protein.[1] The fact that the lymph contains this relatively small concentration of protein suggests that the capillaries, from which the interstitial fluid was derived, are normally only slightly permeable to this type of molecule. The observation that all crystalloidal material in the blood appears in the lymph in about the same concentration as in plasma indicates, on the other hand, a permeability of the capillary walls to these substances. A study of the

[1] The concentration of protein in lymph is highly variable ; the figure presented in Table XII was obtained with lymph from the leg of a dog ; in the liver the concentration is as high as 5·3 per cent.

formation and circulation of the interstitial fluid, and of the exact mode by which a substance passes from blood to tissue cell, demands a knowledge of the equilibria between a virtually protein-free solution and plasma, separated by a membrane, impermeable to protein but permeable to water and all other solutes. We may therefore profitably discuss the *Gibbs-Donnan Equilibrium*.

TABLE XII

Chemical Composition of Plasma and Thoracic Duct Lymph. (*After Drinker & Yoffey*, 1941.)

	Plasma	Lymph
Protein (per cent.) . .	6·85	2·61
Sugar (mg./100 ml.) .	123	124
Non-protein nitrogen (mg./100 ml.) . .	27·2	27
Urea (mg./100 ml.) . .	22	23·5
Amino-acids (mg.N/100ml.)	4·9	4·8
Calcium (mg./100 ml.) .	10·4	9·2
Chloride (mg./100 ml.) .	392	413

The Gibbs-Donnan Equilibrium

Let us consider the system shown in Fig. 112, consisting of a solution of NaCl separated from one of NaCl plus NaP, where P^- is an anion to which

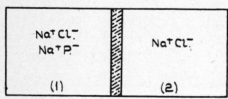

FIG. 112. A mixture of a protein salt, NaP, and NaCl separated from NaCl by a membrane permeable to salt and water.

the membrane is impermeable ; the membrane is permeable to all the other ions of the system and to water. To simplify the calculation, let us assume to begin with that the volumes of the two compartments are maintained constant, *i.e.*, that during the distribution of the ions in accordance with the Gibbs-Donnan equilibrium, osmotic exchanges are excluded. The Gibbs-Donnan rule tells us that the products of the diffusible ions on both sides of the membrane are equal at equilibrium :

$$[Na^+]_1 \times [Cl^-]_1 = [Na^+]_2 \times [Cl^-]_2 \quad \ldots \ldots (9)$$

Since there are equal concentrations of positive and negative ions in each compartment, we may put $[Na^+]_2$ equal to $[Cl^-]_2$, whence :

$$[Na^+]_1 \times [Cl^-]_1 = [Cl^-]_2^2 \quad \ldots \ldots (10)$$

Now $[Na^+]_1$, is clearly greater than $[Cl^-]_1$, since part of the Na^+ ions in compartment (1) are associated with Cl^- ions and part with P^- ions ; thus the left-hand side of Equation (10), being the product of two unequal quantities, may be represented by a rectangle, and the right-hand side by a square, and it is easy to show that the sum of the sides of a rectangle is greater than the sum of the sides of a square of equal area, *i.e.*, that :

$$[Na^+]_1 + [Cl^-]_1 > 2[Cl^-]_2$$
$$> [Na^+]_2 + [Cl^-]_2 \quad . \quad . \quad . \quad . \quad (11)$$

the sum of the concentrations of the diffusible ions being greater on side (1) than on side (2). Writing this excess by e, we have :—

$$[Na^+]_1 + [Cl^-]_1 = [Na^+]_2 + [Cl^-]_2 + e ; \quad . \quad . \quad . \quad . \quad (12)$$

hence the total osmotic concentration of substance on side (1) is :—

$$[Na^+]_1 + [Cl^-]_1 + e + [P] ; \text{ on side (2) it is : } [Na^+]_2 + [Cl^-]_2.$$

Thus the ions distribute themselves in such a way, at equilibrium, that there is a difference of osmotic pressure, equal to $(e + [P])$ RT, between the two solutions, in such a direction that water tends to pass into solution (1). From the purely osmotic point of view, therefore, the system is only in equilibrium if the volumes are maintained constant. Suppose we allow osmotic equilibrium to be achieved by letting water diffuse into solution (1); as a result, the equilibrium distribution of ions will be disturbed, and they will therefore re-distribute themselves in accordance with the Gibbs-Donnan rule, *i.e.*, in such a way that there is an excess of osmotic material on side (1). Consequently, in the absence of any restraint on the relative volumes of the two compartments, these two processes, diffusion of water and NaCl into (1), will proceed continuously until compartment (1) has absorbed all the water and NaCl from compartment (2). To prevent this osmosis a pressure must be exerted on compartment (1) equal to the difference of osmotic pressure [1] $(e + [P])$ RT.

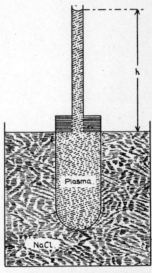

Fig. 113. Plasma separated from isotonic NaCl ; the external solution penetrates the sac until the hydrostatic pressure, h, is equal to the colloid osmotic pressure.

To choose a practical example of the Gibbs-Donnan equilibrium, we could consider blood plasma, which consists of a mixture of salts and protein, separated from a solution of NaCl by a collodion membrane which is permeable to the salts of plasma, and to water, but impermeable to protein, which exists in the form of a sodium salt, NaP (Fig. 113). The Gibbs-

[1] We may note that the failure to achieve osmotic equilibrium in the absence of a mechanical restraint on the volume of one compartment is not peculiar to systems characterised by the Donnan Equilibrium ; thus if, instead of NaP, we had an undissociated substance such as gum acacia, the salts would be in this case distributed in equal concentrations in both compartments, but we should still have an excess of osmotic material on the gum acacia side which could not be equalled out by osmosis of water. The condition is essentially the same as with an *Arbacia* egg suspended in isotonic glycerol solution, considered on p. 158.

Donnan rule tells us that the salts will be distributed in such a way as to give an excess of osmotic material in the collodion sac. The membrane is permeable to water which enters the sac, thereby tending to level out the difference of osmotic pressure ; as we have seen, however, even though water penetrates the sac, the salts will re-distribute themselves in such a way as to maintain a difference of osmotic pressure, so that unless there is some force to prevent the entry of water into the sac it will continue to penetrate until all the NaCl solution outside has passed in. In the experimental arrangement shown by Fig. 113, the entrance of water builds up a hydrostatic pressure which prevents the penetration of water beyond a certain limit. The condition for osmotic equilibrium is that the height, h, of fluid in the tube in the collodion sac above the level of the outside fluid, should exert a hydrostatic pressure equal to the difference of osmotic pressure :—

h (mm.) = Osmotic Pressure Difference in mm. NaCl solution.

We may note that the difference of osmotic pressure is called the *colloid osmotic pressure*.

The Starling Hypothesis

As Starling was the first to point out, a condition almost exactly equivalent to that depicted in Fig. 113 is given by the blood plasma,

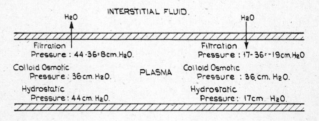

Fig. 114. Schematic representation of the fluid exchanges across a capillary. At the arterial end the capillary pressure exceeds the colloid osmotic pressure of the plasma proteins, so that fluid passes out into the interstitial space ; at the venous end the conditions are reversed.

separated from the interstitial fluid by the capillary membrane. We may therefore expect to find a difference of osmotic pressure between plasma and interstitial fluid. This excess of pressure represents a tendency for water to pass out of the interstitial spaces into the blood-stream, and unless there is an opposing tendency, driving water in the opposite direction, we have seen that all the interstitial fluid would be eventually drawn into the protein-containing fluid, *i.e.*, into the vascular system. The opposing force that prevents this in the intact organism is the hydrostatic pressure of the blood in the capillaries. The blood pressure is a simple hydrostatic pressure, and may be represented as a lateral pressure pushing against the wall of the capillary ; the conditions will therefore be as in Fig. 114, the hydrostatic capillary pressure, like the pressure due to the column of saline in Fig. 113, or the force exerted on the piston in Fig. 86 (Chapter VII), opposes the entrance of water into the capillary. For an equilibrium to be established at any point in the capillary the condition would be :—

Capillary Pressure = Colloid Osmotic Pressure.

In actuality the capillary pressure often exceeds the colloid osmotic pressure, so that ultra-filtration takes place whereby fluid, containing all the constituents of plasma except the proteins, passes out of the capillary into the interstitial space. Since this space is limited in volume, there is set up a back pressure, due to the mechanical resistance of the tissues to deformation, and hence the more general condition for equilibrium is :—

Capillary Pressure = Colloid Osmotic Pressure + Tissue Pressure.

The capillary pressure is the driving force tending to express fluid into the tissue spaces ; the colloid osmotic pressure and the tissue pressure resist this driving force. We may note that the tissue pressure is equal to the capillary pressure minus the colloid osmotic pressure, and becomes zero when the capillary pressure equals the colloid osmotic pressure ; it is largely a passive entity, dependent as it is on these two quantities.[1]

The pressure in a capillary decreases from the arterial to the venous end ; the tissue pressure can be considered to be constant since local changes are rapidly transmitted to other parts ; if the colloid osmotic pressure remained constant along the length of the capillary we should have, at the arterial end, according to the Starling hypothesis : *Capillary pressure* > *Colloid osmotic pressure* + *Tissue pressure*, *i.e.*, fluid would be expressed at the arterial end. At the venous end the position would be reversed, owing to the fall in the capillary pressure, consequently the venous end of the capillary would be the site of reabsorption of tissue fluid. In actual fact the colloid osmotic pressure, favouring the penetration of fluid into the capillary, would be rather higher at the venous end since the plasma, having lost fluid at the arterial end, would be more concentrated. Thus there is no doubt that the arterial end of a capillary is a region favouring the *loss* of fluid, by comparison with the venous end which is more suited to reabsorption. Consequently, under normal conditions of flow, Starling considered that the interstitial fluid was constantly being renewed by a process of filtration and reabsorption. On the basis of the theory, the lymphatic system, draining interstitial fluid back into the large veins, can be treated as an overflow mechanism.

Experimental Verification. We are indebted for an unequivocal substantiation of the Starling hypothesis primarily to the work of Landis ; this author introduced micro-pipettes into the lumens of capillaries and determined the pressures within them by estimating the height of a column of coloured fluid, in connection with the pipette, necessary to allow the coloured fluid to flow into the capillary. He also studied the movement

[1] According to Meyer and Holland the tissue pressure beneath the skin of man is only 2–4 cm. H_2O ; it may increase, however, to 14–16 cm. H_2O in the legs on standing quietly for long periods ; within the muscles quite high pressures are registered on contraction, anything from 10–118 cm. being obtained depending on the muscles. On passive standing the pressure within the muscle may rise to 50 cm. H_2O.

of fluid out of the capillaries, first by observing whether dyes, injected into the vessel, left the capillaries ; and, secondly, by the very ingenious method of compressing the capillary so that flow along it could only be due to

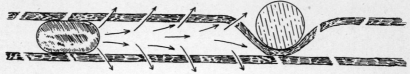

Fig. 115. Illustrating Landis' technique for measuring the rate of outflow from a capillary. The capillary is compressed so that outflow is indicated by the movement of a corpuscle towards the compressed region.

escape through the walls ; and he observed the rate at which a corpuscle approached the blocked end, as in Fig. 115. With the latter technique he was able to measure the rate of filtration or reabsorption of fluid ; whilst a simultaneous determination of the pressure within the capillary enabled

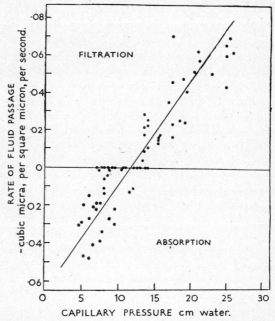

Fig. 116. Fluid exchanges across the frog capillary membrane as a function of the capillary pressure. (Landis. *Amer. J. Physiol.*)

him to correlate flow with pressure. The results for the frog are summarised in Fig. 116 ; it will be seen that the rate of flow increases linearly with the capillary pressure, and that there is a certain region of pressure at which movement, on the average, is zero—between 12·5 and 14 cm. H_2O—a figure agreeing well with White's estimation of the colloid osmotic pressure of the frog's plasma proteins. In the mammal the colloid osmotic pressure of the plasma proteins is much higher,[1] in the region of 30 cm. H_2O, consequently we must expect considerably higher capillary pressures. A number of estimates of capillary pressure in mammals are summarised in Table XIII ; it will be seen that the pressure in the arteriolar capillary is greater than the colloid osmotic pressure, whilst that in the venous limb is less.

TABLE XIII

Colloid Osmotic Pressures of Plasma Proteins and Capillary Pressures of Three Mammals.

		Rat	Guinea Pig	Man
Colloid Osmotic Pressure (cm. H_2O) .	.	25	26·7	36
Cap. Pressure (cm. H_2O) : Arterial .	.	30	38·5	43·5
Venous .	.	17	17	16·5

(Figures for capillary pressure from Landis (1936) ; for colloid osmotic pressure of rat and guinea pig plasma also from Landis ; value for man is median of the large collation of figures presented by Drinker & Yoffey (1941).)

The effects of variation of the colloid osmotic pressure have been studied most recently in the frog by Hyman, and by Danielli ; decreasing the colloid osmotic pressure, other things being equal, should increase the formation of fluid and decrease its reabsorption, thus favouring œdema ; œdema due to this cause is a well-known phenomenon and the question is mainly whether the rate of formation of œdema is in quantitative agreement with predictions on the basis of the Starling hypothesis. The procedure is to perfuse the limb of a frog by way of a cannula, connected to its abdominal aorta, with a fluid whose composition may be varied ; the limb is maintained on a spring-balance so that accumulation of fluid is associated with an increase in weight that can be recorded continuously. Hyman found that variation of the colloid osmotic pressure, by addition of plasma or albumin to the fluid, caused a linear change in the rate of formation of œdema. Danielli investigated the theoretical relationship between colloid osmotic pressure and rate of formation of œdema in detail, and showed that if Poiseuille's Law of fluid-flow held in the capillaries the rate, R, was given by the equation :—

$$R = xp^2 - yp + z$$

where p is the colloid osmotic pressure and x, y, and z are constants. In perfused frog limbs the agreement between experiment and theory was good. A similar type of investigation has been recently carried out by Pappenheimer & Soto-Rivera on a warm-blooded animal ; these authors perfused the hind-limbs of cats and dogs with blood, the plasma protein

[1] According to Scatchard, Batchelder & Brown, the colloid osmotic pressure of the plasma proteins is given by the following empirical formula :—

$$\pi = \frac{268 (1 - 0.64g) c}{1 + (0.4 + 0.9 pH) c}$$

where c is the concentration of protein in g./ml., and g is the ratio of globulin to total proteins.

concentration of which could be varied. They found that the mean capillary pressure at which there was no net transfer of fluid to the tissue, *i.e.*, at which the loss by filtration was just equal to the gain by reabsorption, was some 93 per cent. of the colloid osmotic pressure of the plasma proteins, as determined *in vitro* with a collodion sac. On the basis of this finding they estimated that the tissue fluid contained some 0·8 per cent. of protein. Under the conditions of their experiments, the tissue pressure of the limb was apparently negligible so that quite a small rise in capillary pressure caused œdema. A study of the kinetics of out-flow of tissue fluid gave results in complete accord with the Starling hypothesis.

Lymphatic Drainage. From the point of view of the relationship between colloid osmotic pressure and capillary pressure, the Starling hypothesis seems to be well substantiated ; the theory implies, however, that the capillaries should, on the average, be either impermeable to proteins or sufficiently slowly permeable, by comparison with the permeability to smaller molecules and ions, to warrant the assumption of an effective colloid osmotic pressure of the order of that given by plasma, separated by a collodion sac from its ultra-filtrate. As Table XII shows, the protein concentration of lymph is by no means negligible, even in the resting limb ; and it is increased when this is active. Let us consider the formation of lymph and the function of the lymphatic circulation in more detail. The loss of proteins from the capillaries, whether we regard it as a normal or abnormal phenomenon, has important theoretical implications. This protein can never return directly to the blood by diffusion through the capillaries because, to obtain diffusion, the concentration must be greater than in the plasma ; thus although *fluid* may be reabsorbed from the interstitial space back into the capillaries, the proteins will be left behind. Consequently, in the absence of a mechanism for absorbing the lost proteins back into the blood stream, the tissue fluid would eventually have a concentration of protein equal to that in the plasma. The result of this would be that the factors favouring the loss of fluid from the plasma would predominate, and a condition of œdema would develop. Such a condition is indeed found in blockage of a main lymphatic route, either experimentally in dogs or pathologically in humans, the accumulation of fluid in the interstitial spaces being so great as to warrant the name of *elephantiasis*. The lymphatic capillaries are, presumably, permeable to proteins and other large colloidal molecules, as shown by the ready appearance of these substances in the lymph on subcutaneous injection (*vide, e.g.*, McMaster) ; they may therefore absorb the tissue fluid by a simple flow across their membranes. It is by way of this bulk flow of interstitial fluid into the lymphatic capillaries that the proteins are restored to the blood. The question now is, whether the lymph, collected from the ducts, is representative of the average chemical composition of the tissue fluids. In the resting limb, cannulation of the lymphatic duct produces no measurable flow of lymph, so that in many respects the lymphatics may be regarded as an overflow mechanism coming into operation when the normal filtration-reabsorption process is out of balance. If this is true, the protein concentration of the lymph is by no means representative of that in the tissue fluid in all parts of the limb. Thus let us consider a region in which the capillaries are perfect, *i.e.*, impermeable to protein ; here the factors of filtration and reabsorption are in balance, and there is no excess of fluid demanding lymphatic drainage ; this part of the limb therefore makes no contribution to the lymph found in the lymphatic duct. Consider, now, another region in which there is, on the average, a slow escape of protein ; in time, the concentration in the interstitial fluid mounts to such a value that reabsorption is impeded (the difference of osmotic pressure between the two fluids is inadequate), whilst filtration occurs more rapidly than normal ; in these conditions lymphatic drainage becomes necessary and a flow of lymph takes place, removing the interstitial fluid with its high concentration of protein. As soon as the capillaries become normal again, the necessity for the flow of lymph from this region ceases. Thus, in the resting limb, a flow is only caused by the upset in the normal relations between plasma and interstitial fluid, and the lymph so obtained represents not the normal, or average, interstitial fluid but the abnormal, *i.e.*, the fluid which disrupts, by its presence, the normal filtration-reabsorption equilibrium, and which must be removed before this equilibrium may be re-established. This view of the lymphatics as an overflow mechanism is supported by the studies of Field & Drinker, who observed a great increase in flow of lymph on reduction of the protein concentration in the plasma of dogs by plasmapheresis.[1] A reduction from 7·3 to 3·4 per cent. caused a great increase in flow, but no œdema, thus indicating the value of the lymphatics ; with less acutely induced reductions of plasma proteins the lymph flow did not increase ; the protein concentration of the lymph, however, was very low so that it would seem that a low concentration of plasma proteins, induced slowly, is compensated in some measure by a decreased permeability of the capillaries to proteins. In humans, hunger œdema has been studied extensively ; when the serum albumin concentration falls below 2·5 per cent. (total protein less than 5 per cent.[2]), œdema occurs.

Œdema Fluid. If lymph is to be regarded as an overflow of tissue fluid, it might, at first thought, be expected that it would be very similar in protein concentration to œdema fluid ; it must be borne in mind, however, that œdema fluid is an abnormal accumulation, and care must be taken to distinguish the conditions under which it is formed. When it is due to a lymphatic blockage, as in elephantiasis, we must expect the concentration of protein to be unusually high in the œdema fluid, and this is the case, concentrations varying from 2–3·5 per cent. being found in dogs with obstructed lymphatics. Where œdema is due to a reduced plasma protein concentration, as in the experiments of Weech *et al.*, both lymph and œdema fluid contain very low concentrations of proteins (0·1–0·5 per cent.) ; in blisters caused by mustard gas the protein concentration is very high, due to the increased permeability of the capillaries to protein. If œdema is due to stasis, resulting from a raised venous pressure, reabsorption of fluid into the venous capillaries is reduced considerably, with the result that the

[1] That is, replacement of a large percentage of the blood by isotonic saline solution.
[2] Owing to its relatively low molecular weight, the serum albumin largely determines the colloid osmotic pressure of plasma.

protein concentration in the interstitial fluid never becomes high (*vide, e.g.,* Bramkamp).

The concentrations of the non-protein constituents of œdema fluid require some comment, since they should be governed by the requirements of the Gibbs-Donnan equilibrium. These requirements are, as we have seen, that the product : $[Na]_1 \times [Cl]_1 = [Na]_2 \times [Cl]_2$, *i.e.,* the ratios $[Na]_1 / [Na]_2$ and $[Cl]_2 / [Cl]_1$ should be equal. From a knowledge of the base-binding power of the plasma proteins, *i.e.,* of the fraction of Na^+ neutralised by protein anions, the ratio may be calculated, on the assumption that the activities of the ions are the same as their concentrations. On this assumption, the ratio should be 1·04, *i.e.,* the concentration of Na^+ should be some 4 per cent. higher in the plasma than in the œdema fluid, whilst the concentration of Cl^- should be lower in the plasma by an equivalent amount. Earlier analyses of Loeb, Atchley & Palmer, among others, seemed to bear out this prediction ; however, as Ingraham, Lombard & Visscher have emphasised, the assumption regarding equal activities is probably wrong. They showed that the ratio for Cl^- in plasma and its ultrafiltrate (prepared with a collodion membrane) was about 1·03, whilst that for Na^+ was about 1·07, figures agreeing with the values of Greene & Power [1] for *in vivo* dialysates of plasma, namely 1·02 for Cl^-, and 1·09 for Na^+. More recently Davson, Duke-Elder & Maurice, in a study primarily aimed at deciding whether the aqueous humour was a dialysate of blood plasma or not, found ratios of 1·01 for Cl^- and 1·07 for Na^+ in artificial dialysates. These figures, obtained with artificial ultra-filtrates or dialysates,[2] may be compared with values of 1·04–1·06 for Na^+ in ascitic fluid (*i.e.,* a pathological accumulation of fluid in the peritoneal cavity), and 1·03 for Cl^-, obtained by Greene *et al.,* and 1·02 for dog's peritoneal fluid (Maurer *et al.*). There seems little doubt, therefore, that in so far as the important ions, Na^+ and Cl^- are concerned, the distribution of ions between plasma and œdema-fluid follows approximately the requirements of a simple equilibrium, the " theoretical ratio " of 1·04, computed on the assumption of equal activities, being modified to about 1·07 for positive ions and 1·01 for negative ions, owing to the influence of the plasma proteins. Non-electrolytes should be equally distributed, and according to Gilligan, Volk & Blumgart, this is true of sugar, total non-protein nitrogen and creatinine. Œdema fluid may quite reasonably be taken as representative of interstitial fluid in so far as the Donnan Equilibrium is concerned, although its abnormal conditions of formation

[1] The results of Greene & Power on K^+ reveal surprisingly high ratios, of the order of 1·3 : however these would seem to be due to some technical error since Watchorn & McCance obtained ratios in the region of unity (average 1·01) ; Folk *et al.* obtained high values of K^+ (1·08) due, however, to escape of K^+ from the red cells into the plasma during collection and centrifuging. Their value for Na^+ was 1·04.

[2] The principle of ultra-filtration has already been described (p. 154) ; collodion membranes, as ordinarily prepared, are impermeable to the plasma proteins but permeable to water and non-colloidal constituents ; on exerting a pressure on a collodion sac containing plasma, an ultra-filtrate is exuded. A dialysate is obtained by enclosing plasma in a collodion sac and immersing it in a saline solution of approximately the same composition regarding salts and other non-colloidal substances ; if the volume of plasma is large in relation to the outside solution, an equilibrium is established corresponding approximately to that pertaining between plasma and its ultra-filtrate.

may occasion a much smaller concentration of protein than that in the true interstitial fluid ; recently, however, Maurer punctured muscles and obtained small quantities of normal interstitial fluid, which he analysed for protein and Cl⁻ ; he found a concentration of protein of 1·53 per cent., compared with 4·23 per cent. for plasma (the frog was used), and the ratio :—

$$\frac{[\text{Cl}^-]\ \text{Fluid}}{[\text{Cl}^-]\ \text{Plasma}} \text{ was } 1\cdot01$$

Capillary Permeability

We have so far considered the implications of the presence of a protein-containing fluid, the plasma, in a vessel under pressure, the walls of which were assumed to be impermeable to protein and permeable to smaller molecules and ions ; let us now consider, in more detail, the characteristics of this capillary membrane. The capillary consists of a tube built up of flat cells, cemented together presumably by hyaluronic acid or a similar mucopolysaccharide ; the cement regions are observable microscopically and therefore are very large in comparison with the size of even colloidal molecules, so that it has been suggested that diffusion of material out of the capillary takes place by way of these intercellular spaces, the hyaluronic acid presumably being a watery jelly permitting a fairly rapid diffusion. The fibrous scaffolding of the jelly, however, may be sufficiently tight to prevent the diffusion of protein molecules. The studies of Chambers & Zweifach lend support to the belief that it is the cement substance that largely determines the impermeability, or otherwise, of the capillary to proteins ; these authors perfused the frog's mesentery with fluid containing gelatin, to maintain the colloid osmotic pressure, and carbon particles, the latter being introduced to permit a study of the " stickiness " of the cement. The formation of œdema was estimated in a qualitative fashion. With a Ringer perfusion fluid containing a normal concentration of Ca^{++}, it was found that the carbon particles adhered principally to the intercellular zones, so that the endothelial cells were outlined in black ; raising the perfusion pressure as high as 60 mm. Hg failed to cause any extrusion of the carbon particles through the capillary wall. In the absence of Ca^{++} from the perfusion fluid, carbon particles accumulated in clumps all over the endothelial cells and flow became sluggish. These effects were shown to be most probably due to a rapid dissolution of the cement which caused a rapid outflow of fluid from the capillary ; the holes were too small to permit the passage of the carbon particles, so that the carbon accumulated in the capillary. Raising the capillary pressure to 60 mm. Hg now caused a distention of the wall and rupture, associated with a localised spurting out of masses of carbon. The effects of varying pH were studied in the presence and absence of Ca^{++} and a correlation between the stickiness of the cement, as measured by the tendency for the carbon particles to aggregate on the capillary wall, and the tendency to œdema, was observed. It was concluded that an acid pH, or absence of Ca^{++}, tended to dissolve the cement which became sticky during the first stage of dissolution.

Danielli studied the effectiveness of various substances in preventing œdema ; he confirmed the fact, found originally by Krogh & Harrup, that gum acacia, in spite of possessing a colloid osmotic pressure equal to that of the plasma proteins, was inadequate to prevent the development of œdema ; addition of some serum to the perfusing fluid reduced the œdema considerably, and he was able to show that a significant factor in the effectiveness of serum was the presence of platelets,[1] which presumably were effective in blocking up the holes formed by dissolution of the cement during perfusion. It is unlikely, however, that platelets play an important role in the maintenance of normal capillary permeability in the intact animal, since removal of over 80 per cent. of the platelets from the circulating blood of a cat failed to cause any œdema. It seems that plasma proteins, themselves, have some sort of protective action, possibly forming a layer over the pores of the cement substance ; if this were true, the replacement of these protein molecules by smaller ones might increase œdema ; Danielli found that clupein (p. 77) did indeed have this effect, and later a similar influence of peptone was described by Shleser & Freed. Whether or not this is the whole story remains to be seen ; Zweifach (1940) has drawn attention to the function of particulate matter—either carbon particles or red blood corpuscles—in maintaining an even circulation throughout the capillary bed. With artificial perfusion fluids of adequate colloid osmotic pressure Zweifach found that œdema developed, and this was associated with a complete collapse of the true capillaries ; circulation being exclusively through the *a-v*-bridges. Addition of carbon particles or red blood corpuscles to the perfusion fluid resulted in the opening up of the true capillary circulation and œdema was prevented. The particulate matter apparently exerts a mechanical influence on the flow, causing eddies which maintain the junction between true capillaries and *a-v*-bridges patent ; the strong association between the formation of œdema and closure of the true capillary circulation may be the result of a higher general capillary pressure when flow is confined to the *a-v*-bridges. Particulate matter may also prevent œdema by plugging the naturally occurring holes in the capillary cement as soon as they are formed.

The evidence from these studies suggests that the impermeability of the capillary membrane to plasma proteins depends primarily on the integrity of the cement substance. That a significant increase in permeability to proteins may be brought about by an attack on the individual endothelial cells, however, seems to be true, since Landis found a seven-fold increase in filtration rate due to the presence of a narcotic in the blood ; filtration proceeded to such an extent that capillaries were observed tightly packed with corpuscles. This must have been due to a permeability of the capillary to proteins, otherwise the colloid osmotic pressure of the plasma would have been far too high to have permitted such a loss of fluid. Again, Ponder & Hyman found that saponin, a substance that attacks cell membranes, caused a pronounced œdema ; and, finally, there have been frequent observations on the effects of O_2-lack, and metabolites, such as lactic acid,

---

[1] These are small colourless corpuscles, about 3μ in diameter, considered to play an important role in the clotting of shed blood.

in causing œdema. Abnormal capillary permeability to proteins produced in this way may be due to a passage of protein through the damaged endothelial cell membranes ; however, the capillary is to be regarded as a functional unit, with a normal tone and a continuous power of replacing lost cement. Interference with the true functioning of the endothelial cells might destroy tone, cause the capillary to dilate, and expand the intercellular spaces ; furthermore, an interference with metabolism might prejudice the renewal of the cement substance.[1]

We have so far considered the permeability of the endothelium to proteins ; we may now enquire briefly into the transport of smaller molecules. The measurements of Landis have shown that the passage of water across the capillary wall is extremely rapid in comparison with the observed rates of passage of water across cell membranes ; thus he obtained a figure of $0.03\mu^3$ of fluid flowing across $1\mu^2$ of surface per sec. with a filtration pressure of 5 cm. H_2O, equivalent to the passage of $370\mu^3/\mu^2/min./atm.$ or $7.9.10^{-1}$ cm./sec., a value approximately 100 times that found for the permeability of the erythrocyte to water. By the use of heavy water this rapid rate of exchange has been confirmed ; thus Hevesy & Jacobsen injected heavy water into the blood-stream of rabbits and measured the rate at which it disappeared from this fluid ; the heavy water, leaving the blood, passes first into the interstitial fluid and then, probably much more slowly, into the cells of the tissues ; a study of the rate of disappearance suggested that within half a minute the heavy water was equally distributed between plasma and interstitial fluids, and within half an hour it was distributed throughout all cells of the body. Similar results were found by Flexner and his colleagues. Since, in filtration from a capillary wall, all the non-colloidal constituents are probably taken through at the same rate,[2] we must presume to find not only a high permeability to water but also to all these non-colloidal constituents of the plasma. Work on the penetration of these non-colloidal substances has been mainly qualitative, but the results are in general accord with the notion of a high rate. Thus Hahn & Hevesy measured the rate of disappearance of radioactive K^+, Na^+, PO_4^{--}, Cl^-, and Br^- from the plasma of rabbits, after intravenous injection ; the exchanges were slower than with water, the time required for complete equilibration of Na^+, for example, being about eleven minutes. No difference between Na^+ and Cl^-

---

[1] The cement substance has been considered to be composed of hyaluronic acid, a high-molecular weight polysaccharide found in many transparent structures (p. 102) ; an enzyme, *hyaluronidase*, breaks it down. This enzyme has been described as the *spreading factor* because, when injected into the skin, it favours diffusion of dyes, presumably by breaking down the interstitial structures held together by hyaluronic acid (*vide e.g.*, Day, 1949). Hyaluronidase is said to cause an increase in capillary permeability (*e.g.*, by Elster *et al.*, 1949), but according to Chambers & Zweifach (1947), it has no effect on the cement ; the extravasation of blood from capillaries treated with the enzyme is considered by these authors to be due to a breakdown of the pericapillary sheath ; *cf.* Duran-Reynals (1942). The mode of action of the capillary permeability-increasing substance isolated from inflammatory exudates by Menkin—*leukotaxine*—is not known. It appears to be a polypeptide.

[2] This must happen owing to the difference of osmotic pressure that would be created by a significant lagging behind of the solute molecules. Thus a 1 per cent. difference in the concentrations of NaCl in plasma and its filtrate would establish a difference of osmotic pressure of 65 mm. Hg and thereby bring filtration to a stop.

was observed. It must be appreciated that in these studies all that was measured was the rate of disappearance from the plasma of the radioactive isotope ; the rate of loss will depend, quite apart from the rate of penetration of any membranes, on the relative concentrations of the non-radioactive isotope in the fluids outside the vascular system. If only diffusion into the interstitial fluids were being studied, the relative rates of loss of radioactivity would measure the relative rates of loss from the capillaries, since the relative concentrations of all these ions are approximately the same in plasma and interstitial fluid. However, once out of the capillaries, some of the substances can enter the tissue cells, and the observed rate will depend on the concentration of the non-active material in the cell. Thus the observed rate of loss of K^+ will be greater, because there is such a large concentration of non-radioactive K^+ within the cells with which the radioactive isotope can exchange ; whereas, with Na^+ and Cl^-, the observed rates of loss will be smaller, because the cells contain very low concentrations of these ions. These differences will be quite apart from any differences due to differing rates of migration across the membranes in the paths of these ions. It is therefore impossible to deduce the relative rates of transfer across the capillary membrane from the figures of Hahn & Hevesy and of Flexner. Studies of the penetration of maltose and galactose, two substances differing in molecular weight by a factor of two, show that they both penetrate the intercellular space at the same rate ; this is, at first thought, surprising if one assumes a simple diffusion through water-filled pores (*i.e.*, the intercellular cement substance); however, as Danielli & Davson have pointed out, this simply means that these substances, as well as the other non-colloidal solutes in the plasma, are brought into the interstitial spaces not by simple diffusion but by a bulk flow due to filtration ; the rate of entry is thus determined by the rate of flow of water and not by the individual diffusion constants of the various substances. Before passing to a consideration of the volume of the interstitial fluid, we may note that Rous and his colleagues have suggested that the capillary membrane shows a variable permeability along its length, being highest at the venous end. Thus they observed that dye-stuffs that left the capillary slowly appeared to leave it more rapidly at the venous end than at the arterial end. As Danielli & Stock have pointed out, however, the observation really consisted of the fact that the fluid surrounding the venous end of the capillary had a higher concentration of dye than that surrounding the arterial end ; now the venous end is the site of reabsorption, but since the concentration of dye is greater in the plasma than in the interstitial fluid, dye will not pass back into the plasma. The venous end is thus the site of a local accumulation of the dye ; moreover, most dyes are adsorbed to the plasma proteins, so that a high concentration in any region generally indicates a high concentration of plasma proteins, and this will be expected at the venous end because this is the site of reabsorption of fluid, the proteins being left behind.

Volume of the Interstitial Fluid

The determination of that fraction of the volume (or weight) of a tissue occupied by the extracellular fluids is a matter of great practical importance in the study of the transport of material from blood to tissue cells ; since, moreover, the interstitial fluid is derived from the blood plasma, the volume of the former at any moment is a dominant influence on the volume of fluid available for circulation through the vascular tree. The tissue most frequently studied from the point of view of extracellular fluid is striated muscle, the long fibres of which are bathed with a thin film of this fluid. Chemical analysis of whole muscle reveals, as with other highly cellular tissues, a high concentration of K^+ and relatively low concentrations of Na^+ and Cl^- ; analyses of cells such as erythrocytes, which may be packed so tightly together by centrifugation that the interstitial space is very small, reveals, moreover, that K^+ is the predominant and nearly exclusive cation present in the internal environment, so that it is customary to speak of K^+ as an intracellular cation whilst Na^+ is said to be predominantly extracellular [1] ; in the case of muscle, Cl^- is also thought to be mainly extracellular, the anions within the muscle cells being made up principally of phosphate, protein, etc. (p. 258). Here, then, is a basis for establishing the volume of the extracellular space since, if Cl^- is present only in the extracellular fluid, it will have the same concentration as that in an ultrafiltrate of plasma, and analyses of the Cl^- in plasma and whole muscle provide the necessary figures for the computation of the volume of this space.[2]

The figure derived on this basis is called the *chloride-space* of the tissue and is, of course, only equal to the extracellular space if the cells are truly free of Cl^-. Alternatively the *sodium-space* may be determined. Chloride- and sodium-spaces, computed by Manery & Hastings for various tissues of the rabbit, are shown in Table XIV, where the figures represent grammes of fluid per 100 grammes of blood-free, fat-free tissue. For muscle the chloride- and sodium-spaces are in the region of 11 per cent., whilst in nervous tissue the figure is considerably higher ; tendon is essentially non-cellular and thus gives a very high value. The *thiocyanate-space* has been considered as a substitute for the chloride-space since the CNS^--ion apparently distributes itself in the same manner as Cl^- ; in Table XV some comparative estimates of the chloride- and thiocyanate-spaces in various muscles of the cat are shown, the results being expressed as ml. of fluid in 100 g. of tissue ; the correspondence between the two estimates is fairly good.

The use of radioactive isotopes has simplified the technique for the determination of the sodium-space and permits, moreover, a more reliable estimate of the true extracellular space, *i.e.*, a correction may be made for

---

[1] Certain cells make exceptions to this rule ; thus the erythrocytes of the cat, dog, sheep and ox contain more Na^+ than K^+ ; according to Wilson & Manery, the leucocytes of the rabbit contain about equal concentrations of the two ions.

[2] Thus : " Chloride Space " $= \dfrac{Cl^- \text{ in Muscle (meq./kg.)} \times 100}{Cl^- \text{ in Plasma (meq./kg.)}}$ per cent.

the amount of Na^+ that is intracellular. Thus, after injection of Na^{24}, equilibration with the extracellular fluid takes place very rapidly (within

TABLE XIV

Chloride- and Sodium-Spaces for Rabbit Tissues, Expressed as g. of Fluid per 100 g. of Blood-Free, Fat-Free Tissue. (*Manery & Hastings*, 1939.)

Tissue	Chloride-Space	Sodium-Space
Gastrocnemius	10·7–10·9	10·8–11·2
Brain	33·2–37·6	36·6–40·0
Spinal cord	37·5–32·4	40·3–44·3
Stomach	38·6–50·8	21·3–23·3
Tendon	59·5–68·3	47·3–55·2

TABLE XV

Comparative Values for the Chloride- and Thiocyanate-Spaces of Various Muscles of the Cat. (*Lands, Larson & Cutting*, 1939.)

Muscle	Biceps f.	Gastroc-nemius	Sterno-mastoideus	Diaphragm	Heart
Cl-Space (ml./100 g.) .	13·2	12·4	24·8	29·3	30·2
CNS-Space (ml./100 g.) .	13·6	16·2	24·0	32·9	32·9

three minutes) so that simultaneous determinations of the Na^{24}-activity in muscle and plasma, a short time after the intravenous injection, should provide the basis for a determination of the extracellular space ; a few results on the gastrocnemius of the rat are summarised in Table XVI. The Table gives the extracellular spaces, computed as the *chloride-space*, the ordinary (Na^{23}) *sodium-space*, and the Na^{24}-*space*, at different times after injection.[1] It will be seen that the Na^{24}-space after three minutes was 7·1 per cent., comparing with the classical chloride-space of 10·5 per cent. With the progress of time the Na^{24}-space increased to about 15 per cent., when the chloride-space was 12 per cent., *i.e.*, eventually the Na^{24}-space became considerably greater than its value after three minutes, and even larger than the chloride-space ; these results prove that there is a definite fraction of the Cl^- and Na^+ within the muscle cells (p. 258). Consequently chloride- and sodium-spaces, determined by classical methods, are undoubtedly too high as estimates of the volume of the extracellular fluid.

The ideal method of determining the extracellular space would involve the addition of some foreign substance to the blood that would definitely not penetrate the tissue cells ; thus sucrose and maltose are thought to be suitable and inulin, a high molecular-weight polysaccharide, not too big to be restrained by the muscle capillaries, is probably ideal. Most studies with inulin have been carried out with the intention of estimating the

[1] Of course different animals had to be used for the different periods ; to establish the trends shown in Table XVI, large groups of animals should have been used instead of individuals.

TABLE XVI

Relative Values of Na²⁴-, Cl⁻-, and Na²³-Spaces at Increasing Times After Injection of Na²⁴. (*Manery & Bale, 1939.*)

Time	3 min.	8 min.	8 min.	16 min.	20 min.	60 min.	60 min.
Na²⁴-Space . .	7·1	8·7	11	13	11	15	14
Cl⁻-Space . .	10·5						12·3
Na²³-Space . .		13·4					

Time	120 min.	120 min.	180 min.	12 hours
Na²⁴-Space . .	15	15	13	15
Cl⁻-Space . .	12·1			
Na²³-Space . .			14·3	

extracellular space of the whole animal rather than of single tissues [1]; however, Wilde has compared the inulin- and chloride-spaces in rat muscle. His figures were 17 per cent. for chloride-space as against only 13·5 per cent. for inulin-space, *i.e.*, some of the Cl^- in muscle is definitely intracellular. Again, Conway & Fitzgerald found an inulin-space of only 8·5 per cent. in mammalian muscle compared with 15·2 per cent. for the chloride-space. A great many experiments have been carried out on frog muscles, either soaked in solutions of these substances in Ringer, or perfused with blood substitutes. The muscle, under these conditions, is abnormal in that œdema progressively develops, giving an abnormally high value for the extracellular space. Thus Levi & Ussing found " apparent interspace values " of 27–32 per cent. with muscles soaked in Ringer + Na²⁴, and Danielli & Davson found a progressive increase in the maltose- and chloride-spaces of the perfused sartorius of the frog.

Circulating Volume of Blood. The importance of the accurate determination of the extracellular space lies mainly in the mathematical analysis of the observed rate of penetration of substances from blood into tissue ; before entering the tissue *cells*, a substance must pass into the extracellular space, so that the rate of penetration from blood into cells is determined by the time taken to pass from blood to space and space to cells ; only if the volume of the space is known is a mathematical analysis possible (*vide, e.g.,* Levi & Ussing ; Harris & Burn). In this connection it should be mentioned that the actual volume of circulating blood in the tissue may be of significance in a kinetic analysis ; this may be evaluated from a determination of hæmoglobin in the tissue (Danielli) or by the use of " labelled corpuscles." Thus Nieset *et al.* have shown that incubation of erythrocytes with radioactive phosphate (P³²) at 37° C. for two hours allows them to take up a large percentage of the active phosphorus (40 per cent. of a total of 50 millicuries is taken up by 10 ml. of blood) ; this

---

[1] In the whole animal Kruhoffer finds an inulin-space of 20 per cent., comparing with 30 per cent. for the CNS⁻-space ; Gaudino and Levitt found 19·4, 33·8, and 33·8 per cent. for the inulin-, CNS⁻- and Na²⁴-spaces respectively. Since inulin cannot penetrate at all into some extracellular regions, *e.g.*, the aqueous humour, cerebrospinal fluid and nervous tissue, it does not reveal the true extracellular space of the whole animal.

apparently combines with organic substances within, or on the surface of, the cells and escapes again only very slowly when the erythrocytes are injected into an animal. Consequently a determination of the radioactivity of a tissue after the injection of the labelled corpuscles gives an approximate measure of the volume of blood in it.[1] That the circulating volume of blood in a tissue may be a considerable fraction of the extracellular space is shown by Danielli's finding of 5 per cent. for the " vascular space " of the frog's gastrocnemius and 10·5 per cent. for the sartorius, so that the total extracellular space of a muscle, with a well-filled vascular system, is of the order of 16–20 per cent. ; the figure of 11 per cent., on the other hand, given for the gastrocnemius of the rat (p. 221), is based on the blood-free tissue.

Maintenance of Blood Volume

The volume of the blood plasma must, other things being equal, decrease as the volume of the extracellular fluid increases ; the maintenance of a fairly constant volume of blood is important from the dynamic aspect of maintaining a regular circulation ; a large decrease in circulating volume, for example, leaves the heart with insufficient fluid to fill it adequately during diastole, the blood pressure falls, and the condition of shock ensues. Hence the inter-relationship of blood and extracellular fluid is of great physiological importance, as first recognised by Starling. As we have seen, filtration from the arterial end of the capillaries is associated with reabsorption at the venous end ; there is thus a constant interchange of plasma and interstitial fluid, the rapidity of which may be judged from Flexner's studies with Na^{24}, from which he computed that 60 per cent. of the Na^+ in the plasma is replaced each minute by Na^+ from an extra-vascular source. Now, the greater the loss of fluid at the arterial end of a capillary, the greater will be the concentration of protein in the plasma passing to the venous end, so that the difference of osmotic pressure, and thus the force pulling water back into the plasma, increases with increasing loss at the arterial end. The system is therefore in some measure self-compensating, the greater the loss of fluid at the arterial end of a capillary, the greater the return at the venous end. Consequently the effect of an increase in capillary pressure, which of course increases the filtration tendency all along the capillary, is partly compensated by the increased difference of osmotic pressure created by this extra filtration. The ingestion of a large quantity of water causes, in the first place, a dilution of the plasma proteins (as shown for example by Smirk) ; this dilution reduces the colloid osmotic pressure, with the result that more fluid is filtered into the tissue spaces than before ; and these spaces therefore act as a buffer in taking up a part of the extra water-load. The intravenous

---

[1] Hevesy and Zerahn (1942) were the first to describe this technique. Maneely *et al.* have used radioactive iron (Fe^{59}) in essentially the same manner ; corpuscles are labelled with this atom by feeding the radioactive isotope ; it is incorporated into the hæmoglobin of the newly formed cells ; later the blood is withdrawn and injected into another animal. The ensuing radioactivity of the blood is a measure of the dilution of the radioactive corpuscles by the blood of the recipient, and thus the blood volume can be calculated. Reeve and Veall have recently improved the P^{32} technique.

injection of isotonic NaCl dilutes the plasma proteins and hence increases filtration ; any rise in capillary pressure caused by the increase in circulating volume also tends to favour filtration, so that in consequence of these two compensatory tendencies the increase in blood volume produced in this way is only transient. Injection of strongly hypertonic NaCl solutions produces temporary changes in the pressure relationships which may be of importance, although the final effect on the blood volume [1] may be the same as with the injection of an isotonic solution. The capillary membrane is permeable to NaCl, so that mixing can be achieved by the diffusion of NaCl alone into the tissue fluid, without the osmosis of water in the opposite direction. In these circumstances we have seen that no permanent change in volume of the two fluids will occur (p. 159), but a temporary one is possible, namely the osmosis of water from the more dilute interstitial fluid to the more concentrated plasma. Hence the injection of hypertonic NaCl causes a passage of fluid from the interstitial spaces followed by a return, later, as the NaCl diffuses in the opposite direction. The difference of osmotic pressure between plasma and interstitial fluid may be more permanently increased by the injection of a concentrated solution of a substance which cannot penetrate the capillary membrane with ease, *e.g.*, gum acacia or plasma proteins. In this case the filtration tendency is reduced and the blood volume is increased, and remains at this higher value until the foreign material is eliminated. In serious hæmorrhage the general vascular pressures, including the capillary pressure, fall ; the filtration tendency is thus decreased, whilst the reabsorptive tendency increases, with the result that hæmorrhage is accompanied by a movement of fluid from the tissue spaces into the capillaries. If the loss of blood is too severe, however, the various compensatory mechanisms of the organism may be inadequate, so that circulatory failure may ensue unless the fluid volume is made up by injection. We have seen that the injection of isotonic NaCl creates conditions which lead to its loss to the interstitial spaces ; consequently the value of such an injection is small. The injection of gum acacia, or plasma protein solutions, on the contrary, has a more permanent effect. The most serious threat to the constancy of the volume of circulating fluid is the loss of the impermeability of the capillary membrane to proteins, since now the compensatory mechanism is undermined ; it would seem that this is the state of affairs in many forms of shock.[2]

[1] Ignoring for the moment the water loss that will result from the renal excretion of the extra salt (p. 353).

[2] According to Cope & Moore and Fine & Seligman, shock is not necessarily due to a generalised increase in capillary permeability to proteins, extending beyond the site of injury. These authors tagged the plasma proteins, either by injecting Evans Blue, treated with Br^{82}—the radioactive dye-stuff combining chemically with the plasma proteins—or by injecting plasma proteins previously treated with I^{131} ; the time-course of development of radioactivity of the lymph was therefore a measure of the escape of plasma proteins from the capillaries. Whereas local burns caused a rapid increase in radioactivity in the lymph from the burned limb, there was no apparent change in the course of development of radioactivity in lymph obtained from other regions of the body.

References

ABELL, R. G. (1946). " The Permeability of Blood Capillary Sprouts and Newly Formed Blood Capillaries as Compared to that of Older Capillaries." *Amer. J. Physiol.*, **147**, 237.

AMBERSON, W. R., NASH, T. P., MULDER, A. G. & BINNS, D. (1938). " Relationship between Tissue Chloride and Plasma Chloride." *Amer. J. Physiol.*, **122**, 224.

ANDERSON, R. S. (1942). " The Use of P^{32} for Determining Circulating Erythrocyte Volume." *Amer. J. Physiol.*, **127**, 539.

BARON, H. & CHAMBERS, R. (1936). " A Micromanipulative Study on the Migration of Blood Cells in Frog Capillaries." *Amer. J. Physiol.*, **114**, 700.

CHAMBERS, R. & ZWEIFACH, B. W. (1944). " Topography and Function of the Mesenteric Capillary Circulation." *Amer. J. Anat.*, **75**, 173.

CHAMBERS, R. & ZWEIFACH, B. W. (1947). " Intercellular Cement and Capillary Permeability." *Physiol. Rev.*, **27**, 436.

CONWAY, E. J. & FITZGERALD, O. (1942). " Diffusion Relations of Urea, Inulin, and Chloride in some Mammalian Tissues." *J. Physiol.*, **101**, 86.

COPE, O. & MOORE, F. D. (1944). " Study of Capillary Permeability in Experimental Burns and Burn Shock Using Radioactive Dyes in Blood and Lymph." *J. clin. Inv.*, **23**, 241.

COWIE, D. B., FLEXNER, L. B. & WILDE, W. S. (1949). " Rate of Transcapillary Exchange of Cl^- in the Guinea Pig as Determined with Cl^{38}." *Amer. J. Physiol.*, **158**, 231.

DANIELLI, J. F. (1940). " Capillary Permeability and Œdema in the Perfused Frog." *J. Physiol.*, **98**, 109.

DANIELLI, J. F. (1941). " A Method for Estimating the Fraction of the Volume of a Muscle Contained in the Vascular System." *J. Physiol.*, **100**, 239.

DANIELLI, J. F. & DAVSON, H. (1941). " The Volume of the Vascular System, and Penetration of Sugars from the Vascular System into the Intercellular Space." *J. Physiol.*, **100**, 246.

DANIELLI, J. F. & STOCK, A. (1944). " The Structure and Permeability of Capillaries." *Biol. Rev.*, **19**, 81.

DARROW, D. C., HOPPER, E. B. & CARY, M. K. (1932). " Plasmapheresis Œdema. I. The Relation of Reduction of Serum Proteins to Œdema and the Pathological Anatomy Accompanying Œdema." *J. clin. Inv.*, **11**, 683.

DAVSON, H. & DANIELLI, J. F. (1943). " The Permeability of Natural Membranes." Cambridge.

DAVSON, H., DUKE-ELDER, W. S. & MAURICE, D. M. (1949). " Changes in Ionic Distribution following Dialysis of Aqueous Humour against Plasma." *J. Physiol.*, **109**, 32.

DAY, T. D. (1949). " Mode of Reaction of Interstitial Connective Tissue with Water." *J. Physiol.*, **109**, 380.

DRINKER, C. K., FIELD, M. E. & HOMANS, J. (1934). " The Experimental Production of Œdema and Elephantiasis as a Result of Lymphatic Obstruction." *Amer. J. Physiol.*, **108**, 509.

DRINKER, C. K. & YOFFEY, J. M. (1941). " Lymphatics, Lymph, and Lymphoid Tissue." Harvard Univ. Press.

DURAN-REYNALS, F. (1942). " Tissue Permeability and the Spreading Factors in Infection." *Bact. Rev.*, **6**, 197.

ELSTER, S. K., FREEMAN, M. E. & DORFMAN, A. (1949). " Effect of Hyaluronidase on the Passage of Fluid and of T-1824 Through the Capillary Wall." *Amer. J. Physiol.*, **156**, 429.

FIELD, M. E. & DRINKER, C. K. (1931). " Rapidity of Interchanges between Blood and Lymph in the Dog." *Amer. J. Physiol.*, **98**, 378.

FINE, J. & SELIGMAN, A. M. (1944). " A Study of ' Lost Plasma ' in Hæmorrhagic, Tourniquet, and Burn Shock by the Use of Radioactive Iodo-Plasma Protein." *J. clin. Inv.*, **23**, 720.

FLEXNER, L. B., COWIE, D. B. & VOSBURGH, G. J. (1948). " Studies on Capillary Permeability with Tracer Substances." *C.S.H. Symp.*, **13**, 88.

FOLK, B. P., ZIESLER, K. L. & LILIENTHAL, J. L. (1948). " Distribution of K^+ and Na^+ between Serum and Certain Extracellular Fluids in Man." *Amer. J. Physiol.*, **153**, 381.

GAUDINO, M. & LEVITT, M. F. (1949). " Inulin Space as a Measure of Extracellular Fluid." *Amer. J. Physiol.*, **157**, 387.

GILLIGAN, D. R., VOLK, M. C. & BLUMGART, H. L. (1933). "The Simple Dialysate Nature of Œdema Fluids Contrasted with the Specialised Composition of Cerebrospinal Fluid." *J. clin. Inv.*, 12, 975.

GREENE, C. H. & POWER, M. H. (1931). "The Distribution of Electrolytes between Serum and the *In Vivo* Dialysate." *J. biol. Chem.*, 91, 183.

HARRIS, E. J. & BURN, G. P. (1949). "Transfer of Na+ and K+ between Muscle and Surrounding Medium." *Trans. Farad. Soc.*, 45, 508.

HAHN, L. & HEVESY, G. (1940). "Rate of Passage of Ions Through the Capillary Wall." *Acta Phys. Scand.*, 1, 347.

HEVESY, G. & JACOBSEN, C. F. (1940). "Rate of Passage of Water Through Capillary and Cell Walls." *Acta Phys. Scand.*, 1, 11.

HEVESY, G. & ZERAHN, K. (1942). "Determination of the Red Corpuscle Content." *Acta Physiol. Scand.*, 4, 376.

HYMAN, C. (1944). "Filtration Across the Vascular Wall as a Function of Several Physical Factors." *Amer. J. Physiol.*, 142, 671.

INGRAHAM, R. C., LOMBARD, C. & VISSCHER, M. B. (1933). "The Characteristics of Ultrafiltrates of Plasma." *J. gen. Physiol.*, 16, 637.

KAHN, R. H. & POLLAK, F. (1931). "Die aktive Verengerung des Lumens der capillaren Blutgefässe." *Pflüg. Arch.*, 226, 799.

KEYS, A. (1937). "Apparent Permeability of the Capillary Membrane in Man." *Trans. Farad. Soc.*, 33, 930.

KROGH, A. & HARROP, G. A. (1921). "On the Substance Responsible for Capillary Tonus." *J. Physiol.*, 54, P125.

KRUHOFFER, P. (1946). "Inulin as an Indicator for the Extracellular Space." *Acta Physiol. Scand.*, 11, 16.

KRUHOFFER, P. (1946). "The Significance of Diffusion and Convection for the Distribution of Solutes in the Interstitial Space." *Acta Physiol. Scand.*, 11, 37.

LANDIS, E. M. (1927). "Relation between Capillary Pressure and Rate at which Fluid Passes Through the Walls of Single Capillaries." *Amer. J. Physiol.*, 82, 217.

LANDIS, E. M. (1933). "Poiseuille's Law and the Capillary Circulation." *Amer. J. Physiol.*, 103, 432.

LANDIS, E. M. (1934). "Capillary Pressure and Capillary Permeability." *Physiol. Rev.*, 14, 404.

LANDS, A. M., LARSON, P. S. & CUTTING, R. A. (1939). "Size of the Extracellular Compartment of Skeletal Muscle." *P.S.E.B.M.*, 41, 606.

LEVI, H. & USSING, H. H. (1948). "Exchange of Na+ and Cl− Across the Fibre Membrane of the Isolated Frog Sartorius." *Acta Physiol. Scand.*, 16, 232.

LOEB, R. F., ATCHLEY, D. W. & PALMER, W. M. (1922). "Equilibrium Condition between Blood Serum and Serous Cavity Fluids." *J. gen. Physiol.*, 4, 591.

LOESCHKE, H. & LOESCHKE, E. (1934). "Pericyten, Grundhäutchen und Lymphscheiden der Kapillaren." *Z. mikr. anat. Forsch.*, 35, 533.

MANEELY, G. R., WELLS, E. B. & HAHN, P. F. (1947). "Application of the Radioactive Red Cell Method for Determination of Blood Volume in Humans." *Amer. J. Physiol.*, 148, 531.

MANERY, J. F. & BALE, W. F. (1939). "The Distribution of Injected Na24 and P32 in Tissues." *Amer. J. Physiol.*, 126, 578.

MANERY, J. F. & BALE, W. F. (1941). "The Penetration of Na24 and P32 into the Extra- and Intra-Cellular Phases of Tissues." *Amer. J. Physiol.*, 132, 474.

MANERY, J. F. & HAEGE, L. F. (1941). "The Extent to which Radioactive Chloride Penetrates Tissues and its Significance." *Amer. J. Physiol.*, 134, 83.

MANERY, J. F. & HASTINGS, A. B. (1939). "Distribution of Electrolytes in Mammalian Tissues." *J. biol. Chem.*, 127, 657.

MAURER, F. W. (1938). "Isolation and Analysis of Extracellular Muscle Fluid from Frog." *Amer. J. Physiol.*, 124, 546.

MAURER, F. W., WARREN, M. F. & DRINKER, C. K. (1940). "The Composition of Mammalian Pericardial and Peritoneal Fluids. Studies of Their Protein and Chloride Contents, and the Passage of Foreign Substances from the Blood Stream into these Fluids." *Amer. J. Physiol.*, 124, 635.

MCMASTER, P. D. (1941–2). "Lymphatic Participation in Cutaneous Phenomena." *Harvey Lectures*, 37, 227.

MENKIN, V. (1938). "The Role of Inflammation in Immunity." *Physiol. Rev.*, 18, 366.

MEYER, F. & HOLLAND, G. (1932). "Die Messung des Druckes in Geweben." *Arch. f. exp. Path. u. Pharm.*, 168, 580.

MEYER, K. (1947). "The Biological Significance of Hyaluronic Acid and Hyaluronidase." *Physiol. Rev.*, 27, 335.

MICHELS, N. A. (1936). "Structure of Capillaries, etc." *Anat. Rec.*, 65, 99.

MUNTWYLER, E., WAY, C. T. & POMERENE, E. (1931). " A Comparison of the Chloride and Bicarbonate Concentrations between Plasma and Spinal Fluid and Plasma and Ascitic Fluid in Reference to the Donnan Equilibrium." *J. biol. Chem.*, **92**, 733.

NIESET, R. T., PORTER, B., TRAUTMAN, W. V., BELL, R. M., PARSON, W., LYONS, C. & MAYERSON, H. S. (1948). " Determination of Circulating Red Blood Cell Volume with P^{32}." *Amer. J. Physiol.*, **155**, 226.

PAPPENHEIMER, J. R. & SOTO-RIVERA, A. (1948). " Effective Osmotic Pressure of the Plasma Proteins and Other Quantities Associated with the Capillary Circulation in the Hindlimbs of Cats and Dogs." *Amer. J. Physiol.*, **152**, 471.

PONDER, E. & HYMAN, C. (1943). " The Cytolytic Effect of Saponin on the Walls of Vessels." *Amer. J. Physiol.*, **138**, 432.

REEVE, E. B. & VEALL, N. (1949). " Simplified Method for the Determination of Circulating Red Cell Volume with P^{32}." *J. Physiol.*, **108**, 12.

ROUS, P. and collaborators (1930–1932). " The Gradient of Vascular Permeability." *J. exp. Med.*, **51**, 807 ; **53**, 195, 219 ; **54**, 499 ; **55**, 203 ; **56**, 371.

SCATCHARD, G., BATCHELDER, A. C. & BROWN, A. (1944). " The Osmotic Pressure of Plasma and of Serum Albumin." *J. clin. Inv.*, **23**, 458.

SHLESER, I. H. & FREED, S. C. (1942). " The Effect of Peptone on Capillary Permeability and its Neutralisation by Adrenal Cortical Extract." *Amer. J. Physiol.*, **137**, 426.

SMIRK, F. H. (1932). " Changes in Blood Composition Following Ingestion of Water and Saline." *J. Physiol.*, **75**, 81.

VAN SLYKE, D. D. (1926). " Factors Affecting the Distribution of Electrolytes, Water, and Gases in the Animal Body." Philadelphia.

WATCHORN, E. & MCCANCE (1933). " The K^+ in Serum, Serum Ultra-Filtrate and Cerebrospinal Fluid." *Biochem. J.*, **27**, 1107.

WEECH, A. A., GOETTSCH, E. & REEVE, E. B. (1934). " Flow and Composition of Lymph in Relation to the Formation of Œdema." *J. exp. Med.*, **60**, 63.

WELLS, H. S., YOUMAN, J. B. & MILLER, D. G. (1938). " Intracutaneous, Subcutaneous, and Intramuscular Tissue Pressure as Related to Venous Pressure." *J. clin. Inv.*, **17**, 489.

WHITE, H. L. (1924). " On Glomerular Filtration." *Amer. J. Physiol.*, **68**, 523.

WILDE, W. S. (1945). " The Chloride Equilibrium in Muscle." *Amer. J. Physiol.*, **143**, 666.

WILSON, D. L. & MANERY, J. F. (1949). " Permeability of Leucocytes to Na^+, K^+, and Cl^-." *J. cell. & comp. Physiol.*, **34**, 493.

ZWEIFACH, B. W. (1939). " The Character and Distribution of the Blood Capillaries." *Anat. Rec.*, **73**, 475.

ZWEIFACH, B. W. (1940). " The Structural Basis of Permeability and Other Functions of Blood Capillaries." *C.S.H. Symp.*, **8**, 216.

ZWEIFACH, B. W. (1940). " The Distribution of Blood Perfusates in Capillary Circulation." *Amer. J. Physiol.*, **130**, 512.

ZWEIFACH, B. W. & KOSSMAN, C. E. (1937). " Micromanipulation of Small Blood Vessels in the Mouse." *Amer. J. Physiol.*, **120**, 23.

CHAPTER X

THE CEREBROSPINAL FLUID

Specialised Tissue Fluids

THE extracellular fluid discussed earlier is, in normal circumstances, little more than a thin film covering the more solid elements of a tissue, such as muscle. In two regions, namely the eye and the central nervous system, there is a tissue fluid in relatively larger amounts, the *aqueous humour* and the *cerebrospinal fluid* respectively.[1] The superficial similarity of these fluids to protein-free filtrates from blood plasma suggested that they were formed in a manner similar to that of extracellular fluid in other parts of the body ; but, as a result of more careful studies of their chemical composition, the conclusion has now been reached that they are fluids, elaborated by specialised cells, with a chemical composition different in many important respects from what would be expected of a simple filtrate. Space will not permit of an elaborate account of the experimental studies on both fluids ; since, however, the two have many characteristics in common, it will be sufficient for our purpose to describe only one—the cerebrospinal fluid.[2]

Anatomical Aspects

The central nervous system develops from a hollow *neural tube* filled with fluid, and it retains this character as a hollow organ throughout life, enclosing in its *ventricles and canals* the almost protein-free *cerebrospinal fluid ;* on the outer surfaces of the brain and spinal cord, too, there is a space, the *subarachnoid space*, filled with the same fluid, so that the whole tissue rests on a fluid cushion. The brain is covered by three membranes, or *meninges ;* the *dura mater*, a tough protective coat, and two much thinner layers, the *arachnoid* and *pia mater*. It is the cavity between these last two membranes that is spoken of as the subarachnoid space ; it contains a spongy meshwork of connective tissue through the interstices of which the cerebrospinal fluid percolates. The pia adheres closely to the surface of the brain whilst the arachnoid tends to bridge over the gaps formed by the irregularities of the brain's surface, so that there are formed many large spaces between the membranes (Fig. 117). The pia is highly vascular, containing most of the vessels from which the superficial layers of

---

[1] The *synovial fluid*, which acts as a lubricant in synovial joints, is generally classified with these two ; its composition has been reviewed by Bauer, Ropes & Waine, who consider it to be a filtrate from blood plasma, as opposed to a secretion by the synovial membrane ; it reveals the intervention of secretory activity, however, by the presence of a mucoid.

[2] I have chosen the cerebrospinal fluid because it is a long time since the subject was reviewed ; actually, as a result of recent intensive studies, the aqueous humour is the better understood ; it has been recently reviewed by Davson, and by Friedenwald.

nervous tissue are supplied with blood, the vessels plunging into the nervous tissue. The arachnoid, on the other hand, is avascular. The outer and inner surfaces of the arachnoid, the trabeculæ uniting this membrane to the pia, and the outer surface of the latter membrane, are lined with a layer of squamous mesenchymal epithelial cells, so that the barrier to diffusion between blood and subarachnoid fluid is constituted by the capillary endothelium of the pial capillaries, and this epithelial layer. Within the nervous tissue the fluid is enclosed in four ventricles ; the lateral ventricles of the cerebral hemispheres, the third ventricle in the mid-brain region, and the fourth ventricle in the medulla ; all four ventricles are in connection (Fig. 118) ; moreover, the fluid in the fourth ventricle is in direct communication, at its caudal (lower) end, with the

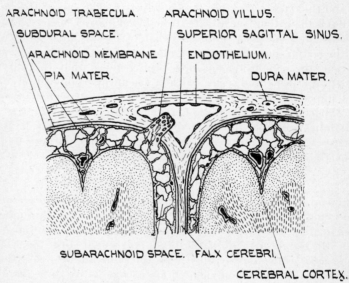

Fig. 117. Illustrating the meninges and an arachnoid villus projecting into the superior sagittal sinus. (After Weed. *Amer. J. Anat.*)

spinal canal which likewise contains cerebrospinal fluid, although in adult life it may be more or less obliterated. The interconnection of the subarachnoid and ventricular systems is brought about by way of certain *foramina*, three channels leading from the fourth ventricle to the *cisterna magna*, a large subarachnoid space over the medulla and below the posterior border of the cerebellum (Fig. 118). Since the subarachnoid spaces are all continuous with each other, the possibility of a continuous circulation of the fluid may be envisaged ; the circulation seems to consist of a continuous formation of new fluid at localised regions, and a drainage away into the venous system. The walls of the ventricles are specialised in certain regions called the *choroid plexuses ;* here the wall consists of a membrane, the *lamina epithelialis*, a thin layer of epithelium which becomes differentiated from the cells lining the rest of the ventricle. The pia covering it becomes extremely vascular, to form the *choroid plexus*, the two membranes being referred to, in this region, as the *tela choroidea ;* they are very much folded so as to increase the area exposed to the ventricular fluid ; and it is these regions that are regarded as the main sources of production of cerebrospinal fluid. The drainage of fluid seems to take place into the large endocranial venous sinuses, whose dural sheaths are perforated in certain places by numerous protrusions of arachnoid membrane, which form finger-like evaginations into the lumen of the sinus

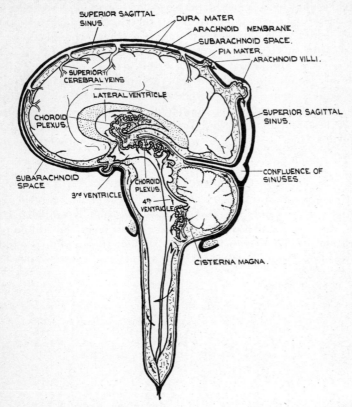

Fig. 118. Illustrating the circulation of the cerebrospinal fluid. (After Rasmussen. *The Principal Nervous Pathways.* Macmillan.)

(Fig. 117) ; the subarachnoid fluid inside these protrusions, or *arachnoid villi* as they are called, is thus separated from the blood within the sinus by only a very thin mesothelial membrane through which filtration and osmosis into the blood undoubtedly occur.

The cerebral tissue, consisting as it does of large aggregates of metabolising nerve cells, requires a suitable supply of nutrient material ; this is achieved primarily by the cerebral system of vessels, the arteries penetrating the substance of the brain and breaking up into capillaries. Although the vessels of the pia mater likewise supply arteries to the brain tissue, this pial, or *meningeal,* system of blood vessels provides only a small fraction of the total blood supply to the brain ; the meningeal circulation, however, gives rise to the choroid plexuses and it is therefore to be regarded as the main source of the cerebrospinal fluid, whereas the cerebral vessels, proper, supply the nervous tissue directly. Since diffusion of material from the cerebrospinal fluid directly to the nervous tissue cannot be excluded, it is possible that this fluid may be regarded as a nutrient medium. The brain is not supplied with a lymphatic system, so that any excess of interstitial fluid, if it is formed, probably finds its way back to the subarachnoid fluid by way of the perivascular spaces of the vessels leaving the pia, these spaces opening freely at the brain surface into the subarachnoid spaces. These perivascular spaces are thought also to be continuous with similar spaces around the nerves (perineural spaces). As we shall see, the specialised nature of the nervous capillaries probably precludes any significant escape of protein into the interstitial fluid of the nervous tissue ; hence it may well be that the normal mechanism of filtration and reabsorption is completely adequate to maintain fluid balance in these regions, and the postulate of a continuous flow, by way of the perineural and perivascular spaces into the subarachnoid, may be unnecessary.

Chemical Composition

The literature contains a vast array of chemical analyses of the cerebrospinal fluid ; in general, the chemical composition resembles, in broad outlines, that of a filtrate of plasma ; however, the differences in concentration of various substances are sufficiently great to exclude this mechanism of the origin of the fluid, and we must postulate some secretory

TABLE XVII

Concentrations of Solutes in Plasma and Cerebrospinal Fluid of Man.
(Collated from figures presented by Katzenelbogen, 1935.)

Solute	Plasma mM per kg. H_2O	C.s.f. mM per kg. H_2O	$\dfrac{\text{Plasma}}{\text{C.s.f.}}$
Cl	109	126	0·865
K	6·35	3·5	1·8
Na	—	—	1·04
Mg	1·1	1·3	0·845
Ca	2·56	1·23	2·1
Glucose	—	—	1·4–2·0
Urea	47 (mg./100 ml. H_2O)	42 (mg./100 ml. H_2O)	1·1
Creatinine	7·4 (mg./100 ml. H_2O)	3·6 (mg./100 ml. H_2O)	2·05
Protein	7,500 (mg./100 ml. H_2O)	25 (mg./100 ml. H_2O)	300

activity in its formation. Thus it will be seen from Table XVII that the ratios of the concentrations of glucose, urea, and creatinine in the two fluids are far removed from unity, the concentration in the cerebrospinal fluid being the smaller ; inorganic ions likewise show considerable deviations from the requirements of the Gibbs-Donnan equilibrium ; thus the ratio of the concentrations of Mg^{++} in plasma and spinal fluid is in the region of 0·85 ; since, moreover, only 75 per cent. of the Mg^{++} in plasma is ultra-filtrable (the remainder presumably being bound as a complex with protein and therefore not entering into the equilibrium), the theoretical ratio is approximately 1·35. McCance & Watchorn obtained the following relative figures for the concentrations of Mg^{++} in serum, cerebrospinal fluid and serum ultra-filtrate :

Serum	C.s.f.	Ultra-filtrate
100	119	74·2

There can be no doubt, therefore, that Mg^{++} is concentrated by secretory or accumulative activity in the cerebrospinal fluid. A comparison of the concentrations of Ca^{++} in the three fluids suggested, on the other hand, that this ion was distributed between serum and cerebrospinal fluid in accordance with simple equilibrium requirements :—

Serum	C.s.f.	Ultra-filtrate
100	51·6	53·6

K^+ seems to be maintained at a lower concentration in the cerebrospinal fluid than in plasma. The Cl^--ion, on the other hand, is definitely too highly concentrated in the fluid to warrant the assumption of a Gibbs-Donnan equilibrium ; thus Muntwyler *et al.* found a value of 0·96 for the ratio : $[Cl^-]_{Plasma}/[Cl^-]_{Asc.}$ for ascitic fluid whilst the ratio : $[Cl^-]_{Plasma}/[Cl^-]_{c.s.f.}$ was 0·858 ; similarly Dailey found a ratio of 0·87 ; he found, moreover, a value of 1·04 for the ratio $[Na^+]_{Plasma}/[Na^+]_{c.s.f.}$, so that if the ratios for the Donnan equilibrium are 0·98 and 1·08 respectively (p. 216), it would appear that both Na^+ and Cl^- are actively secreted into the fluid. The low value for the concentration of glucose in the cerebrospinal fluid may be due to the active metabolism of the nervous tissue, and it is interesting that the vitreous body, in contact with the retina—which is an outgrowth of the central nervous system—gives a comparable ratio. The deficiencies of urea and creatinine likewise suggest a secretory origin, and an instructive study by Flexner of the distribution of urea between the fluid and plasma of pigs during fœtal development bears out this viewpoint ; in fœtuses less than forty-three days old, the ratio : $[Urea]_{Plasma}/[Urea]_{c.s.f.}$ was unity, whilst beyond this period the ratio became progressively larger, to reach a value of 1·25 at term. Similarly the ratio : $[Cl^-]_{Plasma}/[Cl^-]_{c.s.f.}$ changed from about 1·0 to 0·77. Solomon and his colleagues have shown that the individual amino-acids of the blood—arginine, histidine, etc.—are all present in a much lower concentration in the fluid than in the plasma, ratios from 4 to 15 being found ; in general, of the non-electrolytes studied, it would appear that all except ascorbic acid are in lower concentration in the cerebrospinal fluid than in the plasma. Ascorbic acid seems definitely to be in a higher concentration in the fluid ; thus Booij found concentrations varying from

0·3 to 1·44 mg./100 ml. in the plasma and from 0·3 to 3·8 mg./100 ml. in the cerebrospinal fluid. According to Blegen, the total osmotic pressure of the cerebrospinal fluid is less than that of the plasma ; presumably the excess of NaCl in the fluid is more than offset by the deficiencies of amino-acids, glucose, etc.

The Blood-Brain Barrier

When a substance is injected into the blood, it may diffuse rapidly into the cerebrospinal fluid, it may enter only very slowly, or it may not enter at all ; it is therefore customary to speak of a *blood-brain barrier* which may be given a quantitative expression by the speeds with which different substances enter the fluid from the blood. That the barrier has a definite selectivity was shown long ago by Goldman who found that Trypan blue, injected into the blood, leaves the cerebral vessels and tissue completely unstained, whereas the vessels of the choroid plexus and the vessels and tissues of most of the other parts of the body are stained. If the dye is injected into the cerebrospinal fluid, on the other hand, the nervous tissue is strongly stained. It would thus seem that nervous tissue is insulated in a special way from Trypan blue ; this insulation results from an impermeability of the cerebral capillaries to this substance ; so far as the meningeal circulation is concerned it is possible that the capillaries are actually permeable to the dye but that the latter is prevented from passing onwards into the cerebrospinal fluid by the epithelial linings of the choroid plexuses. The existence of this barrier was put on a firm experimental basis by the qualitative studies of Stern, who introduced a variety of substances into the blood and determined, by chemical methods, whether they penetrated into the cerebrospinal fluid ; in many instances she also analysed the brain tissue, and found that the barrier between the blood and cerebrospinal fluid was, at least qualitatively, identical with that between blood and brain tissue ; in the sense that those substances that were excluded from the one were excluded from the other. In general, Stern found that Br^-, CNS^-, salicylate, strychnine, morphia and atropine penetrated the barrier, whereas I^-, ferrocyanide, curare and adrenaline failed to penetrate. All substances, however, if introduced directly into the ventricular fluid, found their way out into the blood rapidly, presumably by a drainage process through the arachnoid villi directly into the venous blood.

As we have indicated, the blood-brain barrier may be studied in two ways : by measuring the rate of penetration of a substance into either the cerebrospinal fluid or the brain tissue ; in the latter case we are concerned with the penetration into the interstitial space of the nervous tissue. The estimates of the chloride and sodium-spaces of nervous tissue, given earlier (p. 222), revealed remarkably high values, in the region of 30 per cent. Injection of Na^{24} into the intact animal shows, as we have seen, a rapid exchange of the isotope with the Na^+ in the interstitial fluid of muscle and many other tissues, the process being complete within two or three minutes. With brain and sciatic nerve, on the other hand, various investigators have found only a very slow uptake of this ion ; thus after three minutes the

Na^{24}-space was only 3·1 per cent., and even in twelve hours it only amounted to 24 per cent. in Manery & Bale's experiments, whilst the true sodium-space is in the region of 30 per cent. Similar results were obtained by Hahn & Hevesy, who found that nearly thirty-two hours were required to achieve Na^{24}-equilibrium ; moreover, Br^- penetrated the spaces slowly too, and Hiatt has shown that perfusion of nervous tissue with a solution of Na_2SO_4 fails to wash out the Cl^-, although a solution of $NaNO_3$ does so slowly, a result indicating that SO_4^{--} is unable to escape from the brain capillaries to exchange with Cl^-. These studies therefore indicate the unequivocal difference in permeability characteristics of the nervous and muscle capillaries, and justify the term " blood-brain barrier." Quantitative studies on the penetration of substances into the cerebrospinal fluid indicate, likewise, a slow rate of equilibration ; of the more recent studies those of Wallace & Brodie are of particular interest ; these authors injected Br^-, I^-, and CNS^- into the blood, and estimated their concentrations in both cerebral tissue and cerebrospinal fluid after different periods, comparing these values with the concentrations of Cl^- in the same samples. If the Br^-, for example, came into rapid equilibrium with the tissue fluid of the brain, we should expect to find the ratio of Cl^- to Br^- the same in both plasma and tissue after a short period ; if, on the other hand, diffusion equilibrium were slow of achievement, the ratio Cl^-/Br^- would be higher in the tissue than in the plasma. Studies of these ratios showed that they were invariably greater than unity even after many hours ; *i.e.*, they showed that Br^- penetrated slowly into the tissue spaces. The striking finding, however, was that the ratio in the tissue was always the same as that in the cerebrospinal fluid ; so good was the agreement that they decided (as Stern had done many years before) that the cerebrospinal fluid was the intermediary between blood and cerebral tissue. This conclusion is questionable, however, although the evidence inviting it is strong ; instead, we must deduce that the two barriers have essentially the same characteristics, with the result that the relative rates of penetration into the cerebrospinal and cerebral-interstitial fluids are approximately the same.[1] The extreme slowness with which Br^-, for example, penetrates the blood-cerebrospinal fluid barrier is shown by the following figures from Wallace & Brodie :

Time	Serum	C.s.f.	r
40 min. .	32	6	5·3
80 min. .	32	7·8	4·0
7 hr.. .	31	13·3	2·3
24 hr.. .	27	22·6	1·4
32 hr.. .	26	22·0	1·2
27 days .	16·4	11·8	1·4

[1] This is not to rule out some interchange between the two ; the evidence suggests, however, that drainage of interstitial fluid is in the direction of the subarachnoid fluid, *i.e.*, away from the ventricles.

It will be noted that Br^- apparently never achieved diffusion equilibrium, *i.e.*, the ratio : $[Br^-]_{serum}/[Br^-]_{c.s.f.}$ never reached the value typical for the Gibbs-Donnan equilibrium ; this may be due to the adsorption of Br^- on to the plasma proteins ; similar and larger deficiencies occurred with I^- and CNS^-, which are more adsorbable ions. Weir has investigated the distribution of Br^- between plasma and cerebrospinal fluid and has shown that the ratio : $[Br]_{serum}/[Br]_{c.s.f.}$, determined some twenty-four hours after an intravenous injection of Br^-, varied with the plasma concentration; thus with a low concentration (1–10 mM) it was 1·78 whilst with a very high concentration (70–95mM) it was 1·09. This finding is quite compatible with an adsorption of Br^- on to the plasma proteins ; as the concentration is raised the percentage adsorbed becomes smaller, and therefore the ratio should approach unity.

Recently Greenberg and his collaborators have reported on an extensive study of the penetration of radioactive isotopes into the cerebrospinal fluid of dogs ; unfortunately, however, these authors drained the cisterna magna continuously during the time the isotopes were in the blood ; the intra-cranial pressure must have been very low and it is likely that the conditions of formation were abnormal. At intervals, the fluid collected was analysed for the particular radioactive isotope. The relative rates of appearance were in the following order :

$$K^+ > Na^+ > Br^- > Rb^+ > Sr^{++} > \text{Phosphate} > I^-$$

the rate of flow of fluid was some 384 ml. per twenty-four hours. The equilibrium ratios, obtained by allowing the isotopes to remain in the blood for a long time, were as follows :

Substance Concn. in plasma Concn. in c.s.f.	Na^+	K^+	Rb^+	PO_4^{--}	Sr^{++}	I^-	Br^-
	0·91	1·7	2·9	6·7	2·5	20	1·1–1·0

The significance of the very high ratios awaits further study ; it will be recalled that many of the substances studied by classical chemical techniques likewise show striking deficiencies in the cerebrospinal fluid. An important factor may be the circumstance that the penetration from blood into the fluid is difficult, *i.e.*, it occurs slowly, whilst the egress, by the arachnoid villi, is easy.[1] If we imagine that the secretory cells of the choroid plexus are continually emptying a fluid into the ventricles, the rate at which a foreign substance in the blood, *e.g.*, Br^-, appears in the cerebrospinal fluid will be determined by the ease with which it joins this fluid, either by entering the secreting cells or passing round them. The final concentration of this substance, at infinite time, will depend in some measure on the relative ease with which it may enter and leave the fluid, since the fluid is being continually washed away ; thus, so long as the necessary energy is available to perform the osmotic work required for maintaining a concentration difference, the existence of a constant flow of

---

[1] For example Brodie & Wallace showed that Br^-, I^-, etc., introduced into the cerebral ventricles, disappeared in 3–4 hours, whereas a much longer time was required for Br^-, diffusing from the blood, to achieve equilibrium.

cerebrospinal fluid, coupled with a differential rate of penetration and exit of its constituents, makes possible a non-equilibrium distribution of these constituents, the slower the rate of penetration the greater the deviation from the equilibrium distribution. It is easy to show that the filtration pressure available in the capillaries is quite inadequate to supply this osmotic energy, and it is for this reason, among others, that we must invoke the use of chemical or secretory energy to permit such a state of affairs to develop.[1]

The blood-brain barrier may be partially destroyed in inflammatory conditions, such as meningitis, in which case the cerebrospinal fluid tends to approach in composition a filtrate from blood plasma, *e.g.*, the concentration of Mg^{++} falls whilst those of K^+ and sugar rise ; the effect seems to be due to a dilatation of the blood capillaries, increasing their general permeability and thus suppressing their selectivity. This point brings us to a consideration of the physiological significance of the blood-brain barrier. The special composition of the cerebrospinal fluid, as contrasted with that of a filtrate of plasma, is the result of secretory processes presumably in the choroid plexuses [2] ; it is not known why Mg^{++}, for example, has a relatively high concentration in this fluid but the fact is doubtless of importance in the economy of the brain tissue. The layers of nerve cells in the immediate neighbourhood of the ventricles and sub-arachnoid spaces are exposed to Mg^{++} in this concentration, and by a process of diffusion it is possible, nay likely, that the more remote layers acquire this concentration too, provided that the capillaries of the cerebral tissue do not carry the excess of Mg^{++} rapidly away into the blood. Thus, in order that the nervous tissue be bathed with fluid of markedly different ionic constitution from that of plasma, it is essential that the capillaries be much less permeable than in other parts of the body where diffusion equilibrium is reached in a matter of minutes, otherwise the secretory activity of the choroid plexuses would be largely wasted and different regions of nervous tissue would have different external fluids surrounding them. Consequently, the essential requirement for a uniform cellular environment in the brain is a barrier between blood and tissue-fluid uniform in all regions, *i.e.*, extending not only to the blood-cerebrospinal fluid barrier but also to the blood-nervous tissue barrier.

[1] This is an important point ; it is always possible to envisage a partial or complete separation of a blood constituent by a process of ultra-filtration ; thus plasma may be filtered free of proteins, as we have seen, but the pressure required to do this must be available, *i.e.*, the colloid osmotic pressure of these proteins ; in a similar way a fluid free of K^+, for example, could be formed by the use of a membrane impermeable to this ion, but now the necessary pressure is the osmotic pressure difference between a fluid containing 6 mM. KCl and one free from this, *i.e.*, 212 mm. Hg. Kinsey & Grant (1942) were the first to suggest this explanation of the low concentrations of certain non-electrolytes in an analogous fluid—the aqueous humour. The explanation is valid because the secretory activity of the cells lining the ciliary body is able to provide the necessary energy.

[2] The possibility that the capillary endothelium can exert secretory activity must not be completely ruled out, although there is no evidence on which to base such a supposition.

Intracranial Pressure

The factors determining the maintenance of the intracranial pressure are by no means completely elucidated ; of prime importance, undoubtedly, are the rate of formation of fluid—presumably by secretory activity in the choroid plexuses—and the rate of drainage. The former process may be fairly constant whereas the latter may be variable. Thus the fluid in the arachnoid villi is almost free from protein, whereas the blood on the other side is not ; cerebrospinal fluid will therefore be drained by the difference of osmotic pressure ; moreover the fluid pressure is in the region of 100 or more mm. H_2O, well above the blood pressure in the venous sinuses, and this hydrostatic pressure will add to the osmotic forces withdrawing fluid. The extent to which variations in the vascular pressures within the skull will modify both the cerebrospinal fluid pressure and its circulation have been discussed recently by O'Connell ; according to him, the changes of blood pressure during the cardiac cycle should be reflected in changes of fluid pressure which should contribute to an active circulation of the fluid. The normal pressure is usually given as 100 mm. H_2O.

Aqueous Humour and Cerebrospinal Fluid Compared

It will be profitable to conclude this description of the cerebrospinal fluid by pointing out certain strong similarities between it and the aqueous humour. The latter fluid occupies the space in front of the iris and lens— the anterior chamber (Fig. 280, p. 621)—the remainder of the eye cavity being occupied by a transparent gel, the *vitreous body*.[1] Chemically the two fluids have much in common ; they are more or less protein-free ; the concentrations of most of the non-electrolytes studied are lower in the fluid than in the plasma whilst the reverse holds for ascorbic acid which may be, in certain species, twenty times more concentrated in the aqueous humour than in the plasma. Careful studies of the ionic distribution have shown an excess of NaCl in the fluid over that required by the Gibbs-Donnan distribution. From the chemical point of view, therefore, the two fluids must be regarded as secretions, in the sense that the mechanical force of filtration would be quite inadequate to account for the large discrepancies from equilibrium distribution ; whether the fluids are completely elaborated within secretory cells—the epithelial cells of the ciliary body or choroid plexus—or whether they are primarily formed as filtrates and subsequently modified by secretory activity, is still undecided, although opinion tends to favour the former view. The aqueous humour—like the cerebrospinal fluid—circulates ; being formed by the ciliary body and drained away in a specialised region—the angle of the anterior chamber— into channels connecting directly to the venous system (canal of Schlemm). The *blood-aqueous barrier* has been studied in more detail than the blood-cerebrospinal fluid barrier ; it exhibits a high degree of selectivity. As with the cerebrospinal fluid, the escape of substances from the aqueous humour is non-selective, apparently taking place mainly by fluid-flow

---

[1] There is a small amount of aqueous humour in the *posterior chamber*, a small space between the lens and the iris (Fig. 280).

across a highly permeable membrane (the endothelial lining of the angle of the anterior chamber, in the case of the eye, and the mesothelial lining of the arachnoid villi, in the case of the brain). The pressure of fluid within the eye—*the intraocular pressure*—is altogether higher than the intracranial pressure, being some 25 mm. Hg ; the factors modifying the pressure are probably similar, however.

References

BAUER, W., ROPES, M. W. & WAINE, H. (1940). "The Physiology of Articular Structures." *Physiol. Rev.*, **20**, 272.

BEDFORD, T. H. B. (1939). "The Effect of Monosaccharides on Water Absorption from the Subarachnoid Space." *J. Physiol.*, **96**, 392.

BLEGEN, E. (1939). "Comparison of Osmotic Pressure in Blood and c.s.f." *Scand. Arch. Physiol.*, **81**, 29.

BOOIJ, J. (1940). "Vitamin-C Content of Blood and c.s.f." *Rec. Trav. Chim.*, **59**, 713.

BROMAN, T. (1941). "Weitere Untersuchungen u. d. Farbindikatormethode als Funktionsprobe d. Bluthirnschranke im Tierexperiment." *Acta Physiol. Scand.*, **2**, 83.

DAILEY, M. E. (1931). "Distribution of Na between c.s.f. and Blood Serum." *J. Biol. Chem.*, **93**, 5.

DAVSON, H. (1949). "Physiology of the Eye." London. Churchill.

DAVSON, H. (1949). "The Aqueous Humour and the Blood-Aqueous Barrier." *Ophthal. Lit.*, **3**, 254.

DAVSON, H. (1950). "The Intra-Ocular Pressure and the Mechanism of Formation of the Intra-Ocular Fluid." *Ophthal. Lit.*, **4**, 3.

FLEXNER, L. B. (1934). "The Chemistry and Nature of the Cerebrospinal Fluid." *Physiol. Rev.*, **14**, 161.

FLEXNER, L. B. (1938). "Changes in the Chemistry and Nature of the c.s.f. during Fœtal Life in the Pig." *Amer. J. Physiol.*, **124**, 131.

FLEXNER, L. B. & STIEHLER, R. D. (1938). "Biochemical Changes Associated with the Onset of Secretion in the Fœtal Choroid Plexus. An Organisation of Oxidation-Reduction Processes." *J. biol. Chem.*, **126**, 619.

FRIEDENWALD, J. S. (1949). "The Formation of the Intra-Ocular Fluid." *Amer. J. Ophthal.*, **32**, 9.

FRIEDENWALD, J. S. & STIEHLER, R. D. (1938). "A Mechanism of Secretion of the Intra-Ocular Fluid." *Arch. Ophth.*, **20**, 761.

GREENBERG, D. M., AIRD, R. B., BOELTER, M. D. D., CAMPBELL, W. W., COHN, W. E. & MURAYAMA, M. M. (1943). "A Study with Radioactive Isotopes of the Permeability of the Blood-c.s.f. Barrier to Ions." *Amer. J. Physiol.*, **140**, 47.

HAHN, L. & HEVESY, G. (1940). "Rate of Passage of Ions through the Capillary Wall." *Acta Physiol. Scand.*, **1**, 347.

HIATT, E. P. (1939). "Replacement of Cl^- in Tissues and Body Fluids of Dogs by NO_3^-." *Amer. J. Physiol.*, **126**, 533P.

KATZENELBOGEN, S. (1935). "The Cerebrospinal Fluid and its Relation to the Blood." Baltimore, Johns Hopkins Press.

KINSEY, V. E. & GRANT, W. M. (1942). "The Mechanism of Aqueous Humour Formation inferred from Chemical Studies on Blood-Aqueous Humour Dynamics." *J. gen. Physiol.*, **26**, 131.

MANERY, J. F. & BALE, W. F. (1941). "Penetration of Na^{24} and P^{32} into the Extra- and Intra-Cellular Phases of Tissues." *Amer. J. Physiol.*, **132**, 474.

McCANCE, R. A. & WATCHORN, E. (1931). "Inorganic Constituents of the c.s.f. I. Ca and Mg." *Quart. J. Med.*, **24**, 371.

MUNTWYLER, E., WAY, C. T. & POMERENE, E. (1931). "A Comparison of the Chloride and Bicarbonate Concentrations between Plasma and Spinal Fluid and Plasma and Ascitic Fluid in Reference to the Donnan Equilibrium." *J. biol. Chem.*, **92**, 733.

O'CONNELL, J. E. A. (1943). "Vascular Factors in Intracranial Pressure and Maintenance of c.s.f. Circulation." *Brain*, **66**, 204.

RANSON, S. W. & CLARK, S. L. (1947). "The Anatomy of the Nervous System." Philadelphia, Saunders.

RASMUSSEN A. T.. "The Principal Nervous Pathways." MacMillan. (Quoted by Ranson & Clark.)

STERN, L. & GAUTIER, R. (1921). "Recherches sur le Liquide Céphalorachidien." *Arch. int. Physiol.*, **17**, 139.

STERN, L. & GAUTIER, R. (1923). "Recherches sur le Liquide Céphalorachidien." *Arch. int. Physiol.*, **20**, 403.

SOLOMON, J. D., HIER, S. W. & BERGEIM, O. (1947). "Free Amino Acids in c.s.f." *J. biol. Chem.*, **171**, 695.

STIEHLER, R. D. & FLEXNER, L. B. (1938). "A Mechanism of Secretion in the Choroid Plexus." *J. biol. Chem.*, **126**, 603.

WALLACE, G. B. & BRODIE, B. B. (1939). "The Distribution of I, CNS, Br and Cl in Central Nervous System and Spinal Fluid." *J. Pharm.*, **65**, 220.

WALLACE, G. B. & BRODIE, B. B. (1940). "The Passage of Br, I, and CNS Into and Out of the c.s.f." *J. Pharm.*, **68**, 50.

WATCHORN, E. & McCANCE, R. A. (1932). "Inorganic Constitution of the c.s.f. II. Ultrafiltration of Ca and Mg from Human Sera." *Biochem. J.*, **26**, 54.

WATCHORN, E. & McCANCE, R. A. (1933). "The K in Serum, Serum Ultra-Filtrate and c.s.f." *Biochem. J.*, **27**, 1107.

WEED, L. H. (1923). "The Absorption of c.s.f. into the Venous System." *Amer. J. Anat.*, **31**, 191.

WEIR, E. G. (1942). "The Influence of the Serum Bromide Concentration upon the Distribution of Bromide Ion between Serum and Spinal Fluid." *Amer. J. Physiol.*, **137**, 109.

WEIR, E. G. (1945). "The Effects of Intracisternal Injection of Sodium Bromide upon the Blood-Spinal Fluid Barrier." *Amer. J. Physiol.*, **143**, 83.

CHAPTER XI

IONIC EQUILIBRIA, BIOELECTRIC POTENTIALS, AND ACTIVE TRANSPORT

Ionic Equilibria in the Erythrocyte

THE erythrocyte in its plasma presents a rather more complicated system than that consisting of plasma and tissue fluid. Apart from the academic interest in explaining the events taking place in this cell on physico-chemical grounds, it must be appreciated that a full understanding of the maintenance of the acid-base equilibrium of the mammal, and its respiratory exchanges, is impossible without a satisfactory interpretation of these phenomena.

The approximate concentrations of the more important ionic

TABLE XVIII

Relative Concentrations (meq./l.H_2O) of Certain Solutes in Plasma and Erythrocytes.

	K^+	Na^+	Ca^{++}	Mg^{++}	Cl^-	HCO_3^-	Glucose
Plasma .	5·35	144	3·2	1·07	111	27·8	4·3
Cells .	150	12–20	—	2·8	73·5	26·9	4·3

constituents of human erythrocytes and plasma are given in Table XVIII. To make the position clearer, the relative concentrations of the different ions may be expressed diagrammatically as in Fig. 119 in which the magnitudes of the concentrations are represented by the heights of the columns. In the plasma we have the predominant cation Na^+ and as anions Cl^- and HCO_3^-, obeying the condition for electrical neutrality :

$$[Na^+]_p = [Cl^-]_p + [HCO_3^-]_p ;$$

the plasma proteins have been ignored for simplicity's sake, their influence on the equilibria being small compared with that of the hæmoglobin. In the cells, the cation is mainly K^+ and the anions are Cl^-, HCO_3^-, and Hb^- (standing for ionised hæmoglobin), obeying the relationship :

$$[K^+]_c = [Cl^-]_c + [HCO_3^-]_c + [Hb^-]$$

The concentration of hæmoglobin [1] is expressed in millimoles of univalent ions per litre (mM/l.) ; it is essential to grasp thoroughly the implications of

---

[1] For simplicity, the impermeable anions of the erythrocyte have been represented exclusively as Hb^- ; actually, according to the work of Farmer & Maizels, diphosphoglycerate, adenosine triphosphate, and other complex anions probably contribute as much base-binding power to the human erythrocyte as does hæmoglobin.

this procedure. In actuality hæmoglobin is a polyvalent anion under physiological conditions, so that perhaps as many as 7 to 10 K^+-ions are neutralised by each hæmoglobin ion, *i.e.*, the formula for the potassium salt of hæmoglobin might be written ; K_{10} Hb ; consequently, although the concentration of hæmoglobin in the cells is only about 5 mM/l., the concentration, expressed as mM of a univalent anion, is about 7 to 10 times this amount, *i.e.*, about 50 mM. Thus, electrically, Hb provides about 50 mM of negative anions per litre, but *osmotically* it acts as only 5 mM/l., *i.e.*, it has an almost negligible osmotic pressure compared with that of the remaining ionic constituents of the cell. For this reason the column representing hæmoglobin is hatched, to indicate that its contribution to the osmotic pressure is negligible for the purposes of this discussion.

The cell is in osmotic equilibrium with its plasma, consequently the sum of the osmotically active ions in the cell should be equal to that in the plasma, *i.e.*, the unhatched area, representing the cell concentrations, should be equal to the area representing the plasma concentrations. In the diagram this is shown to be the case, and it is immediately evident that the concentration of K^+ in the cells is greater than that of Na^+ in the plasma ; moreover, the concentrations of Cl^- and HCO_3^- in the cells are respectively less than those in the plasma. Thus a pictorial representation, based simply on the principle of electrical neutrality and osmotic equality, enables us to explain the main characteristics of the distribution of ions in this system, provided that we may assume that the membrane is permeable to negative non-colloidal ions and effectively impermeable to Na^+ and K^+.

Applying now the Gibbs-Donnan Equilibrium to the case of the erythrocyte, we may note first that any effects produced by the effective impermeability of the membrane to K^+ must be counter-balanced by equal and opposite effects due to the impermeability of the membrane to Na^+, so that the impermeable ion which will cause a Gibbs-Donnan effect is the Hb^- ion. The Gibbs-Donnan formula only relates to the diffusible ions, consequently it can only tell us how the negative ions will be distributed ; the formula in this case is as follows :—

$$[Cl^-]_c / [Cl^-]_s = [HCO_3^-]_c / [HCO_3^-]_s = [OH^-]_c / [OH^-]_s = r$$

As before, the magnitude of r depends on the concentration of the impermeable ion ; since this is much larger than that of the P^- ion discussed earlier (p. 208), we may expect a larger deviation from unity ; in actuality the ratio of the concentrations of Cl^- in cells and plasma has been found to be about 0·7 at body pH, *i.e.*, the concentration of Cl^- in cells is only 0·7 times that in the plasma.

Hamburger Shift. It was observed as long ago as 1878 that bubbling CO_2 into blood caused (*a*) an increase in the concentration of HCO_3^- in the plasma ; (*b*) the passage of Cl^- from the plasma into the cells (the so-called *Hamburger Shift*), and (*c*) a swelling of the erythrocytes.

CO_2 penetrates rapidly into erythrocytes, so that an equal distribution of this substance between plasma and cells may be expected within a second or two ; without much inaccuracy we may consider the dissolved CO_2 to be in the form : H_2CO_3. As a result of the entry of CO_2 the pH of the

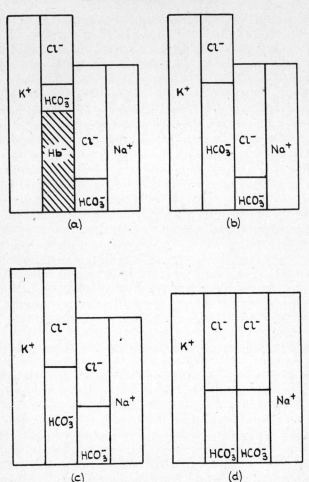

Fig. 119. Illustrating the mechanism of the Hamburger shift. (*a*) Normal distribution of ions ; (*b*) addition of CO_2 to the blood has caused accumulation of HCO_3^- within the cells ; (*c*) The Cl^--HCO_3^- exchange has taken place ; (*d*) Water has penetrated the cells. (After Van Slyke.)

cells has been decreased, so that some of the KHb becomes $KHCO_3$ in accordance with the following reaction :—

$$KHb + H_2CO_3 \rightarrow KHCO_3 + HHb$$

whereby some of the Hb^--ions lose their charges to be converted to undissociated HHb ; the K^+-ions in association with these negative Hb^--ions become associated with the newly formed HCO_3^--ions. The condition of the cells is now represented by (*b*) of Fig. 119. In consequence of the reaction of KHb with H_2CO_3 three things follow : (i), owing to the reduction of the H_2CO_3 concentration in the cells, more CO_2 diffuses into them to equalise the concentrations ; (ii), owing to the increase in the HCO_3^--ions in the cells, the equilibrium is disturbed and some diffuse out.

In order to preserve electrical neutrality, however, other negative ions must enter, so that (iii), Cl⁻ enters the cells. These processes are continuous ; as fast as H_2CO_3 diffuses into the cells, it is largely converted into HCO_3^--ions ; more and more KHb takes on the undissociated form of HHb, so that, if enough CO_2 is bubbled into the cells, condition (c) of Fig. 119 is the end result : a large increase in the concentration of $NaHCO_3$ in the plasma with a reduction in its concentration of Cl⁻ and an increase in the concentration of Cl⁻ in the cells. To appreciate the cause of the swelling of the cells following CO_2 treatment, mentioned earlier, the diagrammatic representation of Fig. 119 is a great help. In (a) and (c) the initial and final concentrations of ions in cells and plasma are shown, on the assumption that no changes in volume have occurred. Now each negative charge in the cells, contributed by Cl⁻ and HCO_3^-, behaves osmotically as a single particle, whereas we have seen that the negative charges due to ionised hæmoglobin contribute only about one-tenth of an osmotically active particle ; consequently, owing to the replacement of the hæmoglobin negative ions by Cl⁻ and HCO_3^-, the total number of osmotically active ions within the cells has increased, and the difference in osmotic pressure is levelled out by the migration of water from plasma to cells (Fig. 119, d).

In a similar manner, the reverse phenomenon of a passage of Cl⁻ out of the cells associated with shrinkage, when CO_2 is removed from the blood, may be explained. In general, it follows from Fig. 119 that any change that modifies the amount of ionised hæmoglobin in the cells will modify their water-content ; thus reduction of the O_2-tension or lowering the temperature decreases this quantity and therefore causes the cells to swell.

We may note that, as before, r, the Gibbs-Donnan ratio which determines the relative concentrations of diffusible negative ions in cells and plasma, depends on the concentration of indiffusible negative ions, in this case Hb⁻ ; when this is zero, r is unity and the concentrations are equal. In the case depicted by Fig. 119 it has been assumed that in the final state all the KHb has been converted to unionised HHb, hence [Hb⁻] is zero and r is unity. The Hamburger shift therefore represents the re-adaptation of the cell-plasma system to a change in the value of r necessitated by a change in the [Hb⁻] of the cells.

It is worth remarking that the uneven distribution of negative ions between cells and plasma is imposed by the presence of an indiffusible

$$(a) \qquad\qquad\qquad (b)$$

Fig. 120. Behaviour of the erythrocyte in a non-electrolyte medium.

negative ion, Hb⁻ ; expressed more generally, a *concentration gradient* of one ion can impose a concentration gradient on other ions. An interesting example of this is given by the system formed by the addition of erythrocytes to a non-electrolyte medium as in Fig. 120. Cl⁻ and HCO_3^-

can diffuse through the membrane, but the demands of electrical neutrality require that negative ions replace those lost ; in a non-electrolyte medium the only negative ions are OH^--ions, obtained from the dissociation of water. OH^--ions therefore pass into the cells in exchange for Cl^- and HCO_3^-, giving the condition shown in Fig. 120b. The KOH, formed in the cells, reacts with the hæmoglobin to form KHb, *i.e.*, the amount of ionised hæmoglobin is increased and it therefore follows that the cells should shrink ; the loss of OH^- from the non-electrolyte medium causes the latter to become acid. The condition for equilibrium is that :

$$[Cl^-]_{Cell} / [Cl^-]_{Medium} = [OH^-]_{Cell} / [OH^-]_{Medium} = [H^+]_{Medium} / [H^+]_{Cell}$$

It has been found experimentally that the cells do certainly shrink in a non-electrolyte medium and that this becomes acid ; in this instance the high concentration gradient of Cl^- and HCO_3^- imposes a concentration gradient of OH^- and H^+. The effects described above may be very large, amounting to a thousand-fold difference in hydrogen-ion concentration between cells and plasma (Jacobs & Parpart, 1933).

These are just two examples of the adaptation of the erythrocyte to disturbances of its equilibrium ; it will be evident that the changes in volume depend mainly on changes in the ionisation of the hæmoglobin in the cells, an increase in this causing them to shrink and *vice versâ*. Consequently the effects of alkalinity, increased O_2-tension, and increased temperature will be a shrinkage of the cells, all these influences being such as to increase the ionisation of hæmoglobin at physiological pH. Jacobs & Parpart (1931) and, more recently, Jacobs & Stewart (1947) have devised general equations for the solution of problems connected with equilibria under a variety of conditions.

Active Transport by the Erythrocyte

The studies of the permeability of the erythrocyte to ions, briefly discussed earlier, have revealed a rapid exchange of the univalent anions and a virtual impermeability to cations (with the possible exception of H^+) ; the assumption of complete impermeability to cations has permitted computations of the effects of changes in pH and O_2-tension that were not belied by the facts. These facts, however, were derived from experiments of short duration by comparison with the life of the erythrocyte [1] and it could very well have been that studies carried out over longer periods would have brought to light significant exchanges of cations. The practice of storing human blood for periods of weeks at low temperatures has provided an opportunity for investigations of very slow permeability processes, which have disclosed some remarkable facts. Before considering these findings, which demand a reconsideration of the assumption of an impermeability of the erythrocyte membrane to cations, it is worth considering the consequences, on the basis of simple equilibrium theory, of a normal permeability of the erythrocyte to both anions and cations. One marked difference between the system of plasma, separated from its

---

[1] About 124 days in the dog according to Hawkins & Whipple.

ultra-filtrate, and the system of the erythrocyte, separated from plasma, has probably occurred to the reader ; this is that, although there is a Gibbs-Donnan equilibrium in both instances, in the former case osmotic equilibrium is only attained by the exertion of a hydrostatic pressure on the fluid containing the indiffusible anion, whereas in the latter, osmotic equilibrium may be achieved without any such pressure. The reason for this difference in the two systems is the effective impermeability of the erythrocyte membrane to cations, besides to the Hb^--ion ; with this impermeability it is possible to balance the osmotic pressure of the indiffusible protein in the cell. Without such an impermeability, on the other hand, no such balance could be achieved, as the following examples will show. If the membrane is made permeable to Na^+ besides the anions, a cell suspended in plasma is now equivalent to one suspended in isotonic glycerol solution (p. 158), *i.e.*, penetration of NaCl and $NaHCO_3$ proceeds together with that of water until the cell bursts. If the membrane is permeable to Na^+ and K^+ besides anions, K^+ will leak out and Na^+ will penetrate, and finally the ions will distribute themselves in such a way that there is an excess of osmotic pressure inside the cell equal to $(e + [P])$ RT, where e is the excess concentration of diffusible ions and [P] is the protein concentration ; this difference of osmotic pressure causes penetration of water and eventual hæmolysis. Thus, from the point of view of osmosis, the integrity of the erythrocyte would appear to depend on its impermeability to cations ; any agent that destroys this impermeability should cause hæmolysis.

Colloid Osmotic Hæmolysis. Confirmation for this viewpoint has been provided by a number of studies. Thus the red cell is hæmolysed by many lipoid-soluble or surface-active substances, such as alcohols, carbamates, chloroform, ether, saponin, taurocholate, digitonin, etc. It was considered for a long time that the hæmolysis was due simply to the rupture of the cell membrane with the result that holes appeared, sufficiently large to allow of the escape of the large hæmoglobin molecule. In 1938, however, Davson & Danielli showed that hæmolytic agents generally caused the erythrocyte to become permeable to cations, and suggested that this abnormal permeability was the primary event in the hæmolysis subsequently taking place, *i.e.*, it was not necessary to destroy the membrane to such an extent that hæmoglobin could escape, but only to weaken it so that the normal impermeability (or very low permeability) was broken down. Studies by Davson & Ponder (1940) on photodynamic hæmolysis (p. 578) confirmed this viewpoint. Since then, the results of a number of workers [1] have supported this theory. This does not mean, of course, that hæmolytic agents are incapable of destroying the cell membrane ; thus saponin continues to break up the " ghosts " remaining after the cells have hæmolysed (stromatolysis) ; it means only that the first stage in

[1] The most extended study is that of Wilbrandt (1941), who showed that hæmolysis may be prevented by addition of sucrose to the medium, *i.e.*, a non-penetrating molecule. Ponder (1947) has carried out analytical studies of the cation movements, and Jacobs & Willis (1947) and Willis, Love & Jacobs (1947), have given brief accounts of indirect studies. Space prevents a detailed description of the phenomena of hæmolysis. Fortunately, Ponder (1948), has recently published an excellent modern account.

destruction is an abnormally high permeability to cations which itself is adequate to complete the destruction by osmotic means. It is very likely that most cells, *e.g.*, muscle, nerve, eggs, and so on, containing as they do a large concentration of proteins, maintain osmotic equilibrium with their environment in virtue of their effective impermeability to certain ions, and it is significant that many agents, which one might expect to cause increased permeability, do cause a swelling and lysis of these cells. Before concluding that a given environmental change destroys the cell membrane, therefore, we must satisfy ourselves that the primary event is not a change in permeability relationships. Two further examples will suffice to demonstrate the importance of this point. Lyman found that a reduction of the concentration of Ca^{++} in the blood of the snapping turtle, *Chelydra serpentina*, *e.g.*, by adding oxalate, caused rapid hæmolysis, and he showed that this was due to the high permeability of the cell membrane to salts in the presence of concentrations of Ca^{++} less than 0·001 M. An uncritical explanation of the phenomenon would be that oxalate destroyed the cell membrane, allowing the hæmoglobin to escape. Again, it has been shown that the dog erythrocyte undergoes hæmolysis in KCl solution ; this erythrocyte contains Na^+ as its principal cation, so that if K^+ enters the cell more rapidly than Na^+ leaves it, we may expect an osmotic type of hæmolysis similar to that taking place in isotonic solutions of a penetrating non-electrolyte, such as urea. This was shown to be the case (Davson, 1942) ; and the hæmolytic action of potassium salts is therefore not due to a primary destruction of the membrane as was originally thought. Thus simple equilibrium theory *demands* an impermeability of the erythrocyte to both Na^+ and K^+, or, alternatively, some mechanism of actively accumulating K^+ and extruding Na^+ in the face of a continued loss and gain by diffusion. In the latter case, the membrane would be *apparently* impermeable to Na^+ and K^+, since a steady state would be achieved with no net loss or gain of these ions, provided that the energy requirements were satisfied. Nevertheless there would be a *definite flux of ions* across the membrane in both directions, so that the addition of isotopic potassium (K^{42}), for example, would cause the appearance of radioactivity within the cell as a result of exchange with ordinary, inactive, K^+. The condition for a steady state would then be that the flux [1] across the membrane be the same in both directions, *i.e.* :—

$$k_{In} [K^+]_{Out} = k_{Out} [K^+]_{In}$$

where k_{In} is a permeability constant indicating the rate of migration of K^+ inwards and k_{Out}, the constant for outward movement. So far as the simple equilibrium theory is concerned, it is quite possible that a system in which the impermeability to cations was only apparent would behave in the same way as one in which the impermeability was real ; the excellent concordance obtained by Jacobs and Peters, among others, between theory and experiment indicates that, within the limits of experimental error, the simple equilibria are not affected by the active transfer which, as we shall

---

[1] By flux is meant the number of ions passing in the given direction across unit area of the membrane in unit time, *e.g.*, moles/cm²/sec.

see, takes place across the membrane. This is not to suggest, however, that the two systems would be identical.

Stored Blood. DeGowin, Harris & Plass observed that human erythrocytes, stored at 2–5° C., lost K⁺ at a steady rate, reaching an equilibrium in about twenty to twenty-five days. It might have been argued, however, that this loss was due to degenerative changes in the cell membrane, especially as there was a tendency for the cells to hæmolyse, *i.e.*, it could have been similar to the pro-lytic losses of K⁺ described by Davson and Ponder (p. 192). However, Harris made the striking discovery that on warming the blood to 37° C. after it had lost, say, 30 per cent. of its K⁺, the escape ceased and some of the lost K⁺ actually returned to the cells. This return of the K⁺ to the cells obviously occurred against a concentration gradient, so that the phenomenon is classed as one of *active transport*, the energy of the metabolic processes within, or at the surface of, the erythrocyte being utilised in the transfer. The addition of 0·02 M fluoride, which inhibits glycolysis, prevented the return of K⁺, in fact it accelerated the escape as described earlier (p. 196). The explanation for these phenomena is doubtless that the erythrocyte, in its normal environment at 37° C., has a significant permeability to K⁺ ; the losses resulting from the continuous leak are made good by an active transport dependent on glycolysis, *i.e.*, the utilisation of glucose. Cooling the blood has two effects : (*a*) it reduces or abolishes the metabolic processes and (*b*) it reduces the permeability but does not abolish it. Consequently a slow escape of K⁺ is observable. Raising the temperature permits the metabolic processes to start again, with the result that some of the lost K⁺ is restored to the cells.

The energy required to maintain the normal concentration of K⁺ will depend on the permeability of the cell to this ion ; this will be made clear by a description of the calculation. We imagine that, for a short time, say one second, the active transfer mechanism ceases ; as a result there is a loss of K⁺ given by

$$kA \left(C_{In} - C_{Out}\right)$$

We now imagine that the transfer process starts again and the lost K⁺ is restored. The work done in transferring x moles from a concentration C_{Out} to a concentration C_{In} is equal to :—

$$x \, RT \ln \frac{C_{In}}{C_{Out}}$$

so that the work done in one second is [1] :—

$$kA \left(C_{In} - C_{Out}\right) RT \ln \frac{C_{Out}}{C_{In}} \qquad \cdots \cdots \cdot (13)$$

From Equation (13) it is quite clear that the larger the value of k, the

---

[1] For simplicity's sake the effects of a difference of potential across the membrane have been ignored ; the work really consists of two terms, the osmotic term considered above, and an electrical term : πxzF, where z is the valency of the ion, F is Faraday's constant, π is the difference of potential, and x the number of gram-ions transported.

more work must be done per second. Thus injury of the membrane by a variety of substances causes an escape of K^+ because k then becomes so great that the product kA $(C_{In} - C_{Out})$ $RT \ln \dfrac{C_{Out}}{C_{In}}$ exceeds the available rate of energy-output of the cell. In this way we may explain the very rapid loss of K^+ that occurs with 0·05 M NaF ; it is not simply due to the cessation of the metabolism, but to an increase in k as well.

The general viewpoint that the normal concentration of K^+ is maintained by metabolic energy has been confirmed by further work of Harris and later investigators. Thus Danowski showed that, if human blood is kept at 37° C., the level of *plasma* K^+ falls for several hours, indicating an active transport of K^+ out of the plasma into the cells ; after this, however, the process is reversed, K^+ escaping from the cells [1] ; addition of glucose, however, delayed very considerably this reversal, a finding which suggests that the point in time at which K^+ begins to be lost from the erythrocyte is that at which glucose is used up. Further work on the behaviour of stored human erythrocytes has been described by Maizels ; he studied the exchanges of both Na^+ and K^+ during storage and subsequent incubation of the cells at 37° C. He confirmed the fact that the loss of K^+ during cold-storage is associated with a rise in the concentration of Na^+ in the cells. The rise in Na^+ was actually greater than the loss of K^+, with the result that there was an increase in the total base within the cells, which swelled as a consequence of the increased osmotic activity. Thus the normal average $[Na^+ + K^+]$ for human erythrocytes is 108–124 meq./l. of cells. After cold-storage for several days the value may reach 140–150 meq./l. In general, it would appear that the greater the total base in the stored cells, the more vigorous is the subsequent expulsion of Na^+ and accumulation of K^+ on incubating at 37° C. ; definite conclusions, however, could not be drawn, owing to the pronounced effect of pH on the accumulation process. It would seem that a pH of 7·4 is optimal for the extrusion of Na^+ and accumulation of K^+, whilst above and below this pH the extrusion of Na^+ seems to be prejudiced although accumulation of K^+ still occurs. Other findings of Maizels were (a) a good correlation between the availability of glucose and the ability of the cell to extrude Na^+ and gain K^+ ; (b) that Li^+, allowed to penetrate during cold-storage, is not extruded on subsequent incubation of the cells at 37° C. ; and (c) that the erythrocyte normally maintains a concentration of Na^+ within it about one-eighth of that in the plasma, these being the relative concentrations at which a balance between inward diffusion and outward extrusion is struck.

This work on the human erythrocyte illustrates the simple facts of accumulation of K^+ and extrusion of Na^+, taking place against concentration gradients.

Isotope Studies. That such processes probably take place in the erythrocytes of other species had, actually, already been shown by Henriques & Ørskov in 1936, although the experiments did not receive the notice they deserved. Thus they showed that Pb, in very small

---

[1] It is this escape of K^+ that has been so frequently observed at 37° C. in various species of erythrocytes, *e.g.*, by Davson and by Solomon, Hald & Peters ; the last-mentioned authors noted that it was accompanied by an increase in cell Na^+.

concentrations, causes the erythrocyte to lose K^+ both *in vitro* and *in vivo* ; this effect seems to be due to a partial destruction of the cell membrane and is an example of pro-lytic K^+ loss (p. 192) ; the losses of K^+ were not associated with gains of Na^+. Henriques & Ørskov noticed that 4·5–32 hours after an injection of Pb into the blood, the concentration of K^+ in the cells started to rise. This was not due to an increased formation of new erythrocytes and so must have been due to the recovery of the cells as the concentration of the Pb fell in the plasma. Presumably they re-assumed

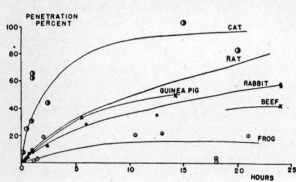

FIG. 121. Penetration of K^{42} into erythrocytes of various species. Ordinates : Specific activity of cells expressed as percentage of that in outside medium. Abscissæ : Time in hours. (Mullins, Fenn, Noonan & Haege. *Amer. J. Physiol.*)

their low permeability to K^+ and were thus able to re-accumulate that lost earlier. Similar recoveries of lost K^+ were observed after injections of distilled water and phenylhydrazine. Further evidence pointing to an active accumulation mechanism in non-human erythrocytes is given by the proof that many erythrocytes are normally permeable to both Na^+ and K^+. The unequivocal demonstration of this permeability under normal conditions was only possible by the use of radioactive isotopes. Results at first were conflicting, but with the improvement of technique a definite exchange of K^{42} in the plasma with ordinary K^+ in the cells has been established for human, rat, cat, dog, rabbit, guinea-pig and frog erythrocytes ; some examples are given in Fig. 121 from Mullins *et al.* [1]; similar results on the exchange of Na^+ between plasma and cells of the cat and dog (in which the concentrations of Na^+ are very high, p. 247), have been provided by Cohn & Cohn and by Mullins *et al.* Permeability constants for penetration of K^+ and Na^+ into the erythrocytes may be computed and in Table XIX some values are shown :—

TABLE XIX

Values of k_{In} for Three Species of Erythrocyte.

Species	Na^+ (cm./sec.)	K^+ (cm./sec.)	Na^+/K^+
Frog . .	$5·5.10^{-10}$	$1·1–2·2.10^{-8}$	0·022–0·05
Cat . .	$3·6.10^{-10}$	$8·9.10^{-9}$	0·041
Man . .	$2·7.10^{-10}$	$6·7.10^{-9}$	0·040

[1] The following values of the permeability constant, k_{Out}, for outward diffusion may be calculated from these curves :

Species	Dog	Cat	Rabbit	Man	Guinea Pig	Rat	Frog
k_{Out} (cm./sec. $\times 10^{-9}$) .	1·8	3·4	0·65	0·82	1·0	1·65	0·19

Later work by Raker *et al.* and Sheppard & Martin suggests that the value for the human erythrocyte is $0·24.10^{-9}$.

It will be noted that the inward permeability to Na^+ is about 1/25th that to K^+, a fact suggesting that the speed of inward migration is determined by the size of the hydration layer on the ion, that of Na^+ being considerably the greater, in fact E. J. Harris has suggested, on the basis of a comparison of the heats of hydration of K and Na salts, that the chance of a Na^+-ion being as little hydrated as a K^+-ion is about 1/45.

The computation of the permeability constants for ionic penetration from data obtained with radioactive isotopes must now be described. In studying the penetration of ions we must take into account the possibility that the rates of transport across the membrane are different in the two directions, we must therefore make use of two constants instead of one, the simple permeability equation becoming :—

$$\frac{dS}{dt} = k_{In} \, AC_{Out} - k_{Out} \, AC_{In} \qquad \ldots \ldots \ldots (14)$$

where k_{In} is the permeability constant in the direction Out-to-In, and k_{Out} that for the reverse direction. As before the k's have the dimensions of cm./sec.

If the system is in a steady state, or at equilibrium, the number of ions passing in each direction in unit time is the same, and $dS/dt = 0$, so that :—

$$\frac{k_{In}}{k_{Out}} = \frac{C_{In}}{C_{Out}} \qquad \ldots \ldots \ldots \ldots (15)$$

the ratio of the concentrations of the ion inside and outside the cell in the steady state being equal to the ratio of the permeability constants.

Let us now consider a cell, with an internal concentration, C_{In}, of the particular ion being studied, surrounded by a large volume of external medium containing the concentration of the ion, C_{Out}, together with a concentration C^*_{Out} of radioactive isotope. The isotope exchanges with the inactive ion within the cells, its rate of penetration being governed by the same permeability constant as that applying to the inactive ion. Thus :

$$\frac{dS^*}{dt} = k_{In} \, AC^*_{Out} - k_{Out} \, AC^*_{In}$$

Since S*, the *amount* of radioactive ion that has entered the cell by the time, t, is related to the *concentration* of radioactive ion in the cell by the formula :

$$\frac{S^*}{V} = C^*_{In} \, ;$$

$$\frac{dS^*}{dt} = V \frac{dC^*_{In}}{dt}$$

Hence

$$\frac{dC^*_{In}}{dt} = k_{In} \frac{A}{V} \cdot C^*_{Out} - k_{Out} \frac{A}{V} \cdot C^*_{In} \qquad \ldots \ldots \ldots (16)$$

Before proceeding further we may note that $\dfrac{k_{In}A}{V}$ and $\dfrac{k_{Out}A}{V}$ are often constant during the course of an experiment so that they may be replaced by new constants, k'_{In} and k'_{Out} ; thus $k'_{Out} = \dfrac{k_{Out}A}{V}$ and has the dimensions of 1/sec. Frequently " permeability constants " are represented in this way, but it must be appreciated that they are not comparable from one cell to another if A/V is not the same.

The problem now is to find an equation containing only k_{In} or k_{Out}. If we let the ratio $\dfrac{C^*}{C}$ be called the *specific activity*, a, the specific activity within and without the cell at any time, t, is given by :

$$a_{In} = \frac{C^*_{In}}{C_{In}} \; ; \quad a_{Out} = \frac{C^*_{Out}}{C_{Out}}$$

Dividing Equation 16 by C_{In}, we get :

$$\frac{1}{C_{In}} \frac{dC^*_{In}}{dt} = \frac{k_{In}A}{V} \frac{C^*_{Out}}{C_{In}} - \frac{k_{Out}A}{V} \frac{C^*_{In}}{C_{In}}$$

i.e.,

$$\frac{da_{In}}{dt} = \frac{k_{In}A}{VC_{In}} \cdot C^*_{Out} - \frac{k_{Out}A}{V} a_{In}$$

Now

$$\frac{C_{In}}{C_{Out}} = \frac{k_{In}}{k_{Out}}, \; i.e., \; k_{In} = \frac{k_{Out} \cdot C_{In}}{C_{Out}}$$

Thus

$$\frac{da_{In}}{dt} = \frac{k_{Out}A}{V} \frac{C^*_{Out}}{C_{Out}} - \frac{k_{Out}A}{V} a_{In}$$

$$= \frac{k_{Out}A}{V} (a_{Out} - a_{In})$$

Which on integration at constant a_{Out} gives :

$$-\frac{1}{t} \ln \left(1 - \frac{a_{In}}{a_{Out}}\right) = \frac{k_{Out}A}{V} \qquad \ldots \ldots \quad (17)$$

In this way k_{Out} may be computed, whence k_{In} may be obtained[1] by substituting in Equation 15.

It will be noted that a difference in the values of k_{In} and k_{Out} implies that, at the steady state, the concentrations of the ion inside the cell and outside will be different. Thus in the case of the erythrocyte, the ratio : $\dfrac{C_{In}}{C_{Out}}$ for K^+ is of the order of 25, so that K^+ must penetrate inwards some 25 times more easily than it leaves. Concentrations of Na^+ are in the reverse direction, and we should therefore expect to find a value of k_{Out} greater than k_{In} ; recently Harris & Maizels have submitted this point to experimental test. Under normal conditions at $37 \cdot 5°$ C., k_{In} for human blood lies between $1 \cdot 7$ and $4 \cdot 4.10^{-10}$ and k_{Out} between $1 \cdot 7$ and $4 \cdot 4.10^{-9}$. This differential permeability is presumably the manifestation of an extrusion mechanism—the metabolic activity hastening the Na^+ out of the cell ; if this is true we may expect the two values of k to become equal

---

[1] The permeability constant used by Krogh is equivalent to k_{Out}, whereas that used by Conway is k_{In}.

when metabolic activity is zero. At 4° C. this is indeed true, the constants approaching equality at about 7.0×10^{-11} cm./sec. Again, low concentrations of fluoride (0.004M) tend to reduce k_{Out} leaving k_{In} relatively unaffected. As we shall see, this differential permeability of an ion must have certain electrical consequences (assuming that it passes in both directions as an ion) ; further understanding of the theory and consequences of ionic accumulation can therefore only be achieved with some knowledge of the phenomena of electrical potentials in solutions.

Bioelectric Potentials

Wherever the experimental methods have been sufficiently refined to permit the demonstration, it has been shown that the individual cell maintains a difference of electrical potential between its internal and external environments. The maintenance of these potential differences would seem to require the constant utilisation of chemical energy ; hence it is likely that a large proportion of the " maintenance energy " of the organism, discussed earlier, is expended in this manner. For a long time the existence of the potential gradient across the cell wall could only be inferred from the grosser potential gradients observed by placing electrodes on different portions of isolated tissue, the so-called *resting* or *injury potentials*. Thus if one electrode is placed on a damaged portion of a muscle, or nerve, and another on an intact portion, a potential difference amounting to perhaps 30 mV, or more, may be recorded, the injured portion being negative in respect to the intact portion. By assuming that the electrode on the injured tissue made electrical contact with the interiors of the injured cells, whilst that on the intact surface made contact with their exteriors, the injury potential was considered to be a measure of the potential difference occurring across any individual cell of the tissue. Whilst this assumption is true, since two electrodes on intact tissue generally give no potential difference, there is every reason to believe that, because of short-circuiting between the electrodes, the injury potential is considerably lower than the real difference of potential between inside and outside of the individual cells.

The large plant cells of the multinucleate algæ *Halicystis, Valonia, Nitella*, etc., studied by Osterhout and Blinks, permit the insertion of an electrode directly into the sap ; by connecting this electrode through a potential-recording instrument to the surrounding sea-water, quite large potential differences, up to 80 mV, may be obtained with complete regularity. Again, more recently, Hodgkin & Huxley and Curtis & Cole have been able to insert a very fine capillary along the axis of a single nerve fibre, and thus have been able to record the exact potential difference between inside and outside ; their results showed that this resting potential was, in fact, greater than the normally recorded injury potential, as a result of the elimination of the factor of short-circuiting. A similar result was obtained by Graham & Gerard working on impaled single muscle fibres.

Whilst the existence of potential gradients across cell membranes, and their alteration during activity, are well established facts, the manner in which they are established and maintained is still by no means completely elucidated ; before entering upon the description of their experimental study, and the modern theory of their nature, it would be as well to revise our notions as to the origin of electrical potentials in aqueous media.

Electrical Neutrality.   In solution, electrical potential consists of a localised accumulation of ions of one charge with a corresponding accumulation, at another region, of ions of opposite charge ; the flow of electrical current, which may result from this potential difference, will consist in a movement of ions in opposite directions into, and from, the regions of accumulation.   To understand the nature of electrical potentials in aqueous solution we must therefore understand how ions are normally distributed throughout a solution, and the forces that can modify this normal distribution.

Since oppositely charged particles attract each other, we may expect in a solution of NaCl, for example, to find positive Na^+-ions surrounded by negative Cl^--ions.   In the solid crystal state this mutual neutralisation of charges is achieved by a lattice structure, the arrangement of the ions being so orderly that there is no excess of charge in any region of the crystal except the surface.   In solution, the ions are free to move, so that a stable lattice arrangement is impossible, but the next best thing to this is achieved by the electrical *atmosphere*, whereby a given ion tends to be surrounded by oppositely charged ions.   However, owing to the random thermal motions of the individual ions, these atmospheres are continually broken down and rebuilt, so that slight fluctuations in electrical potential occur from point to point in the solution.   Nevertheless, there are so many ions in a given solution of finite concentration that the fluctuations are very numerous and take place as often in one direction as in another, so that placing two identical electrodes in a simple solution of an electrolyte does not give any measurable potential difference.   We may therefore take as our starting point the fact that, in a simple solution of an electrolyte, the parts of the solution will not be charged in respect to each other ; furthermore, since any solution is made up of an equal number of positive and negative ions, two simple solutions will not be expected to be charged in respect to each other.   How then does an electrical potential arise in a solution of an electrolyte ?   Clearly there must be some restraint on the movement of ions of a given type, which will effectually permit them to accumulate in one region.

Membrane and Liquid-Junction Potentials.   In our discussion of the Gibbs-Donnan equilibrium, applying to a solution containing a non-diffusible ion separated from another solution by a membrane, we showed that the concentration of Na^+ was greater on the side containing the indiffusible anion than on the other side, whilst the concentrations of Cl^- exhibited the reverse relationship (Fig. 122).   Since, however, the Na^+- and Cl^--ions are free to move across the membrane as independent units we might expect them to attain *equal* concentrations on both sides ; thus in any given time more Na^+-ions reach the membrane travelling from left to right than Na^+-ions travelling in the reverse direction, and *vice versâ* for the Cl^--ions.   What is it that does, in effect, prevent the levelling up of the concentrations of the individual ions ?   We may note that if the ions did equalise their concentrations, there would be an uneven distribution of charges in the bulk of the two solutions, there being an excess of positive over negative charges in the right-hand solution, and in the left-hand solution an excess of negative charges. Such a separation of electricity would be opposed by the electrostatic attraction of the oppositely charged ions for each other. We may thus view the achievement of equilibrium by the system as the result of the interplay between two mutually exclusive tendencies : (*a*) to achieve equal concentrations of the individual diffusible ions in the two solutions and (*b*) to achieve electrical neutrality throughout the whole of the system. The result of this tug-of-war is the distribution shown above, in which the bulk concentrations are such as to give equal numbers of positive and negative ions in each solution, whilst the tendency for the individual ions to reach equal concentrations is opposed by a potential difference, localised across the membrane, which is directed in such a way as to hinder the rate of passage of Na$^+$-ions from left to right and to promote the passage of Cl$^-$-ions from right to left. Thus, although in any given time more Na$^+$-ions strike the membrane in the direction Left $\longrightarrow$ Right than in the reverse direction, the chance of crossing the membrane from left to right is less ; and the result is, finally, that equal quantities of Na$^+$ pass

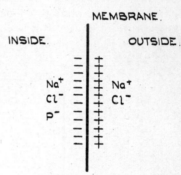

FIG. 122. Illustrating the Gibbs-Donnan membrane potential.

in both directions in any given time. An equilibrium position is thereby maintained with different concentrations of Na$^+$ in the two solutions.[1]

On placing electrodes in the two solutions, the difference in potential across the membrane should give rise to a flow of current on closing the circuit ; in the external circuit the flow of positive current should be from the solution without the indiffusible anions into the solution with them.

The magnitude of this *membrane potential* is given by the formula :—

$$\pi = \frac{RT}{zF} \ln \frac{[Na]_1}{[Na]_2} \qquad \ldots \ldots \ldots (18)$$

where z is the valency of the ion, R is the gas constant, and F is Faraday's Constant, 96,500 international coulombs. When z is unity, and the temperature is 18° C., the formula becomes :—

$$\pi = 58 \log \frac{[Na]_1}{[Na]_2} \qquad \ldots \ldots \ldots (18')$$

the potential being given in millivolts.

[1] The potential difference consists in *localised* accumulations of positive and negative charges, separated by the membrane ; these local accumulations result from the tendency for the positive ions to flow from left to right in virtue of their higher concentration in the left-hand solution ; the *effect* of this potential is to prevent the diffusion process from proceeding to completion, so that the uneven distribution of electrical charges, that would result if the equalisation of ionic concentrations did take place, is confined to a strictly localised part of the system, namely across the membrane.

We may note that the cause of the membrane potential resides in the presence of indiffusible anions in one part of the system ; the potential is established as soon as the two solutions are brought into contact with the membrane, and it remains indefinitely, since the system is in equilibrium ; consequently no expenditure of energy is necessary to maintain the potential.   If the membrane were slightly permeable to the P^--ion, there would be a slow diffusion to a new equilibrium in which NaP would be equally distributed in the two solutions ; as a result, the concentrations of all species of ion would be equal on both sides of the membrane, and the potential would fall to zero.   Consequently if a " leak " in the membrane were to develop, the potential would fall and could only be maintained by the continuous production of more NaP to maintain a higher concentration in the left-hand solution.   This production would, of course, require the expenditure of energy.   It seems likely that the bioelectric potentials in nerve, muscle, and plant cells are not equilibrium potentials of the type illustrated in Fig. 122, but are maintained in the face of a tendency to run down.

An extreme instance of the non-equilibrium type of potential is given by the simple *diffusion potential* or *liquid junction potential* which results from the differing mobilities of the ions of a salt.   Thus with two solutions of NaCl of different concentrations, placed in contact as in Fig. 123, NaCl diffuses from left to right.   The

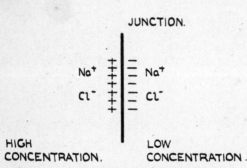

JUNCTION.

HIGH CONCENTRATION.   LOW CONCENTRATION.

Fig. 123.   Illustrating the liquid-junction potential.

Na^+- and Cl^--ions diffuse as separate units and, since Na^+ diffuses more slowly than Cl^-, it tends to get left behind ; the resulting separation of oppositely charged ions establishes a difference of potential at the boundary between the two solutions, the positive side being in the more concentrated solution.   As a result of this potential, the positive ions are accelerated in their passage from left to right whilst the negative ions are retarded ; in consequence, equal amounts of Na^+ and Cl^- diffuse across the boundary in a given time.   As diffusion proceeds, the concentrations tend to become equal and the transport of salt slows down, to cease finally at equilibrium ; since the potential arose out of the tendency for Na^+ and Cl^- to diffuse at different rates, the potential falls until, with the establishment of equilibrium, it becomes zero.   The potential is given by the equation :—

$$\frac{u-v}{u+v}\frac{RT}{F}\ln\frac{C_1}{C_2} \quad . \quad . \quad . \quad . \quad . \quad . \quad . \quad (19)$$

where u and v are the mobilities of the positive and negative ions respectively, and C_1 and C_2 the concentrations of the salt.   When the mobilities of the oppositely charged ions are equal, as with KCl, the diffusion potential is zero. It will be noted that the membrane potential of the type discussed above, is given by putting either u or v equal to zero in the above equation, *i.e.*, by separating the two solutions by a membrane impermeable to one ion ; C_1 and C_2 thus become the concentrations of any one of the diffusible ions.

We have noted that two solutions of KCl should not give a diffusion-potential, since the mobilities of K^+ and Cl^- are equal ; if the two solutions are separated by a dried collodion membrane, however, Michaelis has shown that membrane potentials may be obtained due to the fact that the mobilities of the ions *in the membrane* are different from those in aqueous solution, the membrane tending to slow down the rate of migration of negative ions more than that of positive ions. As diffusion across the membrane proceeds, however, the potential falls, since it is essentially a *concentration potential*, depending on a difference in concentrations of salt on two sides of a membrane ; only if the membrane is completely impermeable to one species of ion will the potential be stable, in which case, as we have seen, it is of the Gibbs-Donnan type. Thus with KCl of concentration 0·1 M separated from 0·01 M KCl by a dried collodion membrane, Michaelis found a difference of potential of the order of 50 mV ; if the mobility of one of the ions were zero the potential difference to be expected would be :

$$\frac{RT}{F} \ln \frac{0\cdot1}{0\cdot01} \text{ or } 2\cdot3 \frac{RT}{F} \log 10$$

At room temperature $RT/F \times 2\cdot3$ is equal to 0·058, consequently the potential should be 0·058 volts, or 58 mV. As the degree of drying of the collodion membrane was increased, the potential obtained became larger and eventually reached this theoretical limiting value, *i.e.*, the membrane became less and less permeable to negative ions until it was finally impermeable. The impermeability of the collodion membrane to negative ions is thought to be due to the presence of negative charges on the pores ; by impregnating the collodion with substances such as protamines, likely to produce a positive charge on the pores, the membrane could be made selectively anion-permeable, in which case the potential was orientated in the reverse direction, the more concentrated solution being positive.

The ionic distribution between the plasma and the erythrocyte has been described earlier ; we may note here that, in virtue of the impermeability of the cell membrane to the negative hæmoglobin-ion, the diffusible negative ions are unevenly distributed between plasma and cell fluid :—

$$\frac{[OH^-]_{Cell}}{[OH^-]_{Plasm}} = \frac{[Cl^-]_{Cell}}{[Cl^-]_{Plasma}} = 0\cdot7 \text{ (approx.)}$$

Such an uneven distribution, with the greater concentration of negative ions in the plasma, can only be maintained in virtue of a potential which slows down the rate of diffusion of negative ions as they pass from plasma into the cell ; *i.e.*, there will be a Gibbs-Donnan potential across the membrane, the outside being positive and the inside negative. With a

Gibbs-Donnan ratio of about 0·7, the potential should be 4·9 mV. With plasma and tissue-fluid the Gibbs-Donnan ratio is only about 0·96, so that the potential here will be very small, only 1 mV.

Resting Potential of Muscle. We have seen that the inside of muscle or nerve appears to be negative in respect to the outside—the resting or injury potential. We have also seen that, to interpret a potential difference across a membrane separating two solutions, we must know the chemical composition of these solutions and the permeability characteristics of the membrane in respect to the various ions. The chemical composition of the muscle fibre and of its external medium (interstitial fluid with approximately the same composition as that of plasma if the plasma proteins are ignored) has been well worked out and is shown in Table XX from Boyle & Conway :

TABLE XX

Chemical Composition of Frog Muscle and Plasma. (*Boyle & Conway*, 1941.)

	Plasma (mM/kg.)	Muscle Fibre (mM/kg. Fibre-Water)
K	2·5	126
Na	104	15·5
Ca	2·0	3·3
Mg	1·2	16·7
Carnosine . . .		16·4
Hexose-mono-phosphoric acid .		2·8
Phosphagen . . .		38·5
ATP		4·8
Protein	0·6	2·3
Chloride	74·3	1·2
Bicarbonate . . .	25·4	0·4
Lactate	3·3	—
Sulphate	1·9	—

Schematically the state of affairs may be represented by the simple diagram of Fig. 124, where A^- represents a group of organic anions many, if not all,

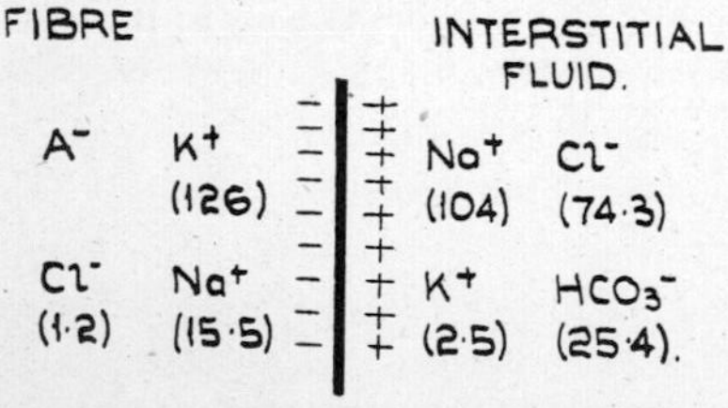

FIG. 124. Schematic representation of the distribution of certain ions between the water in the frog's muscle fibre and interstitial fluid. (Concentrations from Boyle & Conway.)

of which are unable to diffuse across the membrane. The membrane is known to be permeable to K^+, so that the large difference in concentrations of this ion in fibre-water and interstitial fluid must be due to a restraint imposed on the system by the impermeability of some other ion or ions. For a long time it was thought that the fibre-membrane was impermeable to both Na^+ and Cl^-, in which case the high concentration of K^+ would have been due to the impossibility, in the interests of electrical neutrality, for it to diffuse out of the fibre, an exchange with Na^+ being impossible, and a migration outwards in company with a negative ion excluded by the impermeability to Cl^- and the organic anions. The high concentration of K^+ would therefore be maintained by a potential, with such a polarity as to slow the rate of diffusion of K^+ out of the fibre and to accelerate its passage in, *i.e.*, such that the inside of the fibre was negative in respect to the outside. This was thought to account for the observed resting potential. The theoretical magnitude of the potential, on this basis, would be given by the equation :—

$$\frac{RT}{F} \ln \frac{126}{2 \cdot 5} = 99 \text{ mV}$$

considerably higher than the former highest measured value for frog muscle, which was 59 mV. The reason for this discrepancy, as we have indicated earlier, is certainly due to an internal short-circuiting of the potential difference, so that only a portion of the real potential is measured.

Conway has shown, however, that the fibre-membrane is readily permeable to Cl^-, the low concentration of this ion in the muscle fibre being due simply to the fact that the organic anions within the fibre, to which the membrane is impermeable, impose a Donnan Equilibrium on the system similar to, but more extreme than, that found in the erythrocyte. Thus with a membrane permeable to K^+, Cl^-, HCO_3^-, H^+ and OH^- the distribution of these ions should follow the equation :

$$\frac{[K^+]_{\text{In}}}{[K^+]_{\text{Out}}} = \frac{[Cl^-]_{\text{Out}}}{[Cl^-]_{\text{In}}} = \frac{[HCO_3^-]_{\text{Out}}}{[HCO_3^-]_{\text{In}}} = r$$

The ratio of K^+ concentrations is equal to $126/2 \cdot 5 = 50$, whilst that for Cl^- is $74 \cdot 3/1 \cdot 2 = 62$; in view of the difficulty in determining the actual amount of Cl^- within the fibre, as opposed to that within the interstitial fluid of the muscle, the discrepancy between the ratios is not alarming, and we may tentatively conclude that the uneven distribution of Cl^- follows from the impermeability of the fibre-membrane to organic anions (and, of course, to Na^+). We may note that the system is thermodynamically stable, with the existing concentrations of ions, only so long as the membrane is impermeable to Na^+ as well as to the organic anions ; if Na^+ could diffuse into the cell, both Na^+ and Cl^- would enter and so break down the difference in concentration of Cl^- ; as a result, K^+ could leak out.

Whether the membrane is assumed to be permeable to Cl^- or not, the theoretical potential is given by the same formula containing the ratio of the concentrations of K^+. As Conway points out, however, the influence of varying concentrations of KCl in the outside medium will be different according to which view is correct. For example, if the concentration of K^+ in the outside medium is increased by the addition of a small amount of KCl, the concentration of K^+ within the cell will be barely affected by this addition, if the membrane is impermeable to Cl^-; so that the new potential will be given by :

$$\pi' = \frac{RT}{F} \ln \frac{[K^+]_{\text{In}}}{[K^+]'_{\text{Out}}}$$

where $[K^+]'_{Out}$ is the new external K^+-concentration. If the membrane were permeable to Cl^-, on the other hand, a change in the external concentration of K^+ should be reflected in a significant and predictable change in the concentration of K^+ inside, and the potential should follow a more complex equation. For the frog, this more complex equation may be simplified to :—

$$\pi = \frac{RT}{F} \ln \frac{c}{2[K^+]_{Out}} \quad\quad\quad\quad\quad (20)$$

where c is the total concentration of ions in the outside medium. Adding KCl to the medium surrounding a muscle increases c as well as $[K^+]_{Out}$, with the result that the influence of the added KCl on the potential is smaller on the basis of a permeability to Cl^- than on the basis of impermeability to this ion.

Effects of External $[K^+]$. Before considering the resting potential further, we may enquire into some of the recent evidence on the basis of which the modern theory of its origin is established. If the muscle fibre is permeable to both K^+ and Cl^-, by replacing some of the NaCl, in the Ringer solution bathing the muscle, with KCl, the former Donnan-equilibrium is disturbed, since now the ratio : $\dfrac{[K^+]_{In}}{[K^+]_{Out}}$ is less than r, the Donnan ratio, whilst the ratio $\dfrac{[Cl^-]_{Out}}{[Cl^-]_{In}}$ is greater than r ; in order that the two ratios may be equal, *i.e.*, that a new Donnan equilibrium be established, K^+ and Cl^- must enter the fibre until a new position is reached fulfilling the requirement :—

$$[K^+]_{In}\,[Cl^-]_{In} = [K^+]_{Out}\,[Cl^-]_{Out}$$

The resulting migration of KCl into the muscle fibres should raise the osmotic pressure within them ; this should cause the osmosis of water into the fibres and increase the total volume of the muscle. Replacing some of the external NaCl by KCl should therefore cause the muscle to swell and its total contents of K^+ and Cl^- to increase. Such an increase in volume had been observed many years ago by Overton but was attributed, at any rate by later workers, to " colloidal effects " of the salt. The careful analyses of Conway have shown, however, that the changes in volume are accompanied by the penetration of K^+ and Cl^-, in quantitative agreement with the demands of the Gibbs-Donnan equilibrium. If, instead of replacing NaCl by KCl, thereby maintaining a constant external osmotic pressure, KCl is added in increasing quantities, the osmotic pressure of the bathing medium is increased progressively ; as a result, there is an initial tendency for water to leave the muscle fibres ; the penetration of K^+ and Cl^-, on the other hand, tends to reverse the difference of osmotic pressure, and the final volume of the muscle may actually be larger than normal. In general, however, it may be shown that, if the concentration of NaCl in the bathing medium of an excised frog muscle is approximately equal to that in the interstitial fluid, the final volume of the muscle is constant ; in fact V is given by the simple equation :—

$$V = \frac{105 \cdot 5}{[Na]_{Out}}$$

When $[Na]_{Out}$ is 105·5, $V = 1$, the original volume. The equation holds for wide variations in the osmotic pressure of the bathing fluid brought about by the addition of KCl ; this can only mean, of course, that KCl accumulates in the fibres to greater and greater extents, the greater the amount of KCl added to the bathing medium. The actual concentrations of K^+ in the muscle are easily predictable ; in Fig. 125 the concentration of K^+ in muscle has been plotted against the external K^+-concentration ; the line in the figure represents the calculated concentrations whilst the plotted points represent the concentrations actually found. The line fits the plotted points so well that there can be little doubt that the theoretical treatment—which assumes that the membrane is impermeable to Na^+ and

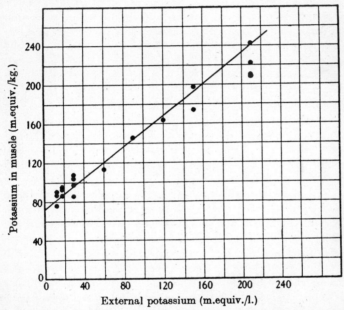

FIG. 125. Total potassium concentration in sartorii against potassium concentration in external fluid containing constant sodium concentration (85·9 meq./l.). The line gives the theoretical relationship deduced on the basis of a Gibbs-Donnan equilibrium. (Boyle & Conway. *J. Physiol.*)

permeable to K^+ and Cl^-—is a good approximation. Further confirmation of the validity of the treatment is given by a direct test of the Gibbs-Donnan equation. According to this, the product $[K^+]_{In} [Cl^-]_{In}$ should be equal to $[K^+]_{Out} [Cl^-]_{Out}$; it is found that these products are equal for external concentrations of K^+ varying from 12 to 300 meq./l. At lower concentrations, however, there is a significant deviation from this equality. This fact, and the observation that, when an excised muscle is placed in a medium containing the same concentration of K^+ as that in plasma (2·5 meq./l.), there is a steady loss of this ion from the fibres, suggest either that the excised muscle is not strictly normal, or that the theoretical treatment ignores some important factor. Earlier experimenters have shown that there is a certain " maintenance concentration " of K^+ in a perfusion fluid, necessary to prevent the leakage of this ion from the muscle ; this maintenance concentration was definitely above the normal plasma level.[1] Conway's work on excised muscle has shown that the maintenance concentration must be considerably higher than that required for perfusion (29 meq./l.), and he attributes this finding to his more artificial conditions in comparison with those prevailing during perfusion, where the muscle is intact. According to Conway, the excised muscle is unable to tolerate the high potential across the fibre-membrane associated with the normal distribution of K^+ (99 mV) ; as a result, the impermeability to Na^+, or organic anions, or to both, breaks down temporarily with a resulting escape of K^+ and gain of Na^+ and Cl^- by the fibres. Only when these exchanges have reduced the resting potential to about 60 mV (*i.e.*, the value usually obtained on excised muscle) does the membrane recover its normal state and prevent the further migration of Na^+ and Cl^-. If, on the other hand, the excised muscle is bathed in a solution containing K^+ in a concentration of 29 meq./l., the potential is smaller and insufficient to break down the barrier to Na^+ ; this concentration is therefore a mainten-ance concentration. At lower temperatures (2–3° C.) the maintenance concentration is lower, 10 meq./l., but still greatly in excess of normal. There is no obvious reason, however, why the fibre should be able to tolerate a higher potential difference at a low temperature than at a high temperature, so that Conway's explanation, plausible as it seems at first sight, cannot be easily accepted. As we shall see, the fundamental assumption that the membrane is normally impermeable to Na^+ has been shown, by studies with radioactive tracers, to be wrong ; it need not be surprising, therefore, that theoretical predictions as to the normal resting potential and distribution of K^+ between fibre and surrounding fluid should not be completely confirmed by experiment.

p*H of Fibre*. Since the H^+- and OH^--ions may be assumed to diffuse across the fibre-membrane, we must expect them to be distributed in the same ratio as those found for K^+ and Cl^-. With a concentration ratio of 11·4, this would correspond with an internal p*H* of 6·2 (external p*H* 7·3) ; with a concentration ratio of about 50, namely that found *in vivo*, the internal p*H* should be 5·9 compared with a p*H* of 7·6 for plasma. According to Rous, who studied the changes in colour of injected indicators, the p*H* in the fibre is at least as acid as 5·6. Another method, open however to serious objections, is that of Hill & Kupalow ; here the amount of CO_2 taken up as HCO_3^- by the excised muscle was used to calculate the cell p*H* in accordance with the Henderson-Hasselbach equation [2] ; these authors claimed that a p*H* of the order of 5·6 would require a quite

---

[1] According to Goffart & Perry, adrenaline may partially inhibit the loss of K^+ from a muscle maintained in Tyrode solution.

[2] The Henderson-Hasselbach equation relates the p*H* of a mixture of a salt and weak acid (*e.g.*, $NaHCO_3$ and H_2CO_3) to the dissociation constant of the acid, $k_a = \dfrac{[H^+][A^-]}{[HA]}$, and the concentrations of salt and acid :—

$$pH = pk_a + \log \frac{[Salt]}{[Acid]}$$

pk_a being the negative logarithm of k_a.

impossible tension of CO_2. Conway has shown, however, that this conclusion is not necessarily valid since adequate account was not taken of the losses of K^+ and gains of Cl^- and HCO_3^- that take place on washing the excised muscle in Ringer solution ; the muscles employed in the investigation had probably lost sufficient K^+ and gained anions to give a fibre pH of 6·7, a figure not incompatible with the CO_2 bound as HCO_3^- found by Hill & Kupalow. In mammalian muscle, moreover, Conway & Fearon have shown that a great deal of the CO_2 is bound in a complex, *i.e.*, it is not in the form of HCO_3^- or free CO_2 ; when allowance is made for this, the pH within the fibre is probably 6·0, and the ratio of the concentrations of HCO_3^- inside and outside the fibre is equal to the ratio for Cl^-.

Demarcation Potentials. If our interpretation of the injury potential is correct, there is, in the muscle, a difference in potential between the interior and exterior of the fibres which depends, in a more or less predictable manner, on the ratio : $[K^+]_{In}/[K^+]_{Out} = [Cl^-]_{Out}/[Cl^-]_{In}$. If,

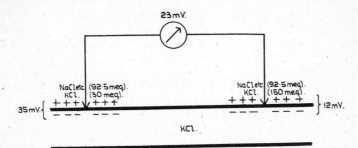

Fig. 126. Illustrating the demarcation potential. Owing to the different potassium concentrations under the two electrodes, the resting potentials are different, the right-hand electrode being less positive than the left-hand one.

at localised regions on the surface of the muscle, different external concentrations of K^+ are maintained, we must expect the resting potentials to differ, as in Fig. 126, where at one contact the external concentration is 30 meq./l. KCl, whilst at the other it is 150 meq./l., the total external ionic concentrations being 245 and 485 meq./l. respectively. A is more positive than B ; by applying Equation (20[1]), the two potentials can be calculated, and thence the difference of potential between A and B (called the *demarcation potential*). The latter amounts to 23 mV, a figure agreeing well with the experimental value. Studies of the potentials obtained in this way, using different salts at one of the contacts, have often been made (*e.g.*, by Höber) with a view to determining whether the muscle fibre-membrane is permeable to given ions. It is clear that the potential difference depends on the impermeability of the fibre to Na^+ ; if the Na^+ in one of the contact solutions were replaced by a cation capable of penetrating the fibre, the resting potential should fall and the potential difference between the two contacts should change. Evidence derived from this kind of study suggests that the fibre is permeable to H^+, Rb^+, Cs^+, NH_4^+ and K^+ (and a number of alkyl substituted ammonium ions, Wilbrandt, 1937) and impermeable to Na^+, Li^+, Ca^{++}, and Mg^{++} so far as cations are concerned ; with anions the following are thought to penetrate the fibre : OH^-, Br^-, I^-, Cl^-, NO_3^- whilst CH_3COO^-, SO_4^{--}, and HPO_4^{--} are thought not to.

Normal Permeability Relationships. It has been emphasised more than once already that the classical interpretation of the resting potential relies on an assumed impermeability of the fibre to certain organic anions and to Na^+ ; the potential is envisaged as a purely physical phenomenon, independent of vital activity so long as the membrane retains its impermeability to these ions. We must not gloss over the fact, however, that as soon as the excised muscle is placed in Ringer solution it immediately loses K^+ and gains Na^+ and Cl^- ; only when the concentration of K^+ is some twelve times the normal value does the system remain stable from a physico-chemical standpoint. With the application of the tracer-technique, using radioactive isotopes, more light has been shed on the problem.

According to the work of Greenberg on the rat, and of Hahn, Hevesy & Rebbe on the frog, the fibre-membrane is definitely permeable to K^+ ; the results of these workers left some doubt, however, as to whether there was complete exchangeability [1] of the fibre and extra-cellular K^+. The most recent work of Harris has answered this question in the affirmative ; thus it was found that a muscle may be soaked for long periods in phosphate solution and retain its normal concentration of K^+, as opposed to the ordinary Ringer solution in which, as we have seen, it steadily loses this ion. If K^{42} is added to the phosphate solution, it is found that it distributes itself completely throughout the K^+ in the muscle (at 18°C.). The main assumption at the basis of the interpretation of the resting potential is thus proved. A comparative study of the rates of penetration of K^{42} from outside the fibre inwards, and in the reverse direction, also lends support to this interpretation ; the high concentration of K^+ is maintained in the fibre largely, if not entirely, by virtue of the difference in potential which hinders the escape, and promotes the penetration. The ratio of the concentrations inside and outside the fibre should be given by the ratio of the permeabilities for inward and outward movement :—

$$\frac{[K^+]_{In}}{[K^+]_{Out}} = \frac{k_{In}}{k_{Out}}$$

if the internal concentration is to be maintained. From dissected muscles a leakage of K^+ goes on, as discussed earlier, and Harris has compared the losses, calculated from the difference :—

$$(k_{In} \times [K^+]_{Out} - k_{Out} \times [K^+]_{In}) \times \text{Time}$$

---

[1] Fenn, Noonan, Mullins & Haege found a complete exchangeability of muscle-K^+ ; they point out that the presence of only 0·01 per cent. of Na^{24} as an impurity in the K^{42} would give results consistent with an apparent exchangeability of only 50 per cent. of the fibre-K^+.

with those found analytically. Typical figures are :—

Ringer with :	k'_{Out} (hr.$^{-1}$)	Fraction of $[K^+]_{In}$ lost per hr.
0·015 per cent. KCl 0° C.	0·03	0·02
0·03 per cent. KCl 0° C.	0·06	0·03
0·06 per cent. KCl 0° C.	0·07	0·02
0·06 per cent. KCl 18° C.	0·13	0·02
0·09 per cent. KCl 18° C.	0·20	0·08

The concordance between the analytically determined and theoretically computed rates of loss of K^+ is an excellent proof that the concentrations of K^+ inside and outside the fibre are determined by the values of k_{In} and k_{Out}, so that it would be difficult to attribute the high internal concentration of K^+ to " binding " in undissociated compounds.

According to all theories of the potential, however, the fibre should be impermeable to Na^+, and although workers in this field seem to have accepted this as being true under normal physiological conditions, there has certainly accrued, in the last ten to twenty years, an amount of evidence that shakes confidence in this assumption. For example, Heppel fed rats on a K^+-deficient diet and found that the K^+ in the fibre tended to be replaced by Na^+ ; that this Na^+ could exchange with external Na^+ was proven, moreover, by injections [1] of Na^{24}. The difficulties in ascertaining a normal permeability of the fibre membrane to Na^+ are great, since the great bulk of the Na^+ in the muscle is in the interstitial space, so that the presence of Na^{24} in the muscle, after an intravenous injection, is no evidence *per se* of penetration into the fibres. Nevertheless an analysis of the kinetics of penetration and escape indicates that Na^{24} may normally enter the fibre and leave it. Thus Levi & Ussing found that the washing-out of Na^{24} from muscle, previously allowed to equilibrate with this isotope, showed two phases which could be analysed into (a) a rapid loss from the extracellular spaces and (b) a slower loss from the fibres. Similar results were obtained with Cl^{39}, the rate of penetration of this ion being greater than that of Na^+. Levi & Ussing estimated the extra-cellular space to be 27–32 per cent. of the muscle volume, and the concentration of Na^+ in the fibre-water to be 23 meq./l. ; the corresponding figure for fibre-K^+ was 73 meq./l. The figures for interspace are doubtless abnormally high, however, since the muscles were soaked for some time in Ringer. Harris & Burn found the ratio of internal to external concentrations of Na^+ to be 0·05 to 0·13, and they computed the extracellular space to be 18 per cent. They also found that the Na^+ in the fibres exchanged with that in the extracellular fluid. Later Harris found that the cellular Na^+ is extruded by what must be a complex process, apparently involving two successive steps. He suggested that these might be transfer through the membrane and desorption from the surface. The time-course of the loss of cellular Na^+ was such that an erroneously high value for the extracellular Na^+

[1] According to Conway & Hingerty the Na^+ is rapidly extruded from the muscle fibres and replaced by K^+ on returning the animals to a diet adequate in K^+.

might be inferred, and this would certainly account for the very high values computed recently by Levi & Ussing.   The rate of extrusion was found to be affected by the time of storage of the dissected muscles, the influence of storage being apparently on the rate of transfer across the fibre-membrane rather than on the subsequent desorption process.

On purely thermodynamic grounds, however, the demonstration of a permeability of the fibre membrane to Na^+ by no means completely invalidates the general interpretation of the bioelectric potential ; if the fibre is permeable to K^+ and Cl^-, a potential must be present across the membrane to prevent the equalisation of the concentrations.   If the membrane is completely impermeable to Na^+ and organic anions, the condition is described as one of thermodynamic equilibrium, and the effects of varying the concentrations of various ions in the bathing medium are completely predictable.   If, on the other hand, there is a permeability to Na^+, then we must invoke a special mechanism for the extrusion of Na^+-ions as fast as they penetrate.   Such a mechanism is not incompatible with the existence of a concentration potential of K^+ and Cl^-, and the remarkable agreement between theory and experiment found by Conway strongly suggests that, so far as gross influences of changes in the external medium at least are concerned, considerations based on thermodynamic equilibria are in the main valid.   Nevertheless it is difficult to believe that the secretory mechanism itself would be completely unaffected by variations in the medium surrounding the fibre ; and changes in the rate and mode of extrusion of Na^+ must react on the distribution of other ions and so produce complications not predictable on simple thermodynamic theory.   The concept of a " sodium pump," by which Na^+ is continually removed from the fibre, is somewhat question-begging, in that the mechanism whereby this can occur is not stated.   In essence, however, the concept implies that the migration of Na^+ across the fibre-membrane is to a large extent, if not completely, independent of the gradient of electrical potential across the fibre.   This assumption implies that, in one stage of its path, the sodium-atom enters into an undissociated complex.

Before passing to a consideration of the resting potential of nerve we may consider the permeability of the muscle fibre to phosphate.   The quantitative assessment of such a permeability is laden with difficulties owing to the continuous formation and breakdown of organic phosphates during glycolysis (p. 501).   Early work, by classical chemical techniques, suggested that the fibres were impermeable to inorganic phosphate, the amount taken up from a solution being that required for the extracellular space to come into equilibrium.   The application of P^{32} has done a little to clarify the situation ; Hevesy & Rebbe showed that some of the injected P^{32} was taken up in organic phosphate fractions, and more recently Causey & Harris have shown that the phosphate taken up by muscle is very highly concentrated on the surface of the fibres (Fig. 127, Pl. VIII) ; this suggests that the phosphorus is involved in some complex, and it is possible that many of the phosphorylations, considered to take place within the fibre, actually take place on its surface.

Nerve.   The nerve, like muscle, exhibits a resting, or injury, potential between the lead from a crushed region and that on the normal surface ; the magnitude of the potential obtained from a whole nerve, *i.e.*, a bundle of fibres, is variable, depending as it does on probable short-circuits and injury during dissection. Cowan reported an average figure of 30 mV in non-medullated Crab nerve (*Maia*), although values ranging from 10 to over 40 mV were recorded. Cowan also carried out accurate chemical analyses of the concentrations of K^+ in the crab's blood and nerve. The concentration was high in the nerve, 150 meq. per litre of nerve, corresponding to about 200 meq. per litre of axoplasm if allowance is made for the extracellular space of invertebrate nerve (*ca.* 25 per cent., Fenn *et al.*, 1934). This compares with a concentration of only 10·4 meq./l., in the blood and 10 meq./l. in Plymouth sea-water. A much more extensive analysis of crab, lobster, and myelinated frog nerve is that of Fenn, Cobb, Hegnauer & Marsh ; some of their results on frog nerve are shown in Table XXI, where the concentrations have been computed in terms of

TABLE XXI

Composition of Frog Myelinated Nerve and Plasma ; Concentrations are in meq. per kg. of Water. (Fenn, Cobb, Hegnauer & Marsh, 1934.)

	Na^+	K^+	Ca^{++}	Cl^-
Nerve . .	37	173	9·6	0
Plasma . .	108	2·6	2·1	77·5

All the Cl^- has been assumed to be extracellular.

water within the fibre. In myelinated nerve the extracellular space is high, Fenn *et al.* computing that 100 g. of nerve contain only 27 g. of water in the axoplasm ; this, however, is on the assumption that all the Cl^- is extracellular. The giant axon from the stellar nerve of the squid *Loligo*, described by J. Z. Young, has permitted a direct analysis of the composition of the interior of the fibre ; although the nerve has a diameter which may be as great as 1 millimetre, it is a single axon and not a bundle of smaller fibres ; the axoplasm of this fibre may be squeezed out in sufficient quantity to allow of reasonably accurate determinations of Na^+, K^+ and Cl^-. The results of some studies by Steinbach & Spiegelman are shown in Table XXII :—

TABLE XXII

Concentrations of Ions in Axoplasm of Squid Nerve and in Sea-water (Steinbach & Spiegelman).

	Concentrations (meq./l. H_2O)		
	K^+	Na^+	Cl^-
Nerve (freshly isolated) . . .	369	44	39
Nerve (sea-water treated) . .	321	101	82
Sea-water	13	498	520

(Chloride concentrations from Steinbach, 1941, on the assumption of 10 per cent. of solid matter in axoplasm ; sodium concentration in sea-water from Osterhout, 1931.)

It will be noted that there is a significant concentration of Na^+ in the axoplasm and that this is increased at the expense of K^+ on washing the nerve in sea-water, the composition of which is very similar to that of squid's blood. On soaking the nerve in K^+-free sea-water, the loss of K^+ is even more striking [1] ; if the sea-water is progressively fortified with K^+, a point is reached—at 100–150 meq./l.—where no loss of K^+ occurs ; when the concentration is raised above these limits, up to some 300–400 meq./l., the nerve shows an increase in concentration of K^+. Thus for the squid giant fibre, the *maintenance concentration* of K^+ is some ten times the normal concentration in the blood, a fact indicating that it is difficult to maintain an isolated nerve in sea-water, in the same way that the isolated frog muscle loses K^+ in frog Ringer.

Permeability studies on nerve have been by no means so extensive as on muscle ; the work of Keynes has shown that crab nerves, soaked in sea-water containing K^{42}, take up the isotope to reach a final concentration of 206 meq./l. of axoplasm. On replacing the nerves in normal sea-water, the K^{42} leaked out with an average " half-life " of 1·4 hours. Rothenberg has published results which suggest that a large fraction (90 per cent.) of the internal K^+ of the axoplasm of the squid giant fibre is not exchangeable with K^{42} in the outside medium ; the exchange of Na^{24} with internal Na^+ was, on the other hand, complete. This result suggests that a large part of the internal K^+ is in a bound form, *i.e.*, that it does not consist of thermodynamically active ions. It is difficult to reconcile such a result, however, with the high internal electrical conductivity of the axoplasm, nor yet with the requirement that the interpretation of the resting potential, on thermodynamic grounds, requires an internal concentration of active potassium ions at least ten times, if not twenty times, that in the outside medium.[2]

As with muscle, it has generally been inferred that the " anion-deficit " of nerve, *i.e.*, the difference in concentrations of inorganic cations and anions, is made up by organic anions ; thus Schmitt, Bear & Silber estimated the anion-deficit in lobster nerve to be some 390 meq./l. of H_2O. If allowance is made for inorganic phosphate and bicarbonate, it is concluded that some 300 meq./l. of unidentified anions are present in the axoplasm ; further investigations by Silber indicated that these anions are probably dicarboxylic amino-acids (but probably not aspartic and glutamic acids). In the medullated nerve of the frog, the total concentration of cations is 180 meq./l. (Fenn), whilst that of Cl^- is 50 meq./l. After allowing for phosphate, bicarbonate, lactate and sulphate, the deficit is only 70 meq./l. This is only partly covered by amino-acids, a circumstance attributed by Schmitt to the phospholipids of the medullary sheath, which probably behave as fixed anions in association with the excess of base.

[1] There is some, but not very conclusive, evidence that the losses obtained by washing the nerve in K^+-free sea-water are reversible on restoring the nerve to normal sea-water.

[2] Two sources of error must be guarded against ; the isotopes may not be pure so that a great deal of radioactivity may be associated with isotopes that cannot enter the cell ; secondly the axon may lose K^+ in its isolated condition. Unfortunately Rothenberg failed to carry out parallel classical chemical analyses of Na^+ and K^+.

PLATE VIII

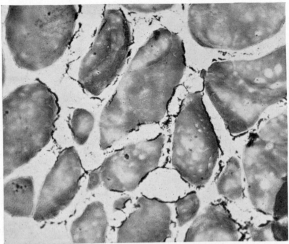

FIG. 127. Radioautograph of muscle. The black regions show accumulation of P^{32} around the muscle fibres. (Causey & Harris. *Biochem. J.*)

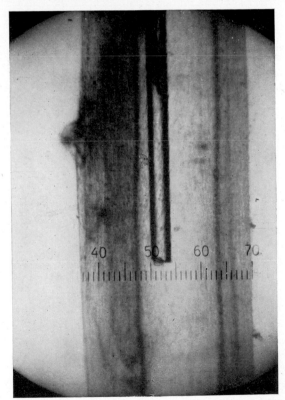

FIG. 129. Photomicrograph of electrode in giant axon. Adjacent tissues have not been completely removed from the fibre, which shows as a clear space. One scale division equals $33\,\mu$. (Hodgkin & Huxley. *J. Physiol.*)

[To face p. 268.

Thus, whilst it is very likely that the organic anions in nerve and muscle are different (and probably different in non-medullated and medullated nerves), it would seem from the chemical analyses that the fundamental factor in the resting potential is, in all cases, the high concentration gradient of K^+ across the fibre-membrane. The effects of varying the external concentration of K^+ on the resting potential were studied by Cowan ; he found that the logarithmic relationship, predictable on the basis of a simple membrane potential, held over a fairly wide range of concentration of K^+. Curtis & Cole (1942) studied the same effect on the single axons of the squid and found that the logarithmic relationship does not hold in the region of comparatively low concentrations of K^+, *i.e.*, when they were from one-tenth to about three times that in normal sea-water. The potential becomes zero with an external concentration of K^+ of about 18 times the sea-water value, *i.e.*, 230 meq./l., well below the concentration in the axoplasm as computed by Steinbach. If the ionic permeability relationships in muscle and nerve are similar, we may expect that replacement of NaCl in the outside medium by KCl will cause the nerve to swell in accordance with Conway's deductions. Shanes has drawn attention to a swelling of this type in the spider-crab nerve.

The True Resting Potential. A concentration ratio of K^+ equal to about

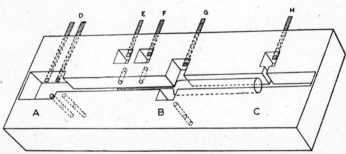

Fig. 128. Schematic drawing of the cell used for measuring membrane resting potential. A clean axon was placed in the trough with its ends in the enlargements at A and B. The micro-pipette, filled with KCl, was placed in the trough with its tip in the B enlargement, and, after piercing the cell wall, was pushed along to the position shown. All chambers were then filled with sea-water, and covered with a glass plate. Membrane potentials were measured at the E and H electrodes. (Curtis & Cole. *J. cell. & comp. Physiol.*)

30, found between the squid axon and its surrounding sea-water, should give a membrane potential of about 85 mV. Measurements of the injury potential of nerve bundles, as we have seen, give values in the region of 30 mV, values attributable to short-circuiting. The recent development of ingenious techniques for inserting micro-pipettes into single nerve fibres, by Hodgkin & Huxley and Curtis & Cole (1940), and in muscle fibres by Graham & Gerard, has permitted measurements of the true resting potential. The experimental arrangement employed by Curtis & Cole is illustrated in Fig. 128, and a micro-photograph of a giant axon with the micro-electrode in place is shown in Fig. 129, Pl. VIII from Hodgkin & Huxley.

On the average, Curtis & Cole found a resting potential of 51 mV ; after making allowance for certain junction potentials at the electrodes, which they estimated to add up to 10 mV, the potential actually existing across the axon was computed to be some 61 mV. The resting potentials found by Hodgkin & Huxley in the squid axon were of the same order of magnitude ; in single axons of *Carcinus* and *Homarus*, however, they were definitely lower. Thus, as with muscle, the measured resting potential is smaller than that expected theoretically ; whether this is due to the abnormal condition of the fibre during the experiment, or to the complicating effects of the " sodium-pump " mechanism, cannot yet be stated ; the work of Steinbach strongly suggests that the isolated axon in sea-water is abnormal, in that it rapidly loses K^+ and gains Na^+ and Cl^-, so that it is quite likely that the measurements of Curtis & Cole and Hodgkin & Huxley provide low estimates of the true resting potential in the intact animal. This view is confirmed by the recent studies of Graham & Gerard on impaled muscle fibres ; these authors inserted a micro-pipette into the sarcoplasm of single fibres with the muscle *in situ* ; the muscle consequently suffered a minimum of damage. The average resting potential was found to be 97·6 mV, when allowance was made for the contact potentials at the electrodes ; this value is thus very close to the theoretical one of 99 mV. deduced from the relative concentrations of K^+ in fibre and interstitial fluid. Even with this technique, the resting potential gradually fell, presumably as a result of damage.[1]

Potentials in Large Plant Cells. We have indicated earlier that the existence of a potential has been demonstrated between the inside (vacuolar) and outside surfaces of certain plant cells. The multinucleate cells of the marine alga *Valonia*, for example, attain the size of a hen's egg and can live for weeks after being pierced by a capillary ; it is therefore possible to make direct measurements of the potential difference. Moreover, the volume of the internal fluid is so large that chemical analyses of its more interesting constituents may be made with ease. If the potential difference between the inside and outside of *Valonia* were the exact analogue of the injury potential of nerve, we might expect that researches on the large plant cells would have gone far to elucidate the injury potential. Unfortunately the analogy does not extend so far ; the injury potential is a potential difference between the inside and outside of a single cell bounded by a plasma membrane, *i.e.*, between the protoplasm and the fluid surroundings ; an impaled *Valonia* cell provides the difference of potential between the *vacuolar sap* and the outside sea-water, the sap being

---

[1] Nastuk & Hodgkin, applying the same technique, found an average resting potential of 88 mV, whilst Huxley & Stämpfli, applying an ingenious technique to medullated nerve (which did not involve puncture with a micro-electrode) found a mean value of 71 mV. These authors have tabulated the values obtained by various authors and have indicated the probability that deviations from the theoretical potential, computed from the concentrations of K^+ inside and outside the cell, are due to the leakage of K^+ and gain of Na^+ that occur during the measurement. Huxley & Stämpfli have measured, and discussed at length, the effects of the external concentration of K^+ on the resting potential ; the deviations from the theoretical effects predicted on thermo-dynamic grounds, noticed by Curtis & Cole and Ling & Gerard (for muscle), are best accounted for by a leakage of K^+.

separated by an intact layer of protoplasm from the outside medium. The potential difference is therefore not one between the inside of protoplasm and outside. The conditions are illustrated in Fig. 130. The potential in *Valonia* is therefore the algebraic sum of the potential differences between sea-water and protoplasm, on the one hand, and vacuolar sap and protoplasm on the other ; for example, if the outside sea-water were 120 mV. positive in respect to the interior of the protoplasm, and the inside sap were 40 mV positive to the protoplasmic interior, the potential difference across the protoplasm would be 80 mV, the outside being positive in respect to the inside. Such a potential would conventionally

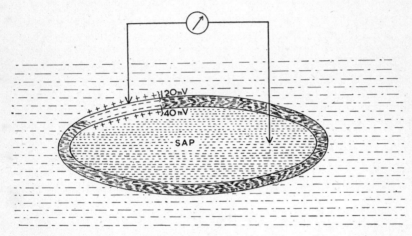

Fɪɢ. 130. Illustrating the origin of the potential between inside and outside of an impaled alga. At the sea-water/protoplasm surface there is a p.d. of 120 mV, whilst the p.d. at the sap/protoplasm surface is only 40 mV. The recorded potential is therefore 80 mV, the sap being negative with respect to the outside of the cell. (After Blinks.)

be given a positive sign. In *Halicystis* the potential is $+ 70$ to $+ 80$ mV ; in *Valonia* it is $- 10$ mV.

The existence of these potentials is the result of an asymmetry in the system ; an asymmetry resulting partly from the different concentrations

Tᴀʙʟᴇ **XXIII**

Relative Compositions of the Sap of some Giant Plant Cells and o their Surrounding Media (meq./l.).

	Valonia sap	*Halicystis* sap	Sea-water	*Chara* sap	Brackish water surrounding *Chara*	*Hydrodictyon* (Blinks & Nielsen, 1940)	Pond water bathing *Hydrodictyon*
Cl . .	597	603	580	225	73	55·3	1·1
Na . .	90	557	498	142	60	4·0	1·3
K . .	500	6	12	88	1·4	76·3	0·019
Ca . .	1·7	8	12	5·3	1·8	1·8	1·1
Mg . .	—	16·7	57	15·5	6·5	—	0·9
SO₄ . .	—	—	36	3·9	2·8	8·2	0·8

of ions in sap and sea-water, Table XXIII, and partly from an essential difference between the sea water-protoplasm and sap-protoplasm interfaces. If the potential across the protoplasm depended only on the difference in chemical composition of sap and sea-water, placing sap on the outside of a cell should abolish its potential. This does not happen. In general, it would seem that the concentration of K^+ in the sap is less important than that in the outside medium ; thus Blinks has shown that the potential of *Halicystis ovalis* is quite unaffected by substituting sea-water for the sap in the vacuole, although such a substitution involves a change of internal concentration of K^+ from 300 meq./l. to some 13 meq./l. Moreover, at least one species, viz., *Halicystis Osterhoutii*, does not accumulate K^+ in its sap, but nevertheless shows a steady resting potential of 70 mV. Small modifications of the outside concentration of K^+, on the other hand, may profoundly modify the potential. In *Halicystis*, for example, KCl applied to the surface tends to make the outside of the cell negative, *i.e.*, it tends to reduce the resting potential to zero. This effect could be obtained, on purely thermodynamic grounds, if K^+ diffused very much more rapidly into the protoplasm than Cl^-. If the Cl^- of the surrounding sea-water is substituted by SO_4^{--} or NO_3^-, the potential may fall to zero or even be reversed ; this effect is attributed to the low mobilities of SO_4^{--} and NO_3^- in the protoplasm. Thus, if the potential difference between protoplasm and outside medium depended on the difference in mobilities of the positive and negative ions, the low mobility of SO_4^{--} in relation to Na^+ would tend to make the outside of the protoplasm negative, as opposed to its normal condition of positivity ; in consequence, the potential-drop across the whole layer of protoplasm would be reduced and might even be reversed. The striking effects of anion substitutions led Blinks to the conclusion that it is the anions in the protoplasm that play a dominating role in the maintenance of the observed potentials ; if these have very low mobilities across the interface between protoplasm and the surrounding media, in comparison with those of the positive ions, we may expect that there will be a potential difference between protoplasm and sea-water, on the one hand, and between protoplasm and sap on the other, the protoplasm being negative in respect to both sap and sea-water. If, now, the relative mobilities of the positive and negative ions are markedly different in the region of the sea-water/ protoplasm interface from those in the sap/protoplasm interface, there will be a marked difference of potential across the whole protoplasm as Fig. 130 shows. All the evidence goes to show that it is at the sea-water/ protoplasm interface that the large differences in mobility between positive and negative ions occur, since modifications in the composition of the sap contribute little to the final potential difference across the cell ; moreover, such effects as do take place are consistent with the idea of a potential difference between sap and protoplasm of the same type as, but smaller than, that existing at the other interface. According to the estimate of Blinks, the relative values of the potentials are those indicated in Fig. 130, sea-water being some 100 to 120 mV positive in respect to protoplasm, and the sap being some 20–40 mV positive in respect to protoplasm ; the resting potential, being the algebraic sum of these two potentials, thus amounts to some 100 to 60 mV. On this basis the relative mobilities of K^+, Cl^-, Na^+, and NO_3^- in protoplasm are 20 : 1 : 0·3 : 0·1.

This, in rough outline, seems to be the state of affairs in *Halicystis* ; the picture is based essentially on membrane diffusion potentials ; and such a system must represent a steady-state rather than a thermodynamic equilibrium, since there is nothing in the postulated mobilities to prevent a final equalisation of concentrations between sea-water and sap. The system, to remain in this steady-state, must perform work ; consequently we may expect the potentials to be affected by factors that influence the cell's metabolism. In O_2-lack it is found that the potential falls from its normal value of 80 mV to about 10 mV, but is rapidly restored on readmitting O_2 (or by illumination, the organism being photosynthetic). This fall in potential is associated with a *rise* in the electrical resistance of the membrane from about 500 to 5,000 ohm.cm.², due presumably to a more selective permeability (p. 386). Apparently the cell, as a result of this metabolic interference, which tends to allow the concentrations to equalise throughout the system, seals itself by a general all-round decrease in permeability to ions.

Space has not permitted detailed accounts of several other types of bioelectric potential. The *electrokinetic potential* is the potential difference between a particle and its surrounding medium, *e.g.*, an ionised protein molecule, and is manifested by the migration of the particle in an electric field (*electrophoresis*) similar to the movement of ions in electrolysis. All the cells that have been studied possess this type of potential but its significance in terms of cell function has not been ascertained (Abramson, Moyer & Gorin). Because of their differing molecular weights and electrokinetic potentials, the molecules of a mixture of proteins will migrate at different speeds in an electric field, and the Tiselius electrophoresis apparatus is a valuable instrument in the separation and identification of proteins. The *phase-boundary potential* results from the differing partition coefficients of the ions of a salt between oil and water ; they have been studied mainly by Beutner. Oxidation consists essentially in the loss of one or more electrons, *e.g.*, in the oxidation of Fe^{++} to Fe^{+++} ; two mixtures of Fe^{++} and Fe^{+++} salts, in different proportions, will show a potential difference if metallic electrodes, capable of conducting electricity, are inserted in the solutions ; the " redox potential " of a system, capable of reversible oxidation and reduction, is a valuable measure of its oxidising or reducing tendency, but whether the differences in redox potential across a membrane are capable of modifying ionic movements, or not, is a matter of uncertainty. Friedenwald & Stiehler have invoked this type of potential to explain certain aspects of secretory activity. The surface potential results from the presence of fixed dipoles in the molecules constituting a surface film (Fig. 106) ; thus if the polar end-groups in the interface are carboxyl-groups, the dipole is such that the C-atom is positive in respect of

the O-atom of the carbonyl group, $^+C\diagdown_{OH}^{-O}$, consequently the aqueous phase tends to be negative. The potentials are described by Adam, and their significance in relation to ionic permeability has been discussed by Davson & Danielli (1936).

Active Transport

This lengthy digression into the realm of bioelectric potentials has enabled us to appreciate the special problems of active transport in nerve, muscle and large plant cells. Studies with radioactive isotopes have demonstrated an unmistakeable permeability of the nerve and muscle cells to both Na^+ and K^+ ; since the high concentration of K^+ and the low concentrations of Cl^- and HCO_3^- in the fibre may be explained simply on the basis of the Gibbs-Donnan equilibrium (provided that the membrane is impermeable to Na^+), no energy would be required to maintain this state of affairs.[1] In the presence of a permeability to Na^+, on the other hand, the system would " run down," the K^+- and Na^+-ions exchanging across the membrane. Since this permeability to Na^+ has been established, energy must be supplied to prevent the Na^+ from diffusing in, *i.e.*, in some way metabolic energy must be supplied to enable this ion to pass out of the cell more readily than it enters. It is possible to calculate the minimum amount of energy required along the lines already discussed, remembering that the extrusion of 1 mole of Na^+ will be against an electrical potential gradient. According to Ussing's computation from his figures for the rate of penetration of Na^{24}, this comes to 50 cals./kg. muscle-water/hr. comparing with some 400 cals./kg. muscle-water/hr. for the resting heat production at $18°$ C. found by Hill, *i.e.*, about 10–20 per cent. of the total resting heat. This is a large fraction, since heat production is not a measure of the energy actually available for use, and only if the efficiency of the process is known can we say how high is the proportion of useful energy expended in this way. If Na^+ diffused back and forth across the membrane of the

---

[1] The K^+ and Cl^--ions are said to have the same *electro-chemical potential* inside and outside the fibre. The condition for equilibrium is that the work done in transferring an infinitely small quantity of a constituent from one point to another is zero ; thus with two solutions of a non-electrolyte separated by a membrane, equilibrium is given when the quantity : $dm\ RT\ ln \dfrac{C_1}{C_2}$ is zero, *i.e.*, when C_1/C_2 is unity. The two solutions, under these conditions, may be said to be at equal *electro-chemical potential*, where this is given by $RT\ ln\ C$. With solutions of electrolytes conditions are not so simple, since now it is possible to have an equilibrium in which a given ion is more concentrated on one side of the membrane than the other, *i.e.*, in which the term $RT\ ln \dfrac{C_1}{C_2}$ is not zero. The work done in transferring dm-ions from one solution to another, however, now consists of two terms, osmotic work plus electrical work. The osmotic work is, as before : $dm\ RT\ ln \dfrac{C_1}{C_2}$, and the electrical work is $dm\ z\ F\ \pi$, z being the valency, F the Faraday constant, and π the potential difference. The two terms have opposite signs since, in transferring an ion against the concentration gradient, osmotic work is done *on* the system, whilst the system does electrical work in accelerating the ion down the potential gradient. When these terms are equal, the total work is zero and the system is in equilibrium. If the potential difference is written as a difference, $\pi_1 - \pi_2$, the electro-chemical potential of an ion may be written as : $RT\ ln\ C_1 + zF\pi_1$ in the solution of concentration C_1, and $RT\ ln\ C_2 + zF\pi_2$ in the other. When the difference between these two quantities is zero, the system is in equilibrium in respect to this ion.

muscle or nerve cell as an ion, it would be subjected to the potential difference imposed by the unequal distributions of H^+ and K^+ and Cl^-, and move more readily inwards than outwards ; it would consequently exhibit a concentration gradient in the same direction, *i.e.*, it would be accumulated to the same extent as K^+. Since this does not occur, we must conclude that the migration of Na is fundamentally different, *e.g.*, that it crosses the membrane as an undissociated complex. The importance of the argument leading to this conclusion cannot be over-estimated since it represents the logical basis for all conclusions as to which of the ions in any secretory system are actively transported, and which of them migrate by passive diffusion. In brief it is this. If the distribution of an ion inside and outside the cell is consistent with the difference of potential across the membrane, it is at equal chemical potential inside and outside, and there is no reason to suppose an active transport mechanism involved in its distribution, the ratio : C_{In}/C_{Out} being determined by the ratio k_{In}/k_{Out} which is itself determined by the difference of potential across the membrane, k_{In} being

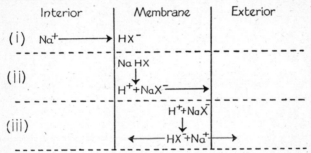

FIG. 131.   Scheme illustrating active extrusion of sodium.

greater than k_{Out} in the case of K^+ because the potential difference accelerates the inward passage and decelerates the outward passage. Where no such relationship exists between the concentrations and the potential, as with Na^+, we must assume an active transport mechanism, the difference between k_{In} and k_{Out}, and thus the difference between the concentrations inside and outside the cell, being determined possibly by the formation of a complex within the membrane.

Now the inward permeability constant for Na^+ seems to be of the order expected for this ion by comparison with that of K^+, *i.e.*, it is some 25 times smaller ; it would therefore seem that the active process is applied to accelerating the Na^+ outwards ; *e.g.*, when the Na^+-ion enters the cell it forms a complex which then diffuses back and dissociates at the outer surface. It is idle to speculate in detail as to the mechanism of this complex-formation and its subsequent dissociation, but the general scheme may be illustrated by Fig. 131. Na^+ within the cell forms a complex NaHX which breaks down to H^+ plus a negative complex NaX^-, the latter being accelerated out of the cell by the potential difference. At the external surface it becomes once again Na^+ whilst the HX^- diffuses back. The one-way character of the permeability would be provided by the tendency for the complex to be formed within the cell, and dissociated at its external surface. (It may well be, as Ussing has pointed out, that a molecule of the complex, reaching the external surface, would exchange its Na for the Na in the outside medium and then be carried back to exchange with a Na^+-ion of the internal medium. This " shuttle service " would make for an exchange of ions without any net transfer—*exchange diffusion* as Ussing calls it—so that the actual tendency for the cell to *gain* Na^+ would be much less than that computed from a knowledge of its permeability, as indicated by isotope studies.)

Returning now to the case of the erythrocyte, we may note that in many species K^+ is accumulated to about the same extent as in muscle and nerve ; one fundamental difference is that the erythrocyte contains, by comparison, high concentrations of Cl^- and HCO_3^-. This is due to the smaller concentration of indiffusible anions, by comparison with muscle and nerve. The two systems may be roughly compared as follows :—

Frog Muscle

Inside		Outside
126 meq./l... $\begin{cases} K^+ & A^- \\ K^+ & Cl^- \end{cases}$		104 meq./l...Na^+ Cl^-
15·3 meq./l.....Na^+ Cl^- $\Big\}$ 1·2 meq./l.		2·5 meq./l...K^+ Cl^- $\Big\}$ 74·3 meq./l.
		HCO_3^- *ca.* 32 meq./l.

Human Erythrocyte

Inside		Outside
150 meq./l... $\begin{cases} K^+ & Hb^- \\ K^+ & Cl^- \end{cases}$		144 meq./l...Na^+ Cl^-
26 meq./l... Na^+ Cl^- $\Big\}$ 74 meq./l.		5 meq./l...K^+ Cl^- $\Big\}$ 111 meq./l.
		HCO_3^- *ca.* 38 meq./l.

The concentrations of K^+ and Cl^- inside and outside the muscle fibre are approximately determined by the Gibbs-Donnan equilibrium :—

$$\frac{[K^+]_{In}}{[K^+]_{Out}} = \frac{[Cl^-]_{Out}}{[Cl^-]_{In}} = 25 \ ca.$$

It is quite clear, on the other hand, that no such relationship pertains between the K^+- and Cl^--ions in the erythrocyte, in fact, as we have seen (p. 242), the equilibrium may be described on the basis of a membrane impermeable to both Na^+ and K^+, and permeable to Cl^- and HCO_3^- ; only the ratios of the negative ions being constant. Now a definite permeability to both Na^+ and K^+ has been well established for the erythrocyte, so let us see how the notion of an active extrusion of Na^+, which explained the accumulation of K^+ in muscle and nerve, can be applied to the erythrocytes. We will assume, then, that K^+ is not actively transported, so that it is at equal chemical potential inside and out ; there will thus be a potential across the membrane given by :

$$\frac{RT}{F} \ln \frac{C_{In}}{C_{Out}}$$

This potential must impose on the system a reverse distribution of the diffusible negative ions of equal magnitude, *i.e.*, the ratio : $\dfrac{Cl^-_{Out}}{Cl^-_{In}}$ should be about 25, the ratio of the K^+-ion concentrations. Since this clearly does not occur, the ratio $\dfrac{Cl^-_{Out}}{Cl^-_{In}}$ being only about 1·5, we must conclude, either that Cl^- is actively transported across the membrane as a complex, or that K^+ is ; all studies so far made have failed to reveal any evidence of active transport of anions in the erythrocyte, so that we must conclude that in this cell both Na^+ and K^+ are actively transported, a mere extrusion of Na^+ being quite inadequate to explain the observed concentrations of diffusible ions. The reason why a Na^+-extrusion mechanism may explain the accumulation of K^+ in muscle, and not in the erythrocyte, resides in the concentrations of indiffusible anions in the two cells ; in the muscle this is so high that the extrusion of Na^+ demands its replacement, in the interest of electrical neutrality, by K^+ ; in the case of the erythrocyte, the extruded Na^+ may be accompanied by a negative ion, Cl^- or HCO_3^-.

The mechanism of the K^+-accumulating process in the erythrocyte is still completely unknown. It is doubtless connected with the complex series of chemical events described as glycolysis, which involves the phosphorylation of sugar and its breakdown through a series of organic phosphates to lactic and pyruvic acids (p. 501. At 7° C. Solomon, Hald & Peters found that the organic acid-soluble phosphorus remained unchanged within the cells, apparently incapable of diffusing across the membrane ; at 37° C., on the other hand, a large amount of organic acid-soluble phosphorus was broken down to give inorganic phosphate, which passed out of the cells, these changes being associated with a large increase in the Na^+-content of the cells and a smaller escape of K^+. It is futile, as yet, to speculate in detail on the mechanism of active transport, but, as we have indicated above, it seems likely that some complex of sodium and of potassium must be formed which permits their more ready penetration in one direction than the other, and it is possible that some organic phosphate, which is probably formed at the surface of the erythrocyte, represents the carrier. In this discussion of the active transport aspects of ionic permeability we have confined attention to comparatively few types of animal cell ; work on others has been by no means so consistent ; a few pointers to the literature may, however, be useful. Wilson & Manery (1949) have shown that Na^{24} exchanges across the leucocyte membrane with a " half-life " of less than one hour ; the membrane seems also to be anion-permeable. Frog eggs, according to Abelson & Duryee (1949), exchange Na^{24} with a half-life of fifteen minutes ; radioautographs (*i.e.*, pictures obtained by placing the radioactive cell on a photographic plate, the blackening being caused by the emitted radiations), failed to indicate a well defined barrier to Na^{24} at the egg surface. Davson & Shapiro (1941) have reported on some preliminary work on accumulation by the *Arbacia* egg, whilst Krogh (1943) has studied active transport of K^+ and Na^+ across the chorion of the hen's egg.

Accumulation by Plant Roots

Plant cells, in general, contain high concentrations of such ions as K^+, Mg^+, Ca^+, and NO_3^- in comparison with the medium from which they derive them ; the roots of such plants must therefore have a highly efficient mechanism for the absorption and accumulation of salts against concentration gradients. Some idea of the extent of the accumulation that normally takes place is given by the following figures for the concentrations (in meq./kg. fresh wt.) of certain ions in the tissues of young wheat plants (taken from Lundegårdh) :—

	K^+	NO_3^-	Ca^{++}	PO_4
Roots .	89	4	5·4	19
Straw .	191	4·4	6·2	24
Leaves.	174	2·3	14·5	23

The concentrations in a typical soil fluid,[1] given by Hoagland, are as follows (meq./l.) :—

NO_3^-	PO_4	Ca^{++}	Mg^{++}	Na^+	K^+
2·8	0·017	7·1	8·2	2·1	0·62

By growing plants in an artificial aqueous medium, moreover, it has been found that, even with as small a concentration of K^+ as 5 parts per million (0·13 meq./l.), normal growth is obtained.

Since the primary process of accumulation must occur in the root, we may profitably concentrate on the behaviour of this tissue. Fig. 132 is a schematic cross-section of a typical root, which consists essentially of an outer agglomeration of cells comprising—from outside inwards—the *epidermis*, *cortex*, *endodermis*, *pericycle*, and an inner conducting system, the *stele*, comprising the *phloem* and the *xylem*. The xylem is a series of woody tubes, resulting from the death and subsequent lignification of long cells,

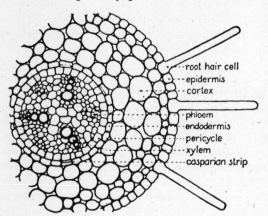

FIG. 132.   Schematic cross-section of root. (Crafts & Broyer. *Amer. J. Bot.*)

which run the length of the root and are continuous with similar tubes in the stem ; it is the analogue of the vascular system of animals and conducts the sap, elaborated by the cellular elements in its neighbourhood, from its site of formation up into the plant. The surface available for

---

[1] It is of course difficult to assess the actual concentrations of dissolved substances in the soil, which is essentially a colloidal suspension of solid matter with a very variable proportion of the aqueous medium ; most of the ions present are adsorbed to the solid phase and are only gradually leached out by water. The experimental procedure for obtaining a sample of soil fluid is to pass water through a layer of soil under pressure until it acquires a constant composition on emerging ; it is an analysis of this solution that is presented above.

absorption from the soil is extensive as a result of the development of root hairs, prolongations of the epidermis cells.

The cells of the root tissue contain a high concentration of salts in relation to the soil solution ; the primary step in this accumulation is doubtless located in the root hair-cells [1] ; from these, the accumulated salts are presumably transferred to the cells of the inner layers (translocation) whence they are secreted in part into the xylem. Whether this translocation results from a protoplasmic continuity between the various layers of cells, or whether each cell tends to absorb at its outer side and exude at its inner side, is not clear although Crafts & Broyer have suggested a mechanism based on the former process. If all the cells are permeable to water there will be a tendency for it to pass into them as a result of the large difference of osmotic pressure between the soil solution and the cell contents ; this is the cause of the cell turgor. The fluid exuded into the xylem, moreover, namely the root sap, having, as we shall see, a concentration of salts greater than that of the soil solution, will also attract water osmotically so that the sap will have its own " turgor pressure " and thus flow to regions where this is lower, *i.e.*, up the vascular system into the stem and leaves. This flow will take place in spite of the fact that the cells, in relation to the xylem, have a higher osmotic pressure than that of the sap, since the determining factor in the flow of water is the difference of osmotic pressure between the sap and outside medium. For example, if we imagine three compartments of different osmotic pressure as below :—

Sap	Tissue Cell	Outside Medium
P_1 (·020 M)	P_2 (0·1 M)	P_3 (0·001 M)

water will actually flow across the tissue cell into the sap, the force driving it being determined by the difference of osmotic pressure between outside medium and sap. That this force may be very great is shown by White's observation of root pressures (*i.e.*, pressures driving sap upwards) in tomato plants of the order of 6–7 atmospheres—pressures more than adequate to maintain a column of liquid some 70 metres high. Thus it was observed that, even though the sap was being formed against a pressure of 6 atmospheres, its rate of formation was not very much smaller than that of a root forming sap under atmospheric pressure alone. We may note in passing that the requirements for the development of these pressures is a membrane, effectively impermeable to salts, separating sap from outside medium. This is apparently provided by the tissue cells ; if it were possible for the soil solution to seep round the various cells, as an interstitial fluid, there would be no osmotic barrier and the necessary pressures could not be developed, mixing of soil solution with sap occurring

[1] Overstreet & Jacobson (1946) have studied the relative rates of absorption of Rb and P by different parts of the root ; maximal absorption was found a few mm. from the tip, the root cap apparently not absorbing significantly ; since root hairs occurred 5·2 mm. from the tip, these were not very active in absorption of these ions.

by simple diffusion of sap-salts into the interstitial fluid across the freely permeable xylem wall.

The general problem as to the membrane, across which the difference of osmotic pressure between soil and sap becomes operative, is still unsolved ; it would seem, from plasmolysis studies, that the layer of cells constituting the endodermis may be regarded as a complete physiological seal, separating the outer layers from the stele, in the sense that the protoplasm of this layer is, in effect, continuous. Leakage of salts from the stele past this barrier may therefore be ruled out, whilst water can pass across it. If this is true, water can pass from soil into the endodermis and develop a pressure within the cells which will drive fluid into the xylem, as the path of least resistance. The translocation of salts involves a rather more difficult problem ; if the protoplasm of the cortical cells were continuous, not only between cortical cells but also with adjoining layers, the salt accumulated by the cortical hair cells could pass, by diffusion and protoplasmic streaming, inwards towards the xylem. According to the hypothesis developed by Crafts & Broyer, the presence of large intercellular spaces between the outer cells would favour aeration and thus accumulation of salt, whilst the more anaerobic conditions in the interior of the root tissue would promote loss of salt which would find its way into the xylem. The alternative supposition would be that each cell accumulated salt and passed some of its accumulated material into the interstitial space of a neighbouring cell which, itself, accumulated it, so that the accumulated material was relayed inwards ; such a process, however, would be thermodynamically most inefficient, the work of accumulation having to be performed successively by each cell.

The absorption of salts and water occurs predominantly in the apical part of the growing root and in the zone of growing root hairs, the vessels being established as close as about 2 mm. to the vegetation point in the wheat root. Thus, as Lundegårdh has shown, this growing region may be regarded as an osmometer cell, the upper part of the vessels acting as a manometer tube (Fig. 133). If the regions, over which absorption of salts and of water takes place, differ in extent, the sap flowing up the stem will differ radically in chemical composition from the fluid formed in the apical zone. Experimentally this sap—the *bleeding-sap*—is collected as it oozes from the cut end of the root, at its junction with the stem.

Bleeding-Sap. Passing now to a description of some of Lundegårdh's experiments on the bleeding-sap, we may see his experimental set-up illustrated in Fig. 134 ; young wheat plants were grown in an artificial nutrient medium for fifteen days and then transferred to a circulation chamber, the green parts being cut off some 3–4 cm. above the seed. The cut ends of the roots were covered with a piece of cotton-wool to absorb the bleeding-sap flowing from them. At intervals, the cotton wool was weighed and analysed, and at the same time the fluid in the circulation chamber was removed and analysed. Some idea of the amount and composition of bleeding-sap formed in one hour by one gramme of roots is given by the following typical experiment, the roots being maintained in a solution of 1 mM KNO_3 :—

Amount of Sap	.	.	0·022 ml./g./hr.
Concn. of K^+	.	.	18 meq./l.
Concn. of NO_3^-	.	.	18 meq./l.
Concn. of Ca^{++}	.	.	1·3 meq./l.

i.e., the sap is essentially a dilute KNO_3 solution (it is generally almost completely free of organic matter). If we compare these figures with the

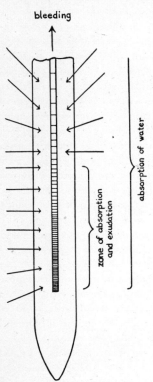

FIG. 133. Illustrating the stele. In the lower region salts are exuded into the xylem ; as the sap moves up the xylem it is diluted by the osmosis of water into it. (Lundegårdh. *Ark. Bot.*)

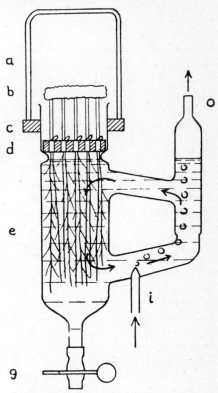

FIG. 134. Lundegårdh's experimental arrangement for the study of the bleeding sap. (*a*), Glass cover to prevent evaporation ; (*b*), cotton wool ; (*d*), cork holder with 14 plants ; (*i*), inlet for O_2, air, or N_2 ; (*o*), outlet. Arrows indicate circulation effected by stream of air bubbles. (Lundegårdh. *Ark. Bot.*)

analysis of the tissues in the plant (p. 278), we see that, although the sap is some 18 times more concentrated than the nutrient medium (1 mM) from which it was derived in the last analysis, the cells through which it passed have very much higher concentrations of K^+ ; NO_3^-, on the other hand, is lower in concentration in the root tissue and therefore exudation seems to be the result of a secretory mechanism. When the roots are placed in distilled water, the flow of sap does not cease immediately and the fluid collected contains appreciable amounts of salts which are, in this case, derived from the root tissues ; thus the root cells give up some of their salts in favour of the sap, even when they cannot replace these losses from the outside medium ; the same phenomenon is observed in intact plants, grown in salt-deficient media or soils, large quantities of K^+, for example, being sacrificed by the root to supply the green tissues.

If the flow of sap is determined (under these experimental conditions of course) (a) by the exudation or secretion of salts into the xylem and (b) by the osmotic flow of water from the nutrient medium to xylem, we should expect a rough correspondence between the concentration of sap and its rate of flow, the greater the concentration the greater the flow. This expectation is confirmed ; and we may conclude that the difference of osmotic pressure is an important factor in the flow of sap. The effects of increasing the concentration of material in the nutrient medium will be complex, since both the rate and degree of salt excretion into the xylem will be modified, as well as the difference of osmotic pressure ; in general it is found that the flow of sap increases with increasing external concentration; due, at least partly, to the increased secretion of salt.

The rate of bleeding rarely exceeded 0·5 ml./hr. per bunch of 14 roots, whereas the intact seedlings transpired (*i.e.*, lost water through the leaves) at a maximum rate of 2·6–3·0 ml./hr. Undoubtedly the " suction," caused by the loss of water on the leaves, accelerates the rate of flow of sap beyond that caused by the difference of osmotic pressure in the root. Under conditions of high humidity, transpiration cannot be an operative mechanism in promoting the flow of sap, so that we may regard the osmotic mechanism, involving the secretion of salt into the xylem, as the fundamental process ensuring this flow independently of transpiration ; the latter process may be regarded as a flow of water superimposed on this fundamental activity, a point of view confirmed by the finding of Hoagland that the actual absorption of salts by a root may be the same whether it is transpiring or not.[1]

We need not follow the investigations into the bleeding sap farther, except to emphasise that in the root we must distinguish two fundamental processes ; (a) the absorption of salts by the root-tissue cells and (b) the exudation of salts into the xylem. The first process is very closely linked to aerobic metabolism, since removal of O_2 from the roots causes an almost instantaneous cessation of absorption, in fact salts start to flow out of the tissue into the medium. The formation of sap under these conditions is reduced, after a time, but carries on for at least several hours at the diminished rate, so that it is possible that anaerobic metabolism is responsible for a part of the exudative process ; on the other hand, bleeding under these conditions may be a passive process resulting from the loss of salts from tissue cells into the xylem, a loss that would increase the difference of osmotic pressure between nutrient medium and sap ; thus with cyanide poisoning it is found that the bleeding sap contains large

[1] For example, Broyer & Hoagland found that when plants grew in high humidity and in the dark, or in low humidity and in the light, the total Br^- and K^+ absorbed was the same, whereas the H_2O taken up by transpiration differed by a factor of five or more.

amounts of K^+ but very little NO_3^-, corresponding to the low concentration of nitrate in the cells.

"**Anion Respiration.**" Studies of the root tissue by Hoagland, and by Lundegårdh, have thrown some light on the details of the accumulation process ; according to Lundegårdh, metabolic energy is supplied only in the transport of anions, the accumulation of cations being regarded as a necessary electrostatic consequence of the former process. Lundegårdh bases this conclusion mainly on the observation that respiration of plant roots, measured in terms of the evolution of CO_2, can be expressed as a simple function of the amount of accumulated anion as follows :—

$$R_t = R_g + kA$$

where R_t is the total respiration, R_g is the *Grundatmung* or *fundamental respiration,* which continues in the absence of accumulative activity, A is the number of millimoles of anion accumulated, and k is a constant which is equal to 2 for NO_3^-, 3 for Cl^- and 12 for SO_4^{--}, when the CO_2 evolution is expressed in millimoles. Thus the respiration is considered to be made up of two parts, the Grundatmung and the *Anionatmung,* the latter being given by kA, and is six times as great in accumulating SO_4^{--} as that required for accumulating an equal quantity of NO_3^-. The evidence Lundegårdh presents in support of this separation of respiration into two components is striking ; for instance it is generally found that the amounts of cation and anion taken up by a root in a given time are different ; Lundegårdh found that with the same amount of anion taken up, and different amounts of cations, the respiration remained the same ; further, when the same amount of cation was taken up from various solutions, the respiration varied linearly with the amount of anion taken up. The value of k, the constant indicating the amount of respiration associated with the uptake of a given anion, did vary with the cation present ; in general k increased in the series :—

$$Na < K < Mg < Ca < NH_4 < Sr < Ba < H$$

being 1·5 with $NaNO_3$ and 4·9 with HNO_3.

According to Lundegårdh, the anion-respiration is set off by the presence of anions capable of being absorbed, so that in distilled water we might expect to have no anion-respiration ; again, roots in $KHCO_3$ do not show accumulation of HCO_3^- and the respiration in bicarbonate solutions should be only the Grundatmung. Nevertheless, as Hoagland has pointed out, the root actively accumulates K^+ in this medium, so that some energy must be involved beyond the Grundatmung. Lundegårdh postulates the presence of a positive group, R^+, in the protoplasm of the plant cell which, at the external surface, reacts with an anion to give an uncharged complex, RA ; this is carried to the inner surface where an oxidative reaction involving glucose provides the energy for the dissociation of the complex into R^+ and A^- ; the anion accumulates at the inner boundary and becomes associated with base which is thought to diffuse in passively. The actual processes are doubtless far more complicated than this simple scheme might suggest ; thus it is known that the root produces large amounts of organic acids besides CO_2 (*e.g.*, malic acid) ; these can presumably diffuse out of the root. To some extent at least, the entry of K^+, for example, is an exchange process [1] with H^+. Finally, Hoagland has shown that, according to the nutritive condition of the plant (*i.e.*, according to the amount of salts and glucose the roots contain), the relative amounts of anions and cations absorbed during a given period may vary greatly, so that a simple anion-absorption process, associated with passive diffusion of cations, must be inadequate to explain all the facts.

Studies on Expressed Root Sap.   Whatever the truth regarding the existence of anion-respiration, the close association of ionic accumulation with metabolism has been well established both by Lundegårdh's work and that of other investigators, particularly by Hoagland & Broyer. These authors expressed the sap from the root tissue, frozen after varying periods in different solutions, and analysed this fluid. They showed that, under anaerobic conditions, active accumulation of Br^- did not occur, the root merely absorbing sufficient to provide equal concentrations in the sap and outside medium. Under anaerobic conditions large amounts of CO_2 are formed, so that a simple mechanism of accumulation based on the production of acid, followed by an exchange of anions, cannot apply. Studies with K^{42} showed, as we should expect, that this isotope, within the root, exchanged with inactive K^{39} in the outside solution, in spite of the fact that a net transfer of K^+ was taking place into the root tissue ; the study of the effect of temperature on the outward movement revealed a very low Q_{10}, of the order of 1·1, whereas the actual accumulation of K^+ was very strongly affected by temperature, showing a Q_{10} of nearly 3 between 0·5° and 20° C. This indicates that the migration outwards represents, probably, a simple diffusion process whereas the inward flow is determined by metabolic reactions. This result strongly suggests that K^+ is accelerated inwards by metabolic processes which become active as the temperature is raised, although it could be argued that the active accumulation of *anions* at the higher temperature creates a potential such that the inside is negative to the outside, and it is this potential which produces the high rate of inward penetration of K^+.[2]

Exchange Adsorption.   We may note that, for convenience in experimentation, the absorption by plant roots has been mainly studied in plants maintained in an artificial liquid medium ; Jenny & Overstreet have emphasised the importance of the natural soil medium ; thus they have shown that, although plants can retain their K^+ for as long as ten hours when placed in distilled water, they lose this ion continuously if exposed to clay suspensions containing an adsorbed cation such as Na^+, NH_4^+ or H^+. The mechanism is one of *exchange adsorption*. If the roots and clay are separated from each other by a collodion membrane, no such

---

[1] The importance of H^+ cannot be overstressed when the extraction of cations from the soil colloids is considered ; the availability of K^+ in the soil is largely determined by the ability of the root to exchange H^+ with K^+, electrostatically attracted in the colloidal lattice.

[2] Lundegårdh has measured the p.d. between the cut end of the plant stem and the outside of the root ; large p.d.'s were found, 150–200 mV, which were strongly dependent on the *p*H of the medium ; the outside of the root was positive in respect to the cut end.

exchanges are observed, consequently Jenny & Overstreet postulate a " contact exchange " between the plant root and the clay particle, as

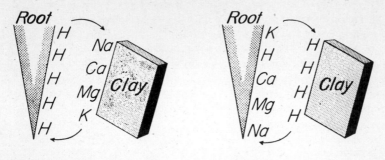

CONTACT INTAKE   CONTACT DEPLETION

FIG. 135. Illustrating *contact exchange* of ions between root and soil colloid. (Jenny & Overstreet. *Soil Science.*)

indicated in Fig. 135, the root and clay particle having to be sufficiently close, if exchange is to occur, for the " oscillation volumes " of the ions to overlap.

Salt Accumulation. It is unwise to speculate far as to the intimate mechanism of accumulation of salts in plant roots ; the contention of Lundegårdh that accumulation is dominated by an active absorption of anions, brought into play by the presence of these anions in the outside

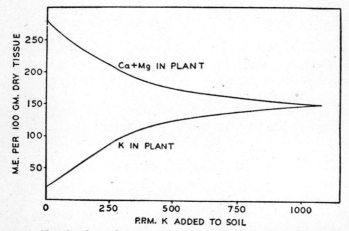

FIG. 136. Showing how the accumulation of K, Ca, and Mg by the plant is affected by the concentration of K in the outside medium ; as this increases, K is accumulated at the expense of Ca and Mg. (Hoagland. *Lectures on the Inorganic Nutrition of Plants.* Waltham, U.S.A.)

medium, has been severely criticised by Hoagland and by Steward, and it would certainly be wise to admit the possibility of an active accumulation of K^+ as well as of anions. Plant roots produce large quantities of organic acids, *e.g.*, malic acid, and this is specially evident during the accumulation of K^+ in $KHCO_3$ solutions ; the exchange of these organic acid anions with external anions would cause an accumulation of the latter, but the real process of accumulation is doubtless much more complex. With regard to cations, there is no doubt that not only K^+, but Mg^{++} and Ca^{++} may be accumulated ; moreover, although K^+ exhibits accumulation in the most pronounced form, when this ion is deficient in the outside medium it may be replaced in the tissue, to some extent at least, by Ca^{++}, Mg^{++} or Na^+ ; thus Fig. 136, from Hoagland & Martin shows the effects of varying the K^+-content of the soil on the K^+, Ca^{++} and Mg^{++} contents of tomato plants, and it will be seen that, as more and more K^+ is available to the plant, more is accumulated whilst less Mg^{++} and Ca^{++} is found in the tissue. Too little is still known about the relative accumulations of the various cations normally found in the plant, and the degrees to which they are interchangeable, for any dogmatic statements on the importance of any given ion ; nevertheless, the almost universal accumulation of K^+ in high concentration within plant and animal cells would suggest the presence of an active secretory mechanism devoted to maintaining these high concentrations. The importance of the absorption of NO_3^- in the plant's economy has doubtless necessitated the development of a highly efficient anion-accumulation mechanism which seems to work nearly as efficiently in accumulating Br^- and Cl^- ; it is not surprising therefore that Lundegårdh should have been so impressed with the anion secretion as to attribute a minor role to absorption of cations.

Translocation. Absorption of salts by the roots, and the photosynthesis of carbohydrate by the green leaves, are the primary metabolic events in the plant's economy ; it is beyond the scope of this simple exposition of secretory phenomena to discuss in detail the relations between these two processes ; the synthesised carbohydrate must be transported downwards to the roots, to provide energy for the absorption of salts ; since the flow of sap is upwards in the xylem, it is thought that the transport of glucose downwards takes place by way of the phloem cells. Thus Rabideau & Burr employed the isotope C^{13} to label the CO_2 absorbed by the leaves ; the labelled carbon was found in the stem-tip and roots, both metabolically active regions ; it failed to pass through killed areas of the stem, even though the xylem system was intact. The labelled carbon was presumably in the form of carbohydrate ; and we may conclude that the translocation of this material depends on an active transport mechanism mediated by the phloem cells. An upward transport of minerals through the phloem has been demonstrated by Gustafson. The studies of Stout & Hoagland on the migration of radioactive elements through the plant indicate, moreover, that salts may pass out laterally from the central conducting tubes, so that all cells have direct access to the salts accumulated by the roots. We have already indicated how transpiration can modify the flow of sap ; in the case of plants with normally low root pressure it may well be that transpiration plays the dominant role in circulation ; for example, Hoagland has shown that in a highly humid atmosphere no Br^- passes up the stem of the squash during one hour, this plant having a low root pressure. On the other hand the root pressure may, under certain circumstances, dominate the circulation ; this is well exemplified in the phenomenon of *guttation*, the exudation of a fluid from the leaves under conditions of high humidity ; placing the plant roots in distilled water, or in nutrient solution in the absence of O_2, causes the guttation to cease because, under these conditions, the secretion of salts into the xylem is inhibited. In this connection it is worth noting that Grossenbacher found a diurnal fluctuation in the root pressure of sunflowers, the maximal pressure being at mid-day and the minimum at about midnight, in spite of the fact that the plants were maintained continuously in the dark. Apparently the secretory activity of the cells has an inherent rhythmicity, the greatest activity occurring during maximal photosynthesis by the leaves (under normal conditions).

Active Transport of Ions by Yeast and Bacteria

Yeast. Pulver & Verzàr observed that K^+ migrated from the nutrient medium into yeast cells during the fermentation of sugar, and returned to the medium after the sugar has been used up. Rothstein & Enns have investigated this phenomenon in more detail. They showed that accumulation of K^+ was rapid, the concentration rising from a negligibly small value to nearly 120 meq./l. within forty minutes after the addition of glucose to the medium ; the external concentration of K^+ being 30 meq./l., there was a four-fold accumulation. The accumulation was not associated with the penetration of anions in significant quantities, so that an exchange of K^+, in the medium, for H^+, formed within the cell, was postulated and confirmed by the appearance of a marked acidity of the medium during fermentation, the amount of K^+ accumulated by the cells being approximately equal to the amount of acid appearing outside them. At least 25 per cent. of the acid turned out to be succinic acid ; when K^+ was present in the medium the H^+-ion of this acid merely exchanged with K^+, with the result that potassium succinate accumulated ; if the medium contained no salts, however, succinic acid diffused out of the cells, either as $H^+ + $ Succinate^{--} or as the undissociated acid. That the yeast is much more permeable to K^+- and H^+-ions than to anions is doubtless the cause of this accumulation ; thus if the rate of production of acid is measured, it is found to be rapid at first, as K^+ exchanges for H^+ ; when the limit of accumulation is reached, *i.e.*, when the concentration-ratio for K^+ is about 4 or less, the rate of development of acidity in the medium is reduced, since now organic acid must leave the cells.

After the glucose had been completely utilised, the accumulated K^+ began to return to the medium, and the acid to return to the cells ; however, a definite amount of K^+ remained accumulated, and this was apparently associated with the synthesis of carbohydrate by the yeast. Yeast does not break down all the glucose it absorbs, but stores as much as 18–31 per cent. as a polysaccharide. The greater the amount of polysaccharide formed, the greater was the retention of K^+ ; for every mole of glucose assimilated, one equivalent of K^+ being retained by the cells. During starvation the carbohydrate reserves are used up and the retained K^+ is liberated, 1·3 equivalents of retained K^+ being lost per mole of dissimilated glucose. This correspondence suggests that the retention of K$^+$ against a concentration gradient is due to its incorporation within the reserve carbohydrate molecule. This conclusion is supported by the observation of Hevesy & Nielsen that K^{42}, added to a yeast medium, will only exchange with the K^{39} in the yeast when carbohydrate is present, *i.e.*, when the cells are actively metabolising ; under these conditions the K^{42} is, presumably, incorporated into newly formed carbohydrate-potassium complexes whilst the K^{39} already present is released. The accumulation process, *per se*, however, does not demand this ; any cell, producing acid, and more permeable to K$^+$ and H$^+$ than to anions, must accumulate K$^+$ to some extent during the production of acid ; when this has ceased, the system must run down unless the K$^+$ is bound in some complex. The ability of yeast to utilise glucose, and to store carbohydrate, in the absence of K$^+$, however, shows that accumulation *per se* is not an obligatory function. It will be noted that these experiments were carried out in media containing K$^+$ as the only cation ; in pure Na-citrate, for example, the evidence suggested that the rate of appearance of acid in the medium was determined by the rate of migration of succinic and other organic acids, *i.e.*, that Na$^+$ could not replace K$^+$ as an ion exchangeable with H$^+$; thus in a mixture of Na$^+$ and K$^+$ salts, yeast would *preferentially* accumulate potassium.[1]

The most exhaustive study of the accumulation of K$^+$ by yeast cells is that of Conway and his colleagues, and they seem to have been the first to emphasise the high degree of acidity (*p*H as low as 1·4) that may be attained in the outside medium. They observed, in common with Rothstein & Enns, that when KCl was in the outside medium K$^+$ exchanged with H$^+$ almost quantitatively, whereas in the absence of KCl the external acidity was the result of the appearance of succinic acid which, according to Brady, is mostly pre-formed within the cells (at any rate that appearing outside during short-period fermentations). Thus in the absence of KCl we may say that succinic acid is excreted from the cells, whilst in its presence H$^+$-ions are excreted which exchange for K$^+$ in the outside medium. Conway & Brady (1950) observed that when yeast had been well oxygenated for some 24–48 hours before fermentation, the excretion of succinic acid was negligible, so that in the absence of KCl the development of external acidity was profoundly depressed ; in the presence of KCl the developed acidity was very high, and was associated with the appearance of large quantities of bicarbonate within the cells. A careful analysis showed that the amount of bicarbonate formed within the cell was equivalent to the acid appearing outside, *i.e.*, that essentially the excretion of each H$^+$-ion was accompanied by the fixation of one OH$^-$-ion

---

[1] The accumulation of K$^+$ in *Valonia* has been studied in great detail by Osterhout and his colleagues, who here assumed an essentially similar mechanism to operate as that actually found in yeast, *i.e.*, the continuous liberation of acid in the cell ; however, Osterhout assumed that K$^+$ penetrated as an undissociated complex with a membrane constituent, a mode of transport that gave it an advantage over Na$^+$ which, it was assumed, could not form a similar complex. Various models were built up, consisting of a layer of oil separating two aqueous solutions, the oil containing guaiacol, a substance with which K$^+$ combines ; accumulation was observed, as one would expect, but the mechanism was very inefficient. Brooks' studies with Rb$^+$ and radioactive isotopes show that the process is highly complex.

($CO_2 + OH^- \rightarrow HCO_3^-$). In the poorly oxygenated cells, therefore, the succinic acid neutralises the accumulated K^+ to give succinate, whereas in the well oxygenated cells this is achieved by carbonic acid. The process of accumulation was inhibited by azide—a poison specific for heavy-metal catalysts—and it was concluded that an enzyme of this type was responsible for the production of an organic acid which subsequently produced CO_2 or carbonic acid. Schematically the reaction could be written :

$$Ct^{++} + RH_2 \rightarrow Ct + R + 2H^+$$

the enzyme being reduced (*i.e.*, gaining electrons) by the hydrogen-donor, RH_2, with the liberation of two H^+-ions. If, now, the catalyst were re-oxidised it would be ready to form more H^+-ions :

$$Ct + R_1 + 2H^+ \rightarrow Ct^{++} + R_1H_2$$

We may note, however, that such a reversal of the original process would lead to the absorption of H^+-ions, *i.e.*, it would cancel the original acidity. Conway & Downey have brought forward convincing evidence, however, that the acidifying reactions of the yeast cell are confined to a peripheral region, constituting some 10 per cent. of the volume, and probably corresponding to the cell wall. If, now, the acidifying reaction occurred here whilst the subsequent reversal, involving absorption of H^+-ions (*i.e.*, the development of alkalinity) took place within the cytoplasm, the conditions for the continuous excretion of H^+-ions by the cyclical oxidation and reduction of a catalyst would be present. The H^+-ions, so formed, could exchange with K^+-ions in the external medium, if these were present, or could migrate in company with succinate ions. Since the accumulated K^+ is definitely not confined to the cell wall, but is found in the cytoplasm, it is considered by Conway that it is carried, possibly as a complex, into the cytoplasm by the catalyst ; again, when succinic acid is being excreted, it is considered that the acid is carried by the catalyst from the cytoplasm outwards. That some sort of active transfer must be invoked both for K^+ and succinate was shown by Conway & Downey, who found that in the non-fermenting cell succinate did not penetrate farther than the outer wall, *i.e.*, that the membrane separating the cytoplasm from the wall was impermeable to this substance. Again, Conway & Moore have shown that the penetration of K^+ into the resting cell is very slow compared with that taking place during fermentation. If Conway's thesis is correct, the accumulation of K^+ is not the simple result of the formation of acid within the cell, such as could be imitated by bubbling CO_2 into a solution separated from another solution by a membrane ; such a system would show an overall increase in acidity, due to the added CO_2, whereas on Conway's theory the acidity developed at the surface of the cell is accompanied by an alkalinity within it ; it is of great interest, therefore, that the cytoplasm does become alkaline and that, when the cells of a fermenting suspension are destroyed, the acidity of the medium is neutralised, the alkalinity of the cytoplasm just compensating the acidity developed by the excreted H^+-ions. As we shall see, the simultaneous formation of acid outside a cell, and alkali within it, as exemplified by yeast, bears a strong analogy to the secretion of acid by the gastric mucosa, a point emphasised by Conway & Brady in 1947.

In conclusion, we may note that it is highly probable that accumulation in yeast, as in many other cells, is intimately connected with glycolysis which, as we shall see (p. 501), involves a variety of phosphorylation reactions, whereby organic phosphates are formed and subsequently broken down.   Simultaneous studies of potassium and phosphorus exchanges have not been made, but Mullins has reported on the exchange of P^{32} with normal phosphorus within the yeast cell.   As with potassium, the exchange of P^{32} with its non-radioactive isotope depends critically on the presence of sugar in the medium, very little exchange occurring in the absence of this metabolite.   The exchange is sensitive to temperature and O_2-tension and, according to Lawrence, Erf & Tuttle, is inhibited by fluoride ; consequently we may presume that penetration of phosphate takes place to a significant extent only when phosphorylated derivatives of glucose are formed.   As with the accumulation of potassium, the amount of newly incorporated phosphorus passes through a maximum and then subsides to a lowlevel.

Accumulation by *Escherichia coli*.   Leibowitz & Kupermintz showed that *E. coli* accumulates K^+ rapidly during the fermentation of glucose ; as with yeast, the accumulation was not permanent, a loss of K^+ setting in before all the sugar was utilised, and the initial conditions being restored by the end of fermentation ; during the brief period in which the absorption of K^+ took place, the disappearance of glucose was far more rapid than the appearance of acid, so that storage as polysaccharide occurred, as in yeast. The accumulation of K^+ in *B. coli communis* was demonstrated very neatly by Ørskov ; he observed that, when the bacteria were well washed with NaCl solution, they could be made to shrink in hypertonic glucose ; this shrinkage was followed by a very gradual return to normal volume, which indicated that osmotically active material was slowly entering ; if K^+ was present in the medium the return to normal volume was very rapid, suggesting that this ion was being actively accumulated.   Similar results were obtained when the shrinkage was caused by a medium made up of hypertonic NaCl, so long as K^+ and glucose were present.   The evidence presented by Ørskov suggests that the accumulation of K^+ in these bacteria subserves the function of osmotic regulation, the accumulation being stimulated by the initial shrinkage of the cells.   Quite recently Cowie, Roberts & Roberts have reported on a study of *E. coli* in which they employed Na^{24} and K^{42} ; they have shown that the permeability to these ions is rapid, equilibrium being established within the time required to centrifuge the cells from their medium (five minutes).   When glucose was added to the medium, a rapid accumulation of K^+ took place, but in contrast with the Na^+-ions, some of the accumulated K^+ in the cells appeared to be bound, and inexchangeable with its radioactive isotope. Further studies by these authors (Roberts *et al.* 1949, 1950) have confirmed the existence of " bound potassium " in the cells ; apparently the cell, when given glucose, takes up K^+ at a very rapid initial rate ; after a time, a steady state is achieved, the newly incorporated K^+ being balanced by K^+ lost by diffusion out of the cell. It is not clear how the K^+ is bound, and all attempts at isolating a complex have so far failed ; evidence derived from paper chromatography suggests that the K^+ is bound as a hexose phosphate (Bolton, 1950). The demonstration that these bacteria are readily permeable to Na^+ makes it unlikely that accumulation of K^+ results merely from an exchange with internal H^+ ; some other factor, presumably the formation of the complex with K^+, must be concerned, otherwise Na^+ would accumulate too. We may note, finally, that the rate of growth of the bacteria studied by Roberts was markedly affected by a deficiency of K^+ in the medium, the rate of increase becoming linear instead of exponential ; apparently K^+ is necessary to permit the organic syntheses to take place in the bacterial cell, but so far the exact relationship between glucose metabolism and accumulation of K^+ has eluded discovery ; the fact that the effects of depletion of K^+ are more pronounced when the substrate is glucose than when it is lactate or pyruvate, suggests that K^+ is involved in one of the early steps in glycolysis (p. 501).

References

ABELSON, P. H. & DURYEE, W. R. (1949). " Na^{24} Permeability and Exchange in Frog Eggs." *Biol. Bull.*, **96**, 205.

ABRAMSON, H. A., GORIN, M. H. & PONDER, E. (1940). " Electrophoresis and the Chemistry of Cell Surfaces." *C.S.H. Symp.*, **8**, 72.

ABRAMSON, H. A., MOYER, L. S. & GORIN, M. H. (1942). " Electrophoresis of Proteins and the Chemistry of Cell Surfaces." New York, Reinhold.

ADAM, N. K. (1938). " The Physics and Chemistry of Surfaces." Oxford.

BEAR, R. S. & SCHMITT, F. O. (1939). " Electrolytes in the Axoplasm of the Giant Nerve Fibres of the Squid." *J. cell. & comp. Physiol.*, **14**, 205.

BEUTNER, R. (1944). " Bioelectricity." Medical Physics, Ed. Glasser. Chicago Year Bk. Pub. Co.

BLINKS, L. R. (1940). " The Relations of Bioelectric Potentials to Ionic Permeability and to Metabolism in Large Plant Cells." *C.S.H. Symp.*, **8**, 204.

BLINKS, L. R. & NIELSEN, J. P. (1940). " The Cell Sap of *Hydrodictyon*." *J. gen. Physiol.*, **23**, 551.

BOLTON, E. T. (1950). " Potassium Compounds Associated with Carbohydrate Metabolism of *Escherichia Coli*." *Fed. Proc.*, **9**, 153.

BOYLE, P. J. & CONWAY, E. J. (1941). " Potassium Accumulation in Muscle and Associated Changes." *J. Physiol.*, **100**, 1.

BRADY, T. G. (1948). " Succinic Acid in Yeast." *Biochem. J.*, **42**, lxi.

BROOKS, S. C. (1939). " Ion Exchanges in Accumulation and Loss of Certain Ions by the Living Protoplasm of *Nitella*." *J. cell. & comp. Physiol.*, **14**, 383.

BROOKS, S. C. (1940). " The Intake of Radioactive Isotopes by Living Cells." *C.S.H. Symp.*, **8**, 171.

BROYER, T. C. & HOAGLAND, D. R. (1943). " Metabolic Activities of Roots and Their Bearing on the Relation of Upward Movement of Salts and Water in Plants." *Amer. J. Bot.*, **30**, 261.

CAUSEY, G. & HARRIS, E. J. (1951). " Uptake and Loss of Phosphate by Frog Muscle." *Biochem. J.* (in press).

COHN, W. E. & COHN, E. T. (1939). " Permeability of Red Corpuscles of the Dog to Sodium Ions." *P.S.E.B.M.*, **41**, 445.

COLE, K. S. (1940). " Permeability and Impermeability of Cell Membranes for Ions." *C.S.H. Symp.*, **8**, 110.

CONWAY, E. J. (1945). " The Physiological Significance of Inorganic Levels in the Internal Medium of Animals." *Biol. Rev.*, **20**, 56.

CONWAY, E. J. (1946). " Ionic Permeability of Skeletal Muscle Fibres." *Nature*, **157** 715.

CONWAY, E. J. (1949). " Biological Interlinkage of Acid-Alkali Formation with Ion Transport and Synthetic Reduction." *Irish J. med. Sci.*, **288**, 787.

CONWAY, E. J. & BRADY, T. (1947). " Mechanism of High Acid Production by Yeast and its Bearing on HCl Formation in the Stomach." *Nature*, **159**, 137.

CONWAY, E. J. & BRADY, T. G. (1950). " Quantitative Relations of Succinic and Carbonic Acids to the Potassium and Hydrogen Ion Exchange in Fermenting Yeast." *Biochem. J.*, **47**, 360.

CONWAY, E. J., BRADY, T. G. & CARTON, E. (1950). " Biological Production of Acid and Alkali. Redox Theory for the Process in Yeast with Application to the Production of Gastric Acidity." *Biochem. J.*, **47**, 369.

CONWAY, E. J. & BREEN, J. (1945). " An ' Ammonia-Yeast ' and Some of its Properties." *Biochem. J.*, **39**, 368.

CONWAY, E. J. & DOWNEY, M. (1950). " An Outer Metabolic Region of the Yeast Cell." *Biochem. J.*, **47**, 347.

CONWAY, E. J. & DOWNEY, M. (1950). " pH Values of the Yeast Cell." *Biochem. J.*, **47**, 355.

CONWAY, E. J. & FEARON, P. J. (1944). " The Acid-Labile CO_2 in Mammalian Muscle and the pH of the Muscle Fibre." *J. Physiol.*, **103**, 274.

CONWAY, E. J., FITZGERALD, O. & MACDOUGALD, T. C. (1946). " K Accumulation in the Proximal Convoluted Tubules of the Frog's Kidney." *J. gen. Physiol.*, **29**, 305.

CONWAY, E. J. & HINGERTY, D. (1948). " Relations between K^+ and Na^+ Levels in Mammalian Muscle and Blood Plasma." *Biochem. J.*, **42**, 372.

CONWAY, E. J. & MOORE, P. T. (1950). " The Azide Effect in Yeast with respect to Potassium and Phosphate Permeability." *Biochem. J.*, **47**, iii.

CONWAY, E. J. & O'MALLEY, E. (1946). " The Nature of the Cation Exchange during Yeast Fermentation with Formation of 0·02 N H-Ion." *Biochem. J.*, **40**, 59.

COWAN, S. L. (1934). " Action of Potassium and Other Ions on Injury Potential and Action Currents in *Maia* Nerve." *Proc. Roy. Soc.*, B, **115**, 216.

COWIE, D. B., ROBERTS, R. B. & ROBERTS, I. Z. (1949). " Potassium Metabolism in *Escherichia Coli*. I. Permeability to Na and K Ions." *J. cell. & comp. Physiol.*, **34**, 243.

CRAFTS, A. S. & BROYER, T. C. (1938). " Migration of Salts and Water into Xylem of the Roots of Higher Plants." *Amer. J. Bot.*, **25**, 529.

CURTIS, H. J. & COLE, K. S. (1942). " Membrane Resting and Action Potentials in Giant Fibres of Squid Nerve." *J. cell. & comp. Physiol.*, **19**, 135.

DANOWSKI, T. S. (1941). " The Transfer of Potassium Across the Human Blood Cell Membrane." *J. biol. Chem.*, **139**, 693.

DAVSON, H. (1941). " The Effect of some Metabolic Poisons on the Permeability of the Rabbit Erythrocyte to Potassium." *J. cell. & comp. Physiol.*, **18**, 173.

DAVSON, H. (1942). " The Hæmolytic Action of Potassium Salts." *J. Physiol.*, **101**, 265.

DAVSON, H. & DANIELLI, J. F. (1936). " Alleged Reversal of Ionic Permeability at Alkaline Reaction." *Biochem. J.*, **30**, 316.

DAVSON, H. & DANIELLI, J. F. (1938). " Studies on the Permeability of Erythrocytes. V. Factors in Cation Permeability." *Biochem. J.*, **32**, 991.

DAVSON, H. & DANIELLI, J. F. (1943). " The Permeability of Natural Membranes." Cambridge. C.U.P.

DAVSON, H. & PONDER, E. (1940). " Photodynamically Induced Cation Permeability and its Relation to Hæmolysis." *J. cell. & comp. Physiol.*, **15**, 67.

DAVSON, H. & SHAPIRO, H. (1941). " Permeability of the *Arbacia* Egg to K." *Biol. Bull.*, **81**, 295.

DEAN, R. B. (1941). " Theories of Electrolyte Equilibria in Muscle." *Biol. Symp.*, **3**, 331.

DEGOWIN, E. L., HARRIS, J. E. & PLASS, E. D. (1940). " Studies on Preserved Human Blood. II. Diffusion of Potassium from the Erythrocytes during Storage." *J.A.M.A.*, **114**, 855.

FARMER, S. N. & MAIZELS, M. (1939). " Organic Anions of Human Erythrocytes." *Biochem. J.*, **32**, 280.

FENN, W. O., COBB, D. M., HEGNAUER, A. H. & MARSH, B. S. (1934). " Electrolytes in Nerve." *Amer. J. Physiol.*, **110**, 74.

FENN, W. O., NOONAN, T. R., MULLINS, L. J. & HAEGE, L. (1941). " The Exchange of K^{42} with Body K^{39}." *Amer. J. Physiol.*, **135**, 149.

FERREBEE, J. W., PARKER, D., CARNES, W. H., GERITY, M. K., ATCHLEY, D. W. & LOEB, R. F. (1941). " Certain Effects of Desoxycorticosterone. The Development of ' Diabetes Insipidus ' and the Replacement of Muscle Potassium by Sodium in Normal Dogs." *Amer. J. Physiol.*, **135**, 230.

FLYNN, F. & MAIZELS, M. (1949). " Cation Control in Human Erythrocytes." *J. Physiol.*, 110, 201.

FRIEDENWALD, J. S. & STIEHLER, R. D. (1938). " A Mechanism of Secretion of the Intra-Ocular Fluid." *Arch. Ophth.*, 20, 761.

GOFFART, M. & PERRY, L. M. (1951). " Action of Adrenaline on the Rate of Loss of K from Unfatigued Striated Muscle." *J. Physiol.*, 112, 95.

GRAHAM, J. & GERARD, R. W. (1946). " Membrane Potentials and Excitation of Impaled Single Muscle Fibres." *J. cell. & comp. Physiol.*, 28, 99.

GREENBERG, D. M., JOSEPH, M., COHN, W. E. & TUFTS, E. V. (1938). " Studies on the K Metabolism of the Animal Body by Means of K⁴²." *Science*, 87, 438.

GROSSENBACHER, K. A. (1938). " Diurnal Fluctuations in Root Pressure." *Plant Physiol.*, 13, 669.

GUSTAFSON, F. G. (1939). " Upward Transport of Minerals through the Phloem of Stems." *Science*, 90, 306.

HAHN, L. & HEVESY, G. (1941). " Potassium Exchange in the Stimulated Muscle." *Acta Physiol. Scand.*, 2, 51.

HAHN, L. A., HEVESY, G. C. & REBBE, O. H. (1939). " Do the Potassium Ions Inside Muscle Cells and Blood Corpuscles Exchange with those present in the Plasma? " *Biochem. J.*, 33, 1549.

HARRIS, E. J. (1950). " Transfer of Na⁺ and K⁺ between Muscle and Surrounding Medium. II. The Na⁺ Flux." *Trans. Farad. Soc.*, 46, 872.

HARRIS, E. J. & BURN, G. P. (1949). " The Transfer of Na⁺ and K⁺ between Muscle and Surrounding Medium." *Trans. Farad. Soc.*, 45, 508.

HARRIS, E. J. & MAIZELS, M. (1951). " Permeability of Human Erythrocytes to Na." *J. Physiol.* (in press).

HARRIS, J. E. (1940). " The Reversible Nature of the Potassium Loss from Erythrocytes during Storage of Blood at 2–5° C." *Biol. Bull.*, 79, 373.

HARRIS, J. E. (1941). " The Influence of the Metabolism of Human Erythrocytes on their Potassium Content." *J. biol. Chem.*, 141, 579.

HAWKINS, W. B. & WHIPPLE, G. H. (1938). " Life Cycle of the Erythrocyte in the Dog." *Amer. J. Physiol.*, 122, 418.

HENRIQUES, V. & ØRSKOV, S. L. (1936). " Die Änderung der Kaliumkonzentration in den Blutkörperchen nach einem Aderlass, nach Vergiftung mit Phenylhydrazin und nach Einführung von destillierten Wasser in die Blutbahn." *Scand. Arch. Physiol.*, 74, 63.

HENRIQUES, V. & ØRSKOV, S. L. (1936). " Änderung des Kaliumgehalts der Blutkörperchen bei Bleivergiftung." *Scand. Arch. Physiol.*, 74, 78.

HEPPEL, L. A. (1939). " The Electrolytes of Muscle and Liver in Potassium-Depleted Rats." *Amer. J. Physiol.*, 127, 385.

HEPPEL, L. A. (1940). " The Diffusion of Na²⁴ into the Muscles of Potassium-Deprived Rats." *Amer. J. Physiol.*, 128, 449.

HEVESY, G. (1941). " Potassium Interchange in the Human Body." *Acta Physiol. Scand.*, 3, 123.

HEVESY, G. & NIELSEN, N. (1941). " Potassium Interchange in Yeast Cells." *Acta Physiol. Scand.*, 2, 347.

HEVESY, G. & REBBE, O. (1940). " Rate of Penetration of Phosphate into Muscle Cells." *Acta Physiol. Scand.*, 1, 171.

HILL, A. V. & KUPALOV P. S. (1930). " The Vapour Pressure of Muscle." *Proc. Roy. Soc. B*, 106, 445.

HOAGLAND, D. R. (1940). " Salt Accumulation by Plant Cells with Special Reference to Metabolism and Experiments on Barley Roots." *C.S.H. Symp.*, 8, 181.

HOAGLAND, D. R. (1944). " Lectures on the Inorganic Nutrition of Plants." Waltham, Mass Chronica Botanica.

HOAGLAND, D. R. & BROYER, T. C. (1942). " Accumulation of Salt and Permeability in Plant Roots." *J. gen. Physiol.*, 25, 865.

HOAGLAND, D. R. & MARTIN, J. C. (1935). " Absorption of K⁺ by Plants and Fixation by the Soil in Relation to Certain Methods of Estimating Available Nutrients." *Trans. 3rd Int. Congr. Soil Sci.*, 1, 99.

HÖBER, R. (1945). " Physical Chemistry of Cells and Tissues." Philadelphia. Blakiston; London, Churchill.

HÖBER, R., ANDERSH, M., HÖBER, J. & NEBEL, B. (1939). " Influence of Organic Electrolytes and Non-Electrolytes on the Membrane Potential of Muscle and Nerve." *J. cell. & comp. Physiol.*, 13, 195.

HODGKIN, A. L. & HUXLEY, A. F. (1945). " Resting and Action Potentials in Single Nerve Fibres." *J. Physiol.*, 104, 176.

HOPKINS, D. L. (1946). " The Contractile Vacuole and the Adjustment to Changing Concentrations in Fresh Water *Amoebae*." *Biol. Bull.*, 90, 158.

HUXLEY, A. F. & STÄMPFLI, R. (1951). " Direct Determination of Membrane Resting Potential and Action Potential in Single Myelinated Nerve Fibres." *J. Physiol.*, **112**, 476.

HUXLEY, A. F. & STÄMPFLI, R. (1951). " Effect of K+ and Na+ on Resting and Action Potentials of Single Myelinated Nerve Fibres." *J. Physiol.*, **112**, 496.

JACOBS, M. H. & PARPART, A. K. (1931). " Influence of pH, Temperature and O₂-Tension on Hæmolysis by Hypotonic Solutions." *Biol. Bull.*, **60**, 95.

JACOBS, M. H. & PARPART, A. K. (1933). " Influence of the Escape of Salts on Hæmolysis by Hypotonic Solutions." *Biol. Bull.*, **65**, 512.

JACOBS, M. H. & STEWART, D. R. (1947). " Ionic and Osmotic Equilibria with a Complex External Solution." *J. cell. & comp. Physiol.*, **30**, 79.

JACOBS, M. H. & WILLIS, M. (1947). " Preparation and Properties of Cation-Permeable Erythrocytes." *Biol. Bull.*, **93**, 223.

JACOBSON, L. & OVERSTREET, R. (1947). " A Study of the Mechanism of Ion Absorption by Plant Roots using Radioactive Elements." *Amer. J. Bot.*, **34**, 415.

JENNY, H. & OVERSTREET, R. (1939). " Cation Interchange between Plant Roots and Soil Colloids." *Soil Science*, **47**, 257.

KEYNES, R. D. (1948). " Leakage of K⁴² from Stimulated Nerve." *J. Physiol.*, **107**, 35P.

KEYNES, R. D. (1949). " Movements of Na²⁴ during Nervous Activity." *J. Physiol.*, **109**, 13P.

KEYNES, R. D. (1949). " Movements of Radioactive Ions in Resting and Stimulated Nerve." *Arch. des Sci. Physiol.*, **3**, 165.

KROGH, A. (1943). " The Uptake of Potassium into the Chorionic Membrane from the Hen's Egg." *Acta Physiol. Scand.*, **6**, 203.

KROGH, A. (1946). " The Active and Passive Exchanges of Inorganic Ions through the Surfaces of Living Cells and through Living Membranes Generally." Croonian Lecture. *Proc. Roy. Soc.*, B, **133**, 140.

LAWRENCE, J. H., ERF, L. A. & TUTTLE, L. W. (1941). " Intracellular Radiation." *J. app. Physics*, **12**, 333.

LEIBOWITZ, J. & KUPERMINTZ, N. (1942). " Potassium in Bacterial Fermentation." *Nature*, **150**, 233.

LEVI, H. & USSING, H. H. (1948). " The Exchange of Na+- and Cl⁻-Ions Across the Fibre Membrane of the Isolated Frog Sartorius." *Acta Physiol. Scand.*, **16**, 232.

LING, G. & GERARD, R. W. (1949). " The Normal Membrane Potential of Frog Sartorius Fibres." *J. cell. & comp. Physiol.*, **34**, 383.

LING, G. & GERARD, R. W. (1949). " The Influence of Stretch on the Membrane Potential of Frog Muscle Fibres." *J. cell. & comp. Physiol.*, **34**, 397.

LING, G. & GERARD, R. W. (1950). " External K+ and the Membrane Potential of Single Muscle Fibres." *Nature*, **165**, 113.

LING, G. & WOODBURY, J. W. (1949). " Effect of Temperature on the Membrane Potential of Frog Muscle Fibres." *J. cell. & comp. Physiol.*, **34**, 407.

LUNDEGÅRDH, H. (1944). " Bleeding and Sap Movement." *Ark. Bot.*, **31A**, 97.

LUNDEGÅRDH, H. & BURSTRÖM, H. (1933). " Untersuchungen u. d. Salzaufnahme der Pflanzen. III. Quantitative Beziehungen zwischen Atmung u. Anionenaufnahme." *Biochem. Z.*, **261**, 235.

LUNDEGÅRDH, H., & BURSTRÖM, H. (1935 and 1937). " Untersuchungen u. d. Atmungsvorgänge in Pflanzenwurzeln." *Biochem. Z.*, **277**, 223 ; **290**, 104.

LYMAN, R. A. (1945). " The Anti-Hæmolytic Function of Calcium in the Blood of the Snapping Turtle, *Chelydra Serpentina*." *J. cell. & comp. Physiol.*, **25**, 65.

MACVICAR, R. & BURRIS, R. H. (1939). " Translocation Studies in Tomato using Ammonium Sulphate Labelled with N¹⁵." *Amer. J. Bot.*, **26**, 567.

MAIZELS, M. (1949). " Cation Control in Human Erythrocytes." *J. Physiol.*, **108**, 247.

MAIZELS, M. (1951). " Factors in the Active Transport of Cations." *J. Physiol.*, **112**, 59.

MANERY, J. F. (1939). " Electrolytes in Squid Blood and Muscle." *J. cell. & comp. Physiol.*, **14**, 365.

MICHAELIS, L. (1925). " Contribution to the Theory of Permeability of Membranes for Electrolytes." *J. gen. Physiol.*, **8**, 33.

MULLINS, L. J. (1942). " The Permeability of Yeast Cells to P³²." *Biol. Bull.*, **83**, 326.

MULLINS, L. J., FENN, W. O., NOONAN, T. R. & HAEGE, L. (1941). " Permeability of Erythrocytes to K⁴²." *Amer. J. Physiol.*, **135**, 93.

NASTUK, W. L. & HODGKIN, A. L. (1950). " The Electrical Activity in Single Muscle Fibres." *J. cell. & comp. Physiol.*, **35**, 39.

NOONAN, T. R., FENN, W. O. & HAEGE, L. (1941). " The Distribution of Injected K⁴² in Rats." *Amer. J. Physiol.*, **132**, 474.

ØRSKOV, S. L. (1945). "Investigations on the Permeability of Yeast Cells." *Acta path. et microbiol. Scand.*, 22, 523.

ØRSKOV, S. L. (1948). "Experiments on Active and Passive Permeability of *Bacillus Coli Communis*." *Acta path. et microbiol. Scand.*, 25, 277.

OSTERHOUT, W. J. V. (1931). "Physiological Studies of Single Plant Cells." *Biol. Rev.*, 6, 369.

OVERSTREET, R. & JACOBSON, L. (1946). "The Absorption by Roots of Rubidium and Phosphate Ions at Extremely Small Concentrations as Revealed by Experiments with Rb[86] and P[32] Prepared without Inert Carrier." *Amer. J. Bot.*, 33, 107.

PONDER, E. (1947). "Prolytic Loss of K from Red Cells." *J. gen. Physiol.*, 30, 235.

PONDER, E. (1947). "K-Na Exchange Accompanying Prolytic Loss of K from Human Red Cells." *J. gen. Physiol.*, 30, 479.

PONDER, E. (1948). "Hæmolysis and Related Phenomena." New York, Grune & Stratton ; London, Churchill.

PONDER, E. (1950). "Accumulation of Potassium by Human Red Cells." *J. gen. Physiol.*, 33, 745.

PULVER, R. & VERZÁR, F. (1940). "Connexion between Carbohydrate and K Metabolism in the Yeast Cell." *Nature*, 145, 823.

RABIDEAU, G. S. & BURR, G. O. (1945). "The Use of C[13] Isotope as a Tracer for Transport Studies in Plants." *Amer. J. Bot.*, 32, 349.

RAKER, J. W., TAYLOR, I. M., WELLER, J. M. & HASTINGS, A. B. (1950). "Rate of Potassium Exchange of the Human Erythrocyte." *J. gen. Physiol.*, 33, 691.

ROBERTS, I. Z. (1950). "Role of Potassium in Cellular Metabolism." *Fed. Proc.*, 9, 219.

ROBERTS, R. B. & ROBERTS, I. Z. (1950). "Potassium Metabolism in *Escherichia Coli*. III. Interrelationship of Potassium and Phosphorus Metabolism." *J. cell. & comp. Physiol.*, 36, 15.

ROBERTS, R. B., ROBERTS, I. Z. & COWIE, D. B. (1949). "Potassium Metabolism in *Escherichia Coli*. Metabolism in the Presence of Carbohydrates and their Metabolic Derivatives." *J. cell. & comp. Physiol.*, 34, 259.

ROTHENBERG, M. A. (1950). "Ionic Movements Across Axonal Membranes." *Biochim. Biophys. Acta*, 4, 96.

ROTHENBERG, M. A. & FELD, E. A. (1948). "Rate of Penetration of Electrolytes into Nerve Fibres." *J. biol. Chem.*, 172, 345.

ROTHSTEIN, A. & ENNS, L. H. (1946). "The Relation of Potassium to Carbohydrate Metabolism in Baker's Yeast." *J. cell. & comp. Physiol.*, 28, 231.

ROTHSTEIN, A. & MEIER, R. (1948). "Phosphatases in the Cell Surface of Living Yeast Cells." *J. cell. & comp. Physiol.*, 32, 77.

ROUS, P. (1925). "Relative Reaction within Living Mammalian Tissues." *J. exp. Med.*, 41, 739.

SACKS, J. (1940). "P[32] as a Tracer in Anaerobic Muscular Contraction." *Amer. J. Physiol.*, 129, 227.

SACKS, J. & ALTSHULER, C. H. (1942). "P[32] Studies on Striate and Cardiac Muscle Metabolism." *Amer. J. Physiol.*, 137, 750.

SCHMITT, F. O., BEAR, R. S. & SILBER, R. H. (1939). "Organic and Inorganic Electrolytes in Lobster Nerves." *J. cell. & comp. Physiol.*, 14, 351.

SHANES, A. M. (1946). "A Neglected Factor in Studies on Potassium Distribution in Relation to the Resting Potential of Nerve." *J. cell. & comp. Physiol.*, 27, 115.

SHEPPARD, C. W. & MARTIN, W. R. (1950). "Cation Exchange between Cells and Plasma of Mammalian Blood. I." *J. gen. Physiol.*, 33, 703.

SILBER, R. H. (1941). "The Free Amino-Acids of Lobster Nerve." *J. cell. & comp. Physiol.*, 18, 21.

SILBER, R. H. & SCHMITT, F. O. (1940). "The Role of Free Amino-Acids in the Electrolyte Balance of Nerve." *J. cell. & comp. Physiol.*, 16, 247.

SOLOMON, R. Z., HALD, P. M. & PETERS, J. P. (1940). "State of the Inorganic Components of Human Red Blood Corpuscles." *J. biol. Chem.*, 132, 723.

SPIEGELMAN, S. & REINER, J. M. (1942). "A Kinetic Analysis of Potassium Accumulation and Sodium Exclusion." *Growth*, 6, 367.

STEINBACH, H. B. (1940). "Electrolyte Balance of Animal Cells." *C.S.H. Symp.*, 8, 242.

STEINBACH, H. B. (1941). "Chloride in the Giant Axons of the Squid." *J. cell. & comp. Physiol.*, 17, 57.

STEINBACH, H. B. & SPIEGELMAN, S. (1943). "The Na and K Balance in Squid Nerve Axoplasm." *J. cell. & comp. Physiol.*, 22, 187.

STEWARD, F. C. (1935). "Mineral Nutrition of Plants." *Ann. Rev. Biochem.*, 4, 519.

STEWARD, F. C., PREVOT, P. & HARRISON, J. A. (1942). "The Absorption and Accumulation of RbBr by Barley Plants. The Localisation in the Root of Cation Accumulation and of Transfer to the Shoot." *Plant Physiol.*, 17, 411.

Stout, P. R. & Hoagland, D. R. (1939).   " Upward and Lateral Movement of Salts in Certain Plants as Indicated by K^{42}, Na^{24}, & P^{32} Absorbed by Roots." *Amer. J. Bot.*, **26**, 320.

Ting, T. P. & Zirkle, R. E. (1940).   " The Nature and Cause of the Hæmolysis Caused by X-Rays." *J. cell. & comp. Physiol.*, **16**, 189.

Ting, T. P. & Zirkle, R. E. (1940).   " The Kinetics of the Diffusion of Salts Into and Out of X-Irradiated Erythrocytes." *J. cell. & comp. Physiol.*, **16**, 197.

Ussing, H. H. (1947).   " Interpretation of the Exchange of Na^{24} in Isolated Muscle." *Nature*, **160**, 262.

Ussing, H. H. (1949).   " Transport of Ions Across Cellular Membranes." *Physiol. Rev.*, **29**, 127.

Ussing, H. H. (1949).   " The Active Ion Transport through the Isolated Frog Skin in the Light of Tracer Studies." *Acta Physiol. Scand.*, **17**, 1.

Van Slyke, D. D. (1926).   " Factors Affecting the Distribution of Electrolytes, Water, and Gases in the Animal Body." Philadelphia, Lippincott.

White, P. R. (1938).   " ' Root Pressure '—an Unappreciated Force in Sap Movement." *Amer. J. Bot.*, **25**, 223.

Wilbrandt, W. (1937).   " Effect of Organic Ions on the Membrane Potential of Nerve." *J. gen. Physiol.*, **20**, 519.

Wilbrandt, W. (1941).   " Osmotische Natur sogenannter nicht osmotischer Hämolysen (Kolloidosmotische Hämolyse)." *Pflüg. Arch.*, **245**, 22.

Willis, M., Love, W. E. & Jacobs, M. H. (1947).   " Observations on the Hæmolytic Action of Sodium Taurocholate." *Biol. Bull.*, **93**, 202.

Wilson, D. L. & Manery, J. F. (1948).   " Na, K and Cl in Leucocytes." *Fed. Proc.*, **7**, 135.

Wilson, D. L. & Manery, J. F. (1949).   " Permeability of Rabbit Leucocytes to Na, K and Cl." *J. cell. & comp. Physiol.*, **34**, 493.

Young, J. Z. (1939).   " Fused Neurons and Synaptic Contacts in the Giant Nerve Fibres of Cephalopods." *Phil. Trans.*, **229**, 465.

CHAPTER XII

ABSORPTION FROM THE INTESTINE

THE main site of intake of exogenous material is the gut, which serves to digest the material into a form suitable for its subsequent *absorption* into the blood ; it is this aspect of intestinal function with which we shall be concerned here, since in this organ the processes of active transport are highly developed, in regard to both dissolved material and water. The intestine [1] is lined with epithelium, the surface of which is considerably enlarged by minute prolongations of the mucous membrane, 0·5–1·5 mm. long, being most numerous in the upper segments (nearest the stomach), namely the duodenum and jejunum where there are some 20–40 per sq. mm. These *villi* are composite organs, as Fig. 137 shows, containing, besides a net-work of capillaries derived from vessels passing through the muscular layers of the intestine, a lymph capillary, or *lacteal*, which begins under the epithelium covering the tip of the villus and leads into a lymphatic plexus which gathers up the lymph from many villi ; the lymph so collected is carried in larger trunks with the mesenteric blood vessels to the retroperitoneal tissue. The distal end of the lymph capillary (nearest the epithelium) is closed, as in other parts of the body. Absorption from the intes-

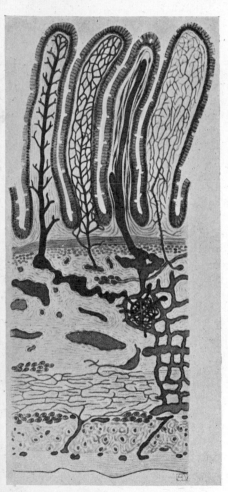

FIG. 137. Semi-diagrammatic section of small intestine. Four villi are shown illustrating, from left to right, the venous, arterial, lymphatic and nervous supplies. (Verzár & McDougall, after Schaffer. *Absorption from the Intestine.* Longmans, London.)

[1] The experiments described in this chapter relate to the *small intestine*, consisting of the duodenum, jejunum and ileum, as opposed to the *large intestine*, or *colon*. We may note that there is little or no absorption of sugars from the large intestine (Davidson & Garry, 1939).

tine is possible either by a direct migration across the epithelium into the blood capillaries or, alternatively, by migration across the epithelium into the lacteal. The absorption of fat would appear to be predominantly by the latter route. In this connection we may note that, as a result of the periodic contraction of the gut wall—which must periodically dam the blood back in the veins thereby raising the capillary pressure—there will be a vigorous turn-over of interstitial fluid ; moreover, the individual villi are contractile, so that a rhythmical shortening of these organs doubtless promotes flow of lymph along the lacteals.[1]

It has been known for many years that, if an animal's own blood plasma is placed in a loop of its small intestine, the plasma is completely absorbed into the blood stream (Voit & Bauer ; Heidenhain) ; similarly a Ringer solution of approximately the same salt concentration as that in plasma is rapidly absorbed. The existence of an active transport mechanism to explain this absorption need not necessarily be invoked, since it is possible that the proteins of autogenous serum are first broken down to diffusible amino-acids ; as a result, the colloid osmotic pressure of the plasma, circulating in the gut capillaries, will be greater than that of the intestinal fluid and this will result, as we have seen, in the migration of the fluid from gut to plasma.[2] Recent work on the absorption of the specific constituents of the intestinal content, such as sugars, salts and water has, however, revealed the unequivocal presence of very efficient absorbing mechanisms.

Absorption of Water and Salts

Studies with classical chemical techniques have established that water and a large variety of univalent ions may migrate from blood into the intestinal lumen and in the reverse direction ; thus, on placing water into the intestine, Na^+, Cl^+ and HCO_3^- pass first from blood to gut, so that, within ten minutes after placing water in the stomach of the rat, Follansbee found that the fluid withdrawn from the gut was isosmotic with blood. Again, on placing hypertonic solutions into the gut, water passes first from blood to gut. Consequently we may state that there is no absolutely irreciprocal permeability in the direction of gut-to-blood, as has sometimes been suggested. Specific absorptive processes are therefore the result of accelerated movement of one or more ions in the gut-to-blood direction ; the active absorption of water could be due to the same phenomenon, but before deciding that such a mechanism exists we must be sure that the

---

[1] There seems to be some uncertainty on this point ; thus Wells & Johnson deny that shortening of the villi empties the lacteals ; Schmidt-Nielsen, however, makes the contrary assertion.

[2] This suggestion was made by Starling ; it has been supported more recently by Wells, who studied the pressures within the intestine required to prevent absorption ; these pressures were of course negative, i.e., suctional, and could be simply expressed in terms of the colloid osmotic pressure of the plasma ; he also showed that absorption was apparently preceded by an œdematous condition of the villi due to vascular engorgement ; only when this engorgement had subsided was absorption considered to take place. Thus Wells considers that the first stage of absorption is an exudation from the capillaries into the tissue spaces of the mucosa ; the material in the gut comes into diffusion equilibrium with this exudate, and only later is absorbed. For many interesting details the reader is referred to the original papers ; however, the main contention of Wells is not substantiated by the great bulk of recent work.

water really is migrating from a region of lower chemical potential to one of higher. Thus if Na^+ or Cl^- were to be actively transported from a NaCl solution in the gut, the osmotic pressure of the latter would fall and water would pass out into the blood in conformity with the demands of osmotic equilibrium. Nevertheless, some fifty years ago, Heidenhain observed that, although he placed hypertonic solutions in the gut and these solutions tended towards isotonicity, there was absorption of the solutions while they were still hypertonic ; clearly the solutions were approaching isotonicity because salt was being absorbed more rapidly than water, but water was passing from gut to blood against a difference of osmotic pressure working in the opposite direction.

Absorption of Autogenous Serum. The processes taking place when autogenous serum is absorbed have been analysed in some detail by Visscher ; the concentrations of various ions in the fluid before, and forty

TABLE XXIV

Changes in Composition of Autogenous Serum placed in Gut.
(Visscher, Roepke & Lifson, 1945.)

	Cl^-	Na^+	pH	CO_2	Osmotic Activity	Volume
Initial Concentration . .	110	154	7·4	27	159	100
Concentration after 40 min.	74	144	7·4	47	145	66

minutes after, the serum was placed in the gut are shown in Table XXIV ; it will be seen that in this time 34 per cent. of the fluid was absorbed and that there was a significant fall in concentration of salt, so that the osmotic pressure fell ; the solution thus became hypotonic by some 12·8 mM/l. in respect to plasma, a result that could not have been achieved by the hydrolysis of the proteins, followed by absorption as an isosmotic solution. Poisoning the intestine with $HgCl_2$ inhibited most of the changes and actually caused the volume of the serum in the intestine to increase.

Absorption of Salt Mixtures. The unequivocal demonstration of active transport of salts has been largely due to the studies of Visscher and his school. Visscher showed that, if a mixture of equal parts of isotonic solutions of NaCl and Na_2SO_4 is placed in the dog's small intestine, the solution is rapidly impoverished of Cl^-, so that eventually there may be a 200-fold difference between the concentrations of this ion in blood and intestine. The phenomenon is due to the presence of SO_4^{--}, which is not absorbed to any great extent, with the result that the active removal of NaCl, even if associated with an isosmotic removal of water, causes a decrease in concentration of Cl^-. The course of the changes in concentration of various ions in the gut is shown in Fig. 138 ; the concentration of SO_4^{--} tends to rise, since it is not appreciably absorbed, whilst water is being lost ; the concentration of Na^+ tends to remain the same at first, indicating that most of the Cl^- is taken up as isotonic NaCl. Replacement of Na^+ with K^+, *i.e.*, placing a mixture of isotonic KCl and K_2SO_4 in the gut, gave a similar impoverishment of Cl^- ; here, however, there is a strong concentration gradient of K^+ in the gut-to-blood direction ; and the concentration of this ion falls, as a result of exchange with Na^+ in the plasma. Poisoning the gut with $HgCl_2$, arsenite or fluoride completely inhibits the impoverishment of chloride, thus confirming that the process involves secretory activity (Fig. 138). In parenthesis it should be noted that the presence of the relatively indiffusible SO_4^{--} in the gut creates

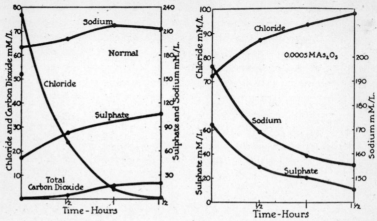

FIG. 138. Showing changes in concentration of Na^+, Cl^-, SO_4^{--}, and total CO_2 in ileum of dog after insertion of an isotonic mixture of NaCl and Na_2SO_4. Left : Normal intestine. Right : Intestine poisoned with arsenite. (Ingraham & Visscher. *Amer. J. Physiol.*)

a temporary Gibbs-Donnan distribution of diffusible ions ; if this were the only factor governing the distribution we should have :—

$$[Na^+]_{In} \times [Cl^-]_{In} = [Na^+]_{Out} \times [Cl^-]_{Out}$$

the concentration of Na^+ in the gut being higher than the concentration in the plasma, and the concentration of Cl^- lower. However, the extremely low concentration of Cl^- in the gut cannot be accounted for in this simple manner ; thus the product in the plasma was : 149×112 mM/l., whilst after one and a half hours, in one experiment, the product in the intestinal fluid was : $229 \times 1 \cdot 8$ mM/l. The system was clearly not in equilibrium, and the absorption of Cl^- was definitely from a region of lower to higher chemical potential ; nevertheless the higher concentration of Na^+ in the gut than in the plasma may have been due, in part, to this Gibbs-Donnan type of distribution.

That the active absorptive process is not confined to anions, but is also exhibited in respect to Na^+, is shown by the use of mixtures of NaCl and $MgCl_2$, the Mg^{++}-ion being, like SO_4^{--}, relatively slowly absorbed ; under these conditions the concentration of Na^+ falls progressively, to give a final concentration in the region of 5 mM/l. compared with 139 mM/l. in the plasma. The concentration of Cl^-, now initially much higher than that in the blood, falls with the absorption of Na^+ but not appreciably below the level in the blood. Finally, in a mixture of NaCl and $MgSO_4$ there was impoverishment both of Na^+ and Cl^- in relation to the plasma level, the $MgSO_4$ being largely retained, whilst the NaCl was actively absorbed.

Roughly, the three main conditions may be represented by Fig. 139. In case (a) the concentration of Cl^- tends to fall to zero ; in case (b) the concentration of Na^+ shows the biggest fall, whilst in case (c) both Na^+ and Cl^- fall ; this is a gross over-simplification since HCO_3^- is present in the plasma and will diffuse into the gut (a rise in concentration of HCO_3^- was always observed ; Fig. 138) ; moreover, the SO_4^{--}- and Mg^{++}-ions are absorbed, although slowly ; and finally there is an active transport of

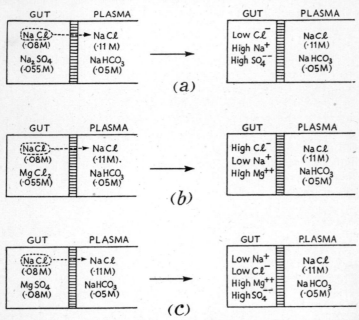

FIG. 139. Illustrating the effects of absorption of NaCl from the three mixtures studied by Visscher.

water which will continuously modify the concentration and volume of the gut fluid.

All regions of the small intestine are not equally efficient in the absorption of Cl^- ; in general the efficiency of the process increases aborally, i.e., from the duodenum to the ileum.[1]

Isotope Studies. The studies with Na^{24} and Cl^{39} of Visscher and his colleagues confirm in general outline the notion of an active transport of these ions ; thus, even when Cl^- is being strongly absorbed from a Cl^--SO_4^{--} mixture, Cl^{39} passes from blood to gut ; consequently the net absorption is due to an active removal of ions as fast as they enter, i.e., it is a dynamic process, just as the accumulation of K^+ is due, in muscle, to an active extrusion of Na^+ from the cell as fast as it enters. The difference

---

[1] Studies with Na^{24} show that the colon is even more efficient than the ileum in the absorption of salt.

between the rates of inward and outward migration of an ion determines the magnitude and direction of the active transport ; Visscher finds that this difference is maximal in the colon, *i.e.*, that the colon is more efficient in absorbing salt than the upper segments of the gut. The total rate of exchange of Na^+ between blood and gut is large, all the Na^+ in the plasma passing into the gut within about eighty-three minutes.

Absorption of Water. So far as the behaviour of water is concerned, it is not easy to distinguish between an active transport of this molecule, in the direction of blood-to-gut, from the effects of the active absorption of salts. The active absorption of salts has been well established by the facts set out above ; according to Visscher & Roepke, the net absorption of water into the blood seems only to occur when the osmotic pressure of the blood is the greater, *i.e.*, it is largely passive ; nevertheless a net intake of water from the blood may sometimes occur even when the fluid in the gut is hypotonic, so that an active control over the migration of water is likely. In general, the net effects of active transfer of salt and water are such as to make the fluid within the ileum hypotonic, *i.e.*, the gut tends to conserve the salt content of the body to a greater extent than the water content. Visscher has suggested that the exchanges between gut and blood are best explained on the assumption of a forced flow of fluid across the intestinal epithelium, in both directions simultaneously, at different loci ; differences in the concentrations of solute in the two streams, and in the relative flow-rates of the streams, would thus determine the magnitude of the net transport of any given substance.

Absorption of Sugars

That active transport is concerned with the absorption of at least some sugars is now well established. If only simple diffusion were concerned in the transport, the pentoses, being smaller than hexoses, might be expected to be absorbed the more rapidly ; however, Cori and Wilbrandt & Laszt have shown that the sugars are absorbed from the rat's intestine at rates in the order shown in Table XXV :—

TABLE XXV

Relative Rates of Absorption of Sugars from Small Intestine.
(Cori and Wilbrandt & Laszt.)

	Cori & Cori	Wilbrandt & Laszt	
		Normal	Poisoned
Galactose (C_6) . . .	110	115	53
Glucose (C_6) . . .	100	100	33
Fructose (C_6) . . .	43	44	37
Mannose (C_6) . . .	19	33	25
Xylose (C_5) . . .	15	30	31
Arabinose (C_5) . . .	9	29	29

Addition of metabolic poisons reduced the rate of absorption of glucose and galactose from isolated loops of small intestine, whilst the absorption of the other sugars remained approximately the same, so that it would appear that these two sugars are actively absorbed whilst the others are not.

As we shall see, however, deductions from the relative rates of absorption of homologous compounds are dangerous ; unequivocal evidence for an active absorption of glucose has been provided only comparatively recently by Bárány & Sperber, who analysed the blood and intestinal fluid during the course of absorption and demonstrated that the glucose was passing up a concentration gradient. They showed also that the absorptive mechanism is easily saturated, in the sense that the rate of absorption is limited by the power of the mucosa to transport the sugar into the blood, rather than by the amount of sugar available ; the rate of absorption was *not* completely independent of the concentration in the intestine, as has sometimes been claimed ; this is reasonable since it has been computed (*e.g.*, by Verzár & Wirz) that about 65 per cent. of the transport is by an active process, whilst the remainder can be attributed to simple diffusion.

Phosphorylation Theory. Verzár has developed the thesis that the first stage in the active absorption of sugar is its phosphorylation, *i.e.*, conversion to organic phosphate. Since pentoses are said not to be phosphorylated *in vivo*, this would account for their much slower rates of absorption. Within recent years a number of flaws in this hypothesis have appeared ; thus Davidson & Garry have shown that, in the caudal region of the rat's small intestine, xylose and glucose are absorbed at the same rate,[1] and Campbell & Davson have shown that a synthetic glucose derivative that is almost certainly not phosphorylated *in vivo*, namely 3-methylglucose, is not only absorbed rapidly (84 per cent. of the rate for glucose), but is definitely absorbed against a concentration gradient in the cat. To prove this, the concentration of 3-methylglucose in the blood was maintained continuously at a higher level than that in the gut ; nevertheless the 3-methylglucose was absorbed. Again, Öhnell & Höber have shown that the results of poisoning with iodoacetate must be accepted with great caution ; iodoacetate interferes with the process of glycolysis, which certainly involves phosphorylation ; nevertheless it is generally toxic and damages the tissues with which it comes into contact, so that one cannot attribute a decreased absorptive rate entirely to a poisoning of a specific phosphorylation process. Moreover, even if the absorption of certain substances, such as xylose, is unaffected by the poison, this need not mean that it is normally not actively absorbed ; the poison may block the absorptive process but increase passive diffusion as a result of damage to

---

[1] These authors (1941) have confirmed the observation, originally made by Westenbrink in the pigeon, that the naturally occurring *d*-xylose is absorbed more rapidly than the *lævo*-isomer (as 17 to 10) ; they find that *d*-xylose is more rapidly absorbed than arabinose, confirming Wilbrandt & Laszt (Table XXV). The series of relative rates of absorption in the rat may therefore be compiled from the work of Wilbrandt & Laszt, Davidson & Garry, and Campbell & Davson as follows :—

Galactose (115), Glucose (100), 3-Methylglucose (84), Fructose (44), and Pentoses (30).

the intestinal epithelium, leaving the absorption rate about the same.[1] Consequently, in order that the active transport of any substance may be definitely proved or excluded, experiments designed to show whether the substance moves against a concentration gradient must be carried out. Thus Bárány & Sperber proved the active absorption of glucose and, as indicated above, Campbell & Davson proved the active absorption of 3-methylglucose, by simultaneous analyses of the gut-fluid and blood. In this connection some interesting work of Fisher & Parsons may be mentioned ; these authors maintained completely isolated portions of rat intestine alive by circulating oxygenated Ringer through the lumen of the excised portion of gut, whilst the outside was bathed by the same

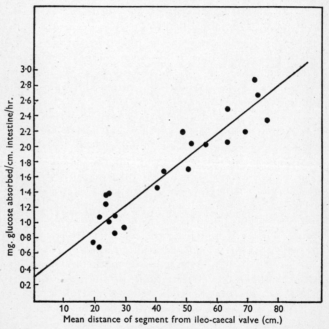

FIG. 140.   Illustrating the variation in the rate of absorption of glucose with distance from the ileo-cæcal valve.   (Fisher & Parsons. *J. Physiol.*)

fluid, the important element in the technique being to maintain the normal blood circulation intact until the lumen is perfused, so that the epithelial cells are never subjected to lack of oxygen. They studied the transfer of glucose from the inside to the outside ; they confirmed that transfer could occur against a concentration gradient, and drew attention to the fact that the tissue utilises for its own metabolism a certain proportion of the glucose presented to it ; Fisher & Parsons therefore draw a distinction between absorption for metabolic needs and *translocation*, the active transfer out of the gut. Their results bring out very clearly the fact, appreciated earlier, that the rate of absorption is greater at the duodenal than at the jejunal end of the small intestine (Fig. 140).

[1] Öhnell & Höber remark on the great variability in the rate of absorption from the gut of the poisoned animal.

Phlorizin, a metabolic poison which abolishes reabsorption of glucose by the kidney tubule (p. 340), reduces the active absorption of glucose, as Lundsgaard and Wertheimer have shown ; Fisher & Parsons have demonstrated a similar effect with the isolated intestine and have shown that, whereas glucose does not normally pass from outside to inside, in the presence of phlorizin this occurs to some extent.

Absorption of Alcohols, Amides, and Amino-Acids

Höber & Höber have studied the absorption of a number of organic substances from the intestine ; in general, they have shown that physiologically insignificant substances, such as the polyhydric alcohols and acid amides, exhibit absorption characteristics that require no hypothesis of active transport, the rate of absorption being apparently determined by the molecular volume, in the case of strongly water-soluble substances, and by the oil-water partition coefficient in the case of less strongly water-soluble substances ; some typical results are shown in Table XXVI :—

TABLE XXVI

Relative Rates of Absorption of Substances from the Intestine Compared with Relative Molecular Volumes and Ether-Water Partition Coefficients.
(*Höber & Höber*, 1937.)

Substance	M.V.	Ether-Water Partition Coefficient	Relative Rate
Glycerol . . .	88	0·00066	89
Erythritol . . .	130	0·00011	41
Mannitol . . .	189	0·00001	0
Valeramide . . .	135	0·023	81
Lactamide . . .	98	0·0006	69
Malonamide . . .	104	0·00008	27

and it will be seen that, with the amides, absorption is determined by partition coefficient ; whilst with the alcohols by molecular size. Further evidence for the view that these substances enter only by simple diffusion is given by the observation that the amount absorbed in a given time is linearly dependent on the concentration in the intestinal fluid (*i.e.*, it depends on the concentration gradient) whereas it has been shown in the case of glucose and galactose that this does not hold, the percentage absorbed in a given time falling off with increasing concentration, a fact suggesting the saturation of an absorptive mechanism.

Amino-acids, as one might expect, are actively absorbed, their rates of absorption being generally more rapid than those of compounds of similar molecular volume ; as with glucose, the percentage absorption in a given time tends to fall off with increasing initial concentration ; the rate of absorption is decreased by metabolic poisons, such as iodoacetate, but not by phlorizin which is thus, apparently, a poison specifically concerned with carbohydrate absorption. Schofield & Lewis fed various amino-acids to rats and after a fixed time analysed the gut contents ; they obtained the following figures for the relative rates of absorption :—

Amino-acid :	dl-alanine	d-alanine	l-alanine	β-alanine	dl-serine	dl-isoserine
Abs. Coefft. :	80·5	61·6	81·5	51·4	67·1	14·1

the differences between the absorption rates being shown to be significant by statistical tests except for that between dl- and l-alanine. Thus, as with the sugars, there is a difference in rates of absorption between optical isomers. Similar, but more striking, differences have been recently reported by Clark, Gibson, Smyth & Wiseman.

Absorption of Fats

It is not proposed to embark here on a detailed discussion of the mode of absorption of fats from the intestine ; the subject is one on which controversy has raged for just half a century and is still not settled ; we must confine ourselves, therefore, to little more than a statement of the problems involved in fat absorption. Within a few hours of the ingestion of olive oil, the epithelial cells and the lacteals of the villi are seen to contain minute globules of fat, and the lymph, collected during fat digestion, consists of a fine emulsion. It has been suggested, e.g., by Munk, that the neutral fat [1] is finely emulsified as a result of the movements of the intestine, aided by the presence of bile salts, which have been shown to be necessary for fat absorption ; the minute droplets so formed (chylomicra) are then supposed to pass into and out of the epithelial cells. In opposition to this viewpoint we have the opinion of Pflüger, supported and modified more recently by Verzár among others, that absorption results from the splitting of fat in the intestine by an enzyme, lipase (secreted by the pancreas), followed by absorption of its components— fatty acid and glycerol—into the epithelial cells, where it is resynthesised to neutral fat and ejected, by some undirectional mechanism, into the lacteal. The latter hypothesis has received a very thorough experimental test by Verzár, and has been largely substantiated ; nevertheless Frazer has recently brought forward some convincing experiments in favour of the direct absorption of undecomposed fat, so that it is possible that both mechanisms operate to some extent. Let us consider first Verzár's experiments.

If the small intestine is thoroughly washed out (so as to remove enzymes already present), and a neutral fat, such as olive oil, is placed in the lumen, absorption only occurs if both lipase and bile salts are added too ; that the bile salts are not merely necessary to aid in splitting the fat by lipase is shown by the fact that fatty acids, such as oleic acid, are not significantly absorbed unless the bile salts are present. Verzár imputed the function of the bile salts, in promoting absorption, to their power of making long-chain fatty acids effectively water-soluble by the formation of complexes. The physiologically important bile acids are, according to Verzár, glycocholic and taurocholic acids ; and, if these are added to a milky suspension of

---

[1] That is, the combination of glycerol with three molecules of fatty acid.

fatty acid in water, the turbidity clears, indicating that the micellar units have become very much smaller ; the existence of a very fine opalescence, however, shows that at least some of the particles retain colloidal dimensions. If more and more fatty acid is used, with a fixed quantity of bile acid, the opalescence increases ; and various experiments go to show that the proportion of larger micelles increases under these conditions. In general, it would seem that the water-insoluble fatty acid molecule is surrounded by a number of glycocholic or taurocholic acid molecules in such a way that the polar groups of the latter are directed outwards towards the water phase, the non-polar group of the fatty acid being screened to give a water-soluble complex. As the number of available bile-acid molecules decreases, the relative proportion of fatty acid to bile acid decreases, so that in order that the polar groups may be effectively screened, the size of the particle must increase (since the larger the particles the smaller the total surface area for a given quantity of fatty acid). Thus the system may pass insensibly from a true solution into what is known as a stable emulsion —discrete droplets of fat being protected from coalescence by the presence of an adsorbed layer of surface-active material (Fig. 141). The secretion of bile acids into the intestine by the liver thus serves a dual purpose ; emulsification of the neutral fat is favoured so that a large surface is presented to the action of lipase—the fat splitting enzyme—and then, when the fat has been split, the long-chain fatty acids are maintained in effective solution and are able to pass into the epithelial cells. As Schmidt-Nielsen has pointed out, the molecular

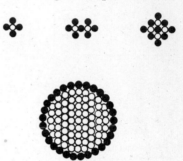

FIG. 141. Black dots indicate bile acid molecules ; white dots indicate lipid molecules. As the proportion of lipid to bile acid increases, the particle size must also increase. (After Verzár & McDougall. *Absorption from the Intestine.* Longmans, London.)

weight of a fatty-acid/bile acid complex would be in the region 2,000–4,000, a fact that may well be prejudicial to its chances of penetration. It is likely, therefore, that the complex is in dynamic equilibrium with smaller units— soaps—and that it is these smaller units that penetrate the epithelium. The theory that the hydrolysed fat penetrated as a soap was suggested by Pflüger, but fell into disrepute with the demonstration, *e.g.*, by Kostyál, that the pH of the intestinal fluid was generally not alkaline but on the acid side of pH 7·0 ; however, it has been recently revived by Schmidt-Nielsen who carried out titration curves of fatty acids in the presence of a long-chain sulphonic acid, which keeps the fatty acid in solution, and showed that at pH 7·0 and pH 6·0 as much as 25 and 10 per cent. respectively of the fatty acid is present as soap. Thus the picture emerging from Verzár's and Schmidt-Nielsen's work is of an emulsification of the fat, followed by splitting to soap, glycerol, and free fatty acid, the last being held in stable solution by complex-formation ; soap and glycerol penetrate the epithelial cell where resynthesis of neutral fat takes place ; as soap is lost, more is formed by dissociation of the bile-acid/fatty-acid complex.

Before considering the fate of the fatty acid and glycerol, absorbed into the epithelial cells, we may consider the results of Frazer's investigations. This author found in 1938 that in human subjects, given a test meal of oleic acid and glycerol, there was no increase in the number of circulating fatty droplets (chylomicra) in the blood, whereas it is well known that a meal of an equivalent amount of olive oil produces a marked increase in the chylomicron count. Moreover, if extra lipase was given with an oil meal, there was practically no increase in the count; these results

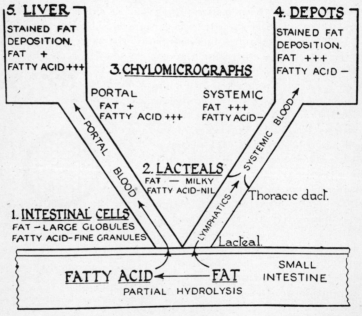

Fig. 142. Frazer's general scheme for the absorption of fats from the intestine.
(Frazer. *J. Physiol.*)

suggested that the fat particles in the blood were due to a direct absorption, as such, and in 1942 Frazer showed that, if paraffin oil [1] is finely emulsified, some 60 per cent. is absorbed from the intestine, *i.e.*, to the same extent as olive oil in the same period. Moreover, the paraffin oil caused an increase in the chylomicron count from a value of 20–30, when the paraffin was given in an unemulsified form, to 200 when given in finely emulsified form. Hence Frazer's results strongly suggest that fat particles, about $0·5\mu$ in diameter, can pass directly out of the intestinal lumen; his subsequent work, moreover, has made it very likely that at least a part of the neutral

---

[1] This is a hydrocarbon thought not to undergo any chemical change in the intestine; it must be absorbed as such. Frazer showed in a later paper (Frazer, Schulman & Stewart), that paraffin is not emulsified in the gut, so that it must be fed as a fine emulsion; this possibly explains the disparity with earlier results of Henriques & Hansen, Mellanby and others who found no absorption of paraffin from the gut.

fat entering the intestine is absorbed in this direct fashion, in fact it seems very likely that the fat appearing in the lacteals, and subsequently in the lymph, is the result of this transport, whilst the fat that is absorbed after lipolysis (as soap and glycerol) probably passes directly into the blood stream (into the portal circulation of the liver). Thus absorption of neutral fat is accompanied by milky lacteals, whereas absorption of fatty acid is said not to be ; the fatty acids, moreover, are found to be deposited in the liver whilst the neutral fat finds its way to the fat depôts of the body. Again, the appearance of fat droplets in the blood after absorption of neutral fat can be prevented by giving extra lipase with the fat meal. Consequently neutral fat, absorbed directly, appears to pass into the lymph, where it empties into the systemic blood by way of the thoracic duct, *i.e.*, it by-passes the liver ; fatty acids, whether ingested as such, or formed by splitting of neutral fat in the intestine, pass into the blood and are taken up by the liver. The general scheme proposed by Frazer is indicated in Fig. 142.

In studies of a more physico-chemical nature Frazer, Schulman & Stewart investigated the conditions favouring emulsification of fat, and showed that the presence of partially split fat (monoglyceride), together with bile salt, was an extremely favourable factor, emulsification to give a particle size of less than 0.5μ taking place almost spontaneously over a wide range of pH. The reasons for this combination's being so favourable are amply discussed by Frazer *et al.* ; the probable arrange-

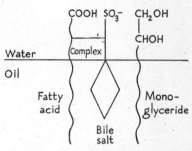

Fig. 143. A mixture of monoglyceride, bile salt and fatty acid gives a highly stable surface film at an oil-water interface ; the mixture will therefore act as an excellent emulsifying agent. (Frazer, Schulman & Stewart. *J. Physiol.*)

ment of the molecules is indicated in Fig. 143, the SO_3^- group of the bile acid providing a charged group over a wider range of pH than oleic acid could, thereby favouring the maintenance of an oil-in-water type of emulsion. The monoglyceride probably assists greatly, by virtue of its hydroxy-groups, in maintaining the stability of the emulsion, but is inadequate by itself, *i.e.*, in the absence of bile salts, because of the absence of charge.

The simple absorption of fat droplets presents us with no other problem than the mechanism of transport of these comparatively large particles (some 50 times thicker than a cell membrane) into and out of the epithelial cells ; it will be recalled in this connection that Chambers & Kopac were able to introduce oil droplets of much greater size into individual cells, but the result was always, in the end, a localised destruction of the surface in the region of penetration. The chemical mode of transport, which undoubtedly occurs simultaneously with the former, begs the question of whether, indeed, the split fat is resynthesised in the epithelial cells and, if so, whether the same type of fat is re-formed, or a new type. There is too much evidence to favour some resynthesis of fat from fatty acids to reject this hypothesis [1] and some confirmation of it has been given by Jeker's histological studies during fat absorption ; if his differential staining of neutral fat and fatty acid can be validated, his results show that, during the first 1–2 hours, the amount of fatty acid steadily increases in the epithelial cells, and that later this tends to be replaced by neutral fat which appears also in the lacteals. With regard to the process of resynthesis of fat, the work of Bloor, and later of Sinclair, has suggested that the formation of phospholipids is an essential step in translocation of fat ; thus Bloor found that phospholipids are produced during ingestion of fat, and Sinclair has shown that if highly unsaturated fats are fed there is a rapid increase in the unsaturation of the phospholipids in the body ; moreover, during fat absorption, the amount of phospholipid in the enteric lymph increases some three-fold ; and Verzár & Laszt showed that the absorption of fatty acids is promoted by addition of both glycerol and phosphate to the intestine, but not by glycerol alone. The more recent studies of Schmidt-Nielsen, in which radioactive phosphorus was employed, have shown that, whereas the total amount of phospholipid in the mucosa of the intestine is unaffected by the absorption of fat, the rate of formation of phospholipid is increased several times during the absorption of oleic acid, so that fat absorption is associated with an increased *turn-over* of phospholipid in the intestine. Quantitative studies show, however, that it is most unlikely that the absorbed fatty acids combine with phosphorus and glycerol to give phospholipids, which are then transported away ; the quantities of the necessary components in the mucosa are inadequate and the amounts of extra phospholipid in the blood during fat absorption are not large (Hevesy & Lundsgaard).[2] It would seem, then, that the formation of phospholipid may well be a step in the translocation of fatty acid, but that the phosphorus cannot be considered as the vehicle for its transport away from the intestine.

The absorption of fat may be inhibited by high concentrations of phlorizin ; and Verzár has postulated a phosphorylation process as being fundamental to fat absorption, an argument that, as we have seen, cannot be sustained on the basis of this finding alone, especially as the concentration required is much higher than that required to prevent the phosphorylation of glucose and its absorption. Schmidt-Nielsen found that the turn-over of phospholipids in the intestine was unaffected by this poison.

Very little work has been done on the relative rates of absorption of the fatty acids ; Deuel and his collaborators have shown that there are

---

[1] In fact, Berry & Ivy (1950) question the whole basis of Frazer's hypothesis ; they point to the fact that a *fatty acid* meal causes large amounts of *neutral* fat to appear in the thoracic duct (Freeman & Ivy, 1935), presumably converted to this form on its way through the epithelium ; moreover, they state that mineral oil, emulsified to give droplets as small as $0 \cdot 2$–$0 \cdot 5\mu$, does not appear in the lacteals or thoracic duct, a claim agreeing with the earlier statement of Lundbæk & Maaløe (1947), that finely emulsified liquid paraffin was not absorbed from the rat's intestine. In a recent communication, however, Daniel, Frazer, French & Sammons have rebutted the criticisms of Berry & Ivy and Lundbæk & Maaløe.

[2] Elkes & Frazer have shown that the chylomicra in the plasma are stabilised by a film of lecithin, a phospholipid ; this may well account for an increase in phospholipid turnover.

pronounced and unpredictable variations in the rates when fed to rats, their results being as follows :—

Acid	Acetic	Propionic	Butyric	Valeric	Caproic	Heptoic
Abs. Coefft. . .	26·6	21·4	39·7	23·3	38	25·8

only minimal quantities of lauric acid (C_{12}) being absorbed. That the absorption of acids involves an active process is suggested—but not proved—by the observation of Garry & Smith that the *lævo*-isomer of *dl*-mandelate is preferentially absorbed.[1]

[1] The absorption of iron compounds is of interest clinically ; according to Groen, Van den Broek & Veldman, it seems only to be absorbed in the ferrous condition ; at pH 6 (the pH of the gut), all the iron is either in complex form or as ferric ion, hence there is no normal absorption of iron, however administered. If reducing agents such as ascorbic acid (vitamin C), cysteine, glutathione, etc., or organic acids, are added, absorption takes place.

References

BÁRÁNY, E. & SPERBER, E. (1939). " Absorption of Glucose Against a Concentration Gradient by the Small Intestine." *Scand. Arch. Physiol.*, 81, 290.

BERRY, I. M. & IVY, A. C. (1950). " Partition Hypothesis for Intestinal Absorption of Fat." *Amer. J. Physiol.*, 162, 80.

BLOOR, W. R. (1915). " Fat Absorption and the Blood Lipoids." *J. biol. Chem.*, 23, 317.

BLOOR, W. R. (1916). " Fat Assimilation." *J. biol. Chem.*, 24, 447.

BURNS, H. S. & VISSCHER, M. B. (1934). " The Influence of Various Anions of the Lyotropic Series upon the Na and Cl Content of Fluid in the Intestine." *Amer. J. Physiol.*, 110, 490.

CAMPBELL, P. N. & DAVSON, H. (1948). " Absorption of 3-Methylglucose from the Small Intestine of the Rat and Cat." *Biochem. J.*, 43, 426.

CLARK, E. W., GIBSON, Q. H., SMYTH, D. H. & WISEMAN, G. (1951). " Selective Absorption of Amino-Acids from Thiry-Vella Loops." *J. Physiol.*, 112, 46P.

CORI, C. F. (1925). " Rate of Absorption of Hexoses and Pentoses from the Intestinal Tract." *J. biol. Chem.*, 66, 691.

DANIEL, J. W., FRAZER, A. C., FRENCH, J. M. & SAMMONS, H. G. (1951). " Absorption of Paraffin." *J. Physiol.*, 113 (in the press).

DAVIDSON, J. N. & GARRY, R. C. (1939). " The Absorption of Monosaccharides from the Large Intestine of the Rat under Urethane Anæsthesia." *J. Physiol.*, 96, 172.

DAVIDSON, J. N. & GARRY, R. C. (1940). " The Absorption of Monosaccharides from the Distal Small Intestine of Anæsthetised Cats." *J. Physiol.*, 97, 509.

DAVIDSON, J. N. & GARRY, R. C. (1941). " The Absorption of Pentoses from the Small Intestine of the Rat under Urethane Anæsthesia." *J. Physiol.*, 99, 239.

DAVSON, H. & DANIELLI, J. F. (1943). " The Permeability of Natural Membranes." Cambridge. C.U.P.

DENNIS, C. & VISSCHER, M. B. (1940). " Studies on the Rates of Absorption of Water and Salts from the Ileum of the Dog." *Amer. J. Physiol.*, 131, 402.

DENNIS, C. & WOOD, E. H. (1940). " Intestinal Absorption in the Adrenalectomised Dog." *Amer. J. Physiol.*, 129, 182.

DEUEL, H. J., HALLMAN, L. & REIFMAN, A. (1941). " The Rate of Absorption of Various Fatty Acids by the Rat." *J. Nutrit.*, 41, 373.

ELKES, J. J. & FRAZER, A. C. (1943). " The Relationship of Phospholipin to the Absorption of Unhydrolysed Fat from the Intestine." *J. Physiol.*, 102, 24P.

ELKES, J. J., FRAZER, A. C. & SCHULMAN, J. H. & STEWART, H. C. (1944). " The Mechanism of Emulsification of Triglyceride in the Small Intestine." *J. Physiol.*, 103, 6P.

ELSDEN, S. R., GIBSON, Q. H. & WISEMAN, G. (1950). " Selective Absorption of Amino-Acids from the Small Intestine of the Rat." *J. Physiol.*, 111, 56P.

FISHER, R. B. & PARSONS, D. S. (1949). " A Preparation of Surviving Rat Small Intestine for the Study of Absorption." *J. Physiol.*, 110, 36.

FISHER R. B. & PARSONS, D. S. (1949). " Glucose Absorption from Surviving Rat Small Intestine." *J. Physiol.*, 110, 218.

FRAZER, A. C. (1942). "Emulsification and Absorption of Fats and Paraffin in the Intestine." *Nature*, 149, 167.

FRAZER, A. C. (1943). "Differentiation in the Absorption of Olive Oil and Oleic Acid in the Rat." *J. Physiol.*, 102, 306.

FRAZER, A. C. (1943). "Lipolysis and Fat Absorption." *J. Physiol.*, 102, 329.

FRAZER, A. C. (1946). "The Absorption of Triglyceride Fat from the Intestine." *Physiol. Rev.*, 26, 103.

FRAZER, A. C., SCHULMAN, J. H. & STEWART, H. C. (1944). "Emulsification of Fat in the Intestine of the Rat and its Relationship to Absorption." *J. Physiol.*, 103, 306.

FRAZER, A. C., STEWART, H. C. & SCHULMAN, J. H. (1942). "Emulsification and Absorption of Fats and Paraffins in the Intestine." *Nature*, 149, 167.

FREEMAN, S. & IVY, A. C. (1935). "Synthesis of Neutral Fat by the Intestine of Diabetic Dogs." *Amer. J. Physiol.*, 114, 132.

GARRY, R. C. & SMITH, I. A. (1943). "Factors Affecting the Absorption of Na *dl*-Mandelate from the Intestine of Cats." *J. Physiol.*, 101, 484.

GROEN, J., VAN DEN BROEK & VELDMAN, H. (1947). "Absorption of Iron Compounds from the Small Intestine." *Biochim. Biophys. Acta*, 1, 315.

HENRIQUES, V. & HANSEN, C. (1900). "Zur Frage der Fettresorption." *Zbl. Physiol.*, 14, 313.

HEVESY, G. & LUNDSGAARD, E. (1937). "Lecithinæmia Following the Administration of Fat." *Nature*, 140, 275.

HÖBER, R. & HÖBER, J. (1937). "Experiments on the Absorption of Organic Solutes in the Small Intestine of Rats." *J. cell. & comp. Physiol.*, 10, 401.

INGRAHAM, R. C. & VISSCHER, M. B. (1936). "The Production of Chloride Free Solutions by the Action of the Intestinal Epithelium." *Amer. J. Physiol.*, 114, 676.

INGRAHAM, R. C. & VISSCHER, M. B. (1936). "The Influence of Various Poisons on the Movement of Chloride Against Concentration Gradients from Intestine to Plasma." *Amer. J. Physiol.*, 114, 681.

INGRAHAM, R. C. & VISSCHER, M. B. (1938). "Further Studies on Intestinal Absorption with the Performance of Work." *Amer. J. Physiol.*, 121, 771.

JEKER, L. (1936). "Mikroskopische Untersuchungen u. d. Fettresorption, etc." *Pflüg. Arch.*, 237, 1.

KOSTYÁL, L. (1926). *Magy. orv. Arch.*, 27, 276. (Quoted by Verzár.)

LUNDBÆK, K. & MAALØE, O. (1947). "Non-Absorption of Finely Emulsified Paraffinum Liquidum in the Intestine of the Rat." *Acta Physiol. Scand.*, 13, 247.

LUNDSGAARD, E. (1933). "Die Wirkung von Phlorrhizin auf die Glukoseresorption." *Biochem. Z.*, 264, 221.

MELLANBY, J. (1927). "Petroleum Emulsion in the Small Intestine." *J. Physiol.*, 64, 33P.

ÖHNELL, R. & HÖBER, R. (1939). "The Effect of Various Poisons on the Absorption of Sugars and Some Other Non-Electrolytes from the Normal and the Isolated Artificially Perfused Intestine." *J. cell. & comp. Physiol.*, 13, 161.

PETERS, H. C. & VISSCHER, M. B. (1949). "On the Mechanism of Active Absorption from the Intestine." *J. cell., & comp. Physiol.*, 13, 51.

ROEPKE, R. R. & VISSCHER, M. B. (1939). "Osmotic Relationship between Blood Plasma and Intestinal Fluid during Absorption." *P.S.E.B.M.*, 41, 500.

SCHMIDT-NIELSEN, K. (1946). "Investigations on the Fat Absorption in the Intestine." *Acta Physiol. Scand.*, 12, Suppl. 37.

SCHOFIELD, F. A. & LEWIS, H. B. (1947). "A Comparative Study of the Metabolism of α-Alanine, β-Alanine, Serine and Isoserine. I. Absorption from the Gastro-intestinal Tract." *J. biol. Chem.*, 168, 439.

SINCLAIR, R. G. (1936). "Blood Phospholipid as a Transport Mechanism." *J. biol. Chem.*, 115, 211.

VERZÁR, F. (1935). "Die Rolle von Diffusion und Schleimhautaktivitt bei der Resorption von verschiedene Zuckern aus dem Darm." *Biochem. Z.*, 276, 17.

VERZÁR, F. & LASZT, L. (1934). "Untersuchungen u. d. Resorption von Fettsäure." *Biochem. Z.*, 270, 24.

VERZÁR, F. & LASZT, L. (1935). "Die Hemmung der Fettresorption durch Phlorrhizin." *Biochem. Z.*, 276, 1.

VERZÁR, F. & McDOUGALL, E. F. (1936). "Absorption from the Intestine." London. Longmans, Green.

VERZÁR, F. & SÜLLMANN, H. (1937). "Die Bildung von Phosphorsäureestern in der Darmschleimhaut bei der Resorption." *Biochem. Z.*, 289, 323.

VERZÁR, F. & WIRZ (1937) "Weitere Untersuchungen u. d. Bedingungen der selektiven Glucoseresorption." *Biochem. Z.*, 292, 174.

VIRTUE, R. W., VIRTUE, M. E. D., SMITH, D. I. & GREENBLATT, J. (1942). "Effect of Bile Salts on Absorption of Sodium Oleate from Jejunal Loops in Dogs." *Amer. J. Physiol.*, **135**, 776.

VISSCHER, M. B., FETCHER, E. S., CARR, C. W., GREGOR, H. P., BUSHEY, M. S. & BAKER, D. E. (1944). "Isotopic Tracer Studies on the Movement of Water and Ions between Intestinal Lumen and Blood." *Amer. J. Physiol.*, **142**, 550.

VISSCHER, M. B. & ROEPKE, R. R. (1945). "Water and Electrolyte Concentration Relationship during Absorption of Salt Solutions from Ileal Segments." *Amer. J. Physiol.*, **144**, 468.

VISSCHER, M. B., ROEPKE, R. R. & LIFSON, N. (1945). "Osmotic and Electrolyte Concentration Relationships during the Absorption of Autogenous Serum." *Amer. J. Physiol.*, **144**, 457.

VISSCHER, M. B., VARCO, R. H., CARR, C. W., DEAN, R. B. & ERICKSON, D. (1944). "Sodium Ion Movement between the Intestinal Lumen and the Blood." *Amer. J. Physiol.*, **141**, 488.

WELLS, H. S. (1931). "The Passage of Materials through the Intestinal Wall. I. The Relation between Intra-Intestinal Pressure and the Rate of Absorption of Water." *Amer. J. Physiol.*, **99**, 209.

WELLS, H. S. (1932). "II. The Osmotic Pressure of the Colloids of Lymph from the Lacteals as a Measure of the Absorbing Force of the Intestine." *Amer. J. Physiol.*, **101**, 434.

WELLS, H. S. & JOHNSON, R. G. (1934). "The Intestinal Villi and Their Circulation in Relation to Absorption and Secretion of Fluid." *Amer. J. Physiol.*, **109**, 387.

WERTHEIMER, E. (1933/4). "Phloridzinwirkung auf die Zuckerresorption." *Pflüg. Arch.*, **233**, 514.

WESTENBRINK, H. G. K. (1936). "Über die Spezifität der Resorption einiger Monosen aus dem Darme der Ratte und der Taube." *Arch. néerl. Physiol.*, **21**, 433.

WILBRANDT, W. & LASZT, L. (1933). "Untersuchungen u. d. Ursachen der selektiven resorption der Zucker aus dem Darm." *Biochem. Z.*, **259**, 398.

CHAPTER XIII

SECRETION OF ACID BY THE STOMACH

WE may now consider a phenomenon that has excited the interest and captured the imagination of physiologists for over two hundred years, namely the secretion of an approximately 0·15 N solution of HCl into the stomach, a concentration of acid that is rapidly lethal to a wide variety of cells. Because of its spectacular nature, an enormous amount of work has been devoted to this form of secretion; the experimental difficulties associated with its study have, however, been a serious barrier to advance, and it may well be that secretions such as the saliva or sweat would have repaid a similarly intensive study by contributing more definitely to our knowledge of secretory processes in general.

The Gastric Mucosa

The stomach is a differentiated portion of the gut in which the first stages of digestion of protein are carried out; unlike the intestine, it does not combine digestive with specific absorptive functions, so that the active transport exhibited by its cells is devoted to the *inward* transfer of substances that are necessary to maintain a suitable medium for digestion, namely acid and the enzyme *pepsin*; in addition, a layer of mucin —presumably a complex containing hyaluronic acid or a related muco-polysaccharide— is continuously secreted as a protective layer over the whole internal surface.

The complex inner layer of the stomach, like that of the intestine, is described as the *mucosa*, consisting of numerous folds of epithelium (mucous membrane) which are described as *gastric glands*, a longitudinal section through one being illustrated in Fig. 144. Its length varies between

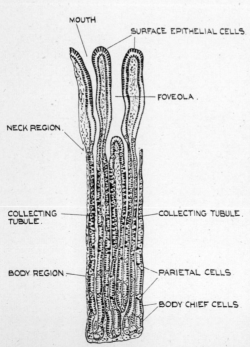

FIG. 144. Longitudinal section through gastric gland. (After Zimmermann. *Ergeb. d. Physiol.*)

314

about 1·3 and 3·5 mm., and it consists essentially of a number of *tubules* (in the region of four), made up of cells of different types, opening into the surface folds or *foveolæ*.[1] The walls of the tubule are differentiated by histologists into *crypt, isthmus, neck,* and *body regions.* The cells constituting the gland are of four types, *columnar* or *surface cells,* on the surface of the mucosa, which elaborate mucus ; *chief cells of the body of the gland,* which secrete the enzyme pepsin ; the cuboidal cells in the neck of the gland, *chief cells of the neck,* probably secreting mucus ; and the *parietal* or *oxyntic cells,* occurring in maximum density in the neck and upper part of the body of the gland, and presumably responsible for the secretion of HCl.[2] The relationship of a parietal cell to the tubule is shown schematically in Fig. 145, the secretion being apparently carried by *intercellular canals,* which open at one end into the lumen of the tubule and at the other into

a tree-like expansion *inside* the parietal cell—the *intracellular canaliculus.* This last has been shown, by a variety of staining techniques, to represent a genuine series of branching tubes in connection with the outer canal, the diameters varying with phases of activity.

As far back as 1865 Heidenhain and Langley attributed the secretion of HCl to the parietal cells. Attempts at exact localisation of the secretory activity by histochemical techniques have been, up till very recently, unsuccessful, so that the main evidence for the

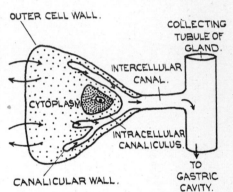

Fig. 145. Diagrammatic representation of the relationship between a parietal cell and the gastric tubule. (After Hollander. *Gastroenterology.*)

function of the parietal cells has been provided by studies on the distribution of acid in excised portions of mucosa and the correlation of this with the distribution of parietal cells, *e.g.,* by Linderstrom-Lang, Holter & Ohlsen.

Chemical Composition of the Parietal Secretion

The parietal cells are by no means the only ones to secrete into the stomach—the gastric gland is a mixed gland—so that the gastric secretion collected from a pouch [3] is normally a mixture of the secretory products of different cells ; it has thus been impossible so far to analyse the true parietal secretion, but this has not prevented a number of ingenious

[1] Also described as *crypts,* or *pits.*

[2] The gastric gland described above is typical of the whole of the gastric mucosa except for two regions, the *cardiac* and *pyloric* areas ; it is therefore common to speak of the *fundus glands,* the *cardiac glands* and the *pyloric glands.*

[3] For the experimental study of gastric secretion a portion of the stomach is usually isolated, by surgical procedure, from the rest to give a pouch, *e.g.,* the Heidenhain pouch, Pavlov pouch, etc. In Frémont's preparation the whole stomach is short-circuited by sewing the œsophagus to the duodenum, and a tube (gastric fistula) is sewn into the stomach. The various techniques have been summarised by Babkin.

attempts to obtain an approximate estimate by extrapolation, particularly in recent years by Hollander, by Gray, and by Teorell. Hollander estimated the variation in total acidity and total chlorides of the gastric, secretion collected at different rates of flow [1], and confirmed and extended the earlier observation of Pavlov that, with increasing rate of secretion, the acidity increased. Hollander found, however, that this increase was not indefinite, but that the concentration of acid flattened off to a maximal value in the region of 150 meq./l., and he suggested that this might be the concentration in the pure secretion. The secretion contained not only HCl but other chlorides (*neutral chlorides*, presumably KCl and NaCl), and, as the acidity increased, the concentration of neutral chlorides fell. On plotting neutral chloride concentration against acidity, a straight line was obtained which, on extrapolation to zero concentration of neutral chloride, indicated that the collected fluid would have no neutral chloride when its concentration of acid was, on the average, 168 meq./l., *i.e.*, that it would be approximately isotonic HCl. The conclusion drawn from this observation was that the parietal cells secreted a fluid of constant composition, isotonic HCl, and that this was diluted by secretion

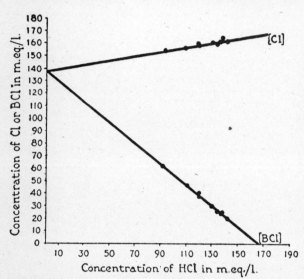

FIG. 146. Relationships between the concentrations of the chloride fractions of gastric juice. As the acidity of the juice increases, the concentration of neutral chloride (BCl) falls. (Gray. *Gastroenterology*.)

from other cells, the so-called *Verdunnungs-Sekretion*, with the result that the fluid actually collected was less acid. Increasing the rate of secretion of acid reduced the proportion of the " dilution-secretion " and so increased the acidity of the collected fluid. The diluting fluid was thought to be mainly sodium and potassium bicarbonates, the acid reacting with them as below to give neutral chloride and CO_2, the latter being lost to the blood.

$$HCl + NaHCO_3 \rightarrow NaCl + H_2CO_3 \rightarrow CO_2 + H_2O$$

[1] The stomach does not secrete acid without a stimulus ; the drug histamine is used most frequently to provoke secretion, the necessary threshold concentration in the blood being as low as one part in 150 million ; increasing the concentration increases the rate of secretion so that the rate of flow may be adequately controlled by maintaining suitable levels of histamine in the blood. Pilocarpine is another drug that provokes secretion of acid.

On this basis the osmotic pressure of the secretion should show definite changes with increasing rate of secretion, being high with rapid rates, low with intermediate rates, and higher again with very slow rates. This point was studied by Visscher and his colleagues and the predicted variation was observed.

The same mode of extrapolation has been applied by several other investigators ; thus Gray and his colleagues plotted the neutral chloride concentration against acidity and obtained a straight line extrapolating to 165 meq./l. (Fig. 146), the maximal acidity obtained being some 153 meq./l. with a total chloride concentration of 166 meq./l., *i.e.*, an excess of 13 meq./l. of neutral chloride. Gray studied the concentrations of Na^+ and K^+ individually ; the concentration of K^+ remained constant whilst that of Na^+ fell with increasing acidity. The constancy of the concentration of K^+ led Gray to conclude that the primary acid secretion was not pure HCl, but a mixture of 159 meq./l. HCl and 7 meq./l. KCl. A more detailed analysis of gastric secretion under variable conditions of flow has been made recently by Gudiksen ; in Table XXVII is shown the composition at the highest rate of flow (21 ml. per hr. by the whole cat stomach) ; it will be seen that K^+ is a significant constituent of the fluid. Gudiksen found that the concentration of K^+ was variable, ranging from 10·6 to 18·8 meq./l., with no correlation with rate of secretion ; however, the K^+/Na^+ ratio decreased with increasing rate, and the concentration of Na^+ showed an inverse relationship with the degree of acidity. Thus, except

TABLE XXVII

Concentrations of Various Ions in Gastric Juice formed at Secretion Rate of 21·2 ml./hr. (Gudiksen, 1943.)

Ion	Concn. (meq./l.)
Cl^- . . .	182
H^+ . . .	163
Na^+ . . .	4·5
K^+ . . .	11·2
NH_4^+ . . .	1·5
Ca^{++} . . .	0·3
Mg^{++} . . .	0·0
Total Cations . .	180·5
$Na^+ + K^+$ . .	15·7
K^+/Na^+ . . .	2·5

in regard to the concentration of K^+, his results are in essential agreement with those of Gray and Hollander. On the assumption of a constant rate of dilution by the " dilution secretion," the concentrations of the different constituents of the hypothetical primary acid secretion were computed as :—

$$Cl^- \quad 185\text{--}195 \text{ meq./l.}$$
$$HCl \quad 169\text{--}174 \text{ meq./l.}$$
$$K^+ \quad 10\text{--}22 \text{ meq./l.}$$
$$Na^+ \quad 2 \text{ meq./l.}$$

However, as the author himself points out, the assumptions made to arrive at these results are by no means likely, so that it is impossible to allocate a definite composition to the primary secretion, nor yet to state whether it is really formed at constant composition under a variety of conditions of flow.[1]

Teorell Hypothesis. Whilst the general thesis that the primary acid secretion suffers some dilution by other secretions is indisputable, the possibility of a continuous loss of H^+ by diffusion exchanges with these other cells—and eventually the blood—can by no means be ruled out, in fact it would be very unlikely that such an exchange could be precluded. Thus Teorell found that the increases in CO_2, resulting from a hypothetical neutralisation of the HCl by bicarbonate, did not take place and he was the first to postulate such an exchange of H^+ with alkali metal ions, such as Na^+ and K^+. In confirmation of his viewpoint he found that, on introducing HCl directly into the tied-off stomach, the rate of loss of acidity was directly proportional to the concentration of H^+ at any moment in the stomach fluid (Fig. 147). On the basis of this, and other experiments, he proposed the eminently reasonable theory

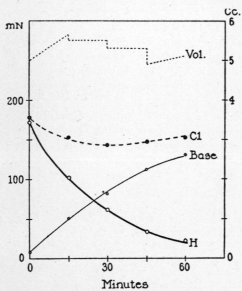

FIG. 147. The effects of introduction of isotonic HCl into a cat's stomach. Note the exponential decrease in the acidity (H) and the simultaneous increase in the concentration of alkali cations, without any appreciable change in volume. (Teorell. *J. gen. Physiol.*)

that the composition of the primary acid secretion was modified more or less exclusively by an exchange of H^+ with Na^+ in the plasma. At rapid rates of secretion a steady-state would be established with a high concentration of H^+, whilst at slow rates the concentration of this ion at the steady-state would be low, and that of Na^+ high. A model of the supposed process is illustrated in Fig. 148, taken from a recent paper by Teorell in which he treats the problem in an elementary

[1] Fisher & Hunt have recently made a rational mathematical analysis of the implications of the *Verdunnungsekretion Theory* and have emphasised that a principal assumption in the extrapolations, carried out to determine the acidity of the parietal secretion, is that the rate of secretion of the non-parietal component is constant.

mathematical way. So far as his model experiments are concerned there is, as one would naturally expect of so simple a system, a good correspondence between theory and experiment. In the case of the animal stomach, however, a lack of definite knowledge of the values of the permeability constants of the different ions through the gastric mucosa, and of their variation in the different regions (canaliculi, tubules, etc.) introduces grave uncertainties into the deductions ; nevertheless some qualitative predictions have been confirmed. Thus the acidity is expected to increase with increasing rate of secretion, the dependence at low rates being marked, whilst at high rates the variation is not large.

Consequently an apparent constancy, similar to that reported by Hollander, is not completely incompat- ible with the Teorell "*diffu- sion theory.*" Again, the concentration of Na^+ should vary inversely with the acidity, a fact confirmed by Hollander and many others, but attributed to the effects of a diluting secretion. It was also predicted that the concentration of Cl^- should pass through a minimum at low rates of secretion ; since the total Cl^- determines the osmotic pressure, it is interesting that Visscher and his colleagues, as men- tioned earlier, found a minimum osmotic pressure of the gastric secretion at moderate secretion rates. Studies on the non-secret- ing isolated frog stomach

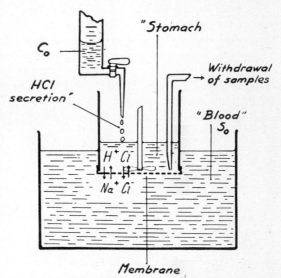

FIG. 148. Illustrating Teorell's model imitating stomach inter-diffusion. Acid, at constant con- centration, C_o, drips into a compartment separ- ated from an NaCl solution by a membrane. A steady state is immediately established with concentrations of Na^+ and H^+ determined by the rate of " secretion of HCl." (Teorell. *Gastro- enterology.*)

mucosa by Terner confirm the fact that HCl diffuses passively out of the stomach, a diffusion coefficient of $0·04.10^{-5} cm.^2/sec.$ being obtained, comparing with $2·5.10^{-5} cm.^2/sec.$ for HCl in water.[1] When the mucosa was actively secreting, on the other hand, the picture was by no means so simple, the back-diffusion through a secreting mucosa being

---

[1] In this connection we may note that the stomach appears to exhibit a low order of permeability to many lipoid-insoluble substances such as glucose and amino-acids ; the absorption of alcohol and of iodide on the other hand has been well established (*vide., e.g.,* Edkins & Murray for alcohol and Mislowitzer *et al.* for iodide). If Teorell's conception of an exchange of H^+ with alkali cations is correct, we should expect a ready permeability to Na^+ and K^+ and this has been demonstrated by Teorell ; this author has extended his observations, reported in 1933, and has shown (Teorell, 1939) that the mucosa is readily permeable to strong acids such as $HClO_4$, H_2SO_4, etc., as well as the weak acids such as CH_3COOH.

of a much lower order, in fact the diffusion could altogether cease on stimulating a mucosa with histamine.   These considerations must give us pause in applying too literally the simple model proposed by Teorell.

Applying his finding that the rate of loss of H^+ from the stomach is determined by the concentration of this ion, Teorell devised a method for determining the concentration of H^+ in the primary secretion.   It consisted of introducing a known volume of an isotonic buffer into the stomach, stimulating secretion by histamine, and subsequently removing the buffer plus secretion.   The acid of the secretion reacts with the buffer (glycine) so that the concentration of H^+, following the secretion of a given amount of acid, is much less than if the buffer had not been there ; diffusion of the secreted H^+ out of the stomach was therefore minimised and hence an estimation of the composition of the secreted fluid was possible.   For example, in one experiment 5 ml. of glycine solution were placed in the stomach ; this solution had a pH of 5·9 but after being in the stomach its pH on withdrawal was 2·75, whilst its volume increased to 6·5 ml.   It was found that 2·8 ml. of N/10 NaOH were required to bring the pH of the fluid back to 5·9 ; consequently the acid secreted was that contained in 2·8 ml. of N/10 HCl, *i.e.*, 0·28 meq. This acid was contained in 1·5 ml., so that it was secreted in a strength of :—

$$\frac{0\cdot 28}{1\cdot 5} \times 1{,}000 \text{ meq./l.} = 186 \text{ meq./l.}$$

On the average, a figure of 208± 6 meq./l. was obtained.   In a later paper the method was elaborated still further.   The main error in the above estimate (admitting the assumptions behind the computation) was in the assessment of the increase in volume of the added glycine secretion ; only when the rates of secretion were high could the values be considered at all valid.   However, by estimating the concentration of glycine in the stomach at the end of the secretion period, the dilution it had undergone by the addition of gastric secretion could be determined accurately.   As a result of this improvement in technique, the concentration of acid in the primary secretion could be estimated at low rates of secretion ; the results indicated a marked increase in acidity with decreasing flow, computed values as low as 350 meq./l. being obtained for the slowest rate, compared with 170 meq./l. when the rate was some twenty times faster.   On extrapolating to zero rate of flow the concentration obtained was 464 meq./l.

The objection to the method, in the writer's opinion, is the implied assumption that the secretion of HCl takes the form of a fluid of definite composition, independent of the pH of the fluid within the gastric tubules. A more reasonable picture of the process of secretion may be established by applying our notions of cellular secretory activity, derived from studies of the frog-skin, the kidney tubules, the erythrocyte, and muscle fibres.   The muscle cell, for example, can carry out secretory activity (in this case probably the extrusion of Na^+) until a definite concentration-ratio of K^+ inside and outside is reached, this ratio depending in some measure on the physiological condition of the fibre.   The existence of a definite limit to the degree of concentration of a secreted substance is probably true for all forms of secretion (*e.g.*, the accumulation of phenol red by the kidney tubule), so that an increased net transfer may be obtained by removal of the accumulated substance as fast as it is transported (*e.g.*, the accumulation of Ag^+ by *Astacus* gills can proceed indefinitely because the Ag^+ is precipitated within the secretory cells as fast as it is transported, and the limiting concentration-ratio is never exceeded). The same consideration must apply to the secretion of HCl by the parietal cells. Thus let us imagine a parietal cell producing an acid secretion ; as we shall see, the histochemical evidence precludes the accumulation of HCl in the cytoplasm, so that we must assume that the parietal cell actively transports water and acid, from its surrounding interstitial fluid, into the canaliculi and tubule in precisely the same way that the kidney tubule cell transports phenol red without showing any large accumulation of this substance within its cytoplasm (p. 344). Since it is by no means certain that H_2O flows passively in response to osmotic gradients established by the active transport of HCl, we may picture the complete process of secretion as one involving the active transfer of both H_2O and HCl into the canaliculi, the *acidity* of the secreted fluid depending on the relative amounts of these transported in unit time. The secretion involves the performance of osmotic work by the parietal cell, and the amount of work done in transporting a given quantity of HCl is given by [1] :—

$$W = n\mathrm{RT} \, ln \frac{[H^+]_{\mathrm{Can.}}}{[H^+]_{\mathrm{Cell}}}$$

where n is the number of gramme-ions of H^+ transported ; it thus depends on the ratio of concentrations of hydrogen ions in the cell and canalicular fluid, so that the same amount of energy can be expended in transporting a lot of HCl at a low concentration-ratio or a small amount of HCl at a high concentration-ratio. The finding of Hollander and others, that the concentration of H^+ is high and constant for a wide variety of rates of flow of gastric secretion above a certain limit, indicates that the capacity to deliver osmotic work is elastic ; it implies, moreover, that the parietal cells tend to establish a fixed ratio of H^+-concentrations across the canalicular wall, *i.e.*, the rates of transport of HCl and water are adjusted to give a secretion of constant acidity. Tentatively we may assume that this limiting concentration-ratio represents the maximum accumulation of which the parietal cells are capable,[2] so that the energy-output varies directly with the amount of acid secreted. Suppose now that the fluid in the gastric tubule and canaliculi is buffered by the diffusion of added glycine from the surface of the mucosa ; the cells must now transport a great deal more HCl, with a given amount of water, to establish the maximal concentration-ratio of H^+-ions, *i.e.*, the proportion of H^+ to transported water is increased, and it will consequently appear that the

---

[1] Ignoring the potential term (p. 274).

[2] It is important to appreciate that this maximum ratio is not determined by the capacity for performing osmotic work ; a cell capable of transferring large amounts of K^+ against a 20-fold concentration gradient could not transfer any against a 100-fold gradient, in the same way that a 2-volt battery would be unable to operate a 220-volt motor, however much energy it was capable of delivering at 2 volts.

secretion is more concentrated than in the absence of glycine ; moreover, the slower the rate of secretion, *i.e.*, of water transport, the more time will there be for the cells to transport HCl in an endeavour to establish the maximal concentration ratio of H^+, so that the slower the rate of secretion the more acid will it be.[1] Thus Teorell's observations find a ready explanation on this basis, but it is incorrect to deduce, from these studies of buffered gastric contents, that the secretion formed in the absence of a buffer would contain the same amount of HCl and water, *i.e.*, that at low rates the fluid would approach a concentration of some 464 meq./l. In the absence of a crucial test of the various hypotheses, therefore, we may picture the secretory process as above, the transport of water and HCl being adjusted to maintain, in normal circumstances, a fixed acidity of the fluid passing into the gastric tubule. As the fluid passes along the tubule and over the surface of the gastric mucosa, there will be an effective dilution of the HCl by an exchange of H^+ with Na^+ and K^+, and by mixture with the secretions of other cells, *e.g.*, the chief cells of the neck. The more rapid the rate of secretion, the nearer will the collected juice approximate in composition to that of the fluid elaborated in the canaliculi ; and the results of Hollander suggest that this retains a fair constancy of acidity. The possibility must not be ignored, however, of an eventual falling off in the ability of the secretory cells to perform the necessary osmotic work, although numerous studies testify to the remarkable power of the stomach to continue to secrete HCl under the most adverse conditions.

Site of Acid Secretion

We have stated that histochemical studies preclude the possibility of a significant accumulation of acid by the cytoplasm of the parietal cells ; these studies are too numerous to cite in detail, and it will suffice to mention only a few. Hoerr & Bensley in 1936 injected rabbits and guinea-pigs with 1 per cent. neutral red—a dye stuff that penetrates cells and appears in the gastric secretion—and examined the excised mucosa after freezing and drying and subsequent fixation. The gastric contents stained a deep crimson, indicating acidity ; the crypts or foveolæ were also crimson, whilst the lumen of the deeper parts of the gland, and the cytoplasm of the parietal cells, either showed no colour or only a pale yellow, indicating a neutral or alkaline reaction. These workers quote in support of their findings an observation of Chambers [2] that micro-injection of a single parietal cell with neutral red gave only a pale yellow. Again, Gersh, using the same freezing-drying technique (the Altmann-Gersh method as it is called) treated the frozen excised mucosa with $AgNO_3$ and showed that the precipitated chloride was confined to the extracellular regions (foveolus, etc.), and that there was no significant difference between the picture presented by secreting or resting mucosæ. As a result largely of these histochemical studies, the notion that the acid formed by the parietal cells

[1] This interpretation of Teorell's results is supported by a recent paper of Heinz (1951) who has calculated that a significant diffusion of H^+-ions from the tubule to the buffer in the mouth of the gastric gland is likely, *i.e.*, that as fast as H^+-ions are secreted a significant fraction will be neutralised by the buffering action of the glycine.

[2] In the *Lancet-Clinic* of Cincinnati, 1915.

is secreted into the canaliculi and gastric tubules as a neutral complex, which is subsequently hydrolysed, originally propounded by Harvey & Bensley in 1912, has been revived. This hypothesis, together with a rather similar one which assumes the secretion of a dilute acid into the base of the gastric tubule, followed by its concentration through the reabsorption of water as it passes towards the crypt, has been strongly attacked by Hollander and by Davenport. They have argued that the secretion of a solution of HCl at pH 5, and the reabsorption of water to bring the pH to 0·5, would involve the secretion of 16,000 litres of primary fluid for every litre of juice collected ; again, the secretion of HCl bound with an organic base would result in an increase in the percentage of organic matter in the secretion with increasing rates of flow, whereas the reverse is found. Thus we may reject, without much compunction, these two hypotheses whilst admitting the main fact on which they are based, namely the absence of accumulation of acid in the parietal cytoplasm. As pictured above, therefore, the secretion of HCl takes place as a transport of acid from blood to gastric tubule ; and it is reasonable to adopt, as the supposed site for the outward transfer, the boundary between the cytoplasm and the canaliculi, the last mentioned being regarded as a special differentiation of these secreting cells. The crux of the problem is thus to demonstrate that the contents of the canaliculi are strongly acid during secretion.

Quite recently Bradford & Davies have studied the secretion of a large variety of dye-stuffs by the isolated frog's mucosa, submitting the mucosa to direct microscopical investigation. All of the basic dye-stuffs tried were secreted, *e.g.*, acridine, toluidine blue, methylene blue, phenol red, etc. Many of these were acid-base indicators, sensitive to different ranges of pH, so that the degree of acidity of the various parts of the mucosa could be estimated in a rough manner. Thus, with neutral red, the lower regions of the mucosa and the cytoplasm of the parietal cells were slightly alkaline (pH 7·2–7·6), whilst the canaliculi and the lumen of some of the tubules and the secreting surface of the mucosa were acid (pH 6·8). The green fluorescence of acridine in ultra-violet light indicated that some tubules had a pH of less than 4·85, whilst the red colour of toluene-azo-amino-toluene-2 : 1 : 1 : 4 : 3 indicated a pH of less than 1·4 in the same regions. The site of secretion seemed to be definitely at or near the walls of the canaliculi.

Mechanism of Secretion

These recent studies with acid-base indicators therefore confirm the view of the parietal cell as a *transporter* of H^+ from the blood to the canaliculi and tubular lumen.[1] If this view is accepted, we may expect the blood leaving the stomach to be more alkaline—with an increased CO_2-combining power—than the arterial blood, in contrast to the state of affairs in other organs where the opposite pertains. Some evidence for a difference of pH during active secretion has been provided by the work of

[1] In contrast to the view of the cell as a manufacturer of acid which diffuses passively into the canaliculi.

Hanke, Johannesen & Hanke, the arterial blood being said to be some 0·07 to 0·09 pH units more acid than the gastric venous blood, whereas in the absence of secretion the difference was not so marked ; moreover the actual CO_2-combining power was considerably lower in the arterial blood. On the other hand, some evidence, which was thought to suggest that the parietal cells actually manufactured the acid, was presented by Davenport who found an excellent correlation between the concentration of carbonic anhydrase—the enzyme that accelerates the reaction : $CO_2 + H_2O \rightarrow H_2CO_3$—in the mucosa and the density of parietal cells ; moreover, the activity in the cat's stomach was some 5–6 times the activity in the erythrocyte where carbonic anhydrase is important in converting the CO_2 in the plasma to H_2CO_3 in the cells, and *vice versâ*. Nevertheless, the production of a concentration of H^+ in the region of 170 meq./l. by a weak acid like carbonic acid is, as Davenport himself indicated, out of the question ; furthermore, inhibitors of carbonic anhydrase, such as sulphanilamide, did not inhibit secretion of HCl.

Before considering the function of carbonic anhydrase and the significance of Davenport's results we may note that the secretory transport of H^+ into the stomach may be viewed as the production of both H^+ and OH^- by the cells of the mucosa, from their own water, as follows :—

$$H_2O \rightarrow H^+ + OH^-$$

the H^+ being secreted out of the cell and the OH^- diffusing back into the blood ; so far as the effect on the blood pH and CO_2-combining power is concerned, the effect will be the same as if only H^+ had been abstracted from the blood. Evidence in support of this viewpoint has been strengthened recently by the studies of Davies and his collaborators on the isolated amphibian gastric mucosa. As long ago as 1930, Delrue described a technique for demonstrating the transport of acid by a strip of mucosa separating a nutrient Ringer solution from distilled water, pH values as low as 1·6 being obtained in the distilled water in contact with the mucosal surface. A rapid secretion could be provoked by histamine, and it was claimed that both Ca^{++} and HCO_3^- in the nutrient medium were essential for acid production. Later Gray applied the same technique, obtaining pH values as low as 1·4 on the mucosal side, and he proved that the acid transport was definitely unidirectional, *i.e.*, from serosal to mucosal surfaces.[1] He obtained evidence indicating that the serosal side became alkaline. The more extensive studies of Davies have shown that the amount of acid liberated is almost exactly equivalent to the amount of base formed ; thus, on incubating a mucosal sac in Brodie solution, a large absorption of CO_2 was observed whilst acid was produced within the sac. The absorption of CO_2 was shown to be due to the formation of bicarbonate, as the result of the diffusion of alkali from the sac into the surrounding Brodie medium ; *i.e.*, the mucosa produced H^+ which diffused into the sac and OH^- which diffused out. Cl^- presumably diffused from the outside medium into the sac in exchange for OH^- which thus reacted

---

[1] The outer surface of the mucosa is described as the *serosa* or *serosal surface*.

with CO_2 to become HCO_3^-, the enzyme carbonic anhydrase being necessary for this reaction :—

$$CO_2 + H_2O \longrightarrow H_2CO_3 \dashrightarrow \overset{+}{H} + HCO_3^-$$
$$(\text{Carbonic Anhydrase}) \quad \overset{+}{OH^-}$$
$$\downarrow$$
$$H_2O$$

The net effect of such a production of acid is to increase the concentration of HCO_3^- in the outside medium and to form HCl inside. Isolated strips of mucosa (as opposed to mucosal sacs) failed to cause any absorption or liberation of CO_2 from the medium, an observation showing that H^+ and OH^- are produced in equivalent amounts, and that it is only when the HCl is insulated from the outside medium (*i.e.*, in a mucosal *sac*) that secretion is followed by an absorption of CO_2 from this medium. A comparison of the amounts of O_2 consumed by the tissue with the amounts of acid secreted showed that two equivalents of acid were produced for each equivalent of O_2 consumed ; this proves that the formation of HCl cannot be due to a simple formation of organic acid, *e.g.*, pyruvic acid, the H^+-ions of which are secreted out of the cell whilst the remainder is metabolised to produce OH^--ions (Bull & Gray). It must be appreciated, however, that Davies' work only shows that the production of acid is associated with the simultaneous appearance of alkali in the blood ; this could be achieved, as he suggests, by the secretion of H^+ from the water inside the cell into the lumen of the gastric tubule, associated with a passive diffusion of OH^- in the direction of cell-to-blood. Alternatively it could result simply from the transport of H^+ from the blood, as suggested earlier, the loss of H^+ from the blood being reflected necessarily in an increase in the concentration of OH^-, since the product : $[H^+] \times [OH^-]$ must always be constant. Davies' work does, however, dispose of the suggestion that H^+-ions are derived simply from organic acids produced by the cell, and also of such possibilities as the reaction :—

$$2NH_4^+ + 2C\ell^- + CO_2^- \dashrightarrow O = C \overset{\displaystyle NH_2}{\underset{\displaystyle NH_2}{\big\langle}} + 2H^+ + 2C\ell^-$$
$$\text{Urea}$$

the formation of acid according to this reaction not being associated with an equivalent amount of alkali.[1]

The function of carbonic anhydrase in the secretion of HCl appears now, according to Davies' work, in the " mopping up " of the OH^--ions

---

[1] Urea has been invoked in a reverse manner, the formation of NH_4^+ from it by the enzyme *urease* being considered as a primary step in the formation of acid by the reaction : $NH_4^+ \ldots . NH_3 + H^+$, or, alternatively, the NH_4^+-ion may exchange for H^+ from the blood (Glick). Davies & Kornberg (1950) have disposed of the hypothesis by showing that neither the concentration of urea, nor the urease activity, of gastric mucosa is adequate for the observed formation of acid.

liberated by the secretory process. How then can we explain the observation that inhibitors of carbonic anhydrase, such as sulphanilamide, do not inhibit gastric secretion ? The answer is given by the work of Davies & Edelman who have shown that, in the isolated gastric mucosa of the frog, complete inhibition of acid formation is brought about by suitable concentrations of p-toluene sulphonamide ; and they have argued that the earlier failure to observe this in the intact animal, *e.g.*, that of Feldberg, Keilin & Mann, was due to the concentration of the sulphonamide being insufficiently high to inhibit all activity.[1] An interesting observation, lending support to the notion of an alkalising of the blood during secretion, is that of Kurtz & Clark to the effect that the amount of CO_2 obtainable from the stomach on blowing a current of N_2 through it, was inversely proportional to the rate of acid secretion, *i.e.*, the more acid that was formed the less CO_2 that could be washed out. They had found earlier that the rate at which CO_2 enters the current of N_2 is directly proportional to the partial pressure of CO_2 in the blood, so that the simplest deduction from this observation is that the partial pressure of CO_2 in the blood falls during secretion (*i.e.*, its CO_2-combining power increases).[2]

Gastric Potentials

A potential between the inside and outside of the stomach was first described in 1834 by Donne ; in 1927 Mond reported some experiments on this potential in the frog's stomach ; its direction is such that the inside— mucosa—is negative in relation to the outside—serosa—in the external circuit. This potential has since been described in detail by several workers and promises to become as popular as the frog-skin potential was some twenty to thirty years ago. It must be appreciated at the outset, however, that these tissue potentials are highly complex, and that it is only since the serious application of radioactive isotopes to the study of the ionic permeability relationships in the frog-skin that we have begun to be able to interpret this particular potential, and even then only tentatively (p. 359). In the case of the stomach we are far more ignorant of the ionic permeability relationships, so that at present the results can contribute little to the interpretation of the secretory mechanisms in the gastric glands. Mislowitzer & Silver showed that, in the anæsthetised cat, the potentials could be as high as 100–125 mV and that they fell to zero with the death of the animal. Histamine, which stimulates acid secretion, generally, but not always, reduced the potential, and various salts had the same effect, the anions being in the following order of activity in reducing the potential :—

$$SO_4^{--}, \text{Acetate}^- < Cl^- < \text{Citrate}^{---} < I^- < CNS^-$$

The effect of CNS^- was the most striking, a decrease to zero being obtained by a 3·8 per cent. solution (it had been long known that CNS^- inhibits

---

[1] If it had been sufficiently high there would have been sufficient interference with respiratory exchanges to be fatal.

[2] The more alkaline the blood, the more its total CO_2 is bound as HCO_3^- ; hence the partial pressure of CO_2 falls with alkalinity and increases with acidity.

gastric secretion of acid). Of the cations, Li$^+$ was the most effective, the order being :—

$$NH_4^+ < Na^+ < Rb^+ < K^+ < Li^+$$

Narcotics, such as the alcohols, reduced the potential. Mislowitzer, Silver & Rothschild made the interesting observation that the absorption of I$^-$ was accelerated by the addition of Li$^+$ and CNS$^-$, ions that reduce the potential strongly. Quigley *et al.* seem to have been the next to study the potential ; in dogs, they stated that histamine and pilocarpine had *no effect*, nor yet the introduction of solutions of pH varying from 1 to 9 ; a marked fall was obtained with glucose solutions. This claim regarding histamine has not been substantiated by later work ; *e.g.*, Rice & Ross found a marked depression of the potential, which was sometimes associated with an increased secretion and sometimes not. More elaborate studies of the gastric potential have been made by Gray and Rehm in America and by Davies in England. Rehm showed that the potential difference across the dog's stomach was some 40–60 mV and that it could be maintained in spite of shunting it across a resistance, so that it was capable of performing electrical work. By inserting an electrode between the mucosa and the outer muscular coat of the stomach, Rehm showed that the potential difference measured by him was definitely across the mucosa, the muscle wall having no influence. Histamine and pilocarpine decreased the potential, whilst they provoked secretion ; and, in general, factors favouring secretion produced a drop in potential, although the correlation between rate of secretion and magnitude of the fall in potential was by no means perfect ; for example, after administration of pilocarpine or mecholyl, the potential fell and remained fairly steady, whilst the secretion continued to increase in rate for a long time. Ethyl alcohol, moreover, lowered the potential across a resting stomach but did not provoke secretion ; on the other hand, when the stomach was already secreting, alcohol lowered both the potential and secretion rate. Rehm showed that, by applying a potential across the mucosa in such a way as to increase its normal potential difference (*i.e.*, by putting the negative electrode on the mucosal side and the positive on the serosal side), the rate of secretion provoked by histamine could be increased, whilst it could be decreased on reversal of the polarity of the applied potential. Histamine, as Mislowitzer found, decreased the potential whilst CNS$^-$, which inhibits gastric secretion, raised the potential back to normal. For example, the resting potential of one dog was 75 mV ; with histamine it fell to 39 mV, whilst with CNS$^-$ plus histamine it fell only to 73 mV. CNS$^-$ had no significant effect on the potential of the resting stomach, in contrast to the finding of Mislowitzer & Silver.

Many of the findings described by Rehm in the dog have been confirmed and extended by Davies on the isolated frog mucosa ; he found the potential to be, on the average, 30 mV, and confirmed that current could be withdrawn without appreciable polarisation, the greatest theoretical power-output being of the order of $7\mu W/cm.^2$ which compares with a maximal value found by Rehm of $22\mu W/cm.^2$ with an external resistance equal to the resistance of the mucosa. This output of energy corresponds, in the frog, to some 10 per cent. of the O_2-consumption of its mucosa. Davies confirmed that the secretion, provoked by histamine, caused a fall in potential, and that an applied electric current increased the secretion. He has elaborated a complex system of chemical reactions to explain the finding, but until more is known about the elementary facts this seems premature. Nevertheless, we need not refrain entirely from speculation as to the origin of the potential and its relation to secretion. It will be seen (p. 359) that the inside of the frog-skin is positive in relation to the outside, *i.e.*, apparently the reverse of the state of affairs in the mucosa.[1] The frog's skin-potential has been interpreted by Ussing as due to a secretion of Na^+ inward more rapidly than Cl^- may follow ; to transpose a similar mechanism to the stomach we might suppose that Cl^- is secreted into the tubules faster than H^+, thus giving a negative potential inside. However, this is to ignore a fundamental difference between the two, namely that the frog-skin secretes continuously, so that the observed potential reflects the *secretory activity*, whilst the stomach potential exhibits the potential at its highest value when it is *not secreting*, showing a *fall* when secreting. Thus it is the fall of potential that must be related to secretion, *i.e.*, the tendency of the mucosal surface to become positive. Consequently a secretion of H^+ into the stomach, associated with a slower passive diffusion of Cl^-, would explain the fall in potential.[2] This is as far as we can go until careful studies, with the use of isotopic tracers, have been carried out to determine which ions are actively transported. The finding that secretion is aided by an applied potential must also be taken into account in any interpretation ; the effect may conceivably be due to an acceleration of the H^+-ions inwards, the contrary effect on the negative ions being less significant than the beneficial effect on the positive ion.

[1] Viewing the gastro-intestinal tract as an invagination of the surface ectoderm, however, the inside of the stomach may be regarded quite legitimately as the surface of the body.

[2] A passive diffusion of Cl^- is supported by the observation of Davenport & Fisher that over a wide range of plasma Br^- concentrations the ratio : $\dfrac{[Br^-]_{Plasma}}{[Cl^-]_{Plasma}}$ is equal to the ratio $\dfrac{[Br^-]_{Gastric}}{[Cl^-]_{Gastric}}$, *i.e.*, Br^- and Cl^- seem to be treated indifferently by the secretory mechanism.

References

BABKIN, B. D. (1944). " Secretory Mechanism of the Digestive Glands." New York, Hoeber.

BERGGREN, S. M. & GOLDBERG, L. (1940). " Absorption of EtOH from the Gastro-Intestinal Tract as a Diffusion Process." *Acta Physiol. Scand.*, 1, 246.

BRADFORD, N. M. & DAVIES, R. E. (1950). " The Site of Hydrochloric Acid Production in the Stomach as Determined by Indicators." *Biochem. J.*, 46, 414.

BRUNSCHWEIG, A. & SCHMITZ, R. L. (1940). " Rapidity of Passage of Chloride Ions from Blood into Gastric Juice of Stimulated Stomach." *P.S.E.B.M.*, 43, 438.

BRUNTON, C. E. (1933). " The pH of the Arterial Blood during Gastric Secretion." *J. Physiol.*, 79, 4P.

BULL, H. B. & GRAY, J. S. (1945). " Secretion of HCl by the Stomach." *Gastro.*, 4, 175.

CONWAY, E. J. (1949). " Biological Interlinkage of Acid-Alkali Formation with Ion Transport and Synthetic Reduction." *Irish J. med. Sci.*, 288, 787.

CONWAY, E. J. (1949). " A Redox Theory of HCl Production by the Gastric Mucosa." *Irish J. med. Sci.*, **288**, 801.
CONWAY, E. J. & BRADY, T. (1947). " Mechanism of High Acid Production by Yeast and its Bearing on HCl Formation in the Stomach." *Nature*, **159**, 137.
CONWAY, E. J., BRADY, T. G. & CARTON, E. (1950). " Redox Theory for the Process in Yeast with Application to the Production of Gastric Acidity." *Biochem. J.*, **47**, 369.
CRANE, E. E. & DAVIES, R. E. (1949). " Transport of Na²⁴ and K⁴² through Gastric Mucosa." *Biochem. J.*, **45**, xxiii.
CRANE, E. E., DAVIES, R. E. & LONGMUIR, N. M. (1948). " Relation between Secretion and Electrical Phenomena in Frog Gastric Mucosa." *Biochem. J.*, **43**, 321.
CRANE, E. E., DAVIES, R. E. & LONGMUIR, N. M. (1948). " The Effect of Electric Current on HCl Secretion by Isolated Frog Gastric Mucosa." *Biochem. J.*, **43**, 336.
CRANE, E. E., DAVIES, R. E. & LONGMUIR, N. M. (1948). " Relations between Hydrochloric Acid Secretion and Electrical Phenomena in Frog Gastric Mucosa." *Biochem. J.*, **43**, 321.
DAVENPORT, H. W. (1939). " Gastric Carbonic Anhydrase." *J. Physiol.*, **97**, 32.
DAVENPORT, H. W. (1940). " The Inhibition of Carbonic Anhydrase and of Gastric Secretion by Thiocyanate." *Amer. J. Physiol.*, **129**, 505.
DAVENPORT, H. W. (1942). " The Secretion of Water as a Component of Gastric Secretion." *Amer. J. Dig.*, **9**, 416.
DAVENPORT, H. W. & FISHER, R. B. (1940). " The Mechanism of the Secretion of Acid by the Gastric Mucosa." *Amer. J. Physiol.*, **131**, 165.
DAVIES, R. E. (1948). " HCl Production of Isolated Gastric Mucosa." *Biochem. J.*, **42**, 39.
DAVIES, R. E. & EDELMAN, J. (1948). " The Function of Carbonic Anhydrase in Gastric Mucosa." *Biochem. J.*, **43**, lvii.
DAVIES, R. E. & KORNBERG, H. L. (1950). " Gastric Urease and HCl Secretion." *Biochem. J.*, **47**, ii.
DAVIES, R. E. & OGSTON, A. G. (1950). " On the Mechanism of Secretion of Ions by Gastric Mucosa and by Other Tissues." *Biochem. J.*, **46**, 324.
DAVIES, R. E. & TERNER, C. (1949). " Effects of Applied Pressure on Secretion by Isolated Amphibian Gastric Mucosa." *Biochem. J.*, **44**, 377.
DELRUE, G. (1930 ; 1933). " Étude de la Sécrétion de l'Estomac." *Arch. int. Physiol.*, **33**, 196 ; **36**, 129.
EDKINS, N. & MURRAY, M. M. (1924). " Influence of CO_2 on the Absorption of Alcohol by the Gastric Mucosa." *J. Physiol.*, **59**, 271.
FELDBERG, W., KEILIN, D. & MANN, T. (1940). " Activity of Carbonic Anhydrase in Relation to Gastric Mucosa." *Nature*, **146**, 651.
FISHER, R. B. & HUNT, J. N. (1950). " The Inorganic Components of Gastric Secretion." *J. Physiol.*, **111**, 138.
GERSH, I. (1938). " Distribution of Chloride in the Gastric Mucous Membrane of the Dog." *P.S.E.B.M.*, **38**, 70.
GLICK, D. (1949). " Urease in the Human Stomach with Respect to Acid Secretion in Ulcer and Cancer." *J. Nat. Canc. Inst.*, **10**, 321.
GRAY, J. S. (1943). " The Physiology of the Parietal Cell with Special Reference to the Formation of Acid." *Gastro.*, **1**, 390.
GRAY, J. S. & ADKISON, J. L. (1941). " The Effect of Inorganic Ions on Gastric Secretion *In Vitro*." *Amer. J. Physiol.*, **134**, 27.
GRAY, J. S., BUCHER, G. R. & HARMAN, H. H. (1941). " The Relationship between Total, Acid, and Neutral Chlorides of Gastric Fluid." *Amer. J. Physiol.*, **132**, 504.
GUDIKSEN, E. (1943). " Investigations on the Electrolyte Content of Gastric Juice." *Acta Physiol. Scand.*, **5**, 39.
HANKE, M. E. (1937). " The Acid-Base and Energy Metabolism of the Stomach and Pancreas." *Science*, **85**, 54.
HANKE, M. E., JOHANNESEN, R. E. & HANKE, M. M. (1931). " Alkalinity of Gastric Venous Blood during Gastric Secretion." *P.S.E.B.M.*, **28**, 698.
HARVEY, C. H. & BENSLEY, R. R. (1912). " Formation of HCl in the Foveolæ, etc." *Biol. Bull.*, **23**, 225.
HEINZ, E. (1951). " Über die primäre Azidität der Magensäure." *Biochim. Biophys. Acta*, **6**, 434.
HOERR, N. L. (1936). " Cytological Studies by the Altmann-Gersh Freezing-Drying Method. III. The Mechanism of Secretion of HCl by the Gastric Mucosa." *Anat. Rec.*, **65**, 417.
HOLLANDER, F. (1932). " Variations in the Chloride Content of Gastric Juice and Their Significance." *J. biol. Chem.*, **97**, 585.

HOLLANDER, F. (1934). "The Composition of Gastric Juice as a Function of its Acidity." *J. biol. Chem.*, **104**, 33.

HOLLANDER, F. (1936). "The Composition of the Gastric Secretion." *Amer. J. Dig. Dis. & Nutr.*, **3**, 651.

HOLLANDER, F. (1942). "The Chemistry and Mechanics of Hydrochloric Acid Formation in the Stomach." *Gastro.*, **1**, 401.

HORSTMANN, P. (1947). "Contribution to the Understanding of the Regulation of the Gastric Acidity." *Acta Physiol. Scand.*, **14**, 27.

KURTZ, L. D. & CLARK, B. B. (1947). "The Inverse Relationship of the Secretion of HCl to the Tension of CO_2 in the Stomach." *Gastro.*, **9**, 594.

LIFSON, N., VARCO, R. L. & VISSCHER, M. B. (1941). "Relationship between Osmotic Activity and Na Content of Gastric Juice." *P.S.E.B.M.*, **47**, 422.

LINDE, S., TEORELL, T. & OBRINK, K. J. (1947). "Experiments on the Primary Acidity of the Gastric Juice." *Acta Physiol. Scand.*, **14**, 220.

LINDERSTRØM-LANG, K., & HOLTER H. (1935). "Localisation of Acid in the Gastric Mucosa of Pigs." *C. r. Lab. Carlsberg*, **20**, No. 11, 33.

LINDERSTRØM-LANG, K., HOLTER, H. & OLSEN, A. S. (1935). "Distribution of Enzymes in the Stomach of Pigs as a Function of its Histological Structure." *C. r. Lab. Carlsberg*, **20**, No. 11, p. 66.

MISLOWITZER, E. & SILVER, S. (1932). "Uber die Potentiale der Magenschleimhaut." I. *Biochem. Z.*, **256**, 423. II. "Magenschleimhaut Potential und Resorption." *Biochem. Z.*, **256**, 444.

MOND, R. (1927). "U. d. elektromotorische Kräfte der Magenschleimhaut vom Frosch." *Pflüg. Arch.*, **215**, 468.

OBRINK, K. J. (1948). "Studies on the Kinetics of the Parietal Secretion of the Stomach." *Acta Physiol. Scand.*, **15**, Suppl. 51.

QUIGLEY, J. P., BARCROFT, J., ADAIR, G. S. & GOODMAN, E. N. (1937). "The Difference in Potential Across the Gastric Membranes and Certain Factors Modifying the Potential." *Amer. J. Physiol.*, **119**, 763.

REHM, W. S. (1943). "Electrical Energy Output of the Resting Stomach as Determined by Shunting its Potential." *Amer. J. Physiol.*, **139**, 1.

REHM, W. S. (1944). "Positive Injury Potential of the Stomach." *Amer. J. Physiol.*, **140**, 720.

REHM, W. S. (1945). "The Effect of Electric Current on Gastric Secretion and Potential." *Amer. J. Physiol.*, **144**, 115.

REHM, W. S. (1946). "Evidence that the Major Portion of the Gastric Potential Originates between the Submucosa and Mucosa." *Amer. J. Physiol.*, **147**, 69.

REHM, W. S. & ENELOW, A. J. (1945). "The Effect of Thiocyanate on Gastric Potential and Secretion." *Amer. J. Physiol.*, **144**, 701.

REHM, W. S. & HOKIN, L. E. (1947). "The Effect of Pilocarpine, Mecholyl, Atropine, and Alcohol on the Gastric Potential and the Secretion of HCl." *Amer. J. Physiol.*, **149**, 162.

RICE, H. V. & ROSS, R. T. (1947). "Factors Affecting the Electrical Potential of the Gastric Mucosa." *Amer. J. Physiol.*, **149**, 77.

ROBACK, R., GROSSMAN, M. I. & IVY, A. C. (1950). "Intragastric Pressure which Abolishes Secretion of Acid." *Amer. J. Physiol.*, **161**, 47.

TEORELL, T. (1933). "Untersuchungen uber die Magensaftsekretion." *Scand. Arch. Physiol.*, **66**, 225.

TEORELL, T. (1939). "On the Permeability of the Stomach Mucosa for Acids and some other Substances." *J. gen. Physiol.*, **23**, 263.

TEORELL, T. (1940). "On the Primary Acidity of the Gastric Juice." *J. Physiol.*, **97**, 308.

TEORELL, T. (1947). "Electrolyte Diffusion in Relation to the Acidity Regulation of the Gastric Juice." *Gastro.*, **9**, 425.

TERNER, C. (1949). "The Reduction of Gastric Acidity by Back Diffusion of H^+ through the Mucosa." *Biochem. J.*, **45**, 150.

THOMAS, J. E. & FRIEDMAN, M. H. F. (1949). "Digestive System." *Ann. Rev. Physiol.*, **11**, 103.

ZIMMERMANN, K. W. (1925). "Beitrag zur Kenntnis der Fundusdrüsen im menschlichen Magen." *Ergebn. d. Physiol.*, **24**, 281.

CHAPTER XIV

THE KIDNEY AND OSMOTIC REGULATION

THE MECHANISM OF THE KIDNEY

THE main requirements implied by the so-called " constancy of the internal environment " are first, that the total concentration of dissolved material, predominantly [1] NaCl and NaHCO$_3$, in the circulating fluid should not fluctuate widely, since this " osmotic activity " largely determines the amount of water within the cells. Secondly, the level of the resting potential, and the excitability of conducting tissue, depend critically on the concentrations of K$^+$ and Ca^{++} in the interstitial fluid, so that these must not vary greatly ; and, again, the integrity of cell membranes is bound up, in some way not clearly understood, with the maintenance of suitable proportions of Ca^{++}, Mg^{++}, K$^+$ and Na$^+$ in the outside medium ; hence, not only the total osmotic activity of the plasma, but also the relative concentrations of its various constituents, must be maintained within a suitable range. Thirdly, the pH of the blood must be maintained very constant since it is known that very small changes may cause death of the organism ; the metabolic reactions of the body result in the continuous net production of acid ; a proportion of this is lost as CO$_2$ in the lungs, but other mechanisms are also necessary for its elimination. Finally, a number of other products of metabolism, *e.g.*, urea, must be eliminated from the body. In the higher forms of life it is the kidney that takes the dominant rôle in the maintenance of this constancy of the internal environment ; the mechanisms employed involve, as we shall see, the process of active transport ; and the specialised cells responsible for this transfer of dissolved material and water against concentration gradients must clearly exhibit this phenomenon in respect to a wider range of substances than any other cells so far considered.

In mammals, birds, amphibians and most fishes [2] the process by which the kidney maintains the constancy of the composition of the blood is the indiscriminate removal of fluid from the circulation into tubules, from which substances such as sugar, amino-acids, and most of the salts and water, are *selectively* removed back again into the blood, whilst unnecessary metabolic products and exogenous materials are left behind in the tubules, whence they are excreted as urine. In actuality, whole blood is not removed, as such, from the circulation ; instead it is ultra-filtered into the tubules, the plasma proteins and the formed elements of the blood being left behind in the vascular system, so that it is the *filtrate* that is actually removed from the circulation and subsequently partially reabsorbed.

---

[1] As we shall see, in the elasmobranch fishes, such as the shark, the concentration of urea is a significant factor in the total osmotic activity of the blood.

[2] The exceptions are the so-called *aglomerular* fishes such as *Lophius piscatorius* (toad fish), and *Opsanus tau* (goose fish).

Structure of the Kidney

The anatomy of the kidney may now be discussed briefly in the light of its function as (*a*) a filtration apparatus for the removal of blood-filtrate from the circulation and (*b*) a reabsorption apparatus for the restoration of necessary components of the filtrate to the circulation. The fundamental unit of the kidney is the *nephron* (Fig. 149), consisting of the *renal corpuscle* and the *convoluted tubule*. The renal corpuscle may be regarded as a skein of capillaries, the *glomerular tuft*, enclosed by the blind dilated end of the proximal tubule which is known as *Bowman's capsule*. The

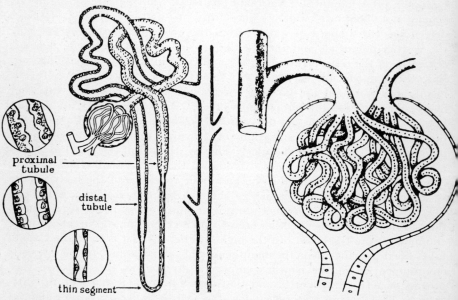

proximal tubule

distal tubule

thin segment

Fig. 149. The nephron. (Homer Smith. *Physiology of the Kidney*. New York, O.U.P.)

Fig. 150. Schema of the human glomerulus (Richards, after Vimtrup. *Proc. Roy Soc.*)

capillaries of each glomerular tuft rise from a twig of an interlobular artery, the *afferent arteriole*, and collect together again to form the *efferent arteriole* (Fig. 150). It is in the renal capsule that the filtration of the plasma occurs, the anatomical features of the circulation being such as to favour a high pressure of fluid within the glomerular tuft of capillaries (thus the efferent arteriole has only one-fifth of the diameter of the afferent). Since, other things being equal, the rate of filtration will be determined by the pressure in the glomerular tuft, a nervous or hormonal control over the rate of filtration may be attained by modification of the relative diameters of the afferent and efferent arterioles.[1] The tubule in the mammal is divided into

[1] There is still some uncertainty as to the hydrodynamics of the situation. The rate of filtration is remarkably constant (*vide, e.g.*, Shannon, 1936), even under the action of adrenaline which constricts arterioles (Smith *et al.*, 1940) ; it seems very likely that variations in constrictor tone occur in the efferent arteriole ; thus increased constriction will raise the pressure in the glomerulus and increase the *fraction* of the blood passing

three parts, the *proximal tubule*, the *loop of Henle*, and the *distal tubule*. The proximal tubule is continuous with Bowman's capsule through a short neck and leads to the distal tubule by means of a U-shaped portion, the *ascending* and *descending limbs* of *Henle's loop*. The distal tubule leads into a collecting tubule which in turn leads into a papillary duct emptying into the ureter at the renal pelvis. The efferent arteriole, leading from the glomerulus, breaks up into capillaries which ramify round the tubules and Henle's loop, so that the selective reabsorption of necessary materials from the blood filtrate in the tubule occurs across the tubular epithelium into these capillaries.

The capsular wall consists of a *visceral* and a *parietal* layer, the former closely invests the capillary membranes and consists of a supporting *basement membrane* and an outer covering of flat epithelial cells ; the parietal layer consists of squamous cells which become cuboidal near the point where the capsule joins the tubule (Fig. 150). The walls of the proximal tubule consist of a single layer of columnar epithelial cells, and they differ from the walls of the distal tubule and Henle's loop by possessing delicate vertical striations on their free borders—the *brush* or *bristle border*. The kidney is divided into an outer layer, the *cortex*, and an inner portion, the *medulla*, and, between these, the intermediate layer containing the larger branchings of the renal blood vessels. The glomeruli are situated in the cortical layer, and the loops of Henle pass into the medullary layer as rays. It is unnecessary for our purpose here to enter into further details of the circulation of the blood through the kidney ; it will be seen that blood passes first through the glomeruli and only later through the small vessels supplying the tubules. Recent anatomical studies have shown, however, that there are several possibilities of a short-circuiting of the blood, so that not all of it that emerges from the renal vein can be said to have been submitted to the purifying process of filtration and subsequent reabsorption (Shonyo & Mann).

Aglomerular Kidneys. In certain species of fishes, *e.g.*, the goose fish, the glomerulus is lacking in the nephron, and we must conclude that the urine is formed in these circumstances by the direct transport of substances from the blood into the tubule ; *i.e.*, that there is no filtration and reabsorption, but simply the selective transfer of waste products and some water into the tubular lumen. This we may describe as *tubular secretion*, and it has become clear that even in the glomerular kidney the two processes of filtration and reabsorption are not sufficient to account for the quantitative aspects of urine formation, and that we have, superimposed on these, the phenomenon of tubular secretion. On this basis, urine is formed by three processes :—

(*a*) Filtration.

(*b*) Tubular reabsorption of necessary substances.

(*c*) Tubular secretion of certain waste products.

Let us now consider each of these three mechanisms in some detail.

through that is filtered (the *filtration fraction*), but will at the same time decrease flow of blood through the kidney ; these two factors are self-compensating, and tend to keep the *amount* of filtrate formed constant. Any nervous control over kidney secretion must operate on this aspect, tubular reabsorption and secretion being the same in a transplanted kidney as in a normal one (Maluf).

Filtration

The filtration process is essentially the same as that involved in the formation of the interstitial fluid (p. 210) ; the driving force causing filtration is the glomerular capillary pressure, and, acting against this, there is the colloid osmotic pressure of the plasma proteins and the resistance to flow along the tubules. If the capillary pressure is just balanced by the colloid osmotic pressure, no filtration will occur and urine formation will cease. In the frog, the glomeruli and tubules are more superficially disposed than in the mammalian kidney so that Hayman found it possible to measure the pressures in the afferent arterioles and in the glomerular capillaries. The average values for more than 100 frogs were $31 \cdot 6 \pm 6 \cdot 0$ and $20 \cdot 2 \pm 6 \cdot 8$ cm. H_2O respectively. The colloid osmotic pressure of frog's plasma is about 10 cm. H_2O, hence in the frog there is, on the average, an excess pressure of about 10 cm. H_2O driving fluid into Bowman's capsule and along the tubules.

Composition of Glomerular Fluid. The accessibility of the glomeruli of the frog and *Necturus* has led to an extremely valuable series of experiments by Richards and his collaborators on the chemical composition of the fluid in Bowman's capsule. By insertion of a fine capillary into the capsule, the glomerular filtrate could be withdrawn and submitted to chemical analysis by methods specially adapted to the small quantities obtained.[1] It was found that, within the limits of experimental error of the methods, the concentrations of Cl^-, urea, phenol red, indigo carmine, inorganic phosphate, creatinine and uric acid, and the osmotic pressure, were the same in the glomerular fluid as in a filtrate of blood plasma. The chemical findings, together with the results of the determination of the available filtration pressure in the glomerulus, thus lead to the conclusion that the function of the latter, at least in the amphibian kidney, is to filter off a part of the crystalloidal contents of the blood in an unselective manner. There is no reason to postulate, therefore, any selective removal of substances from the blood by the epithelium of Bowman's capsule.

In the mammal, indirect methods of study have almost invariably been used [2] ; from the mechanical point of view the factors of venous pressure, systemic arterial pressure and intra-renal pressure have been studied, particularly by means of the perfused isolated kidney, the organ being supplied by blood through the renal artery from an artificial perfusion apparatus. Qualitatively, the changes in rate of flow of urine, when these factors were varied under these very artificial conditions, were in accord with expectation ; since the fundamental facts of renal physiology are now so universally accepted, we need not enter into further discussion of this aspect except to point out that Krogh & Rehberg have deduced from Landis' measurements of capillary permeability to water (p. 212), that the

---

[1] One cannot but admire the ingenuity displayed both in the collection of the fluid and in the adaptation of standard methods of analysis to the extremely small quantities of fluid obtainable (1–4 mm.[3] were obtained after one hour of drainage) ; essentially the methods depend on carrying out the reactions in capillary tubes and comparing the colour with standards in tubes of the same diameter.

[2] For a review of this aspect see Winton.

minimal filtration pressure required to cause a normal flow of urine is some 80 mm. Hg ; allowing a colloid osmotic pressure of 40 mm. Hg (the value for the most concentrated plasma present in the glomerulus), and a drop of pressure along the tubules of 25-80 mm. Hg, it would seem that the pressure of blood in the glomeruli would be inadequate to cause an adequate flow of urine. However, it may well be that measurements on capillary permeability in the skin are not applicable to a specialised tissue like the kidney glomerulus.

Clearance. In the intact animal the measurement of the actual rate of the primary filtration process is fundamental to all studies on renal function ; it is quite clear from our sketch of the essential steps in the formation of urine—filtration followed by partial reabsorption of the filtrate—that the rate of flow of urine, alone, can give no measure of the actual rate of filtration, in the ignorance of the extent of the reabsorption of water. However, if some substance in the blood were known *not* to be reabsorbed after filtration, then, by measuring its simultaneous concentrations in plasma and urine, together with the rate of flow of urine, the rate of filtration could be determined with precision. Thus suppose a concentration of this hypothetical substance equal to 5 mg./ml. was found in the urine, and the amount of urine collected in one hour was 100 ml. ; 500 mg. would have been filtered from the blood, since none was reabsorbed. If the concentration in the plasma was 0·2 mg./ml., the amount of plasma that had to be filtered to give this 500 mg. was $500/0·2 = 2,500$ ml., *i.e.*, 2,500 ml. of plasma were filtered per hour, or 41 ml. per minute. More generally, if B is the plasma concentration, U the urine concentration, and V the flow of urine in ml. per minute, the amount excreted per minute is $U \times V$, and the amount of filtrate formed is UV/B if the substance is not reabsorbed. For any substance, whether it is reabsorbed or not, the factor UV/B is called the *clearance* of that substance ; it represents the amount of plasma that *would have to be* completely filtered to give the quantity of substance found in the urine in one minute of flow. If, as we have seen, the substance is not reabsorbed (nor yet secreted directly into the tubule), the clearance measures the rate of filtration ; thus inulin, a high-molecular weight polysaccharide, is not reabsorbed, and the *inulin clearance* measures the filtration rate. If reabsorption occurs, clearly the product $U \times V$ no longer tells us how much material actually passed into the glomerulus, it is obviously too small ; thus the clearance of a substance that is partially reabsorbed is less than the inulin clearance ; similarly if, besides by filtration, a substance may enter the tubule by secretion, its clearance will be greater than the inulin clearance. It is a simple matter to calculate, from the simultaneously observed clearances of inulin and any other substance, the extent of reabsorption or tubular secretion, assuming, of course, that both reabsorption and secretion of the same substance do not occur simultaneously.[1] We can thus understand how important it

---

[1] The possibility that a substance is both secreted and reabsorbed cannot be completely ruled out ; *e.g.*, K⁺ is normally reabsorbed but in certain circumstances an actual tubular secretion has been described, *e.g.*, by Berliner & Kennedy and by Mudge, Foulks & Gilman.

is to know whether there exists a substance that is neither reabsorbed from, nor secreted by, the tubules. The discovery that the inulin clearance measures the rate of filtration [1] is due independently to the laboratories of Homer Smith and A. N. Richards ; before this, creatinine was the

$$HN=C \overset{NH——CO}{\underset{N[CH_3].CH_2}{<}} \qquad HN=C \overset{NH_2}{\underset{N[CH_3].CH_2.COOH}{<}}$$

Creatinine   Creatine

favourite substance used, although there was some uncertainty as to its value ; later work has shown that only in certain animals, *e.g.*, the dog, rabbit, sheep, and seal, is the creatinine clearance identical with the inulin clearance ; in man, creatinine is secreted by the tubules (Shannon, 1941). Besides that of inulin, the clearances of sorbitol, mannitol, dulcitol, and sorbitan in man and the dog may be used to measure filtration rate ; from a practical point of view, thiosulphate, which is easy to determine chemically, has recently been recommended. Thus Newman, Gilman & Philips (1946) stated that its clearance in man was the same as that of inulin, and Gilman, Philips & Koelle (1946) and Pitts & Lotspiech (1947) made the same claim in respect of the dog (creatinine clearance in this case). A thorough investigation of its clearance in the cat by M. G. Eggleton & Habib (1949) has shown, however, that thiosulphate is secreted by the tubules. The secretion is depressed by *p*-aminohippuric acid, *i.e.*, there is competition. Thiosulphate is not without effect on the normal function of the kidney, exerting a depressant action on both glomerular filtration and tubular function ; since these effects have about the same magnitude, it appears that individual nephrons are put out of action by thiosulphate.

Filtration Fraction. The actual fraction of the plasma passing through the kidney that is filtered—the *filtration fraction*—is another quantity that is of interest, especially clinically ; this may be found by injecting inulin and withdrawing blood simultaneously from an artery and the renal vein ; the loss in concentration in the vein is due to the filtration, the greater the fraction filtered the greater the loss in concentration. It is of interest

[1] The validity of the inulin clearance as a measure of filtration rate has been recently called into question by Barclay and his colleagues, who have shown that there is a correlation between inulin clearance and plasma inulin level, and by Eggleton & Habib, who have made a careful comparison of the inulin and creatinine clearances in the cat under a variety of conditions. The last-mentioned authors have shown that the inulin clearance exhibits a maximum at plasma levels of about 50 mg./100 ml., declining at levels above and below this ; if inulin clearance were a true measure of filtration rate, we should expect it to be reasonably independent of plasma level. The falling off of the clearance at high plasma levels might be explained by defective filtration, owing to the low permeability of the glomerular membranes to this substance, but this explanation would not apply to the decline at low plasma levels. In the cat, at any rate, it would seem that the creatinine clearance is the more reliable measure of filtration rate. It is worth noting that an injection of creatinine depresses the clearance of inulin. These recent results have thrown the subject of renal physiology into some confusion, and it may be that a grea t deal of published work will have to be revised when filtration rates can be unequivocally related to the clearance of some substance.

that the fraction is not the same for inulin and creatinine, being on the average 0·2 for the former and 0·26 for the latter in man.[1] In view of the large difference in molecular size of the two substances this is not surprising ; during ultra-filtration, substances passing the filtering membrane with great difficulty will tend to be left behind.

Proteins. Before passing to a consideration of the process of tubular reabsorption, we may note that the urine is generally spoken of as being free, normally, from protein ; this suggests that the glomerular capillaries are capable of retaining proteins more efficiently than the peripheral capillaries (p. 207), which probably lose protein continuously ; thus if the glomerular filtrate of man contained only 10 mg./100 ml., *i.e.*, the same amount as in the so-called protein-free tissue fluids such as the aqueous humour or cerebrospinal fluid, this would correspond to a loss of 18 g. of plasma protein per day, a serious drain if this passed into the urine, so that we must assume, either that the barrier between blood and Bowman's capsule is more selective than the blood-brain barrier, or that there is some reabsorption of protein ; some evidence for the latter alternative has been provided by recent studies of Smetana in rats. Of interest in this connection is a study of Bayliss *et al.* on the renal excretion of various proteins ; the results of this study are shown in Table XXVIII, and it will be seen that hæmoglobin occupies an intermediate position, being excreted only if the plasma concentration exceed a certain value ; albumin, the smallest of the plasma proteins, is retained.[2] Gelatin is not only excreted but it also causes the excretion of plasma proteins ; thus Lowell *et al.* found that, of 50 g. of gelatin given intravenously, 30–50 per cent. was excreted during

TABLE XXVIII

The Excretion of Proteins by the Cat and Rabbit and the Isolated Perfused Kidney of the Dog. (*Bayliss, Kerridge & Russell*, 1933.)

Proteins excreted :	Molecular Weight
Gelatin	35,000
Bence Jones . . .	35,000
Egg albumin . . .	34,500
Hæmoglobin . . .	68,000
Proteins not excreted :	
Hæmoglobin . . .	68,000
Serum albumin . . .	67,500
Serum globulin . . .	103,800
Edestin	208,000
Casein	188,000
Hæmocyanin . . .	5,000,000

[1] In man the renal venous blood has been drawn by the rather frightening technique of passing a cannula up the cubital vein of the arm, through the right auricle and on through the vena cava up to the renal vein itself.

[2] In the cases when plasma proteins do appear in the urine the proportion of albumin greatly exceeds that of the others, due doubtless to its smaller size.

the first day together with 10–15 g. of serum protein ; this effect is not peculiar to gelatin, for example ovalbumin does the same and it may be due, as Danielli has suggested, to the replacement of the larger adsorbed albumin and globulin molecules in the capillary pores, thereby increasing the size of the latter ; on the other hand it may be due, as Dock has suggested, to a blockage of reabsorption, supposing that this is a normal process taking place continuously.

Reabsorption

The normal urine is free from glucose except when the concentration of this substance in the blood is very high ; it is quite evident that the transfer of this substance involves its passage up a concentration gradient, so that active transport on the part of the tubular epithelium is involved. Again, the urine of the frog may be free from Cl^-, hence, in this animal at least, Cl^- must be transferred against a concentration gradient. A partial reabsorption of a substance is possible, however, without any active mechanism directed towards this individual component of the glomerular filtrate. Thus the partial or complete absorption of NaCl from the filtrate must, of itself, make the fluid hypotonic ; water will therefore pass from tubule to blood, so that any substance, not actively absorbed, becomes concentrated, and diffuses from tubule to blood, provided it can pass the tubular membranes. That such a mechanism is responsible for the partial reabsorption of urea in the dog and man has been proved by numerous experiments, *e.g.*, those of Shannon, who showed that at least 40 per cent. of the filtered urea is reabsorbed and that the actual percentage varied inversely with the rate of flow of urine, *i.e.*, the more rapidly the fluid was carried through the tubules, the less chance was there for this back diffusion.[1]

Maximal Reabsorptive Capacity. Where active reabsorption occurs, as with glucose, amino-acids, phosphate and ascorbic acid, among other substances, the phenomena are generally different, there being a definite limit to the amount of substance that may be reabsorbed, which is apparently independent of the rate at which it is presented to the tubules, in marked contrast to the case of urea. Thus in Fig. 151 the results of a typical series of experiments on glucose are given ; the excretion of glucose in the urine was measured at the same time as the excretion of inulin, so that the amount of glucose filtered in unit time was known. The difference between this amount and that appearing in the urine therefore represented the amount reabsorbed. At low blood concentrations the urine was free from sugar, the amount reabsorbed being equal to the amount filtered ; as the blood-sugar was raised, the urine remained free from sugar up to a certain concentration ; up to this point, therefore, the

---

[1] A mathematical treatment of the problem of reabsorption of urea, at varying rates of filtration and urine flow, has revealed complexities in the situation, which may, however, be resolved if it is assumed that reabsorption occurs at two loci, in the proximal tubule first and later, as a consequence of the " facultative " reabsorption of water, in the distal tubule (Dole, 1943). If compounds of the urea type depend only on simple diffusion for reabsorption, an increase in lipoid-solubility should favour the process ; Nicholes & Herrin have found that thiourea, phenylthiourea, etc., are reabsorbed to a greater extent than urea.

amount reabsorbed increased. Increasing the blood concentration beyond this point produced excretion of glucose, but the amount reabsorbed remained constant ; thus, on plotting the amount of reabsorbed glucose against the concentration of glucose in the blood, we obtain a straight line which, at the critical point, runs horizontal, indicating that the maximal rate of reabsorption has been reached. The existence of this sharp threshold implies that the glomerulus and tubule of each nephron are adjusted to each other's capacities, so that the tubules belonging to the faster filtering glomeruli are capable of a greater maximal reabsorption than the tubules with the slower filtering glomeruli ; if this were not true, no such sharp threshold would be observed (Shannon, Farber & Troast) ; that this adjustment is present in spite of wide variations in the size of the glomeruli and tubules shows how well adjusted the nephron is for fulfilling its

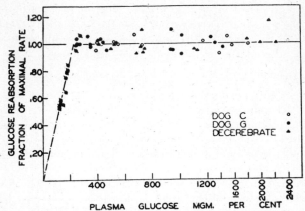

Fig. 151. Illustrating the reabsorption maximum for glucose. As the concentration of glucose in the plasma is raised, the amount reabsorbed increases only up to a certain limit, when the *maximal reabsorptive capacity*, T_m, is reached. (Shannon & Fisher. *Amer. J. Physiol.*)

functions ; moreover, to a first approximation, this fact permits us to treat the whole kidney as a single nephron.

Competition. The results typified by Fig. 151 indicate the presence of a limit to the reabsorptive capacity of the tubules in respect to glucose ; moreover, when different sugars are presented to the tubules simultaneously, it is found that the total amount of sugar reabsorbed remains the same, but that the presence of one sugar depresses the reabsorption of the other. These facts led Shannon & Fisher to postulate, as a mechanism for reabsorption, the reaction of sugar with a substance in the tubular epithelial cell to form a complex which was later decomposed at the tubule-blood boundary to give the original sugar, which passed into the blood stream. As with all such postulated mechanisms of active transfer, the process must be linked with the metabolism of the cell, so that the energy for the osmotic work can be derived from the chemical energy of metabolism. If the same hypothetical substance were involved for all sugars, the phenomenon of competition for reabsorption would be intelligible. The much smaller efficiency of the mechanism for the reabsorption of galactose and of xylose [1] is considered to be due to the smaller affinity of the hypothetical substance for these sugars. The state of affairs is essentially the same for the amino-acids and creatine, in the sense that the tubules exhibit a *maximal reabsorptive capacity* (indicated by the symbol T_m) for these amino-compounds. As with the sugars, the amino-acids exhibit competition ; according to Beyer *et al.*, arginine competes with lysine and histidine, but not with glycine and leucine ; leucine competes with isoleucine, but not with glycine ; and, finally, isoleucine does not compete with glycine. Creatine, according to Pitts, competes with glycine for reabsorption. On the other hand, no competition has been observed between sugars and amino-acids, so that separate hypothetical compounds must be invoked. It should be noted that, unlike the state of affairs with glucose, there is no sharp threshold for amino-acid excretion ; instead, the amount reabsorbed falls off gradually with increasing amounts filtered *i.e.*, before the maximal reabsorptive capacity is reached some amino-acid passes out into the urine. Pitts observed considerable differences in the reabsorptive rates of the amino-acids, the order being :—

Glycine > Alanine > Glutamic acid > Arginine [2]

Phlorizin. The reabsorption of glucose may be completely blocked in the dog by the administration of the drug *phlorizin*, a typical *phlorizin diabetes* being produced ; this blockage is of great interest, and since the same drug blocks the absorption of sugars from the intestine, where an active transport by way of an intermediate phosphorylated sugar has been postulated, a similar mechanism has been invoked, *e.g.*, by Lundsgaard, for the reabsorption of glucose in the tubule ; *i.e.*, at the inside surface of the tubule epithelial cell the sugar is said to be converted to an organic phosphate by a specific enzyme, *kidney phosphorylase*, and transported, as such, through the cell ; at the tubule-blood boundary the sugar is said to be liberated by *alkaline phosphatase*, a phosphate splitting enzyme, and to disappear in the blood stream. This explanation has been recently subjected to a rigid experimental test by Shapiro ; he has shown that phlorizin is not specific in poisoning phosphorylation reactions, it actually

---

[1] For example, approximately 40 per cent. of the galactose presented to the tubules is reabsorbed under conditions where 100 per cent. of glucose would have been ; the figure for xylose is only 27 per cent. The relative rates of reabsorption by the frog's kidney are in the order :—

Glucose > Galactose > Mannose > Fructose > Xylose > Arabinose

similar, in their general trend, to the series found for intestinal absorption. We may note that the reabsorptive mechanism is able to distinguish between optical isomers, *e.g.*, the natural l (+)-lactic acid is reabsorbed in preference to the dextro-compound (Craig, 1946).

[2] Ascorbic acid exhibits a maximal reabsorptive rate, and must be classed with the amino-acids and sugars ; according to Friedman *et al.* it is never completely reabsorbed ; moreover the maximal rate is easily exceeded so that at high blood concentrations the clearance is nearly the same as that of inulin ; glucose reabsorption seems, according to Selkurt, to interfere with the reabsorption of ascorbic acid. Lactic acid, on the other hand, is very efficiently reabsorbed since it is barely excreted even when the blood concentration reaches 100 mg./100 ml. ; its reabsorption is apparently unaffected by the presence of glucose so that once again we must invoke a new hypothetical substance with which it may combine in the tubule cell.

inhibits a wide variety of enzymes, *e.g.*, the oxidation of pyruvic and citric acids by the kidney ; moreover, as Lundsgaard showed, the kidneys from a completely phlorizinised animal (*i.e.*, one in which reabsorption of glucose is completely blocked) can phosphorylate sugars *in vitro*. Shapiro's studies suggest that the primary inhibiting action of phlorizin is exerted on certain oxidative processes which are coupled with the phosphorylation of adenylic acid. Adenylic acid reacts with phosphate to give ATP (p. 501) ; and, if this substance is either directly or indirectly concerned in the supply of metabolic energy to the active transport mechanism, any interference with its synthesis will block secretion. Since, moreover, phlorizin reduces the tubular *secretion* of diodrast and creatinine, and the reabsorption of ascorbic acid, it is much more likely that it interferes in a general way with the metabolic activities of the tubule cell, rather than specifically in the first stage of the process of active transport. Support for this more general view of the action of poisons on tubular secretion is provided by the recent work of Mudge & Taggart who have established a good correlation between the inhibition of tubular secretory activity by 2, 4-dinitrophenol and its inhibition of the cyclophorase system of the kidney, *i.e.*, by its inhibition of that series of enzymes concerned with the oxidative generation of energy-rich phosphates (pp. 31, 501). An actual increase in the maximal secretory rate of *p*-aminohippuric acid was obtained by injections of the intermediary metabolites, acetate and lactate.

Permeability. Of some interest with regard to the mechanism of reabsorption in the tubule is the observation by Höber of an effective impermeability of the tubular membrane, in the direction : blood-to-tubule, to all the sugars that are actively reabsorbed. Thus, on perfusing the renal portal vein of the frog with glucose,[1] galactose, etc., no sugar was found in the urine. In other secretory systems, in spite of the existence of an active transfer in one direction, a permeability in both directions has been observed (*e.g.*, Hoagland's work on the absorption of K^+ by plant roots, p. 284 ; Visscher's on the absorption of salt and water from the intestine, p. 301 ; and so on) so that it is possible that glucose can, indeed, pass in both directions but that the secretory activity effectively prevents any *net transfer* ; against this is the observation that in the presence of phlorizin no permeability from blood to tubule was observed. Höber also observed that lipoid-soluble substances penetrated rapidly in both directions across the tubular membrane, and found no evidence for their active absorption. Of the more lipoid-insoluble substances, molecular size seemed to be important ; *e.g.*, the amino-compounds studied gave the following order of penetration :—

Acetamide > thiourea > methylurea > lactamide > malonamide > butyramide > creatinine > asparagine

[1] The blood supply to the renal tubules in the frog is functionally separate from that to the glomeruli ; by perfusing the abdominal aorta, substances in the perfusion fluid reach the glomeruli, whereas, by perfusion through the renal portal vein, substances may be presented directly to the tubules. Perfusion of the renal portal vein with a mixture of cyanol and phenol red effects an excellent separation of these dyes because cyanol is not secreted by the tubules and can only enter the urine by way of the glomerular filtrate.

the last mentioned not penetrating at all. This observation has led Höber to believe that the passive diffusion of substances across the tubular membrane is largely a matter of passing water-filled pores, *e.g.*, pores in the intercellular cement, but the evidence for this is by no means conclusive.

The reabsorption of salts and water from the tubule is closely bound up with the more general problem of ionic and osmotic regulation ; the discussion of this subject may therefore be profitably deferred till later, and we may now pass on to the subject of tubular secretion.

Tubular Secretion

The clearances of certain substances have been found to be greater than the simultaneous inulin clearance. This can only mean that these substances are eliminated by tubular secretion in addition to filtration. Certain foreign substances, *e.g.*, diodrast,[1] hippuran, and *p*-aminohippuric acid with formulæ indicated below :—

Diodrast   Hippuran   p-aminohippuric acid

exhibit this secretion to a remarkable degree, to such an extent indeed that they may be completely eliminated from the blood in a single circuit through the kidney, provided that the concentration in the blood does not exceed a definite value.[2]

Maximal Secretory Capacity. As the concentration of any of these substances in the blood is raised, just as with the reabsorption of sugars, a *maximal secretory capacity*, T_m, is attained, further increases in rate of excretion being due entirely to filtration. In Fig. 152 the filtration and secretion components of the excretion of phenol red by the dog have been plotted against the plasma concentration by Pitts. As the concentration rises, the amount excreted by filtration increases linearly (Curve B). The *actual amount excreted*, *i.e.*, the total of *filtered* and *secreted* phenol red, increases rapidly at first (Curve A), but the curve eventually runs parallel with the filtration curve, indicating that, beyond a concentration of about 5 mg./100 ml., further increases in excretion, following a rise in the blood level, are due only to increased amounts in the glomerular filtrate. On subtracting the ordinates of curve B from those of curve A, the curve C is

[1] "Diodrast Compound Solution" is really a mixture of this compound and its diethanolamine salt.

[2] This is probably a completely true statement if reference is made to the blood actually passing through the tubular blood capillaries ; as indicated above, short-circuiting may occur so that in actuality the blood issuing in the renal vein is not completely depleted of *p*-aminohippuric acid ; for example, at a plasma concentration of 2·5 mg./100 ml., the *extraction ratio* is 0·88.

obtained, indicating the amount of phenol red secreted by the tubules ; this treatment brings out the important fact that a secretory maximum is reached.[1] Secretory maxima of this type have been demonstrated for a wide variety of substances ; and Shannon has applied similar concepts to explain these maxima to those used to explain the maximal reabsorptive capacity. As with the latter, tubular secretion exhibits competition, *e.g.*, phenol red, diodrast, hippuran, *p*-hydroxy-, *p*-amino-, *p*-acetylamino-, *m*-amino-, *m*-hydroxy-hippuric acids, 2-pyridine-1-acetic acid, cinnamoyl-glycine, and penicillin, all compete with each other and thus, on the basis of Shannon's interpretation, are said to be transported by combination with the same tubular component.[2] In this connection it is worth noting that the maximal reabsorptive capacity for a given substance may be decreased by the saturation of the tubular secretory process, *e.g.*, that of ascorbic acid by saturating with *p*-aminohippuric acid, and that of uric acid by saturation with diodrast. It could be argued that the tubule cells are capable of a certain limited rate of performing secretory work ; if a large part of the available energy is used in secreting, less will be available for reabsorption. Against this, however, is the observation that the secretion of *p*-aminohippuric acid is unaffected by maximal reabsorption of glucose.

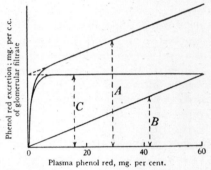

Fig. 152. Curves describing the excretion of phenol red. Curve A shows the total phenol red excreted with varying plasma levels ; Curve B shows the amount filtered ; Curve C is the difference between Curves A and B, and indicates the variation in the amount excreted by tubular secretion with varying plasma levels. Note that the rate of secretion reaches a maximum. (Pitts. *J. cell. & comp. Physiol.*)

Phlorizin, as we have seen, inhibits the secretion of diodrast ; a phosphorylation mechanism has therefore been suggested to explain this process too ; apart from the objections already raised, however, we may note that the reabsorption of glucose does not compete with the excretion of diodrast ; if phosphorylation is important, the absorption of glucose should have some influence ; moreover, diodrast is unlikely, on chemical grounds, to be phosphorylated, and all the substances that compete with it for secretion are equally unlikely to undergo this reaction.

Tissue-Culture Studies. Some contribution to our understanding of the mechanism of tubular secretion has been provided by the tissue-culture

[1] The measurement of the maximal secretory capacity, T_m, for *p*-aminohippuric acid may be used to determine the functional activity of the tubules ; similarly the maximal reabsorptive capacity for glucose has been employed. In this connection we may note that Eggleton & Habib have shown that, if very high concentrations of *p*-aminohippuric acid are established in the blood, the back-diffusion of this substance becomes significant, to such an extent, in fact, that the amount excreted may be less than that filtered.

[2] The finding that the secretion of penicillin may be depressed by *p*-aminohippuric acid may be useful in maintaining the concentration of penicillin in the blood at a therapeutic level for long periods ; however, *p*-aminohippuric acid is expensive to prepare.

studies of Chambers on the developing chick kidney (mesonephros). Transplanted fragments of proximal tubules were found to grow into closed cylinders as a result of the migration and rearrangement of cells ; these closed tubes soon became distended cysts owing to the secretion of material into the lumen. According to Keosian, the fluid is hypotonic to the outside culture medium and thus represents a true secretion, involving the performance of osmotic work ; the obvious tension within the cyst, moreover, betokens an active secretion of water into the lumen, since the difference of osmotic pressure would otherwise draw water into the medium. The cysts exhibited a well-marked power of concentrating phenol red from the medium, producing more than a 20-fold accumulation in the lumen, whilst the cells showed only a moderate accumulation ; secretion is therefore something more, in this case, than the mere accumulation of a substance within the cell, followed by passive diffusion outwards. The secretory activity could be completely and reversibly blocked by metabolic poisons such as cyanide and iodoacetate ; moreover, if a cyst containing a high concentration of phenol red was cooled, the dye returned to the outside medium ; re-warming allowed a further accumulation. Evidently the cyst is permeable to phenol red in both directions, the accumulation within the lumen resulting from a more rapid penetration inwards than outwards ; cooling the cyst reduces the rate of supply of energy necessary to maintain this differential permeability and thus allows the cyst to " run down." An important observation of Chambers was that tubule cells only accumulated phenol red when they were organised in cysts ; isolated cells always remained colourless. Another interesting point was that distal tubules never became distended, nor did they accumulate dye in their lumen ; consequently, in the chick at least, tubular secretion is probably a function of the proximal tubule.

Secretion of Dye-Stuffs. Finally, on the subject of the mechanism of tubular secretion, we may mention Höber's work on the frog. Höber & Woolley studied the secretion of a large number of dye-stuffs and showed that, in general, it was those substances with a polar and non-polar group at opposite ends of the molecule that tended to be secreted, whereas if polar groups were situated at both ends no secretion occurred. This " head-and-tail " nature of the molecule strongly favours adsorption at solid-water interfaces ; it may well be, therefore, that the first stage in the active secretion of these dye-stuffs is adsorption on the surface of the tubule. These dyes are, of course, highly artificial substances, and there is no doubt that other mechanisms are involved in the active secretion of creatinine, for example, by man, and of urea by the frog.

SITE OF REABSORPTION AND STABILISATION OF THE INTERNAL ENVIRONMENT

Water-Balance

So far, the three processes of filtration, reabsorption and tubular secretion have been treated as separate phenomena and no attempt has been made to integrate them or to give a clear picture of the relation of excretion to stabilisation of the internal environment. The types of kidney discussed have been the amphibian and mammalian ; the former class lives in a fresh-water environment ; it does not drink water but it absorbs it continuously through the skin, whilst excretion in normal circumstances takes place almost exclusively by way of the urine. The main problem of the amphibian, so far as the kidney is concerned, therefore, is the retention of salt and the elimination of the large volumes of water that are continuously absorbed through the skin.[1] In the mammal, on the other hand, *conservation* of water is usually the more important consideration, partly because water is lost in significant quantities in the interests of thermoregulation, and partly because the diet normally contains an excess of salt over daily requirements. It is not surprising to find, therefore, that

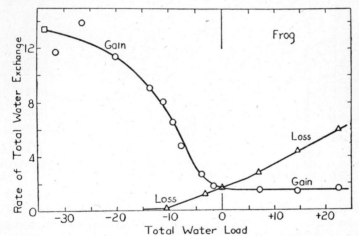

Fig. 153. Rates of water exchange in relation to initial water load. Frog. Rates are all computed from the first 0·5 hour of recovery. The square represents 10 individuals that did not survive. (Adolph. *Physiological Regulations.* Jacques Cattell Press, Lancaster, Pa.)

the amphibian urine is strongly hypotonic in relation to the blood, and is often free of Cl^-, whilst the mammalian urine is hypertonic. The importance of the kidney in the matter of osmotic regulation is shown by Figs. 153 and 154, so-called *equilibration diagrams* (Adolph) in respect to water balance ; here the rate of total water exchange (which may be a gain or a loss) is plotted against the total water load, a negative load indicating that the animal has been dehydrated and a positive value that it has been forced to take water. The curve marked " Gain " shows that the frog gains water continuously (by absorption through the skin), even when its load is positive ; on the other hand, the rate of gain becomes increasingly great with increasing negative loads. At equilibrium, or the state of *water-balance*, water is gained and lost at equal rates ; even with a negative load as great as 10 per cent. of the body weight, the formation of urine continues, showing that the kidney must continue its other

[1] For seven months in the year the frog may remain under water without feeding ; during this time it cannot gain salts from food.

functions as a purely excretory organ, eliminating urea, etc. The diagram for the dog shows a similar trend, but this animal does not have to compete with a continuous intake of water, the amount of water produced by oxidation of organic matter being normally small in comparison with the other exchanges. Once again it will be seen that the rate of urinary loss does not become zero with the negative loads studied, and that the rate of elimination by the kidneys increases with positive loads. The remarkable feature of the curves is the drinking response to negative loads ; the rate

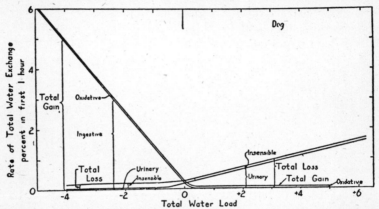

FIG. 154. Rates of water exchanges at various water-loads. Equilibration diagram for the dog. (Adolph. *Physiological Regulations.* Jacques Cattell Press, Lancaster, Pa.)

is not only adjusted to the degree of water deficiency but (what the curves do not show), the dog drinks almost precisely the amount of its deficit.

Site of Reabsorption. The mechanism, whereby differing volumes of urine are excreted in accordance with the state of water-balance, resides in the tubular reabsorptive process ; it is of interest to inquire first, therefore, where the various constituents of the glomerular filtrate are absorbed, *i.e.*, whether in the proximal or distal tubule, or loop of Henle. We may note first that an almost entire reabsorption of most of the constituents of the plasma, including water, is necessary ; thus the human kidney produces some 120 ml. of filtrate per minute, even when the production of urine is as low as 0·5 ml. per minute ; this involves, therefore, a reabsorption which may amount to more than 99 per cent. of the volume of filtrate.[1] As to the site of reabsorption, we may note first, before entering into the experimental aspect, that the most economical mode of reabsorption of dissolved material is the so-called isosmotic absorption, *i.e.*, absorption of solute and water in the proportions in which they occur in the filtrate, so that differences of osmotic pressure between blood and tubular fluid are kept to a minimum ; the work done in such circumstances

---

[1] The lower limit is given by the ratio of the concentrations of inulin in urine and plasma at maximal rates of urine flow, *i.e.*, during diuresis ; according to Chasis & Smith this ratio is never less than 10, *i.e.*, 90 per cent. of the filtrate is reabsorbed even in maximal diuresis when the kidney is operating at its maximum rate to eliminate water from the body.

is at a minimum. However, if the frog is to excrete a hypotonic urine, this is not feasible since it must excrete more water in proportion to solute ; nevertheless a considerable economy of energy can be achieved by deferring, till the latest possible moment, the final *dilution* of the filtrate (*i.e.*, the reabsorption of salts which brings about hypotonicity). Thus, if the dilution occurred in the proximal tubule, there would be a difference of osmotic pressure driving water out of the fluid into the blood all along its course through the loop of Henle and the distal tubule ; the epithelial lining of these segments would therefore have to perform osmotic work to *maintain* the diluted condition established by the proximal tubule. On the grounds of economy, therefore, we may expect to find an isosmotic absorption of the great bulk of the filtrate in the proximal tubule, whilst

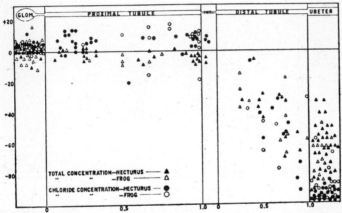

FIG. 155. Showing differences between blood plasma and fluid collected from various levels of the tubules with respect to total concentration and Cl⁻ concentration. Sites of collection of tubule fluid can be identified by reference to the diagrammatic tubule. Zero on the ordinates represents the plasma level. For chlorides, figures above and below the horizontal line represent percentage differences from plasma ; for total concentration the units are arbitrary. (Walker, Hudson, Findley & Richards. *Amer. J. Physiol.*)

the establishment of differences of osmotic pressure (dilution in the case of the amphibian kidney, concentration in the mammalian kidney) will be deferred to the distal tubule. The distal tubule of the frog may therefore be expected to show an active reabsorption of salts, capable of making the urine hypotonic, whilst the distal tubule of the mammal, by the same token, may be expected to show an active reabsorption of water, making the urine hypertonic. In the proximal tubule, reabsorption of solutes will be determined largely by active processes, since only in this way will sugar, for example, be completely reabsorbed ; excretory products will be left behind, to an extent depending on their ability to cross the tubule wall by simple diffusion, and isotonicity will be approximately maintained by the rapid diffusion of water along osmotic gradients. So far as the mammal is concerned, therefore, we may speak of an *obligatory* absorption of water in the proximal tubule, associated with the isosmotic withdrawal of solute ;

this represents some 90 per cent. of the filtrate ; the remaining 10 per cent. is subjected to a partial reabsorption depending on the water balance of the animal ; and this reabsorption may be called *facultative* (Homer Smith).

Richards, by withdrawing fluid from different regions of the amphibian nephron, has applied his micro-techniques to the problem of the actual site of reabsorption of the various constituents of the glomerular filtrate. Because of the tangled appearance of the tubules, it was difficult to assess, by direct observation, the distances from the glomerulus at which the punctures were made ; however, by injecting India ink after withdrawal of the fluid, the particular nephron punctured could afterwards be identified by histological techniques, and the point of puncture established in relation to the glomerulus. Contamination of the withdrawn fluid with

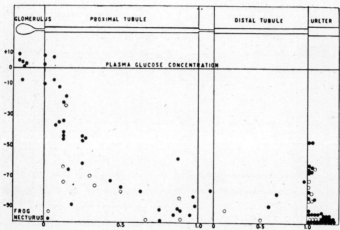

FIG. 156.   Showing percentage differences between glucose concentration of blood plasma and fluid collected from various levels of the renal tubules of normal *Necturi* and frogs.   Zero on the ordinates represents the plasma level.   (Walker & Hudson.   *Amer. J. Physiol.*)

that derived from other parts of the nephron was prevented by establishing a blockade of the tubule immediately distal to the point of the pipette by injecting, before removal of the fluid, a drop of mercury or oil. Fig. 155 shows some results on the osmotic pressure and concentration of Cl⁻ ; it is seen that they tend to remain the same until the distal tubule has been reached, when both fall rapidly, as predicted above on purely energetic grounds. This experiment does not decide for us, however, whether there has been any reabsorption of salt in the *proximal* tubule, since the absorption of both water and salt in isosmotic proportions would leave the *concentration* unaffected. The reabsorption of glucose takes place entirely in the proximal tubule as Fig. 156 shows ; moreover, on perfusion of the distal tubule with a glucose-Ringer, Richards has shown that none is absorbed by this segment. In the phlorizinised proximal tubule there is no evidence of reabsorption of glucose, in fact the concentration rises by some 25 per cent. This rise in concentration is doubtless due to the reabsorption of water, so that we can conclude from this result, and the observation that

PLATE IX

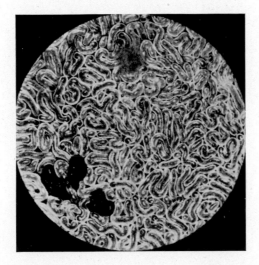

FIG. 157. Appearance of the ventral surface of a guinea-pig's kidney, when observed under the conditions described by Walker & Oliver. India ink has been injected into a single tubule segment, and has filled the three coils of a proximal convolution shown at 7 o'clock. The rounded interruption at 12 o'clock is a glomerulus. Photograph of a drawing by Miss Edna Hill. (Walker & Oliver. *Amer. J. Physiol.*)

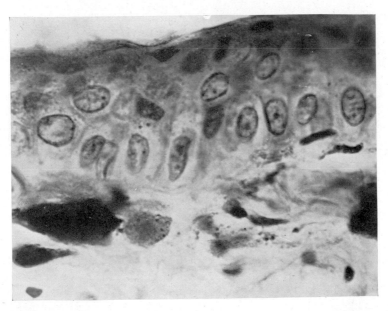

FIG. 160. Cross-section of frog's skin. (Ussing. *Acta Physiol. Scand.*)

[*To face p.* 348.

the concentration of Cl⁻ is unchanged, that reabsorption of both water and salts does take place in the proximal tubule. In the frog kidney about one-third of the water and salts are reabsorbed in the proximal tubule, and two-thirds of the salts in the distal tubule.

Evidence on the site of reabsorption in the mammalian nephron was lacking until Walker & Oliver punctured the tubules of the guinea pig

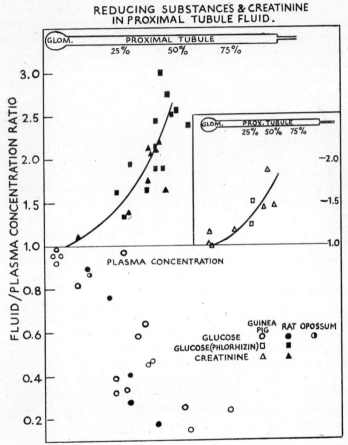

Fig. 158. Showing concentration ratios between blood plasma and fluid, collected from glomerulus and proximal tubule, with respect to exogenous creatinine and to reducing substances, with and without preliminary injection of phlorizin. Site of collection of fluid may be identified by reference to schematic tubule. *Inset.* Results on guinea pigs, separated from those on rats because fluid/plasma ratios were of a different order. Curves drawn to indicate concentration ratios which would result from the reabsorption of 12·5 per cent. (inset, 7·5 per cent.) of glomerular filtrate for each 10 per cent. of tubule length. (Walker, Bott, Oliver & Macdowell. *Amer. J. Physiol.*)

and the rat in 1941. The surface appearance of the mammalian kidney is shown in Fig. 157, Pl. IX—a confusing mass of twisted tubules, mainly the proximal portions; only rarely can a glomerulus be discerned. By injection of phenolsulphonaphthalein into the animal the distal tubules could be made to stand out by virtue of their accumulation of this dye-stuff. A micro-needle was inserted into a tubule, and the position of puncture determined subsequently by histological techniques. Fig. 158 illustrates some of the results obtained ; the concentration of glucose falls as the fluid passes along the proximal tubule, being zero about half-way along. In the phlorizinised animal the concentration of glucose actually increases, as a result of reabsorption of fluid, some 12·5 per cent. of the water being reabsorbed per 10 per cent. of the tubule length ; thus half-way down the tubule about 60 per cent. of the glomerular filtrate has been reabsorbed, and a conservative estimate suggests that some 80 per cent. would be reabsorbed by the whole tubule. The osmotic pressure remains approximately the same, indicating an isosmotic reabsorption. In the distal tubule the fluid actually became slightly hypotonic, corresponding to the hypotonic urines obtained under the experimental conditions employed.[1]

Smith's hypothesis of an obligatory reabsorption of water in the proximal tubule, accompanying the isosmotic reabsorption of salts and essential non-electrolytes, receives a striking confirmation from these brilliantly executed measurements of Walker and his colleagues. We may therefore regard the distal tubule as the site of the facultative reabsorption of water, but to what extent the loop of Henle is concerned in reabsorption is not clear ; on phylogenetic grounds [2] it has been argued that this region is associated with the power of excretion of a hypertonic urine, and it is therefore conceivable that the process of concentration, *i.e.*, the selective reabsorption of water, takes place here, at least in part.

Anti-Diuretic Hormone. The reabsorption of varying amounts of water and salts is, as we have seen, the principal means whereby the animal maintains its internal environment constant, from the point of view of osmotic pressure ; we may therefore expect a sensitive mechanism for regulating the output of these substances ; moreover, since the mammal, in contrast to the frog or fresh-water fish, is subjected to a continuous loss of water in the interests of thermoregulation, it would not be surprising if water were conserved at the expense of salt ; in actual fact a rise in osmotic pressure of the blood, caused by the injection of hypertonic NaCl, causes, in the first place, a retention of water instead of an increased excretion of salt. The reabsorption of water is controlled by a hormone, the *anti-diuretic hormone* of the posterior lobe of the pituitary gland ; the liberation of this hormone into the blood-stream is determined by nervous influences originating in the supra-optic nucleus, presumably after the activation of *osmo-receptors*, as Verney has called them. Thus the profuse diuresis following the ingestion of water by the dog does not occur rapidly ; there is a time-lag in its development corresponding to the time required for the normal amount of anti-diuretic hormone in the blood to be

---

[1] Accurate observation was only possible by paralysing the animal's respiratory movements, so that the kidney was probably not completely normal.

[2] The thin segment of the loop of Henle reaches its highest development in mammals and is absent in amphibia and fishes.

destroyed or eliminated ; again, the diuresis may be inhibited by the injection of small amounts of the hormone into the blood. The fact that the water-balance is controlled by an *anti*-diuretic hormone is of interest, and shows, once again, the greater importance attached to the retention, rather than the loss, of water in the mammal.

Reabsorption of Salts

The reabsorption of salts has only recently come in for quantitative study on the mammal ; Pitts has shown that the characteristics of this process in regard to both Cl^- and HCO_3^- are intermediate between those of urea—where reabsorption results from a passive back-flow—and sugar, where there is a definite maximal rate of reabsorption. In general, the reabsorptive capacity is well adjusted to the rate of filtration, an increase in the rate of filtration being reflected in an increase in the rate of reabsorption ; when the plasma level is increased beyond a certain amount, excretion takes place, but, unlike the situation with glucose, this is not when the reabsorptive mechanism is saturated, since an increased rate of filtration will not cause all the extra Cl^- presented to the tubules to be excreted. Presumably the excretion of Na^+, and of many other ions, is determined by a similar mechanism, *i.e.*, one that assures that, irrespective of the rate of filtration, the amount of salt returned to the blood is such as to keep its concentration constant. K^+ has been studied recently, and some evidence of an active tubular secretory process, as well as one of active reabsorption, has been presented by Berliner and by Mudge ; in normal circumstances the excretion of K^+ may be accounted for on the assumption that the tubules reject some 10 per cent. of the amount presented to them in the filtrate, *i.e.*, the body normally has to deal with an excess of K^+ taken in the diet. When KCl is infused into the dog, the clearance of K^+ is frequently greater than the simultaneous inulin clearance, so that it would seem that some tubular secretion occurs in these circumstances. Work on the excretion of K^+, in the light of this finding, and its relation to the excretion of other ions, such as Na^+, is in active progress, but it is still too soon to make any definite statement as to the critical factor that determines the extent of reabsorption and the tubular secretion. According to a recent paper by Mudge, Foulks & Gilman, dehydration of an animal may provoke tubular secretion of K^+, presumably as a result of the raised intracellular concentration of K^+. In general, because of the remarkable constancy of the relative concentrations of the ions in plasma, *e.g.*, of Ca^{++}, Mg^{++}, K^+, we must postulate separate mechanisms, regulating the extent of the reabsorption of the ions ; presumably this is largely autonomous, being determined by the concentration of the ion in the plasma ; with Na^+, on the other hand, because this ion contributes predominantly to the osmotic pressure of the blood, we may expect to find a specific control over its reabsorption ; recently it has been found that the hormones liberated by the adrenal cortex cause a retention of NaCl, extirpation of the gland resulting in a considerable loss of salt.

Acid-Base Balance

While we are considering the maintenance of the constancy of the ionic concentrations in the plasma, we may profitably consider the hydrogen ion, *i.e.*, the mechanism for the maintenance of a constant pH of the plasma. It is clear that if the reabsorption of cations and anions is brought about by separate processes, the kidney could profoundly modify the relative concentrations of, say, Na^+ and Cl^- in the blood, so long as electrical neutrality was maintained ; thus the reabsorption of all the Na^+ and only a part of the Cl^- could be achieved by an exchange of some Na^+ in the filtrate with H^+ from the blood ; the urine would become acid and the blood alkaline. This, in essence, is one of the mechanisms for the elimination of excess acid from the blood, but in detail it is not quite so simple, being mediated by the phosphates of the blood. The urine does indeed show wide fluctuations in pH, varying from 4·8 to 7·8 ; since the normal man absorbs some 30–80 mM of excess acid[1] in a day, it is clear that a mechanism for the continuous excretion of this excess must exist. The phosphate in plasma at pH 7·4 exists as a mixture of 4 parts of Na_2HPO_4 and one part of NaH_2PO_4 and it is in these proportions that they occur in the tubules ; clearly, if, in the tubules, there were an exchange of Na^+ in the fluid for H^+ in the plasma, the proportion of acid phosphate (NaH_2PO_4) in the fluid would be increased. Pitts & Alexander have investigated the reabsorption of phosphate with special reference to the acid-base balance, and have shown that the most probable mechanism is that considered above, namely the exchange of H^+ in the tubule cells with Na^+ in the tubular fluid. The H^+ is presumably derived from acid produced in the tubule cell ; thus if the cell produced CO_2 this could be converted into H_2CO_3 by the action of carbonic anhydrase ; the H_2CO_3 would dissociate partially into H^+ and HCO_3^-, and the H^+ would then be ready to exchange with Na^+ ; the $NaHCO_3$ formed in the tubule cell, as a result of the exchange, would then diffuse into the blood.[2] The advantage of the intervention of phosphate in this mechanism resides in its buffering capacity ; the mere selective reabsorption of Na^+ in exchange for H^+ would leave the urine very acid indeed ; however, because of the buffering power of the phosphates, the exchange of Na^+ and H^+ results in a much smaller shift in pH. Besides this mechanism, the kidney can—and does so continuously—make use of the synthesis of ammonia to neutralise a part of the excess of acids in the organism ; thus some 20–50 mM of the excess potential acid are accounted for by this process ; NH_4^+, formed in the tubule cells by the breakdown of glutamine (Van Slyke), exchanges for Na^+ in the filtrate and thus spares base. According to Walker's micro-analytical studies of tubular fluid, ammonia is added to the fluid in the distal 2/3 of the distal tubule.

[1] That is, as a result of metabolism, acid is produced in excess of base absorbed.

[2] There are alternative mechanisms which are discussed by Pitts & Alexander ; their experiments, however, confirmed this view ; they made dogs acidotic by ingestion of HCl and infused intravenously large amounts of phosphate ; they found that the amount of H^+ excreted was greater than could have been filtered by the glomeruli in the same time. The fact that carbonic anhydrase is involved is suggested by the observation that sulphanilamide, which inhibits this enzyme, depresses acid excretion.

The characteristics of the reabsorption of phosphate have been studied by Pitts & Alexander ; the ion is similar to glucose in showing a maximal reabsorptive capacity, but, as with the amino-acids, excretion in the urine begins before the maximal reabsorptive capacity is reached ; a competition with glucose exists but the reabsorption is unaffected by phlorizin.[1] There is thus an active process at work in its reabsorption. The site of the acidification of the urine is the distal tubule in the frog, as Richards has shown ; in man there is a little pathological evidence suggesting that this region of the nephron is likewise involved in acidification.

Co-ordination of Salt and Water Excretion

Osmotic constancy is maintained by the regulation of the reabsorption of water and salt ; both processes are to some degree limited, in the sense that the reabsorption of water can only proceed until a certain critical difference of osmotic pressure between blood and urine is established. The magnitude of this limit is equivalent to a difference in concentration of NaCl of 1·2–1·5 M, and there is no doubt that urea contributes very significantly to the total osmotic activity of the urine. Thus in the normal mammal, in water-balance, the urine contains some 400 mM/l. of urea, and when the urine is strongly concentrated it is doubtless very much higher (of the order of 1 M) ; the salt concentration is of the order of 300 mM/l., *i.e.*, with a mammal in water-balance the salts are concentrated about two-fold in respect to the plasma concentration, whilst urea nearly a hundred-fold. Because of this limitation on the reabsorption of water, the ingestion of sea-water is useless to quench thirst, the concentration of salts in this fluid being some 500 mM/l., whilst urines containing higher salt concentrations than about 500 mM/l. of NaCl are rare (Adolph, 1923 ; McCance & Young, 1944).

Again, the reabsorption of salts is limited ; for each ml. of urine formed, a minimum amount of 1·2 mg. of Cl⁻ being excreted. Nevertheless the salt loss of the normal individual is so restrained that it is difficult to produce experimentally a salt-deficiency by merely regulating the diet ; in dogs, Darrow & Yannet and Gilman caused an experimental salt-deficiency by injecting intraperitoneally large amounts of isotonic sugar solution and withdrawing the same volume of fluid from the peritoneum after it had come into equilibrium with the plasma, *i.e.*, after it had attained the same salt concentration. In spite of the considerable loss of salts (approximately 20 per cent.), less than 1·5 per cent. of the water-content of the animal was lost, so that a depletion of salt was tolerated in preference to the loss of water that would have been necessary to retain the normal osmotic pressure of the plasma ; nevertheless, since the animals exhibited symptoms of decreased blood volume, a significant amount of the plasma water passed into tissue cells as a result of the difference of osmotic pressure caused by the loss of salt from the blood. McCance obtained salt-deficiency in humans by the combined effects of sweating and regulation of the diet, the concentration of Na⁺ in the plasma

---

[1] According to Lotspeich (1947), the characteristics of the reabsorption of sulphate are quite similar to those of phosphate.

12

falling to 132 meq./l. The effects of the deficiency were severe, so that any movement involved great effort ; the signs were probably attributable to a decrease in the volume of the circulating blood.[1] Thus the loss of salt initially caused a reduction in the osmotic pressure of the blood ; this probably caused an increased excretion of water in an attempt to maintain the osmotic pressure constant (the human subjects took water *ad libitum* and observed a marked diuresis) ; moreover, the reduced osmotic pressure was partly compensated by the migration of water into the tissue cells, which reduced the volume of circulating blood.

Some of the phenomena of *water-intoxication* appear to be related to those of salt-deficiency, in that similar symptoms may be evoked by the forced ingestion of large volumes of water. Here the *minimal diuretic excretion* of Cl^- exerts its effect, the copious excretion of a dilute urine being associated with an obligatory loss of NaCl. Thus Swingle *et al.* found it easier to evoke the symptoms of water-intoxication in adrenalectomised dogs (with impaired reabsorption of NaCl) than in normals, the final effect of water-intoxication being a salt depletion of the body and its accompanying dehydration. The phenomenon of dehydration, due to deficient intake of water, is essentially similar in its effects to that of water-intoxication ; the deficiency of water tends to raise the osmotic pressure of the plasma, water is retained and salts are excreted ; but, as the deficiency is maintained, the total volume of circulating fluid falls ; for example Wiley & Wiley found that the losses of water and salts go hand in hand but generally there is more salt lost than its osmotic equivalent of water, with the result that the blood becomes hypotonic and water passes into the tissue cells.[2]

The concept of an obligatory reabsorption of water, consequent on the reabsorption of the bulk of the solutes in the proximal tubule, provides an explanation for the diuresis associated with a high blood sugar, as in diabetes mellitus. The urine, in this condition, is not highly concentrated, having a concentration equivalent to about 0·15 M NaCl, as compared with a normal average of about 0·25–0·50 M. The diuresis is therefore not due to the exceeding of the difference of osmotic pressure that the distal tubule is capable of overcoming in the reabsorption of water. The cause is to be sought, primarily, in the proximal tubule ; the high concentration of glucose overloads the reabsorptive mechanism for this substance, so that appreciable amounts are retained in the tubular fluid ; the presence of this glucose restricts the isosmotic reabsorption of water in the proximal tubule with the result that the distal tubule is presented with a greater than normal

[1] It is interesting that all sense of smell and taste was lost, it returned rapidly with the ingestion of 15 g. of NaCl.

[2] The effects on the water-balance of continuously ingested water, or of intravenous infusions of saline solutions of different concentrations, are probably more complex than suggested here ; some recent studies on the problem are those of Wolf (1945), Cizek & Holmes (1948), Stewart & Rourke (1942) and Coon *et al.* (1941). Wolf finds three concentrations of saline which, when infused into the blood, cause excretion of salt in the same concentration as in the saline, these are in the region of 600, 140, and 1,700 mg. Cl^-/ 100 ml. The first is called the *threshold of retention* and is about equal to the plasma concentration of Cl^-, the second and third are the *minimal* and *maximal isorrheic concentrations* respectively.

volume of fluid to reabsorb. If it is appreciated that a reduction of only 10 per cent. in the reabsorption of fluid in the proximal tubule means doubling the amount presented to the distal tubule for reabsorption, it will be understood that the capacity of the distal tubule to reabsorb may easily be overloaded, with a resultant diuresis. The diuresis is therefore due to the presentation to the distal tubule of too great a *bulk* of fluid rather than to the presentation of a too concentrated solution.

Hormonal Control. Before passing to a consideration of osmotic regulation in other animals, we may consider briefly the hormonal control of the water and salt content of the mammal. We have seen that a prime factor in the excretion of water is the anti-diuretic hormone, secreted by the posterior lobe of the pituitary body ; mention has also been made of the function of the adrenal cortex in controlling the reabsorption of salts. Since the retention of water is closely linked with the retention of salts, we may expect the cortical hormones to influence the water-balance of the animal. Extirpation of the adrenals produces the syndrome classically known as Addison's disease, the concentration of NaCl in the blood falling whilst that of K^+ rises ; the cortical hormones therefore promote the reabsorption of NaCl and inhibit that of K^+ ; associated with the fall in concentration of NaCl in the blood, there is a diuresis, as we should expect. Injection of adrenal cortical extract, or more especially the synthetic desoxycorticosterone (" **DOCA** "), into a normal animal, causes the retention of salt and a low [1] blood-K^+, and leads to a form of " diabetes insipidus " superficially similar to that produced by extirpation of the posterior pituitary. This latter manifestation is not easy, at first sight, to understand. Retention of salt should lead to retention of water ; however, the polyuria is probably due mainly to the increased tendency to drink water—*polydipsia*—so that the primary factor is probably the sensation of thirst associated with the retention of salt. This is not the whole story, however ; the cortical hormones seem definitely to have the power of *inhibiting* the reabsorption of water, the failure of an adrenalectomised animal to cope with the forced ingestion of water, described by Swingle *et al.*, being due mainly to its inability to inhibit the reabsorption of water and only to a less extent to defective retention of salt. The adrenal cortex thus exerts two opposing influences on the water-balance of the organism—salt retention,[2] favouring the retention of water, and inhibition of reabsorption of water, favouring the excretion of fluid. The relationship between the pituitary and adrenal cortical hormones in the control of the water-balance of the animal has been discussed at length by Gaunt, Birnie & Eversole ; the matter is complicated by the circumstance that the anterior lobe of the pituitary controls the adrenal cortex by a hormone, the *adrenocorticotrophic hormone* ; extirpation of the whole pituitary therefore does not leave the animal in control of the adrenal cortex, since this becomes non-functional. Finally, extirpation

---

[1] The muscular weakness resulting from injections of DOCA is due to the replacement of muscle-K^+ by Na^+ in consequence of the low plasma-K^+ (Ferrebee, Parker, Carnes, Gerity, Atchley & Loeb, 1941).

[2] According to Little, Wallace, Whatley & Anderson (1947), the pituitary hormone inhibits the reabsorption of salt.

of the adrenals seems to increase the sensitivity of the renal water-excreting mechanism to the anti-diuretic hormone.

Desert Mammals

Schmidt-Nielsen and his colleagues have drawn attention to the remarkable ability of certain desert rodents to remain in water-balance without drinking, namely the kangaroo-rat and pocket mouse of the Arizona desert. Their diet consists of dried seeds. When fed on an experimental diet of rolled oats and barley, containing only 5–10 per cent. of water, they remained in water-balance indefinitely ; the water obtained from metabolic oxidations, together with that in the diet, being sufficient for the animals' requirements. This can only mean that the kidneys of these rodents are capable of a more efficient reabsorption of water than is customarily found in mammals ; in confirmation of this it was found that the urine was twice as concentrated in respect to electrolytes as that of white rats on a similar diet, and the concentration of urea was 1·6 times. If the rodents were kept on a high-protein diet, *e.g.*, soya bean, the necessity to eliminate large quantities of urea placed too great a strain on the water-reabsorptive mechanism, and their survival was impaired ; the extreme limits of urea concentration found in the urines of these desert rodents, of the white rat, and of man were respectively : 3·6, 2·5 and 1·0 M/l. Thus, in contrast to other desert animals such as the camel, antelope, donkey, etc., which survive in virtue of their ability to store water and to undergo considerable dehydration, the kangaroo-rat and pocket mouse survive because their kidneys permit the maintenance of perfect water-balance without drinking.

If the kangaroo-rat is able to concentrate salts to a high degree, it is likely that it can utilise sea-water as a normal drinking fluid ; in some recently described experiments Schmidt-Nielsen & Schmidt-Nielsen have put this to the test and shown that animals, allowed to drink sea-water regularly, thrived and showed no accumulation of salt ; urines as concentrated as 1·2 M in respect of salts being obtained. The urines were not always highly concentrated, however ; for example, one sample was 1·04 N and 2·01 M in respect of salt and urea respectively, whilst another was 0·15 N and 0·42 M, and it would seem that the kangaroo-rat periodically excretes a highly concentrated urine in the interests of osmotic regulation, whilst at other times the concentration falls within the customary mammalian range. That at least one extra-renal factor, however, is important in the adaptation of desert mammals to their habitat, is shown by the observation of the Schmidt-Nielsens that the pulmonary loss of water by these rodents is considerably less than that of man (0·5 mg./ml.O_2 compared with 0·84 mg./ml.O_2).

Marine Mammals

Marine mammals, such as the whale and seal, have a concentration of salt in their blood very similar to that of terrestrial mammals ; thus the concentrations of important ions, in mM/l., together with the depression of freezing-point,[1] in human and whale serum may be compared with those for sea-water as follows :—

	Δ°C.	Na$^+$	K$^+$	Ca^{++}	Mg^{++}	Cl$^-$	SO$_4{}^{--}$	PO$_4$
Man	·54–·59	135–145	3·5–5·0	2·3–2·8	0·5–1·0	99–105	2·3	1·4
Sperm Whale	·66–·72	170	2·6	0·2	2·3	120	—	—
Sea Water	2·3	490	9·8	10	54	540	27	—

The whale lives on marine crustacea which have a salt concentration in their body-water the same as that of sea-water, consequently, although the whale does not drink sea-water, any water ingested as food has a concentration of salt equal to that in this fluid. According to Fetcher's computation, the water of the diet, plus that produced by metabolism, should be sufficient to maintain the whale in water-balance, since a marine mammal is not exposed to the losses of water by way of the skin which the terrestrial mammals suffer in the interests of thermo-regulation. Nevertheless, the problem arises of the elimination of the relatively large amounts of salt, ingested as food.

The urine of the whale appears to be definitely more concentrated than that of the normal human, but the concentration is nevertheless rarely sufficiently high to permit the necessary elimination of salt on a crustacean diet (Fetcher computes that the concentration should be some 0·66–0·75 M NaCl). Consequently Fetcher suggests that the buccal glands of the whale's mouth may be modified to permit the elimination of salt by an active transport mechanism ; the rather higher osmotic concentration of the whale's blood (Δ°C. of 0·69 compared with 0·58 for man) may be regarded, possibly, as a step towards adaptation to the sea-water environment.

The seal lives on a fish diet with a salt concentration equivalent to about 1 per cent. NaCl, so that its salt-elimination problem is not so acute. Irving *et al.* have submitted the problem of the seal's water-balance to an exact analytical test ; they compute that for every 1,000 Calories derived from a herring diet (1,250 g. of herring), 1,121 g. of water are made available (1,000 g. from the herring ; 50 g. from oxidation of fat and 71 g. from protein) ; of this, 106 g. are used to saturate the air with water vapour during the period in which the 1,000 Calories are liberated as heat, and 200 g. are lost to the fæces, leaving some 800 g. for urine. This involves an excretion of urea in 6 per cent. concentration, a very high value but not beyond the known limits of carnivores such as the cat ; also the salt concentration would have to be equivalent to 1·56 per cent. NaCl (0·27 M), a value within the range of the human kidney. Thus the water-balance of the seal may be explained without invoking any special adaptation.

---

[1] A non-volatile solute depresses the vapour pressure and freezing-point of the solvent ; for a dilute solution the depression of freezing-point (Δ°) is given by :—

$$\Delta° = K_f C$$

where K_f is the *molal depression constant*, and C is the concentration of solute in moles/l. For water, K_f is 1·86. Thus a plasma with a Δ° of 0·54° C. has a total osmotic concentration of 0·54/1·86 = 0·30 M approx., which is equivalent to 0·15 M for a dissociated electrolyte such as NaCl.

OSMOTIC REGULATION IN LOWER FORMS THAN THE MAMMAL

The Frog

We may now consider in further detail the mechanisms of osmotic regulation in lower forms than the mammal, in forms, namely, where the kidney does not play so dominant a rôle ; our consideration of the general subject in relation to the kidney has focussed attention on *loss* or *retention* both of water and salts, but, of course, not on *gain* of these substances. The fact that the frog's skin is a significant area of exchange with its outside aqueous medium [1] would suggest that there is a mechanism to prevent the loss of salts by diffusion ; moreover, the frog's urine probably always contains a little salt (in summer frogs the average concentration was found to be some 4·6 mM) which must be replaced by methods other than those of simple diffusion ; since the frog may spend seven months of the year submerged in fresh water we may expect to find, in the skin, an active transfer mechanism for salt. It will be impossible here to review the multiplicity of studies on the isolated frog-skin, purporting to demonstrate an irreciprocal permeability to ions and to relate this to the potential difference measured across it. The weight of evidence suggests that the absorption of water through the skin is a passive process, its rate being dependent on the difference of osmotic pressure between outside medium and blood, so that in isotonic NaCl (0·11 M) there is apparently no absorption of water ; when the osmotic pressure outside is greater, the frog loses water. An irreciprocal permeability to water, in the sense that water passes more rapidly in one direction than the other, is therefore unlikely, and studies with heavy water by Hevesy, Hofer & Krogh have shown that the actual rates of transfer are the same in both directions. On the other hand, an active transport of ions inwards has been conclusively proved ; thus Krogh [2] (1937) artificially depleted frogs of salt by spraying them with distilled water ; on transferring them to dilute salt solutions an active absorption could be shown. For example, NaCl is absorbed from aqueous NaCl solutions, whilst only Cl^- from KCl, NH_4Cl and $CaCl_2$, *i.e.*, K^+, NH_4^+ and Ca^{++} are apparently not actively absorbed, the absorption in the last mentioned cases being an exchange with HCO_3^- from the blood.

Skin Potential and Active Transport. More precise studies have been made with the use of Na^{24} by Ussing ; if there were no active transport the flux of Na^{24} across the skin should be the same in both directions ; as Fig. 159 shows, the influx (measured as mol./cm.²/hr.) was always greater than the outflux, in spite of large variations in the outside concentration of NaCl ; it will be noted from the figure that the inward flux increases with the outside concentration whilst the outward flux is barely affected. It has been known for a long time that there is a potential difference, of

---

[1] This is shown by the fact that a frog may be rapidly dehydrated by placing it in hypertonic salt solutions.

[2] Two years earlier (1935), Huf showed that Cl^- can be actively transported by a piece of isolated frog-skin separating two solutions of NaCl of the same concentration.

the order of 50 mV, between the two sides of the isolated frog-skin, the inside being positive in relation to the outside ; consequently the active transport of Na^+ would involve, not only osmotic, but also electrical, work if it were transported as an ion. The relationship between this potential and the secretory activity of the skin has been studied frequently ; for example, Huf showed that cyanide, which blocks the active transport, reduces the potential to zero. Ussing, following on the recent studies of Meyer & Bernfeld, established that those factors, *e.g.*, pH and salt concentration, that made the inside of the skin more positive in relation to the outside, increased the inward flux of Na^+, the influx of Cl^- running more or less parallel with that of Na^+. With regard to Cl^-, a simple

calculation showed that the potential is probably adequate to account for its transport against a concentration gradient, *i.e.*, to a first approximation this ion is normally at equal electro-chemical potential (p. 274) on both sides of the skin, active transport being manifested towards Na^+. Fig. 160, Pl. IX shows a cross-section through the frog's skin ; it consists essentially of two layers, a mesodermal chorion and an ecto-dermal epithelium. The former consists of blood-vessels, connec-tive tissue, etc., whilst

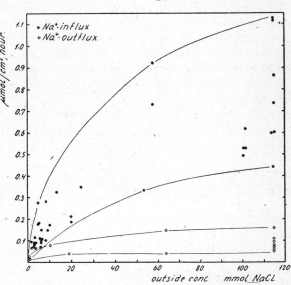

FIG. 159. The Na^+-influx (•) and the Na^+-outflux (○) through the isolated frog's skin as functions of the outside NaCl concentration. (Ussing. *Acta Physiol. Scand.*)

the latter is made up of two or three layers of tightly packed cells, the innermost layer is called the *stratum germinativum* ; outside this there are one or more layers of cells, many of which are undergoing keratinisation. On histological grounds secretory activity is likely to be predominantly associated with the cylindrical cells of the stratum germinativum, and it is of interest that conspicuous influences of pH on the potential and influx of Na^+ can only be produced by changing the *inside* pH. Consequently Ussing inclines to the view that active transport of Na^+ results from an active *extrusion* of this ion, confined to the basal region of the inner layer of cells. This active transport may take place by the formation of an undissociated complex in the cell membrane ; its result is to produce a flux of Na^+ from without inwards ; if Cl^- cannot pass through the skin as rapidly as Na^+ is transported, clearly the inside of the skin will be positive in relation to the outside ; and it now becomes intelligible why the potential difference across the frog's skin should be so intimately related to the transport of Na^+. The potential difference and the active transport are very sensitive to the pH of the inside medium ; an increase in pH causing an increase in the rate of transport and elevating the potential, in fact the inside of the skin behaves faithfully as a glass-electrode, responding rapidly and regularly to changes in hydrogen-ion concentration. An increase in the hydrogen-ion concentration inside will tend to decrease the potential, because H^+ moves faster than Cl^-, thus tending to make the inside negative (less positive) ; the increased amount of H^+ entering the cells will presumably react on the transport process, according to Ussing, by causing the supposed sodium-complex to dissociate, thereby prejudicing the rate of inward transfer. Finally we may mention the dependence of the inward flux of Na^+ on the outside concentration ; the active transport presumably results from the extrusion of Na^+ from the basal parts of the cells of the stratum germinativum ; to obtain the Na^+ the cells must rely on an inward diffusion, hence the greater the outside concentration the more readily will Na^+ be available for extrusion.

Fish

The main area of functional contact of the fish with its watery environment is by way of the gills, exchanges through the skin, especially

TABLE XXIX

Depression of Freezing-point ($\Delta°C.$) of Body Fluids and External Environment of Different Organisms (after Schlieper, 1930).

Species	Body Fluid	External Medium
Cœlenterate		
Alcyonium palmatum	2·20	2·2
Echinoderm		
Asterias glacialis	2·30	2·2–2·36
Annelid		
Sipunculus nudus	2·3	2·3
Mollusc		
Octopus vulgaris	2·16	2·11–2·14
Arthropod		
Limulus polyphemus	1·90	1·82
Homarus vulgaris	2·29	2·27–2·28
Carcinus mœnas	2·17	1·96–1·99
Elasmobranch		
Scyllium canicula	2·22	2·15
Raja undulata	1·89	1·84
Teleost		
Conger vulgaris	0·77	2·14
Pleuronectes platessa	0·79	1·9
Mollusc (Fresh water)		
Anodonta cygnea	0·09	—
Annelid (Fresh water)		
Hirudo officinalis	0·43	—
Crustacean (Fresh water)		
Potamobius astacus	0·80	—
Teleost (Fresh water)		
Leuciscus dobula	0·45	—
Salmo fario	0·57	—
Anguilla anguilla	0·62	—

in scaly fishes, being relatively small. Marine fish are thus subjected to an outside salt concentration of about 520 mM, some three times the equivalent concentration of the body fluids of mammals ; unless their blood is likewise concentrated, therefore, they are presented with the problem of fighting against a continuous osmotic withdrawal of water through the gills. Fresh-water fish, on the other hand, are exposed to a continuous osmotic *entry* of water, as in the case of the frog. Although the great majority of fish are *stenohaline, i.e.*, they can only survive within a limited range of salinity, certain species are *euryhaline*, being able to pass from sea-water to fresh-water, *e.g.*, the salmon, eel and stickleback, so that they must be able to contend with drastic modifications of their external osmotic pressure. The osmotic relations of a number of species are exhibited in Table **XXIX** which shows the depression of freezing-point of the body fluids compared with that of the outside medium ; it will be seen that the elasmobranch fishes (*e.g.*, the shark) are slightly hypertonic to the sea-water, in sharp contrast to the teleosts (*e.g.*, the eel or herring) which are strongly hypotonic, having freezing-point depressions much closer to the figure characteristic of mammals and fresh-water fish.

Elasmobranchs. An analysis of the actual concentration of salt in the elasmobranch blood reveals a value similar to that of the teleosts, the hypertonicity being caused by a high concentration of urea ; the gill membranes are apparently impermeable to this substance, with the result that water is continuously drawn into the blood; it is not surprising, therefore, that the elasmobranch fishes do not drink sea-water. The urine is hypotonic, as a result of the active reabsorption of urea and salts, the elasmobranch nephron being characterised by special segments (between the glomerulus and proximal tubule, and distal to these) which are thought to be responsible for this active reabsorption of urea. Homer Smith found the concentration of urea in the urine to vary considerably, so that it is likely that osmotic regulation is brought about by the reabsorption of varying amounts of this substance in accordance with the water require-ments of the fish. In fresh-water elasmobranchs the picture is rather similar ; here, however, the total osmotic concentration of the blood is very much less than that of sea-water, owing to the much lower concentration of urea in the blood which, however, is still some thirty times that tolerated by the teleost fishes.

Teleosts. The teleosts do not maintain blood hypertonicity, consequently we must expect a continuous loss of water from the gills ; moreover, it has been well proved by Homer Smith that these fish normally drink sea-water, which is absorbed, together with its salts, into the blood. The excretion of these salts by the mammal would require, as we have seen, an extremely efficient concentrating mechanism in the distal tubule, but since the urine of these fish is actually slightly hypotonic to the blood we must postulate the existence of what Smith calls an *extra-renal* salt excretory mechanism. Definite evidence that the gills are responsible for the active transfer of salt outwards from the blood into the sea-water has been provided, in the case of the eel, by Keys who perfused the gills with saline solutions by way of the blood vessels, whilst the mouth and branchial cavities, *i.e.*, the outside of the gills, were bathed with another saline solution. The rate of excretion increased with increasing internal concentration, the maximal rate being equivalent to about 1 mM/kg./hr., a value agreeing fairly well with the rate of extra-renal excretion computed to be necessary for water-balance in sea-water. Schlieper showed that the excretion of Cl^- could be independent of any net transport of water, as for example when the media on the inside and outside of the gills were identical ; he showed also that hypertonicity, induced by Na_2SO_4, sucrose, and glucose, as well as by NaCl, stimulated the active transport of Cl^-, whilst urea and $NaNO_3$ were ineffective. Keys & Willmer identified certain " chloride secreting cells " in the gill leaflets of the eel which were quite different in appearance from the epithelial cells through which respiratory exchanges occur ; later, Copeland found similar cells in *Fundulus*. If the latter fish was adapted to sea-water, the cells contained vesicles which were thought to have an excretory function ; on adaptation to fresh-water, the vesicles disappeared. Whether or not the same cells are responsible for the *absorption* of salts when the fish is adapted to fresh-water remains to be proved (Pettengill & Copeland). We may conclude, therefore, that osmotic regulation in these marine teleosts is not a function of the kidney, and it is perhaps significant that there are several species of marine fish, *e.g.*, the goose fish and toad fish (*Lophius piscatorius* and *Opsanus Tau*) in which the glomeruli have become vestigial, the function of the kidney being carried out entirely by tubular secretion. It is thought that teleosts have a fresh-water ancestry, so that in a remote period the ancestors of the present-day goose fish excreted a hypotonic urine by glomerular filtration and reabsorption of salts ; the migration to a sea-water environment required the development of a salt-excreting and water-conserving mechanism, and thus the osmo-regulatory function of the kidney was dispensed with, glomeruli becoming unnecessary since tubular secretion can take care of the excretory function of the kidney.[1]

Fresh-water teleosts have osmotic concentrations in the region of 130–170 mM, of which about 75 per cent. is made up of chlorides ; they do not drink water and so gain it entirely by osmosis through the gills and skin (apart from that taken in the food). As we should expect, therefore, the urine is dilute and copious (100–300 ml./kg./day, equivalent to 8–24 litres a day in an 80 kg. man) ; since it is not by any means free

---

[1] It is of interest that the urine of the aglomerular fishes is slightly hypotonic to the blood, like that of other teleosts. According to Marshall & Smith the provertebrate kidney was aglomerular, a series of tubes (like the nephridial organs of crustacea, (p. 364), connecting the cœlom with the exterior ; the glomerulus was evolved, in an early fresh-water chordate, to permit of a more ready elimination of the large amounts of water taken in osmotically, *i.e.*, the glomerulus was an " advantageous juxtaposition of the blood-vascular system to the already existing tubular system draining the cœlom." With the assumption of a marine habitat, or terrestrial existence, water-conservation became more important and the glomerular system was either discarded or amended. Thus in birds the ventral capillaries of the glomeruli have become non-functional by replacement with a dense syncytium, and in mammals the thin segment of the loop of Henle is thought to be a development to allow of more efficient water-reabsorption. It is interesting that a return to fresh-water, as in the aglomerular pipe-fish (*Microphis boaja*), does not result in the re-establishment of the glomerular system.

from salt (it contains some 2–10 mM Cl^-), there must be some salt-absorbing mechanism to compensate for this continual loss ; and the elaborate experiments of Krogh have demonstrated the existence of this very thoroughly. Krogh showed that fish—for example the gold-fish *Carassius auratus*—could be greatly depleted of salt by injuring the skin, or by placing the fish in distilled water, changed at frequent intervals ; on replacing the fish in water containing, for example, 1 mM NaCl, salt was rapidly absorbed ; by placing the fish in a chamber divided into two compartments, the relative contributions of the skin and gills could be studied ; it was shown that the absorption of salt was confined to the gills. Osmotic regulation is therefore attained by the elimination of a hypotonic urine, combined with the active absorption of salts through the gills ; and is thus very similar to that of the amphibian, active transport of salt by the latter taking place, however, through the skin. The permeability of the gills of the gold-fish to water may be computed from Krogh's measurements of water absorption by the head of a fish with a gill area of 55 cm.^{2} ; it works out at $0.04\mu^3/\mu^2/min./atm.$ or $8.6.10^{-5}$ cm./sec., and is of the low order expected if the osmo-regulatory processes are to succeed in maintaining a stable blood concentration.[1]

The actual changes taking place in a euryhaline fish on rapid transfer from a marine to a fresh-water environment, or *vice versâ*, are well exemplified by the studies of Keys on the eel, *Anguilla vulgaris*. His work shows that, when the fish is adapted to one or other environment, its osmotic regulation is characteristic of the stenohaline teleosts in this environment ; on rapid transfer from one medium to another, however, it suffers changes in weight due to osmotic absorption or loss of water, presumably through the gills. The transfer is outwards when placed in sea-water (*i.e.*, a loss of weight), and inwards when transferred to fresh-water. Thus on placing a fresh water-adapted eel in sea-water, the loss amounts to some 4.5 per cent. of its body-weight in about ten hours ; after this, however, evidence of an active process becomes manifest and the fish begins to gain weight ; and it finally establishes an equilibrium with a lower weight than it had in fresh-water. When the sea water-adapted eel is placed in fresh-water, the rise in weight is equally rapid, and equilibrium is established in about seventy-two hours at a weight corresponding to that possessed in sea-water (allowing for the metabolic loss taking place in a starving fish). A definite difference in the depression of freezing-point of the plasma of eels, adapted to sea-water (0.73° C.), and fresh-water (0.61° C.), was confirmed. The active process of osmotic regulation—excretion of hypotonic urine in fresh-water and swallowing of sea-water and excretion of salt in sea-water—begins only when considerable changes in blood composition have been suffered.

[1] The details of the active transport of ions have been studied by Krogh ; in the gold-fish, for example, he found Cl^- and Br^- actively taken up from salts of Na^+, K^+, NH_4^+ and Ca^{++}, whilst I^-, CNS^-, and NO_3^- were not. Whereas Na^+ was usually taken up with Cl^-, K^+ or NH_4^+ was definitely not, so that the gill could separate a mixture of NaCl and KCl ; when no cation was taken up (as for example in KCl), it was proved that Cl^- exchanged with HCO_3^- ; similarly the absorption of Na^+ without an anion was associated with an increased elimination of ammonia by the gills.

Crustacea

The crustaceans have a restricted area of interchange between the outside medium and blood, in virtue of the development of a thick calcareous exoskeleton ; in consequence, osmotic exchanges take place almost entirely across the gills, whilst a primitive form of kidney is largely responsible for maintaining the constancy of composition of the blood.

Nephridial Organ. The nephridial organ (*green gland, antennary gland*) may be typified by that of *Astacus* (cray-fish ; *Potamobius*), in the case of a fresh-water crustacean, and that of *Carcinus mœnas*, the common shore-crab, in the case of a marine form (Fig. 161). It consists of a *cœlomic sac*, which passes through the *labyrinth* and thence, by way of the *nephridial canal*, to the bladder. In the fresh-water cray-fish this canal is long, with

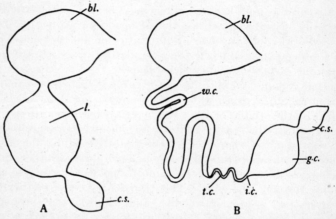

FIG. 161. Excretory organs of the decapods (diagrammatic) : A, *Carcinus* ; B, *Potamobius*. *bl.*, bladder ; *c.s.*, cœlomic sac ; *g.c.*, green canal ; *i.c.*, intermediary canal ; *l*, labyrinth ; *t.c.*, transparent canal ; *w.c.*, white canal. (Picken, after Marchal. *J. exp. Biol.*)

a large surface development, whilst in the marine crab, *Carcinus mœnas,* the connection is much more direct. The bladder opens on to the surface of the body at the base of the antenna. The cœlomic sac is richly supplied with blood through a number of vessels and lacunæ ; it is thought that a filtrate from blood passes into the cœlomic sac, and that this, after suitable modification by secretion inwards and reabsorption of salts, issues as urine. Thus Picken has shown that the hydrostatic pressure within the sternal sinus of *Astacus* is 20 cm. H_2O whilst the colloid osmotic pressure of the blood is 15 cm. H_2O ; hence the necessary filtration pressure is present ; similarly in *Carcinus mœnas* the pressures were 13 and 11 cm. H_2O respectively. Against this view of the nephridial organ as a filtration-reabsorption mechanism there is the cytological evidence put forward by Maluf who regards the formation of urine as consisting of the *tubular secretion* of a hypotonic solution. Maluf observed that the distal portions of the tubule were composed of large columnar cells containing a clear apical vacuole ; when the cray-fish was kept in a hypertonic medium, *i.e.*, fresh-water to which salts had been added, the vacuoles disappeared, and the formation of urine almost ceased ; on return to fresh-water the vacuoles reappeared and the formation of urine resumed.

Cray-Fish. The blood of the cray-fish has a high total osmotic concentration, being of the order of 235 mM as determined by the depression of freezing-point ; the urine is dilute, on the average 47 mM. Peters punctured the nephridial organ at different points and analysed the fluid withdrawn ; the concentration of Cl^- fell from a value equal to that in the blood in the cœlomic sac and labyrinth (ca. 196 mM/l.) to about 90 mM in the nephridial canal, whilst the concentration in the bladder was 10 mM. According to Herrmann, the average production of urine is 3·8 per cent. of the live weight in twenty-four hours (corresponding to about 3 litres a day in an 80 kg. man), so that this continuous elimination of a dilute urine is to be regarded as a defence against a continuous osmotic entry of water ; this is confirmed by the finding that, in an external solution of 250 mM salt, the formation of urine ceases. The thick chitinous exoskeleton surrounding the animal makes a significant gain of water (or loss of salts) by way of the body surface unlikely ; only in the gills will osmotic exchanges be important. Krogh found that cray-fish, maintained for some days in distilled water and then transferred to dilute salt solutions, actively absorbed Cl^- and Br^- from Na^+ and Ca^{++} salts, and Schmidt-Nielsen has shown that silver is actively accumulated from solutions of concentration as low as 0·01 mM ; the site of absorption could be identified by the blackening of the silver, which was found accumulated in the flat and thin cells of the gill filaments. In strongly hypertonic media, *e.g.*, 66 per cent. sea-water, the blood of *Astacus* became isotonic with its outside medium [1] ; nevertheless an effort was still made to regulate the ionic composition of the blood, the concentrations of Ca^{++} and K^+, for example, being maintained well above those of the diluted sea-water.

Crab. The common shore-crab, *Carcinus mœnas*, differs greatly from fresh-water crustacea in that its urine is approximately isotonic with its blood, which itself is practically isotonic with sea-water. According to recent studies of Webb, the blood is usually slightly hypertonic [2] ; moreover, the ionic make-up is different from that of sea-water in several respects. Thus, if concentrations are expressed as percentages of what would be expected of a simple dialysis-equilibrium with sea-water, the following figures are given by Webb :—

Ion :	Na^+	K^+	Ca^{++}	Mg^{++}	Cl^-	SO_4^{--}
Percentage	110	118	108	34	104	61

Since the concentrations of Mg^{++} and SO_4^{--} are high in urine, and are increased still further when the sea-water is enriched with $MgSO_4$, there

---

[1] Like many fresh-water organisms, including fish, *Astacus* is only homoiosmotic in a limited sense, retaining its normal osmotic pressure only until that of the outside medium has equalled that of its blood ; thus Duval gradually increased the salt concentration in the outside medium of a carp ; the fish, although normally stenohaline, survived a marked degree of hypertonicity, its blood acquiring the same osmotic concentration as that of the outside medium ($\triangle 1°$ C.).

[2] According to Picken the blood may be iso-, hyper-, or hypotonic to sea-water, and the urine iso-, hyper-, or hypotonic to blood.

is no doubt that these ions are selectively excreted by the kidney ; the maintenance of hypertonicity, however, must result from an active transport of salt from the surrounding sea-water into the blood, since the urine is not always hypotonic. Moreover, when *Carcinus mœnas* is placed in diluted sea-water, Schlieper, among others, has shown that, although the osmotic pressure of the blood falls, it nevertheless remains strongly hypertonic to its outside medium, a fact indicating the presence of an active osmo-regulatory mechanism, and in conformity with the well known fact that this crab can normally withstand gross changes in the concentration of salt in its outside medium. In no case is it possible to account for this osmo-regulation by the excretion of a dilute urine, and it seems likely that the gills are responsible.

PROCERODES ULVAE *Gunda Ulvæ*

This primitive worm lives in tidal estuaries and is therefore of great interest from the point of view of osmotic regulation, since it is alternately subjected to sea-water and fresh-water. Its adaptations to these wide fluctuations have been studied by Pantin and by Beadle. Studies on the effects of progressive dilution of the worm's sea-water environment showed that the animal was permeable to water, a progressive increase in the volume of the body occurring with increasing dilution ; in tap-water, however, the worm swelled up rapidly and disintegrated, whereas in natural stream-water it swelled to only a limited extent and then shrank. The difference in response to tap- and stream-water was shown to be due to the presence of Ca^{++} in the latter, so that the worm could be kept alive in tap-water plus 1·6 mM $CaCl_2$. The fact that, in the presence of Ca^{++}, the worm can compensate for the continuous absorption of water, indicates the existence of an active osmo-regulatory process ; the importance of Ca^{++} being that it restricts, to manageable proportions, the permeability of the worm to water. After swelling rapidly in stream-water, the worm subsequently shrinks ; Pantin showed that this was associated with the escape of salts ; osmo-regulation therefore consists, at least in part, in the loss of osmotically active material ; this is not the whole story, however, since in tap-water the loss of salts is even greater, yet osmo-regulation fails ; consequently water must be secreted outwards by the worm in stream-water. The picture of osmotic regulation is consequently that of a loss of salts, which reduces the difference of osmotic pressure and thereby slows osmotic penetration,[1] together with an active secretion of water out into the surrounding medium ; when sufficient salts have been lost, the outward secretion of water may exceed the inward osmosis, so that the worm may shrink back to its normal volume. That an active secretory process is at work is shown by Beadle's observation that in diluted sea-water the O_2-consumption of the worm is increased, and that in O_2-lack the animals swelled to a greater extent in diluted sea-water than in the presence of O_2 ; admission of O_2 allowed the worm to shrink ; finally, 1 mM cyanide had the same effect as O_2-lack. The exact mechanism of the excretion of water

---

[1] The loss may be very extensive, leaving a final concentration of only 34–56 mM, compared with an initial value of 520 mM.

is not clear ; Beadle observed in swollen worms large vacuoles of steadily increasing size in the entodermal cells, and showed that the vacuoles did not discharge into the gut ; as Krogh suggests, the final outlet may be into the protonephridial system.   When the worm swelled in the presence of cyanide,   the   entodermal   cells   did   not   vacuolate ;   instead,   the parenchymatous and ectodermal cells became swollen. *Gunda ulvæ* may be classed as a euryhaline organism, in that it can withstand a large change of external osmotic pressure ; it is partially homoiosmotic in so far as it can maintain hypertonicity of its internal environment in stream-water.

Protozoa

Unicellular organisms are found in both fresh-water and marine environments ; in fresh-water we may expect a difference of osmotic pressure between the cell's internal and external environments ;   the magnitude of this is not accurately known, although Mast & Fowler estimated a difference equivalent to 2·5 mM NaCl in *Amœba* whilst Kitching obtained a figure of 25 mM NaCl in a fresh-water peritrichium, and Picken obtained 25 mM for a heterotrichous ciliate, *Spirostomum ambiguum*.[1] Thus, unless the fresh-water organisms have some power of withstanding the difference of osmotic pressure, either by structural rigidity or by elimination of water, we must expect them to burst.   According to Picken the internal presssure is only about 5 cm. H_2O, so that there must be an active elimination of water.   The permeability of various marine and fresh-water protozoa to water has been well established by numerous experiments which showed that they tend to shrink in hypertonic media and swell in hypotonic ; Mast & Fowler, for instance, measured the rate at which *Amœba proteus* changed in volume when the external tonicity was varied,[2] and computed a permeability constant between 0·009–0·047 μ^3/min./μ^2/atm. with a mean of 0·026 (5·6 . 10^{-5} cm./sec.).   It is significant, in view of the fact that *Amœba* has to compete with a continuous intake of water by osmosis, that this permeability is low by comparison with many other membranes.[3]

Contractile Vacuole. How, may we ask, does this group of unicellular organisms excrete the superfluous water entering by osmosis ?   The answer may be given by the *contractile vacuole*, which, as its name implies, is a localised collection of fluid—attaining a size of approximately 30-50μ

---

[1] Picken measured the lowering of vapour pressure of a cell suspension ; Mast & Fowler and Kitching used indirect methods ; thus the last author observed that peritrichia in tap-water plus 50 mM sucrose shrank, as a result presumably of vacuolar output ; in the same solution plus cyanide, in which output was zero, the cell did not shrink, consequently its internal osmotic pressure was considered to be equivalent to 25 mM NaCl or 50 mM sucrose.

[2] It may well be asked how the volume of an organism so variable in shape was measured ; essentially the method consisted of drawing the *Amœba* into a capillary tube, when it assumed a cylindrical shape.

[3] We may note that severe shrinkage of *Amœba* eventually leads to its death by disintegration, although, if it is transferred back to a less hypertonic medium before disintegration, it recovers fully ; the proportion of plasmagel to plasmasol (p. 11), at first decreases, then increases and finally decreases precipitately so that disintegration probably results from the loss of plasmagel, in some way due to the dehydration of the organism.

in *Amœba proteus*—which is repeatedly emptied through the surface of the body. In those organisms that have a variable shape, the vacuole is likewise impermanent, whereas in the *Paramœcia*, which maintain their shape within the limits of the elasticity of their pellicles, the vacuole retains its position and has a more organised character, containing a number of channels (Fig. 162). The vacuole repeatedly passes through stages described as *diastole* and *systole*, gradually increasing in size in diastole and then collapsing in systole, emitting its contents through a temporarily formed hole in the surface, the *pore*. This pore represents a weak spot in the cell wall, and it is clear that, with the " roving vacuoles," an essential part of the process of excretion must reside in the establishment of this weak spot each time a new position is taken up. The vacuolar duration varies greatly among protozoa, from about seven seconds for a *Ciliata Heterotricha* to several minutes in *Amœba*. The function of the vacuole as an excreter of water has been established by indirect methods ; thus it is found more frequently in fresh- and brackish-water genera than in marine forms ; it is found in zoospores and other developmental stages of many algæ, provided that they do not have a hard, water-impermeable, boundary ; on placing the fresh-water *Paramœcium* in a hypertonic medium its vacuole ceases to contract ; on transferring an *Amœba* to " conductivity water " it develops new vacuoles ; finally, on diluting the sea-water surrounding a vacuolated marine form, the frequency of contraction increases (Fig. 163).

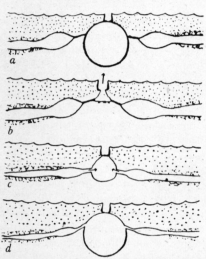

Fig. 162. Stages in the vacuolar cycle of *Paramœcium*. (*a*) End of diastole of vesicle ; vesicle spherical ; canals shut off from vesicle and still dilating. (*b*) End of systole ; canals dilated maximally. (*c*) Early stage in diastole ; canals discharging into vesicle. (*d*) Late stage in diastole ; discharge of canals into vesicle complete. (Kitching, from Gelei. *Biol. Rev.*)

By measuring the frequency of contraction, and the maximal volume attained by the vacuole, the volume of water excreted by the protozoon may be estimated ; fresh-water organisms excrete their own volume of water in four minutes to three-quarters of an hour ; from these figures the rate of elimination of water in $\mu^3/\mu^2/min.$ may be calculated. With *Amœba*, giving times varying from 3·9–13·2 minutes, the rate of excretion comes out at $0·036–0·090/\mu^3/\mu^2/min.$ According to Mast & Fowler, water enters at the rate of $0·026/\mu^3/\mu^2/min.$ per atmosphere difference of osmotic pressure, and, since the difference of osmotic pressure between *Amœba* and freshwater is unlikely to be more than 1·2 atmospheres, the rate of excretion can keep pace with the rate of entry.

With regard to the mechanism of the excretory process, we are still very much in the dark ; the problems to be solved include the following :—

1. *The Nature and Origin of the Membrane Separating the Water in the Vacuole from the Protoplasm.* Presumably it is lipoid but whether derived from protoplasmic granules, is not certain. The vacuole may begin as a very small coacervate consisting of a part of the protoplasm surrounded by a layer of lipoid ; as a result of secretory activity in the region of the vacuolar membrane, water may be forced in and, as it expands, new lipoid material may be supplied.

2. *The Nature of the Secretory Forces.* Kitching's work has demonstrated unequivocally the dependence of vacuolar excretion on metabolism, fresh-water organisms swelling, and losing their power of excreting, in dilute cyanide solutions, and marine organisms showing a diminished resistance to dilution of their sea-water environment on addition of the poison. To what extent simple diffusion and osmosis may operate in the collection of fluid in the vacuole is not yet clear. Mast & Hopkins have shown that the hyaline vacuoles in *Amœba mira*, a marine form, increase in size when there are no granules in

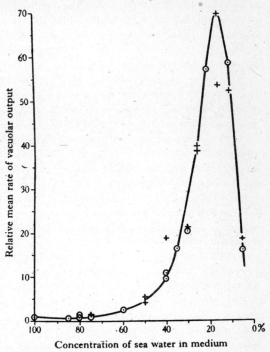

FIG. 163. Variation in vacuolar output with concentration of sea-water for *Zoothamnium marinum* (circles) and *Cothurnia curvula* (crosses). (Kitching. *Biol. Rev.*)

them ; cessation of growth by these vacuoles is associated with the appearance of granules. Mast & Hopkins suggest that growth of the vacuole is normally due to the presence of a higher concentration of osmotically active material inside the vacuole than in the cytoplasm, and that growth is inhibited by a precipitation of this material in the form of a granule. Growth of hyaline vacuoles does not take place when the *Amœba* is not feeding ; and it may well be that the primary function of these organelles is the excretion of useless products of digestion ; the fluid eliminated at the same time contributing to osmotic regulation.

3. *The Contractile or Systole Mechanism.* Here opinions are divided as to whether systole results from a contraction of the vacuolar membrane, or from a change in pressure induced by changes in the cytoplasm. The

fact that the vacuole *completely* empties periodically indicates the periodical recurrence of a leak, *i.e.*, the appearance of the pore. If we assume, as seems very likely from the work of Mast, of Howland & Pollack, and of Gelei, that systole results from a pressure developed in the cytoplasm —either osmotically or by tension developed in the gelated cortex— complete emptying and subsequent refilling can only follow if the pore remains open for a definite time and then closes. That cytoplasmic pressure is not the only factor, *i.e.*, that the local conditions surrounding the vacuole are also important, is shown by Gelei's observation that in multi-vacuolated organisms there was no synchronism of the vacuolar contractions.

We may note, finally, that the osmo-regulatory system of *Amœba* is similar to that of *Gunda*, in the sense that the primary adjustment to a large change in external osmotic pressure is a very considerable change in the concentration of solutes in the cell. Thus Hopkins showed that *Amœba lacerata*, normally cultured in fresh-water, may be adapted to solutions of high salinity (up to 100 per cent. sea-water). Indirect estimates of the osmotic pressure of the contents of the cell, under these conditions, indicated that it was not greatly different from that of its environment, so that the internal concentration can change from a very low value, in the fresh water-cultured organism, to one corresponding to sea-water, in an organism adapted to this medium. On suddenly transferring *Amœba* to a hypertonic medium, the cell shrinks but later resumes its normal size ; again, in a hypotonic medium it swells and subsequently shrinks to normal volume. It is safe to conclude, therefore, that the cell membrane is permeable to both water and salts. It will be recalled (p. 246) that a cell, permeable to water and salts, must be unstable owing to the Gibbs-Donnan difference of osmotic pressure that causes the absorption of both water and salts. In the absence of a water-excreting mechanism, therefore, *Amœba* must be unstable ; and it would appear that the contractile vacuole provides the necessary stabilising mechanism. This is not to say, however, that the excretory mechanism is capable of maintaining large differences of osmotic pressure between the inside and outside of the cell ; we have already seen that this does not happen in *Amœba lacerata*, and Mast & Hopkins have shown the same for a marine form, *Amœba mira*. Thus, in a hypertonic medium, *Amœba* adapts itself first by shrinkage and the absorption of salts, until approximate equality of osmotic pressure is attained ; the distribution of salts, however, is always such as to leave a residual Gibbs-Donnan excess driving fluid back into the cell. Consequently the *Amœba* subsequently swells ; on reaching its normal size the excretory mechanism comes into play and prevents further swelling.[1]

[1] Hopkins has rejected the osmo-regulatory function of the vacuole precisely because *Amœba* cannot maintain a large difference of osmotic pressure across its membrane when the external tonicity is varied. If osmo-regulation is confined to excretion of the fluid which must enter as a result of the Gibbs-Donnan, or colloid-osmotic, swelling, his argument falls to the ground.

References

ADOLPH, E. F. (1923). " The Excretion of Water by the Kidneys." *Amer. J. Physiol.*, **65**, 419.

ADOLPH, E. F. (1943). " Physiological Regulations." Lancaster, Pa., Jaques Cattell Press.

ANSLOW, W. P., WESSON, L. G., BOLOMEY, A. A. & TAYLOR, J. G. (1948). " Chloruretic Action of Pressor-Antidiuretic Fraction of Posterior Pituitary Extract." *Fed. Proc.*, **7**, 3.

AYER, J. L., SCHIESS, W. A. & PITTS, R. F. (1947). " Independence of Phosphate Reabsorption and Glomerular Filtration in the Dog." *Amer. J. Physiol.*, **151**, 168.

BALDWIN, D., KAHANA, E. M. & CLARKE, R. W. (1950). " Renal Excretion of Na and K in the Dog." *Amer. J. Physiol.*, **162**, 655.

BATEMAN, J. B. & KEYS, A. (1932). " Chloride and Vapour-Pressure Relations in the Secretory Activity of the Gills of the Eel." *J. Physiol.*, **75**, 226.

BAYLISS, L. E., KERRIDGE, P. M. T. & RUSSELL, D. S. (1933). " Excretion of Protein by the Mammalian Kidney." *J. Physiol.*, **77**, 386.

BEADLE, L. C. (1931). " Effect of Salinity Changes on the Water Content and Respiration of Marine Invertebrates." *J. exp. Biol.*, **8**, 211.

BEADLE, L. C. (1934). " Osmotic Regulation in *Gunda Ulvæ*." *J. exp. Biol.*, **11**, 382.

BERLINER, R. W. & KENNEDY, T. J. (1948). " Renal Tubular Secretion of Potassium in the Normal Dog." *P.S.E.B.M.*, **67**, 542.

BERLINER, R. W., KENNEDY, T. J. & HILTON, J. G. (1950). " Renal Mechanism of Excretion of K+." *Amer. J. Physiol.*, **162**, 348.

BEVELANDER, G. (1935). " A Comparative Study of the Branchial Epithelium in Fishes, with Special Reference to Extra-Renal Excretion." *J. Morph.*, **57**, 335.

BEYER, K. H., WRIGHT, L. D., SKEGGS, H. R., RUSSO, H. F. & SHANER, G. A. (1947). " Renal Clearance of Essential Amino-Acids : Their Competition for Reabsorption by the Renal Tubules." *Amer. J. Physiol.*, **151**, 202.

BROCH, O. J. (1945). " Studies on the Regulation of the Serum Electrolytes with a Survey of the Salt and Water Metabolism of the Organism." *Acta Med. Scand.*, Suppl. 166.

CHAMBERS, R. & KEMPTON, R. T. (1933). " Indications of Function of the Chick Mesonephros in Tissue Culture with Phenol Red." *J. cell. & comp. Physiol.*, **3**, 131.

CHASIS, H. & SMITH, H. W. (1938). " The Excretion of Urea in Normal Man and in Subjects with Glomerulonephritis." *J. clin. Inv.*, **17**, 347.

CIZEK, L. J. & HOLMES, J. H. (1948). " Studies of the Mechanism of Increased Chloride Excretion during Osmotic Diuresis." *Fed. Proc.*, **7**, 21.

COLE, W. H. (1940). " The Composition of Fluids and Sera of Some Marine Animals and of the Sea Water in which They Live." *J. gen. Physiol.*, **23**, 575.

COON, J. M., NOOJIN, R. O. & PFEIFFER, C. (1941). " Optimal NaCl Concentration for Oral Saline Diuresis." *Amer. J. Physiol.*, **134**, 723.

COPELAND, D. E. (1948). " The Cytological Basis of Chloride Transfer in the Gills of *Fundulus Heteroclitus*." *J. Morph.*, **82**, 201.

CRAIG, F. N. (1946). " Renal Tubular Reabsorption, Metabolic Utilisation and Isomeric Fractionation of Lactic Acid in the Dog." *Amer. J. Physiol.*, **146**, 146.

DARROW, D. C. & YANNET, H. (1936). " Changes in Body Electrolyte and Distribution of Water Induced Experimentally by Deficit of Extracellular Electrolyte." *J. clin. Inv.*, **15**, 419.

DAVSON, H. & DANIELLI, J. F. (1943). " The Permeability of Natural Membranes." Cambridge. C.U.P.

DOCK, W. (1947). " The Kidney." *Ann. Rev. Physiol.*, **9**, 225.

DOLE, V. P. (1943). " Back-Diffusion of Urea in the Mammalian Kidney." *Amer. J. Physiol.*, **139**, 504.

DUVAL, M. (1925). " Recherches sur le Milieu Intérieur des Animaux Aquatiques. Modifications sous l'Influence du Milieu Extérieur." *Ann. Inst. océanogr.*, **2**, 232.

EGGLETON, M. G. & HABIB, Y. A. (1949). " Sodium Thiosulphate Excretion in the Cat." *J. Physiol.*, **110**, 98.

EGGLETON, M. G. & HABIB, Y. A. (1949). " Excretion of Para-Aminohippurate by the Kidney of the Cat." *J. Physiol.*, **110**, 458.

EGGLETON, M. G. & HABIB, Y. A. (1951). " Mode of Excretion of Creatinine and Inulin by the Kidney of the Cat." *J. Physiol.*, **112**, 191.

EILER, J. J., ALTHAUSEN, T. L. & STOCKHOLM, M. (1944). " Absorption of Galactose by Renal Tubules of the Dog." *P.S.E.B.M.*, **56**, 67.

FERREBEE, J. W., PARKER, D., CARNES, W. H., GERITY, M. K., ATCHLEY, D. W. & LOEB, R. F. (1941). "Certain Effects of Desoxycorticosterone. The Development of 'Diabetes Insipidus' and the Replacement of Muscle K by Na in Normal Dogs." *Amer. J. Physiol.*, 135, 230.

FETCHER, E. S. (1939). "The Water Balance in Marine Animals." *Quart. Rev. Biol.*, 14, 451.

FLEMISTER, L. J. (1942). "Distribution of Available Water in the Animal Body." *Amer. J. Physiol.*, 135, 430.

FRIEDMAN, G. J., SHERRY, S. & RALLI, E. P. (1940). "The Mechanism of Excretion of Vitamin C by the Human Kidney at Low Normal Plasma Levels of Ascorbic Acid." *J. clin. Inv.*, 19, 685.

FRIEDMAN, M., BYERS, S. O. & ABRAHM, P. M. (1948). "Renal Clearance of Allantoin as a Measure of Glomerular Filtration Rate." *Amer. J. Physiol.*, 155, 278.

GAMMELTOFT, A. & KJERULF-JENSEN, K. (1943). "The Mechanism of Renal Excretion of Fructose and Galactose in Rabbit, Cat, Dog and Man." *Acta Physiol. Scand.*, 6, 368.

GAUNT, R., BIRNIE, J. H. & EVERSOLE, W. J. (1949). "Adrenal Cortex and Water Metabolism." *Physiol. Rev.*, 29, 281.

GELEI, J. (1935). *Math. term. Közl.*, 37, 1. (Quoted by Kitching, 1938.)

GILMAN, A. (1934). "Experimental Sodium Loss Analogous to Adrenal Insufficiency, etc." *Amer. J. Physiol.*, 108, 662.

GILMAN, A., PHILIPS, F. S. & KOELLE, E. S. (1946). "Renal Clearance of Thiosulphate with Observations on its Volume Distribution." *Amer. J. Physiol.*, 146, 348.

HAYMAN, J. M. (1927). "Estimation of Afferent Arteriole and Glomerular Capillary Pressure in the Frog Kidney." *Amer. J. Physiol.*, 79, 389.

HERRMANN, F. (1931). "U. d. Wasserhaushalt des Flusskrebses." *Z. vgl. Physiol.*, 14, 479.

HEVESY, G., v. HOFER, E. & KROGH, A. (1935). "Permeability of the Skin of Frogs to Water as Determined by D_2O and H_2O." *Scand. Arch. Physiol.*, 72, 199.

HÖBER, R. (1933). "Über die Ausscheidung von Zuckern durch die isolierte Froschniere." *Pflüg. Arch.*, 233, 181.

HÖBER, R. (1940). "Correlation Between the Molecular Configuration of Organic Compounds and Their Active Transfer in Living Cells." *C.S.H. Symp.*, 8, 40.

HÖBER, R. (1945). "Physical Chemistry of Cells and Tissues." Philadelphia. Blakiston ; London. Churchill.

HÖBER, R. & BRISCOE-WOOLEY, P. M. (1940). "Conditions Determining the Selective Secretion of Dyestuffs by the Isolated Frog Kidney." *J. cell. & comp. Physiol.*, 15, 35.

HÖBER, R. & BRISCOE-WOOLEY, P. M. (1940). "Further Studies on Conditions Determining the Selective Renal Secretion of Dyestuffs." *J. cell. & comp. Physiol.*, 16, 63.

HOPKINS, D. L. (1946). "The Contractile Vacuole and the Adjustment to Changing Concentration in Fresh Water Amœbæ." *Biol. Bull.*, 90, 158.

HOWLAND, R. B. & POLLACK, H. (1927). "Significance of Gelation in the Systole of the Contractile Vacuole of *Amœba Dura*." *P.S.E.B.M.*, 24, 377.

HOWLAND, R. B. & POLLACK, H. (1927). "Micro-Injection of Urea into the Protoplasm of *Amœba Dura*." *loc. cit.*, p. 378.

HOWLAND, R. B. & POLLACK, H. (1927). "Micrurgical Studies on the Contractile Vacuole." *J. exp. Zool.*, 48, 441.

HUF, E. (1935). "Versuche u. d. Zusammenhang zwischen Stoffwechsel, Potential-bildung und Funktion der Froschhaut." *Pflüg. Arch.*, 235, 655.

IRVING, L., FISHER, K. C. & McINTOSH, F. C. (1935). "The Water Balance of a Marine Mammal, the Seal." *J. cell. & comp. Physiol.*, 6, 387.

KEOSIAN, J. (1938). "Secretion in Tissue Cultures. III. Tonicity of Fluid in Chick Mesonephros Cyst." *J. cell. & comp. Physiol.*, 12, 23.

KEYS, A. (1933). "The Mechanism of Adaptation in Varying Salinity in the Common Eel and the General Problem of Osmotic Regulation." *Proc. Roy. Soc.*, B, 112, 184.

KEYS, A. & WILLMER, E. N. (1932). "'Chloride Secreting Cells' in the Gills of Fishes with Special Reference to the Common Eel." *J. Physiol.*, 76, 368.

KITCHING, J. A. (1936). "The Physiology of Contractile Vacuoles. II. The Control of Body Volume in Marine Peritrichia." *J. exp. Biol.*, 13, 11.

KITCHING, J. A. (1938). "The Physiology of Contractile Vacuoles. III. The Water Balance of Fresh-Water Peritrichia." *J. exp. Biol.*, 15, 143.

KITCHING, J. A. (1938). "Contractile Vacuoles." *Biol. Rev.*, 13, 403.

KRITZLER, R. A. & GUTMAN, A. B. (1941). "'Alkaline' Phosphatase Activity of the Proximal Convoluted Tubules." *Amer. J. Physiol.*, 134, 94.

KROGH, A. (1937). "Osmotic Regulation in the Frog by Active Absorption of Chloride." *Scand. Arch. Physiol.*, **76**, 60.

KROGH, A. (1939). "Osmotic Regulation in Aquatic Animals." Cambridge. The University Press.

KROGH, A. (1946). "The Active and Passive Exchanges of Inorganic Ions through the Surfaces of Living Cells and through Living Membranes Generally." *Proc. Roy. Soc., B*, **133**, 140.

KUBICEK, W. C., HARVEY, R. B. & KOTTKE, F. J. (1948). "The Adrenalin Sensitivity of the Denervated Dog Kidney." *Fed. Proc.*, **7**, 68.

LIENEMANN, L. J. (1938). "The Green Glands as a Mechanism for Osmotic and Ionic Regulation in the Crayfish (*Cambarus Clarkii Girard*)." *J. cell. & comp. Physiol.*, **11**, 149.

LITTLE, J. M. & DAMERON, J. T. (1943). "Plasma Retention, Urinary Excretion and Effect upon Circulatory Total Red Cell Volume of Intravenous Gelatin in Normal Dogs." *Amer. J. Physiol.*, **139**, 438.

LITTLE, J. M., WALLACE, S. L., WHATLEY, E. C. & ANDERSON, G. A. (1947). "Effect of Pitressin on the Urinary Excretion of Chloride and Water in the Human." *Amer. J. Physiol.*, **151**, 174.

LOEB, R. F. (1941/2). "The Adrenal Cortex and Electrolyte Behaviour." *Harvey Lectures*, **37**, 100.

LOTSPEICH, W. D. (1947). "Renal Tubular Reabsorption of Inorganic Sulphate in the Normal Dog." *Amer. J. Physiol.*, **151**, 311.

LOTSPEICH, W. D., SWAN, R. C. & PITTS, R. F. (1947). "The Renal Tubular Reabsorption of Chloride." *Amer. J. Physiol.*, **148**, 445.

LOWELL, A., KENDALL, C. F. E., PATEK, A. J. & SEEGAL, D. (1946). "Comparison of the Effects of High and Low Viscosity Gelatins after their Intravenous Injection in Man." *J. clin. Inv.*, **25**, 226.

LUNDSGAARD, E. (1933). "Hemmung von Esterifizierungsvorgängen als Ursache der Phlorrhizinwirkung." *Biochem. Z.*, **264**, 209.

LUNDSGAARD, E. (1935). "Effect of Phloridzin on the Isolated Kidney and Isolated Liver." *Scand. Arch. Physiol.*, **72**, 265.

MALUF, N. S. R. (1940). "The Uptake of Inorganic Electrolytes by the Crayfish." *J. gen. Physiol.*, **24**, 151.

MALUF, N. S. R. (1941). "Experimental Cytological Evidence for an Outward Secretion of Water by the Nephric Tubule of the Crayfish." *Biol. Bull.*, **81**, 127.

MALUF, N. S. R. (1943). "Role of Renal Innervation in Renal Tubular Function." *Amer. J. Physiol.*, **139**, 103.

MARSHALL, E. K. & SMITH, H. W. (1930). "Glomerular Development of the Vertebrate Kidney in Relation to Habitat." *Biol. Bull.*, **59**, 135.

MAST, S. O. (1926). "Structure, Movement, Locomotion and Stimulation in *Amœba*." *J. Morph.*, **41**, 341.

MAST, S. O. & FOWLER, C. (1935). "Permeability of *Amœba Proteus* to Water." *J. cell. & comp. Physiol.*, **6**, 151.

MAST, S. O. & HOPKINS, D. L. (1941). "Regulation of the Water Content of *Amœba Mira* and Adaptation to Changes in the Osmotic Concentration of the Surrounding Medium." *J. cell. & comp. Physiol.*, **17**, 31.

McCANCE, R. A. (1936). "Experimental Sodium Chloride Deficiency in Man." *Proc. Roy. Soc., B*, **119**, 245.

McCANCE, R. A. & YOUNG, W. F. (1944). "The Secretion of Urine during Dehydration." *J. Physiol.*, **102**, 415.

MEYER, K. H. & BERNFELD, P. (1946). "Potentiometric Analysis of Membrane Structure and its Application to Living Animal Membranes." *J. gen. Physiol.*, **29**, 353.

MUDGE, G. H., FOULKS, J. & GILMAN, A. (1948). "The Renal Excretion of Potassium." *P.S.E.B.M.*, **67**, 545.

MUDGE, G. H., FOULKS, J. & GILMAN, A. (1950). "Renal Secretion of K in the Dog during Cellular Dehydration." *Amer. J. Physiol.*, **161**, 159.

MUDGE, G. H. & TAGGART, J. V. (1950). "Effect of 2,4-Dinitrophenol on Renal Transport Mechanisms in the Dog." *Amer. J. Physiol.*, **161**, 173.

MUDGE, G. H. & TAGGART, J. V. (1950). "Effect of Acetate on the Renal Excretion of *p*-Aminohippurate in the Dog." *Amer. J. Physiol.*, **161**, 191.

NEWMAN, E. V., GILMAN, A. & PHILIPS, F. S. (1946). "Renal Clearance of Thiosulphate in Man." *Bull. Johns Hopkins Hosp.*, **79**, 229.

NICHOLES, H. J. & HERRIN, R. C. (1941). "The Tubular Reabsorption of Urea, Thiourea and Derivatives of Thiourea in the Dog Kidney." *Amer. J. Physiol.*, **135**, 113.

OLIVER, J. (1944/5). " New Directions in Renal Morphology : a Method, the Results, and its Future." *Harvey Lectures*, **40**, 102.

PANTIN, C. F. A. (1931). " The Origin of the Composition of the Body Fluids in Animals." *Biol. Rev.*, **6**, 459.

PANTIN, C. F. A. (1931). " Adaptation of *Gunda Ulvæ* to Salinity." I—III. *J. exp. Biol.*, **8**, 63, 73, 82.

PETERS, H. (1935). " U. d. Einfluss des Salzgehaltes im Aussenmedium auf den Bau u.ʳd. Funktion der Exkretionsorgane dekapoder Crustaceen." *Z. Morph. Ökol.*, **30**, 355.

PETTENGILL, O. & COPELAND, D. E. (1948). " Alkaline Phosphatase Activity in the Chloride Cell of *Fundulus Heteroclitus* and its Relation to Osmotic Work." *J. exp. Zool.*, **108**, 235.

PHILLIPS, R. A. (1949). " The Kidney." *Ann. Rev. Physiol.*, **11**, 493.

PICKEN, L. E. R. (1936). " The Mechanism of Urine Formation in Invertebrates. I. The Excretion Mechanism in Certain Arthropods." *J. exp. Biol.*, **13**, 309.

PICKEN, L. E. R. (1936). " A Note on the Mechanism of Salt and Water Balance in the Heterotrichous Ciliate, *Spirostomum Ambiguum.*" *J. exp. Biol.*, **13**, 387.

PITTS, R. F. (1938). " Excretion of Phenol Red by the Chicken." *J. cell. & comp. Physiol.*, **11**, 99.

PITTS, R. F. (1943). " A Renal Reabsorptive Mechanism in the Dog Common to Glycine and Creatine." *Amer. J. Physiol.*, **140**, 156.

PITTS, R. F. (1944). " A Comparison of the Renal Reabsorptive Processes for Several Amino Acids." *Amer. J. Physiol.*, **140**, 535.

PITTS, R. F. (1946). " The Kidney." *Ann. Rev. Physiol.*, **8**, 199.

PITTS, R. F. & ALEXANDER, R. S. (1944). " The Renal Reabsorptive Mechanism for Inorganic Phosphate in Normal and Acidotic Dogs." *Amer. J. Physiol.*, **142**, 648.

PITTS, R. F. & ALEXANDER, R. S. (1945). " The Nature of the Renal Tubular Mechanism for Acidifying the Urine." *Amer. J. Physiol.*, **144**, 239.

PITTS, R. F., AYER, J. L. & SCHIESS, W. A. (1948). " Reabsorption and Excretion of Bicarbonate in Normal Man." *Fed. Proc.*, **7**, 94.

PITTS, R. F. & LOTSPEICH, W. D. (1947). " Use of Thiosulphate as a Measure of Glomerular Filtration Rate in Acidotic Dogs." *P.S.E.B.M.*, **64**, 224.

RICHARDS, A. N. (1938). " Processes of Urine Formation." *Croonian Lecture. Proc. Roy. Soc.*, B, **126**, 398.

RICHARDS, A. N., BOTT, P. A. & WESTFALL, B. B. (1938). " Experiments Concerning the Possibility that Inulin is Secreted by the Renal Tubules." *Amer. J. Physiol.*, **123**, 281.

ROWNTREE, L. G. (1926). " The Effects on Mammals of the Administration of Excessive Quantities of Water." *J. Pharm. exp. Ther.*, **29**, 135.

SCHLIEPER, C. (1930). " Die Osmoregulation Wasserlebender Tiere." *Biol. Rev.*, **5**, 309.

SCHLIEPER, C. (1933). " Die Wasserdurchlässigkeit und der angebliche Wassertransport der Aalkiemen bei hypertonischem Aussenmedium." *Z. vgl. Physiol.*, **19**, 68.

SCHLIEPER, C. (1935). " Neuere Ergebnisse und Probleme aus der Gebiet der Osmoregulation Wasserlebender Tiere." *Biol. Rev.*, **10**, 334.

SCHMIDT-NIELSEN (1941). *K. danske vidensk. Selsk. Biol. Medd.*, **16**, 6. (Quoted by Krogh, 1946.)

SCHMIDT-NIELSEN, B. & SCHMIDT-NIELSEN, K. (1950). " Do Kangaroo Rats Thrive When Drinking Sea Water ? " *Amer. J. Physiol.*, **160**, 291.

SCHMIDT-NIELSEN, B. & SCHMIDT-NIELSEN, K. (1950). " Pulmonary Water Loss in Desert Rodents." *Amer. J. Physiol.*, **162**, 31.

SCHMIDT-NIELSEN, B., SCHMIDT-NIELSEN, K., BROKAW, A. & SCHNEIDERMAN, H. (1948). " Water Conservation in Desert Rodents." *J. cell. & comp. Physiol.*, **32**, 331.

SCHWARTZ, B. M., SMITH, P. K. & WINKLER, A. W. (1942). " Renal Excretion of Sulphate." *Amer. J. Physiol.*, **137**, 658.

SELKURT, E. E. (1944). " Influence of Glucose Renal Tubular Reabsorption and p-NH$_2$-hippuric Acid Tubular Secretion on the Clearance of Ascorbic Acid." *Amer. J. Physiol.*, **142**, 182.

SHANNON, J. A. (1936). " The Excretion of Inulin and Creatinine at Low Urine Flows by the Normal Dog." *Amer. J. Physiol.*, **114**, 362.

SHANNON, J. A. (1936). " Glomerular Filtration and Urea Excretion in Relation to Urine Flow in the Dog." *Amer. J. Physiol.*, **117**, 206.

SHANNON, J. A. (1938). " The Tubular Reabsorption of Xylose in the Normal Dog." *Amer. J. Physiol.*, **122**, 775.

SHANNON, J. A. (1942). " Control of Renal Excretion of Water." *J. exp. Med.*, **76**, 387.

SHANNON, J. A., FARBER, S. & TROAST, L. (1941). " Measurement of Glucose T_m in the Normal Dog." *Amer. J. Physiol.*, 133, 752.

SHANNON, J. A. & FISHER, S. (1938). " The Renal Tubular Reabsorption of Glucose in the Normal Dog." *Amer. J. Physiol.*, 122, 765.

SHAPIRO, B. (1947). " The Mechanism of Phloridzin Glucosuria." *Biochem. J.*, 41, 151.

SHONYO, E. S. & MANN, F. C. (1944). " Experimental Investigation of Renal Circulation." *Arch. Path.*, 38, 287.

SIMS, E. A. H. & SELDIN, D. W. (1949). " Reabsorption of Creatine and Guanidoacetic Acid by the Renal Tubules." *Amer. J. Physiol.*, 157, 14.

SMETANA, H. (1946). " Permeability of Renal Glomeruli for Proteins in Lower Animals." *Fed. Proc.*, 5, 227.

SMITH, H. W. (1936). " Composition of the Urine of the Seal." *J. cell. & comp. Physiol.*, 7, 465.

SMITH, H. W. (1937). " Physiology of the Kidney." New York. O.U.P.

SMITH, H. W. (1939/40). " Physiology of the Renal Circulation." *Harvey Lectures*, 35, 166.

SMITH, H. W., CHASIS, H., GOLDRING, W. & RANGES, H. A. (1940). " Glomerular Dynamics in the Normal Human Kidney." *J. clin. Inv.*, 19, 751.

SMITH, H. W., GOLDRING, W. & CHASIS, H. (1938). " Measurement of Tubular Excretory Mass, Effective Blood Flow and Filtration Rate in the Normal Human Kidney." *J. clin. Inv.*, 17, 263.

STEINITZ, K. (1940). " The Renal Excretion of Sucrose in Normal Man ; Comparison with Inulin." *Amer. J. Physiol.*, 129, 252.

SWINGLE, W. W., REMINGTON, J. W., HAYS, H. W. & COLLINGS, W. D. (1941). " Effectiveness of Priming Doses of DOCA in Protecting the Adrenalectomised Dog against Water Intoxication." *Endocrin.*, 28, 531.

USSING, H. H. (1945). " The Reabsorption of Glycine and other Amino-Acids in the Kidney of Man." *Acta Physiol. Scand.*, 9, 193.

USSING, H. H. (1949). " Active Ion Transport Through the Isolated Frog Skin in the Light of Tracer Studies." *Acta Physiol. Scand.*, 17, 1.

VAN SLYKE (1943). " Glutamine as Source Material of Urinary Nitrogen." *J. biol. Chem.*, 150, 481.

VERNEY, E. B. (1947). " The Antidiuretic Hormone and the Factors which Determine its Release." *Croonian Lecture. Proc. Roy. Soc.*, B, 135, 25.

WALKER, A. M. (1940). " Ammonia Formation in the Amphibian Kidney." *Amer. J. Physiol.*, 131, 187.

WALKER, A. M., BOTT, P. A., OLIVER, J. & MacDOWELL, M. C. (1941). " The Collection and Analysis of Fluid from Single Nephrons of the Mammalian Kidney." *Amer. J. Physiol.*, 134, 580.

WALKER, A. M. & HUDSON, C. L. (1937). " Reabsorption of Glucose from the Renal Tubule in Amphibia and the Action of Phlorhizin upon it." *Amer. J. Physiol.*, 118, 130.

WALKER, A. M., HUDSON, C. L., FINDLEY, T. & RICHARDS, A. N. (1937). " Total Molecular Concentration and Chloride Concentration of Fluid from Different Segments of the Renal Tubule of Amphibia." *Amer. J. Physiol.*, 118, 121.

WALKER, A. M. & OLIVER, J. (1941). " Methods for the Collection of Fluid from Single Glomeruli and Tubules of the Mammalian Kidney." *Amer. J. Physiol.*, 134, 562.

WEBB, D. A. (1940). " Ionic Regulation in *Carcinus Mænas*." *Proc. Roy. Soc.*, B, 129, 107.

WESSON, L. G., PARKER, W. & SMITH, H. W. (1948). " The Renal Excretion of Strong Electrolytes." *Fed. Proc.*, 7, 132.

WHITE, H. L. (1940). " The Effects of Phlorizin on Renal Plasma Flow, on Glomerular Filtration and on Tubular Excretion of Diodrast in the Dog." *Amer. J. Physiol.*, 130, 582.

WILEY, F. H. & WILEY, L. L. (1933). " The Inorganic Salt Balance during Dehydration and Recovery." *J. biol. Chem.*, 101, 83.

WINKLER, A. W. & SMITH, P. K. (1943). " Renal Excretion of Potassium Salts." *Amer. J. Physiol.*, 138, 94.

WINTON, F. R. (1937). " Physical Factors Involved in the Activities of the Mammalian Kidney." *Physiol. Rev.*, 17, 408.

WOLF, A. V. (1943). " The Relative Retention of Infused Chloride, Urea and Water." *Amer. J. Physiol.*, 138, 191.

WOLF, A. V. (1945). " The Dehydrating Effect of Continuously Administered Water." *Amer. J. Physiol.*, 143, 567.

WOLF, A. V. (1945). " The Retention and Excretion of Continuously Administered Salt Solutions." *Amer. J. Physiol.*, 143, 572.

CHAPTER XV

EXCITABILITY AND PROPAGATION OF THE IMPULSE

IN an earlier chapter (p. 258) we have discussed the nature of the potential difference between the inside and outside of certain cells, in particular of nerve and muscle fibres, without, however, attempting to elucidate their functional significance. In the present section we shall be concerned with the problems of excitation and transmission, phenomena that are associated with modifications of these bioelectric potentials. In the complex organism the effects of a stimulus are transmitted by way of specialised cells—*neurones*; transmission is not peculiar to these, however, since a muscle, for example, may exhibit the spread of an excited state in an essentially similar manner to that found in nerve, and even unicellular organisms exhibit responses to local stimulation that are not necessarily confined to the stimulated point. The spread of excitation may thus be a general characteristic of living tissues, attaining, however, a maximal degree of efficiency and speed in the specialised nervous cells. The spread of excitation over a muscle fibre is probably related to the uniform development of contraction, and is thus an important element in its behaviour; nerve and muscle therefore represent specialised tissues in which we may expect to find the properties of excitability and transmission highly developed, so that in this section we may confine attention almost exclusively to them.

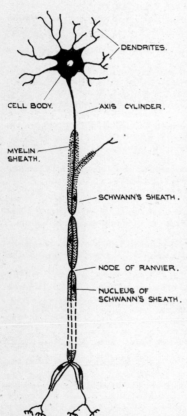

FIG. 164. Typical motor neurone.

The Neurone

A typical vertebrate nerve consists of a bundle of hundreds of fibres, each one of which is an extension of a single nerve cell, or neurone; a typical neurone, Fig. 164, is essentially a cell with a series of processes, one of which, the *axon*, is much longer than the remainder, the *dendrites*. The axon leaves the cell body (soma or perikaryon) as the axon hillock, and eventually makes connection with an effector organ—in this case a number of muscle fibres—or another neurone; the dendrites connect with the

axons of other nerve fibres of the central nervous system.[1] As we shall
see, these junctional regions, the *nerve-muscle junction* and the nerve-nerve
synapse, are specialised regions permitting a close association of the two
elements ; nevertheless there is reason to believe that the fundamental
continuity of the plasma membrane over the protoplasmic surface of the
nerve cell is maintained even in these regions, *i.e.*, there is probably no
cytoplasmic fusion, so that the neurone is a true unit in transmission. The
axon consists, from without inwards, of an outermost sheath or *neurilemma*
(*Schwann's sheath*) ; a *myelin sheath* of mainly lipoid material which acts
as an insulating layer, and which may be thick in the typical *myelinated*
(or *medullated*) *nerves* of vertebrates or very thin in the *non-myelinated*
nerves typically found in invertebrates and in some parts of the vertebrate
nervous system. The limiting plasma membrane, the presence of which
can only be inferred, separates the internal *axoplasm* from the outer layers.
The thick myelin sheath of the medullated nerve is interrupted at regular
intervals—about 1 mm. in man and 3 mm. in the frog—to give
constrictions, or *nodes of Ranvier*, which are therefore to be regarded as
localised regions of low insulating resistance (p. 413). In each internodal
region there is a nucleus belonging to a cell of the Schwann sheath or
neurilemma.

Ultra-Structure. The ultra-structure of the nerve axon has been a matter
for speculation and controversy for many years ; the extruded material, or
axoplasm, is gelatinous,[2] but in histological preparations it appears to consist
of a number of fibrils embedded in a matrix, the fibrils being continuous
with an interlacing network in the body of the cell. Like so many of the
structures identified by classical histological techniques, the neurofibrils
have been described as artefacts, but the studies of Weiss & Wang on living
ganglion cells cultivated *in vitro* suggest that they are definite entities ;
in the very young cell, according to these workers, the fibrils are not
evident as discrete units, but within seven days of explantation they may
be observed (about 20 in a large axon). The polarisation-optical studies
of Bear, Schmitt & Young on squid giant axons indicate a submicroscopic
organisation of the axoplasm, the weak birefringence observed being most
probably due to the presence of orientated rodlets of protein parallel to the
axis of the fibre ; within the cell body, according to Chinn, the particles
are orientated in a direction tangential to the surface. More recent studies
with the electron-microscope by Robertis & Schmitt on fixed preparations,
submitted to sonic vibrations to induce fragmentation, have suggested the

[1] The distinction between axon and dendrite is made on both morphological and
functional grounds ; it is sufficient for our purpose to note that the neurone is so disposed
that impulses pass normally into the dendrites through the cell body and thence along
the axon. The long processes, constituting the sensory nerves of the spinal ganglia
(p. 437), are often described as axons, though functionally they behave as dendrites.

[2] Hodgkin & Katz have shown that the physical state of the extruded axoplasm
of the squid giant axon depends critically on the concentration of Ca^{++} in the fluid into
which it is extruded. In a medium free of Ca^{++}, the axoplasm retains its cylindrical
shape ; but in a concentration of 20 mM Ca^{++} dissolution occurs in a matter of minutes.
The evidence for the belief that the axoplasm is a solid gel within the axon has
been summarised by Hodgkin & Katz ; they conclude that the concentration of Ca^{++}
within the axon must be less than some 0·5 mM.

existence of so-called *neurotubules*, long bodies, about 500A in diameter, which appear to be hollow tubes. The authors do not consider them to be artefacts of fixation and have shown that they disappear from a degenerating nerve contemporaneously with the disappearance of electrical excitability. Against this view, however, we have the more recent electron-microscopical studies of Fernández-Morán (1950) who considers the neurotubules to be no more than collagen fibrils belonging to the external sheath layer. The myelin sheath is strongly birefringent ; according to the polarisation-optical studies of W. J. Schmidt and F. O. Schmitt, the birefringence is complex, being due to layers of lipoid molecules, with their long axes directed radially, interspersed with " leaflets " of protein disposed tangentially, as in Fig. 165. The micellar birefringence of the lipoid molecules dominates the appearance of the nerve fibre in the myelinated nerve ; the presence of a lipoid sheath in the " non-myelinated " nerve can be deduced from the change in birefringence that occurs when the

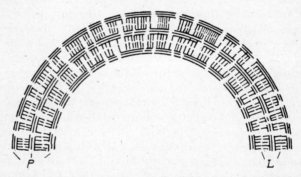

Fig. 165.   Schematic representation of the lipids (L) and protein lamellæ (P), in the myelin sheath. (W. J. Schmidt. *Z. f. wiss. Mikr.*)

nerve is impregnated with glycerine ; under these conditions, form birefringence is more or less neutralised, and the remaining micellar birefringence is due to lipoid molecules orientated with their long axes radially.[1] The X-ray studies of the myelin sheath carried out by Bear, Palmer & Schmitt, have been discussed in another connection (p. 200) ; the general picture emerging from these studies is in full agreement with that derived from the measurement of birefringence. Fernández-Morán's electron-microscopical studies are likewise in agreement, since he observed that the sheath is made up of concentric layers, some 80A thick ; on extraction of the lipids much thinner concentric laminæ—some 30–40A thick—remained. Fernández-Morán described also an *internal sheath wall*,

---

[1] As Schmitt & Bear have pointed out, the distinction between the myelinated and non-myelinated nerve is arbitrary, the birefringence due to the sheath varying from one nerve to another in a continuous fashion. Fibres with a very small amount of lipid will be normally positively birefringent (referred to the axis of the fibre), as the form birefringence of the concentric leaflets of protein then predominates ; on treatment with glycerol this form birefringence is neutralised, the sheath becoming negatively birefringent ; this is the so-called *metatropic reaction* of Göthlin ; Schmitt & Bear describe this thin sheath as a *metatropic sheath* in contrast to the *myelotropic sheath* of the thickly myelinated fibre.

corresponding to the axolemma of the histologists, consisting of a dense set of interlacing fibrils, some 100–200A wide. The general picture emerging from Fernández-Morán's work is illustrated in Fig. 166.

The nodes of Ranvier represent regions in which the myelin sheath is absent ; according to v. Muralt, in these regions the continuity of the axoplasm is broken by the interposition of *transverse membranes* at each node. In the electron-microscope, however, there is no evidence of a discontinuity in the axoplasm at the node, and it would seem from recent studies of Lüthy that the transverse membranes are optical artefacts of the type known as " Becke Lines." The myelin sheath in each Schwann

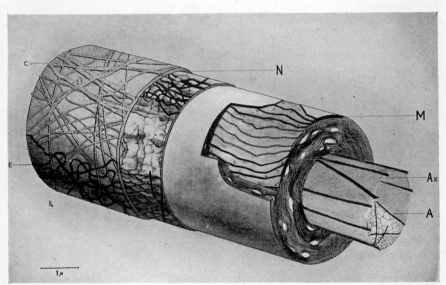

Fig. 166. Schematic diagram of the internodal portion of a medullated nerve fibre to illustrate the general features. The neurilemma (N), with attached collagen fibril bundles (C) and smooth rigid fibrils (E), envelops a scaly surface structure corresponding to the outer layers of the myelin sheath (M). The latter is represented schematically as a series of 50 thin-walled tubes fitted concentrically into each other, and separated by irregular oval crevices distributed at random throughout the sheath. The internal fibrous membrane, probably corresponding to the axolemma (Ax), is depicted with its longitudinal trabecular reinforcements. Drawing by Prof. R. Lucchetti. (Fernández-Morán. *Exp. Cell. Res.*)

segment is interrupted by several oblique partitions, the *incisions* or *clefts of Schmidt-Lantermann*, easily recognisable in polarised light, and recently identified in the electron-microscope by Rozsa, Morgan & Szent-Györgyi. According to these workers the neurilemma is only some 500A thick, and is probably built up on a fibrillar basis. The individual fibres of a nerve trunk are bound together into fascicles by connective tissue constituting the *endoneurium* and *epineurium*. The fibrils of the former fill the spaces between the nerve fibres, whilst the epineurium surrounds each fascicle as a sheath. Individual fascicles are held together by the *perineurium*. In the electron-microscope many of these connective tissue fibrils exhibit the typical collagen banding (p. 102), with a repeat-period of 640A ; others have a period of only 200A. It is customary to treat the epineurium as a mere connective tissue sheath, but Huxley & Stämpfli (1951) have drawn attention to its probable function as a diffusion barrier between the axons and surrounding interstitial fluid. Thus a whole nerve responds to alterations in the composition of its environment, such as a reduced concentration of Na⁺, in a matter of hours, whereas, if the epineurium is stripped off, the time is a matter of seconds. These authors quote the description of the epineurium by Ranvier—" delicate fibrous sheets each covered by a complete, or almost complete, layer of flat ' endothelial ' cells " ; and it seems likely that it is the epineurium that constitutes the diffusion barrier between blood and nervous tissue remarked on earlier (p. 234).

The Action Potential (Classical Representation)

Monophasic Action Potential. It will be recalled that the nerve or muscle fibre has a potential between inside and outside—the resting potential—the inside being negative in respect to the outside. During the

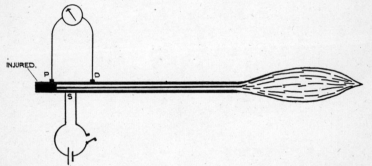

Fig. 167.   Stimulation and recording set-up for nerve-muscle preparation.

passage of an impulse a characteristic change in the resting potential takes place ; thus Fig. 167 illustrates a muscle with its nerve, the so-called nerve-muscle preparation ; one electrode is placed on the cut end and another, nearer the muscle, on an intact portion. Both are connected to a device for the recording of potential differences, which will thus indicate the resting or injury potential. If, now, the nerve is stimulated at an intact portion, say at S between the electrodes, the muscle contracts but, before this happens, the resting potential passes through a characteristic cycle, falling rapidly to zero and returning to its original value, the whole cycle lasting perhaps only a few thousandths of a second (msec.). If the difference of potential between P and D is plotted against time, we should obtain a curve similar to that in Fig. 168 (*a*), the potential of the electrode D, in respect to P, being first 30 mV positive, falling to zero, and then rising to its initial value. It is more usual, however, in making records, to balance out the resting potential with a potentiometer, so that, before stimulation, the recorded potential between the electrodes is zero. Stimulation results in a change of potential such that D now becomes negative in respect to P, and the action-potential record, obtained by plotting the potential of D against time, is turned upside down as in Fig. 168 (*b*), potentials above the abscissæ being called *negative*. The detailed nature of the action potential and its full interpretation will be dealt with later ; for the moment we may note that the record is called a *negative spike*, and that the transmission of the effect of stimulation seems to be associated with a transient fall in the resting potential to zero.[1] This fall could happen if the effect of the propagated disturbance were to abolish the potential difference between

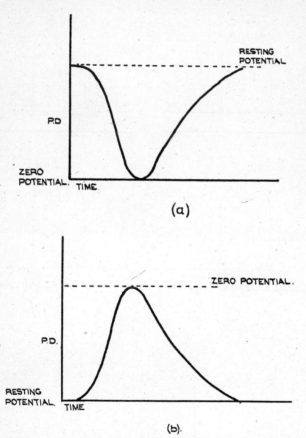

FIG. 168. Monophasic action potential, classically regarded as a falling to zero of the resting potential.

inside and outside of the cell at the point D, *i.e.*, if the electrical condition of the point P were unaffected. That this is the truth of the matter is shown by the fact that the time at which the spike occurs depends on the distance of the point of stimulation from D, and not on its distance from P. Thus the membrane is said to be depolarised by the passage of the propagated disturbance.

An essentially similar type of action potential is obtained by stimulation

[1] As we shall see, the action potential consists of something more than a *fall* in the resting potential ; the sign is actually reversed.

of the plant cell, *Nitella*, but in this case the process is very much slower, lasting some fifteen seconds.

Diphasic Action Potential. If the conducted effect of the stimulus—the propagated disturbance—consists essentially of the abolition of the resting potential across the wall of the cell, then, since this disturbance travels at a measurable rate, we may expect to find characteristic changes

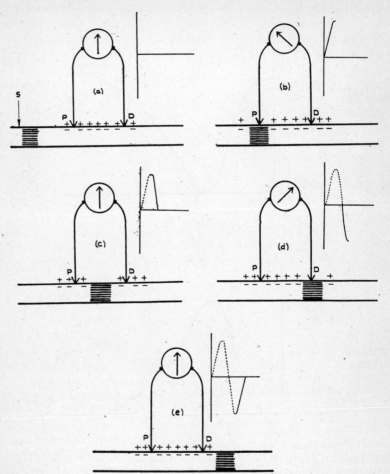

Fig. 169.   Schematic illustration of the diphasic action potential.

in the difference of potential between two electrodes on intact nerve as the disturbance passes first under one electrode and then under the other. We may expect the changes illustrated in Fig. 169. At (*a*) the disturbance has not reached either electrode : both of these are on intact nerve so that their potential difference is zero.   At (*b*) the disturbance has reached the proximal electrode, P, to abolish its resting potential ; consequently P becomes negative in respect to the distal electrode, D, and positive current flows through the recording instrument from D to P.   At (*c*) the disturbance is between the electrodes, and the resting potential at P has been re-established ; there is thus no difference of potential between the electrodes —the *isoelectric phase*. At (*d*) the disturbance has reached the distal electrode, abolishing its resting potential. D thus becomes negative in respect to P and current now flows in the external circuit, *i.e.*, through the recording system, in the reverse direction. Finally, at (*e*) the disturbance has passed on and the resting potential at D has been re-established ; there is now no difference of potential between the two electrodes. If, now, we plot the potential of the proximal electrode, P, in respect to the other electrode, against time we obtain a *diphasic record*, as shown in Fig. 169, where negativity of P is marked by points above the horizontal axis. The shape of the diphasic record will clearly depend on the distance between the electrodes, and the velocity of transmission, among other factors ; as the electrodes are brought closer together the isoelectric phase tends to disappear ; when the electrodes are very close, the development of negativity at P is followed so closely by the development of negativity at D that the effect is to produce what is described as the " first differential " of the monophasic action potential, *i.e.*, the record exhibits the variation in the *rate of change* of potential under the first active electrode. By integrating this record it is possible to deduce the form of the monophasic action potenital.

The resting potential depends on the unequal distribution of ions across the fibre membrane ; the propagated disturbance, the action potential, is a decrease in this potential—a depolarisation. Since the maintenance of the unequal distribution of ions depends on the permeability characteristics of the membrane, the simplest explanation of the depolarisation is that it results from a localised change in permeability which, if it were maintained for long enough, would permit the high internal concentration of K^+ to fall and the low concentration of Na^+ to rise. Such a change in permeability should be reflected in a change in such electrical properties of the membrane as its resistance and capacity ; let us therefore consider the significance of these characteristics.

Electrical Properties of the Membrane

Impedance. The bioelectric potentials have been described in terms of the mobilities of certain ions through the plasma membrane of the cell. The selectivity displayed by the plasma membrane should be reflected in other characteristics besides the potential across it. Thus on passing a current through the membrane, *e.g.*, by placing electrodes inside and outside a cell, the flow of current should encounter an ohmic resistance, compounded of that due to the resistance of the solution within the cell, the resistance of the membrane, and the resistance of the extracellular fluid. (By *ohmic* resistance is meant a resistance such that the current is always a definite fraction of the applied voltage.) The membrane, representing as it does a layer, or several layers, of lipoid material, is made of poorly conducting material ; in this event the concept of electrical resistance must be extended to include the effects of *specific inductive capacity* or *dielectric constant*. When a potential difference is established across a non-conductor, an electric charge is stored in the material and the electric, or static, capacity is given by the ratio of the quantity of electricity stored over the applied voltage. Thus, if the material is completely non-conducting, a certain amount of current flows during the charging process; when this is complete, the flow ceases. In an alternating current, on the other hand, the applied potential changes its sign repeatedly; during each cycle current flows in a charging and discharging process, so that it is permissible to speak of a flow of alternating current *through* the condenser although it is non-conducting. The resistance to flow of the alternating current is therefore made up of a simple ohmic resistance plus a "capacitative" resistance, the two together producing what is called the "*impedance*" of the system. The cell membrane allows a constant current to flow through it if a voltage is applied across it; during the establishment of the steady flow, however, the fluctuations of current intensity reveal the presence of a capacitative

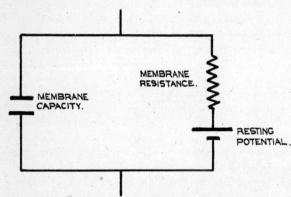

element in the circuit, *i.e.*, the membrane behaves as a condenser. The course of the flow of current, after the sudden application of a potential difference, is described as a *direct current transient*, and from its characteristics important information regarding the capacity and resistance of the system can be deduced. On applying an alternating potential differ-

FIG. 170.   The membrane regarded as a leaky condenser.

ence to the cell membrane, the impedance may be measured; this varies with the frequency of alternation and thereby reveals the presence of a capacitative element. The pioneering studies of Fricke, and of Cole & Curtis, on the impedance of suspensions of cells and of nerve fibres indicate that the cell membrane may be represented, to a first approximation, as a condenser with a resistance in parallel as in Fig. 170; such a system might be called a "leaky" condenser since current can flow through the shunt resistance. On applying a potential difference across the cell membrane we may expect, on this basis, that current will flow rapidly at first until the condenser charges; when the maximum charge is attained, the flow will be entirely through the shunt resistance. The process of charging the condenser consists, in reality, of the accumulation of ions of opposite charges at the surfaces of the membrane, and may be described as a *polarisation of the membrane*, the potential on the two sides of the membrane building up to oppose the applied potential.

In the case of the large plant cells, the resistance across the membrane could be directly measured (*e.g.*, by Blinks) through electrodes within and without the cell. The studies of Cole & Curtis on *Nitella* and the giant axon of the squid have been largely measurements of alternating current impedance between two electrodes placed transversely across the cell ; the impedance so measured had to be analysed into a capacity and a resistance, but the amount of current flowing across the membrane was so small that no accurate estimate of the latter quantity could be obtained ; by making use of Blinks' figure, determined as described above, however, the capacity could be calculated. A method more suited for measuring the resistance consists in applying a potential across two electrodes placed axially so that current flows mainly along the axis of the nerve ; this method has been applied with success by Cole & Hodgkin to the squid's giant axon, and by Hodgkin & Rushton to single fibres of the non-medullated nerve of the lobster. In these measurements the following aspects had to be studied : (*a*) the spread of potential around the electrodes during the application of a current too weak to excite ; (*b*) the rate of rise of potential ; (*c*) the ratio of the applied current to the voltage recorded between cathode and anode and a distant extrapolar point, and (*d*) the voltage gradient in the region midway between two distant electrodes. From the results, the electric resistance of the fluid within and without the fibre, and the resistance and capacity of the membrane were calculated. Finally, the recently developed technique of impaling single axons with micro-electrodes has permitted direct measurements across the fibre wall, as with *Nitella*. Some values obtained are shown in Table **XXX**. The

TABLE XXX

Electrical Constants of Certain Cells (after Katz, 1948, and Cole, 1942).

	RESISTANCE			CAPACITY
	Internal ohm.cm.	Outside Medium ohm.cm.	Membrane ohm.cm.^{2}	Membrane μF/cm.^{2}
75μ Axon of *Homarus vulgaris* .	60	20	600–7,000	1·3
Axon of *Carcinus Mœnas* 30μ .	90	20	2,000–16,000 Mean: 8,000	1·1
Giant axon of Squid. *Loligo.* 500μ	29	20	400–1,100 Mean : 700	1·1
Nitella	58		2·5.10^5	0·94
Erythrocyte . . .	140			0·8
Frog muscle (75μ). (Bundles of add. magnus) . . .	200	87	1,500	6
Frog muscle. (Extensor dig. IV, 45μ)	260	87	4,000	4·5
Frog egg . .			170	2·0
Arbacia egg. Resting . .	180		> 100	1·1
Fertilised . .	210		> 100	2·8

results indicate in general that the capacity of the membrane is remarkably constant at about 1 microfarad per sq. cm., whether we consider different nerve fibres, the large plant cell, *Nitella*, or the erythrocyte. The transverse resistance, on the other hand, is highly variable, being some 250,000 ohm.cm.^{2} in *Nitella*, 8,000 ohm.cm.^{2} in crab single fibres, and only 700 ohm.cm.^{2} in the squid giant axon ; moreover, small differences in technique seem to bring about large changes in the resistance ; thus Cole & Curtis' study on impaled axons of the squid gave a value as low as 23 ohm.cm.^{2}. This variability suggests that it is in its transverse resistance, as opposed to its capacity, that physiological changes are reflected. Thus the resistance is essentially a measure of the power of electrolytes to penetrate the membrane whilst the capacity represents its ability to accumulate charge. The appearance of quite a small area of membrane (in comparison with the total) permitting free diffusion would very considerably modify the electrical resistance whilst the change in capacity might be barely measurable. Hodgkin (1947) has calculated that a layer of sea-water as thick as the plasma membrane (say 100A) would have a resistance of only 2.10^{-5} ohm.cm.^{2}, *i.e.*, less than one ten-millionth of that of the squid axon ; if only 1 per cent. of the area became freely conducting, the resistance of the membrane as a whole would fall to less than a thousandth of an ohm.cm.^{2}.

Katz has applied the method of Hodgkin & Rushton to determine the electrical constants of muscle fibres ; the theoretical treatment and the experimental findings were consistent, and suggested a fundamental similarity between nerve and muscle, viewed as sources of potential and conducting units. Quantitatively there were differences ; thus the membrane capacity was $4 \cdot 5$–6μF/cm.^{2}, considerably higher than the values found for all other membranes studied ; the membrane resistance was 1,500–4,000 ohm.cm.^{2}, and the internal and external resistivities were 200–267 and 87 ohm.cm. respectively.[1]

Change in Impedance with Activity. Cole & Curtis have measured simultaneously the action potential and the impedance of the membrane of *Nitella*, and of the squid giant axon. The action potential, we will remember, may be considered to be a falling off of the normal resting potential. The latter, we have seen, depends on the permeability characteristics of the membrane, and thus on the electrical impedance. A decrease in the resting potential could be brought about by a permeability

---

[1] The different terms used to describe the electrical resistance of biological structures and fluids, and the units in which they are expressed, are likely to cause confusion. The measured resistance varies inversely as the area, and directly as the thickness of the material being examined, *i.e.*, Resistance $= Rl/A$. When A is 1 cm.^{2}, and l is 1 cm., and the resistance is measured in ohms, the constant, R, becomes the *specific resistance* or *resistivity* ; the units are : ohms $\times$ cm.^{2}/cm. $=$ ohm.cm. Frequently it is useful to employ the resistance per unit length of the structure, *e.g.*, the axoplasm. If this is regarded as a cylinder, the specific resistance, R, will be given by : $R = \pi\rho^2 r$, where ρ is the radius and r is the resistance per unit length of axoplasm, with units of ohm.cm. Where a membrane of unknown thickness is concerned, the quantity, l, cannot be measured, hence the transverse membrane resistance must be expressed in units independent of this quantity ; the *specific transverse resistance* of the membrane, R_m, is equal to the specific resistance of the membrane multiplied by its thickness in cm., and its units are ohm.cm. $\times$ cm. $=$ ohm.cm.^{2}. Finally, the transverse resistance of unit length of the membrane, r_m, is often used ; since the resistance decreases with increasing length of membrane, the quantity required is the resistance times the length, and the unit is ohm.cm. With a cylindrical membrane, r_m is related to the specific transverse resistance, R_m, by : $2\pi\rho r_m = R_m$.

of the membrane to previously non-penetrating organic anions, or by an increased permeability to Na^+ ; both of these effects should be reflected in a decrease in membrane resistance. The record of Fig. 171 shows unmistakably that the transverse impedance decreases as the wave of action potential passes between the impedance-recording electrodes ; as we shall see, the time at which the impedance change occurs corresponds to the point on the action potential curve where it is thought that the critical change of membrane potential takes place. A single measurement of a change of impedance is not sufficient to permit of an analysis into a change of capacity and change of resistance ; by repeating the experiment at different frequencies of alternating current, however, the analysis could be made, and it was shown that the main change consisted in a fall of resistance to about 28 ohm.cm.^{2}, *i.e.*, a fall of nearly 97 per cent. The

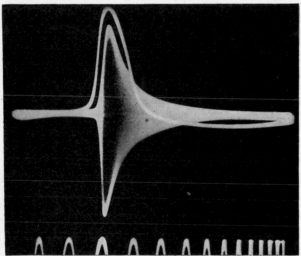

Fig. 171. Superimposed records of the action potential and change in transverse impedance of the giant axon of the squid. (Cole & Curtis. *J. gen. Physiol.*)

change in membrane capacity was very small, only 2 per cent. In *Nitella* essentially similar results were obtained, the capacity decreasing by only about 15 per cent., whilst the resistance decreased from about 10^5 ohm.cm.^{2} to about 500.

Effect of Ions on Membrane Conductance. If the nerve membrane is more permeable to K^+ than to Na^+, as the theory of the resting potential demands, we must expect current to be carried through the membrane, as the result of an applied potential, mainly by K^+ and Cl^-. Increasing the concentration of K^+ in the external medium should, therefore, by increasing the concentration of available carriers of electricity, increase the conductance of the membrane. Qualitative effects of this kind have been observed in *Nitella* by Blinks and Osterhout. Hodgkin (1947) has made a detailed study of the effects of ions on the membrane conductance of isolated axons of *Carcinus mœnas* ; Rb^+, K^+, and Cs^+ increase the membrane conductance ; the greater effect of Rb^+ being probably due to the fact that the nerve membrane is more permeable to this ion than to K^+. Na^+ and Li^+ produced only very small increases in membrane conductance when added to the Ringer solution. A study of the membrane capacity revealed very small,[1] if any, effects of K^+.

Effect of Stimulation on Electrolyte Content

The passage of an action current along a nerve is associated with a transient collapse of the fibre's polarisation ; if this is due to a transient change in the ionic permeability relationships, whereby Na^+ may diffuse into the fibre and K^+ leak out, we must expect to be able to measure a leakage of K^+ from a nerve repeatedly stimulated. Cowan found that stimulation of crab nerve for five minutes at 40 to 140 shocks per second caused a measurable escape of K^+. A. C. Young observed a similar leakage in the leg nerve of *Limulus,* and Arnett & Wilde a definite but limited loss of K^+ from medullated nerve. More recently Keynes has shown, with the aid of radioactive isotopes, that Na^+ penetrates the fibre during repetitive stimulation. We have referred to the increased membrane conductance resulting from raising the concentration of K^+ in the external medium of an isolated axon ; Hodgkin & Huxley (1947) have used this change as an index to the loss of K^+ resulting from stimulation. The isolated axon, being surrounded by a layer of sea-water only a few microns thick, any escape of K^+ as a result of stimulation should cause a significant increase in membrane conductance. An increase of four-fold in this quantity was actually observed, following one minute of stimulation ; the conductance returned smoothly to its normal value in about five minutes, a recovery presumably due to reabsorption of the lost K^+ by the axon ; if the axon was placed in a large volume of sea-water immediately after stimulation, the recovery of normal conductance was almost instantaneous, due this time to the washing away of the K^+ from the surface of the fibre. The loss-per-impulse was computed to be about 1.10^{-12} moles per $cm.^2$ of membrane ; this actually represents only about 1/100,000 of the total quantity of K^+ in the fibre. If the fibre is treated as a condenser with a capacity of 1.35 microfarads per $cm.^2$, across which is the resting potential of 61 mV, it is possible to calculate the loss of K^+ necessary to discharge the condenser ; it was computed by Hodgkin & Huxley that the actual loss measured was twice that necessary. With the aid of Na^{24} and K^{42}, Rothenberg has confirmed that K^+ is lost during stimulation (2.6–$6.5 . 10^{-12}$ meq./$cm.^2$) ; moreover, Na^+ apparently penetrates at the same time. We may note, finally, that Noonan, Fenn & Haege failed to observe an increased rate of

---

[1] We may mention here the rectifying properties of nerve. According to Cole (1941), passage of a constant current causes a thirteen-fold increase in the conductance at the cathode and an eight-fold decrease at the anode ; thus it is easier for current to pass in one direction than the other. The differences in relative concentrations of ions inside and outside the membrane will also cause a rectifier effect (Labes & Zain). According to Steinbach *et al.* (1944), the rectifier effect should be more sensitive to environmental effects than the impedance ; K^+ decreased it whilst an excess of Ca^{++} prevented this decrease. Three recent and highly competent discussions of the subject are those of Hodgkin, Huxley & Katz (1949), Teorell (1949), and Cole (1949).

exchange of K^{42} with K^{39} on stimulating an isolated muscle. This tissue, however, is unsuited for this kind of study owing to the rapid fatigue that sets in on repeated stimulation.

Resting and Action Potentials.   Quantitative Considerations

On the basis of a simple view of the action potential as a depolarisation of the membrane, we may expect it to be at most equal to the resting potential, *i.e.*, the proximal recording lead, used for obtaining a diphasic response, should develop a negativity at most equal to the negativity of the lead on the cut end of a nerve, or muscle fibre. For many years this was thought to be true, although the correct magnitudes of the

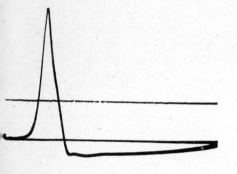

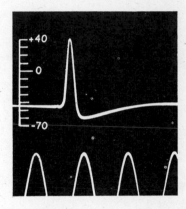

Fig. 172.   Membrane action potential of the squid axon. The two horizontal traces are 50 mV apart ; the resting potential was 58 mV. Thus the upper horizontal line approximately represents zero potential difference across the membrane, the lower line the resting potential (outside positive), and the action potential, starting from the resting potential, swings to 110 mV (outside negative). Time intervals at the bottom are 0·2 msec. (Curtis & Cole. *J. cell. & comp. Physiol.*)

Fig. 173.   Similar to Fig. 172 ;   action potential recorded between inside and outside of squid giant axon.   The vertical scale indicates the potential of the internal electrode in mV, the sea-water outside being taken as zero potential.   Time marker, 500 cyc./sec. (Hodgkin & Huxley. *J. Physiol.*)

resting and action potentials were a matter of some doubt owing to the short-circuiting that must have taken place with the usual recording devices. However, the most recent measurements on single fibres of the nerve (Hodgkin & Huxley, 1939, Curtis & Cole, 1942) and muscle (Graham & Gerard, and Nastuk & Hodgkin) have provided accurate quantitative data not only on the resting potential but also on the action potential. As we have seen, the resting potential of the squid giant axon, measured directly across the membrane by means of an inserted micro-electrode, is some 61 mV, and that of isolated fibres of the frog sartorius about 88 mV ; the action potential, measured under the same conditions by Curtis & Cole, turned out to be considerably greater, varying between 77 and 168 mV with an average value of 108 mV (Fig. 172).   Hodgkin & Huxley obtained essentially similar results on the axon of the British squid, *Loligo forbesi*, although the absolute magnitudes of their potentials were consistently smaller.   Fig. 173 illustrates a typical finding ; the scale on the record indicates the potential of the electrode inside the fibre in relation to a similar electrode in sea-water, the potential of the latter being put equal to zero.   The resting potential was thus 44 mV.   On the classical view the spike should rise to the zero level on the scale, at which point the potential of the internal electrode becomes equal to that of the external one in sea-water.   In fact, the potential reverses in sign before the spike reaches its maximum height, the magnitude of this *positivity* being variable and sometimes as high as 45 mV.   It will be noted also that the action potential of the squid axon is diphasic in the sense that, after falling to zero, the potential difference between inside and outside reverses its sign ; this *positive after-potential* amounts to some 15 mV and is typical of all measurements on the squid axon.

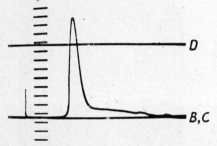

I ΛΛΛΛΛΛΛΛΛΛΛΛΛΛΛΛΛΛΛΛΛΛΙΙΙΙ msec.

Fig. 174.   Resting potential and action potential of muscle fibre.   The ordinate scale indicates steps of 10 mV.   Records B and C were obtained with the micro-electrode inside the fibre in the resting and stimulated conditions ; D, with it outside at the end of the experiment, *i.e.*, D represents zero potential between the electrodes.   (Nastuk & Hodgkin. *J. cell. & comp. Physiol.*)

In their studies of impaled single muscle fibres Graham & Gerard were unable to record accurately individual action-potentials; nevertheless they were able to compute the probable magnitude of a given spike, and showed that it was some 30 mV greater than the resting potential.   This was confirmed by Nastuk & Hodgkin who found, at 18° C., an average resting potential of 88 mV and an action potential of 119 mV (Fig. 174).

An action potential greater than the resting potential must mean that the membrane is not only depolarised but is repolarised with a potential orientated in the opposite direction ; thus if the resting potential is 60 mV, the internal electrode has a potential of − 60 mV compared with the external electrode on the intact outer surface.   When the membrane in the region of the outer electrode is depolarised, the potential between the two electrodes is zero and the spike height is 60 mV ; if now the external electrode became positive in relation to the internal electrode, the flow of current would continue in the same direction and the spike would rise still higher.   A reasonable theory has been put forward by Hodgkin & Katz to account for the reversal of the resting potential.   They suggest that the event occurring at the membrane during the passage of a wave of activity consists in a permeability to Na^+ of such magnitude as to cause a diffusion potential of opposite sign to that which would be produced by K^+ diffusing out ; this would mean that Na^+ should penetrate the membrane very much more rapidly, under these " active " conditions, than K^+.   Before discussing the likelihood of a membrane being more permeable to Na⁺ than to K⁺, let us consider some of the evidence presented by Hodgkin & Katz. If the theory is correct, the height of the action potential should depend critically on the external concentration of Na⁺. Moreover, since propagation of an impulse depends on the action potential's acquiring a sufficient height (p. 409), we should expect to find a decrease in excitability of the nerve following a reduction of the concentration of Na⁺ in the external medium, this reduction being independent, to some extent at least, of the resting potential. Overton in 1902 showed that a muscle became inexcitable in solutions containing less than 10 per cent. of the normal plasma concentration of Na⁺, and

Kato and Erlanger & Blair have more recently demonstrated similar losses of excitability with nerve. Hodgkin & Katz have shown, in support of their theory, that reducing the concentration of Na⁺ in sea-water, by addition of increasing proportions of isotonic dextrose solution, progressively decreases the height of the action potential (recorded by their microelectrode technique with one electrode inside the squid axon), whilst the size of the resting potential which depends essentially on the outside concentration

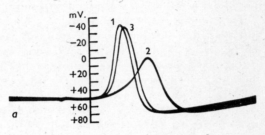

Fig. 175. Action of sodium-deficient solution on the resting and action potentials. 1, response in sea-water ; 2, after 16 minutes in 33 per cent. sea-water, 67 per cent. isotonic dextrose ; 3, 13 minutes after re-application of sea-water. The scale gives the potential difference across the nerve membrane (outside—inside) with no allowance for the junction potential between the axoplasm and the sea-water in the micro-electrode. (Hodgkin & Katz. *J. Physiol.*)

of K⁺ and should not be greatly changed by these substitutions) remained effectively constant. Some typical effects are shown in Fig. 175. On a simple theory, the magnitude of the reversed potential difference, *i.e.*, of the positive component of the action potential, should depend on the logarithmic ratio : $\log \dfrac{[\text{Na}]_{\text{test}}}{[\text{Na}]_{\text{sea-water}}}$. On plotting the change in action potential against this ratio, a straight line should be obtained ; for both nerve and muscle the agreement between theory and experiment was very satisfactory. The effect of *increasing* the concentration of Na⁺ should be the reverse ; however, such an increase must cause such rapid and profound changes in the osmotic relationships that it is questionable whether experiments using hypertonic solutions have much significance ; it is of interest, nevertheless, that quite definite, though transient, increases in the height of the action potential were observed with Na⁺-rich solutions, increases which were of the order of magnitude predicted on the basis of simple membrane theory. In further confirmation of the theory it was found that the *rate of rise* of the action potential depended on the outside concentration of Na⁺ ; thus in Fig. 175 it is quite evident that the action potential is not only reduced in height but also that its rate of rise is reduced when the external concentration is made equal to 33 per cent. of normal. Essentially similar results were obtained with impaled frog muscle fibres by Nastuk & Hodgkin.

It may be argued that the effects observed are due not so much to dilution of the Na^+ but to reducing the concentration of Cl^- or of some other ion ; that Cl^- was not a significant factor was shown by substituting choline chloride for NaCl in sea-water ; a solution made up of equal parts of isotonic choline chloride and sea-water gave a positive phase of the action potential equal in magnitude to that found with a mixture of equal parts of sea-water and isotonic dextrose solution.

The fundamental assumption at the basis of Hodgkin & Katz's interpretation of the action potential is that Na^+ penetrates the membrane during its active phase, considerably more rapidly than K^+ leaves the fibre ; if this can be proved to be an impossibility, the theory falls to the ground. The difference in permeability in the active phase must be large ; thus with relative permeabilities to K^+, Na^+ and Cl^- of $1 : 20 : 0.45$ it is possible to compute that the action potential would be of the order found, i.e., Na^+ must penetrate the membrane about 20 times more rapidly than K^+. For many years it had always been assumed that Na^+ necessarily penetrated biological membranes more slowly than K^+, on account of the greater ionic diameter of the hydrated Na^+-ion. Unfortunately most of the studies of ionic permeability in living systems have been indirect and qualitative ; however, Davson's work on the cat erythrocyte, described earlier, has revealed that, under the conditions existing in these experiments, Na^+ generally penetrates considerably more rapidly than K^+. Thus there is no doubt that in a biological system Na^+ *may* penetrate a membrane more rapidly than K^+ in spite of the greater hydration, and therefore the greater ionic diameter, of Na^+. It was observed, moreover, that the permeability to Na^+ was extremely sensitive to environmental changes ; thus narcotics only increased permeability to K^+ whilst they were capable of completely *inhibiting* Na^+-permeability ; a careful study of the influences of pH and temperature revealed, furthermore, that there were an optimal temperature and an optimal pH for Na^+-permeability, the optimal conditions being those pertaining in the intact animal, i.e., 38° C. and pH 7·2–7·4. Davson & Reiner concluded that the penetration of Na^+ was mediated by an " enzyme-like " factor sensitive to pH, temperature, narcotics, etc., whilst the penetration of K^+ was probably a simple permeability process. One striking fact emerging from this work was that the high permeability to Na^+ only manifested itself in K^+-rich solutions ; in this sense the erythrocyte membrane had to be " activated " to reveal its permeability to Na^+. Turning now to the action potential, we see that the analogy between the systems of activated nerve and erythrocyte in K^+-rich solutions is very strong ; the action potential of nerve is abolished by narcotics although the resting potential may remain constant (Bishop p. 424), i.e., the narcotic barely influences the mobility of K^+ through the resting fibre membrane but inhibits the Na^+-permeability necessary for the development of the propagated action potential. Further research is eeded to establish the analogy more definitely, *e.g.*, a detailed study of the effects of temperature and *p*H on the height of the action potential in single ibres under Hodgkin & Katz's conditions ; the effects of graded oncentrations of narcotic on the height of the potential, and so on. So ar, then, the studies of permeability rather support than contradict the undamental assumption at the basis of Hodgkin & Katz's interpretation of the action potential. To return to the experiments on the axon we may note that the theory of Hodgkin & Katz implies that the first stage of the ction potential consists in a flow of current which may be described as " capacity current," in the sense that it is a discharge of a condenser without an appreciable movement of ions across the membrane ; the next tage consists of a flow of current due to the rapid inward penetration of Na^+, whilst the final stage, corresponding to the falling phase of the action potential, is due to an outward flow of K^+. The most recent studies lesigned to ascertain whether these types of current-flow do actually take place (Hodgkin, Huxley & Katz) tend to confirm the theory. We may note, lso, that exchanges and transfers of electrolytes are likely to be associated with changes in the volume of an axon owing to the osmotic shifts of water hat must take place. D. K. Hill & Keynes observed a reversible decrease n the opacity of the crustacean nerve trunk during stimulation, and ubsequent work of D. K. Hill made it very probable that this change was result of an increase in volume of the axons. The simple exchange of K^+ for Na^+ might, at first thought, be expected to result in no change in vater content ; however, the smaller hydration of the K^+-ion—3·8 nolecules of H_2O per ion—compared with that of the Na^+-ion—8 molecules —must result in an increase in the water content of the axon when K^+ xchanges for Na^+ ; excitation, moreover, is accompanied by a definite penetration of Na^+ and Cl^-, in addition to the K^+—Na^+ exchange, onsequently a marked increase in volume is to be expected. According to Iill, the changes in volume of the axons, deduced from the changes in pacity, are of the correct order to be accounted for by ionic movements.

ELECTRICAL EXCITATION

The primary facts of electrical stimulation of nerve and muscle are, in ffect, simple ; nevertheless the development of mathematical theories to escribe the phenomena has prompted such exhaustive investigations, in which practically every possible variable has been altered, that the ewcomer into the field is presented with a bewildering mass of facts and highly specialised terminology. In the present section it must be our aim o throw the main facts into prominence and to indicate the mode in hich the modern investigator chooses to interpret them, bearing in mind, lways, that the final aim must be to relate the electrical phenomena with ne distribution of electrolytes across the plasma membrane of the xcitable tissue, the restraints placed on ionic movement across this nembrane, and the relationship of metabolic processes to these factors.

The Stimulus

Let us consider two electrodes, say 1 cm. apart, on the intact surface of a nerve, connected to a source of e.m.f. by way of a morse-key. On closure of the circuit the nerve is stimulated, and a wave of action potential passes in both directions along the nerve. The wave starts at the negative electrode and, if the applied current is strong enough, may be extinguished when it reaches the positive electrode—there is an *anodic depression* of excitability ; consequently, the more effective stimulus to a nerve-muscle preparation is obtained when the negative electrode, or *cathode*, is the nearer to the muscle, *i.e.*, when the stimulating current is *descending*, since with the electrodes in the *ascending* position the action potential may be blocked at the anode in many, if not all, of the nerve fibres. Only one action potential is usually obtained on making the circuit, so that we may think of the nerve as having *accommodated* itself to the new conditions imposed by the passage of a current through it. If the nerve consists of a bundle of fibres, their thresholds will be different ; consequently, on raising the applied voltage, successively larger responses may be obtained —either measured as the height of the action potential or as the muscular contraction in a nerve-muscle preparation—until all the fibres are stimulated. Raising the voltage above this point has no further effect on the magnitude of the response, a phenomenon that has given rise to the expression " *All-or-None Law*," by which is meant that a given nerve or muscle fibre responds with a fixed size of action potential (or muscular contraction) which depends on its physiological condition but not on the strength of the applied stimulus. The action potential recorded from a bundle of nerve fibres is the summated effect of changes occurring in many individual fibres ; as we have seen, short-circuiting results in losses of potential at the recording leads, so that the measured action potential is only a fraction of the true electrical change ; with a large number of fibres activated, the recorded action potential is greater than with a small number, just because of these short-circuiting losses. With a single fibre on the other hand, if the all-or-none law holds, the action potential should be of fixed height independently of the strength of stimulus ; this is indeed, found to be the case, and the same is true of single muscle fibre and of the wave of action potential in *Nitella*.

On breaking the circuit, provided that the current has been strong enough, a new response is elicited from the nerve ; this time it begins at the anode. These simple phenomena suggest that it is the *establishment* of a definite flow of current, rather than the flow itself, that is the effective stimulus ; in fact we have seen that the propagated action potential may be suppressed by the anode when the current is flowing. If the stimulus consists in the establishment of the action potential, which then propagates along the nerve, we may treat the action potential at any given point along the nerve as the effective stimulus to an immediately adjoining point which will make *it* active and pass on its activity to a more remote point and so on. The suppression of the action potential by the anodal current may therefore be regarded as an expression of some tendency working against stimulation, *i.e.*, the *excitability* may be said to be lowered in the region of the anode. The effects of the passage of a constant current through a nerve on its excitability were described long ago by Pflüger, and gave rise to the concept of *electrotonus* ; in general, it is found that the excitability of nerve is greatest in the region of the cathode and least around the anode during the flow of a constant current. This phenomenon we may call " *Pflüger's electrotonus*," since the term electrotonus is now used in a rather more special sense to describe the changes in potential in the region of the stimulating electrode during the first few milliseconds of the application of an external electromotive force. The Pflüger electrotonus is a rather more complex phenomenon than this simple account suggests, since it changes its sign on increasing the intensity of the constant current sufficiently, *i.e.*, the nerve in the region of the anode may become the more excitable ; according to Rosenblueth its sign and magnitude also depend on the distance between the electrodes.[1]

Latent Addition. If the applied stimulus is too weak to excite, *i.e.*, to set up a propagated disturbance, this does not mean that it has no influence

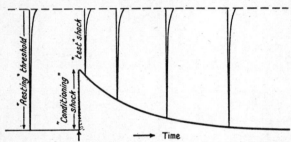

Fig. 176.   Illustrating *latent addition*. As a result of a conditioning shock, the threshold to the test shock is reduced. (Katz. *Electric Excitation in Nerve*. O.U.P.)

on the excitability of the tissue ; a second stimulus, of the same subliminal strength, falling within a few msec., may excite—the phenomenon of *subliminal summation* or *latent addition*. Thus, on plotting the strength of stimulus necessary to excite at different times after the first, *conditioning*, stimulus, against time after the conditioning stimulus, we obtain the change in excitability with time as in Fig. 176. Alternatively we may estimate the excitability, at a fixed time following a conditioning stimulus, at different points in the regions of both electrodes ; it is found that excitability is greatest in the region of the cathode and least around the anode ; between the electrodes is a neutral point at which the increased *cathodic excitability* is just balanced by the *anodic depression*.

---

[1] The changes occurring with constant currents of long duration—the Pflüger electrotonus—are closely related to the phenomenon of " cathodic depression," the depression of excitability at the cathode following lengthy application of a potential difference. Thus, to say that the polarity of the electrotonus is reversed is rather misleading, since what probably happens is that the nerve under the cathode becomes relatively inexcitable, in which case excitation is easier at the anode. The cathodic depression is due, presumably, to a decrease in membrane resistance resulting from the continued outflow of K+, which produces a condition essentially similar to that pertaining in the refractory state.

Strength-Duration Curve. To elicit a response in a nerve, the stimulus must be applied for a finite time ; the weaker the current the longer the time required for stimulation. By plotting the current-strength against the duration required to excite, we get the well-known *strength-duration curve* shown in Fig. 177. We may note that if the strength is below a certain minimum quantity—the *rheobase*—the current may flow indefinitely without exciting. The time necessary for stimulation on applying a current of twice the rheobase is called by Lapique the *chronaxie*, and is said to be a measure of the excitability of a given tissue. With very brief pulses of current it was found by Gildemeister that the total *quantity* of current required to excite was constant, *i.e.*, $i \times t = k$. This *constant-quantity* relationship clearly does not apply to comparatively long times of current-

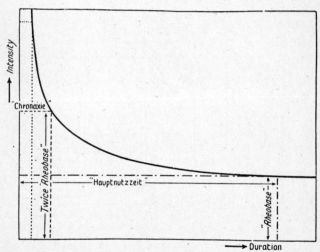

Fig. 177. Diagram of the strength-duration curve, illustrating the relation between the threshold strength and the duration of a rectangular current pulse. (Katz. *Electric Excitation in Nerve.* O.U.P.)

flow, since otherwise the strength-duration curve would be a rectangular hyperbola.

Minimal Current Gradient. One further characteristic of the electrical stimulus, of great theoretical importance, is the phenomenon of a *minimal current gradient*. It is not sufficient to state that a current of a definite magnitude, flowing for a definite time, will excite ; if the current is established slowly, *i.e.*, if the applied voltage is built up gradually, it may not excite, whereas the sudden application of the same voltage may excite. For any strength of current capable of exciting, therefore, there will be a minimum rate of growth below which the current will be ineffective (Fig. 178). This phenomenon reveals an adaptive, or *accommodative*, change in nerve, which may be regarded as a progressive increase in the threshold of excitability during the process of stimulation.

Nernst Theory. Much mathematical ingenuity has been displayed in interpreting the strength-duration curve and related phenomena of electrical stimulation ; the most significant contributions in this direction have been the *membrane theory* of Nernst and the *core-conductor theory* of Hermann, in that they represent definite attempts to relate the phenomena of electrical excitation with the known physico-chemical characteristics of excitable tissue. Nernst was impressed with the fact that alternating currents of very high frequency failed to stimulate at all. He argued that the effect of passing an electric current through a tissue would be to cause a local accumulation of ions in the region of the electrodes ; this accumulation could reach significant proportions if there were membranes, capable of slowing the passage of ions, interposed in the path of the current through the tissue. Such an accumulation would require an appreciable time to attain any specified magnitude, so that, if a certain critical

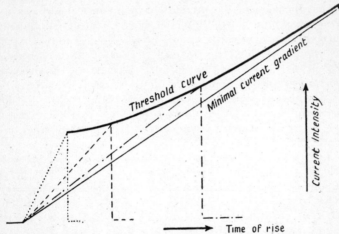

FIG. 178. Diagram illustrating the relation between rate of rise and threshold strength of a linearly increasing " triangular " current pulse. The steeper the rate of rise of current intensity, the lower is the threshold. (Katz, after Fabre. *Electric Excitation in Nerve.* O.U.P.)

accumulation of electrical charge at a membrane were necessary for excitation, too rapid an alternation of the current would be useless for stimulating. Nernst developed an equation to describe the accumulation of ions at a membrane, transversely across the axis of a tube of fluid ; as a result of the applied electromotive force, ions of one charge would be accelerated across the membrane whilst those of the opposite charge would accumulate on the other side. Because of diffusion, however, this accumulation would tend to be dissipated, and for any current-strength a steady-state would be achieved with a definite concentration of ions in the region of the membrane. If, now, the requirement for a current to excite be that it produce a critical accumulation, Nernst showed that the product : $i \times \sqrt{t}$ should be constant. Over a certain range of current-strengths this prediction accorded remarkably well with the experimental results. The phenomenon of " rheobase," however, namely the existence of a minimal current-strength, below which an indefinitely long period of current-flow would still fail to excite, put a limit to the applicability of the equation, so that Nernst invoked an accommodative process, during the flow of current, that raised the threshold for stimulation. Too slow a development of the current, or too low a current-strength, failed to excite because the accumulation of ions could not keep pace with the progressive increase of threshold. Nernst's theory has been developed and refined by later workers in an attempt to extend its applicability, but the results of such attempts have not been very impressive and need not be described here.

Hill's Treatment. A better fit of the experimental facts of stimulation with the predictions of theory has been achieved by dropping all attempts at a physical explanation of the underlying phenomena. Instead, it is merely postulated (*e.g.*, by Hill ; see also similar theories of Rashevsky and Monnier) that the passage of a current through a nerve increases a vaguely-defined " *local potential* " (V_o) above its normal resting value, *i.e.*, V_o rises at the cathode to a new value at any time, *t*, equal to V. At the same time the original, resting, threshold, U_o, rises at the cathode at a rate dependent on the rise in local potential. By making certain assumptions about the rate of growth and decay of both the local potential and the change in threshold, a simple equation describing the strength-duration curve was formulated ; the equations, in general, embodied two " time constants," one, represented by the symbol k, indicating the rate of decay of local potential on cessation of the current, and the other, λ, representing the rate of return of the threshold. A current is said, on the basis of this theory, to excite when the local potential, V, reaches the threshold, U, which, of course, changes during the excitation process. The accommodative changes are known to take place much more slowly than the changes in local potential, consequently, by choosing the conditions of stimulation suitably, it is possible to isolate this factor and estimate the magnitude of λ. Similarly, by using currents of short duration, during which the accommodative factor barely enters, the excitation constant, k, may be isolated and shown to be simply related to the chronaxie. In general, the theory of Hill, and the essentially similar theories of Rashevsky and Monnier, provide equations which describe many of the details of electrical stimulation of nerve and muscle. The concept of local potential has not been strictly defined ; and the fundamental equations contain four arbitrary constants, so that a failure of these equations to fit the experimental results might be more surprising than the actual fit. In so far, however, as the theory has led to predictions that have been subsequently verified experimentally, its value cannot be seriously questioned ; moreover, the theory co-ordinates a vast number of the facts of electrical stimulation and allows them to be assessed in terms of the two time constants, k and λ.

Core-Conductor Theory

A more realistic interpretation of the electrical events leading to excitation at an applied electrode is provided by the core-conductor theory, developed from the original concepts of Hermann and Matteucci by Cremer and later workers. On applying electrodes to the surface of a nerve, potentials develop at, and in the neighbourhood of the electrodes, *electrotonic potentials*, which indicate that there is a flow of current along certain specific lines as in Fig. 179. The potential at any point on the surface of the nerve in relation to the potential at a point a long distance away from the electrodes, is called the electrotonic potential ; in the region of the cathode it is negative or *catelectrotonic*, and in the region of the anode it is positive or *anelectrotonic*. The potential change is greatest immediately underneath the electrodes, and falls off exponentially in the extra-

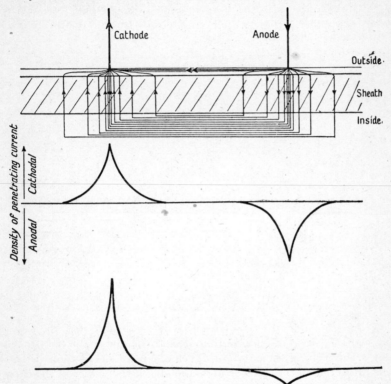

Fig. 179.   Diagram of current distribution in a core-conductor. Upper figure : The direction of current flow through outside, sheath, and inside is indicated by arrows. Lower figure : The lateral spread of the traversing current lines is illustrated, by plotting current density against length of nerve. (Katz. *Electric Excitation in Nerve.* O.U.P.)

polar region ; it requires a measurable time to develop, both at the electrodes and in their immediate neighbourhood.   The development of these potentials, and their associated currents, can best be accounted for if the nerve fibre is treated as a *cable* or *core-conductor*, *i.e.*, as a cylinder of conducting fluid, the axoplasm, surrounded by a layer of conducting medium and separated from this layer by a sheath or polarisable membrane of high electrical resistance (Fig. 180a).[1] This sheath is thought to impose

[1] As Katz (1939) has pointed out, it would be unwise to attempt an exact correlation between the histological structures of the myelinated nerve fibre and these abstract

a capacity on the system, so that the nerve fibre may be viewed as a condenser capable of being charged on application of a potential difference across it. To account for the flow of current that takes place across the sheath, on applying a difference of potential under steady-state conditions, the condenser is said to be leaky ; and it may be treated as a condenser plus a shunting resistance, R, in parallel (Fig. 180b). To account for the time characteristics of the build-up of electrotonic potential, it is necessary to treat the nerve as a series of units, as in Fig. 180c, but the essential principle is the same as in the simpler case shown in Fig. 180b. When a potential is applied across two electrodes, side-by-side on the nerve, the

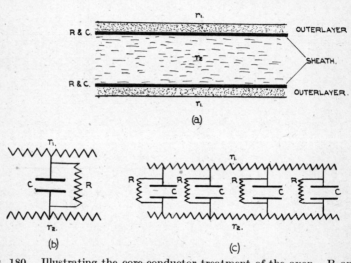

FIG. 180. Illustrating the core-conductor treatment of the axon. R and C are the transverse resistance and capacity of the sheath respectively.

flow of current charges the condensers, with the result that the potential at and near the electrodes builds up and tends to oppose the further flow of current. The form of the curve of development of electrotonus with time may be predicted on the basis of such a model, if the values of the capacity and resistance of the membrane, and the resistances of sheath and core, are known. When the steady-state has been attained, moreover, the distribution of electrotonic potentials around the electrodes can also be computed. Thus, according to Rushton's analysis, the potential, P, at any distance, x, from the electrode, during the passage of a weak current is given by :—

$$P = P_o \, exp - \left(\frac{x}{\sqrt{r_m/r_1 + r_2}} \right)$$

P_o being the peak potential at the electrode, r_m the resistance times unit length of nerve membrane, and r_1 and r_2 the resistances per unit length of

entities : *core, outer layer*, and *sheath*. In the non-myelinated axon the core is the axoplasm, the outer layer is the enveloping fluid plus connective tissue, whilst the plasma membrane constitutes the highly resistant and polarisable " sheath." The myelin sheath of a medullated nerve must contribute to r_m.

outside and axoplasm respectively. The quantity $\sqrt{\dfrac{r_m}{r_1 + r_2}}$ is called the *characteristic length* of nerve ; and it has been shown by Rushton that the equations describing the strength-interpolar distance relationship of stimulation, and also the resistance-length relationship, all contain this length-factor which is, essentially, an index to the degree of electrotonic spread produced by a given potential. Fig. 179 indicates the flow of current during the steady-state. If, now, we accept the hypothesis that the essential feature of an effective stimulus is the build-up of a sufficiently high current density directed outwards through the membrane,[1] or, more precisely, the build-up of a sufficiently high electrotonic potential at a given point, a great many of the phenomena of stimulation may be explained, at least on qualitative grounds. An all-embracing quantitative treatment of electrical stimulation is, however, no more possible on the basis of cable theory than on the basis of Nernst's membrane hypothesis, and until the physico-chemical mechanisms involved in accommodation are elucidated, it is unlikely that progress will be made in this direction ; we may merely note that the equation developed by Cremer to describe the strength-duration curve has a similar form to that developed on the basis of the membrane theory. In the hands of Rushton, Cole & Curtis, Rosenberg, and Hodgkin, the cable theory has been developed to explain the detailed characteristics of the build-up of the electrical stimulus and its propagation ; in this respect (as opposed to the development of an all-embracing theory of the quantitative aspects of electrical stimulation) the theory has been remarkably successful, as the following pages will testify. Before entering into the details of some of the modern studies of the excitation process and its propagation, it will be profitable to indicate certain qualitative explanations of the simpler phenomena of electrical excitation.

The effective stimulus is the establishment of a critical reduction of the membrane potential, over a certain area under the stimulating electrode ; with excitation beginning at the cathode, this means a flow of positive current from the axoplasm outwards. A subliminal stimulus causes too small a flow of current, but since the electrotonic potentials take a measurable time to subside, a new subliminal shock may summate its effects with those of the first, conditioning, shock and so excite. A region of catelectrotonus is therefore a region of increased excitability, and it may be shown that there is a perfect correlation between the electrotonic potentials caused by an applied electromotive force and the changes in excitability at the points where these potentials are measured. At the anode the current-flow is in the opposite direction (anelectrotonus) so that a stimulus, to excite, must drive current against an opposing potential difference ; the applied shock must therefore be greater, and the

[1] Direct confirmation of this is provided by " trans-membrane " stimulation ; Graham & Gerard inserted an electrode directly into the muscle fibre and placed another, above it, on the outside of the fibre. Passage of a current from inside to outside, *i.e.*, when the internal electrode was positive, acted as a stimulus, a quantity of electricity as low as 1.10^{-10} coulombs being effective ; on reversing the polarity no excitation could be obtained, even when the current flow was increased a hundred-fold over that required with the internal anode.

excitability is less. If the stimulating electrodes are very close together, the cathodic and anodic electrotonus will interfere, and the threshold stimulus should be larger than when the separation is greater ; Rushton showed that this was the case.

THEORY OF EXCITATION AND PROPAGATION

On the basis of the core-conductor theory, the effective stimulus is the establishment of a region of catelectrotonus under the stimulating electrode ; *i.e.*, the surface of the nerve fibre is made negative in respect to other portions. It will be recalled that the normal resting potential is directed so that the inside of the fibre is negative in respect to the outside ; electrical stimulation, therefore, consists of the neutralisation, or partial neutralisation, of the resting potential in the region of the cathode. The fibre is said to be *depolarised* by the stimulus. As a result of the stimulus, provided that it is great enough, this local electric effect is propagated as an action potential, which consists of a similar, but more extreme, form of depolarisation, involving a definite breakdown of the membrane. An exact analysis of the electrical changes taking place at the anode and cathode, as a result of a brief stimulus, can therefore throw a great deal of light on the nature of the primary excitation process and its propagation.

Local Sub-Threshold Responses

We will suppose that the shock is applied, and the recording made, as indicated in Fig. 181. A and B are the stimulating electrodes, B being the

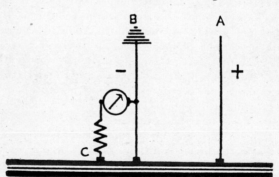

FIG. 181. Stimulating and recording set-up for study of electrotonic and propagated potentials. A and B are stimulating electrodes, whilst recording is from B and C. (After Hodgkin. *Proc. Roy. Soc.*)

cathode from which the propagated disturbance will travel ; the effects of the shock are recorded at B and C, *i.e.*, the electrode B is used both for stimulation and recording. On applying a brief thyratron shock lasting only, say, 60μsec. (Hodgkin, 1938), B becomes progressively negative, as a result of the passive build-up of electrotonic potential which may be likened, as we have seen, to the charging of a condenser. If the stimulus is well below threshold, the potential passes through a maximum and falls to its original value, the rate of fall being slower than the rate of rise since the fall depends on the discharge of a leaky condenser through a high resistance. The course of the electrotonic changes at the cathode is therefore given by the record shown in Fig. 182G from Hodgkin. At the anode quite symmetrical changes are observed (Fig. 182H). The shock has thus produced local changes in electrical potential that are easily predictable from an equivalent electrical circuit.[1]

If the stimulus is above threshold, the same electrotonic changes occur, but are succeeded by electrical events that reveal a more fundamental alteration in the state of the nerve ; the action potential, in effect, makes itself manifest, as in Fig. 182A. The " negativity " of electrode B, in relation to C, builds up to a far greater extent than can be accounted for by the primary electrotonic effect of the applied shock, and is due to the complete breakdown and reversal of the resting potential (p. 389). Moreover, this change is propagated, so that C eventually becomes negative in respect to B, and the change is diphasic. If the stimulus is reduced in intensity, but maintained above threshold, the transition from the passive, electrotonic, to the active condition, as revealed by the development of the action potential proper, is more protracted ; we may therefore speak of a *latent-period* of development of the action potential which, in the record of Fig. 182C, amounts to about 1/3 msec. but is much shorter with stronger stimuli (Fig. 182A). Thus Figs. 182A and C represent the primary, electrotonic, plus the true action, potentials at the cathode resulting from a brief shock ; since only electrotonic

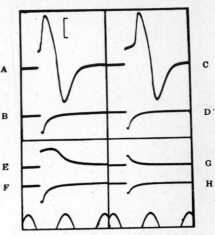

Fig. 182. Records, at the anode and cathode, of electrical changes taking place in nerve as a result of brief stimuli of different relative strengths : A, 1·05 ; B, —1·05 ; C, 1·00 ; D, —1·00 ; E, 1·00 ; F, —1·00 ; G, 0·61 ; H, —0·61. The difference between C and E was due to a slight fluctuation in excitability, since the shock strength was not changed between making these two records. Each pair of records, A, B ; C, D ; etc., thus represents the changes taking place at cathode and anode ; the A—B and C—D records result from a supra-liminal shock ; the E—F records result from a shock high enough to produce a local response, whilst the G—H records indicate the purely electrotonic responses to a definitely sub-threshold stimulus. Scale, 15 mV ; time, 1 msec. (Hodgkin. *Proc. Roy. Soc.*)

changes occur at the anode, and since there is every reason to believe that they are the mirror images of those taking place at the cathode (Fig. 182G and H), we may allow for the electrotonic effects at the cathode by merely taking the algebraic sum of the cathodic and anodic potentials ;

---

[1] That these changes are, nevertheless, a characteristic of living tissue is shown by experiments on dead nerve, in which the electrotonic potentials were only a small fraction of the values obtained on living nerve and were due to some electrode polarisation.

the action potential, uncomplicated by the primary electrotonic effects, is thus obtained, as in Fig. 183.

For a long time it was thought that the transition from a purely electrotonic polarisation to the active state was sharp, so that a nerve could be considered either to have been activated or not, according as the strength of the stimulus was great enough to excite or not. In 1937 Katz, by studying the changes in excitability of nerve in the neighbourhood of

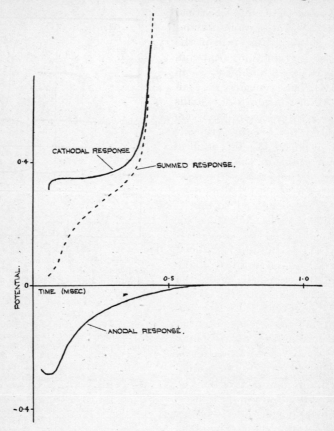

FIG. 183. Showing how the response at the cathode, after allowing for purely electrotonic effects, may be determined. The plotted curve is the algebraic sum of the cathodal and anodal responses. Ordinates : Fraction of the spike height. Abscissæ : Time in msec. (After Hodgkin.)

the cathode, immediately after a just subliminal shock, obtained evidence for the existence of local changes which were too great to be accounted for on the basis of electrotonus, and yet were too small, and were not propagated far enough, to be described as typical action potentials. Following on this, Hodgkin, using the stimulating and recording set-up illustrated in Fig. 181, showed that electrical stimuli of strength greater than half the threshold could produce local changes in potential at the recording lead, which were quite distinct from the purely electrotonic ones induced by the stimulus. Thus in Fig. 182 the electrical changes at the cathode are shown for a definitely sub-threshold shock (G), and for one very close to the threshold (E) ; the first record is one of a typical electrotonic change and is the mirror image of that obtained at the anode (Fig. 182H) ; the potential in the second record, on the other hand, lasts much longer and is quite different from the record at the anode (Fig. 182F). By adding the cathodic and anodic changes algebraically, as in Fig. 184, the local excitatory disturbance, uncomplicated by the electrotonic effects of the stimulus, may be obtained. In this case, the local response had a rising phase of 270μsec. and a total duration of 1,500μsec. The gradual transition from the subliminal to the threshold response (leading to a propagated action potential) is shown in Fig. 185 ; it appears from this figure that it is only when the local potential reaches a certain critical size

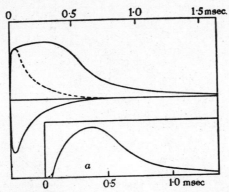

FIG. 184. Cathodic and anodic potentials, traced from records in Fig. 182 E and F. The dotted curve represents the mirror image of the anodal response, and the difference between this curve and that showing the cathodal response represents activity at the cathode, *i.e.*, the local response (inset). (Hodgkin. *Proc. Roy. Soc.*)

that it develops into a true propagated disturbance ; if it fails to achieve this it dies out as a localised monophasic wave—it is said to *decrement* to extinction. It is interesting, moreover, that the latency of the propagated impulse is, in essence, determined by the time required for the local disturbance to build up ; this is evident from Fig. 185. In general, if a given fibre has a long latency, the local build-up of its sub-threshold potential is slow and *vice versâ*.

The local disturbance, following a subliminal stimulus, is not confined to the region of the nerve immediately under the electrode ; in other words, there is some propagation to neighbouring regions. Since the effects do not extend far, however, the study of the spread is difficult (allowance being made, of course, for the spread of electrotonic potential).[1]

These studies of Katz and Hodgkin on the subliminal response are very

---

[1] In fibres with a long latency, the subliminal response may spread over appreciable lengths of the nerve before dying away. If, now, the spreading subliminal response passes into a region of greater excitability, it may grow into a true spike ; in this case, as Hodgkin has shown, a spike may originate at some distance from the cathode.

suggestive ; they indicate that the first element in the series of events leading to the production of a propagated action potential is the establishment of an electrotonic potential of a certain magnitude ; the flow of current across the membrane, thus established, appears to release some mechanism which continues the process of depolarisation. As a result, the local potential, in the region of the cathode, becomes higher than the electrotonic potential. If the conditions are suitable, this process goes to completion, *i.e.*, if the initial electrotonic potential is high enough, or the excitability sufficiently great, the local disturbance grows into an " all-or-none " type of action potential which is propagated away from the cathode. If the conditions are unsuitable, the local disturbance fails to

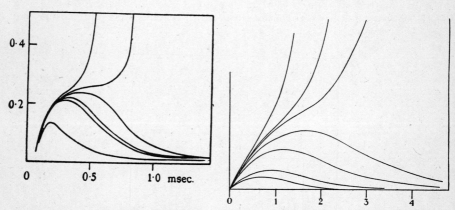

Fig. 185. Showing the transition from the local response to the fully propagated action potential. Left : Differences between cathodal and anodal responses as determined by Hodgkin's technique. Right : Curves derived from excitability changes following threshold and sub-threshold shocks by Katz. (Hodgkin, *Proc. Roy. Soc.*, and Katz, *Proc. Roy. Soc.*)

reach the minimum height necessary for propagation as a true action potential ; it travels a little way, decrementing to extinction.[1]

Refractory State. Immediately after stimulation, or the passage of a wave of action potential, excitable tissue passes through a stage of complete inexcitability, the *absolutely refractory period* ; following this, there is a period of reduced excitability, the *relatively refractory period* ; before returning to its normal resting condition the tissue often passes, finally, through a stage of hyperexcitability, the *supernormal phase*. During the relatively refractory period, the local response to a subliminal stimulus is very considerably reduced, whilst the electrotonic polarisation is virtually unchanged ; during the supernormal phase the local response is accentuated. If, now, we compare the heights to which a local response must rise in order to grow into " orthodox spikes " in the relatively refractory, resting, and supernormal phases we find that they decrease in

---

[1] The question whether subliminal responses may be elicited in medullated nerve has been discussed by Katz (1947), who has brought forward convincing evidence in favour of it. More recently Huxley & Stämpfli (1951) and del Castillo-Nicolau & Stark (1951), have recorded local responses from single medullated fibres.

this order, a large local response, and therefore of course a large stimulus, being necessary to cause a propagated spike in the refractory condition. In this condition, indeed, the difference between a local response which fails to propagate, and a propagated spike, tends to become vanishingly small ; in resting nerve the difference in size may be about five-fold.

Local Circuit Theory

These facts indicate that the ability of a local disturbance, produced at the cathode, to propagate depends on its size in relation to the state of excitability of the tissue. In other words, in order that the locally developed action potential may *move away* from its seat of origin, it must be able to *stimulate adequately an adjoining region*. The rationale for such a stimulation by an adjoining region of tissue is provided by the *local-circuit theory* of propagation. This concept follows directly from the core-conductor theory of stimulation ; essentially it is argued that, during the passage of a wave of action potential, the surface of the active, or depolarised, nerve, being at a different potential from that in an adjoining region, causes a local flow of current which is adequate to activate the adjoining region. The analogy between nerve, with a cathodic electrotonic potential applied externally, and a nerve during the passage of an action potential is illustrated in Fig. 186 from Hodgkin.

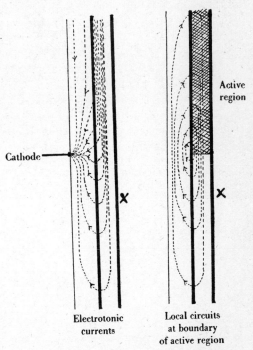

Fig. 186. Illustrating the analogy between the electrotonic currents due to an applied cathode and the local circuits at the boundary of an active region. (Hodgkin. *J. Physiol.*)

The cathode causes electric circuits through the nerve fibre to be made as in Fig. 186, and the electrotonus in the region of this electrode is such as to increase excitability in neighbouring regions, because the effective stimulus is the establishment of a critical potential across the membrane. Now let us consider the state of affairs with active nerve. The surface of the active region becomes negative in respect to the inactive region ; consequently positive current tends to flow from the inactive to the active region of the surface. Within the core, the active region becomes more positive (or less negative) in relation to an adjoining inactive region, so that positive current flows, within the core, from active to inactive regions. A local circuit is thus established causing a flow of current which will be by no means confined to the junction between active and inactive regions ; consequently the condition at the point X may be essentially similar in the two conditions in that, in each case, it shares in the electrotonic spread from an active

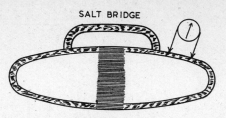

FIG. 187.   The spread of excitation through a salt-bridge.   (After Osterhout & Hill.   *Cold Spring Harbor Symposia*.)

region.   In the immediate neighbourhood of the active region, however, the current density through the membrane is sufficiently great to excite the adjoining, inactive, region which then excites the next point, and so on ; meanwhile the electrotonus extends farther and farther along the nerve.

On the basis of this theory a number of important deductions may be made.   Thus Osterhout & Hill argued that if a tissue is made locally

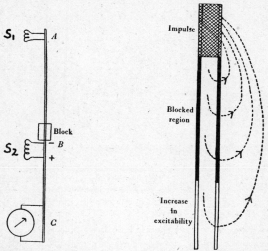

FIG. 188.   Illustrating Hodgkin's study of the spread of electrotonic potential beyond a blocked region.   Left : General scheme of the stimulating and recording set-up.   Right : Showing how the currents, due to local circuits, may modify the excitability beyond a block.   (Hodgkin.   *J. Physiol.*)

inexcitable, *e.g.*, by treating a portion of its surface with chloroform, it should be possible for the wave of activity to be continued around the block by a salt-bridge as in Fig. 187, and they demonstrated that this could indeed occur in *Nitella*.   This is a most convincing piece of evidence in favour of the essentially electrical nature of the transmission process, since it is quite inconceivable that any chemical substance, liberated proximally to the block, could diffuse through the salt-bridge within a short time and affect the distal region of the cell's surface. Again, Hodgkin has pointed out that, since the blockage of a nerve by cold or a narcotic [1] does not affect appreciably its longitudinal electrical resistance, the action potential, when it reaches the block, may influence regions beyond. This point is illustrated in Fig. 188. Hodgkin found in a nerve blocked with cold, that, whereas a maximal stimulus applied to A produced no action potential beyond the block (at C), a sub-threshold stimulus, applied to B 1–2 msec. after the maximal shock at A, produced an action potential at C. Hence the propagated disturbance from the first stimulus, although it failed to pass through the block, increased the excitability of the nerve in the region immediately distal to the block. Changes in threshold down to 10 per cent. of the normal resting value could be obtained under appropriate conditions.

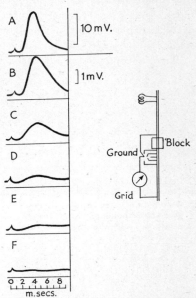

Fig. 189. Extrinsic potentials recorded from a region beyond a block. (Hodgkin. *J. Physiol.*)

Extrinsic Potentials. Clearly, if the active region of nerve proximal to the block, *i.e.*, on the side nearest A in Fig. 188, is modifying the excitability of the region distal to the block, some electrical effects should be observable beyond the block. In Fig. 189 some records of Hodgkin are shown of the action potential proximal to the block (A) and the electrotonic potentials at increasing distances beyond this region (B-F). These potentials are much smaller than the true action potential and, instead of propagating at the same height, they decay logarithmically

---

[1] Conduction through a nerve may be blocked by a number of experimental procedures, *e.g.*, by narcotics applied locally. If the narcotisation is not too severe, however, the action potential, although depressed in height, continues to travel through the region of depressed excitability and re-acquires its former height on emerging into the normal stretch of nerve. For some time it was thought that the nerve impulse experienced *decremental conduction*, *i.e.*, that it was propagated for considerable distances through regions of low excitability with a gradually decreasing spike-height. Such a conclusion has been shown to be wrong (*e.g.*, by Kato and by Davis *et al.*), so that the probable course of events, if the narcotisation is sufficient to suppress excitability completely, is an abrupt cessation of activity at the boundary between normal and narcotised nerve. In the region where excitability is only depressed, and not abolished, we may expect that the propagated disturbance will decrement rapidly to a lower level, at which it will remain constant until it passes back to normal nerve, when it will rise rapidly, but not instantaneously, to normal height. The depression in height of the action potential may be severe ; Davis *et al.*, working with a mixed nerve, found a decrease of 75 per cent., and that this was not due to complete blocking of a significant proportion of the fibres was indicated by the fact that the emerging action potential regained 99 per cent. of its original height.

to $1/e$ of their value in 2 mm. They are called *extrinsic potentials*, since they are due entirely to electrical activity in a region beyond the recording electrodes, being electrotonic effects of the action potential. The strong analogy between the extrinsic potential and the electrotonic effect of an externally applied cathodic potential was shown by further experiments of Hodgkin ; a potential was applied with the cathode in the blocked region, and it was shown that, in the normal region beyond the block, the response obtained could be made almost identical with that caused by a propagated disturbance which died away in the block. Finally, Hodgkin showed that the time-course of development of the change in excitability beyond the block, and of the rise in extrinsic potential, were identical ; the efficiency of an extrinsic potential in raising excitability was found, however, to be some 1·4–2·3 times greater than that of an externally applied voltage.

This concept, of an activated region of nerve acting as a stimulus for an adjoining region, permits of a ready interpretation of the details of the propagated action potential. This potential, it will be recalled, is an expression of the changes of potential taking place at an electrode on the intact surface of the fibre at different times during the approach of a propagated disturbance. When the approaching disturbance has reached a certain distance from the electrode, the electrotonic effects, spreading ahead of the active region, increase the negativity at the electrode. The initial deflection on the recording instrument, the *foot* of the action potential, is thus due to an *extrinsic potential* and is not a sign of " activity " under the electrode. At a certain point in time, when the active region has come sufficiently close, the region under the electrode is excited, and at this point the negativity increases rapidly to a maximum. With the re-establishment of polarisation, which must take a measurable time, the negativity falls.[1]

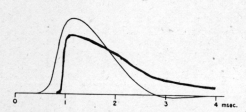

Fig. 190. Membrane conductance increase (heavy line), after approximate corrections for electrode length and bridge amplifier response, and monophasic action potential (light line) obtained from the first derivative, after approximate correction for action potential amplifier response. (Cole & Curtis. *J. gen. Physiol.*)

The point of inflection on the rising phase of the action potential, where the rate of rise of negativity is greatest, represents the moment at which the region of nerve under the electrode becomes fully active, as a result of the

---

[1] The foot of the action potential represents an extrinsic potential, so that the shape and time constants of the rising phase will be largely determined by the velocity of propagation and the characteristics of electrotonic spread. The " wavelength " of the action potential is given by the velocity of transmission divided by the " frequency," *i.e.*, the reciprocal of the duration. A crab fibre, with a velocity of 3–5 m./sec., and a duration of 0·8–1·0 m./sec., has a wavelength of about 4 mm. Myelinated fibres of the frog have a wavelength of about 40 mm. The difference is largely due to the myelin sheath with its high longitudinal resistance which permits a far greater electrotonic spread. Thus in medullated nerve an applied electrotonic potential falls to $1/e$ of its value in 2–3 mm., whereas in single fibres of crab non-medullated nerve it falls to the same extent in only 0·5 mm.

excitatory influence of the electrotonic potential. We have already seen (p. 387) that Cole & Curtis have recorded simultaneously the changes in potential and impedance at a point on the nerve during the passage of a propagated disturbance, and it is of the utmost interest that they observed that the change of impedance did indeed occur at the point of inflection of the action potential curve (Fig. 190).

After-Potentials. The action potential does not fall simply to zero ; studies in the schools of Gasser and Erlanger have shown that the sequence of events is usually : *action potential, negative after-potential, positive after-potential.* The relative prominence of these after-potentials varies with the type of nerve fibre studied ; the negative after-potential is manifest as a failure of the record to return to its base-line, so that its beginning is generally difficult to identify ; the positive after-potential, on the other hand, represents a reversal in sign of the record. Associated with these states of residual negativity and positivity are found conditions of hyper- and hypo-excitability, as one should expect. The after-potentials are clearly of the greatest importance in the interpretation of the effects of repetitive stimulation, since succeeding impulses must traverse regions of diminished or enhanced excitability according to the phase of the preceding action potential that they encounter.[1]

Interaction Between Fibres. A further confirmation of the primarily electrical changes associated with nervous conduction is provided by the

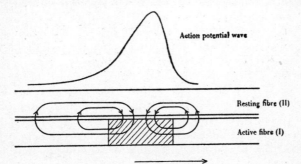

FIG. 191. Local circuit diagram illustrating the penetration of Fibre II by the action currents of Fibre I. The shaded area indicates the " active region " of Fibre I. Note that the direction of the penetrating current reverses twice. (Katz & O. H. Schmitt. *J. Physiol.*)

work of Katz & O. H. Schmitt on the interaction of single nerve fibres in a bundle. A study of the local circuits during a propagated disturbance, illustrated in Fig. 191, shows that positive current tends to flow, within the fibre, from the active to the inactive region and penetrates the

---

[1] In a nerve fibre it might, at first thought, be considered that a train of repetitive stimuli would extinguish themselves at some point along the fibre, due to the progressive build-up of positive after-potential ; this does not occur, however, since the positive after-potential decreases the velocity of propagation ; so that an impulse, entering a depressed region, is slowed and thus gives more distal regions time to recover their full excitability. In a region of discontinuity, however, as for example the myoneural junction (p. 438), it may well be that the after-positivity could build up to blocking height with sufficiently rapid stimulation, as in Wedensky inhibition (p. 464).

membrane, in the inactive region, from within → out. This type of penetration, we have argued, is equivalent to catelectrotonus and should increase excitability. If a resting fibre is lying alongside an active one in close apposition, as in Fig. 191, some of the current tends to flow from the inactive region of the active fibre into the resting fibre in the direction : out → in, *i.e.*, it should depress excitability ; in the region of activity, however, the current-flow through the resting fibre is from in → out, a condition that must increase its excitability. The excitability at a point on a resting fibre must therefore pass through a cycle of changes, during the passage of an impulse along an adjacent fibre, because of the alternate anelectrotonic and catelectrotonic influences of the active region as it passes by. By stimulating only one of a pair of adjacent isolated fibres of a non-myelinated crab nerve, and measuring the change in excitability of the other, results were obtained indicating influences of one fibre on the other that were qualitatively predictable on the basis of the local-circuit theory of propagation. Quantitatively, the threshold lowering amounted to about 20 per cent., *i.e.*, it was sufficiently small to render negligible the possibility of one fibre activating another. Two impulses passing in separate adjacent fibres should interfere, either by summating or cancelling their electrotonic effects, the exact nature of the interaction depending on the phase relationships of the impulses ; these electrotonic interactions should be reflected in changes in velocity of propagation, since this must depend on electrotonic spread (p. 415). The experimental analysis of such possibilities, carried out by Katz & O. H. Schmitt, has shown that if one impulse slightly precedes, it accelerates the rate of conduction of the lagging action potential, an effect leading to a synchronisation of impulses in adjacent fibres if their speeds differ only slightly.[1]

Safety-Margin. If it is the potential difference between adjacent portions of the surface of the nerve fibre that provides the condition for propagation, it follows that the height of the action potential should be equal to, or exceed, the adequate stimulus for the nerve fibre. It is known, moreover, that under conditions approaching nerve block, or during the relatively refractory period, the threshold for stimulation may be increased some five-fold. Under the same conditions the height of the propagated action potential may be reduced to one-half, consequently, during propagation through relatively refractory nerve, the effective stimulus provided by the action potential is only one half as great as normal, and the excitability is only one fifth. The normal action potential should therefore be some ten times higher than necessary if it is to have a *safety-margin* to permit propagation under adverse conditions. An exact quantitative comparison between the potential required to stimulate, and the height of the action potential, is not easy ; according to Hodgkin

---

[1] Rosenblueth (1944) has discussed the possibility that fibre interaction is a factor in *recruitment*, *i.e.*, the systematic increase in the number of nerve fibres stimulated by the successive shocks of a sub-maximal train ; recruitment is not exclusively due to local conditions at the stimulating electrode, and the observation that stimulation of fibres other than those tested gives recruitment certainly suggests that interaction of spike potentials is a factor. Rosenblueth infers that interaction is partly electrical and partly due to the escape of K^+ ; it is considerably enhanced by veratrine (p. 488).

the smallest extrinsic potential in a mixed nerve trunk was 2–3 mV, comparing with an action potential, recorded under the same conditions, of 20–30 mV, *i.e.*, there was a safety-margin of about ten. Moreover, unless the action potential, initiated at the cathode, has a considerable reserve of potential, the propagated disturbance should invariably be wiped out by the electrotonic influence of the anode. It is known, of course, that a propagated impulse *can* be blocked at the anode if the applied voltage is high enough, but a quantitative study reveals that the anodic voltage necessary to block an impulse is some ten to fifteen times the cathodic voltage required to initiate one, *i.e.*, if the anodic polarisation, necessary to cause block, is equivalent to the height of the action potential, the safety-margin is indeed more than ten-fold.

Saltatory Conduction. We have so far supposed the spread of electrotonus along the nerve fibre to take place continuously ; in the non-myelinated fibres of invertebrates this seems to be true, but Erlanger & Blair in 1934 showed that, in medullated nerve, the blocking effects of anodic polarisation showed discontinuities which could most reasonably be attributed to the fact that the polarising current entered the nerve sheath only through the nodes of Ranvier. The evidence for this cannot be presented here, but it is convincing and indicates that a polarising current, passed through a nerve, enters mainly, if not exclusively, at the nodes of Ranvier where the myelin sheath is thinnest. If this is true of externally applied currents, it should also be true of the spread of electrotonic currents from the advancing wave-front of the propagated disturbance. Evidence has been accumulating that this is indeed true [1] and quite recently Huxley & Stämpfli have developed methods of recording the action potentials from very short lengths of nerve fibre so that records could successively be taken from at least three points within one internode, a distance of only 3 mm., on the average, in frog nerve. It was pointed out by Hodgkin that, if current enters the axoplasm only through nodes, the flow of current through any internode, at any moment during the approach of an impulse, must be the same at all points along the internode ; in other words, the recorded action potential should have the same time relations at all points in the internode.[2] A series of records at different points on the internodes of a nerve are shown in Fig. 192, and it will be seen that the groups of records from any internode are practically synchronous, whilst the different groups are displaced in time. This result certainly suggests that the nerve fibre becomes active only at the nodes, or at any rate that the effects of its activity are only propagated through these discontinuities in

---

[1] The earlier work has been summarised by Huxley & Stämpfli and, more fully, by von Muralt (1945) ; credit for the establishment of this point is due particularly to the Japanese worker, Tasaki, and his colleagues ; Pfaffman, using an isolated fibre, obtained larger action potentials from the nodes than from internodal regions. The monophasic action potential, recorded at the internode, was different from that at the node, and suggested that the recorded potential was due to an out-of-phase spread of electrotonic potential originating at the two nodes.

[2] An apt analogy would be that provided by water flowing through a tube ; if there are leaks in the wall the flow will decrease progressively along the tube ; if the leaks are confined to definite nodes, the flow between the nodes will be uniform, although from one segment to another the flow will decrease in accordance with the loss at the nodes.

the sheath. We may note that the records were taken with two electrodes on intact nerve (*i.e.*, the recording would be described as "diphasic") so that the rise and fall of potential are mainly due to activity occurring first at one node and then at the other ; the interval is so small however (the internodal distance is only 3 mm. and the velocity of

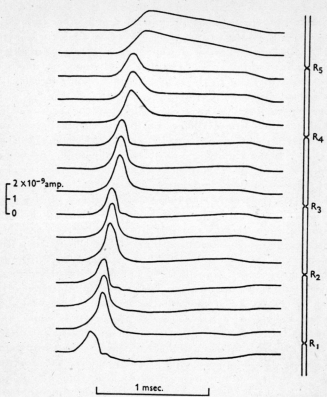

FIG. 192. Saltatory conduction. Tracings of records obtained at a series of positions along a single medullated fibre. Diagram of fibre on right-hand side shows positions where each record was taken. (Huxley & Stämpfli. *J. Physiol.*)

propagation about 23 m./sec., with the result that the time-interval is only 0·13 msec.) that the second phase of the action potential is ill defined, the rising limb of the first phase representing activity mainly at the proximal node and the falling phase activity mainly at the distal node ; according as the leads are taken from points close to the proximal or distal node we may expect the time relations of the different phases of the action potential to change ; this is clear from the graphs of Fig. 192, and an elaborate experimental and theoretical analysis of the effects of the distance of the recording leads from the node tends to confirm the saltatory interpretation of the phenomena, although a certain amount of capacity current-flow does take place through the myelin sheath of the internodes.

Site of Origin of Spike

If the concept of saltatory conduction is correct, a stimulus should originate at the node nearest the cathode with a make shock ; in a non-medullated nerve, on the other hand, it should originate immediately under the cathode. Recent work of Rushton and Rashbass on the sciatic nerve of the frog suggested that this was not true, the spike originating some 3 mm. away from the cathode. However, in a later paper (Rashbass & Rushton, 1949, c) it was shown that the origin of the spike at a distance from the " manifest cathode " was due primarily to the employment of electrodes very close together, but also to the presence of the epineurium —the connective tissue sheath binding the bundles of nerve fibres together in a large nerve like the sciatic. By stripping the epineurium from the nerve, more " orthodox " results were obtained, so that the potential drop across this sheath is a significant factor ; hence the potential of the interstitial fluid within the sheath is different from that applied to the outside of the nerve. An experimental and theoretical study of the influence of the epineurium on the spread of potential from a stimulating electrode provided an adequate explanation of the origin of the spike at a distance from the cathode.

Velocity of Propagation

Diameter of the Fibre. It follows, from Rushton's analysis of the implications of the core-conductor theory, that the velocity of propagation should increase with the diameter of the nerve fibre, other things being equal. The diameters of the medullated fibres in a mixed nerve, such as a frog's sciatic, vary over a wide range, between 3 and 29μ. We must therefore expect the action potential, recorded from a mixed nerve such as this, to represent the summated effects of the action potentials, moving with different velocities, in hundreds of fibres; at the point of initiation of the impulse we may expect the disturbances to be, to some extent, in phase, but as the propagated disturbance travels along the nerve they should fall " out of step " so that at a few centimetres' distance we may expect to record, first, the spikes of the most rapidly conducting fibres ; the spikes of more slowly conducting fibres adding their contributions later. The shape of the action potential, recorded from a bundle of nerve fibres, may therefore be expected to change significantly with distance travelled. The complete action potential of the bull-frog's peroneal nerve, after travelling 13 cm., is shown in Fig. 193 ; it contains a number of spikes, representing the activities of groups of fibres of different conduction velocities ; the fastest fibres produce an A-wave which may be analysed into α-, β-, and γ-elevations, corresponding to groups of fast fibres with conduction velocities decreasing in this order.[1] The waves due to the

[1] There is not complete agreement as to the theoretical effect of internodal distance on velocity of conduction ; practically there is no influence (Sanders & Whitteridge) ; theoretical considerations are given by Offner et al., and by Huxley & Stämpfli ; according to the last authors, theory predicts that the velocity will have a maximum value over a certain range of internodal distances, a range that might be sufficiently wide to make the velocity, in practice, independent of this variable.

slower groups are named B and C. The differences in size of the elevations, due to the three main groups of fibres, were so great that the records had to be amplified to different extents ; thus in the records (d) and (f) the amplification was twenty times that in (a) ; moreover, separate

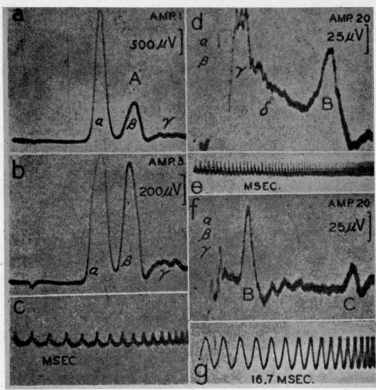

Fig. 193. Complete action potential of bullfrog's peroneal nerve after conducting through a distance of 13·1 cm. The time falls off logarithmi-cally from left to right ; scale c applies to records a and b, whilst scale e applies to record d, and g to record f. Note different amplifications. (Erlanger & Gasser. *Electrical Signs of Nervous Activity.* U. of Penna Press, Philadelphia.)

time-scales were necessary. A painstaking analysis of the action potential records, correlated with measurements of the distribution of fibre diameters,[1] by Erlanger & Gasser has provided the classification of fibre-types shown in Table XXXI. More recently Gasser & Grundfest have

---

[1] The mathematical relationship between velocity and diameter was originally thought by Blair & Erlanger to be of the form : $V \propto D^2$; however, the most recent work of Gasser & Grundfest has established that the relationship is approximately linear in A-fibres of the cat and rabbit saphenous nerves, with diameters ranging from 10–2μ. In the giant axons of the squid Pumphrey & Young found the relationship $V \propto D^{0 \cdot 6}$. It should be noted that Gasser & Grundfest obtained the best linear fit for their results by using the axon, as opposed to the fibre, diameter. The proportion of sheath to whole fibre becomes larger as the fibres become smaller ; thus the ratio : axon diameter/fibre diameter is about 0·75 for fibres of 8μ and larger, but may fall as low as 0·2 for the thinnest myelinated fibres (Taylor ; Gasser & Grundfest).

TABLE **XXXI**

*Classification of Frog Fibres According to Fibre Diameter and
Conduction Velocity.*

Elevation		Fibre Diameter	Velocity
A { α	. .	18·5μ	42 m./sec.
β	. .	14·0μ	25 m./sec.
γ	. .	11·0μ	17 m./sec.
B	. .	—	4·2 m./sec.
C	. .	2·5μ	0·4–0·5 m./sec.

TABLE **XXXII**

*Analysis of Components of Cat and Rabbit Saphenous Nerves (Grundfest,
1940).*

Group	A	B	C
Diameter of fibre (μ)	20–1	3	—
Conduction velocity (m./sec.) . . .	100–5	14–3	2
Duration of action potential (msec.) . .	0·4–0·5	1·2	2·0
Absolute refractory period (msec.) . .	0·4–1·0	1·2	2·0

analysed the components of the cat and rabbit saphenous nerves as in
Table **XXXII**. It should be noted that there is considerable overlap
between the velocities of the A- and B-groups ; their classification is not,
however, exclusively on a basis of conduction velocity. The duration of
the spike, the characteristics of the positive after-potential, the refractory
period, etc., are all taken into account. Thus the slowest fibres of the
A-group in the rabbit's and cat's saphenous nerves are described as the
δ-elevation ; they are actually slower than B-fibres, but differ sufficiently
in other characteristics to warrant their inclusion in the A-group.

Attempts at establishing a correlation between the size of the fibre and
its function were, at first, hopeful ; thus, in general, the motor root contains
only the α-elevation of the A-group, and the C-elevation, the latter being
due to very fine non-myelinated fibres ; the sensory root contains the
whole A- and C-groups ; pre-ganglionic (myelinated) nerves of the
autonomic system give the B-type of elevation. The finding of four
groups of fibres in sensory nerves suggested that different groups
conducted different sensations. Although some correlation between the
extinction of a given elevation and the disappearance of a given type of
sensation has been found, the most recent work on the subject makes it
unlikely that there is a strict segregation of the modalities of sensation
into fibre-groups. The fact that the fibres in a given bundle can differ
in their conduction rates by a factor of about 100 is doubtless significant
from the point of view of central co-ordination ; thus it is possible for
impulses to reach the highest centres before others, travelling along thin
fibres, reach the spinal cord.

14

Thickness of Sheath. Lest it should be thought that conduction velocity is entirely determined by the diameter of the fibre it should be emphasised that, when the fibres of different phyla are compared, there is no strict correlation. Several authors have drawn attention to the thickness of the myelin sheath ; thus the largest squid fibres, with diameters of the orders of 700μ, conduct at about 23 m./sec. whilst the fastest A-fibres of the frog, with a diameter of only 18μ, conduct about twice as fast. In the squid, the myelin layer represents only some 1 per cent. of the thickness of the fibre, whilst it may be as high as 25 per cent. in vertebrates. It would appear, therefore, that a greater relative thickness of the myelin sheath, combined with the presence of nodes, accounts for the higher velocity in the frog fibre. This view is supported by Table **XXXIII** ; in it

TABLE **XXXIII**

Showing Relative Constancy of Product of Birefringence of Sheath Times Diameter of Fibre in Various Nerve Fibres (Taylor, 1942).

	Fibre diam. (μ)	Axon diam. (μ)	Axon diam. / Fibre diam.	Birefringence	Velocity (ca.) (m/.sec.)	Birefringence × Fibre diam.
Squid giant . . .	650	637	0·98	− 0·0001	25	—
Earthworm giant . .	100	90	0·90	0·0010	25	0·10
Shrimp giant . . .	50	43	0·87	0·0024	25	0·12
Frog sciatic . . .	10	7·5	0·75	0·0105	25	0·105
Cat saphenous (calc.) 20° C.	8·7	6·6	0·76	0·014	25	0·12
Catfish	8·8	5·8	0·58	0·012	25	0·105

the birefringences of a number of fibres, all with approximately the same conduction rate, are shown together with the thicknesses of the whole fibres and of the axons. It will be seen that, as the fibre diameter decreases, the proportionate thickness of sheath increases. If the lipid content of the sheath is the important factor, it will be the birefringence that determines its value in aiding conduction ; and it is interesting that the product of the birefringence times the fibre diameter is approximately constant for all the fibres considered. It should be noted, however, that when fibres in a single nerve are compared, the axon diameter seems to be the determining factor (Gasser & Grundfest). In the invertebrate nervous system, the importance of fibre diameter is strikingly indicated by the giant fibres of the squid ; J. Z. Young showed that these fibres, acting as the motor pathway for contraction of the mantle, were developed by the fusion of numerous smaller nerve cells into a syncytium ; this fusion is to be regarded as an adaptive process to enable rapid conduction to the mantle, which is used in propulsion.

External Resistance. The velocity of propagation, according to Rushton's analysis, should depend on the length factor, L (p. 401), which, as we have seen, is a function of the resistances of the outside and inside media of the fibre ; increasing L means that the extrinsic potential will extend farther at any given moment and so activate a given point, ahead of the action potential, sooner. Since L increases with decreasing external resistance, we should expect a nerve to conduct more rapidly in sea-water than in oil. With isolated fibres of the squid giant axon, Hodgkin demonstrated an increase of 80–140 per cent. in conduction velocity on transferring a nerve fibre from oil to sea-water. It is interesting, in this connection, that Auger increased the velocity of propagation of the wave of action potential in *Nitella* by covering the cell with a strip of filter paper moistened with saline solution. Conversely Katz has shown that the conduction velocity in a single nerve fibre is reduced by replacing some of the salt in its outside medium by non-electrolyte.

Spike-Height. The greater the height of the action potential, the greater will be the extent of the extrinsic potential, and hence the greater the conduction velocity. In a narcotised region the action potential propagates at a lower height, so that narcoticisation should be reflected in a lower velocity of propagation. According to Adrian's experiments this is true, the velocity falling, under suitable conditions, to less than a third of normal.

The core-conductor theory is the best attempt, so far made, to describe the events leading up to stimulation, *i.e.*, the events leading to the development of a critical electrotonic potential over a small area of fibre. With its aid, certain broad generalisations can be made with regard to the time relations of excitation, in so far as these are largely determined by the development and spread of electrotonus ; there is, however, one important factor still barely explored, namely the development of the excited state from the purely passive electrotonic condition. From one excitable tissue to another, the time relations of this process may vary enormously, and so obscure any differences due to the differing time relations of electrotonus. Until this development of the excited state is better understood, any relations between conduction velocity, chronaxie, rheobase, absolutely and relatively refractory periods, and so on, must rest on an empirical basis—at least in so far as different tissues are concerned.

Electric Excitation of Muscle

From a teleological point of view it is in the nerve that we must expect excitability and speed of conduction to be developed in their highest forms ; and for this reason the studies described so far have been largely confined to this type of cell ; nevertheless the muscle has been subjected to a large variety of experimental studies in which excitation has been brought about by the direct application of electrodes to the muscle, either *in situ* or excised, or by indirect stimulation through the motor nerve.

Action Potential. With studies on whole muscle, as opposed to individual fibres, the recorded action potential is generally complex, due to one or more of the following causes : (*a*) asynchronism in the potentials in the individual fibres, as it is difficult to stimulate all simultaneously, and they do not always run parallel as in nerves ; (*b*) the spread of electrotonic currents through the highly conducting spaces between the muscle fibres (Gilson & Bishop), and (*c*), in muscle made up of fibres short compared with the distance between electrodes, to the development of series

14—2

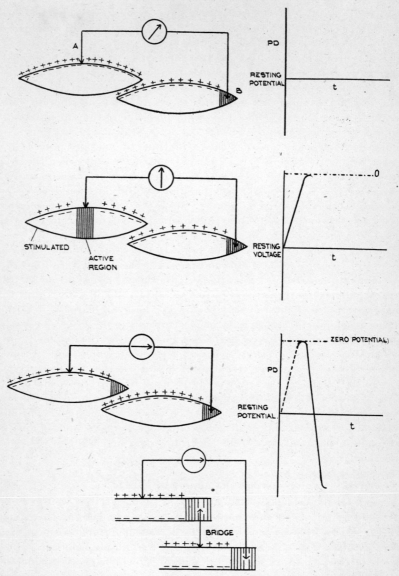

Fig. 194. Showing how a "monophasic recording" can give a diphasic response when the two electrodes are on different fibres. (After Adrian. *J. Physiol.*)

connections between fibres. The last point will be made clear by an example provided by Adrian (1925). Fig. 194 illustrates the case of a "monophasic recording" from the cat's tenuissimus; electrode B is on the injured region of one fibre, whilst electrode A is on another fibre, which is intact; the resting potential is recorded. On stimulating, the depolarisation proceeds towards electrode A; when it passes A, the resting potential falls and returns to its original value. When it reaches the end of the fibre, however, the difference of potential between the electrodes is not the resting potential, but twice this, because the two fibres behave as two cells in series ; the potential record is diphasic.

The influence of current-spread has been investigated theoretically by a number of workers on account of its importance in the interpretation of the electrocardiogram. According to Bishop, the potential at an electrode in the neighbourhood of an advancing wave of action potential becomes first *positive* ; when the wave passes under the electrode this changes to pronounced negativity, and is followed by a final positive phase. Thus the potential changes under a single electrode are triphasic instead of monophasic.

In general, the spike in muscle is slower in development than in nerve and its velocity of propagation is about one-tenth or even less (Göpfert & Schaefer, 1938) ; for example, in the frog's sartorius the velocity is about 2 m./sec. comparing with a velocity in the motor nerve fibres of over 50 m./sec. at 20–25° C. ; the total duration of the negative spike is about 2 msec., the crest is attained in 0·75 msec., and the wavelength is some 7 mm., *i.e.*, only about one-fifth that of myelinated motor nerve fibres, a difference due mainly to the smaller electrotonic spread in the low-resistance muscle sheath. It will be recalled that the wavelength of the action potential in unmyelinated crab nerve is also very small ; thus the distances for " half-decay " in medullated nerve, crab nerve and frog sartorius muscle are 2–3 mm., 0·5 mm., and 1 mm. respectively.

Chronaxie. Ten or fifteen years ago no account of the excitability of muscle would have been considered complete without a lengthy disquisition on the chronaxie of the muscle and its related nerve; the theory of *isochronism* of Lapique and its later extensions ; the controversial subject of α- and γ-excitation, and so on. To-day it is now fairly generally agreed that the electrical stimulation of muscle differs only quantitatively from that of nerve, so that very little space need be devoted to the subject. Chronaxie, as we have seen (p. 396) is a somewhat arbitrary index of excitability, being the minimum time of application of a current of twice the rheobasic strength required to excite. Its unit is therefore one of time and its significance has been extended beyond all reasonable limits (considering that it is no more than a parameter of a strength-duration curve) by Lapique, who described it as the " physiological unit of time " ; for instance it was stated that an impulse " travels 10 cm. in one chronaxie." Such a statement implies a linear relationship between conduction velocity and chronaxie, the shorter the chronaxie the greater the velocity ; the careful studies of Erlanger & Blair on the fibres of a mixed nerve, on the contrary, have shown that no such simple relationship prevails. The great significance of chronaxie, however, arose out of the theory of isochronism which stated that the transmission of a nerve impulse to a muscle was only possible if the chronaxies of the two tissues did not differ by more than a factor of two. It was therefore important for Lapique to establish that the chronaxies of nerve and muscle were more or less equal. The most disturbing evidence against this concept was the appearance of a duality in the behaviour of muscle, on electrical stimulation, which suggested that it had two types of chronaxie differing very considerably ; a short one called γ-chronaxie, similar in magnitude to that of nerve, and a much longer, α-chronaxie. This duality in behaviour was described by Lucas as long ago as 1907 when he used large fluid electrodes, with which to excite ; it was thoroughly investigated by Rushton whose results made it most probable that the α-chronaxie represented the true physiological excitability of muscle. With large fluid electrodes the γ-chronaxie that also appears in the complex strength-duration curve represents the stimulation of the nerve fibres in their intra-muscular course. Lapique, however, used very fine silver electrodes, so-called " stigmatic electrodes," so that the γ-type of chronaxie found by him was definitely a characteristic of the muscle fibres ; thus the problem resolved itself into deciding whether the α-chronaxie or the γ-chronaxie was the artefact ; if the γ-chronaxie, then the bottom fell out of the isochronism theory since the α-chronaxie is very much longer than that of nerve.

Electrotonus and Chronaxie. For years the argument raged but in 1939 Schaefer, Schölmerich & Haass reported their studies on the electrotonic potentials in muscle. They showed that a true electrotonic potential develops at the stimulating electrodes, and that this potential leads directly to the propagated all-or-none type of action potential ; this electrotonic potential dies away exponentially, as with nerve. The " half-time " for decay of electrotonus has been shown by Rosenberg to be equal to the chronaxie, so that if the electrotonic potential is really an expression of the electrical events leading to excitation in muscle, as in nerve, we should expect to find such an equality. Typical results were as follows :--

| Chronaxie (msec.) . | . | . | 7·8 | 8·6 | 3·65 | 3·85 | 2·1 | 3·2 |
| ½-time (msec.) | . | . | 10 | 9 | 3·5–4·4 | 3·5–3·6 | 2·1–2·4 | 3·9 |

These chronaxies are, moreover, α-chronaxies, comparable with the values found by Rushton ; consequently we have here an independent confirmation of Rushton's contention that it is the α-chronaxie that is the true index of excitability of the muscle fibres. The chronaxies of nerve fibres vary with the diameter ; thus it is about 4 msec. for slow fibres conducting at 2 m./sec. and about 1/5 msec. or less for fibres conducting at 26 m./sec. These chronaxies are short compared with that of the muscle fibre, and thus the theory of isochronism, untenable on other grounds, is effectively disposed of by these studies of electrotonus. The chronaxie of muscle depends, apparently, on the size of the electrodes used to measure it, and approaches that of nerve when these are very small ; the studies of Ramsey & Street (1938) with single fibres have given figures for muscle chronaxie similar to those of Rushton for α-chronaxie ; on decreasing the area of contact of one electrode, however, the chronaxie shortened in a similar manner to the shortening with small electrodes with whole muscle. Again, Kuffler (1945) found that in the isolated single nerve-muscle fibre preparation, the α-chronaxie belonged to the muscle and the γ-chronaxie to the nerve. A mathematical analysis by Blair has partly explained the variation in chronaxie on the basis of the core-conductor theory ; it indicates, moreover, that chronaxie itself is a poor index to excitability. A similar conclusion was reached by Davis & Forbes in reviewing the vast literature on chronaximetry, the application of chronaxie measurements to clinical conditions.

METABOLIC ASPECTS OF EXCITATION

The metabolism of muscle is complicated by the fact that it is concerned not only with the conducting, but also with the contractile, mechanism ; so that it would be most profitable to concentrate attention on the metabolism of nerve, where the conduction mechanism has been developed to the greatest extent. The frog nerve, at rest, consumes O_2 and produces heat at rates of the order of 50 mm.^{3}/g.hr. and 0·5 cal./g.hr., respectively.

Effects of Anaerobiosis and Metabolic Inhibitors

In an atmosphere of pure N_2 the resting heat production falls, over a period of two hours, but even after this there is a steady evolution of heat corresponding to one-quarter to one-fifth of the normal resting rate ; on re-admitting O_2 the heat production rises rapidly to overshoot the resting level for about an hour. There is thus developed an " oxygen debt," but the extra consumption of O_2 only represents about 15 per cent. of that missed during anaerobiosis. During anaerobiosis the production of CO_2 continues for some time in spite of the fact that, according to Hill's calculation, all the dissolved O_2 in nerve should be lost in a few minutes ; the relatively slow fall in heat production is therefore said to be due to the presence of an " oxidative reserve," *i.e.*, the presence within the nerve of a hydrogen acceptor capable of taking the place of molecular O_2. It is thought that, when the nerve in N_2 has settled down to its low rate of heat production, the true anaerobic metabolism, presumably involving the formation of lactic acid, is operating alone. The steady anaerobic heat production amounts to some 10^{-3} cal./g.hr., equivalent to the energy obtained from the formation of 2.10^{-4} g. of lactic acid per gramme of nerve per hour ; according to Schmitt & Cori, the actual formation of lactic acid corresponds to 2.10^{-5} g./g.hr.

Conduction Block. In the absence of O_2, the nerve slowly loses its power to conduct an impulse ; Gerard placed several recording electrodes at different positions along the frog's sciatic nerve ; if the impulse had to pass through a portion of nerve exposed to an atmosphere of N_2, the height of the action potential, recorded from a part of the nerve in O_2, fell progressively during a period of an hour or more. For example, in one experiment there was a 3 per cent. loss in fifteen minutes, 13 per cent. in thirty minutes, 49 per cent. in forty minutes and complete block occurred in one hour. The higher the temperature, or the more rapid the resting O_2-consumption, the more rapidly the block occurred ; thus the order of decreasing rates of blockage was : Dog nerve > green-frog > bull-frog, the order of their resting O_2-consumptions. If there is an oxidative reserve, the exhaustion of which causes eventual block, then clearly the rate of block must run parallel with the normal requirements of the nerve.[1] On re-admitting O_2 to the nerve, conduction returned in one minute, the nerve being, for a time, more excitable than in its initial resting condition ; in this connection it is of interest that, in the early stages of asphyxia, the response to stimulation actually increases above normal before falling. The resting potential during asphyxia has been studied by a number of workers ; thus Furusawa said that it may be abolished in the absence of O_2 ; Shanes reported a continuous decrease in anoxia or in the presence of iodoacetate ; Gerard, in the work alluded to, found that the fall in resting potential generally, but not always, paralleled the change in action potential. The work of Bishop, however, suggests a comparative independence of action potential and resting potential under abnormal conditions. For example, in an atmosphere of pure CO_2 the resting potential of nerve was barely affected, but a partial block occurred. In general, Bishop found that substances that brought about block caused only small changes in resting potential ; for example, KCl, aconitine, and CO_2, in the concentrations necessary to produce block, produced only small changes in resting potential whilst cocaine and the aliphatic narcotics caused an *increase in resting potential*, although blocking the nerve.[2] More recently still Shanes & Brown have stated that the resting potential is not completely abolished in anaerobiosis ; they divide the resting potential into anaerobic and aerobic fractions, only the latter being abolished in O_2-lack. In a careful study of the effects of metabolic inhibitors on the resting potential of frog nerve, these authors found that the specific inhibitors of glycolysis—phlorizin, iodoacetate, and fluoride—reduce the resting potential but do not abolish it completely ; by adding lactate or pyruvate the poison could be antagonised,[3] showing that the loss in resting potential was due to the interruption of the glycolytic cycle. They concluded that the oxidation of pyruvate, in the presence of O_2, is fundamentally concerned in the maintenance of the polarised state of the fibre membrane ; moreover, under anaerobic conditions, as in N_2, it was thought that the breakdown of phosphopyruvate to pyruvate is an important process, providing energy to support the resting potential (p. 501). Finally, their results suggested that still another process, this one insensitive to O_2-lack and to temperature changes, was concerned in maintaining a fraction of the resting potential.

In the light of these results there seems to be little doubt that the normal state of polarisation of the nerve fibre membrane requires the continuous performance of work ; whether this work is purely involved in an active excretion of Na^+ from the fibre, or is connected more generally with maintaining the general structure of the membrane, cannot yet be decided.

[1] Wright (1946), has shown that, for nerves of a variety of species, the product : *Survival Time* × *Resting O_2-Consumption* is constant.

[2] Höber's (1939) results seem to be at variance with Bishop's ; Höber stated that novocaine, cocaine, and amyl alcohol depolarised muscle and nerve ; the matter has been re-investigated by Bennett & Chinbury (1946), who find that no depolarisation of frog nerve is caused by just-blocking concentrations of a variety of local anæsthetics, *e.g.*, novocaine, procaine, cocaine, etc. Höber apparently used much higher concentrations than those just required to cause block.

[3] Not, however, in crab nerve (Shanes, 1950).

If the effect of a metabolic inhibitor or O_2-lack is to cause the Na^+-extrusion mechanism to fail, we should expect to find a close parallelism between the failure of the resting potential and the escape of K^+ and gain of Na^+ by the nerve. So far a critical experiment to decide this point in respect to nerve has not been made, although Fenn & Gerschman and Shanes (1950) have shown that nerves lose K^+ in O_2-lack ; perfusing a muscle with O_2-free Ringer fails to cause an escape of K^+ (Fenn, Koenen & Sheridan) ; unfortunately, however, in this work no test of either the resting potential or the excitability of the muscle was made ; moreover, the muscle has such large reserves of anaerobic metabolic energy that anaerobiosis of only one hour's duration would be unlikely to affect the resting potential. According to Dean, a muscle retains its K^+ under conditions of O_2-lack, or if it is perfused with iodoacetate in the presence of O_2 ; when both conditions are applied together, namely anaerobiosis plus iodoacetate, the muscle loses K^+.

The independence of the resting potential and the condition of block, brought out by Bishop's work, was difficult to interpret on the classical theory that the action potential was a simple abolition of the resting potential ; the work of Hodgkin & Katz (p. 390), showing that the action potential represents an actual reversal of the normal polarity across the membrane, would suggest that substances like cocaine and aliphatic narcotics cause block by inhibiting the development of permeability to Na^+ that is thought to be the fundamental element in the action potential. It is interesting that in the cat erythrocyte narcotics inhibit only Na^+-permeability. This could explain why an agent may abolish the action potential and leave the resting potential virtually unaffected. In this connection we may note that Gerard & Doty have raised the question of the relationship between the resting metabolism of a nerve and the extra metabolism concerned with conduction ; by making use of two enzymatic poisons, azide and methyl fluoracetate, they obtained results suggesting that the energy derived from the resting metabolism could be diverted to the process of conduction, *i.e.*, restitution of the polarised state. For example, with an appropriate concentration of azide the resting metabolism of nerve was barely affected ; conduction occurred, but *without* an increase in O_2-consumption. Again, methyl fluoracetate decreased the resting O_2-consumption to about half its normal value, leaving conduction with its attendant increase in O_2-consumption intact.

Anodic Polarisation. A striking observation, originally made by Thörner and confirmed and extended by Lorente de Nó (1946/7) and by Gallego, is that the excitability of nerve, destroyed by anoxia or narcotics, may be restored by anodal polarisation, *i.e.*, by the passage of a weak constant current through the nerve, the tested region being near the positive pole of the polarising electrodes. As Lorente de Nó pointed out, this observation means that the excitability of the nerve fibre is determined primarily by its electrical condition, metabolism influencing the excitability in so far as it is necessary to restore the nerve's original (or approximately so) electrical condition after the depolarisation which follows a stimulus and propagated disturbance. We may mention that Lorente de Nó objects to the simple theory of excitation developed in these pages and championed by Hodgkin, Rushton, and others. He regards the whole process of excitation from a more dynamic viewpoint, the nerve fibre being thought to respond actively to any applied potential in such a way as to minimise its effect. He also divides the resting potential into two main components, differing in the influence of environmental changes on them ; Gerard's recent studies on resting potentials in impaled muscle fibres have led him to a similar position (Ling & Gerard, 1949,c), the potential being divided into an A-fraction, which is abolished by iodoacetate, and a residual B-fraction, only abolished by an attack on the integrity of the fibre membrane. This fractionation is difficult to justify on theoretical grounds, however convenient it may be from a descriptive point of view.

Before leaving this aspect of the resting potential, three points may be briefly considered. First, it by no means follows that the abolition of the resting potential should be immediately followed by a levelling up of the concentrations of K^+ in the fibre and extracellular fluid ; the potential depends on a restraint placed on the migration of K^+ by the impermeability of certain anions ; the removal of this restraint will rapidly abolish the potential, although it may take a considerable time for the K^+ to leak away from the fibre. Moreover, we must not rule out the possibility that the fibre is able to protect itself against large losses of K^+ by developing a decreased permeability to K^+ in response to the metabolic or other disturbance; such an effect has already been described (p. 273) during O_2-lack in *Halicystis*. Secondly, a word of caution on the interpretation of results obtained with metabolic inhibitors. Fluoride is an inhibitor of glycolysis ; in 0·01 M concentration it causes the erythrocyte to lose K^+ rapidly (p. 195) ; a detailed study of the process has revealed, however, that it would be quite wrong to treat the effect as simply the putting out of action of a secretory mechanism that normally accumulates K^+ in the cell. Thus much higher concentrations of fluoride have no effect, yet they abolish glycolysis just as effectively, so that it has been concluded that it is essentially the accumulation of metabolites, which would normally be converted to lactic acid, that is the cause of the escape of K^+.

Finally, we may draw attention to the possibility, suggested recently by Arvanitaki, that the redox potentials, associated with metabolic activity, may influence the electrical condition of the nerve. Thus oxidation is essentially a loss of electrons (p. 273), hence a localised accumulation of oxidative enzymes may make this region electrically negative in respect of another region, and, provided that there is a mechanism for the transfer of these electrons, local circuits may be envisaged carrying current from one region to another. In the ganglia of *Aplysia* (a large gastropod mollusc known as the " sea-hare ") there are two pigments, the one a carotenoid and the other a chlorophyll-like compound ; they are probably connected with respiratory activities, and Arvanitaki has shown that the rhythmic activity of these ganglion cells may be modified by irradiating them with those wavelengths of light that are strongly absorbed by the pigments.

Heat Production During Activity

As a result of a propagated disturbance the nerve fibre is depolarised, and subsequently, during the refractory periods, re-establishes its resting polarised condition. We may expect these two phases of activity to be associated with an increase over the basal heat production—the *initial* and *recovery* heats respectively. The absolute amounts of heat are very small and they present serious technical problems in their measurement, especially since the rate of liberation is rapid. The history of the analysis of the heat production of nerve during activity is thus the history of the development of suitable thermopiles, thermostats, and galvanometers. Space will not permit a description of the apparatus, developed in its most refined form by A. V. Hill, but if it is appreciated that the rise in temperature of nerve, accompanying a high frequency tetanic stimulation lasting one second, is only 6.10^{-6} °C., the high sensitivity of the thermopile, and the accuracy of the temperature regulation, become evident.

The heat liberated as a result of a single shock is too small to measure, even with the utmost refinements of technique at present available, so that the effects of a volley of impulses in several nerves must be studied; and the curve, obtained by plotting the heat liberated against time of stimulation, must be analysed into components corresponding to the initial and recovery heats. Thus, during a faradic discharge at, say, a frequency of 40 per sec., the heat liberated at any moment represents the sum of the initial heat, due to the impulse at that moment, plus the accumulation of the recovery heat from many of the preceding stimuli; the number of these preceding stimuli contributing to the instantaneous heat production must clearly depend on the duration of the recovery heat; if this lasts for thirty minutes, then the first stimulus must contribute heat to the instantaneous heat production for the first thirty minutes of repetitive stimulation. It will be clear, too, that at this point, *i.e.*, when the stimulation has lasted for the duration of the recovery heat, a steady-state of heat production will be reached.

The response to a faradic stimulus lasting for sixteen seconds is shown in Fig. 195, the rate of heat production, computed from an analysis of the galvanometer deflection, being plotted against time. There is a rapid rise at the beginning of stimulation and a rapid decline at the end, both of which may be attributed to the initial heat. The slower rise in rate of heat production is due to the cumulative effect of the delayed heat of preceding impulses, plus a steady component of initial heat which may be assumed to remain constant. If the frequency of stimulation is not too high, a steady-state may be reached in about 25–40 minutes in frog nerve at 20° C., hence the total duration of the recovery heat lies within this range. If the stimulation is stopped when the steady-state has been reached, there is a sudden fall in heat production, followed by a more gentle fall lasting over the same period as that required to establish the steady-state. The sudden fall is due predominantly to the falling out of the initial heat, and the slower one to the gradual decrease in the recovery heat. A study of the rate of fall of heat production in these circumstances shows that the recovery heat may be divided into a very rapid " A-component," which is half-completed in 2–3 seconds, and a slow " B-component," half-completed in 4–5 minutes. The total heat liberated during the rapid recovery process is about equal to that liberated as initial heat, and is doubtless equivalent to the heat liberated during the rapid re-establishment of excitability during the absolutely refractory phase. The slower phase, lasting half-an-hour, is probably an oxidative process which restores the energy utilised in the rapid phase. Hill's results show that the greatest rate of extra heat production, due to steady stimulation, is of the order of 40μcal./g. sec. ; the rate, of course, depends on the frequency of stimulation, since the greater the

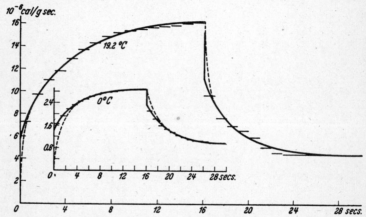

Fig. 195.   Extra heat production of nerve during and after a 16-sec. tetanus. The extra heat liberated has been computed from the galvanometer deflection over successive 1-sec. intervals, as indicated by the short horizontal lines. The full curves are drawn through these lines, it being assumed that the initial rise of heat production on stimulation, and the fall on cessation of the stimulus, are sudden. The broken curves are drawn on the assumption that the initial rise and final fall of heat production are continuous, not sudden. (Feng, after Hill. *Ergebn. d. Physiol.*)

frequency the more stimuli occur in one second ; at ten shocks per second the rate is only about 10μcal./g. sec. and reaches the maximal figure with about 100 shocks/sec. At this frequency, the heat liberated *per impulse* is of the order of 0·4μcal./g. At higher frequencies the heat production per impulse falls.

The initial *rate* of heat production is high compared with that for the delayed heat but, since the duration of the former is so short, the *amount* of delayed heat is very much larger. Thus, for a 32-sec. burst of impulses, the initial heat in one experiment was 4·3μcal./g. sec., giving a quantity of 138μcal./g. ; the total heat liberated as a result of this 32-sec. stimulation was 4,230μcal./g., lasting over a period of about 30 min. The ratio of total to initial heat was 31. If the ratio is determined when the heat production of stimulated nerve is in the steady-state, *i.e.*, subjected to prolonged stimulation, the ratio changes to about 9. Apparently, during lengthy tetanic stimulation, the recovery process is never complete, the nerve " making do " with only a partial restoration of the original resting conditions. The *initial heat per impulse* varies greatly with the frequency of stimulation ; with a frequency of 65/sec., for example, it was 0.05μcal./g. whilst with a frequency of 600/sec. it was 0.01μcal./g. Moreover, the *total heat per impulse* is an inverse function of the frequency of stimulation ; only when the interval between stimuli is 50 msec., *i.e.*, longer than the relatively refractory period of 10 msec., does the heat production per stimulus become maximal. Apparently with high frequency stimulation the nerve operates at a lower level of physiological activity ; it is interesting in this connection that during tetanic stimulation the height of the action potential may be considerably depressed below that obtained with single shocks (*cf.*, *e.g.*, Hodgkin, 1938).

References

ACHESON, G. H. & ROSENBLUETH, A. (1941). " Some Effects of Veratrine on Circulated Mammalian Nerve." *Amer. J. Physiol.*, **133**, 736.

ADRIAN, E. D. (1914). " The Relation between the Size of the Propagated Disturbance and the Rate of Conduction in Nerve." *J. Physiol.*, **48**, 53.

ADRIAN, E. D. (1925). " The Spread of Activity in the Tenuissimus Muscle of the Cat and in other Complex Muscles." *J. Physiol.*, **60**, 301.

ARNETT, V. & WILDE, W. S. (1941). " Potassium and Water Changes in Excised Nerve on Stimulation." *J. Neurophysiol.*, **4**, 572.

ARVANITAKI, A. & CHALAZONITIS, N. (1949). " Inhibition ou Excitation des Potentiels Neuroniques à la Photoactivation Distincte de deux Chromoprotéines (Carotenoide et Chlorophyllien)." *Arch. des Sci. Physiol.*, **3**, 45.

ARVANITAKI, A. & CHALAZONITIS, N. (1949). " Catalyse Respiratoire et Potentiels Bioélectriques." *Arch. des Sci. Physiol.*, **3**, 303.

AUGER, D. (1933). " Contribution à l'étude de la Propagation de la Variation Électrique chez les Characées." *C. r. Soc. Biol.*, Paris, **113**, 1437.

BEAR, R. S., PALMER, K. J. & SCHMITT, F. O. (1941). " X-Ray Diffraction Studies on Nerve Lipides." *J. cell. & comp. Physiol.*, **17**, 355.

BEAR, R. S., SCHMITT, F. O. & YOUNG, J. Z. (1937). " The Sheath Components of the Giant Nerve Fibres of the Squid." *Proc. Roy. Soc.*, B, **123**, 496.

BEAR, R. S., SCHMITT, F. O. & YOUNG, J. Z. (1937). " The Ultra Structure of Nerve Axoplasm." *Proc. Roy. Soc.*, B, **123**, 505.

BEAR, R. S., SCHMITT, F. O. & YOUNG, J. Z. (1937). " Investigations on the Protein Constituents of Nerve Axoplasm." *Proc. Roy. Soc.*, B, **123**, 520.

BENNETT, A. L. & CHINBURY, K. G. (1946). " The Effects of Several Local Anæsthetics on the Resting Potential of Isolated Frog Nerve." *J. Pharm.*, **88**, 72.

BEUTNER, R. & BARNES, T. C. (1948). " A New Concept of Phase-Boundary Potential Applied to the Electro-Physiology of Nerve." *Fed. Proc.*, **7**, 8.

BISHOP, G. H. (1932). " The Action of Nerve Depressants on Potential." *J. cell. & comp. Physiol.*, **1**, 177.

BISHOP, G. H. (1937). " La Théorie des Circuits Locaux Permet-elle de Prévoir la Forme du Potentiel d'Action ? " *Arch. int. Physiol.*, **45**, 273.

BLAIR, H. A. (1941). " Muscle Excitability." *Biol. Symp.*, **3**, 51.

BLAIR, E. A. & ERLANGER, J. (1940). " Interaction of Medullated Fibres of a Nerve Tested with Electric Shocks." *Amer. J. Physiol.*, **131**, 483.

BLINKS, L. R. (1930). " The Direct Current Resistance of *Valonia*." *J. gen. Physiol.*, **13**, 361.

BLINKS, L. R. (1930). " The Direct Current Resistance of *Nitella*." *J. gen. Physiol.*, **13**, 495.

BREMER, F. (1947). " Nerve and Synaptic Potentials." *Ann. Rev. Physiol.*, **9**, 457.

DEL CASTILLO-NICOLAU & STARK, L. (1951). " Local Responses Due to Stimulation at a Single Node of Ranvier." *J. Physiol.*, **113**. (In the press.)

CHAMBERS, R. (1947). " The Shape of Oil Drops Injected into the Axoplasm of the Giant Nerve of the Squid." *Biol. Bull.*, **93**, 191.

CHINN, P. (1938). "Polarisation Optical Studies of the Structure of Nerve Cells." *J. cell. & comp. Physiol.*, **12**, 1.

CHINN, P. & SCHMITT, F. O. (1937). "On the Birefringence of Nerve Sheaths as Studied in Cross Sections." *J. cell. & comp. Physiol.*, **9**, 289.

COLE, K. S. (1941). "Rectification and Inductance in the Squid Giant Axon." *J. gen. Physiol.*, **25**, 29.

COLE, K. S. (1942). "Impedance of Single Cells." *Tab. Biol.*, **19** (2), 24.

COLE, K. S. (1949). "Dynamic Electrical Characteristics of the Squid Axon Membrane." *Arch. des Sci. physiol.*, **3**, 253.

COLE, K. S. & CURTIS, H. J. (1936). "Electric Impedance of Nerve and Muscle." *C.S.H. Symp.*, **4**, 73.

COLE, K. S. & CURTIS, H. J. (1938). "Electric Impedance of *Nitella* during Activity." *J. gen. Physiol.*, **22**, 37.

COLE, K. S. & CURTIS, H. J. (1950). Electric Physiology "Medical Physics." (p. 82). Ed. O. Glasser. Chicago, Year Book Publishers.

COLE, K. S. & GUTTMAN, R. M. (1942). "Electric Impedance of the Frog Egg." *J. gen. Physiol.*, **25**, 765.

COLE, K. S. & HODGKIN, A. L. (1939). "Membrane and Protoplasmic Resistance in the Squid Giant Axon." *J. gen. Physiol.*, **22**, 671.

COWAN, S. L. (1934). "Action of K^+ and other Ions on the Injury Potential and Action Current in *Maia* Nerve." *Proc. Roy. Soc.*, *B*, **115**, 216.

CRESCITELLI, F. (1948). "The Dual Action of Carbamates on the Resting Potential of Frog Nerve." *J. cell. & comp. Physiol.*, **32**, 187.

CURTIS, H. J. & COLE, K. S. (1937). "Transverse Electric Impedance of *Nitella*." *J. gen. Physiol.*, **21**, 189.

CURTIS, H. J. & COLE, K. S. (1938). "Transverse Electric Impedance of the Squid Giant Axon." *J. gen. Physiol.*, **21**, 757.

CURTIS, H. J. & COLE, K. S. (1942). "Membrane Resting and Action Potentials in Giant Fibres of Squid Nerve." *J. cell. & comp. Physiol.*, **19**, 135.

CURTIS, H. J. & COLE, K. S. (1950). Excitation and Propagation of Nerve "Medical Physics." (p. 584). Ed. O. Glasser. Chicago, Year Book Publishers.

DAVIS, H. & FORBES, A. (1936). "Chronaxie." *Physiol. Rev.*, **16**, 407.

DAVIS, H., FORBES, A., BRUNSWICK, D. & HOPKINS, A. McH. (1926). "The Question of Decrement." *Amer. J. Physiol.*, **76**, 448.

DAVSON, H. & DANIELLI, J. F. (1943). "The Permeability of Natural Membranes." Cambridge, C.U.P.

DAVSON, H. & REINER, J. M. (1942). "Ionic Permeability : an Enzyme-like Factor Concerned in the Migration of Na through the Cat Erythrocyte Membrane." *J. cell. & comp. Physiol.*, **20**, 325.

DEAN, R. B. (1940). "Anaerobic Loss of K from Frog Muscle." *J. cell. & comp. Physiol.*, **15**, 189.

DUNCAN, D. (1934). "A Relation between Axone Diameter and Myelination Determined by Measurement of Myelinated Spinal Root Fibres." *J. comp. Neurol.*, **60**, 437.

ERLANGER, J. & BLAIR, E. A. (1934). "Manifestation of Segmentation in Myelinated Axons." *Amer. J. Physiol.*, **110**, 286.

ERLANGER, J. & BLAIR, E. A. (1938). "Action of Isotonic Salt-Free Solutions on Conduction in Medullated Nerve Fibres." *Amer. J. Physiol.*, **124**, 341.

ERLANGER, J. & GASSER, H. S. (1937). "Electrical Signs of Nervous Activity." Philadelphia. Univ. of Penn. Press.

VON EULER, H., VON EULER, U. S. & HEVESY, G. (1946). "The Effect of Excitation on Nerve Permeability." *Acta Physiol. Scand.*, **12**, 261.

FENG, T. P. (1936). "The Heat Production of Nerve." *Ergebn. d. Physiol.*, **38**, 73.

FENG, T. P. & HILL, A. V. (1933). "The Steady State of Heat Production of Nerve." *Proc. Roy. Soc.*, *B*, **113**, 356.

FENG, T. P. & HILL, A. V. (1933). "Effect of Frequency of Stimulation on the Heat Production of Frog's Nerve." *Proc. Roy. Soc.*, *B*, **113**, 366.

FENN, W. O. & GERSCHMAN, R. (1950). "The Loss of Potassium from Frog Nerves in Anoxia and other Conditions." *J. gen. Physiol.*, **33**, 195.

FENN, W. O., KOENEMANN, R. H., FAVATA, B. V. & SHERIDAN, E. T. (1940). "The Role of Lactic Acid in the Movements of Potassium." *Amer. J. Physiol.*, **131**, 494.

FENN, W. O., KOENEMANN, R. H. & SHERIDAN, E. T. (1940). "The Potassium Exchange of Perfused Frog Muscle during Asphyxia." *J. cell. & comp. Physiol.*, **16**, 255.

FERNÁNDEZ-MORÁN, H. (1950). "Sheath and Axon Structures in the Internode Portion of Vertebrate Myelinated Nerve Fibres." *Exp. Cell. Res.*, **1**, 309.

FESSARD, A. (1936). " Propriétés Rhythmiques de la Matière Vivante." Paris, Hermann.

FURUSAWA, K. (1929). " The Depolarisation of Crustacean Nerve by Stimulation or Oxygen Want." *J. Physiol.*, **67**, 325.

GALLEGO, A. (1948). " On the Effect of Ethyl Alcohol upon Frog Nerve." *J. cell. & comp. Physiol.*, **31**, 97.

GASSER, H. S. & GRUNDFEST, H. (1936). " Action and Excitability in Mammalian A Fibres." *Amer. J. Physiol.*, **117**, 113.

GASSER, H. S. & GRUNDFEST, H. (1939). " Axon Diameter in Relation to the Spike Dimension and Conduction Velocity in Mammalian A Fibres." *Amer. J. Physiol.*, **127**, 393.

GERARD, R. W. (1932). " Nerve Metabolism." *Physiol. Rev.*, **12**, 469.

GERARD, R. W. (1932). " The Response of Nerve to Oxygen Lack." *Amer. J. Physiol.*, **92**, 498.

GERARD, R. W. (1936). " Metabolism and Excitation." *C.S.H. Symp.*, **4**, 194.

GERARD, R. W. & DOTY, R. W. (1950). " Nerve Conduction without Increased Oxygen Consumption : the Action of Azide and Fluoracetate." *Biochim. Biophys. Acta*, **4**, 115.

GILSON, A. S. & BISHOP, G. H. (1937). " The Effect of Remote Leads on the Form of Recorded ECG." *Amer. J. Physiol.*, **118**, 743.

GÖPFERT, H. & SCHAEFER, H. (1938). " Uber den Direkt und Indirekt Erregten Aktionstrom und die Funktion der Motorische Endplatte." *Pflüg. Arch.*, **239**, 597.

GRAHAM, J. & GERARD, R. W. (1946). " Membrane Potentials and Excitation of Impaled Single Muscle Fibres." *J. cell. & comp. Physiol.*, **28**, 99.

GRUNDFEST, H. (1939). " Properties of Mammalian B Fibres." *Amer. J. Physiol.*, **127**, 253.

GRUNDFEST, H. (1940). " Bioelectric Potentials." *Ann. Rev. Physiol.*, **2**, 213.

GRUNDFEST, H. (1946). " Bioelectric Potentials in the Nervous System and in Muscle." *Ann. Rev. Physiol.*, **9**, 477.

HAHN, L. & HEVESY, G. (1941). " Potassium Exchange in Stimulated Muscle." *Acta Physiol. Scand.*, **2**, 51.

HERTZ, H. (1947). " Action Potential and Diameter of Isolated Nerve Fibres Under Various Conditions." *Acta Physiol., Scand.*, **13**, Suppl. 43.

HILL, A. V. (1932). " A Closer Analysis of the Heat Production of Nerve." *Proc. Roy. Soc., B*, **111**, 106.

HILL, A. V. (1933). " The Three Phases of Nerve Heat Production." *Proc. Roy. Soc., B*, **113**, 345.

HILL, A. V. (1936). " Excitation and Accommodation in Nerve." *Proc. Roy. Soc., B*, **119**, 305.

HILL, D. K. (1950). " Effect of Stimulation on Opacity of Crustacean Nerve Trunk and its Relation to Fibre Diameter." *J. Physiol.*, **111**, 283.

HILL, D. K. (1950). " Volume Change Resulting from Stimulation of a Giant Nerve Fibre." *J. Physiol.*, **111**, 304.

HILL, D. K. & KEYNES, R. D. (1949). " Opacity Changes in Stimulated Nerve." *J. Physiol.*, **108**, 278.

HÖBER, R. (1947). " Studies on the Physiological Effects of Non-Polar Organic Electrolytes. I. The Influence upon the Resting Potential of Frog Muscle." *J. gen. Physiol.*, **30**, 389.

HÖBER, R., ANDERSH, M., HÖBER, J. & NEBEL, B. (1939). " Influence of Organic Electrolytes and Non-Electrolytes on the Membrane Potentials of Muscle and Nerve." *J. cell. & comp. Physiol.*, **13**, 195.

HÖBER, R., LANGSTON, M. & STRAUSSER, H. (1948). " Studies on the Physiological Effects of Non-Polar Organic Electrolytes." II. *J. gen. Physiol.*, **32**, 111.

HODGKIN, A. L. (1937). " Evidence for Electrical Transmission in Nerve." I & II. *J. Physiol.*, **90**, 183, 211.

HODGKIN, A. L. (1938). " The Subthreshold Potentials in a Crustacean Nerve Fibre." *Proc. Roy. Soc., B*, **126**, 87.

HODGKIN, A. L. (1939). " The Relation between Conduction Velocity and the Electrical Resistance Outside a Nerve." *J. Physiol.*, **94**, 560.

HODGKIN, A. L. (1947). " The Membrane Resistance of Non-Medullated Nerve Fibre." *J. Physiol.*, **106**, 305.

HODGKIN, A. L. (1947). " The Effect of Potassium on the Surface Membrane of an Isolated Axon." *J. Physiol.*, **106**, 319.

HODGKIN, A. L. (1948). " The Local Electric Changes Associated with Repetitive Action in a Non-Medullated Axon." *J. Physiol.*, **107**, 165.

HODGKIN, A. L. & HUXLEY, A. F. (1939). " Action Potentials Recorded from Inside a Nerve Fibre." *Nature*, **140**, 710.

HODGKIN, A. L. & HUXLEY, A. F. (1945). "Resting and Action Potentials in Single Nerve Fibres." *J. Physiol.*, **104**, 176.

HODGKIN, A. L. & HUXLEY, A. F. (1947). "Potassium Leakage from an Active Nerve Fibre." *J. Physiol.*, **106**, 341.

HODGKIN, A. L., HUXLEY, A. F. & KATZ, B. (1949). "Ionic Currents Underlying Activity in the Giant Axon of the Squid." *Arch. des Sci. Physiol.*, **III**, 129.

HODGKIN, A. L. & KATZ, B. (1949). "Effect of Na+ on the Electrical Activity of the Giant Axon of the Squid." *J. Physiol.*, **108**, 37.

HODGKIN, A. L. & KATZ, B. (1949). "Effect of Ca++ on the Axoplasm of Giant Nerve Fibres." *J. exp. Biol.*, **26**, 292.

HODGKIN, A. L. & RUSHTON, W. A. H. (1946). "The Electrical Constants of a Crustacean Nerve Fibre." *Proc. Roy. Soc.*, *B*, **133**, 444.

HURSH, J. B. (1939). "Conduction Velocity and Diameter of Nerve Fibres." *Amer. J. Physiol.*, **127**, 131.

HUXLEY, A. F. & STÄMPFLI, R. (1949). "Evidence for Saltatory Conduction in Peripheral Myelinated Nerve Fibres." *J. Physiol.*, **108**, 315.

HUXLEY, A. F. & STÄMPFLI, R. (1951). "Direct Determination of Membrane Resting Potential and Action Potential in Single Myelinated Nerve Fibres." *J. Physiol.*, **112**, 476.

HUXLEY, A. F. & STÄMPFLI, R. (1951). "Effect of K+ and Na+ on Resting and Action Potentials of Single Myelinated Nerve Fibres." *J. Physiol.*, **112**, 496.

KATO, G. (1936). "Excitation, Conduction and Narcotisation of Single Nerve Fibres." *C.S.H. Symp.*, **4**, 43.

KATZ, B. (1937). "Experimental Evidence for a Non-Conducted Response of Nerve to Subthreshold Stimulation." *Proc. Roy. Soc.*, *B*, **124**, 244.

KATZ, B. (1939). "Electrical Excitation in Nerve." Oxford. O.U.P.

KATZ, B. (1947). "Subthreshold Potentials in Medullated Nerve." *J. Physiol.*, **106**, 66.

KATZ, B. (1947). "The Effect of Electrolyte Deficiency on the Rate of Conduction in a Single Nerve Fibre." *J. Physiol.*, **106**, 411.

KATZ, B. (1948). "Electrical Properties of the Muscle Fibre Membrane." *Proc. Roy. Soc.*, *B*, **135**, 506.

KATZ, B. (1950). "Electrical Properties of Muscle Fibre." *Research*, **3**, 359.

KATZ, B. & SCHMITT, F. O. (1940). "Electric Interaction between Two Adjacent Nerve Fibres." *J. Physiol.*, **97**, 471.

KEYNES, R. D. (1948). "The Leakage of Radioactive Potassium from Stimulated Nerve." *J. Physiol.*, **107**, 35P.

KEYNES, R. D. (1949). "The Movements of Radioactive Sodium during Nervous Activity." *J. Physiol.*, **109**, 13P.

KUFFLER, S. W. (1945). "Electric Excitability of Nerve-Muscle Fibre Preparations." *J. Neurophysiol.*, **8**, 75.

LABES, R. & ZAIN, H. (1928). "Ein Membranmodell für eine Reihe Bioelektrischer Vorgänge." *Arch. exp. Path. Pharm.*, **126**, 284.

LLOYD, D. P. C. & McINTYRE, A. K. (1949). "Bioelectric Potentials in the Nervous System and Muscle." *Ann. Rev. Physiol.*, **11**, 173.

LORENTE DE NÓ, R. (1946–7). "Correlation of Nerve Activity with Polarisation Phenomena." *Harvey Lectures*, **42**, 43.

LÜTHY, H. (1950). "Optische Interpretation der Quermembran im Ranvierschen Schnürring." *Experientia*, **6**, 381.

MARRAZZI, A. S. & LORENTE DE NÓ, R. (1944). "Interaction of Neighbouring Fibres in Myelinated Nerve." *J. Neurophysiol.*, **7**, 81.

McCOUCH, G. P. (1945). "Conduction and Synaptic Transmission." *Ann. Rev. Physiol.*, **7**, 455.

MONNIER, A. M. (1934). "L'Excitation Electrique des Tissus." Paris, Hermann.

VON MURALT, A. (1946). "Die Signalübermittlung im Nerven." Basel, Birkhäuser.

VON MURALT, A. (1947–8). "Signal Transmission in Nerve." *Harvey Lectures*, **43**, 230.

NASTUK, W. L. & HODGKIN, A. L. (1950). "The Electrical Activity in Single Muscle Fibres." *J. cell. & comp. Physiol.*, **35**, 39.

NERNST, W. (1908). "Zur Theorie des Elektrischen Reizes." *Pflüg. Arch.*, **122**, 275.

NOONAN, T. R., FENN, W. O. & HAEGE, L. (1941). "The Effects of Denervation and of Stimulation on Exchange of Radioactive Potassium." *Amer. J. Physiol.*, **132**, 612.

OFFNER, F., WEINBERG, A. & YOUNG, G. (1940). "Nerve Conduction Theory. Some Mathematical Consequences of Bernstein's Model." *Bull. Math. Biophys.*, **2**, 89.

OSTERHOUT, W. J. V. (1936). "Some Ways to Control Electrical Behaviour." *C.S.H. Symp.*, **4**, 43.

OSTERHOUT, W. J. V. & HILL, S. E. (1930). "Salt Bridges and Negative Variations." *J. gen. Physiol.*, **13**, 547.

PALMER, K. J., SCHMITT, F. O. & CHARGAFF, E. (1941). "X-Ray Diffraction Studies of Certain Lipide Protein Complexes." *J. cell. & comp. Physiol.*, **18**, 43.

PFAFFMAN, C. (1940). "Potentials in the Isolated Medullated Axon." *J. cell. & comp. Physiol.*, **16**, 407.

PUMPHREY, R. J. & YOUNG, J. Z. (1938). "The Rates of Conduction of Nerve Fibres of Various Diameters in Cephalopods." *J. exp. Biol.*, **15**, 453.

RAMSEY, R. W. & STREET, S. F. (1938). "The Alpha Excitability of the Local and Propagated Mechanical Response in Isolated Single Muscle Fibres." *J. cell. & comp. Physiol.*, **12**, 361.

RASHBASS, C. & RUSHTON, W. A. H. (1949). "Space Distribution of Excitability in the Frog's Sciatic Nerve Stimulated by Slot Electrodes." *J. Physiol.*, **109**, 327, see also pp. 343, 354.

RASHBASS, C. & RUSHTON, W. A. H. (1949). "The Relation of Structure to the Spread of Excitation in the Frog's Sciatic Trunk." *J. Physiol.*, **110**, 110.

RASHEVSKY, N. (1936). "Physico-Mathematical Aspects of Excitation and Conduction in Nerves." *C.S.H. Symp.*, **4**, 90.

DE RENYI, G. ST. (1929). "The Structure of Cells in Tissues as Revealed by Micro-dissection. II. The Physical Properties of the Living Axis Cylinder in Myelinated Fibre of the Frog." *J. comp. Neurol.*, **47**, 405.

RICHARDS, A. G., STEINBACH, H. B. & ANDERSON, T. F. (1943). "Electron Microscope Studies of Squid Giant Nerve Axoplasm." *J. cell. & comp. Physiol.*, **21**, 129.

DE ROBERTIS, E. & SCHMITT, F. O. (1948). "An Electron Microscope Analysis of Certain Nerve Axon Constituents." *J. cell. & comp. Physiol.*, **31**, 1.

DE ROBERTIS, E. & SCHMITT, F. O. (1948). "The Effect of Nerve Degeneration on the Structure of Neurotubules." *J. cell. & comp. Physiol.*, **32**, 45.

ROSENBERG, H. (1937). "Electrotonus and Excitation in Nerve." *Proc. Roy. Soc.*, B, **124**, 308.

ROSENBERG, H. (1937). "The Physico-Chemical Basis of Electrotonus." *Trans. Farad. Soc.*, **33**, 1028.

ROSENBLUETH, A. (1941). "The Effects of Direct Current upon Electrical Excitability of Nerve." *Amer. J. Physiol.*, **132**, 57.

ROSENBLUETH, A. (1943). "The Interaction of Myelinated Fibres in Mammalian Nerve Trunks." *Amer. J. Physiol.*, **140**, 656.

ROTHENBERG, M. A. (1950). "Ionic Movements Across Axonal Membranes." *Biochim. Biophys. Acta*, **4**, 96.

ROZSA, G., MORGAN, C., SZENT-GYÖRGYI, A. & WYCKOFF, R. W. G. (1950). "Electron Microscopy of Myelinated Nerve." *Biochim. Biophys. Acta*, **6**, 13.

RUSHTON, W. A. H. (1932). "Identification of the Gamma Excitability in Muscle." *J. Physiol.*, **75**, 161.

RUSHTON, W. A. H. (1933). "Lapique's Theory of Curarization." *J. Physiol.*, **77**, 337.

RUSHTON, W. A. H. (1937). "The Initiation of the Propagated Disturbance." *Proc. Roy. Soc.*, B, **124**, 201.

RUSHTON, W. A. H. (1949). "The Site of Excitation in the Nerve Trunk of the Frog." *J. Physiol.*, **109**, 314.

SANDERS, F. K. & WHITTERIDGE, D. (1946). "Conduction Velocity and Myelin Thickness in Regenerating Nerve Fibres." *J. Physiol.*, **105**, 152.

SCHAEFER, H., SCHÖLMERICH, P. & HAASS, P. (1938). "Der Elektrotonus und die Erregungsgesetze des Muskels." *Pflüg. Arch.*, **241**, 310.

SCHMIDT, W. J. (1937). "Uber die Formdoppelbrechung der Osmierten Markscheide des Nerven." *Z. wiss. Mikr.*, **54**, 159.

SCHMITT, F. O. (1950). "Morphology in Muscle and Nerve Physiology." *Biochim. Biophys. Acta*, **4**, 68.

SCHMITT, F. O. & BEAR, R. S. (1937). "The Optical Properties of Vertebrate Nerve Axons as Related to Size." *J. cell. & comp. Physiol.*, **9**, 261.

SCHMITT, F. O. & BEAR, R. S. (1939). "The Ultrastructure of the Nerve Axon Sheath." *Biol. Rev.*, **14**, 27.

SCHMITT, F. O., BEAR, R. S. & PALMER, K. J. (1941). "X-Ray Diffraction Studies of the Nerve Myelin Sheath." *J. cell. & comp. Physiol.*, **18**, 31.

SCHMITT, F. O. & CORI, C. F. (1933). "Lactic Acid Formation in Medullated Nerve." *Amer. J. Physiol.*, **106**, 339.

SCHMITT, F. O. & PALMER, K. J. (1940). "X-Ray Diffraction Studies of Lipid and Lipid-Protein Systems." *C.S.H. Symp.*, **8**, 94.

SCHOEPFLE, G. M. & ERLANGER, J. (1941). "The Action of Temperature on the Excitability, Spike-Height and Configuration, and the Refractory Period Observed in the Responses of Single Medullated Nerve Fibres." *Amer. J. Physiol.*, **134**, 694.

SHANES, A. M. (1944). " The Effect of High Potassium Concentrations on the Aerobic and Anaerobic Fractions of Resting Potential of Frog Nerve." *J. cell. & comp. Physiol.*, **23**, 193.

SHANES, A. M. (1949). " Electrical Phenomena in Nerve. I. Squid Giant Axon." *J. gen. Physiol.*, **33**, 57. " II. Crab Nerve," p. 75.

SHANES, A. M. (1950). " Potassium Retention in Crab Nerve." *J. gen. Physiol.*, **33**, 643.

SHANES, A. M. & BROWN, D. E. S. (1942). " The Effect of Metabolic Inhibitors on the Resting Potential of Frog Nerve." *J. cell. & comp. Physiol.*, **19**, 1.

STEINBACH, H. B., SPIEGELMAN, S. & KAWATA, N. (1944). " The Effect of Potassium and Calcium Ions on the Electrical Properties of Squid Axons." *J. cell. & comp. Physiol.*, **24**, 147.

TASAKI, I. (1939). " The Electro-Saltatory Transmission of the Nerve Impulse and the Effect of Narcosis upon the Nerve Fibre." *Amer. J. Physiol.*, **127**, 211.

TAYLOR, G. W. (1940). " Optical Properties of the Earthworm Giant Fibre Sheath as Related to Fibre Size." *J. cell. & comp. Physiol.*, **15**, 363.

TAYLOR, G. W. (1942). " The Correlation between Sheath Birefringence and Conduction Velocity with Special Reference to Cat Nerve Fibres." *J. cell. & comp. Physiol.*, **20**, 359.

TEORELL, T. (1949). " Membrane Electrophoresis in Relation to Bioelectrical Polarisation Effects." *Arch. des Sci. Physiol*, **III**, 205.

THÖRNER, W. (1922). " Elektrophysiologische Untersuchungen am Alterierten Nerven." *Pflüg. Arch.*, **197**, 159.

WEISS, P. & WANG, H. (1936). " Neurofibrils in Living Ganglion Cells of the Chick, Cultivated *In Vitro*." *Anat. Rec.*, **67**, 105.

WERNDLE, L. & TAYLOR, G. W. (1943). " Sheath Birefringence as Related to Fibre Size and Conduction Velocity of Catfish Mauthner, Muller and Peripheral Fibres." *J. cell. & comp. Physiol.*, **21**, 281.

WILBRANDT, W. (1937). " Effect of Organic Ions on the Membrane Potential of Nerves." *J. gen. Physiol.*, **20**, 519.

WRIGHT, E. B. (1946). " A Comparative Study of the Effects of Oxygen Lack on Peripheral Nerve." *Amer. J. Physiol.*, **147**, 78.

YOUNG, J. Z. (1936). " Structure of Nerve Fibres and Synapses in Some Invertebrates." *C.S.H. Symp.*, **4** 1.

CHAPTER XVI

TRANSMISSION OF THE IMPULSE AND THE SENSORY RESPONSE

NEUROMUSCULAR AND SYNAPTIC TRANSMISSION

THE wave of action potential, initiated at any point on the nerve or muscle fibre, travels over its whole surface as a result of the self-propagating characteristic discussed earlier. The transmission of this disturbance from one cell to another, be it from one nerve to another, or from a nerve to a muscle or secretory cell, introduces a new problem, the bridging of a gap in protoplasmic continuity. The existence of regions of functional discontinuity, at least in so far as the nervous organisation is concerned, is clearly necessary if a single impulse is not to excite all nerves with which it is related, either directly or indirectly. The problem of transmission is, therefore, twofold in its nature ; it is concerned with how an impulse bridges a gap in protoplasmic continuity and why, in some circumstances, it fails to do so. So complex are the phenomena of transmission and inhibition, however, that a lucid and full account is beyond the scope of this book ; all that the author can hope to do is to present some of the more striking facts regarding transmission from nerve to muscle and, in certain comparatively simple instances, from nerve to nerve, and to indicate the trends of thought in their interpretation. Before considering, in detail, some of the special problems of transmission, we may first briefly review the general organisation of the vertebrate nervous system.

Neuronal Organisation

The neurone is the unit of conduction, but only in rare cases, in the higher organisms, is it adequate to initiate and complete any response to an environmental change ; in general, such a response is brought about by groups of neurones subserving separate functions, the propagated disturbances initiated in one being passed, by way of the *synapse*, to new, second-order, neurones, which may then pass the impulse on to others, until finally the neurone making relation with the effector organ, *e.g.*, a muscle fibre, is activated. If it is realised that a single neurone may make direct synaptic relations with many other neurones, the complexity of the organisation of the nervous system becomes evident, and the difficulties of physiological study, in terms of the passage of impulses, become only too manifest. In the present treatment of the subject we shall therefore confine attention to those experiments in which there is reason to believe that the pathway is simple, so that, for this purpose, it is necessary only to indicate the neuronal organisation at its lowest level, the nervous pathway involved in the simple *spinal reflex*, and the motor pathway in the *visceral reflexes* mediated by a sympathetic ganglion. Fig. 196*a* is the time-

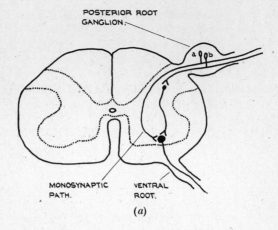

(a)

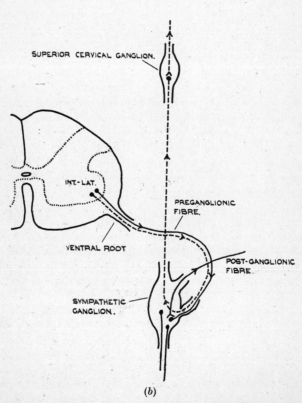

(b)

FIG. 196. (a) Illustrating simple reflex arcs ; a sensory fibre, with its cell body in the posterior root ganglion, may synapse directly with a motor neurone in the ventral grey matter, or indirectly by way of an intercalary neurone. (b) Illustrating the sympathetic outflow. The axons of sympathetic motor neurones emerge by way of the ventral root and enter a ganglion of the sympathetic chain where they may or may not synapse immediately.

honoured representation of the reflex arc ; a sensory nerve, with its cell body located in the *dorsal root ganglion*, has two processes, the peripheral axon[1] ramifying at its termination in the skin, the ramifications becoming specialised to respond to a definite stimulus, *e.g.*, of touch, or heat, and called *receptors*. The central end enters the spinal cord (a group of these fibres constituting the *posterior root*) and makes relations with numerous other neurones ; in the simplest monosynaptic type of reflex—*e.g.*, the myotatic—the impulses may be effectively transmitted directly to the motor neurones, the cell-bodies of which are in the *ventral horn*, their axons passing out at the motor, or *anterior, root* to end in a number of muscle fibres.

The *autonomic* division of the nervous system is concerned with the activation of effectors not under voluntary control, *e.g.*, the pupil of the eye ; the motor pathway of the *sympathetic* division is mediated by motor neurones with their cell bodies in the intermedio-lateral grey matter of the cord ; their axons pass out in the anterior root with the voluntary motor fibres already described, but leave these to pass into one of a chain of ganglia, the *sympathetic chain*, where they may or may not relay, *i.e.*, make synaptic relations with post-ganglionic nerve cells. Thus fibres to the eye (Fig. 196*b*) pass *through* the *stellate ganglion* to synapse in a ganglion higher up, the *superior cervical ganglion*. Fibres to the heart, on the other hand, relay in the stellate ganglion. The motor pathway for the *parasympathetic* is by way of special nerves, most of them emanating directly from the brain, the so-called *cranial nerves* ; they relay in ganglia closely related to the organs they innervate, *e.g.*, the *ciliary ganglion* in the orbit of the eye. Hence in the autonomic system we have to distinguish, in the motor path, between *pre-* and *post*-ganglionic fibres, and in any ganglion we must find out which pre-ganglionic fibres synapse and which pass straight through. The modes of connection between neurones are so various that it is impossible to speak of a typical synapse ; as we have seen, the impulses in a neurone are carried by the axon away from the cell-body or soma ; the axon generally ramifies at its termination, its branches making contact with the dendrites or soma of the post-synaptic neurone. Frequently this contact is made by *terminal boutons*, the fine ramifications ending in swellings which are apposed to the post-synaptic neurone, as in Fig. 197, which gives some idea of the large number of boutons, derived from many axons, that may make relation with a single neurone (*e.g.*, some neurones have 1,200–1,800 boutons which may occupy some 38 per cent. of the cell surface). In other cases a single axonic termination may occupy a large proportion of the synaptic surface (Fig. 197) whilst in still other cases the ramifications of a single axon may constitute the only inter-neuronal connection.[2] In general, we may take it that a post-synaptic neurone receives, or is capable of receiving, impulses transmitted from the axons of several pre-synaptic fibres. If the pre-synaptic fibre is myelinated, its sheath terminates a short distance from

---

[1] Actually a dendrite (p. 377).

[2] Such a system is still described as *polysynaptic*, *e.g.*, by Bodian (1942), since each termination of an axon branch constitutes a synapse ; by a monosynaptic connection is meant a junction involving a single contact, as for example, in certain invertebrate synapses (p. 458).

the contact surface ; moreover, according to the polarisation optical studies of Chinn (1938), there seems to be no equivalent layer over the perikaryon and axon hillock of motor cells, so that the contact between bouton and soma is intimate. The evidence for a protoplasmic discontinuity at the junction is mainly physiological ; histological techniques appear to confirm the viewpoint since the neurofibrils of the axon terminal show no

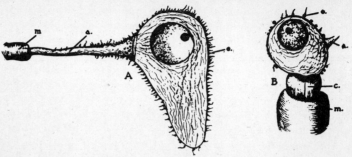

Fig. 197. Synapses. A, large motor-type cell from the reticular formation of the goldfish showing relatively uniform distribution of homogeneous boutons, *e*, on soma and proximal part of axon, *a.* × 960. This type of synaptic system is the most common in the vertebrate nervous system and is characteristic of motor neurones and intermediate neurones. B, cell of reticular formation of the goldfish showing, in addition to small boutons, a single large club ending, *c*, of a myelinated axon, *m.* × 960. (Bodian, after Lorente de Nó. *Physiol. Rev.*)

evidence of continuing into the post-synaptic cell ; a synaptic membrane, or *synaptilemma*, may be demonstrated by suitable staining.

The Neuromuscular Junction

Structure. The detailed structure of the voluntary muscle fibre will be discussed later in relation to its contractile properties (p. 479) ; we may note

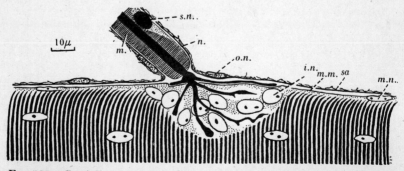

Fig. 198. Semi-diagrammatic view of motor end-plate. The outlines are from a single plate, and the proportions are correct but details have been adjusted to show the relationships clearly. The main nerve fibre and sarcolemma are seen in optical section, but the rest of the plate covers the surface of the muscle fibre. *s.n.*, Schwann nucleus ; *n*, neurilemma ; *m*, myelin ; *o.n.*, outer end-plate nucleus ; *i.n.*, inner end-plate nucleus ; *m.m.*, muscle (sarcoplastic) membrane ; *sa.*, sarcolemma ; *m.n.*, muscle (subsarcolemmal) nucleus. (Gutmann & Young. *J. Anat.*)

here that it is a long cell, containing many nuclei, with fibrillæ embedded in a matrix of sarcoplasm, the whole being surrounded by a connective tissue-type of membrane, the sarcolemma, the functional plasma membrane lying beneath this. The junction between the fibre and its motor nerve fibre is described as the *end-plate* (Fig. 198) ; it is a granular cytoplasmic mass lying beneath the sarcolemma and containing numerous nuclei ; the connective tissue sheath of the nerve fibre (*endoneurium*) joins that of the muscle fibre ; and the axon cylinder, either just before, or on reaching the end-plate protoplasm, branches into smaller twigs which proceed towards the periphery of the end-plate. The fibrils are probably not embedded within the protoplasmic mass of the end-plate but lie on its surface. According to the recent studies of Couteaux (1944) the end-plate has a mixed embryonic origin, the tissues immediately adjacent to the

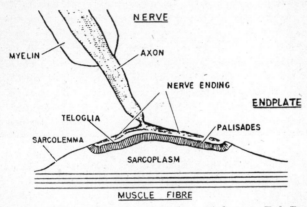

Fig. 199. The neuromuscular junction. (Acheson. *Fed. Proc.*)

nerve fibrils being derived from the Schwann sheath. This material stains specifically with Janus Green (a mitochondrial stain), and appears like a palisade of small rods (Fig. 199) touching what appears to be a limiting membrane around the nerve fibrils. As yet the exact relationships of the nerve fibrils and end-plate, on the one hand, and the end-plate and muscle fibrils, on the other, are quite unknown.

Neuromuscular Block. The neuromuscular junction and the synapse have been recognised as functionally important regions for many years, and are generally considered to be sites especially liable to the action of drugs, of anoxia [1] and fatigue. The phenomenon of block, with repetitive stimulation, is an excellent example ; the tension developed by a muscle, stimulated through its nerve, gradually falls off and finally attains a negligible value ; the failure is due to transmission block since action potentials are still carried by the nerve, and direct stimulation of the muscle reveals

---

[1] This hypersensitivity may be illusory, at any rate in so far as O_2-lack is concerned. Bronk, Larrabee & Gaylor have shown that fibres passing straight through the stellate ganglion, *i.e.*, not making synapses, fail to conduct during O_2-lack at the same time as post-synaptic fibres. According to Posternak & Larrabee, $CHCl_3$ and Et_2O have a preferential blocking action at the synapse, whilst the reverse pertains for alcohols, the axons being the more sensitive.

that it is still excitable. A less severe form of this block has been recently investigated by Brown & Burns, who found that the decrease in tension was due, as had been considered, to the " falling out " of muscle fibres from the contractile process, the tension developed by the whole muscle decreasing in consequence. The matter was, however, not quite so simple as at first thought, since a sudden transition to direct stimulation often caused a rise in tension above the maximal value developed by indirect stimulation.[1] The explanation for this was found to be that, after transmitting a certain number of impulses, a given myoneural junction would block, and thus rest its associated muscle fibre ; after failing to transmit a certain number of impulses, it would recover its ability to transmit and would excite its fibre, which then contracted far more strongly than before. Fatigue, therefore, is a complex process and by no means necessarily due to neuromuscular block ; it will be evident that the junction exerts a protective action on its muscle fibre, preventing it from being over-stimulated ; this view was developed by Göpfert & Schaefer, who have shown that a frog nerve responds faithfully to stimulation with frequencies as high as 100–150 per sec. ; if the frequency is increased still further, the height of the action potential falls as a result of the failure of fibres to respond to each stimulus. The muscle, stimulated directly, responds faithfully to frequencies up to 60–80 per sec. With indirect stimulation, on the other hand, the maximal frequency is only about 50 per sec. The end-plate thus limits the extent to which a muscle may be stimulated, and is regarded by Göpfert & Schaefer as an organ which protects the muscle fibre from over-stimulation. The phenomenon of *Wedensky inhibition* is related to the limit imposed on the frequency of transmission by the end-plate. If the nerve, of a nerve-muscle preparation, is stimulated with a high frequency, the action potential recorded from the muscle (or its tension) decreases progressively with time, a fact indicating the falling out of fibres from the response. If the frequency of stimulation is suddenly reduced, the action potentials rapidly reacquire their original height. Wedensky inhibition is thus a reduction in the maximal frequency to which a nerve-muscle preparation may respond.

Chemical Transmission

Although the problems of nerve-voluntary muscle excitation have enjoyed priority of place in the field of physiological investigation, the ideas of chemical transmission grew out of an observation on the involuntary system. In 1921 Loewi passed saline solution through one isolated beating frog's heart into another ; stimulation of the vagus supplying the first heart caused inhibition of this heart, as expected, but after a short time the second heart was also inhibited. A substance, called the *Vagusstoff*, was apparently liberated at the nerve endings in the heart ; since this substance had the same effect on another heart as that caused by

---

[1] Steiman (1943) had already observed this phenomenon in a single-fibre nerve-muscle preparation ; fatigue was associated with a gradually diminishing tension until the fibre failed to respond ; when it responded again, the contraction became larger, the larger the intervening " rest period."

vagus stimulation, it could be concluded that the nerve acted on the heart by liberating this substance at its endings. As a result of the earlier pharmacological studies of Dale, it became easy to identify the Vagusstoff as *acetylcholine*. Since then, it has been shown that a large group of autonomic fibres, *e.g.*, those causing constriction of the pupil and accommodation, secretion of the salivary glands, constriction of the bronchi, contraction of the walls of the alimentary canal, etc., transmit the effects of their electrical impulses to the effector organ through the liberation of acetylcholine. This substance is broken down locally, during and after its action, by *cholinesterase*,[1] an enzyme which is specifically inhibited by the drug *eserine*. All these nervous actions may, therefore, be mimicked by treatment of the effector with acetylcholine ; such an action of the drug is called a " *muscarine action*," since muscarine has essentially similar effects. With few exceptions, the action of acetylcholine on the effectors of the parasympathetic autonomic system are abolished by atropine ; this drug does not prevent acetylcholine from being formed at the nerve terminals, but prevents it from acting on the effector cell. Eserine, on the other hand, by specifically inhibiting the enzymatic hydrolysis of acetylcholine, potentiates the action of the effector substance or of the nerve.

The classical researches of Elliott and of Cannon showed that another group of effectors, mainly controlled by the sympathetic division of the autonomic system, were stimulated by the liberation of a substance similar to, if not identical with, *adrenaline*, a hormone secreted by the suprarenal gland. For example, the effect of stimulating the accelerator nerves to the heart may be mimicked by intravenous injection of adrenaline. Since the original division of the autonomic system into parasympathetic fibres, liberating acetylcholine, and sympathetic fibres, liberating adrenaline or *sympathin*, has turned out to be inaccurate,[2] it is now customary to describe nerve fibres as either *cholinergic* or *adrenergic*, according to whether their action may be mimicked by acetylcholine or adrenaline.

The responses in these effectors controlled by the autonomic system are slow, so that the concept of a chemical process intervening between the more rapid electrical ones was not considered an insuperable difficulty in the way of acceptance of the chemical mediator hypothesis ; moreover, the fact that the effects of a single nerve volley could persist for some time (several seconds in the case of vagal inhibition of the heart), and that this persistence could be extended by the application of eserine, rather favoured the hypothesis.

Transmission of the nerve impulse through a synapse or myoneural junction is a very rapid process, the delay-time being of the order of one msec. or less ; nevertheless the existence of this delay, together with

[1] Mendel & Rudney have shown that plasma and tissues contain a non-specific esterase, *pseudo-cholinesterase* ; true cholinesterase, specific for acetylcholine, may be separated from the non-specific enzyme.

[2] For example, the sweat glands are innervated by the sympathetic, whilst the nerve-endings apparently liberate acetylcholine. We may note that von Euler has extracted a substance from a number of tissues with an action similar to adrenaline, but differing from it in several important respects. It would seem to be *nor-adrenaline*, a closely related substance. The literature on the subject is growing rapidly.

the specific effects of certain drugs, notably nicotine and curare, on the junctional region, marks the latter off as a possible site for something more than purely depolarisation phenomena in the conduction process. Nicotine, in small doses, was shown by Langley to have a stimulating action on ganglionic synapses, and to cause a muscle to contract if applied to the end-plate region, the effect becoming weaker the farther removed the point of application from the end-plate. Recent work has shown that both the ganglionic synapse, and the end-plate of voluntary muscle, are activated by acetylcholine, so that it is customary to speak of the *nicotine action* of acetylcholine on these structures, to distinguish it from the muscarine action on *autonomic effectors*. The demonstration that acetylcholine is normally present in ganglia, and that it is liberated on stimulating the preganglionic fibres (Witanowski ; Chang & Gaddum), has placed the position of acetylcholine as an important element in the transmission of impulses through ganglionic synapses beyond question.[1] The extension of the hypothesis to include neuromuscular transmission in the vertebrate voluntary effectors has met with more opposition, but to-day even those, who at one time were the most ardent supporters of an electrical theory of neuromuscular transmission, concede that one stage in the process involves the liberation of acetylcholine. Dale, Feldberg & Vogt showed that stimulation of the motor nerve to perfused voluntary muscle liberates acetylcholine into the venous effluent. The effects of intravenous injections of acetylcholine are obscured by its rapid destruction by the enzyme cholinesterase in the blood and tissues ; however, Brown, Dale & Feldberg showed that if the injection is made by way of the artery immediately supplying the muscle, very small quantities, *e.g.*, $2\mu g.$, will cause a contraction as strong as that obtained by maximal nerve stimulation.[2] Curarine, in sufficient doses, completely blocks transmission from nerve to muscle, leaving the excitability of both tissues unaffected ; it does not, however, affect the liberation of acetylcholine at the end-plate, so that its action must consist in preventing the liberated acetylcholine from exerting its normal effects on the muscle tissue ; it is thought that it competes with acetylcholine for the active groups in the end-plate substance. The response to injected acetylcholine is essentially similar to that evoked by repeated nerve stimulation, consisting of a brief asynchronous tetanus with typical all-or-nothing spikes at a frequency of some 200/sec. (Brown, 1937) ; eserine may modify the response to a single nerve volley, from a single twitch to a waning tetanus of the muscle fibres ; moreover, it causes a muscle to twitch spontaneously.[3]

[1] According to Bülbring, the superior cervical ganglion may also be activated by low concentrations of adrenalin ; larger doses have an inhibitory action.

[2] Amphibian voluntary muscle and denervated mammalian muscle are very sensitive to acetylcholine, so that treatment with this drug generally causes the muscle to go into a *contracture*, *i.e.*, the activation of the normal contractile mechanism in which tension, heat and lactic acid are produced, but in which conduction of the mechanical response and a wave of action potential are missing (Gasser). This is probably due, as Brown pointed out, to the relatively smaller amounts of the cholinesterase in these tissues than in normal mammalian muscle.

[3] The effects of eserine are complicated ; it causes the accumulation of acetylcholine, the excitatory effect of which passes into inhibition if the concentration becomes too great ; *vide*, *e.g.*, Cowan, 1940.

We shall see that a single volley of impulses, that is, a single shock applied to all the nerve fibres, in the vertebrate motor nerve produces only a single action potential, and contraction, in the muscle fibres supplied by it ; if transmission is effected by the depolarising action of the liberated acetylcholine in the end-plate region, in order that it should not cause a second depolarisation it must be removed within the refractory period of the muscle fibre, *i.e.*, within about 5 msec. in the frog and about 2 msec. in the mammal. If the acetylcholine theory is correct, therefore, we may expect the rate of hydrolysis of acetylcholine to be rapid. A correlation between the concentration of cholinesterase in any region and the number of end-plates might also be expected ; but we must appreciate that the acetylcholine is liberated in highly localised regions, and it could easily be that diffusion alone would be adequate to lower its concentration sufficiently to render it ineffective ; furthermore, it need not necessarily be removed by hydrolysis, but could be restored to the inactive form from which it had been liberated if, as is thought, it exists as an inactive complex in the resting nerve terminals.

Cholinesterase and Neuromuscular Transmission

The concentration of cholinesterase in muscle as a whole is low ; hence, if the local concentration in the nerve endings were the same as in the muscle generally, the necessary rate of hydrolysis of the liberated acetylcholine would be some 50,000 times too slow to permit its complete elimination during the refractory period ; thus the concentration at the end-plate must be some 50,000 times higher than elsewhere in the muscle.[1] Exact determination of the cholinesterase activity at the end-plate has not been carried out, but Marnay & Nachmansohn have established a definite correlation between the activity in different regions of the frog's sartorius muscle and the number of end-plates. They calculated that at a single end-plate 8.10^9 molecules of acetylcholine could be split during the refractory period ; this compares with Acheson's estimate of 10^{-16} g. liberated per impulse, *i.e.*, about 1.10^5 molecules. Perhaps the most striking result of Nachmansohn's investigations on cholinesterase distribution was the demonstration of the huge quantities of this enzyme in the electric organs of certain fishes.

Electric Organs. The electric organ is highly developed in *Electrophorus electricus*, representing a very large proportion [2] of the animal's tissue and capable of a discharge of 400 volts. The four organs in this species have been accurately described recently by Couceiro & Akerman ; they are large masses of tissue divided into compartments, or *electroplaxes*, by connective tissue laminæ running longitudinally and transversely (Fig.

[1] Recently Koelle & Friedenwald have developed a histochemical method for localising cholinesterase activity, based on the hydrolysis of a sulphur derivative of acetylcholine in the presence of a copper salt and subsequent precipitation of the copper as sulphide. Their published microphotographs reveal a dense accumulation of cholinesterase at the end-plates.

[2] All the viscera of the animal are under the bones of the skull and the first 20 vertebræ, whilst the electric organs occupy the space under the remaining 230 vertebræ ; it is therefore possible to keep an *Electrophorus* alive after amputation of its posterior four-fifths.

200, Pl. X) with dimensions of $30 \times 1 \cdot 8 \times 0 \cdot 1$ to $14 \times 2 \times 1 \cdot 9$ mm. according to their position. The electroplax is a syncytium containing many nuclei, and is activated by a nerve fibre. It has been suggested that the electroplax is equivalent to the end-plate of a voluntary muscle fibre, *i.e.*, it is an end-plate without a muscle. The arrangement of large groups of electroplaxes each capable, on activation, of establishing a potential in relation to inactive portions of the tissue, is essentially equivalent to a voltaic pile, *i.e.*, a group of cells in series ; thus very high potential differences between one end of the organ and the other may be established when the organ discharges (figures as high as 800 volts have been recorded in *Gymnotus electricus* ; in the ray, however, the shock is very weak, just a few volts). Discharges occur rapidly, at rates from 100 to 200 per sec., and all the time-relations of the discharge, *i.e.*, duration, latency, refractory period, are similar to those involved in the action potentials of nerve, so that the electric organ is excellent material for an experimental study of the end-plate. In Table XXXIV, from Nachmansohn & Meyerhof, the maximal discharge, number of plates in series, and the quantity of acetylcholine split by the organ in 1 sec. are shown for three different species of electric organ :—

TABLE XXXIV

Correlation of Voltage, Number of Plates, and Capacity to Split Acetylcholine in Electric Organs (Nachmansohn & Meyerhof, 1941).

Species	Maximum Discharge (Volts)	No. of Plates in Series	mg. AcCh Split by Organ in 1 sec.
Raja undulata . . .	1–3	60–80	0·5–1·0
Torpedo marmorata . .	30–60	400–500	50–100
Gymnotus electricus . .	300–800	5,000–6,000	500–1,000

The parallelism is striking ; moreover, the actual concentration of acetylcholine in the electric organ is of the same order of magnitude as that estimated to be present in the frog's end-plate.

Studies on the distribution of cholinesterase in synapses told essentially the same story, the concentration in the nerve being considerably less than that in the ganglion where it made its synapse ; degeneration of the pre-ganglionic fibres caused a loss of up to 60 per cent. of the activity of the ganglion, a fact suggesting that this proportion is present in the nerve fibres themselves, the remainder being extracellular, and possibly acting as a barrier to prevent the diffusion of acetylcholine away from the synaptic region. An extension of this work to the distribution of cholinesterase in the axon of nerve, however, produced results which appear, at first sight, surprising ; the nerve fibre definitely contains cholinesterase, but in the giant axon of the squid, where a separation of axoplasm and sheath is feasible, the great bulk of the enzyme appears to be in the latter structure. According to Nachmansohn, the high concentration in the end-plate and synapse is due only to the much increased surface-area of the nerve fibres

PLATE X

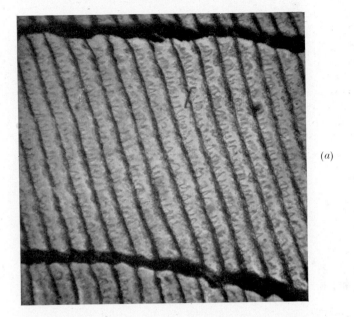

(a)

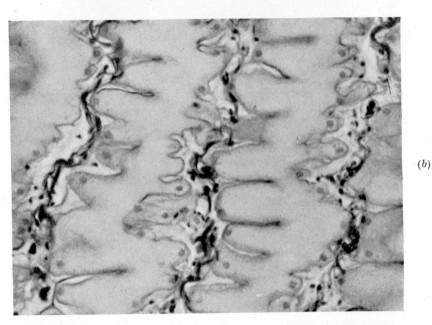

(b)

FIG. 200. The electric organ of *Electrophorus electricus.* (*a*) Low power microphotograph of a vertical section cut parallel to the lateral surface of the principal organ. The two thick lines running horizontally are portions of the longitudinal septa, whilst the thin lines are the transverse septa ; the electroplaxes thus appear as rectangles, being cut transversely. × 46. (*b*) High power microphotograph, showing part of two electroplaxes which are cut transversely. × 500.

[*To face p.* 444.

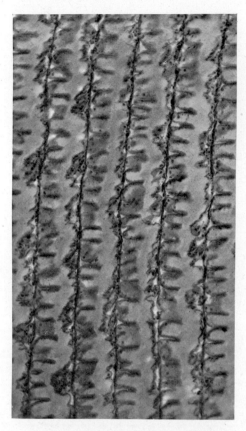

FIG. 200(c). Section parallel to the longitudinal septa, cutting the electroplaxes longitudinally. × 120. In all sections the anterior surface of the electroplax is on the left. (Couceiro & Akerman. *Anais Acad. Bras. de Ciencias.*)

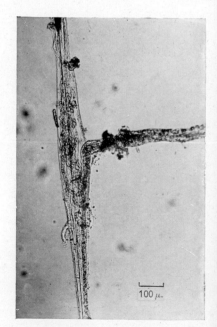

FIG. 212. Photomicrograph of frog muscle spindle, showing capsule, intrafusal muscle fibres and nerve supply. (Katz. *J. Physiol.*)

following their ramification in these organs ; Nachmansohn has argued further that the presence of cholinesterase in the nerve sheath indicates that the conduction of impulses involves the liberation of acetylcholine, in essentially the same way as during conduction through the synapse. In support of this contention he cites the action of the powerful inhibitor of cholinesterase, di-isopropylfluorophosphate (DFP) which, according to his studies, blocks transmission in nerve in proportion to the degree to which it inactivates cholinesterase. This last point will be taken up later ; so far as transmission across junctions is concerned, we may conclude that there is overwhelming evidence in favour of the intervention of acetylcholine at one stage, although it should be noted that the synapses to which this statement applies are those localised in the autonomic ganglia ; the evidence for a humoral transmission in all the synapses of the spinal cord and brain is by no means conclusive.

Electrical Aspects of Neuromuscular Transmission

Up till very recently many physiologists have been inclined to regard the process of neuromuscular transmission as a purely electrical phenomenon, the condition at the junction being represented as similar to that in a partially blocked nerve. Thus Hodgkin's and Tasaki's studies have shown that a discontinuity, consisting of several millimetres of inactive nerve, can be bridged by the extrinsic potential moving ahead of an active region. The objection that the delay at the junction must represent the interposition of some chemical reaction was met by pointing first to the fact that the delay is, in effect, very short, perhaps no longer than the duration of the rising phase of the action potential, and secondly by the studies of Erlanger & Gasser on partial block by anodic polarisation, and of Hodgkin on the new-born impulse. Under conditions of partial block, or where the stimulus is only just liminal, quite long latencies are found as a result of the slow build-up of the active state. Moreover, the phenomena of one-way transmission, temporal summation (or recruitment) could all be simulated in nerve axons under suitable conditions (Erlanger, 1939). Nevertheless, as we have seen above, the tendency now is to consider the liberation of acetylcholine at the end-plate as a first step in the process of transmission, the effect of curarine being attributed to its competition with acetylcholine for the active points of the end-plate tissue. It is important, however, that we should have an exact picture of the electrical events taking place at the end-plate during transmission. Because of the many factors involved, namely the electrotonic action of the arriving nerve impulse, the chemical reactions involved in the liberation and hydrolysis of acetylcholine, and the depolarisation process leading to the initiation of a new spike in the muscle, any measured electrical events are rather more complex than those we have so far considered. For this reason the position is still far from clear, and the recorded results of experimentation are often so complex as to make it very difficult for the ordinary reader to maintain any clear idea of their probable significance.

Neuromuscular Delay. Because of the anatomical characteristics of most muscles, the action potential, recorded from electrodes on the intact surface, is generally tri-phasic ; if one electrode is placed in a localised region where the end-plates are concentrated,[1] and the nerve stimulated, the muscle spike is sharply defined and diphasic, indicating that activity begins immediately under the electrode on the end-plates. A shock applied to the nerve very close to the muscle, in the cat, evoked an action potential after a delay of 0·75–0·85 msec. This delay represents the time of conduction through the remaining intra-muscular course of the nerve twigs, together with the " neuro-muscular delay." Eccles & O'Connor estimated that, in the cat, the delay cannot be more than 0·6–0·7 msec., a similar figure having been estimated for the extra-ocular muscles by Lorente de Nó. In the frog's sartorius the delay is longer, 1·1–1·5 msec.

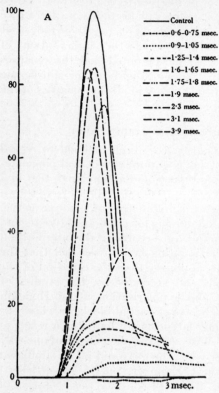

End-plate Potentials. When the nerve supplying the cat's soleus muscle is stimulated with two shocks in rapid succession, a variety of results are obtained at electrodes arranged to record the changes of potential in the end-plate region. The first shock always produces, of course, a diphasic spike ; if the interval between successive shocks is less than 1·9 msec., the contraction of the muscle fibres caused by the first shock is unaffected, and no second muscle spike is recorded ; a refractory condition of the nerve-muscle preparation therefore persists for 1·9 msec. The absolutely refractory period of nerve lasts only 0·4–0·5 msec., so that the failure of the second volley to produce a muscle spike is due to the refractory condition of the muscle or end-plate. If we allow for the diminished rate of refractory condition, we may state that there is a period from about 0·7 to as long as 1·8 msec., after the first

Fig. 201. Time courses of the potential changes, expressed as percentage of the maximum spike potential, produced by a second nerve volley at the indicated intervals after the first volley. The continuous line shows the spike potential set up by a single nerve volley. (Eccles & O'Connor. *J. Physiol.*)

conduction of nerve in its relatively

[1] In the cat's soleus or peroneus tertius this may be done by cutting down nerve fibres to the muscle, leaving intact only a minute twig ; if this twig is chosen correctly it will be found that the muscle fibres innervated by it form a discrete superficial strip, whose end-plates are restricted to a region close to the site of entry of the nerve. In the frog, the sartorius provides a similar type of preparation, most of the muscle fibres being innervated at two or several discrete end-plate zones. (Eccles & O'Connor ; Katz & Kuffler.)

nerve volley, during which a second volley fails to set up a propagated disturbance in any muscle fibre ; moreover, only if the delay is 2·5 msec. can *all* the fibres in the muscle respond. Provided that the delay between volleys is greater than 0·65–1·0 msec., however, the second volley is not entirely without effect on the end-plate region, a potential being recorded which has been called the *end-plate potential*. In the cat it rises after a delay of about 0·7 msec., reaches its maximum about 1·5 msec. later, and disappears in about 10 msec. The time-course of this potential seems to be unaffected by the length of the interval between volleys until this is increased beyond about 1·6 msec., although the height of the potential increases progressively. If the delay is 1·6–1·9 msec. a small non-propagated muscle *aborted spike* appears, and any further increase in the delay leads to an ordinary muscle spike. In Fig. 201 the various end-plate potentials, changing in nature from a slow rise,

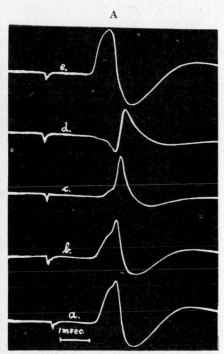

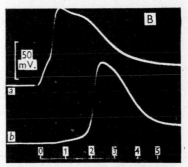

Fig. 202, A. Recording at different positions on a single muscle fibre. (*a*), at the nerve-muscle junction ; *b*, *c*, and *d*, at 80, 230 and 500μ distance from the junction ; *e*, after careful placement of the electrode on the end-plate, no spike action potential is observed. (Kuffler. *J. Neurophysiol.*)

Fig. 202, B. Action potential at the nerve-muscle junction, recorded from the inside of muscle fibre at the nerve-muscle junction (*a*), and 2·5 mm. away (*b*). Time-scale msec. (Fatt & Katz. *J. Physiol.*)

through an "aborted spike" to a true propagated spike are shown. These results were strongly reminiscent of Hodgkin's studies on just subliminal stimuli, and suggested to Eccles & O'Connor that the build-up of the end-plate potential was the first stage in the initiation of the muscle spike.

The end-plate potentials, discovered in this way, are characteristic of the refractory condition of the end-plate ; nevertheless there is good reason to believe that a similar potential rises during the establishment of any spike in muscle, although its time-course can only be deduced indirectly, since it is swamped by the actual spike. Kuffler, studying a single isolated end-plate, presented records suggesting that the end-plate potential in normal muscle may be regarded as something distinct from the rising phase of the action potential taking place in this region. Thus in Fig. 202A the potential changes recorded when the leading electrode was at different points near, and at, the junction are shown ; in *a* the electrode is very close to the junction, and the rising phase has two components, an initial end-plate potential lasting 0·5 msec. and a continuation of this, after a slight delay, which represents the true spike. As the electrode is moved away (*b–d*) the component of end-plate potential represents a smaller contribution, with a slower rate of rise, but no diminution in the latent period ; it thus appears to be an electrotonic spread of electrical events taking place at the end-plate itself. When the electrode is exactly placed on the end-plate, no true spike is obtained (*e*) ; instead, the whole rise has the characteristics of an end-plate potential, although its diphasic nature, and steep fall, indicate that the change has been propagated through the muscle as a spike. When the spike is over, a residual and slowly declining negativity persists, representing the decline of the end-plate potential which definitely outlives the action potential. The method of external recording, as used by Kuffler, does not give the exact time-course of the membrane potential changes at the end-plate, and a more precise indication would be given by the use of a recording electrode inserted directly into the muscle fibre in the manner described by Graham & Gerard and Nastuk & Hodgkin. Very recently Fatt & Katz and Nastuk have recorded end-plate potentials in this manner ; as the upper record of Fig. 202B shows, the potential, recorded exactly at the end-plate, is rather different from the earlier record ; the end-plate potential is manifested as a discrete step, of some 30–55 mV and lasting 0·5 msec. at 20° C., in the development of the action potential, and its persistence, after the muscle spike, is shown as a hump on the descending limb of the record.

Effect of Curarine. Curarine blocks neuromuscular transmission; its effects on the end-plate potential are therefore of great interest ; in Fig. 203 some results of Kuffler on the isolated end-plate are shown ; *a* represents the normal end-plate potential, following on to a spike, in an uncurarised preparation ; *b* to *e* represent progressive effects of curarine, blockage being reached at *e* ; it will be noted that curarine diminishes the initial end-plate potential and progressively lengthens the latent period of the spike. Further increases in dosage of curarine progressively reduce the height of the end-plate potential. If we regard the establishment of a certain critical end-plate potential as a stage in the process of transmission, we may explain the effect of curarine as a progressive lowering of the end-plate potential until it is too small to initiate a propagated impulse in muscle. The fact that block may be obtained without the complete extinction of the end-plate potential makes the curarised nerve-muscle preparation a useful one for the study of the potential, in fact it was first discovered by Göpfert & Schaefer in the curarised frog nerve-muscle preparation ; these authors were inclined to regard it as the electrical sign of events following the liberation of acetylcholine. Eccles, Katz & Kuffler have made an exhaustive study of the end-plate potential in curarised muscle ; their results, which indicate that the spread of potential is electrotonic in nature, may now be briefly described. The spatial decrement of the end-plate potential is considerable, so that if the leading electrode is moved just a few mm. from the end-plate zone no potential is recorded. This decremental phenomenon is strongly reminiscent of the simple electrotonic effects of an applied cathode, and a careful study shows that the decrement is exponential, decaying to half in 0·5–0·9 mm. ; this compares with 2–3 mm. for frog's medullated nerve, 0·5 mm. for crab's nerve and approximately 1 mm. for frog's sartorius muscle.[1]

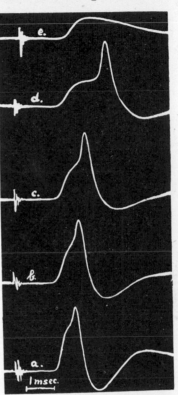

FIG. 203. Effects of curarine on the potentials, recorded at the end-plate region of a single fibre nerve-muscle preparation, in response to nerve stimulus. *a*, Before application of curarine ; *b, c,* and *d*, during progressive curarisation, show the diminution of the initial end-plate potential and the progressive lengthening of the spike latent period ; *e*, pure end-plate potential, no spike being set up. (Kuffler. *J. Neurophysiol.*)

So far as latency is concerned, there is little to distinguish the spike from the end-plate potential ; the much slower rate of extinction indicates a passive decay of electrotonus ; it has a time-constant similar to that for the electrotonic potential of muscle (10 msec. for the frog) and characteristic of the α-excitability of muscle. The analogy between the declining phase of the end-plate potential and a simple electrotonic decay is further emphasised by the negligible effect of temperature on the declining phase. The duration of the rising phase, however, is lengthened nearly three-fold by a decrease of 10° C. This result strongly suggests that the potential, as established, is purely electrotonic, *i.e.*, it involves no " activity " of the end-plate region. The high Q_{10} for the rising phase, on the other hand, indicates that the *process of establishment* of the end-plate potential involves more fundamental changes, possibly a chemical reaction. Further confirmation of the electrotonic nature of the end-plate potential is provided by a study of its interaction with spikes arising in the muscle itself as a result of " anti-dromic " stimulation.[2] It was found that the anti-

[1] The space constant of an excitable tissue depends in some measure on the duration of the applied potential. The figure of 0·5 mm., given for crab's nerve, applies only to very brief shocks ; under steady-state conditions, the more usual value is 2 mm. (Hodgkin, 1938, 1947.)
[2] That is, impulses initiated by direct stimulation of the muscle and travelling towards the end-plate.

15

dromic impulse was slightly speeded up by the end-plate potential, a result to be expected since the extrinsic potential, ahead of the active region of the action potential, meets tissue with excitability that has been increased by the depolarisation. The "foot" of the anti-dromic spike summed with the end-plate potential, whilst the later phases were unaffected ; this, also, is understandable if the end-plate potential is regarded as an electrotonic potential ; the foot of the spike represents only an electrotonic build-up due to the advancing wave of activity, and should therefore sum with another electrotonic potential. In the decaying phase of the action potential, the membrane resistance is broken down (p. 386) and only slowly re-establishes itself ; in this condition electrotonic potentials must leak away rapidly, so that the fact that the end-plate potential barely affects the declining phase confirms its electrotonic character. The fact that the end-plate potential survives the spike, on the

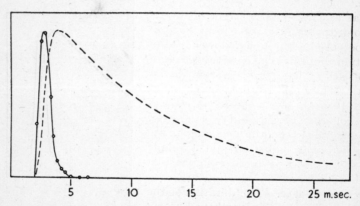

Fig. 204.   End-plate potential and transmitter action.   Broken line represents the end-plate potential of frog's sartorius at 17·5° C., with a time-constant for decay of 9·8 msec.   Full line represents the probable course of the "transmitter action."   Ordinates in arbitrary units.   Abscissæ : Time after nerve stimulus.   (Eccles, Katz & Kuffler.   *J. Neurophysiol.*)

other hand, indicates that the *cause* of the end-plate potential continues to operate, in the same way that an applied catelectrotonus reappears after the passage of a spike.

It is all very well, however, to describe the end-plate potential as a manifestation of electrotonus ; this still begs the question of the factors operating to establish it in the first place.   Some hint of the " transmitter process " may be obtained by a mathematical analysis of the observed rate of decay ; if a given potential decays exponentially at a certain rate, then it is easy to calculate how rapidly it would have to be established, if it is assumed that during the process of establishment the same decay process is taking place.   Fig. 204 represents the result of such an analysis ; it will be seen that a certain *transmitter action* takes place over a period of some 5 msec.   A study of the effect of reduced temperature on the end-plate potential suggests that the transmitter action, deduced in the same way, is very considerably reduced in magnitude but extended in time, a phenomenon that could be best explained on the basis of a chemical reaction, *i.e.*, the liberation of acetylcholine at the end-plate.

A study of the changes of impedance in the end-plate region, by Katz, confirms, generally, the idea that the end-plate potential is induced by a relatively brief transmitter action ; the end-plate potential in curarised muscle is associated with a change in impedance similar to that recently shown to occur with subliminal cathodal currents ; the time-course of decay of change of impedance runs an apparently identical course with that for the end-plate potential, or an applied catelectrotonus ; the rising phase of the impedance change, however, is about twice as rapid as that of the end-plate potential and suggests, once again, the existence of some transmitter action, taking place rapidly and leading up to the slower changes recorded as end-plate potentials. This transmitter action could very well be the liberation of acetylcholine, which may be expected to exert a depolarising action on the membrane of the end-plate ; this activity would be reflected immediately in a change of impedance, whilst the change of potential, spreading electrotonically, would probably show a slower time-course.

Facilitation. It has been known for some time that a neuromuscular block may be overcome by repetitive stimulation of the nerve (Adrian & Lucas ; Bremer), the so-called *facilitation* or *recruitment*. If a single nerve volley leaves behind a state of cathodal electrotonus, *i.e.*, increased excitability, it is quite possible that a new volley, arriving soon after, will build the electrotonus even higher, so high, perhaps, as to cause a propagated spike. That this is possible in a curarised nerve-muscle preparation was shown by Eccles, Katz & Kuffler, the critical value of the summed potentials, necessary for the initiation of a propagated spike, being about 2mV. That the effects of summing two stimuli are not a simple addition of electrotonic potentials, however, is shown by the fact that, in the frog, the second stimulus may evoke an end-plate potential twice as high as that evoked by the first, the total potential being three times the normal. The end-plate is therefore in a supernormal phase following the first stimulus, the duration of this supernormality being strongly affected by temperature. Here, again, the analysis of the electrical phenomena brings into prominence changes that may be attributable to chemical reactions going on in the end-plate.

Invertebrate Junctions. We may note, in parenthesis, that in the normal vertebrate nerve-muscle preparation the summation of successive impulses does not occur, in the sense that an impulse reaching the end-plate is rapidly transmitted ; a second impulse, arriving after an initial one, is not [facilitated by the latter. An entirely different state of affairs is found in certain invertebrate systems, *e.g.*, in the anemone *Calliactis parasitica* (Pantin) or the leg muscles of crabs (Pantin ; Katz, 1936). A study of the end-plate potentials in the crab muscles by Katz & Kuffler has shown that summation occurs, such that, with repetitive stimulation, a potential five times as large as that evoked by a single stimulus may be obtained ; moreover, whereas a single stimulus rarely induces an action potential in a muscle fibre, repetitive stimulation does so ; the crustacean

15—2

nerve-muscle system is therefore similar to the curarised vertebrate system, or to the normal vertebrate synapse (p. 454). The similarity to the synapse extends to the phenomenon of inhibition ; thus Marmont & Wiersma showed that, by a suitable timing of impulses conducted along the inhibitory fibre to a crab muscle, a complete relaxation could be induced, the action potential due to the antagonistic fibre (stimulating) being unaffected ; in the vertebrate system, a skeletal muscle cannot be directly inhibited, relaxation being caused by the inhibition of the normal tonic impulses in the motor nerve, *i.e.*, the motor neurones are inhibited by way of synapses in the spinal cord. It is of interest that the inhibiting impulses apparently produce no electrical effect of their own at the end-plates ; if they arrive before the stimulating impulses, they decrease the end-plate potential due to these. If they arrive after, they may still inhibit, presumably by an action on the contractile mechanism (Kuffler & Katz ; Marmont & Wiersma).

Effect of Eserine. Eserine, by poisoning the enzyme cholinesterase, should prolong the action of acetylcholine at the end-plate and therefore, if liberation of this substance does represent the transmitter process, should lengthen the end-plate potential. It was found by Brown, Dale & Feldberg that eserine causes repetitive discharges in cat's muscle in response to single nerve stimuli, whereas in normal preparations a single impulse in the nerve produces only a single response in any fibre ; corresponding with this phenomenon we have a definite increase in height and duration of the end-plate potential following a single nerve volley. The initial spike response is quite unaffected by eserine ; as the dose is increased, the negativity remaining after the spike, which represents the remainder of the end-plate potential, increases until it is so high as to induce a new propagated response ; by recording from both nerve and muscle simultaneously, it could be shown that the additional muscle spikes sometimes occur alone and sometimes are associated with spikes in the nerve. With very high doses of eserine, impulses are discharged spontaneously from nerve terminals, giving rise to the phenomenon of *eserine twitching* (Masland & Wigton).

The broad effects of eserine thus indicate that the end-plate potential is a secondary phenomenon, depending on the depolarising action of a chemical transmitter ; the more detailed effects are, however, complex, especially when the interactions with curarine are studied. Besides lengthening the end-plate potential, eserine brings out a new component which, with repetitive stimulation, may last for several seconds—the *slow wave of end-plate potential.* It is possible that this slow wave represents the gradual spread of acetylcholine along the muscle fibres, depolarising them partially ; in the normal muscle this would be impossible owing to the barrier of cholinesterase which effectually destroys the acetylcholine. Curarine, as we have seen, depresses the normal end-plate potential (Fig. 203) ; in the eserinised preparation its effects are much more striking, the slow wave being completely abolished. These results of Eccles, Katz & Kuffler, together with many others, present a picture of transmission as consisting primarily of the build-up of an electrotonic potential in the specialised end-plate region. This electrotonic potential seems not to lead to an activated condition in the end-plate tissue itself, but rather to induce this, by electrotonic spread, in the neighbouring muscle tissue, thus leading to the propagated spike. The potential in the end-plate is presumably established by acetylcholine. If this view is correct, we may regard the end-plate protoplasm as peculiar, in that it can be depolarised without the change in membrane properties characteristic of *activation*—as described in the nerve or muscle fibre—and in its sensitivity to acetylcholine.

Synaptic Transmission

The study of the neuromuscular junction has revealed that transmission of the nervous impulse is associated with the development of a slow potential which outlasts the individual spike in the end-plate ; the exact analysis of the end-plate potential has indicated the operation of a certain " transmitter action " whose duration may be greatly extended by eserine, so that there is strong presumptive evidence for the importance of acetylcholine in this phase of activity. The synaptic relationship, for example in a ganglion of the sympathetic system, differs from the neuromuscular one in an important respect ; a single post-ganglionic neurone may make synaptic relations with a number of endings from different preganglionic fibres, so that at any given moment the response of the postganglionic neurone must be determined by the influx of impulses from a variety of fibres, all perhaps discharging rapidly at different frequencies. Only if all these incoming impulses were in phase could we expect a discharge of the postganglionic neurone with a frequency corresponding to that in the preganglionic fibres. The concept of a simple transmission of the preganglionic impulse through a postganglionic fibre, in a similar manner to the transmission of a telephone conversation from one subscriber to another by way of an exchange, is thus far too simple ; instead, we must imagine a postganglionic neurone to be bombarded by a variety of impulses which modify its excitatory state ; the response to this bombardment will be characteristic of the neurone, and of the exact temporal and spatial relationships of the individual impulses reaching it. Some neurones may be so constituted that they discharge rhythmically in the absence of any afferent impulses, in which event the arrival of impulses from the preganglionic fibres may inhibit or accelerate this rhythm ; others may respond repetitively to a single impulse, and so on. The important point, therefore, is that the preganglionic discharge probably loses its identity on reaching the synapse, so that the study of the process of transmission resolves itself mainly into an analysis of the events taking place in the postganglionic neurone as the result of arriving impulses. The synapses most amenable to experimental studies are those in the sympathetic ganglia—*e.g.*, the stellate or superior cervical ganglion ; in addition to these, certain synapses in the spinal cord are being studied extensively. Thus, when the sensory nerves of a spinal root are stimulated submaximally, with the animal under fairly deep anæsthesia, the flow of impulses may be confined to a single synapse between sensory nerve and motor nerve [1] (Fig. 196, p. 436) ; by inserting electrodes into the ventral gray matter Eccles has registered " focal potentials " which may be due to activity at this synapse ; alternatively, electrodes may be placed on the ventral root, in which case, as Barron & Matthews have shown, the electrical spread of events taking place in the motor neurones may be recorded.

We may note, first, the essential similarity in function between the end-plate and the synapse. In both there is a " delay " between the arrival of the impulse and its further propagation ; in the sympathetic ganglia studied, this delay has been estimated to be 1–2 msec. (Brown, 1934), but may be as long as 4 msec. or as short as 0·5 msec. (Eccles, 1936). The synapse imposes a one-way character on the process of transmission so that an antidromic discharge is not propagated from the postganglionic to the preganglionic fibres ; the antidromic impulse leaves the whole of the neurone refractory, however, with the result that an immediately following preganglionic impulse may be extinguished at the synapse.

Facilitation. Facilitation and inhibition are marked characteristics of the synaptic process ; facilitation may take two forms, spatial and temporal, in virtue of the multiple innervation of any ganglion cell. Thus Fig. 205 represents the stellate ganglion of the cat, an assembly of neurones making synaptic connection with fibres from the sympathetic trunk, and sending their axons to the heart (inferior cardiac nerve), and other organs. The number of stimulated pre-synaptic fibres may be varied in this preparation by choice of the roots leading to the sympathetic trunk ; the postganglionic discharge is recorded from the inferior cardiac nerve ; and the height of the action potential, thus recorded, is a measure of the number of stimulated postganglionic neurones. Bronk demonstrated spatial summation by measuring the response to stimulating root A, alone, and together with stimulation of root B ; Fig. 206 shows this type of facilitation. It means that, whereas stimulation of root A or B alone failed to excite all the neurones in the ganglion, it nevertheless increased the excitability of those that failed to respond, with the result that the two together caused maximal discharge. The maximum facilitation is obtained when the stimuli are simultaneous, but the state of increased excitability may last as long as 200 msec., passing after this into a state of diminished excitability. If impulses from one group of fibres can facilitate the passage of impulses initiated in another, we may expect that successive impulses in one group of preganglionic fibres should gradually build up an increasing response, *i.e.*, *recruitment* or *temporal summation* should occur. This does indeed happen, but there is a limit to which this build-up can extend ; if the frequency of preganglionic stimulation exceeds about 20/sec. in the stellate ganglion, the height of the postganglionic action potential decreases. A study of the action potentials in single fibres in these circumstances shows that, when the preganglionic stimulation exceeds

---

[1] This statement must not be read too literally ; under the experimental conditions employed by Eccles, for example, large groups of neurones are stimulated, and thus many synapses activated ; what is meant is that the impulses from any fibre pass through only one synapse, namely that connecting it with a motor neurone.

about 20/sec., the frequency of response ceases to follow the frequency of
stimulation ; instead, the single fibres respond at variable rates and so
fail to give a *synchronised* response in the whole nerve ; this dispersion
of the individual action potentials causes a diminished height of the

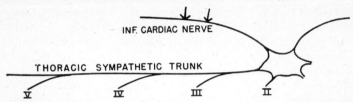

Fig. 205. Diagrammatic sketch of the stellate ganglion of the cat, showing
the preganglionic nerves used for stimulation and the postganglionic nerve
in which the cellular discharge is recorded. (Bronk. *J. Neurophysiol.*)

recorded action potential from the whole nerve. These experiments
of Bronk and his collaborators answer the much debated question
whether the postganglionic response corresponds in frequency with that
of the preganglionic stimulus ; under conditions of electrical stimulation,
all the preganglionic impulses arrive approximately in phase, so that a

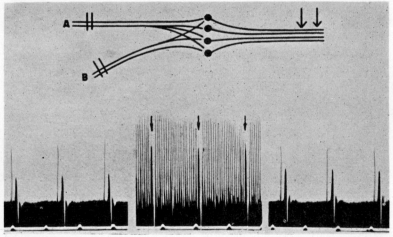

Fig. 206. *Above.* Schematic representation of the innervation of ganglion cells
by fibres from different roots. *Below.* First record : Postganglionic responses to preganglionic volleys in root A. Second record : Arrows
indicate responses to similar volleys during concurrent repetitive
stimulation of root B. Last record : Stimulation of root A alone. Time :
0·2 msec. (Bronk. *J. Neurophysiol.*)

response of the postganglionic neurones with a frequency corresponding to
that of the stimulus is feasible ; Bronk's results show that this does indeed
happen, but only if the frequency of stimulation is below a certain critical
value. The conditions of electrical preganglionic stimulation are, of
course, artificial and, in general, impulses reaching the ganglion from
different fibres are probably out of phase ; it is therefore unlikely that the

frequency of postganglionic response can be identified with the frequency of response in any particular preganglionic fibre.

Acetylcholine. The liberation of acetylcholine in the ganglion, as the result of preganglionic stimulation, has already been referred to, together with the demonstration of the high concentration of cholinesterase necessary for rapid hydrolysis during the refractory state of the postganglionic neurone. The effect of perfusing a ganglion, with acetylcholine in the perfusion fluid, is shown in Fig. 207 from Bronk ; it may be noted that the discharge persists as long as the acetylcholine remains in the perfusion fluid. We may thus take as a fundamental fact the liberation of a chemical transmitter substance at the endings of the preganglionic fibres, capable of activating the postganglionic neurones. It is by no means certain, however, that all the phenomena of spatial and temporal summation, and the action of eserine, are to be attributed to the build-up of unhydrolysed acetylcholine. Thus Larrabee & Bronk have shown a long-lasting facilitation resulting from a few seconds of preganglionic repetitive stimulation, the threshold to impulses in the same fibres being reduced to as little as one-tenth. The threshold to applied

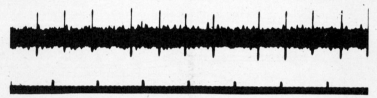

FIG. 207. Effect of perfusing stellate ganglion of cat with 50μg. acetylcholine per ml. of Ringer's fluid. Time : 1 sec. The spikes are recorded from a postganglionic fibre. (Bronk. *J. Neurophysiol.*)

acetylcholine was unaltered, and since this acts, presumably, on the postganglionic neurones we must conclude that the facilitation is due to a phase of hyperexcitability of the preganglionic nerve terminals, *i.e.*, it is *not* due to accumulated acetylcholine. This is confirmed by the observation that the facilitation does not extend to impulses arriving along preganglionic fibres other than those subjected to the original repetitive stimulation. It is necessary, therefore, before assessing the role of acetylcholine in synapses, to discuss the electrical events leading to discharge in the postganglionic fibres.

Synaptic Potentials. The development of negativity at the ganglion, the so-called *synaptic potential*, has been recognised for some time ; thus Barron & Matthews concluded that the wave of negativity—to be distinguished from spike potentials—developing in the motor root of a spinal nerve during activity, was due to the electrotonic spread of a potential developing in the neurones of the motor region of the spinal grey matter. Fig. 208 illustrates the rise in negativity of the lead nearest to the cord, resulting from the entry of afferent impulses by way of the posterior root of the same side. As Barron & Matthews correctly emphasised, the potential is a typical electrotonic one, spreading from the cell bodies of the motor neurones. When the electrotonic potential had built up to a certain critical value, spikes were superimposed on the record, and the picture is thus identical with that of the curarised end-plate discussed earlier, but this time it is the soma of the motor nerve that develops an electrotonic potential which, exceeding a critical value, leads to activation and a propagated spike. Further studies of these *ventral root-potentials* showed that they were diminished (although never altering in sign) when inhibitory impulses entered the cord, so that inhibition of one neurone by another may be due to a reduction of its electrotonic potential. More recent studies of Eccles using a similar locus of recording, and also *focal electrodes*, *i.e.*, electrodes inserted into the nervous tissue of the spinal cord, have generally tended to confirm this view of transmission ; inhibition was actually associated with a reversal of the focal potential, a phenomenon equivalent to anodal polarisation of an axon. Facilitation, on the other hand, appeared to result from the build-up of negative electrotonus (Brooks & Eccles, 1947, 1948 ; Brooks, Eccles & Malcolm, 1948).[1] The finding that eserine and acetylcholine were without apparent effect on these central synaptic potentials, nor yet on facilitation, has led Eccles (1947), and also Bremer, to conclude that, in these synapses at any rate,

Fig. 208. Electrical changes in ventral roots of spinal frog as a result of a stimulus applied continuously to foot. Upward deflection represents negativity of electrode nearest cord. Note rise in negativity leading to the appearance of spikes. (Barron & Matthews. *J. Physiol.*)

transmission is purely electrical. Before considering this mechanism further, however, we may consider the electrical events taking place in sympathetic ganglia.

The potentials in sympathetic ganglia have been thoroughly investigated by Eccles, who has applied essentially similar techniques to those employed in the study of the end-plate potentials. Curarine blocks synaptic transmission ; in this case the synaptic potential is observed as a small wave of negativity which may reach 12 per cent. of the spike-height, and which decays rapidly as the recording lead is moved away from the ganglion along the postganglionic nerve, its magnitude halving at a distance of 1·2 mm. As with the end-plate potential, all the evidence points to the synaptic potential being electrotonic with an exponential course of decay, falling to $1/e$ of its value in 60–80 msec. An analysis of the course of decay, on the basis of Hill's theory of the development of " local potential," suggests that the synaptic potential develops as a result of a relatively brief transmitter action, which reaches its peak in about 3 msec. and lasts for some 10–18 msec. A further analysis of the synaptic potential, during

---

[1] Thus the focal potentials could be separated into the spike of the arriving impulse ; the electrotonic synaptic potential, arising with a delay of 0·3–0·45 msec., and decaying with a half-life of about 1·5 msec. ; and, finally, the spike response of the motor neurone. Facilitation decayed a little more slowly than the synaptic potential.

and after repetitive stimulation of the preganglionic fibres, suggests that there is a progressive lowering of the peak and an increase in the " tail " of the transmitter curve. The increase in the " tail " may be shown to be a result of the summation of the effects of preceding stimuli, and may be due to the accumulation of acetylcholine at, and in the region of, the synapse. It is considered by Eccles that the eventual overcoming of the block in the curarised ganglion by repetitive stimulation (recruitment) is the result of the summation of the " tails " due to successive stimuli. Eserine

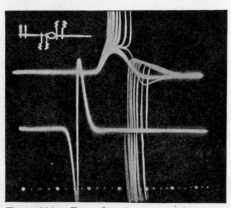

FIG. 209. Record of pre- and post-ganglionic spike potentials from squid synapse during development of fatigue. The stimulating and recording arrangement is shown in the inset, the two vertical lines representing the stimulating electrodes, whilst pairs with terminal zig-zag represent recording electrodes. The records are successive sweeps of a cathode-ray oscillograph, recurring 33 times per sec., a shock being applied at the beginning (left) of each sweep. The upper record represents the post-synaptic spike and, in contrast to the pre-synaptic spike in the lower record, it exhibits fatigue, in that the spike arises later and later from the synaptic potential. Finally the spikes cease, only the synaptic potential being recorded. (Bullock. *J. Neurophysiol.*)

certainly has an effect on the synapse, since very pronounced after-discharges, following a slow rate of stimulation (12/sec.), are observed, whereas only after much more vigorous stimulation is after-discharge observed in the normal stellate ganglion (Bronk). This is easily understandable if eserine causes the accumulation of acetylcholine at the synapse. The effects on the synaptic potential are not striking, however, and it is mainly for this reason that Eccles is inclined to argue in favour of a rapid electrical transmission process, independent of the liberation of acetylcholine, the transmitter substance being mainly concerned with building up the slower phase of the synaptic potential.

Invertebrate Synapse. The vertebrate transmitter systems have been ordered by Eccles in a descending series : neuromuscular junction, peripheral ganglionic synapse, and central synapse,[1] according to the relative importance of acetylcholine. We may, therefore, proceed to consider the possibility of purely electrical transmission ; we may begin with the electrical changes in an invertebrate synapse belonging to the giant fibre system of the squid (Young).

[1] It is probably unsound to speak of " central synapses " without further differentiation ; Feldberg & Vogt have analysed the powers of different regions of the central nervous system to synthesise acetylcholine and have deduced, on the likely assumption that only cholinergic neurones synthesise this transmitter, that transmission at some synapses is mediated by acetylcholine and in others not. The reflex studied by Eccles, involving transmission from a sensory (non-acetylcholine producing) neurone to a motor neurone, does not involve acetylcholine on these grounds ; where impulses are conveyed through a succession of neurones, as, for example, in the sensory pathway to the cerebral cortex, cholinergic and non-cholinergic neurones apparently alternate.

The synapse consists of an apposition of one axon on another (second-order giant fibres on third-order giant fibres) and, in conformity with this apparently simple connection, we find an altogether simple mode of behaviour; in fact, Bullock's studies strongly suggest that the synapse serves no other function than to provide a one-way traffic of impulses, integrative action of the nature of facilitation not being observed. With electrodes on the third-order axon, well-developed synaptic potentials were obtained, leading directly to large spikes; as the junction was fatigued, the spikes arose later and later from the synaptic potentials, as shown in Fig. 209. If fatigue was too great, abortive spikes and, eventually, only synaptic potentials were recorded. The maximal height to which the synaptic potential could rise, before initiating a spike, was some 20 per cent. of the spike-height, which corresponds with the value found by Hodgkin for the transition from local to propagated response in peripheral nerve (p. 404). The actual delay at the synapse was estimated at not less than 0·5 msec., an exceedingly rapid transmission comparable with that found in warm-blooded vertebrate synapses. DFP inhibited transmission through the synapse in the same concentration as that required to block the giant axon, so that there was apparently no specific synaptic effect.

The Ephapse. The results suggest, but do not, of course, prove that the transmission in this synapse is electrical, in an essentially similar manner to transmission across what Arvanitaki calls the *ephapse*, the region of contact between two laterally apposed axons. We have already seen that the impulse in an excited axon may modify considerably the excitability of contiguous axons, in virtue of the flow of current induced by the local negativity in the excited region (p. 411). This flow of current is not sufficient to excite a normal axon, but in fibres whose excitability has been increased, *e.g.*, by treatment with citrate, excitation of one fibre may lead to propagated disturbances in another, especially if the geometrical relationships are suitable. Arvanitaki has applied the general considerations on the changes of potential in the vicinity of an advancing wave of action potential, developed by Bishop (p. 421), to the special case of the ephapse, and has deduced that a relationship indicated by Fig. 210 is favourable for interaction since the final wave of positivity, due to the spike in A, which would prejudice excitation, is avoided at the point P of the " post-ephaptic " axon, B. Stimulation of axon A, under these conditions, led to the development of a non-propagated local potential, *l*, in B, preceded by a positive and negative electrotonus due to current-spread (p. 421). As the excitability of B was increased by treatment with citrate, this response increased until it grew into a true propagated spike (Fig. 210), in a similar manner to the growth of electrotonic potentials into non-propagated and, finally, propagated potentials as described by Hodgkin (p. 406). The " ephaptic delay " was often considerable, as much as 5 msec., and was clearly related to the time required for the local subliminal potential to grow into a propagated response. Frequently the axon B, treated with citrate, developed a spontaneous rhythm of subliminal potential waves; the arrival of an impulse in A, in this case, evoked an action potential in B, the delay depending on the phase of oscillation in which the spike in A arrived. A number of other findings, all with their analogies in true synaptic transmission, led Arvanitaki to point out that the latter process could be a purely electrotonic phenomenon, resulting

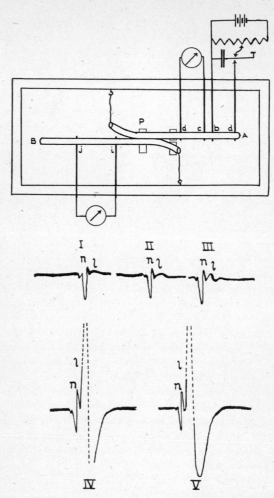

FIG. 210.   The *ephapse*.   Above : Arrangement for stimulating " pre-ephaptic axon," A, and for recording from this and the " post-ephaptic " axon, B. Below : Records from post-ephaptic axon as the excitability is artificially increased by treatment with citrate. The potential wave, indicated by *l*, is the non-propagated local potential from which a spike may arise if the excitability is great enough (IV and V). (Arvanitaki. *J. Neurophysiol.*)

from the spread of extrinsic potential from the advancing spike in the pre-synaptic neurone, in a similar manner to the jumping of blocked regions described by Hodgkin and Tasaki in peripheral nerve. The soma, or dendrite of the recipient neurone, would differ from the axon in a high power of developing graded responses, *i.e.*, local subliminal potentials. The importance of the geometrical relationships between the two fibres led Arvanitaki to the belief that the polarity of the synapse (*i.e.*, the uni-directional nature of conduction) might be related to the peculiar geometrical relationship, pertaining in the synapse, between the pre- and post-synaptic neurones—thus it might be possible for spikes, reaching knob terminals, to induce local potentials which, on summation, would excite, whereas spikes travelling in the reverse direction might, because of the unfavourable spread of current, fail to initiate an anti-dromic spike. Various other artificial synapses have been described, *e.g.*, a region of anodal block [1] by Gasser (1939), and various preparations involving cut nerve trunks by Jasper & Monnier, Renshaw & Therman and Bernhard & Skoglund.[2] These, likewise, have simulated many of the characteristics of synaptic transmission ; the credit for a clear exposition of the possibilities of the ephapse goes, however, to Arvanitaki. Her views have been transposed, in greater detail, by Eccles (1946), to the particular situation of a cylindrical membrane—the axon terminal—in apposition to a large plane membrane—the soma of the postganglionic neurone. According to Eccles, the flow of current, due to an arriving impulse, would result first in a local positivity in the soma, followed by negativity ; the latter would induce a local potential which would spread and summate with other potentials. Inhibition would result from a preponderance of the initial positivity dúe to impulses arriving along inhibitory axons (Brooks & Eccles 1948). Further progress along these lines must await an analysis of the electrical characteristics of the soma of the nerve cell ; some progress in this direction has been made on the giant ganglion cells of *Aplysia*—which may attain 200μ in diameter—the soma of which can be stimulated independently of the axon. Arvanitaki found, for example, that whereas the rheobase for the axon was 7μamp., that for the soma was only 3μamp. Again, Arvanitaki & Chalazonitis recorded with micro-electrodes from different regions of the soma and found a variable activity ; some regions could be quiescent at the same time as others exhibited a rhythmic, subliminal, discharge similar to that observed in invertebrate axons (p. 471). A stimulus, falling on the soma during the rising phase of this rhythmic potential, accentuated the oscillations for several periods, whilst one falling during the descending phase had the opposite effect, so that it could be described as inhibitory.

Chemical Excitation

In concluding this review of the transmission process, we must discuss some of the phenomena connected with the liberation of acetylcholine in more detail. It is not sufficient to say that acetylcholine is liberated at a junctional region, we must ask ourselves how this liberation initiates a new impulse in the effector cell, *i.e.*, how a chemical substance, or a

[1] That is, a region made relatively inexcitable by the passage of a constant current through it, the region considered being near the anode.
[2] In the region of a cut, the excitability of nerve fibres seems to be increased ; impulses travelling along a fibre in a mixed nerve, on reaching the cut, may activate neighbouring fibres, from which spikes may be recorded, travelling back along the trunk, away from the cut.

chemical reaction, can produce the same results as those of an applied electrotonus. In the first place we may note that the phenomena of sensory excitation, to be discussed briefly later, provide many instances of chemical excitation ; the end organs of smell and taste are merely specialised nerve endings adapted to respond to minute changes in the chemical environment ; the retinal receptors are specialised cells capable of responding electrically to a photochemical reaction taking place at their surface ; and so on. It will therefore be nothing new to demonstrate that a substance such as acetylcholine, even in minute concentrations, can initiate impulses in an effector cell.

Depolarisation. We have described electrical excitation, and the propagation of the action potential, as a *depolarisation* phenomenon, and the action of acetylcholine as a *depolarising action* ; let us review the significance of these statements. An applied cathodal potential causes current to flow as in Fig. 179 (p. 399), *i.e.*, in such a way that positive current flows across the membrane from inside to the outside : this flow of current causes the breakdown in impedance of the membrane that gives the full action potential ; and since the flow of current during excitation is such as to break down the normal resting potential, the excitation process is described as one of depolarisation. Propagation is due to the flow of current from the active to the inactive region as indicated in Fig. 186 (p. 407) ; this flow is such as to depolarise the adjoining portion of membrane, and therefore to excite it. Any chemical reagent that is capable of reducing the resting potential at a given point on the surface of an excitable tissue must set up demarcation currents in the same direction as those that normally are responsible for the propagation of the impulse. Now KCl, applied to a nerve or muscle, reduces the resting potential for reasons that are now quite clear (p. 261) ; a localised application of KCl to the nerve should, and actually does, initiate a propagated disturbance, whilst immersion of the whole tissue in a solution with a high concentration of KCl abolishes conduction. Similarly, any reagent that breaks down the selective ionic permeability of the membrane should depolarise it and therefore induce a propagated disturbance. For example, a high concentration of alcohol, by its destructive action on the cell membrane, probably makes it permeable to Na^+ and other ions ; applied locally to nerve it initiates an impulse (Arvanitaki & Fessard) ; in fact the literature is well stocked with examples of chemical compounds which, even in low concentrations, depolarise the membranes of excitable tissues. Thus the dialkylsuccinylsulphates have been shown by Höber to depolarise frog muscle in concentrations in the region of $1.10^{-4}M$. In general, we may distinguish two types of depolarisation ; the first, typified by K^+, is due to a reduction of the resting potential on simple thermodynamic grounds ; its effect can be mimicked by other cations to which the membrane is permeable, *e.g.*, Rb^+, Cs^+, NH_4^+ and probably certain organic derivatives of the ammonium ion (Wilbrandt ; Cowan & Walter) ; to the other class belong substances such as alcohol, bile salts, saponin, etc., whose influence is directly on the cell membrane, breaking down selective permeability when applied in sufficiently high concentration, and causing reversible block in lower concentration. In general, the effects of substances of the first class are reversible whilst those of the second class are only reversible under restricted conditions, the effects on the membrane being often too severe for recovery on removal of the agent.

Acetylcholine has been shown by Kuffler (1943) to cause a repetitive discharge in the single fibre nerve-muscle preparation when applied to the end-plate ; if applied only 2 mm. away from this region, no response at all is found except by increasing the concentration several thousand-fold. A study of the resting potential under these conditions shows that acetylcholine produces a definite decrease, comparable with that obtained by the local application of KCl, which likewise stimulates the end-plate (Kuffler, 1946). When applied to the muscle fibre, however, acetylcholine failed to depolarise [1] so that we must assume that the end-plate region is specially adapted to respond by depolarisation to acetylcholine ; in this connection it should also be mentioned that Lorente de Nó and Hodgkin have shown that neither the myelinated nerve fibre of the frog, nor the unmyelinated crustacean fibre, is depolarised by massive concentrations of acetylcholine. We may now ask : How does acetylcholine depolarise ? It is a quaternary ammonium base of the formula :—

$$(CH_3)_3 \overset{\overset{\displaystyle OH}{|}}{N}\text{-}CH_2 . CH_2OOCCH_3$$

Quaternary ammonium bases are strong bases, so that acetylcholine exists in solution, under physiological conditions, as a cation. If the end-plate tissue were permeable to this cation, and if its local concentration were effectively high, depolarisation could occur as a result of a thermo-dynamic effect rather similar to that of K^+. The local concentration, however, would have to be exceedingly high in comparison with the bulk concentrations that are effective ; thus Kuffler found a concentration of one part in ten million effective on the single-fibre preparation, and Buchtal & Lindhard found the minimal effective dose in the lizard to be 5.10^{-12}g. dissolved in a droplet of saline ; even these quantities are probably 30,000 times the quantities actually liberated at the nerve terminals, so that a simple ionic depolarisation, comparable with that obtained by local application of a diffusible cation, *e.g.*, Rb^+, is hard to imagine. Fatt has made a quantitative analysis of this possibility, when a known amount of acetylcholine is applied to the end-plate ; he has concluded that the end-plate must have an extremely high permeability to acetylcholine if the latter is to be able to depolarise it—in the region of 5.10^{-3} cm./sec. Furthermore, a consideration of the actual amount probably liberated at a nerve terminal has led Fatt & Katz to reject this thermodynamic mode of depolarisation.

[1] Cowan found that acetylcholine applied to the pelvic end of the whole sartorius muscle caused a profound and reversible abolition of the resting potential, measured between this and the injured tibial end ; it is conceivable, however, that the muscle was activated by way of the end-plates (*vide, e.g.*, Fatt, 1949). In the stellate ganglion, Bronk found that acetylcholine did not activate the pre-synaptic fibres, only the post-synaptic neurone.

The alternative hypothesis, that acetylcholine depolarises in virtue of a reversible change in membrane permeability, is easier to reconcile with the facts, since it is known that permeability may be affected by quite low concentrations of certain ions, *e.g.*, Ag^+, or by certain surface-active organic substances. Presumably the end-plate membrane has a specific chemical grouping on its surface capable of reacting with acetylcholine ; as a result of this reaction, it could be supposed that the properties of the membrane would be altered so as to cause a breakdown in the normal resting permeability relationships to give the depolarised condition. Acetylcholine is, of course, not the only known reactive substance so far as the junctional region is concerned ; nicotine, in doses comparable with those of acetylcholine, depolarises the end-plate and causes repetitive stimulation ; this substance has the property in common with acetylcholine of being a base (tertiary, however) ; choline, moreover, although considered as the *inactivated* hydrolytic product of acetylcholine, is capable of stimulating the ganglion, although in concentrations about a thousand times greater than those required for acetylcholine ; a variety of other synthetic quaternary bases have apparently specific effects on the end-plates ; thus the tetramethyl ammonium ion, in certain circumstances, is capable of stimulating muscle in a similar manner to acetylcholine, although in other circumstances it inhibits.

Curarine is a quaternary base like acetylcholine ; it would seem, therefore, that transmitter substances and curarine-like substances react with a certain chemical grouping in the end-plate ; if they are incapable of depolarising, they cause a blockage of transmission by excluding acetylcholine from the same grouping ; if, on the other hand, they can depolarise, their action is similar to that of acetylcholine ; nicotine belongs to the latter class, whilst curarine belongs to the former.

Wedensky Inhibition. An excess of acetylcholine at the nerve terminals in a synapse, or end-plate, depresses transmission and leads to *acetylcholine block*; the cause of this may be simply that the responsive tissue becomes permanently depolarised, and is then equivalent to nerve or muscle in its absolutely refractory condition. Apart from its general interest, the phenomenon of acetylcholine block emphasises the difficulties in the interpretation of end-plate and synaptic phenomena ; this is specially manifest in the phenomenon of Wedensky inhibition (p. 440), the blockage of neuromuscular transmission at high frequencies of stimulation. The phenomenon may be due, as Rosenblueth & Morison have suggested, to a diminution of the quanta of acetylcholine liberated by each impulse as the frequency rises, but it may also be due to the accumulation of an excess of acetylcholine at the junction ; the former type of block would be overcome by injected eserine and acetylcholine, whilst the latter type would be accentuated by the same treatment (Rosenblueth & Morison ; del Pozo).[1]

---

[1] Rosenblueth, Lissák & Lanari describe " five stages of neuromuscular transmission " as follows : (i) Contraction. (ii) Fall in tension. (iii) Slower rise. (iv) Fall in tension. (v) Late rise. (ii) and (iv) are both due to a failure of transmission, but (ii) is said to be due to an excess of acetylcholine, whilst (iv) to a deficiency ; (iv) therefore represents true fatigue. The transition from (iv) to (v) is thought to be due to increased output of

Acetylcholine and Potassium. The effects of acetylcholine become even more complex when we consider the relationship of acetylcholine to K^+. KCl, as we have seen, is able to stimulate the junctional region, its action being explained, on the classical view, as a simple thermodynamic depolarisation. Nevertheless KCl, when injected into the fluid perfusing a ganglion, besides causing a discharge in both post- and pre-ganglionic fibres, liberates acetylcholine (Brown & Feldberg, 1936), so that some of the effects of KCl have been attributed to the liberation of transmitter substance ; that the effects are not exclusively produced in this way, however, is shown by the fact that KCl stimulates a chronically denervated ganglion (*i.e.*, one incapable of liberating acetylcholine), and by the observation that curarine does not abolish the effect of KCl. One of the effects of stimulating a nerve is, as we have seen, the escape of K^+ from its interior ; and it has been suggested that the liberation of acetylcholine at the nerve terminals is due, initially, to the liberation of K^+. This suggestion, however, has not been fruitful ; the acetylcholine is, presumably, *inside* the nerve terminals, *i.e.*, exposed to a very high concentration of K^+ anyway. If it is granted that the depolarisation of the nerve terminals is the effective step in the liberation of acetylcholine, the effects of K^+, applied to the junction, are most simply explained by the depolarisation of the nerve terminals caused by the K^+, *i.e.*, K^+ liberates acetylcholine because it depolarises the nerve terminals. In experimental studies, however, the effects of liberated K^+ at the end-plate must not be ignored ; thus Brown & v. Euler have shown that the increased response of a muscle to nerve stimulation, obtained immediately after a tetanus, was not due to accumulated acetylcholine, as was originally thought, but to the accumulated K^+ which reduced the resting potential of the muscle fibres and allowed them to be excited with a weaker stimulus. K^+ also has a " decurarising " action, in that it reduces the degree of block of a nerve-muscle preparation due to curarine ; in a recent study Quilliam & Taylor have shown that the greater the concentration of K^+ in the medium, the greater is the concentration of curarine necessary to block, the relationship between the two concentrations being linear. Whether this antagonism is simply one of competition for the active groups in the " receptive substance " of the end-plate, or whether it means only that K^+, by increasing the electric excitability of the tissue, permits the liberated acetylcholine to depolarise in the presence of a larger concentration of curarine, is another problem that cannot be answered yet. Katz (1939) has shown that cathodal polarisation of the end-plate region exerts a similar " decurarising " effect, in that a formerly blocked end-plate was enabled to transmit nerve impulses ; a careful study of this decurarising action revealed that it was due to purely electrotonic effects, so that the decurarising action of K^+ may very well be due to its action on the resting potential.[1]

acetylcholine, *i.e.*, an adaptation to repetitive stimulation. Even these categories, however, fail to describe all the phenomena, *vide*, *e.g.*, Rosenblueth & Cannon and Cannon & Rosenblueth (1940).

[1] Buchtal & Lindhard (1942) consider that the neuromuscular junction should be regarded from two aspects : the junction between the neurofibrillar network and the

Acetylcholine and Propagation along the Axon

We may now return to a vexed question ; the significance of cholinesterase in the nerve sheath. According to Bullock, Nachmansohn and their co-workers, the liberation of acetylcholine is a primary step in transmission along the axon as well as at a junction. The main argument adduced in support of this contention is that DFP is said to block nerve conduction in proportion to the degree of inhibition of cholinesterase.[1] This finding has been disputed by Crescitelli and Gerard who find that DFP, in appropriate concentration, may completely inhibit cholinesterase and leave conduction intact ; so that although Nachmansohn seems not to accept their evidence we must consider this, the keystone of the hypothesis, as not yet firmly established. The most serious objection, however, is the finding of Lorente de Nó and Hodgkin (1947) that acetylcholine does not depolarise nerve even in isotonic concentration ; Nachmansohn attempts to avoid this objection by stating that the lipoid sheath of the fibre prevents the acetylcholine from reaching the functional surface, and he furthermore ascribes the same cause to the failure of prostigmine (an eserine-like compound) to abolish conduction, it being water-soluble and less likely to penetrate a lipoid layer than eserine [2] or DFP. It would be unwise to dismiss the Nachmansohn hypothesis out of hand, however, until the true role of the cholinesterase in the sheath is understood [3] ; stimulation of nerve seems to be associated with the loss of acetylcholine, but v. Muralt, who has summarised this work in his monograph, also describes the liberation of another substance which seems to be a derivative of vitamin-B_1, thiamin-disulphide. The electrical studies on the excitation of, and transmission along, nerve provide an imposing body of facts favouring an electrical mode of transmission ; the electrical theory, however, leaves two aspects unexplained : (*a*) the breakdown of the membrane resistance when a critical electrotonus has been reached, and (*b*) the recovery process, or re-polarisation. The failure to observe depolarisation by acetylcholine rules it out as a direct mediator in the breakdown in membrane resistance of the axon, so that it may well be concerned in the recovery process. Thus Nachmansohn & Machado have shown that nervous tissue contains both cholinesterase and another enzyme, *choline acetylase*, which re-synthesises acetylcholine ; the latter enzyme is closely connected with the glycolytic reaction mechanisms [4] (p. 501) and it is of interest that Libet has shown

end-plate, or *sole*, sensitive to acetylcholine, and the junction between the sole and the sarcoplasm, sensitive to K+.

[1] I must confess that, although this argument forms the theme of many papers by Nachmansohn, all of which I have read with care, its cogency has escaped me. The primary effect of an anticholinesterase is to potentiate the action of acetylcholine, *i.e.*, to *increase* and *prolong* its effects. If the liberation of acetylcholine all along the length of the axon determines the propagation of the impulse, why should DFP, which preserves acetylcholine from destruction, cause only blockage ? At some stage in its action it should surely increase the size or duration of the action potential, precisely as happens at the end-plate (Eccles, Katz & Kuffler), but such an effect has never been described.

[2] This view of the cause of the functional difference between eserine and prostigmine seems first to have been propounded by Schweitzer, Stedman & Wright.

[3] Other enzymes, such as succinoxidase and vitamin-B_1 seem to be more concentrated in the axoplasm than in the sheath.

[4] The literature on this point is large and growing rapidly ; it has recently been summarised by Nachmansohn (1950). ATP, an important metabolic compound (p. 501),

that the enzyme that breaks down adenosinetriphosphate (ATPase) is a hundred times more concentrated in the sheath than in the axoplasm. It is possible, therefore, that the blockage of transmission by DFP and eserine is connected with an interference with the recovery process. In this connection we may note that DFP, the substance utilised most in these studies, is a highly lipoid-soluble substance and has recently been found to exhibit a simple non-specific narcotic action on permeability similar to that of a large variety of fat-soluble substances, *e.g.*, alcohols, urethanes, chloroform, etc. (Davson & Matchett, 1951). It is quite possible therefore that, in the relatively high concentrations employed in these studies, the block is due to a simple non-specific narcotic action, rather than a specific anti-cholinesterase activity. That the block is non-specific is made very probable by the observation of Bullock *et al.* (1947) that DFP blocks sensory and adrenergic nerves ; Feldberg & Mann (1946) have shown that sensory nerves are incapable of synthesising acetylcholine, in contrast to motor nerves ; consequently, as they point out, it is very unlikely that acetylcholine is involved in transmission along this type of nerve, nor, probably, at its synapse in the cord. (We may note, however, that naphthaquinone, which specifically inhibits choline acetylase, depresses the action potential and increases the latency of muscle and nerve, according to Torda & Wolff.)

Provisional Sketch of Junctional Transmission

So much for the complexities of the problem ; we may now attempt to build up a simple picture of the events taking place at the end-plate. The wave of action potential in the nerve, arriving at the terminals, meets a gap in protoplasmic continuity. As a result, the potential is no longer propagated, and any electrotonic effects it may produce at the junction are too small to detect. The propagated disturbance at the nerve terminals causes a liberation of acetylcholine from an inactive precursor [1] ; and the work of Fatt & Katz suggests that this escapes in exchange for external Na^+. The acetylcholine causes a rapid depolarisation of the end-plate ; this is reflected in the rapid build-up of the end-plate potential, which grows up to such a height that its electrotonic effects, transmitted to the associated muscle fibre, set off a propagated disturbance. The end-plate itself may be incapable of a propagated type of disturbance, its whole effect being passed on by electrotonic spread to the muscle fibre, in a similar manner to that postulated for the soma of a postganglionic neurone (p. 456). In this connection it must be mentioned that Fessard has shown that the chronically denervated electric organ is incapable of responding to electrical

---

is necessary for the synthesis, but may be replaced by creatine phosphate + adenylic acid, according to Feldberg & Hebb. ATP sensitises muscle to the action of acetylcholine (Torda & Wolff), but the mechanism of the action is by no means clear (*vide*, *e.g.*, Buchtal & Folkow) ; according to Feldberg & Hebb it is not due to the accelerating action of ATP on the synthesis of acetylcholine.

[1] That acetylcholine may exist in a bound form, at least in the central nervous system, seems to be well established ; Schallek has shown that its liberation by K^+ may be due to a cation-exchange ; thus there may be a reciprocal relationship between K^+ and acetylcholine bound by nervous tissue, K^+ liberating acetylcholine and acetylcholine liberating K^+, according to circumstances.

stimulation, a fact suggesting that the muscle end-plate is likewise electrically inexcitable, requiring the specific depolarising action of acetylcholine to build up a potential. The liberated acetylcholine, having exerted its effects on the end-plate, is now rapidly hydrolysed by the cholinesterase concentrated in this region. In the presence of eserine, which inhibits this enzyme, the liberated acetylcholine persists and continues to depolarise the end-plate and thus to cause repetitive discharges until the end-plate accommodates itself. That there is normally some accommodative process is shown by the effects of Ca^{++}-deficiency on the end-plate ; as Bronk has shown, a Ca^{++}-free medium causes repetitive discharges in ganglia, and Kuffler has shown a similar effect at the end-plate of a single-fibre preparation ; in nerve fibres a deficiency of Ca^{++} causes spontaneous discharges, which are attributable to a failure of the tissue to accommodate to a stimulus (p. 470).

It is, perhaps, too early to speculate on the difference between the apparently non-propagated depolarisation of the end-plate and the propagated type of potential change found in the nerve or muscle fibre, but some recent studies of Fatt & Katz suggest that, in the former case, there is a simple breakdown of selective permeability without the development of the selective inward permeability to Na^+, characteristic of the propagated type of depolarisation. The depolarised end-plate would act as a " potential sink," causing the surrounding fibre membrane to discharge sufficiently to excite.

THE SENSORY RESPONSE

We may conclude this account of the phenomena of excitation and transmission with a few considerations on the natural initiation of nervous activity ; electrical excitation is a valuable tool in the study of general mechanisms, on account of the great accuracy with which the stimulus may be controlled ; but of course the natural external stimuli are either mechanical or chemical, and are applied to the sensory nerve terminals usually through the intermediary action of a specialised receptor. This receptor may take the form of a mechanical transmitter of the impulse, as for example in the Pacinian corpuscle which mediates pressure sensations, or it may be a specialised cell in which a propagated disturbance is initiated and transmitted to the sensory nerve fibre through a synapse, as in the case of the rods and cones of the vertebrate retina.

Discharge in Sensory Nerve. The result of stimulating the receptor is the propagation of a series of spikes along the sensory fibre ; they are typically all-or-none, maintaining the same characteristics in spite of wide variations in intensity of stimulus, the only effect of this variable being a change in the frequency of discharge. Thus Fig. 211 shows the response of a stretch receptor—a muscle spindle [1]—which indicates by its responses the state

---

[1] This organ, found in higher vertebrates only, consists of several muscle fibres in a connective tissue capsule (Fig. 212, p. 445), and located mainly at the junction of the muscle with the tendon ; it is supplied with sensory fibres which respond to stretch, and thus mediate the so-called *proprioceptive* impulses which aid in muscular co-ordination.

of tension of the muscle ; as the tension increases, the frequency increases but the spikes maintain a constant shape and height. Again, when fibres mediating different sensations are compared, no differences in the nature of the spikes have been definitively correlated with the type of sensation mediated, so that it is generally considered that the nature of the sensation is determined by the connections the sensory fibre ultimately establishes in the central nervous system. The remarkable feature of the response illustrated in Fig. 211, and characteristic of all sensory discharges, is its discontinuity or *repetitiousness*. The stimulus may be continuous, as with illumination of the retina with a source of constant brightness, but the response is repetitive. A second feature is the tendency of the response, measured as the frequency of the discharge, to decrease—the phenomenon of *adaptation* or *accommodation*. It will be recalled that in isolated

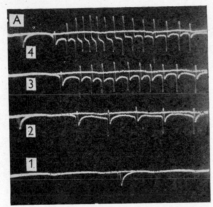

FIG. 211. Response of a stretch receptor recorded from its sensory axon. 1, At " rest " ; 2—4, with increasing intensity of stretching. (Katz. *J. Physiol.*)

vertebrate nerve the application of a constant current causes only one response at " make " ; formally, at least, we may describe the failure to obtain further responses as due to accommodation, the process invoked by Nernst and later workers to account for the failure of a slowly growing current to excite. The nerve fibre may then be regarded as exhibiting accommodation in an extreme form, responding with only one spike to a continuous stimulus, whilst the sensory nerve ending, stimulated through its receptor, shows a smaller power of accommodation.

Repetitive Response in Crustacean Axon. Crustacean nerves have the striking feature of responding repetitively to weak constant currents ; and Katz has applied the notion of accommodation to the problem. On the basis of Hill's theory of excitation (p. 398) the excited state should be reached when the local potential, V, exceeds the threshold value, U, which rises during the passage of the stimulating current. If accommodation is slow,[1] it may be predicted that U — V will be negative (the condition

---

[1] That is, if λ, which measures the rate of return of threshold on cessation of current-flow, is large.

for excitation) for appreciable times ; thus Katz found that the time during which a repetitive discharge lasted was predictable from Hill's equation on the basis of the experimentally determined time-constants. Other, and more extensive, studies of the phenomenon have been carried out by Fessard, by Arvanitaki, and, quite recently, by Hodgkin who has used single crustacean fibres and applied his technique for studying local responses. On making a constant current through certain fibres, a response comparable to that of a receptor was obtained (Fig. 213), beginning with a high frequency and exhibiting typical adaptation ; frequencies from 5 to 150/sec. could be obtained by varying the current intensity. A study of the local sub-threshold potentials under these conditions showed that when the current was very weak the growth was very slow (*e.g.*, as long as 98 msec.) ; as the current-strength increased, the build-up was more rapid and the frequency of discharge increased ; the rate of growth of local sub-threshold potential, from which the spike emerged, thus seemed to determine the frequency of the discharge rather than the refractory period of the fibre. Hence the chain of events would consist of the purely electrotonic charging of the membrane by the applied current ; this would lead to the slow growth of a local, non-propagated response, which finally grew to the height necessary to initiate a propagated spike. Following this, the membrane resistance would be re-established, the current from the electrodes would build up a new electrotonus, and so on. This view, of course, still leaves the central problem untouched, namely why certain axons are repetitive and others not. The idea that fibres possess a natural rhythmicity, particularly favoured by Bronk, is of interest, but still begs the same question. Removal of Ca^{++} from a nerve induces repetitiveness, the Ca^{++}-deficient frog or squid axon having many characteristics in common with the normal crustacean fibre ; moreover, if decalcification is carried far enough, the nerve exhibits spontaneous activity. Arvanitaki observed under these conditions, in the *Sepia* axon, a spontaneous sub-threshold activity, and Fig. 214 illustrates a similar

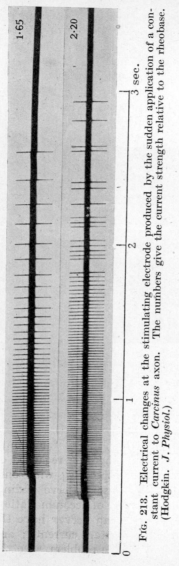

FIG. 213. Electrical changes at the stimulating electrode produced by the sudden application of a constant current to *Carcinus* axon. The numbers give the current strength relative to the rheobase. (Hodgkin. *J. Physiol.*)

nding, in the Ca^{++}-deficient squid axon, by Brink, Bronk & Larra-
ee, the sub-threshold potentials eventually building up into true spikes.
'hese authors have suggested that a nerve fibre, under any set of conditions,
as a fundamental rhythm ; thus the intervals between spikes in a
a^{++}-deficient frog nerve appeared to be simple multiples of 6 msec., so
hat different frequencies of response may have been due to the regular
issing of beats in a fundamental 6 msec. rhythm. It may well be too, as

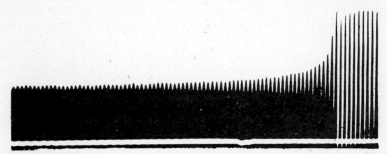

Fig. 214. Local electric response, recorded from a chemically excited region
of a squid giant axon. It is oscillatory and precedes the conducted
impulses. The last ten oscillations on the right of the record initiated
propagated impulses, which are much larger in amplitude than shown.
Stimulation by topical application of isotonic NaCl. (Brink, Bronk &
Larrabee. *Ann. N.Y. Acad. Sci.*)

Bronk suggested in 1929, that the adaptive decrease in discharge of a normal receptor is due to the missing of beats in a fundamental rhythm.

Response in Invertebrate Eye. The repetitive response is, of course, not
peculiar to sense organs [1] ; the motor neurones of the spinal cord give a
repetitive response to a constant current applied to the cord (Barron & Mat-
hews) and the postganglionic sympathetic fibres, already considered, give a
repetitive discharge with frequencies which bear no simple relationship to
the frequencies in the preganglionic fibres. In these cases we have seen that
the spikes apparently discharge as a result of a build-up of electrotonic
potential, and it is of interest that Bernhard has described a similar
phenomenon in the compound eye of the water-beetle *Dytiscus*. Nerve
fibres leading from the excitable retinula cells soon end in the optic ganglion
or optic lobe, a pear-shaped structure tapering off into an optic nerve
which runs to the supra-œsophageal ganglion, the whole distance from
retinula cell to supra-œsophageal ganglion being only 2·5 mm. The optic
lobe consists of neurones which presumably synapse with the fibres of the
retinula cells. By placing electrodes at different points on this sensory
pathway, as indicated schematically in Fig. 215, Bernhard was able to
record the electrical events taking place at different stages. With leads
3 and 5, *i.e.*, on the optic ganglion and supra-œsophageal ganglion, the
record consisted in a slow rise in potential persisting as long as the light-

[1] According to Erlanger & Blair, differences in the electrical characteristics of sensory
and motor nerve axons indicate a greater tendency to repetitiveness in the sensory
fibres ; v. Euler has reached a similar conclusion.

stimulus, the optic ganglion being negative ; superimposed on this wave of negativity were typical spikes ; the farther up the optic nerve the active electrode was placed, the smaller the negativity ; and the record became eventually a typical repetitive discharge of spikes (leads 4 and 5). If the optic ganglion and central parts were severed from the eye, leads 1 and 2 recorded only a slow wave of negativity without spikes. This observation suggests that the first effect of the light-stimulus is the development of an electrotonic negative potential in the receptors (retinula cells), and that this spreads to the optic ganglion and initiates spike potentials in the neurones there. Some support for this viewpoint is

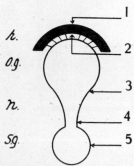

FIG. 215. Schematic drawing of eye of *Dytiscus* prepared for an experiment, showing receptorial layer, *r*, optic ganglion, *og*, optic nerve, *n*, and supra-œsophageal ganglion, *sg*. The numbers 1–4 show the different loci used for the active electrode, whereas 5 is the constant locus of the reference electrode on the supra-œsophageal ganglion. (Bernhard. *J. Neurophysiol.*)

given by a recent study made by Katz (1950) on the sensory discharges in single fibres from a muscle spindle. A very definite electrotonic potential preceded the discharge of action potentials, the greater the potential the greater the frequency of discharge ; the potential was not abolished by concentrations of local anæsthetics that were sufficient to prevent the development of action potentials. A significant feature was that the " spindle potential " preceding the first spike was always smaller than that preceding later ones ; presumably the excitability of the resting fibre is high, whilst in the relatively refractory period following a spike discharge the electrotonic potential, necessary to cause a new spike, is higher. Whether the deductions of Bernhard from his findings in *Dytiscus* can be extended to other eyes and other types of receptor is difficult to say ; that a separate type of cell is necessary to generate the electrotonic potential in all cases is certainly not true, since certain sensory nerves end simply as minute branches in the tissue they supply (*e.g.*, the cornea).

Acetylcholine and the Sensory Response. We may ask, finally, whether the initiation of impulses at the terminals of sensory nerves is brought about by the liberation of acetylcholine. According to Brown & Gray, a cutaneous injection of this substance causes a discharge in the sensory nerve, an effect that may be blocked by large doses of the same substance or nicotine. The important point, however, is that this blocking action does not extend to an inhibition of the effects of mechanical stimulation, and for this reason Brown & Gray answer the question, posed above, in the negative. They point to the different effects of acetylcholine on the neurones of a ganglion ; the postganglionic cell, on the " receiving end," is sensitive to the drug, whereas the preganglionic cell, on the " transmitting end," is not,[1] but

---

[1] Perfusion of the stellate ganglion with a solution containing acetylcholine initiates discharges only in the postganglionic fibres.

it does *liberate acetylcholine*. The sensory nerve is a "receiver" and, in conformity with this viewpoint, should be sensitive to acetylcholine, but should not liberate it. It remains to be seen whether this sensitivity of afferent nerve endings to acetylcholine is an accident. We may recall in this connection that sensory nerves contain cholinesterase, but are incapable of synthesising acetylcholine (p. 467).

References

ACHESON, G. H. (1948). "Physiology of Neuro-Muscular Junctions : Chemical Aspects." *Fed. Proc.*, **7**, 447.

ADRIAN, E. D. & LUCAS, K. (1912). "Summation of Propagated Disturbances in Nerve and Muscle." *J. Physiol.*, **44**, 68.

ARVANITAKI, A. (1939). "La Réponse Oscillatoire Locale de l'Axone Géant Isolé de *Sepia*." *Arch. int. Physiol.*, **49**, 209.

ARVANITAKI, A. (1939–40). "L'Activité Électrique Sous-Liminaire Locale de l'Axone Normal Isolé de *Sepia*." *J. Physiol. Path. gén.*, **37**, 895.

ARVANITAKI, A. (1942). "Effects Evoked in an Axon by the Activity of a Contiguous One." *J. Neurophysiol.*, **5**, 89.

ARVANITAKI, A. & CHALAZONITIS, N. (1949). "Prototypes d'Interactions Neuroniques et Transmissions Synaptiques." *Arch. Sci. Physiol.*, **3**, 547.

ARVANITAKI, A. & FESSARD, A. (1935). "Sur les Potentiels Retardés de la Réponse du Nerf de Crabe. Action de la Vératrine et de la Privation d'Électrolytes." *C. r. Soc. Biol.*, **118**, 419.

AUGER, D. & FESSARD, A. (1941). "Actions de Curare de l'Atropine et de l'Eserine sur le Prisme Electrogène de la Torpille." *C. r. Soc. Biol.*, **135**, 76.

BARRON, D. H. & MATTHEWS, B. H. C. (1938). "The Interpretation of Potential Changes in the Spinal Cord." *J. Physiol.*, **92**, 276.

BERNHARD, C. G. (1942). "Isolation of Retinal and Optic Ganglion Response in the Eye of *Dytiscus*." *J. Neurophysiol.*, **5**, 32.

BERNHARD, C. G., GRANIT, R. & SKOGLUND, C. R. (1942). "The Breakdown of Accommodation. Nerve as Model Sense Organ." *J. Neurophysiol.*, **5**, 55.

BODIAN, D. (1940). "Further Notes on the Vertebrate Synapse." *J. comp. Neurol.*, **73**, 323.

BODIAN, D. (1942). "Cytological Aspects of Synaptic Function." *Physiol. Rev.*, **22**, 146.

BOELL, E. J. & NACHMANSOHN, D. (1940). "Localisation of Choline Esterase in Nerve Fibres." *Science*, **92**, 513.

BOYARSKI, L. L., POSTEL, S. & ROSENBLATT, A. (1948). "Enzyme Inhibitors on Conduction and Respiration of Frog Nerve." *Fed. Proc.*, **7**, 11.

BOYARSKI, L. L., TOBIAS, J. M. & GERARD, R. W. (1947). "Nerve Conduction after Inactivation of Choline Esterase." *P.S.E.B.M.*, **64**, 106.

BREMER, F. (1927). "Sur le Mécanisme de la Sommation d'Influx Nerveux." *C. r. Soc. Biol.*, **97**, 1179.

BREMER, F. (1947). "Nerve and Synaptic Potentials." *Ann. Rev. Physiol.*, **9**, 457.

BREMER, F. & HOMÈS, G. (1930). "Interprétation Théorique de la Sommation d'Influx Nerveux." *C. r. Soc. Biol.*, **104**, 806.

BREMER, F. & KLEYNTJENS, F. (1935). "Nouvelles Recherches sur le Phénomène de la Sommation d'Influx Nerveux." *Arch. int. Physiol.*, **45**, 382.

BRINK, F., BRONK, D. W. & LARRABEE, M. G. (1946). "Chemical Excitation of Nerve." *Ann. N.Y. Acad. Sci.*, **47**, 457.

BRONK, D. W. (1929). "Fatigue of the Sense Organs in Muscle." *J. Physiol.*, **67**, 270.

BRONK, D. W. (1939). "Synaptic Mechanism in Sympathetic Ganglia." *J. Neurophysiol.*, **2**, 380.

BRONK, D. W., LARRABEE, M. G. & GAYLOR, J. B. (1948). "The Effects of Circulatory Arrest and Oxygen Lack on Synaptic Transmission in a Sympathetic Ganglion." *J. cell. & comp. Physiol.*, **31**, 193.

BRONK, D. W., LARRABEE, M. G., GAYLOR, J. B. & BRINK, F. (1938). "Influence of Altered Chemical Environment on the Activity of Ganglion Cells." *Amer. J. Physiol.*, **123**, 24.

BROOKS, C. McC., DOWNMAN, C. B. B. & ECCLES, J. C. (1950). "After Potentials and Excitability of Spinal Motoneurones following Orthodromic Activation." *J. Neurophysiol.*, **13**, 157.

BROOKS, C. McC. & ECCLES, J. C. (1947). "Electrical Investigation of the Mono-synaptic Pathway through the Spinal Cord." *J. Neurophysiol.*, **10**, 247.

BROOKS, C. McC. & ECCLES, J. C. (1948). "An Analysis of Synaptic and Excitator Action." *J. Neurophysiol.*, **11**, 365.

BROOKS, C. McC. & ECCLES, J. C. (1948). "Inhibition of Antidromic Responses of Motoneurones." *J. Neurophysiol.*, **11**, 431.

BROOKS, C. McC., ECCLES, J. C. & MALCOLM, J. L. (1948). "Synaptic Potentials of Inhibited Motoneurones." *J. Neurophysiol.*, **11**, 417.

BROWN, G. L. (1934). "Conduction in the Cervical Sympathetic." *J. Physiol.*, **81**, 22

BROWN, G. L. (1937). "Action Potentials of Normal Mammalian Muscle. Effects of Acetylcholine and Eserine." *J. Physiol.*, **89**, 220.

BROWN, G. L. (1937). "Transmission at Nerve Endings by Acetylcholine." *Physio Rev.*, **17**, 485.

BROWN, G. L. & BURNS, B. D. (1949). "Fatigue and Neuromuscular Block in Mammalian Skeletal Muscle." *Proc. Roy. Soc.*, B, **136**, 182.

BROWN, G. L., DALE, H. H. & FELDBERG, W. (1936). "Reactions of the Norma Mammalian Muscle to Acetylcholine and to Eserine." *J. Physiol.*, **87**, 394.

BROWN, G. L. & v. EULER, U. S. (1938). "The After Effects of a Tetanus on Mam-malian Muscle." *J. Physiol.*, **93**, 39.

BROWN, G. L. & FELDBERG, W. (1936). "The Action of Potassium on the Superio Cervical Ganglion of the Cat." *J. Physiol.*, **86**, 290.

BROWN, G. L. & GRAY, J. A. B. (1948). "Some Effects of Nicotine-like Substances an Their Relations to Sensory Nerve Endings." *J. Physiol.*, **107**, 306.

BROWN, G. L. & MACINTOSH, F. C. (1939). "Discharges in Nerve Fibres Produced b Potassium Ions." *J. Physiol.*, **96**, 10P.

BUCHTAL, F. & FOLKOW, B. (1948). "Interaction between Acetylcholine and Adenosin Triphosphate in Normal Curarised and Denervated Muscle." *Acta Physiol., Scand* **15**, 150.

BUCHTAL, F. & LINDHARD, J. (1942). "Transmission of Impulses from Nerve t Muscle Fibre." *Acta Physiol., Scand.*, **4**, 136.

BULBRING, E. (1944). "The Action of Adrenalin on Transmission in the Superio Cervical Ganglion." *J. Physiol.*, **103**, 55.

BULLOCK, T. H. (1948). "Properties of a Single Synapse in the Stellate Ganglion of th Squid." *J. Neurophysiol.*, **11**, 343.

BULLOCK, T. H., GRUNDFEST, H., NACHMANSOHN, D. & ROTHENBERG, M. A. (1947) "Generality of the Role of Acetylcholine in Nerve and Muscle Conduction." *J. Neurophysiol.*, **10**, 11.

BULLOCK, T. H., GRUNDFEST, H., NACHMANSOHN, D. & ROTHENBERG, M. A. (1947) "Effects of DFP on Action Potential and Cholinesterase of Nerve." II. *J Neurophysiol.*, **10**, 62.

BULLOCK, T. H., GRUNDFEST, H., NACHMANSOHN, D., ROTHENBERG, M. A. & STERLING K. (1946). "Effect of DFP on Action Potential and Cholinesterase of Nerve." *J. Neurophysiol.*, **9**, 253.

BULLOCK, T. H., NACHMANSOHN, D. & ROTHENBERG, M. A. (1946). "Effects o Inhibitors of Choline Esterase on the Nerve Action Potential." *J. Neurophysiol.*, **9** 9.

DU BUY, H. G. (1935). "The Electrical Phenomena of the Crustacean Nerve-Muscl System." *Amer. J. Physiol.*, **114**, 224.

CANNON, W. B. & ROSENBLUETH, A. (1940). "Some Conditions Affecting the Lat Stages of Neuromuscular Transmission." *Amer. J. Physiol.*, **130**, 219.

CHANG, H. C. & GADDUM, J. H. (1933). "Choline Esters in Tissue Extracts." *J Physiol.*, **79**, 255.

COPPÉE, G. (1943). "La Transmission Neuro-Musculaire : Curarisation ; Décurarisa tion et Renforcement à la Jonction Myoneurale." *Arch. int. Physiol.*, **53**, 327.

COUCEIRO, A. & AKERMAN, M. (1948). "Sur Quelques Aspects du Tissu Électrique d l'Électrophorus Électricus (Linnæus)." *Anais da Acad. Bras. de Ciencias*, **20**, 383

COUTEAUX, R. (1941). "Recherches sur l'Histogenèse du Muscle Strié des Mammi fères et la Formation des Plaques Motrices." *Bull. Biol.*, **75**, 101.

COUTEAUX, R. (1944). "Nouvelles Observations sur la Structure de la Plaque Motric et Interpretation des Rapports Myo-Neuraux." *C. r. Soc. Biol.*, **138**, 976.

COUTEAUX, R. & NACHMANSOHN, D. (1940). "Changes of Choline Esterase at End Plates of Voluntary Muscle Following Section of Sciatic Nerve." *P.S.E.B.M.*, **43** 177.

COWAN, S. L. (1936). "The Initiation of All-or-None Responses in Muscle by Acetyl choline." *J. Physiol.*, **88**, 3P.

REFERENCES   475

COWAN, S. L. (1940). " The Actions of Eserine-like Compounds upon Frog's Nerve-Muscle Preparations, and Conditions in which a Single Shock can Evoke an Augmented Muscular Response." *Proc. Roy. Soc., B,* **129**, 356.

COWAN, S. L. (1940). " The Actions of Eserine-like Compounds upon Frog's Nerve-Muscle Preparations, and the Blocking of Neuromuscular Conduction." *Proc. Roy. Soc., B,* **129**, 392.

COWAN, S. L. & WALTER, W. G. (1937). " The Effects of Tetraethyl Ammonium Iodide on the Electrical Response and the Accommodation of Nerve." *J. Physiol.,* **91**, 101.

CRESCITELLI, F., KOELLE, G. B. & GILMAN, A. (1946). " Transmission of Impulses in Peripheral Nerves Treated with DFP." *J. Neurophysiol.,* **9**, 241.

DALE, H. H., FELDBERG, W. & VOGT, M. (1936). " Release of Acetylcholine at Voluntary Motor Nerve Endings." *J. Physiol.,* **86**, 353.

DAVSON, H. & MATCHETT, P. A. (1951). " The Non-Specific Narcotic Action of DFP." *J. cell. & comp. Physiol.* (In the press.)

ECCLES, J. C. (1936). " Synaptic and Neuro-Muscular Transmission." *Ergebn. d. Physiol.,* **33**, 339.

ECCLES, J. C. (1943). " Synaptic Potentials and Transmission in Sympathetic Ganglion." *J. Physiol.,* **101**, 465.

ECCLES, J. C. (1944). " The Nature of Synaptic Transmission in a Sympathetic Ganglion." *J. Physiol.,* **103**, 27.

ECCLES, J. C. (1946). " Synaptic Potentials of Motoneurones." *J. Neurophysiol.,* **9**, 87.

ECCLES, J. C. (1946). " An Electrical Hypothesis of Synaptic and Neuro-Muscular Transmission." *Ann. N.Y. Acad. Sci.,* **47**, 429.

ECCLES, J. C. (1947). " Acetylcholine and Synaptic Transmission in the Spinal Cord." *J. Neurophysiol.,* **10**, 197.

ECCLES, J. C. (1948). " Conduction and Synaptic Transmission in the Central Nervous System." *Ann. Rev. Physiol.,* **10**, 93.

ECCLES, J. C., KATZ, B. & KUFFLER, S. W. (1941). " Nature of the ' End-Plate Potential ' in Curarized Muscle." *J. Neurophysiol.,* **5**, 211.

ECCLES, J. C., KATZ, B. & KUFFLER, S. W. (1941). " Electric Potential Changes Accompanying Neuromuscular Transmission." *Biol. Symp.,* **3**, 349.

ECCLES, J. C., KATZ, B. & KUFFLER, S. W. (1942). " Effect of Eserine on Neuromuscular Transmission." *J. Neurophysiol.,* **5**, 211.

ECCLES, J. C. & KUFFLER, S. W. (1941). " Initiation of Muscle Impulses at Neuromuscular Junction." *J. Neurophysiol.,* **4**, 402.

ECCLES, J. C. & KUFFLER, S. W. (1941). " The Endplate Potential During and After the Muscle Spike Potential." *J. Neurophysiol.,* **4**, 486.

ECCLES, J. C. & MACFARLANE, W. V. (1949). " Actions of Anti-Cholinesterases on Endplate Potential of Frog Muscle." *J. Neurophysiol.,* **12**, 59.

ECCLES, J. C. & O'CONNOR, W. J. (1939). " Responses which Nerve Impulses Evoke in Mammalian Muscles." *J. Physiol.,* **97**, 44.

ERLANGER, J. (1939). " The Initiation of Impulses in Axons." *J. Neurophysiol.,* **2**, 370.

ERLANGER, J. & BLAIR, E. A. (1938). " Comparative Observations on Motor and Sensory Fibres with Special Reference to Repetitiousness." *Amer. J. Physiol.,* **121**, 431.

v. EULER, C. (1948). " Differences between Autonomic and Somatic-C Fibres to Stimulation with Constant Current." *Acta Physiol., Scand.,* **15**, 93.

v. EULER, U. S. (1945). " A Sympathomimetic Pressor Substance in Animal Organ Extracts." *Nature,* **156**, 18.

FATT, P. (1949). " The Depolarising Action of Acetylcholine on Muscle." *J. Physiol.,* **109**, 13P.

FATT, P. (1950). " Electromotive Action of Acetylcholine at the Motor End-Plate." *J. Physiol.,* **111**, 408.

FATT, P. & KATZ, B. (1950). " Membrane Potentials at the Motor End-Plate." *J. Physiol.,* **111**, 46P.

FATT, P. & KATZ, B. (1951). " An Analysis of the e.p.p. Recorded with an Intra-Cellular Electrode." (In the press.)

FELD, E. A., GRUNDFEST, H., NACHMANSOHN, D. & ROTHENBERG, M. A. (1948). " Effect of Di-Isopropyl Fluorophosphate (DFP) on Action Potential and Cholinesterase of Nerve." *J. Neurophysiol.,* **11**, 125.

FELDBERG, W. (1945). " Present Views on the Mode of Action of Acetylcholine in the Central Nervous System." *Physiol. Rev.,* **25**, 596.

FELDBERG, W., FESSARD, A. & NACHMANSOHN, D. (1940). " The Cholinergic Nature of the Nervous Supply to the Electric Organ of the Torpedo." *J. Physiol.,* **97**, 3.

FELDBERG, W. & GUIMARIS, J. A. (1936). "The Liberation of Acetylcholine by Potassium." *J. Physiol.*, 86, 306.

FELDBERG, W. & HEBB, C. (1947). "The Effects of Magnesium Ions and of Creatine Phosphate on the Synthesis of Acetylcholine." *J. Physiol.*, 106, 8.

FELDBERG, W. & MANN, T. (1946). "Properties and Distribution of the Enzyme System which Synthesizes Acetylcholine in Nervous Tissue." *J. Physiol.*, 104, 411.

FELDBERG, W. & VOGT, M. (1948). "Acetylcholine Synthesis in Different Regions of the Central Nervous System." *J. Physiol.*, 107, 372.

FENG, T. P. (1937). "Studies on the Neuromuscular Junction. VIII. The Localised Contraction Around the Neuromuscular Junction and the Blocking of Contraction Waves due to Nerve Stimulation." *Chin. J. Physiol.*, 12, 331.

FESSARD, A. (1946). "Some Aspects of the Activity of Electric Plates." *Ann. N.Y., Acad. Sci.*, 47, 501.

FESSARD, A. & PÉZARD, A. (1940). "Étude Physiologique et Histologique de la Lamelle de *Torpedo Marmorata* Après Section du Nerf Électrique." *C. r. Soc. Biol.*, 134, 525.

FORBES, A. (1939). "Problems of Synaptic Function." *J. Neurophysiol.*, 2, 465.

GASSER, H. S. (1930). "Contractures of Skeletal Muscle." *Physiol. Rev.*, 10, 35.

GASSER, H. S. (1939). "Axons as Samples of Nervous Tissue." *J. Neurophysiol.*, 2, 361.

GERARD, R. W. (1946). "Nerve Metabolism and Function. A Critique of the Role of Acetylcholine." *Ann. N.Y. Acad. Sci.*, 47, 575.

GÖPFERT, H. & SCHAEFER, H. (1938). "Uber den Direkt und Indirekt Erregten Aktionstrom und die Funktion der Motorische Endplatte." *Pflüg. Arch.*, 239, 597.

GRAY, J. A. B. & MALCOLM, J. L. (1950). "The Initiation of Nerve Impulses by Mesenteric Pacinian Corpuscles." *Proc. Roy. Soc.*, B, 137, 96.

GRUNDFEST, H. (1940). "Bioelectric Potentials." *Ann. Rev. Physiol.*, 2, 213.

GRUNDFEST, H. (1946). "Bioelectric Potentials in the Nervous System and in Muscle." *Ann. Rev. Physiol.*, 9, 477.

GRUNDFEST, H., NACHMANSOHN, D. & ROTHENBERG, M. A. (1947). "Effect of DFP on Action Potential and Cholinesterase of Nerve III." *J. Neurophysiol.*, 10, 155.

GUTMANN, E. & YOUNG, J. Z. (1944). "The Re-Innervation of Muscle after Various Periods of Atrophy." *J. Anat.*, 78, 15.

HARVEY, A. M. & MACINTOSH, F. C. (1940). "Calcium and Synaptic Transmission in a Sympathetic Ganglion." *J. Physiol.*, 97, 408.

HAWKINS, R. D. & MENDEL, B. (1947). "Selective Inhibition of Pseudo-Cholinesterase by Di-Isopropyl Fluorophosphonate." *Brit. J. Pharm.*, 2, 173.

HÖBER, R., ANDERSH, M., HÖBER, J. & NEBEL, B. (1939). "Influence of Organic Electrolytes and Non-Electrolytes on the Membrane Potentials of Muscle and Nerve." *J. cell. & comp. Physiol.*, 13, 195.

JASPER, H. H. & MONNIER, A. M. (1938). "Transmission of Excitation between Excised Non-Myelinated Nerves. An Artificial Synapse." *J. cell. & comp. Physiol.*, 11, 259.

KATZ, B. (1936). "Neuromuscular Transmission in Crabs." *J. Physiol.*, 87, 199.

KATZ, B. (1936). "Multiple Response to Constant Current in Frog's Medullated Nerve." *J. Physiol.*, 88, 239.

KATZ, B. (1939). "Electric Excitation in Nerve." Oxford, O.U.P.

KATZ, B. (1939). "The 'Anti-Curare' Action of a Subthreshold Catelectrotonus." *J. Physiol.*, 95, 286.

KATZ, B. (1942). "Impedance Changes in Frog's Muscle Associated with Electrotonic and 'Endplate' Potentials." *J. Neurophysiol.*, 5, 169.

KATZ, B. (1949). "Neuromuscular Transmission in Invertebrates." *Biol. Rev.*, 24, 1.

KATZ, B. (1950). "Depolarisation of Sensory Terminals and the Initiation of Impulses in the Muscle Spindle." *J. Physiol.*, 111, 26.

KATZ, B. (1950). "Action Potentials from a Sensory Nerve Ending." *J. Physiol.*, 111, 248.

KATZ, B. & KUFFLER, S. W. (1946). "Excitation of the Nerve-Muscle System in Crustacea." *Proc. Roy. Soc.*, B, 133, 374.

KOELLE, G. B. (1950). "Histochemical Differentiation of Types of Cholinesterases and Their Localisation in Tissues of the Cat." *J. Pharm.*, 100, 158.

KOELLE, G. B. & FRIEDENWALD, J. S. (1949). "A Histochemical Method for Localising Cholinesterase Activity." *P.S.E.B.M.*, 70, 617.

KUFFLER, S. W. (1942). "Electrical Potential Changes at an Isolated Nerve-Muscle Junction." *J. Neurophysiol.*, 5, 18.

KUFFLER, S. W. (1942). "Further Study In Transmission in an Isolated Nerve-Muscle Preparation." *J. Neurophysiol.*, 5, 309.

KUFFLER, S. W. (1943). " Specific Excitability of the Endplate Region in Normal and Denervated Muscle." *J. Neurophysiol.*, **6**, 99.
KUFFLER, S. W. (1944). " The Effect of Calcium on the Neuromuscular Junction." *J. Neurophysiol.*, **7**, 17.
KUFFLER, S. W. (1945). " Electric Excitability of Nerve-Muscle Fibre Preparations." *J. Neurophysiol.*, **8**, 75.
KUFFLER, S. W. & KATZ, B. (1946). " Inhibition at the Nerve Muscle Junction in Crustacea." *J. Neurophysiol.*, **9**, 337.
LARRABEE, M. G. & BRONK, D. W. (1947). " Prolonged Facilitation of Synaptic Excitation in Sympathetic Ganglia." *J. Neurophysiol.*, **10**, 139.
LIBET, B. (1948). " Adenosinetriphosphatase (ATPase) in Nerve." *Fed. Proc.*, **7**, 72.
LISSÁK, K., DEMPSEY, E. W. & ROSENBLUETH, A. (1939). " Failure of Transmission of Motor Nerve Impulses in the Course of Wallerian Degeneration." *Amer. J. Physiol.*, **128**, 45.
LLOYD, D. P. C. & McINTYRE, A. K. (1949). " Bioelectric Potentials in the Nervous System and Muscle." *Ann. Rev. Physiol.*, **11**, 173.
LOEWI, O. (1923). " Uber Humorale Ubertragbarkeit der Herznervenwirkung." *Pflüg. Arch.*, **189**, 239.
LORENTE DE NÓ, R. (1935). " Electrical Excitability of the Motoneurones." *J. cell. & comp. Physiol.*, **7**, 47.
LORENTE DE NÓ, R. (1935). " Synaptic Delay of the Motoneurones." *Amer. J. Physiol.*, **111**, 272.
LORENTE DE NÓ, R. (1939). " Transmission of Impulses through Cranial Motor Nuclei." *J. Neurophysiol.*, **2**, 402.
LORENTE DE NÓ, R. (1944). " Effects of Choline and Acetylcholine Chloride upon Peripheral Nerve Fibres." *J. cell. & comp. Physiol.*, **24**, 85.
LORENTE DE NÓ, R. (1946–7). " Correlation of Nerve Activity with Polarisation Phenomena." *Harvey Lectures*, **42**, 43.
MARAZZI, A. S. & MARAZZI, R. N. (1947). " Further Localisation and Analysis of Adrenergic Synaptic Inhibition." *J. Neurophysiol.*, **10**, 165.
MARMONT, G. & WIERSMA, C. A. G. (1938). " On the Mechanism of Inhibition and Excitation of Crayfish Muscle." *J. Physiol.*, **93**, 173.
MARNAY, A. & NACHMANSOHN, D. (1938). " Choline Esterase in Voluntary Muscle." *J. Physiol.*, **92**, 37.
MASLAND, R. L. & WIGTON, R. S. (1940). " Nerve Activity Accompanying Facilitation Produced by Prostigmine." *J. Neurophysiol.*, **3**, 269.
McCOUCH, G. P. (1945). " Conduction and Synaptic Transmission." *Ann. Rev. Physiol.*, **7**, 455.
MENDEL, B. & RUDNEY, H. (1943). " Studies on Cholinesterase. I. Cholinesterase and Pseudo-Cholinesterase." *Biochem. J.*, **37**, 59.
VON MURALT, A. (1946). " Die Signalübermittlung im Nerven." Basle, Birkhäuser.
VON MURALT, A. (1947–8). " Signal Transmission in Nerve." *Harvey Lectures*, **43**, 230.
NACHMANSOHN, D. (1946). " Chemical Mechanism of Nerve Activity." *Ann. N.Y. Acad. Sci.*, **47**, 395.
NACHMANSOHN, D. (1950). " Studies on Permeability in Relation to Nerve Function." *Biochim. Biophys. Acta*, **4**, 78.
NACHMANSOHN, D., COATES, C. W. & COX, R. T. (1941). " Electric Potential and Activity of Choline Esterase in the Electric Organ of *Electrophorus Electricus* (Linnæus)." *J. Gen. Physiol.*, **25**, 75.
NACHMANSOHN, D., COX, R. T., COATES, C. W. & MACHADO, A. L. (1942–3). " Action Potential and Enzyme Activity in the Electric Organ of *Electrophorus Electricus.*" I, II. *J. Neurophysiol.*, **5**, 499 ; **6**, 383.
NACHMANSOHN, D., COX, R. T., COATES, C. W. & MACHADO, A. L. (1943). " Action Potential and Enzyme Activity in the Electric Organ of Electrophorus II. Phosphocreatine as Energy Source of the Action Potential." *J. Neurophysiol.*, **6**, 383.
NACHMANSOHN, D. & MACHADO, A. L. (1943). " Formation of Acetylcholine. A New Enzyme : ' Choline Acetylase '." *J. Neurophysiol.*, **6**, 397.
NACHMANSOHN, D. & MEYERHOF, B. (1941). " Relation between Electrical Changes during Nerve Activity and Concentration of Choline Esterase." *J. Neurophysiol.*, **4**, 348.
NACHMANSOHN, D. & STEINBACH, H. B. (1942). " Localisation of Enzymes in Nerves. I. Succinic Dehydrogenase and Vitamin B_1." *J. Neurophysiol.*, **5**, 109.
PANTIN, C. F. A. (1936). " On the Excitation of Crustacean Muscle. II. Neuromuscular Facilitation." *J. exp. Biol.*, **13**, 111.

POSTERNAK, J. M. & LARRABEE, M. G. (1948). "Action of Narcotics on Synapses Compared to Action on Axons in Sympathetic Ganglia." *Fed. Proc.*, **7**, 96.

DEL POZO, E. C. (1942). "Transmission Fatigue and Contraction Fatigue." *Amer. J. Physiol.*, **135**, 763.

PROSSER, C. L. (1946). "The Physiology of Nervous Systems of Invertebrate Animals." *Physiol. Rev.*, **26**, 337.

QUILLIAM, J. P. & TAYLOR, D. B. (1947). "Antagonism between Curare and the Potassium Ion." *Nature*, **160**, 603.

RENSHAW, B. & THERMAN, P. O. (1941). "Excitation of Intraspinal Mammalian Neurons by Nerve Impulses in Adjacent Axons." *Amer. J. Physiol.*, **133**, 96.

ROSENBLUETH, A. (1944). "Recruitment of Mammalian Nerve Fibres." *Amer. J. Physiol.*, **141**, 196.

ROSENBLUETH, A. & CANNON, W. B. (1940). "Some Features of the Early Stages of Neuromuscular Transmission." *Amer. J. Physiol.*, **130**, 205.

ROSENBLUETH, A., LISSÁK, K. & LANARI, A. (1939). "An Explanation of the Five Stages of Neuromuscular and Ganglionic Synaptic Transmission." *Amer. J. Physiol.*, **128**, 31.

ROSENBLUETH, A. & MORISON, R. S. (1937). "Curarization, Fatigue and Wedensky Inhibition." *Amer. J. Physiol.*, **119**, 236.

ROTHENBERG, M. A. (1950). "Ionic Movements Across Axonal Membranes." *Biochim. Biophys. Acta*, **4**, 96.

ROTHENBERG, M. A., SPRINSON, D. B. & NACHMANSOHN, D. (1948). "Site of Action of Acetylcholine." *J. Neurophysiol.*, **11**, 111.

SCHALLEK, W. (1945). "Action of Potassium on Bound Acetylcholine in Lobster Nerve Cord." *J. cell. & comp. Physiol.*, **26**, 15.

SCHALLEK, W. & WIERSMA, C. A. G. (1948). "The Influence of Various Drugs on a Crustacean Synapse." *J. cell. & comp. Physiol.*, **31**, 35.

SCHWEITZER, A., STEDMAN, E. & WRIGHT, S. (1939). "Central Action of Anticholinesterases." *J. Physiol.*, **96**, 302.

SHARPLES, W., GRUNDFEST, H. & NACHMANSOHN, D. (1948). "Adenosinetriphosphatase and Conduction Velocity of the Nerve Impulses." *Fed. Proc.*, **7**, 113.

STEIMAN, S. E. (1943). "Neuromuscular Transmission in the Single Nerve and Muscle Fibre Preparation." *Amer. J. Physiol.*, **140**, 269.

TOMAN, J. P., WOODBURY, J. W. & WOODBURY, L. A. (1947). "Mechanism of Nerve Conduction Block Produced by Anticholinesterases." *J. Neurophysiol.*, **10**, 429.

TORDA, C. & WOLFF, H. G. (1946). "Effect of Compounds Related to Glycolysis in Muscle on the Sensitivity of Muscle to Acetylcholine and Potassium." *Amer. J. Physiol.*, **145**, 419.

TORDA, C. & WOLFF, H. G. (1948). "Effect of Acetylcholine and Alkaloids on Activity of Muscle Adenosinetriphosphatase." *Amer. J. Physiol.*, **152**, 86.

TORDA, C. & WOLFF, H. G. (1949). "Effect of 2-Methyl Naphthaquinone on the Action Potential of Nerve and Muscle." *Amer. J. Physiol.*, **157**, 465.

WELSH, J. H. & SCHALLEK, W. (1946). "Arthropod Nervous Systems : a Review of Their Structure and Function." *Physiol. Rev.*, **26**, 447.

WILBRANDT, W. (1937). "Effect of Organic Ions on the Membrane Potential of Nerves." *J. gen. Physiol.*, **20**, 519.

WITANOWSKI, W. R. (1925). "Uber Humorale Ubertragbarkeit der Herznervenwirkung." *Pflüg. Arch.*, **208**, 694.

YOUNG, J. Z. (1938). "The Functioning of the Giant Nerve Fibres of the Squid." *J. exp. Biol.*, **15**, 170.

YOUNG, J. Z. (1939). "Fused Neurons and Synaptic Contacts in the Giant Nerve Fibres of Cephalopods." *Phil. Trans.*, B, **229**, 465.

CHAPTER XVII

MECHANICAL AND THERMAL ASPECTS

MECHANICAL work of the organism is carried out by muscular, or contractile, tissue which in higher forms is made up of cells highly differentiated to permit of a rapid and reversible shortening and relaxation. As with the conduction of an impulse, it seems very likely that contractility, as such, is a widely spread characteristic of cells, for example, the streaming of the slime mould, *Phycomyces*, has been interpreted on the basis of an inherent contractility of parts of its protoplasm ; and, again, the ciliary action of many unicellular organisms, including some bacteria, may be included in any classification of muscular activity. In the higher forms we may differentiate two main types of specialised contractile tissue, *voluntary* or *skeletal* muscle, controlling the movements of the limbs and other movable structures, and *smooth muscle*, generally arranged in sheets around hollow organs, such as the intestine and bladder.[1]

The unit of the voluntary muscle is the *muscle fibre*, some $10-100\mu$ thick, and with a length that varies considerably with the muscle, from a few millimetres to several centimetres. The fibre results from the fusion of many cells, *myoblasts*, during development and contains many nuclei (in fibres several centimetres long there may be several hundred nuclei). Bundles of fibres are held together with elastic connective tissue. Most muscles are continued at one or both ends into dense tendinous bands which make attachments to the bone or other structure that they operate. The fibres of a given muscle need not necessarily, in fact they most frequently do not, run the whole length of the muscle ; in the frog sartorius they probably do but in other muscles they may begin and end in connective tissue.

Microscopic Structure of the Striated Muscle Fibre

An individual muscle fibre is illustrated in Fig. 216, Pl. XI ; it is striated in both longitudinal and transverse directions, the former being due to the fact that the fibre is built up of numerous fine fibrillæ some 1 to 2μ thick, or less, embedded in a structureless medium, the *sarcoplasm*. The cross striations, which give the name to this type of muscle, are due to alternations in the optical and staining properties of the fibrils along their axes, so that the whole fibre appears to be made up of a series of discs : the A- or *anisotropic* discs,[2] which are highly refractile and appear dark under the microscope ; and the I-, or *isotropic* discs, which are less highly

---

[1] Cardiac muscle occupies a position between these two extremes ; space demands that we confine attention in this book to striated, or voluntary, muscle.
[2] Also called Q discs.

refractile and appear light. As their names imply, the A-discs are doubly refracting, whereas the I-discs are only very weakly so, their double refraction amounting to only about 10 per cent. of that of the A-discs. These optical properties are accompanied by a difference in staining characteristics ; thus with the Heidenhain or methylene blue stains the A-bands become dark and the I-bands remain light, whilst with silver staining the banding is reversed, the I-bands preferentially taking up the stain. Further microscopical studies have revealed other apparent discontinuities along the fibre ; for example, the I-band is crossed by a thin, doubly refracting, *Z-band* (*Krause's membrane*) which creates the appearance of a membrane dividing the whole muscle fibre transversely, since, unlike the A- and I-bands, which are confined to the fibrils, it crosses the axoplasm. When muscle fibres are macerated they tend to break at the Z-band, hence the unit, or *sarcomere*, of the fibre is defined as the region enclosed between two successive Z-bands. Within the A-band an *M-band* has been described which likewise appears as a membrane crossing the fibre ; a region to either side of the M-band, and containing it, is referred to as the *H-band*, whilst two bands to either side of the Z-band are called *N-bands*. To what extent many of these regions are artefacts of fixation and staining is not clear ; according to Dempsey *et al.*, only the A- and I-segments are invariably demonstrable, and Høncke states that the N-bands are not observable in living fibres. In a fixed and stained preparation, however, the electron-microscope has revealed regions of different electron density corresponding with the classically described bands, as Fig. 218, Pl. XI, from the work of Hall, Jakus & Schmitt shows. The existence of fibrils, embedded in sarcoplasm, has often been questioned ; as we shall see, the electron-microscope has settled all reasonable doubts on this score, but it is worth mentioning that in 1932 Chambers & Hale described the formation of ice, in a freezing muscle fibre, as the progressive forward movement of slender longitudinal columns apparently moving in the spaces between the myofibrils ; on twisting the fibre before freezing, the columns moved spirally. Moreover, the more recent studies of Buchtal & Knappeis on the diffraction spectra of muscle suggest the presence of discontinuities between fibrils which may be as wide as 5μ.

Sarcolemma. The muscle fibre is enclosed by a membrane, the *sarcolemma*, which is continuous with the tendinous endings of the muscle ; it has been described by Bairati as a complex structure, consisting of interlacing collagenous fibres arranged as short lengths of stronger fibres, orientated longitudinally and tied together at the ends and sides by finer fibres running circumferentially, the whole being embedded in a matrix. This view has been questioned recently by Barer who studied the membrane by causing " retraction clots " to appear in the fibre, whereby the interior structures retracted locally leaving the sarcolemma exposed as a thin, apparently structureless, membrane with no evidence of a fibrous structure on dark-ground illumination or with the phase-contrast microscope. According to Long the sarcolemma is composed of two layers, an inner apparently structureless one and an outer one composed of delicate reticular fibres closely adherent to the inner layer. The membrane is

PLATE XI

FIG. 216. Part of a rabbit's striated muscle fibre. × 600 approx. (Microphotograph by F. J. Pittock, F.R.P.S., from preparation by K. C. Richardson.)

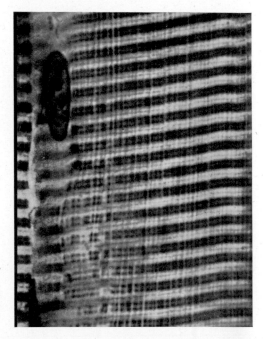

FIG. 217. Electron-micrograph of surface of striated muscle fibre, showing fine fibrils, cross-banded like collagen, and the undulations due to the muscle striations. Gold shadowed. (Reed & Rudall. *Biochim. Biophys. Acta.*)

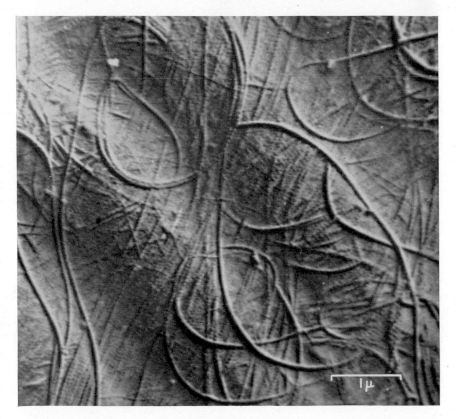

[*To face p.* 480.

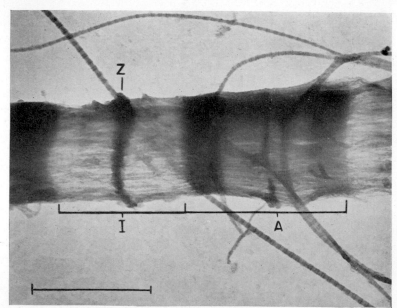

FIG. 218.   Myofibril from frog sartorius, stained with phosphotungstic acid.
Note also the striated collagen fibrils.   × 39,000.   (Hall, Jakus & Schmitt.
Biol. Bull.)

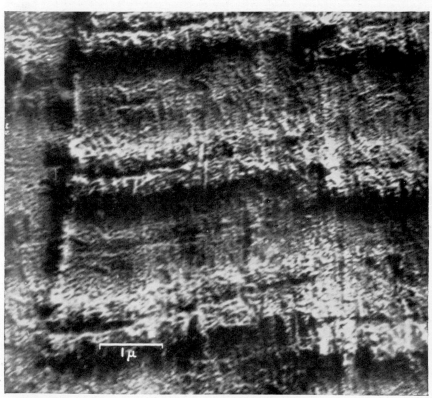

FIG. 219.   Electron-micrograph of stretched myofibril.   Gold shadowed.
(Reed & Rudall.   *Biochim. Biophys. Acta.*)

resistant to treatment with trypsin and also to collagenase, so that the view that it is made up of collagen is apparently unsound ; that fibrils of a collagen-type are closely associated with the surface of the muscle fibre when the sarcolemma has been torn away is revealed, however, by Reed & Rudall's electron-micrograph shown in Fig. 217, Pl. XI (and also in Fig. 218) ; the very thin fibrils have the typical banded collagen appearance (p. 102). According to a recent electron-microscopical study of Rozsa, Szent-Györgyi & Wyckoff (1950) the sarcolemma is, indeed, very thin and without a resolvable structure ; threads are seen in association with it, but they are thought not to be an integral part of the body of the membrane, and to be attached to its surface to form part of a system of threads surrounding the muscle fibre. This view is supported by the study of Draper & Hodge ; the outermost layer of the sarcolemma is, indeed, structureless, in the sense that no fibrillar arrangement can be resolved in the electron-microscope ; and it is this layer that is isolated by the formation of retraction clots. Within this, there are several successive layers characterised by the presence of collagen fibrils, except for the innermost layer, which consists of a matrix of granular material in which are embedded many fine interlacing non-collagenous fibrils, about 100A in diameter. This innermost layer appears to be continuous with, or attached to, the Z-band. The question whether the myofibrils are continuous, through holes in the sarcolemma, with the tendon fibrils has been a subject for controversy for many years ; Long's recent work has demonstrated the absence of such a continuity, the myofibrillæ ending within the sarcolemma. The muscle fibre exerts its pull on the tendon fibre, therefore, through the agency of reticular fibrils, which are continuous with the fibrils of the tendon, and continue over the surface of the muscle fibre as the sarcolemmal and endomysial reticulum.

MECHANICAL ASPECTS

Latency-Relaxation

Stimulation of muscle, as we have seen, is followed by the passage of a wave of action potential extending over its whole length ; immediately after the electrical event the muscle contracts. If the muscle is allowed to lift a constant load, the contraction is said to be *isotonic*, the developed tension being constant once this is equal to the gravitational pull of the load. If the muscle is attached to a rigid spring, so that only a minute change in length occurs, contraction is said to be *isometric* ; a record of an isometric twitch is thus a record of changes in tension of the muscle, whilst that for an isotonic twitch is a record of changes in length. The interval between the direct electrical stimulation of the muscle and the beginning of the upstroke of shortening is the *latent period* ; its duration depends so strongly on the inertia of the ordinary recording apparatus that Roos, who reduced this inertia to a minimum, considered that there was no real latent period. Roos' results have since been criticised by Snyder and by Sandow both of whom critically re-examined the matter. Sandow's technique is worth describing, since it illustrates a method of recording changes in isometric

tension involving practically no change in total length of the muscle.   Fig.
220 illustrates the principle ; the muscle was connected by a metal chain
to a stylus, S, attached to an ordinary gramophone pick-up, P.   The

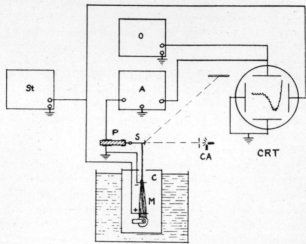

Fig. 220.   Diagram of apparatus for recording latency mechanical changes.
C, moist chamber in constant temperature bath ; M, muscle ; P, crystal
pick-up ; S, stylus of pick-up ; A, amplifying system ; CRT, cathode-ray
tube ; O, oscillator ; St, stimulator ; CA, carbon-arc source of beam for
optical lever used for recording initial and peak tensions of muscle.
(Sandow.   *J. cell. & comp. Physiol.*)

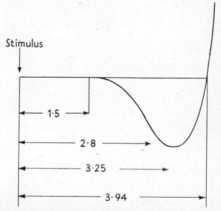

Fig. 221.   Diagrammatic representation of latency-relaxation.   Numbers
indicate times, in msec. after stimulation, at which the various phases
of the tension take place for a muscle loaded with 8g.   (Sandow.   *J. cell.
& comp. Physiol.*)

development of tension in the stylus caused a potential in the piezo-electric
crystal in the pick-up, which was amplified and recorded on a cathode-ray
oscillograph.   The movement of the stylus resulting from maximal tension
in the frog's sartorius was only 0·07 mm., which was only some 0·2 per cent.
of its length.   The cathode-ray oscillograph gave a rapid and inertia-less

record of the time relations of stimulus and initial tension changes ; to
obtain the actual value of the maximal tension developed, a simple optical
recording system was employed. Light from a carbon-arc was reflected off
a mirror attached to the stylus ; movement of the stylus was magnified in
this manner 248 times. Sandow's results confirmed an earlier observation
of Rauh that contraction is preceded by relaxation [1] (Fig. 221), so that the
time-course of events consisted of (a), a quiescent period of about 1·5 msec.

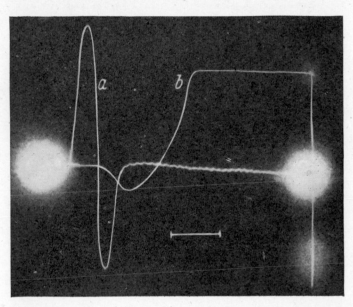

Fig. 222. Two superimposed records obtained from frog's gastrocnemius :
a, action potential ; b, tension, relaxation being indicated by a movement
below the base-line. Note that the first phase of the action-potential
precedes the onset of latency-relaxation. Time-mark, 10 msec. (Schaefer
& Göpfert. *Pflüg. Arch.*)

from the moment of stimulation to the beginning, (b), of the so-called *latency-
relaxation* which lasts for some 1·5 msec. and passes abruptly into (c), the
phase of rising tension, the first 0·5 msec. of which is required to bring the
tension back to its initial value. The latency, as ordinarily recorded, is
thus of the order of 3·5 msec. at 23° C. ; if, however, we take as a measure
of the mechanical latent period the time between the stimulus and the
moment when the tension begins to rise from its minimum value, the period

[1] Schoepfle & Gilson suggest that latency-relaxation is an artefact, due to a fluid wave
disturbance, set up by the contractile process and operating in the opposite sense to that
of shortening, the progress of this wave being more rapid than the propagation of the
contractile process. Sandow, however, disagrees with this view (1947, 1950) and has
brought forward evidence suggesting that the latency-relaxation is a manifestation of
chemical events leading to contraction ; for example, the effects of pH and temperature
on the extent of the relaxation and on the time relationships of its different phases may
be linked with the reaction of the ATP-myosin system (p. 528). The effects of K^+ on
latency-relaxation (Sandow & Kahn ; Kahn & Sandow) are not so easy of interpretation.
Sandow's work indicates the value of the latency-relaxation as a sign of events leading to
the development of tension.

is 3·0 msec.   Fig. 222 is a simultaneous recording of tension and action potential taken from the work of Schaefer & Göpfert.

Studies with whole muscle, and more recently on isolated single fibres by Ramsey & Street and by Buchtal, have shown that contraction does not begin instantaneously along the whole length of the muscle fibre but progresses as a wave from the point of stimulation, so that in the absence of a load the more proximal part of the fibre contracts strongly against the more distal, relaxed, part.   As we shall see, the energy put forth by a muscle varies with the load, and it may well be that the mechanism for this differential liberation of energy is bound up with the differing modes of contraction with differing loads (*vide, e.g.,* Ramsey, 1947).

Summation and Tetanus

When the muscle is stimulated during the period of contraction a process of summation is observed, the second stimulus causing the tension to develop to a considerably higher value ; with repetitive stimulation at a high rate, the summated effects of successive stimuli lead to the development of a tension which may be nearly ten times as great as that developed in a single twitch, the muscle being said to be in *tetanus.* The frequency of stimulation necessary to obtain a complete tetanus will clearly depend on the contraction-time of the muscle, *i.e.,* the time from the beginning of the action potential to the point of maximum tension, a very rapid muscle requiring a high frequency ; whilst a muscle with a long refractory period, extending into the relaxation period, cannot develop a complete tetanus.

Alpha-State. The independence of mechanical and electrical events in muscular contraction is emphasised by D. E. S. Brown's studies on the stimulating effect of pressure.   Exposing a muscle to a uniform hydrostatic pressure of 272 atmospheres for a fraction of a second causes a typical twitch, differing from that obtained by the electrical stimulation of muscle or its nerve by the complete absence of any wave of action potential.   Moreover, it was found that a pressure-stimulus was capable of summating its effect with that of an electrical stimulus.   The pressure-stimulus was unaffected by the refractory state of the muscle following electrical stimulation,[1] so that the effects of summation could be studied with extremely short intervals between the electrical and pressure stimuli. Brown found that the maximum effect was obtained with an interval of 3·5 msec., the limiting period for augmentation being about 5 msec.   From his studies Brown assumed that the first stimulus activates the contractile mechanism to produce a certain *alpha-state* which requires time to develop to a maximum, and follows a curve indicated by Fig. 223 ; a new stimulus, applied during the 5 msec. during which the alpha-state waxes and wanes, is thought to produce a greater effect on the mechanical process the more intense the alpha-state, so that at 3·5 msec. the effect will be greatest and at 5 msec. it will be least.   This does not mean, however, that

---

[1] This is understandable ; the refractory condition is to be regarded as a condition in which the membrane is already depolarised, a new electrical stimulus being only effective when the membrane has recovered in some measure from this depolarisation. The pressure effect is presumably the result of a direct activation of the mechanical contractile process.

two stimuli applied within an interval of greater than 5 msec. will fail to summate ; summation is possible in frog and mammalian muscles over much longer periods. This summation, however, is regarded by Brown as the mechanical effect of the development of two separate cycles of alpha-state. Both stimuli produce alpha-states which, by themselves, would have led to a definite amount of tension ; since the development of tension is a comparatively slow process the two " quanta " of tension will add their effects and ordinary summation of the mechanical effect will take

place. When the interval is less than 5 msec., however, the second stimulus arrives at some phase of the first alpha-state, and its effect will be large or small according as the alpha-state already developed is large or small. If this viewpoint is correct, we may look upon the events following stimulation as a primary activation of the contractile mechanism, or development of an alpha-state ; this is presumably succeeded by the liberation of energy which leads to the development of tension. Both these processes are subject

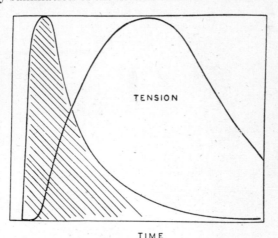

Fig. 223. The course of the *alpha*, or activation, process during an isometric twitch. *Alpha* process is represented by the shaded area. (D. E. S. Brown. *Biol. Symp.*)

to summation within certain periods of time, so that two successive stimuli may add their effects, either by summation of the active, or alpha, state or by a summation of the mechanical tension. The justification for the isolation of a separate process leading up to the later mechanical events must await an elucidation of the mechanism of energy transformation in contracting muscle ; what can be stated with certainty from Brown's work is that in the very early stage of the contractile process the muscle fibres acquire an " active " state in which they may be highly sensitive to a new stimulus ; the fact that this sensitivity does not persist for long indicates that it is succeeded by other changes which preclude or prejudice it in some manner.

The All-or-None Law

Just as with a bundle of nerve fibres, increasing the strength of stimulus above threshold produces increasing muscular responses until the maximal stimulus is reached, when further increase has no effect. That this increase in response was due to the successive entry of new muscle fibres into the total response was suggested by Gotch and demonstrated indirectly by Keith Lucas in 1905 and 1909. According to this viewpoint, a single fibre always responded maximally, *i.e.*, the effect was " all-or-none." In 1919

Pratt confirmed the so-called " quantal " nature of the response by observing single fibres of the frog's sartorius muscle under the microscope while stimulating the surface of the muscle with a pore-electrode, with a diameter of about 7μ. The contraction of individual fibres of this preparation could be recorded by the ingenious device of spraying mercury drops over the surface of the muscle ; on stimulating through the pore-electrode a drop could generally be found whose movements reflected the contraction of just one or two fibres immediately beneath it. The movements of a beam of light, reflected off this droplet, gave a record of the actual contraction. Fig. 224 illustrates the set-up. Observations carried

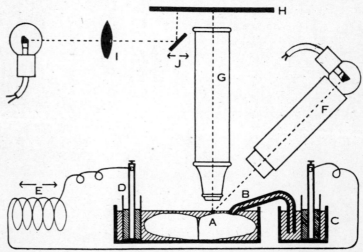

Fig. 224. Diagram indicating essentials of method for studying responses of single fibres. A, section of live preparation ; B, active electrode with pore in contact with muscle surface ; C, bath of Ringer's fluid containing Zn-ZnSO$_4$ terminal ; D, similar terminal in bath of Ringer's fluid covering the preparation—the indifferent electrode ; E, stimulating coil ; F, light projector for illuminating mercury globule over A ; G, recording microscope ; H, photographic plate ; I, lens system for projecting signal image on plate ; J, mirror, movable with coil, E. (Pratt & Eisenberger. Amer. J. Physiol.)

out by Pratt, using this technique, showed that the responses of a single fibre were all-or-none ; when the stimulus-intensity was increased continuously, any increase in response was abrupt, indicating the entry of a new, maximally contracting, unit.

Local Responses. Extension of this technique to the very thin sheet of muscle constituting the retrolingual membrane of the frog—where the isolation of activity in single fibres was more precise—and the development of techniques for the study of single fibres dissected out completely from a muscle, brought to light many apparent contradictions to the all-or-none law. Thus stimulation of a single fibre with increasing strength of stimulus produced contractions of increasing strength ; these graded responses differed in an important respect, however, from the maximal response, in that they were not associated with a wave of action potential ; in keeping with this finding they were generally localised to a limited region in the neighbourhood of the stimulating electrode. In some cases, however, the whole fibre went into a prolonged contraction, as opposed to a twitch, but this differed once again from a normal tetanus in the absence of action potentials. This type of contraction is not confined to single fibres but was observed long before in whole muscles and is described as a *contracture*, generally produced by injurious agents (*e.g.*, NH_4Cl) ; it also develops on prolonged application of high hydrostatic pressures (Brown) ; these phenomena stress the independence, already discussed, of the conducting and contractile mechanisms. It was considered at first, for example by Gelfan, that the local response of the fibre was a consequence of the highly localised conditions of stimulation, the electrotonic currents being so concentrated as to fail to activate the conduction mechanism (*i.e.*, to depolarise a sufficient area of membrane to induce a propagated all-or-none disturbance), yet was sufficient to activate the contractile mechanism. This viewpoint has since been questioned ; thus Steiman has analysed with great care the conditions under which localised and graded responses may be obtained in single fibres of the intact retrolingual membrane. The conclusion that he drew from his analysis was that the production of graded responses was not necessarily dependent on the size of the electrodes, except in so far as a micro-electrode generally caused a localised damage to the fibre, and it was this damage, primarily, that was responsible for the local response. In the fresh uninjured preparation the responses were always maximal and all-or-none even with electrodes as small as $0.25–4.00\mu$ in diameter. By damage through over-stimulation, cutting the fibre, or applying solutions rich in KCl, local responses could always be obtained ; on allowing a fatigued fibre to recover sufficiently, maximal all-or-none responses could generally be recorded, although during the fatigued state the responses were local. Frequency of stimulation was found to be an important factor also ; thus fresh uninjured fibres could be stimulated for as long as 100 minutes, at a rate of 30 per minute, without producing localised responses, whilst with a frequency of 33 per minute partial responses were obtained in a few minutes. Nevertheless, Steiman's conclusions have not been fully accepted ; and it would appear that Gelfan's view is more nearly correct, the local mechanical response being analogous to the local non-propagated electrical responses observed in excitable tissues. The difficulty in demonstrating local responses in normal muscle fibres probably depends on the circumstance that the threshold for activation of the mechanical response is usually very close to the threshold for the fully propagated electrical disturbance, which activates the whole fibre.

Contracture and Activation of the Contractile Process. The exact relationship between the electrical and mechanical events in muscular contraction is still largely a matter of speculation. Their independence under certain conditions is well brought out by the phenomenon of contracture, in which a muscle exhibits a sustained, reversible contraction with the liberation of heat and formation of lactic acid, but shows no propagated spike potentials, as in the sustained contraction of a tetanus.

The contracture is not propagated, in the sense that if only a portion of the fibre is involved, as is most frequently the case, there is no spread to other regions.   A typical agent for producing contractures is veratrine ; on stimulating a veratrine-poisoned muscle it exhibits a twitch followed by a sustained contraction, or contracture ; if only half the muscle is poisoned only half is involved in the contracture.   Strong direct currents, heat, acids, narcotics, potassium, citrate, caffeine, acetylcholine, nicotine, and many other drugs are capable of producing contractures.   The most instructive study of the phenomenon is that of Kuffler (1946) on a single fibre preparation ; a drop of veratrine was applied locally to a fibre, and a subsequent stimulus gave rise to a series of propagated spikes (as many as 300/sec.) which rapidly gave way to a pronounced negativity of the electrode on the poisoned region ; at first the negativity showed oscillations—abortive spikes—but finally became smooth.   The fibre exhibited a local contracture as long as the negative potential lasted.   A number of other facts all pointed to the contracture as being essentially a non-propagated contraction, of which the graded responses described earlier are merely transient examples ; the sustained nature is apparently due to the prolonged depolarisation caused by the agent, be it a maintained constant current (the contracture is at the cathode), acetylcholine, potassium, and so on.   Thus the condition is similar to that of nerve treated by certain blocking agents, in the sense that the conducting mechanism is out of action through depolarisation [1] ; if, however, the contractile mechanism is triggered by a depolarisation of the muscle membrane, we may understand why it is that the fibre remains contracted over the poisoned region.   We have seen that anodal polarisation restores conduction to a nerve, blocked with a narcotic, and it is interesting that the same procedure will cause relaxation of a contracture.   Thus, as Katz has suggested in a recent review of the subject (1950), the phenomena of contracture, or local contractions, strongly indicate that the trigger for activating the contractile mechanism is the depolarisation of the muscle membrane by the wave of action potential, or its negative after-potential ; if the action potential is blocked at any point in its path along the muscle fibre, the contractile process is likewise blocked, and the contraction remains local.   Repolarisation of the membrane brings the contraction to an end, so that any substance interfering with this, such as a narcotic or veratrine, causes a sustained contraction or contracture.   The contracture following on treatment of the end-plate with acetylcholine or nicotine is presumably due to its sustained depolarising action.   How the change in potential at the surface activates the fibre is, as yet, a complete mystery.

Grading of Contraction in Vertebrate and Invertebrate Muscles.   In crustacean muscles an all-or-none contraction seems to be more the exception than the rule ; we have already indicated (p. 451) that these muscles show a remarkable capacity for facilitation, and it was thought for a long time that this feature was significant in the grading of mechanical contractions in a whole muscle.   To make this point clear we may consider,

---

[1] According to Feng, for example, a wave of action potential cannot cross a region of contracture.

first, the grading of contraction in the all-or-nothing type of vertebrate muscle. The tension developed in a single fibre increases as we pass from a single stimulus (the twitch) to repetitive discharges of increasing frequency up to a limit, when the tetanus is perfect. The strength of contraction of a single fibre may thus be varied by varying the frequency of discharge in its nerve fibre. A given motor fibre, in vertebrates, innervates only a small fraction of the fibres in a muscle, so that we may divide the muscle into a number of functional units—the groups of muscle fibres supplied by a single nerve fibre (this may be as small as two or three in the extra-ocular muscles, but may be a hundred or more in others). Further gradation of muscular contraction can be achieved by variation in the number of motor units that are activated. In the crab, the muscle fibres are supplied by the ramifications of just one or two motor fibres ; consequently, in the extreme case of a muscle innervated by one fibre only, if every single impulse could pass the neuromuscular junctions, grading could only be achieved by summation of contractions. If these contractions were of the all-or-none type, this would leave very little play for gradation of the muscle as a whole. A single shock applied to a crustacean muscle rarely produces any response itself, but it facilitates the passage of another stimulus ; consequently, on increasing the frequency of stimulation, a smooth rise in tension is observed which reaches a maximum when the frequency is 250–300 per sec. (in the case of the leg muscle of the crab). Thus, on the supposition that contraction in an individual fibre was all-or-none, it was considered by Pantin and by Katz that gradation was achieved mainly by facilitation, more and more fibres contributing to the tension as the frequency was increased. In 1946 Katz & Kuffler showed that an even more important factor in gradation was the local, non-propagated, responses of single fibres ; at a low frequency of stimulation the contraction was confined to the end-plate region, and no propagated action potentials were observed ; as the frequency increased, the local responses became bigger until a point was reached when propagated action potentials spread over the fibres and their contractions were of the all-or-none type. Thus it is quite possible to stimulate a crab muscle at 50/sec. and observe considerable tension without being able to record a single propagated spike ; instead, end-plate potentials are observed which increase in size with increasing frequency until finally, if the frequency is high enough, they grow into full-size spikes. The crustacean muscle can therefore be graded by three mechanisms, all depending on the frequency of nervous discharge, as follows : (*a*) the build-up of local contractions ; (*b*) the development of tetanus from propagated twitches ; (*c*) the recruitment of individual fibres.

We may note, finally, that certain muscles of the crab, *e.g.*, the closer of the claw, behave more like the vertebrate muscles in responding with a twitch to a single impulse, and in showing little facilitation ; such muscles are classed as " fast " in contrast to the " slow " system already discussed ; Wiersma has shown that some muscles are supplied by two or more motor axons, one being of the " fast," the remainder, of the " slow " type.

Further Mechanical Aspects

Tetanic stimulation of a muscle causes it to develop a greater tension than that manifested in a single twitch ; for any given set of conditions it is, in fact, the maximum tension of which the muscle is capable. We must now investigate the factors modifying the development of tension ; furthermore, it is not sufficient that a muscle develop tension, it must also, when allowed to shorten against an external load, perform mechanical work ; and it becomes necessary to examine the relationship between the amount of work done and the conditions of shortening.

Length-Tension Diagram. If a muscle is fixed rigidly at one end and the tendon is tied with a wire to a rigid " isometric lever," capable of recording the tension ; by varying the amount of slack in the wire, we may record the tension developed by a tetanic stimulation when the muscle is at different

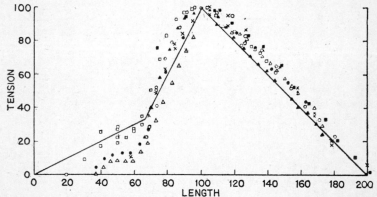

Fig. 225. Length-tension diagram for isolated muscle fibres. Ordinates : Tension developed (total minus resting) in per cent. of maximum developed. Abscissæ : Length, in per cent. of resting length. (Ramsey. *Medical Physics.* Chicago. Year Book Publishers.)

lengths—from its normal, resting, length to that achieved in maximal shortening ; moreover, by stretching the muscle (by tightening its connection to the lever), lengths greater than normal can be obtained. The results may be plotted as the classical *length-tension diagram* (Fig. 225). Certain aspects of this length-tension diagram will be discussed later ; here we may note, first, that the curve represents the tension developed during *activity* at different lengths ; a length-tension diagram of resting muscle may also be constructed, although here we are confined to regions of length greater than resting. The tensions developed in these circumstances are, of course, very small by comparison with active muscle ; there has been some argument as to whether the resting curve represents the behaviour of the muscle substance or only the sarcolemma or connective tissue. Ramsey & Street's studies with single fibres strongly indicate that the elastic behaviour of resting fibres is determined largely by the sarcolemma. If, as seems true, however, the substance of the muscle fibre is made up of long myosin chains (p. 524), which may be unfolded on stretching, some of the elastic properties of the fibres must be due to the muscle substance, although it may well be that the sarcolemma dominates the picture.[1]   Secondly, we may note that the tension developed in active muscle is maximal at resting length, *i.e.*, a stretched or contracted muscle develops less tension than one at resting length.   In normal isolated muscle the length-tension diagram can only be measured over a range of about plus or minus 30 per cent. of the resting length ; with the isolated fibres prepared by Ramsey & Street, lengths ranging between 200 and 20 per cent. of the resting value could be studied (Fig. 225) ; it was found that, over the range of 66 to 160 per cent. of resting length, the phenomena were completely reversible ; when the muscle was stretched beyond 160 per cent., it was found that the total developed tension varied with the previous history of the fibre (*i.e.*, after stretching, say, to 200 per cent. the tension at 170 per cent. was less than if the muscle had only been stretched to this latter length).   If, however, the tension developed, minus the initial resting tension, was plotted (as has been done in Fig. 225), this *increment* of tension due to activity was quite reversible, a fact suggesting that excessive stretching impairs the elasticity of the sarcolemma and leaves the contractile process intact.   Certainly the resting length of the fibre is increased after excessive stretching (Hønck). When the fibres were allowed to contract to less than 60 per cent. of resting length several interesting phenomena became manifest.   The resting muscle made a loop between its two supports ; on stimulation, the loop immediately straightened out, and, on cessation of the tetanus, the muscle relaxed rapidly to form the loop again, so long as the shortening did not proceed to more than 60 per cent. of the resting length.   When greater shortening was permitted, however, the fibre took longer by several seconds to shorten completely and, moreover, remained permanently shortened after cessation of the tetanus.   On forcible re-extension of the fibre, the tension developed was very much less than normal for this new length, in fact the whole length-tension diagram was on a lower scale. Apparently excessive shortening causes an irreversible change in the contractile mechanism ; the new state of the fibre has been termed the *delta-state*.   Corresponding with this abnormal physiological behaviour, cytological studies revealed a severe upset in the organisation of the striations of the fibre, consisting in the appearance of irregularly alternating bands of close, and widely separated, striations.   The appearance was strongly suggestive of similar observations on localised contractures produced by a variety of agents, *e.g.*, caffeine.

Finally, we may note that the area under the length-tension curve provides a measure of the total theoretical work that a muscle is capable of in shortening from twice its resting length to one-fifth of this. For a muscle of 1 sq. cm. of cross-section and 1 cm. of resting length, this comes out at 3,250 gm. cm.   Expressed in terms of the maximum tension the muscle can develop (T_o), the maximal work on shortening from twice to one-fifth resting length is $0.92\,T_o L_o$, where L_o is the resting length.

[1] Sichel (1941) questions the conclusion of Ramsey & Street ; he finds that the sarcolemma has only half the resistance to stretch of a normal muscle fibre.

Viscous-Elastic Properties of Muscle

If we come now to consider the mechanical work done when a muscle shortens against a load, we find that this varies very considerably with the load to be lifted ; experiments on the isolated frog muscle, and on the human forearm, by Hill showed that the work done decreased rapidly as the speed of shortening increased. It was found that the work done could be approximately expressed by the simple equation :—

$$W = W_o(1 - k/t)$$

where W is the work actually done, t is the time of shortening, and W_o and k are constants. Since a small load is lifted more rapidly than a large one, the work done decreases with decreasing load. As Hill pointed out, the conditions of muscular contraction appeared to be similar in many respects to the behaviour of a viscous-elastic system ; as a result of the contractile process, the viscosity of the muscle increased so that contraction was

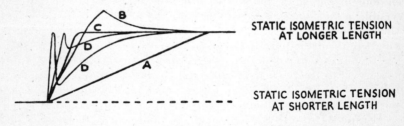

STATIC ISOMETRIC TENSION
AT LONGER LENGTH

STATIC ISOMETRIC TENSION
AT SHORTER LENGTH

ZERO TENSION

Fig. 226.   Illustrating the effects of stretching a frog's sartorius at varying speeds during a maximal tetanus. A, very slow stretch ; D, very rapid ; B, fairly rapid ; C, intermediate between B and D. (Gasser & Hill. *Proc. Roy. Soc.*)

associated with a considerable loss of energy in overcoming internal friction. On this view, W_o is the ideal work which would be obtained when no energy was lost by viscous resistance, *i.e.*, the maximum work calculated from the length-tension diagram. Thus, if the muscle were a simple elastic system, like a wire spring, the work obtainable from it would be entirely determined by the tension it developed at different lengths, and could be calculated from a length-tension diagram.

The fundamental difference between an elastic and a viscous-elastic system is well brought out by further experiments of Gasser & Hill ; these authors studied the effects of applying sudden stretches to a tetanised muscle, or, alternatively, of allowing a tetanised muscle to contract suddenly to a shorter length, and recording the changes of tension in consequence. Fig. 226 illustrates the general results of stretching. The horizontal lines indicate the static isometric tensions developed by the muscle at two lengths. Curve D shows the effect of a sudden stretch ; the tension rises rapidly, as we might expect, but then falls rapidly to rise again slowly to a value characteristic of the greater length. If the stretch is not quite so rapid, the tension rises above the static isometric value and approaches the latter from above (Curve B), whilst a very slow stretch (Curve A) gives a continuous rise in tension to the new level. The reverse phenomena were also described ; a sudden release of a tetanised muscle to a shorter length caused the tension to fall almost to zero and then to rise to the value characteristic of its new length ; only if the shortening was very slow did the tension approach its new value along a straight line. In a passive (unstimulated) muscle, no such phenomena were observable, the muscle adopting a new tension for each length immediately. These effects were considered to fit well with the concept of a damped spring as in Fig. 227, I, or, more simply still, a thin india-rubber balloon filled with a very viscous material.

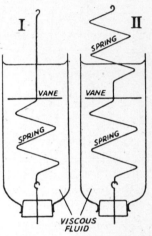

Levin-Wyman Model. Later Levin & Wyman drew attention to the inadequacy of this simple model ; they pointed out that a quick release of the hook attached to the damped spring must result in a *complete loss of tension*, the whole being taken up at first by the viscous resistance of the vane ; only as the spring adopted its new length would the tension rise to the value characteristic of the new length. Now although Hill's results on quick releases indicated a drop in tension below the normal isometric value for the new length, this drop was not to zero unless the shortening was greater than 15 per cent. Levin & Wyman suggested a new model, Fig. 227, II, consisting of a damped viscous-elastic spring in series with an undamped spring. If this model is at equilibrium under a certain tension and is suddenly released, the top spring will shorten first, the lower one being unable to change its length immediately

Fig. 227. Viscous - elastic models to illustrate the behaviour of muscle. System I. Simple damped spring. System II. Damped spring (contractile elements) in series with undamped spring (elastic elements). (Levin & Wyman. *Proc. Roy. Soc.*)

on account of the damping vane. The equilibrium between the two springs will thus be disturbed, the top spring shortening too much at first, the bottom one too little ; the tension exerted at first will therefore be too small, but not zero. Equilibrium will be approached by the shortening of the lower spring and an extension of the upper one. It is possible to calculate the form of the curve obtained by plotting work done, against speed of contraction or relaxation, for the two models. Model I gives a simple straight line, whilst Model II gives an exponential type of curve. Levin & Wyman constructed an ergometer in which both tension and shortening were registered simultaneously, while the isolated tetanised muscle was allowed to shorten at a constant speed, which could be regulated. The resulting record was a length-tension curve (Fig. 228), the area contained by the curve representing the work done (the muscle could also be lengthened by stretch applied during the tetanus, and a length-tension diagram could be obtained representing work done *on* the muscle). Thus in Fig. 228 the muscle has been allowed to contract at several different speeds during the application of a tetanic stimulus. The tension before release is high and is the isometric value at

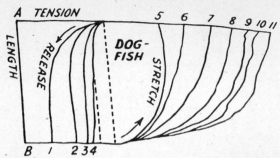

FIG. 228. Length-tension curves from jaw muscle of dog-fish, recorded by the Levin-Wyman ergometer which permits a muscle to contract at constant speed. Numbers indicate order in which observations were made. The corresponding speeds of shortening or stretching are as follows (arbitrary units) : 1, 6·15 ; 2, 0·70 ; 3, 0·27 ; 4, 0·13 ; 5, 0·17 ; 6, 0·25 ; 7, 0·49 ; 8, 1·42 ; 9, 3·47 ; 10, 3·69 ; 11, 6·71. (Levin & Wyman. *Proc. Roy. Soc.*)

the original length ; as the muscle shortens, and lifts the weight, the tension falls, to attain a constant value—the isometric value at the new length. If the shortening is much slower (*i.e.*, if the weight to be lifted is much greater) the fall in tension with shortening is considerably less and the

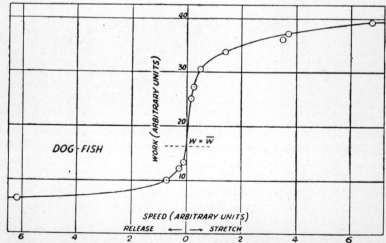

FIG. 229. Curve relating work to speed of contraction or extension of muscle. (Levin & Wyman. *Proc. Roy. Soc.*)

area under the curve (*i.e.*, the work done) is greater. By plotting work (either done on the muscle during extension or done by the muscle during contraction) against speed of contraction or lengthening, we get a typical S-shaped curve (Fig. 229) whose form may be predicted mathematically from the theoretical behaviour of the damped-elastic system depicted in

Fig. 227, II. It will be seen from this curve that the work done increases with decreasing speed of shortening, the curve cutting the ordinates at a value, $\bar{w}$, the work done with zero shortening ; this, of course, is an imaginary quantity since, when the muscle contracts isometrically, the work done is zero.

These mechanical studies, and a host of others, enable us to characterise the behaviour of active muscle in terms of a relatively simple system ; the transposition of this model to muscle in terms of the actual structure, and modifications in this structure, is another matter. We may regard the contractile process as a shortening of the myosin fibrils ; this shortening we may look upon as the shortening of the damped spring, *i.e.*, the rearrangement of myosin chains is by no means frictionless but, on the contrary, is damped, owing to the high viscosity, or molecular friction. The shortening of the fibrils is associated with the stretching of connective tissue, a process similar to the stretching of a metal spring, taking place with little or no frictional loss, so that the elastic energy may be stored as potential energy during shortening. These elastic elements are thus the undamped spring. According to Gasser & Hill's measurements, if a muscle in isometric tetanus is suddenly released to 85 per cent. of its length, the tension falls to zero, whereas with smaller releases some tension remains ; Levin & Wyman conclude, therefore, that in an isometric contraction the undamped elastic elements are stretched by an amount equalling 15 per cent. of the muscle's resting length, whilst Hill (1949*e*) computed, from his more precise measurement, a stretch of 10 per cent. These free elastic elements may be regarded as buffers, protecting the muscle against too sudden changes in tension ; moreover, since they take up the tension developed in the true contractile elements, a very sudden shortening is not associated with a temporary complete loss of tension in the muscle—a very important factor in the smooth performance of muscular tasks.

Fenn Effect. This rather simple scheme of an undamped and a damped elastic system in series accounted for many of the mechanical properties of muscle, and was widely accepted for a long time ; however, Fenn pointed out the true implications of the model and showed that they were inconsistent with some of his findings. Thus the model envisaged contraction as a primary shortening of the damped elements (the lower spring in Fig. 227, II) which, pulling against the elastic elements, stored their contractile energy as potential energy, and it was these elastic elements that were considered to do the mechanical work by subsequently shortening. On this basis, therefore, the muscle, on stimulation, developed a given amount of heat, and a given amount of potential energy in the elastic elements, both these quantities varying with the length of the fibres of the muscle. The amount of this elastic energy that could be recovered as mechanical work would depend on the art of the experimenter with no relation to the energy liberated. Fenn, in 1923, showed that the amount of actual energy liberated by a muscle (*i.e.*, heat plus external work) was not constant for any given initial condition of the muscle, but varied with the load, a large load resulting in the liberation of more energy than a small load. Thus, in some way, the muscle can adjust its output of energy to the task that is to be performed, a property quite foreign to the Levin-Wyman model in its simple form. As Fenn aptly remarked in 1924, we may think of the muscle lifting a weight either by (a) doing work on a spring and then allowing the latter to shorten and lift the weight, or (b) by raising the weight by a chain and windlass ; each link, as it is wound up, requiring extra energy *at the moment of winding* ; the *Fenn effect* disposes of the first alternative. In 1935 Fenn & Marsh re-emphasised the inadequacy of the spring model and showed that, under conditions of isotonic contraction, the rate of shortening should vary linearly with the load if the muscle did indeed behave in the simple manner demanded by the model. For example, in an isotonic contraction, the undamped element would be stretched until it just began to lift the weight, and after this it would retain a constant length and constant force to the end of contraction. The speed of contraction would thus be determined, for this particular load, by the viscous elements. The same would be true of other loads so that, if the model is correct, we must expect.the speed of contraction to vary with the load in the manner predicted of a simple damped system, *i.e.*, it should follow the equation : $P = P_o - kv$, where P is the load, or tension developed, v is the velocity of contraction and P_o the isometric tension ; Fenn & Marsh showed that the relationship was not linear, but could be described by the equation :—

$$P = P_o\, e^{-av} - kv$$

With small loads the velocity of contraction is high ; as the load increases, the velocity falls off, but not so rapidly as would be expected for the Levin-Wyman model ; as Fenn points out, such a relationship would be given by a system in which the energy made available for contraction increased as the load increased.

Effects of Stretches Applied During Contraction. The work of Gasser & Hill on the effect of stretching a contracting muscle has provided some

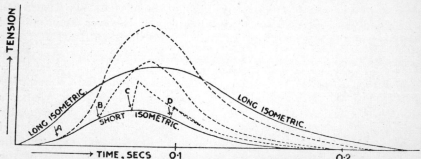

FIG. 230.   Illustrating the effect, on the tension developed, of stretching a
muscle at various moments during a twitch. (After Gasser & Hill. *Proc.
Roy. Soc.*)

information regarding the true time-course of the fundamental contractile process. To appreciate the full value of these experiments we must form a clear picture of the events taking place during a twitch. The stimulus sets off the fundamental contractile process which involves, presumably, a shortening of myosin chains ; the development of tension in the muscle requires time, the elastic elements having to be stretched ; clearly, the tension could be developed more rapidly if the muscle were artificially stretched during the contractile process, the actual tension developed depending on the vigour with which the damped elements were contracting. Some estimate of the force with which these elements could pull, at different times during a twitch, should therefore be obtained by applying stretches at different moments. The results of an experiment of this nature are shown in Fig. 230. The curves in full lines represent the observed tension during isometric twitches at two lengths. With the muscle fixed at the shorter length, it was stretched suddenly to the greater length at different moments after the stimulus ; it will be seen that the tension developed by stretching at A was very considerably greater than that developed by stimulating the muscle at the greater length. Clearly we are tapping here practically all the available force in the contractile

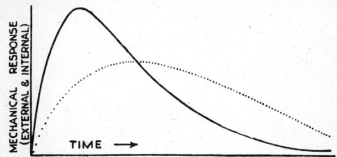

Fig. 231. Diagram of supposed internal (" fundamental ") mechanical change in muscle. Broken line, observed external response, lagging, owing to viscous-elastic forces, behind the internal change. (Gasser & Hill. *Proc. Roy. Soc.*)

process ; as the stretches are applied later and later, the tension developed becomes smaller until, finally, the tension developed during stretch is no greater than that in passive muscle. The results show that the energy of the twitch is made available sooner than is indicated by the curve of isometric tension ; an analysis of the results suggests that the contractile process follows the curve in full lines in Fig. 231, the maximum of the fundamental process occurring at the initial third of the observed rise in tension (we may note here that D. E. S. Brown's analysis reveals a fundamental change in the muscle, the alpha-process, which reaches its maximum even earlier, within one-tenth of the contraction-time ; p. 485).

As Hill has recently emphasised, the fact that, when a muscle in isometric tetanus is released, the time-course of re-development of tension is identical with that of the original development, suggests that the onset of the fully active state is very rapid indeed. Thus in tetanus the fibres are fully active ; on release, the tension falls because the elastic components, which transmit the tension to the recording apparatus, must be re-stretched ; the time-course of the re-development is therefore the time-course of stretching the elastic elements when the contractile elements are in their fully active state at the outset. The fact that this time-course agrees well with that for the initial development of tension suggests that the contractile elements have their maximal force at the outset of contraction likewise. More precise studies of the effects of stretches, applied just at the end of the latent period, showed that the development of maximal activity by the contractile elements was, indeed, very rapid—too rapid for its rate of growth to be assessed. In the more slowly responding tortoise muscle it was possible to determine the course of events with some precision, and it was shown that activity begins about half-way through the latent period, *i.e.*, just about when the latency-relaxation begins. The latency-relaxation may therefore be regarded, according to Hill, as a slight lengthening of the muscle resulting from the altered molecular pattern of the muscle proteins, corresponding with the development of activity. In a single twitch, the state of maximal activity of the contractile elements is not maintained for long, so that, when the muscle as a whole shows its maximal tension, the contractile elements are in a partially relaxed state (Fig. 231) ; the greater tension developed by a tetanus, as compared with a twitch, finds a ready explanation on this basis ; repeated shocks prevent the contractile elements from relaxing, so that they are enabled to exert their maximal force on the fully stretched elastic elements, instead of a reduced force, as in a twitch.

THERMAL ASPECTS OF CONTRACTION

General Considerations

Since the transformations of energy are associated with the liberation of heat, the course of heat production during contraction and relaxation can provide some idea of the timing of chemical events during the process. The hope has frequently been expressed that such thermodynamic studies will also provide useful clues as to the intimate mechanisms involved ; it must be emphasised, however, that unless the exact nature of the chemical and physical processes is already understood, the true interpretation of the time-course of events is impossible. Muscular contraction requires the expenditure of more energy than the normal basal requirements, and this therefore requires the liberation of energy bound up in chemical substances, *e.g.*, adenosine triphosphate, phosphagen, etc., capable of reacting to produce energy in the required forms ; this liberation will be associated with the production of heat, which is to be regarded as a necessary waste ; but unless the efficiencies of the various metabolic steps are well understood, *i.e.*, the amounts of waste heat in proportion to the total amount of energy made available, it is impossible, from purely thermal measurements, to estimate the exact course of events during contraction and relaxation. Thus contraction is probably the result of the folding up of myosin chains, together with the stretching of the elastic components of the muscle—sarcolemma, elastic connective tissue, etc. These may be regarded as purely mechanical events, which may be associated either with the absorption of heat, *i.e.*, cooling, as for example when rubber is stretched, or the liberation of heat, as in a frictional process. The actual rearrangement of the myosin linkages, associated with folding, may require a preliminary supply of chemical energy, and further supplies may be required while contraction is maintained, to prevent the myosin chains from unfolding ; if this is true, the development of tension in the muscle will be preceded and accompanied by the liberation of waste heat associated with the chemical transformations. Relaxation will undoubtedly involve further frictional and elastic recoils which will be associated with the liberation of heat, although some element of this purely mechanical aspect may be accompanied by cooling. On the other hand, it may conceivably be, as Ramsey has argued (p. 513), that the myosin chains are in their highest state of internal energy when they are stretched, so that energy is required to stretch them out after contraction, *i.e.*, in the relaxation process ; in this event, contraction heat and maintenance heat acquire a new significance. The importance of the purely mechanical aspect of heat production is well brought out by the heat production of muscle (*a*), when it is allowed to relax with the weight which it has lifted, and (*b*), when it is allowed to relax without a weight. In the former case Hill has shown that the heat production is greater by an amount equal to the potential energy of the lifted weight ; it follows, therefore, that the potential energy of the weight is transformed completely into heat. The importance of the metabolic aspect, on the other hand, is illustrated by the effect of stretching the actively contracting muscle ; this is associated with a diminished heat production which is best explained by a diminution in the rate of liberation of chemical energy, although the tension developed may be the same as in the shorter muscle.[1] The thermodynamic data, therefore, reveal only gross changes not easily susceptible of interpretation ; nevertheless, the rapidity and accuracy with which they may be recorded, thanks to the experimental skill shown by A. V. Hill and Hartree in particular,[2] have permitted certain interesting, if tentative, conclusions to be drawn.

Heat Production During a Tetanus

Initial and Delayed Heats. The contraction of muscle, be it a twitch or a sustained tetanus, is accompanied by the liberation of excess heat, occurring, under aerobic conditions, in two principal phases, the *initial* and *delayed heats*. The resting heat-rate of frog muscle at 15° C. has been given by A. V. Hill as $6 \cdot 3 . 10^{-5}$ cal./g.sec. With tetanic stimulation, the heat production rises rapidly, as shown in Fig. 232 ; according to Hartree, the heat production during the maintenance of tension is in the region of $2 . 10^{-1}$ cal./g.sec. With cessation of stimulation the heat production falls abruptly to a value in the region of only 0·7 per cent. of the initial rate, and

[1] Hill (1950) has recently presented evidence suggesting that a stretch, applied to a muscle during shortening, actually causes a reversal of the energy-providing reactions. We may mention here that a passive (unstimulated) muscle responds to a stretch by an increased O_2-consumption (Meyerhof *et al.*, 1932 ; Feng, 1932), which is doubtless reflected in the liberation of heat.

[2] As Hill has frequently emphasised, an important factor in the success of this work has been the skill of A. C. Downing in the construction and design of his sensitive galvanometers.

soon falls much lower ; nevertheless this recovery heat is so prolonged that the *total* recovery heat is of the same order of magnitude as the *initial* heat. According to Hill's recent measurements, the ratio of the total energy liberated to the initial energy set free is equal to 2 under a variety of conditions of stimulation, both isometric and isotonic. Under isometric conditions, where all the initial energy appears as heat, this means that the recovery heat and initial heat are equal. When the muscle is caused to contract in N_2 the initial heat is altered very little (Fig. 232), whilst the recovery heat becomes almost zero. An analysis of the events under these conditions indicates that there is a certain quantity of delayed anaerobic

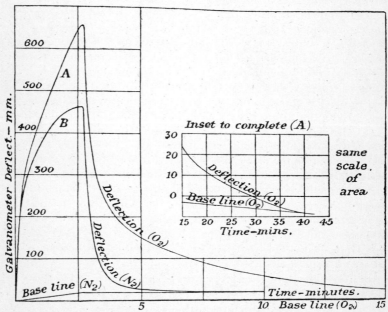

Fig. 232. Galvanometer records of heat-production of muscle in a series of twitches. A, in oxygen ; B, in nitrogen. The total heat is given by the area of each curve above its appropriate base-line. *Inset :* The later part of curve A, reduced in scale five times horizontally, increased five times vertically. The muscle gave 51 twitches during the first 2 mins. 40 secs. of the recording. (Hill. *Proc. Roy. Soc.*)

heat, amounting to about 8 per cent. of the initial heat ; it is liberated within about 20 sec. of cessation of a short tetanus, so that delayed, or recovery, heat of a muscle in N_2 is soon over. The small reduction in the initial heat, on stimulation in N_2, is due entirely to the fact that the recovery heat is abolished, since during a tetanus there must be an element of recovery heat ; this fact, together with the observation that a muscle may develop just as high a tension under anaerobic conditions as when O_2 is present, indicates that the energy required for the contraction of muscle is derived from non-oxidative reactions. The restoration of this energy, on the other hand, relies exclusively on oxidative processes. It will be seen later that the recovery heat is greater when the muscle does mechanical work during its contraction than when it does none, in fact the heat is greater by an amount equal to the thermal equivalent of this work. The recovery heat is the outward manifestation of a metabolic process which restores energy to the muscle ; the heat itself is so much lost energy, so that the *recovery energy required* must be at least equal to this extra heat production plus the energy involved in the work done ; since the heat production involved in doing work is found to be equal to the work done, the extra recovery energy, necessary when the muscle does work, is at least twice the extra recovery heat. Consequently we may tentatively assume that, when a certain amount of *heat* is liberated by muscle in the recovery process, the actual amount of *energy* utilised is twice this ; thus the rate of recovery heat is of the order of 2·8 to 6 times the resting heat, so that the rate of O_2-*consumption* must, in these circumstances, be some 5·6 to 12 times the normal resting value ; calculations made by Hill indicate that such a high rate is possible under the conditions of his experiments.

Chemical Events. The chemical reactions involved in muscular contraction may now be briefly indicated ; the energy for contraction is *ultimately* derived from the oxidation of carbohydrate—glycogen—to CO_2 and H_2O, but the fact that a muscle can contract vigorously for a time in the complete absence of O_2 indicates that the oxidative reaction is concerned with the restitution of energy derived from non-oxidative sources ; this is especially apparent in the greatly increased O_2-consumption of the organism *after* vigorous muscular work has been performed, a phenomenon illustrating the concept of " oxygen-debt," elaborated by A. V. Hill. The currently accepted view of the chain of reactions is as follows :—

(1) Reaction most closely connected in time with contraction :
$$ATP \longrightarrow ADP \qquad + H_3PO_4$$
(Adenosine triphosphate) (Adenosine diphosphate)

(2) Restitution Process (*a*) $ADP + Creatine\ phosphate \longrightarrow Creatine + ATP$
(3) Restitution Process (*b*)   Rephosphorylation of creatine.

Restitution process (*b*) is endothermic and requires energy which is ultimately derived from the breakdown of glycogen. Under *anaerobic conditions* glycogen (or glucose) is " glycolysed " to lactic acid through a number of stages involving the phosphorylation of organic intermediate compounds. The details of the reactions may be found in any modern textbook of biochemistry ; a brief sketch is as follows :—

$Glycogen + H_3PO_4 \dashrightarrow Glucose\text{-}1\text{-}phosphate \longrightarrow Glucose\text{-}6\text{-}phosphate \longrightarrow Fructose\text{-}6\text{-}phosphate$

$Fructose\text{-}6\text{-}phosphate + ATP \longrightarrow Fructose\text{-}1:6\text{-}phosphate + ADP$

$ATP + Creatine \longrightarrow ADP + creatine\ phosphate$

$Fructose\ 1:6\ phosphate \diagup^{Dioxyacetone\ phosphate \longrightarrow 3\text{-}glyceraldehyde\ phosphate}_{\diagdown 3\text{-}glyceraldehyde\ phosphate}$

$3\text{-}Glyceraldehyde\ phosphate + H_3PO_4 \longrightarrow 1:3\text{-}diphosphoglyceraldehyde$

$1:3\text{-}diphosphoglyceraldehyde + CoI \longrightarrow 1:3\text{-}diphosphoglycerate + CoIH_2$

$1:3\text{-}diphosphoglycerate + ADP \longrightarrow 3\text{-}phosphoglycerate + ATP$

$3\text{-}phosphoglycerate - H_2O \longrightarrow Phosphopyruvate$

$Phosphopyruvate + ADP \longrightarrow Pyruvate + ATP$

$Pyruvate + CoIH_2 \dashrightarrow Lactate + CoI.$

It will be noted that ATP appears to be involved in phosphorylation of glucose intermediates besides in transfer of energy to the contractile process.

During glycolysis, a part of the energy set free is restored to the creatine by reconversion to creatine phosphate. We can thus understand how, even under strictly anaerobic conditions, the muscle is able to function normally; lactic acid, however, accumulates and causes an early onset of fatigue; and complete recovery from anaerobic conditions involves a further restitution process, namely the oxidation of part of the lactic acid to CO_2 and H_2O, and the reconversion of the remainder to glycogen. Restitution process (*b*) may be described as :—

$$\underset{\text{Glycogen unit}}{C_6H_{10}O_5} + H_2O \rightarrow \underset{\text{Lactic acid}}{2\ C_3H_6O_3}$$

during the course of which creatine is rephosphorylated ; whilst subsequent restitution consists in :—

$$1/5\left\{2\ C_3H_6O_3 + 6\ O_2 \rightarrow 6\ CO_2 + 6\ H_2O\right\}$$

$$4/5\left\{2\ C_3H_6O_3 \rightarrow C_6H_{10}O_5 + H_2O\right\}$$

Some of the energy of oxidation of lactic acid appears as heat, the remainder being used in the endothermic re-synthesis of glycogen. The cycle is now complete, the heat and mechanical work performed being equivalent to the heat of combustion of the glycogen that has disappeared.

Normally, however, muscular contraction is carried out under adequately aerobic conditions, in which case lactic acid is not formed ; the process of glycolysis takes place only up to the stage of formation of pyruvate but then this compound, instead of being dehydrogenated by lactic dehydrogenase, is oxidised by a highly complex series of reactions to form CO_2 and H_2O, a part of the energy made available by these oxidative reactions being utilised in the synthesis of energy-rich phosphate compounds in a similar (but more generous) fashion to that occurring in glycolysis ; thus the glycolysis of one glycogen unit ($C_6H_{10}O_5$) makes available some 57 Calories of free energy, of which about 30 Calories become available as phosphate-bond energy, whilst the complete oxidation of the same unit liberates some twelve times as much, namely 720 Calories, equivalent to about 36 high-energy phosphate bonds.

It would be idle at the moment to attempt to identify the chemical reactions taking place during the different phases of heat production, beyond indicating the probability that the earliest phases are connected with the breakdown of ATP, although, as A. V. Hill has recently emphasised, so far no one has ever proven a change in the ATP concentration in living muscle except in extreme exhaustion. Delayed heat, as we have indicated earlier, is undoubtedly connected with restitution processes, but since all the ATP in muscle would probably be exhausted within 0·5 sec. of stimulation if it were not replaced, we must conclude that some of the restitution processes take place in the initial phases of heat production. We may note that D. K. Hill has developed a method for the rapid determination of the course of oxygen consumption by stimulated muscle ; he has found that the oxygen consumption occurs entirely after activity, and its time-course follows closely that of the oxidative delayed heat, *i.e.*, the part of the delayed heat that is missing in the absence of oxygen.

Analysis of Initial Heat. The development of rapid methods of heat measurement has permitted a more exact analysis of the time-course of the thermal changes during the period of evolution of initial heat. In general, the period has been divided into a *shortening heat*, a *maintenance heat*, and a *relaxation heat*. Shortening and maintenance heats are well illustrated by Fig. 233 ; with a constant load on the muscle, the magnitude of the steep rise (the shortening heat) increases with the degree of shortening permitted by the experimental set-up ; the maintenance heat is represented by the constant-slope portion of the curve ; since the weight lifted was the

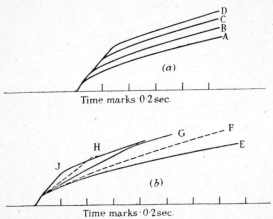

Fig. 233. Heat production during isotonic shortening from the start. Tetanus at 0° C. ; time, 0·2 sec. (*a*) Shortening different distances under constant load of 1·9 g. A, isometric ; B, 3·4 mm. ; C, 6·5 mm. ; D, 9·6 mm. (*b*) Shortening constant distance of 6·5 mm. under different loads. E, isometric ; F, 31·9 g. ; G, 23·7 g. ; H, 12·8 g. ; J, 1·9 g. (Hill. *Proc. Roy. Soc.*)

same in all cases the curves run approximately parallel (and parallel also to the isometric curve, A). It will be noted that even in isometric contraction there is a significant " shortening heat," this may be said to represent the shortening of the contractile component of the muscle, stretching the elastic elements, the tendon and the lever itself. Thus, even if no shortening at all were permitted, *i.e.*, if the contraction were truely isometric, the contractile elements could shorten against inert elastic elements ; only in this way, moreover, can we explain the fact that tension does not develop immediately, in isometric contraction, to its full value. The maintenance heat, represented by the slope of the curve after the initial steep rise, remains remarkably constant, and is not greatly influenced by the length of the muscle. The significance of the maintenance heat will become apparent when we consider the thermal phenomena exhibited by a single twitch ; for the moment we may regard it as entirely independent of the shortening process, and as the necessary accompaniment of tetanic stimulation. The magnitude of the relaxation heat depends greatly on whether the muscle is permitted to lower its load ; if so, and the load is great, the curve shows a rapid up-stroke ; if the muscle has been maintained in the isometric state, on the other hand, only a small hump appears which is probably the mechanical effect of the release of the elastic element (Fig. 234). The relaxation heat may therefore be classed primarily as the degradation of potential energy in the extensile system of the muscle ; metabolic events are, of course, taking place at the same

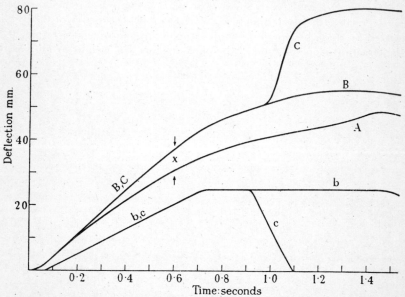

FIG. 234.   Relaxation heat in isometric and isotonic contractions. A, B and C, heat production in 0·6 sec. tetanus at 0° C. with initial load of 3·6 g. A, isometric ; B, isotonic, after-load 38·6 g., held up so that it cannot fall during relaxation ; C, isotonic, same after-load, but free so that load falls during relaxation. When the muscle lengthens under the load, the energy of the load (the work done by the muscle on it) appears as heat, hence the rapid upstroke in C during relaxation. Mechanical records below with corresponding small letters. Note the small relaxation hump on the heat record, A, of the isometric contraction. X, end of stimulus. (Hill. *Proc. Roy. Soc.*)

time, but in this region of the curve they appear to be neither exothermic nor endothermic.

Perhaps the most striking fact discovered by these thermal studies of A. V. Hill is that the shortening heat is a simple linear function of the degree of shortening, independent of the load lifted, *i.e.* :—

$$\text{Shortening Heat} = a.x$$

where x is the shortening. The constant, a, moreover, is related to the maximum tension the muscle can develop (the isometric tension, P_o), so that the ratio :—

$$a/P_o = \text{constant}$$

a and P_o depend on temperature, but the ratio a/P_o is found to be independent of this variable, the mean value for the frog's sartorius being in the region of 0·25 when a is in g.wt./sq.cm. of muscle cross-section, and P_o is in the same unit.

The fact that the heat liberated by a muscle in a tetanus is independent of the work done means that, when work *is* done, more energy is liberated than when no work is done ; this tallies with the finding that the recovery heat is greater when work is done. Hence, in a tetanus, the muscle is able to govern its output of energy in accordance with the mechanical requirements, as Fenn had emphasised. The *constancy* of the shortening heat, with varying amounts of external work, implies more than this, however ; it means that, when the muscle does work, not only is more chemical energy liberated, but also less is dissipated wastefully as heat, *i.e.*, the energy made available is either more efficiently applied to the contractile process, or there is less frictional loss when the muscle does work, although the shortening is the same in both cases. The efficiency of the muscle must clearly increase as the mechanical load is increased ; the manner in which it varies with load, and hence with the speed of contraction, may be quite simply predicted from the established thermal relationships ; according to Hill the maximum efficiency depends only on a/P_o and on K/P_o, where $K = k/b$, k being the maintenance heat constant, *i.e.*,

$$\text{Maintenance Heat} = k \times \text{time}$$

and b is a constant defining the rate of extra-energy liberation as a function of load. The values obtained experimentally for the efficiency were in the region of 20 per cent., agreeing well with the calculated value of 22 per cent.

The relative constancy of the maintenance heat at a given temperature permits the introduction of the concept of *extra-energy liberation* associated with shortening ; thus during an isometric tetanus no work is done ; the heat produced is maintenance heat, and the " extra-energy " is zero. Hill found experimentally that, under a variety of conditions of shortening, the rate of liberation of " extra-energy " was a linear function of the tension developed, *i.e.*,

$$\text{Rate of " Extra Energy "} = b(P_o - P) \quad . \quad . \quad . \quad . \quad (21)$$

where P_o is the isometric (maximal) tension, and P is the actual tension developed during shortening.

When a muscle contracts through a distance, x, against a load, P, the " extra energy " will be made up of the shortening heat and the mechanical work. The shortening heat, as we have seen, is given quite simply by the product ax, whilst the mechanical work is Px. The rate of " extra energy " liberation is therefore given by :—

$$\text{Rate of " Extra Energy "} = av + Pv \quad . \quad . \quad . \quad . \quad (22)$$

where v is the velocity of contraction.

Combining (21) and (22), we have :—

$$v(a + P) = b(P_o - P)$$

or, $\qquad (P + a)(v + b) = (P_o + a)b = \text{Constant} \quad . \quad . \quad . \quad . \quad (23)$

Thus plotting the load, P, against the velocity of contraction, v, should give a rectangular hyperbola with asymptotes at :—

$$P = -a, \text{ and } v = -b$$

Hence a, a thermal constant of the muscle, may be obtained from purely mechanical measurements.

Qualitatively we may say that the greater the rate of contraction the greater the *rate* of extra-energy liberation, the heat production without a load at all being considerably greater than that during an isometric contraction [1] ; thus by increasing the tension in the muscle, other things being equal, we slow the rate of liberation of energy ; this is shown also in

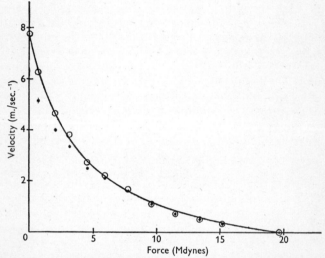

FIG. 235.   Experimental relationship between force and velocity of contraction of muscles of human arm.   (Wilkie. *J. Physiol.*)

experiments in which the muscle is caused to lengthen during a tetanus ; in this case the rate of heat production falls to a value less than that found for the isometric rate. Hill suggests, as a tentative explanation of the thermal phenomena, that shortening is associated with the exposure of a certain number of " reactive spots " in the myosin fibrils ; the greater the shortening the greater the number of spots exposed, and therefore the greater the rate at which energy is liberated ; this might suggest that the maintenance heat would increase with the degree of shortening ; this is true, although the relationship is not very simple, the maintenance heat actually becoming considerably smaller when the shortening is great. According to D. E. S. Brown, the shortening heat and maintenance heat are inversely related when a muscle is allowed to contract under different loads ; the smaller the load, the more the muscle contracts, the greater the shortening heat and the less the maintenance heat.

[1] The following figures have been given by Hill for the relative amounts of energy liberated by muscle : *Under conditions of maximum efficiency :* Maintenance Heat, or Heat of Activation, 40 ; Work, 40 ; Heat of Shortening, 20. *With zero load :* Heat of Activation, 40 ; Work, Nil ; Heat of Shortening, 49.

The fundamental equation of Hill describes the way in which the tension and velocity of contraction are related ; it will be recalled that Fenn & Marsh had already established an empirical equation of the form :—

$$P = P_o e^{-av} - kv$$

to describe their results ; Hill found that the same results could be equally well described by his own equation, which has the merit that the same parameters may be derived from both thermal and mechanical measurements. The phenomena of heat production are primarily connected, doubtless, with the contractile elements, so that Hill has replaced Levin & Wyman's mechanical model by a system in which the contractile elements, obeying the fundamental equation, are linked in series with purely elastic elements. On this basis the curves, showing the development of tension during an isotonic and an isometric twitch, may be predicted with great

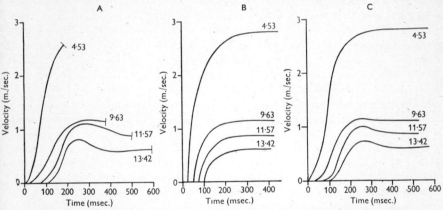

FIG. 236. Velocity-time curves. A, experimental curves ; B, theoretical curves on the assumption that there is no elastic component in series with the contractile elements ; C, theoretical curves on the assumption that there are series elastic elements. Figures on graphs indicate tension (megadynes) against which pull was made. (Wilkie. *J. Physiol.*)

accuracy ; in the latter case the shortening of the muscle as a whole is zero, but the development of tension in a muscle may be regarded as a process of shortening the contractile elements against the extension of the elastic component. More recently Wilkie has applied the same method of analysis to the behaviour of the muscles of the human arm. Fig. 235 illustrates the force-velocity relationship which, like the results of Fenn & Marsh, and of Katz, on isolated frog and cat muscles, fits the fundamental equation. The rate of development of velocity will clearly depend on the interaction between the contractile and elastic components ; if there were no elastic component, the theoretical curve would be given by Fig. 236, B, whereas, if the contractile elements, obeying the fundamental equation while shortening, transmitted some of their energy to the inert elastic elements, the theoretical curve would be different (Fig. 236, c), the initial development of tension being slower, to give an S-shaped curve, and the velocity later passing through a maximum. The actual curves are shown in

Fig. 236, A ; their shapes agree well with those derived theoretically on the assumption of contractile elements in series with inert elastic elements.

Thus the mechanical and thermal studies have left us with a model of the muscle that differs from that of Levin & Wyman only in that the concept of viscous-elasticity has been abandoned ; instead, " contractile elements " have been postulated, which develop tension in accordance with the empirical relationship :—

$$(P + a)(v + b) = \text{Constant}$$

The fundamental innovation is the admission that the rate of liberation of energy is a function of the tension the muscle is allowed to develop.

Thermal Events in Single Twitches

If we may regard the events taking place during a tetanus as simply the additive effects of repeated twitches, we must be able to extend the concepts, derived from tetanic contractions, to the case of the single twitch. Thus, from the thermal point of view, we must find analogues to the maintenance heat, the shortening heat, and the heat of relaxation ; moreover, we must expect the fundamental equation, relating the tension to the rate of contraction, to apply with equal force, and the parameters a/P_o and b, derived from measurements of heat production in a twitch, to be of the same order as those already derived from tetanic contractions. Up till quite recently, the devices for recording the heat production during a single twitch were not adequate to permit an analysis into components separated in time by only a few milliseconds ; recently, however, A. V. Hill, in a series of papers, has shown that the difficulties have been at last overcome.

Maintenance and Activation Heats. Let us consider, first, the significance of the maintenance heat in terms of the single twitch. Fig. 237

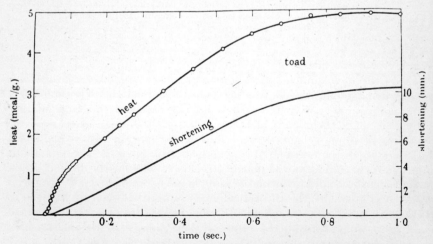

FIG. 237. Heat and shortening, simultaneously recorded in the isotonic twitch of a pair of toad's semi-membranosus muscles at 0° C., under 6 g. load. (Hill. *Proc. Roy. Soc.*)

shows simultaneous records of heat production and shortening of a toad muscle,[1] during the early phases following a single brief condenser shock. It will be seen that there is a rapid outburst of heat, preceding the beginning of shortening, and that the heat production continues, during shortening, but at a slower rate. It would thus appear that there are two components in the initial heat, just as in tetanic contraction ; one, possibly independent of shortening, which, in the case of tetanic contraction, has been described as maintenance heat but, in the case of a single twitch, may be described, with Hill, as *activation heat* ; and another component, the shortening heat. The justification of this concept of an activation

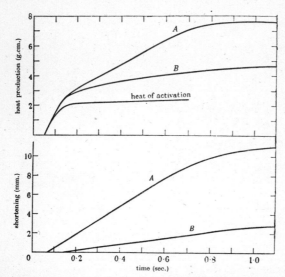

Fig. 238. To show heat of shortening and heat of activation in isotonic twitches. A, no after-load, with the result that shortening heat is large ; B, after-load of 8·6 g. Note that, although the initial course of shortening was different in the two cases, the initial outbursts of activation heat appeared to be simultaneous. Curve showing heat of activation has been calculated as described in the text. Toad sartorii, 0° C. (Hill. *Proc. Roy. Soc.*)

heat, independent of shortening heat, was carried out by Hill along the following lines. It was first necessary to establish that, as in tetanic contractions, it is legitimate to speak of a shortening heat, independent of load and determined entirely by the degree of shortening. This was made very probable by a number of experiments in which muscles were allowed to contract with different loads, thereby shortening to different lengths, and the heat due to shortening was calculated on the assumption that a fixed amount of the liberated heat was the activation heat, whatever the initial length of the muscle. The shortening heat, expressed as gm.cm./cm., was satisfactorily constant. In a later experiment, the assumption, that

[1] Toad muscle was mainly used in this work because it responds more slowly than frog muscle, and thus increases the resolution, in time, of the recording instruments ; the temperature of 0° C. was adopted for this reason also.

the activation heat was independent of the initial length, was avoided by comparing two muscles, both of which were loaded with a small weight, but one of which was after-loaded with a larger weight.[1] Although they both started at the same length, the shortening of the after-loaded muscle was at all times much less than that of the other. Fig. 238 shows the heat and shortening curves ; although the after-loaded muscle started to shorten later than the other, both show a simultaneous rapid rise in heat production ; the rate falls off far more rapidly with the after-loaded muscle (Curve B), indicating that, in the later stages, shortening heat is the dominant, if not the exclusive, factor. If, now, at given moments, the difference in heat produced by the two muscles (ΔH), and the difference in the shortening (ΔS), are computed, it is found that there is a simple linear relationship between the two, as in Fig. 239, the slope of the curve

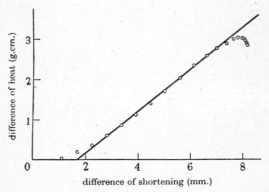

FIG. 239.   Calculation of heat of shortening from curves A and B of Fig. 238. Differences of heat (ΔH) plotted against differences of shortening (ΔS) at corresponding times, from 0·15 sec. to 1·1 sec. Slope of linear portion of line, which gives the shortening heat, is 5·25 g.cm./cm.   (Hill. *Proc. Roy. Soc.*)

giving the ratio $\Delta H/\Delta S$, *i.e.*, the shortening heat expressed as gm.cm./cm. of shortening. This comes out at about 360 gm.cm./cm. per cm.[2] cross-section of muscle, comparing with a figure of 400 for the frog's sartorius, computed earlier from tetanic measurements.

Having established that the shortening heat is a valid concept, we may now determine the course of the activation heat ; it is simply a matter of subtracting from the curve of heat production the computed shortening heat ; the result is incorporated in Fig. 238. By comparing this with the shortening curve it is clear that activation heat is well established before shortening has begun. The actual amount of activation heat is about equal to the maximum heat of shortening in a single twitch, *i.e.*, the heat of shortening with a very small load.[2] Thus we are quite justified in

---

[1] By " after-loading " is meant the mechanical arrangement whereby the muscle only pulls on the load after it has begun to develop tension.
[2] This estimate has been confirmed by Hill with an independent method (1950*a*) ; if the load against which a muscle must pull is made sufficiently large, the heat developed in a twitch is probably purely activation heat, and it is found to be about half the maximum shortening heat with small loads.

regarding the maintenance heat as the summated activation heats of successive stimuli.

The relationship of the activation heat to the course of development of mechanical shortening has been studied with particular care by Hill. It is possible to allow for the effect of the time required for propagation of the stimulus, applied directly to the muscle, on the observed course of development of heat. When this allowance was made, the activation heat of a muscle, theoretically stimulated at all points simultaneously, was shown to begin some 10 msec. after the stimulus (in the frog at 0° C. ; 25 msec. in the case of the toad) ; moreover, the rate of liberation of activation heat apparently starts at its maximum, and then declines to zero as the shortening heat becomes manifest. It was not possible to compute the effects of propagation delays on the development of tension in the muscle, so that neither of the curves in Fig. 238 has been corrected for this factor. The delay in development of heat may possibly be related to the time required for the action potential to reach its maximum, which would be of the order of 7 msec. (Eccles, Katz & Kuffler, 1941) ; thus, as Hill expresses it, the stimulus has a trigger action on some chemical process which develops its maximal rate at the beginning ; the heat developed is the sign of this chemical process, which puts the muscle in a state of activity which may be regarded as a readiness to shorten, to exert a mechanical force, or to do mechanical work.

Relaxation Heat. Tetanic studies indicated that relaxation heat was no more than the degradation of elastic potential energy stored in the muscle. In a single twitch it is a difficult matter, experimentally, to equate exactly the relaxation heat with the work done on the muscle by the weight in falling, so that the clearest proof that relaxation heat is only degraded potential energy is provided by Hill's demonstration that, when the muscle relaxes without a load, there is no relaxation heat. For this purpose a special ergometer was devised which permitted a muscle to lift a load in such a way that at the end of its shortening it cast its load ; it could thus relax under no tension.

Fundamental Equation. Studies with single twitches showed that the fundamental equation applied to all stages of the shortening process ; since, however, the muscle does not develop its maximal tension during a twitch, owing to the onset of relaxation in the contractile elements before the development of maximal shortening of the elastic elements has been completed, the value of P_o, the maximal tension, is obtained by extrapolation of the tension developed at successively increasing loads. The parameters in the equation for toad muscle at 0° C. were :—

$$a/P_o = 0.32 \; ; \; b = 0.26$$

comparing with values of 0·26 and 0·33 respectively in the earlier work on tetanic stimulation of frog muscle.

The All-or-None Principle. Finally we come to a consideration of the all-or-none principle, in so far as it applies to the liberation of energy in a twitch. The effects of tetanic stimulation have shown unequivocally that the behaviour of the muscle is not all-or-none from the point of view of the liberation of energy, a given period of stimulation producing a variable amount of total energy according as the muscle was allowed to shorten and perform work, or not. Thus the energy liberation could be expressed as :

$$E = M + W + ax$$

where M is the maintenance heat, W the work, and ax the shortening heat, the last two terms being variable. The studies on activation and shortening heat in single twitches, mentioned above, indicate that the all-or-none principle cannot apply to the twitch as well, although the earlier work of Hartree & Hill, in which much less sensitive recording apparatus was available, had led to the opposite conclusion, *i.e.*, that a single stimulus always led to the evolution of the same amount of energy, whether this was entirely heat or partly work plus heat. Hill has recently re-investigated this point and shown that, in a single twitch, the conditions are exactly similar to those in a tetanus, the energy liberated being defined by the equation :—

$$E = A + W + ax$$

Thus, with constant shortening (*i.e.*, when ax is kept constant), and a variable load, the heat liberated is $A + ax$ (the muscle being allowed to relax without a load) ; consequently the heat produced should be constant in spite of wide variations in the work performed, and hence the total energy, E, liberated in a twitch, should vary with the load. The following figures, derived from experiments on the special ergometer which allowed variations in work with the same amount of shortening, reveal the remarkable constancy of the heat under these conditions :—

Work/Heat (per cent.) .			6	12	16	19	22	25	27	27	30	32	35
Heat (per cent.) .		.	100	99	99	100	99	93	98	103	100	95	102
Work/Heat (per cent.) .		.	39	45	45	47 mean							
Heat (per cent.) .		.	101	94	100	92	98						

where the upper column indicates the percentage of the total energy appearing as mechanical work, and the lower column represents the heat liberated, expressed as a percentage of that with the smallest load. So far as the all-or-none principle is concerned, therefore, it is only the activation heat that may be regarded as an event independent of the mechanical conditions of contraction.

The Isometric Twitch. The isometric twitch has been studied in the past because errors due to the movement of the muscle over the thermopile [1] could be avoided by this technique. This, however, as Hill has recently emphasised, is unfortunate because the thermal events in an isometric twitch are highly complex and not easily resolved quantitatively. In general, the heat liberated in an isometric twitch is

---

[1] When a muscle on a thermopile contracts, a part of it previously not touching the thermopile comes on to it ; the temperature of this part is above that of the rest because it has not been losing heat by conduction through the thermopile. Contraction thus gives rise to a factitious heat production. In the modern " protected " thermopile dummy portion is included, long enough to ensure that any part of the muscle coming on to the active thermojunctions has been losing heat previously at exactly the same rate as those parts already on them.

made up of four components : (*a*) activation heat ; (*b*) shortening heat of the contractile elements against the elastic ones ; (*c*) the work done by stronger regions extending the weaker portions, which appears mainly as heat in the latter ; (*d*) relaxation heat, *i.e.*, the degradation of the mechanical energy stored in the stretched elastic elements.

Active Contraction or Active Relaxation ?

In this discussion of some of the thermal aspects of muscular contraction it has been tacitly assumed that the shortening heat represented the liberation of energy necessary for the contractile process, and such appears to be the view of A. V. Hill, and others, in this field. Recently, however, Ramsey has suggested that many of the thermal aspects may be just as readily explained on the assumption that the energy is required to restore the potential energy lost by the myosin chains of the muscle fibre during contraction, *i.e.*, that relaxation is an active process requiring the liberation of energy. If this viewpoint is justified, the characteristics of the heat production of muscle must be entirely reinterpreted. There is certainly some evidence to indicate that relaxation is not passive ; a single isolated muscle fibre, suspended from one end in Ringer's solution, after being tetanised, rapidly reassumes its original length, although the weight is so small that under gravitational pull this would take much longer. Moreover, if a single fibre of frog's muscle is allowed to contract beyond two-thirds of its length, it fails completely to relax—it has entered the so-called " delta-state." According to Ramsey this would be because the energy for relaxation is now inadequate. Finally there are many invertebrate muscles, for example, the adductor of the molluscs, which maintain a vigorous contraction over long periods of time, and without fatigue or extra O_2-consumption.[1]

In applying this viewpoint to an interpretation of the thermal data, Ramsey takes as his starting point the length-tension diagram of the single isolated fibre which, according to him, is best represented as three straight lines (Fig. 225), the middle portion representing the normal physiological range (between L_o, the resting length, and $2L_o/3$) ; the left-hand portion corresponds to the delta-state of the fibre, and it is assumed that over this range it is the tension in the sarcolemma that determines the degree of shortening and the slope of the length-tension diagram ; it is suggested that in the absence of a sarcolemma the fibre would shorten very much more than it actually does. Certainly in isolated toad fibres, where the sarcolemma is much tougher, the maximal shortening is very much less. The area under the length-tension diagram may be considered to represent the total potential energy available to the muscle ; thus in

[1] The failure of an unloaded muscle to return to its original length after shortening has been recently commented on by Hill ; he points to the analogy with nylon fibres ; these, until they have been drawn out to cause their molecular chains to orientate along the fibre-axis, are merely plastic, *i.e.*, they show no reversible elasticity. When they have been " cold-drawn," however, they show reversible elasticity. The same may be true of muscle ; we must regard the failure to return, not as due to the absence of enough energy to cause relaxation, but simply as a result of the contractile elements having coiled too far to permit reversible re-extension, *i.e.*, they have achieved a plastic condition.

shortening at maximal tension from the resting length, L_o, to a new length $L_o - \Delta L_o$, the energy of the muscle changes by the factor $T\Delta L_o$, which will be the area contained in the element of space under the curve between the abscissæ corresponding to L_o and $L_o - \Delta L_o$.   From the equation of the middle portion of the curve it may be shown that the potential energy of the muscle at rest is $T_o L_o/3$, whilst at length $2L_o/3$ it is $T_o L_o/9$.   Under conditions of isotonic contraction some of this potential energy is converted into work, whilst the remainder appears as heat due to frictional losses. Ramsey has computed the proportions of these two quantities, for various degrees of shortening, on simple thermodynamic grounds, and they agree remarkably well with the values of the shortening heat (experimentally determined) by A. V. Hill.   Moreover, still arguing on thermodynamic grounds, Ramsey was able to deduce a relationship between tension and velocity of shortening of the same form as the fundamental equation of A. V. Hill.   Hill's equation is entirely empirical, being derived in the first place from simple relationships between heat production and the length of the muscle ; Ramsey's equation, on the other hand, derives theoretically from the length-tension diagram on purely thermodynamic considerations, in which the shortening heat is viewed only as a frictional loss.   If work done, and heat produced, by a muscle during contraction are derived only from potential energy already present in the myosin chains, the liberation of energy by chemical reactions only becomes necessary after the contraction phase ; how, then, are we to interpret the " maintenance heat " ? According to Ramsey it is to be regarded as the manifestation of chemical reactions whose function is, not to maintain contraction, but to restore the lost potential energy of the myosin fibrils resulting from contraction. While contraction is maintained these reactions go to waste, i.e., the liberated energy is dissipated as heat ; immediately after the cessation of the tetanic stimulus, however, the reactions are employed in restoring the potential energy, thereby permitting the fibres to relax.   We need not go into further details of this interesting theory ; the weak point is certainly the requirement that the lost potential energy be restored in a very short time after cessation of the stimulus, since Hill has shown that there is no heat in relaxation ; it is certainly interesting that the same fundamental equation can be interpreted on the basis of diametrically opposed theories, a fact, however, which gives point to the warning uttered earlier, on the attempt to interpret mechanical and chemical processes from thermal data alone.   Until further experimental evidence is adduced in support of Ramsey's thesis, we must incline towards the view, maintained by Hill and by Fenn, that the liberation of energy is associated with the contractile, rather than the relaxation, process ; thus it is by no means certain that a significant component of the initial heat is viscous, since it is quite independent of the speed of shortening ; moreover, Hill has recently found that stretching a muscle during shortening actually causes a reduction in the heat liberated, a finding impossible of explanation on a frictional basis, but which may be interpreted as a reversal of the energy-giving chemical reaction.   Furthermore, if there were an active relaxation process, we should expect the latent period of muscle to vary widely with the length at which it is stimulated. Thus a muscle can be made to adopt considerably smaller lengths than its normal resting length by simply stimulating it without a load, and allowing it to shorten the required amount. Such a muscle retains this new length, *i.e.*, there is no obvious relaxation ; if it is argued that the contractile elements have actually loosened by an active relaxation process, then there will be a considerable slack to take up before the development of tension ; and, since the mechanical latent period is essentially a measure of this taking up of slack, the latent period of this shortened muscle should be longer than that for the same muscle when it is maintained under tension at a greater length. Hill showed that the latent period is approximately the same in the two states— a convincing argument against the active-relaxation theory. In the isolated fibre, the distensibility of the sarcolemma probably puts a limit to the extent of reversible shortening ; if contraction is so vigorous as to damage the sarcolemma, the fibre will shorten irreversibly ; and this condition probably corresponds to the delta-state described by Ramsey & Street ; in the intact muscle, the development of this condition is presumably prevented by the interfibrillar connective tissue.

References

BAIRATI, A. (1937). " Struttura e Proprietà Fisiche del Sarcolemma della Fibra Musculare Striata." *Z. Zellf.*, **27**, 100.

BANUS, M. G. & ZETLIN, A. M. (1938). " Relation of Isometric Tension to Length in Skeletal Muscle." *J. cell. & comp. Physiol.*, **12**, 403.

BARER, R. (1948). " Structure of the Striated Muscle Fibre." *Biol. Rev.*, **23**, 159.

BROWN, D. E. S. (1936). " Effect of Rapid Compression on Events in the Isometric Contraction of Skeletal Muscle." *J. cell. & comp. Physiol.*, **8**, 141.

BROWN, D. E. S. (1941). " Regulation of Energy Exchange in Contracting Muscle." *Biol. Symp.*, **3**, 161.

BROWN, D. E. S. & SICHEL, F. J. M. (1936). " Isometric Contraction of Isolated Muscle Fibres." *J. cell. & comp. Physiol.*, **8**, 315.

BUCHTAL, F. & KNAPPEIS, G. G. (1943). " Propagation of Contraction in the Isolated Striated Muscle Fibre." *Acta Physiol. Scand.*, **5**, 256.

BUCHTAL, F. & KNAPPEIS, G. G. (1943). " Correlation between Changes in Cross Striation and Mechanical Tension, etc." *Acta Physiol. Scand.*, **6**, 123.

BUCHTAL, F. & LINDHARD, J. (1939). " Physiology of the Striated Muscle Fibre." *Det. Kgl. Danske Videnskabernes Selskab. Biologiske Meddelelser*, **14**, 6.

CHAMBERS, R. & HALE, H. P. (1932). " Formation of Ice in Protoplasm." *Proc. Roy. Soc.*, *B*, **110**, 336.

DEMPSEY, E. W., WISLOCKI, G. B. & SINGER, M. (1946). " Observations on the Chemical Cytology of Striated Muscle." *Anat. Rec.*, **96**, 221.

DRAPER, M. H. & HODGE, A. J. (1949). " Studies on Muscle with the Electron Microscope." *Austr. J. Exp. Biol. & Med. Sci.*, **27**, 465.

FENG, T. P. (1932). " The Thermo-Elastic Properties of Muscle." *J. Physiol.*, **74**, 455.

FENN, W. O. (1923). " Quantitative Comparison between the Energy Liberated and the Work Performed by the Isolated Sartorius Muscle of the Frog." *J. Physiol.*, **58**, 175.

FENN, W. O. (1924). " Relation between Work Performed and Energy Liberated in Muscular Contraction." *J. Physiol.*, **58**, 373.

FENN, W. O. (1945). " Muscles." Chap. 33. Physical Chemistry of Cells and Tissues. Ed. Höber. London. Churchill.

FENN, W. O. & MARSH, B. S. (1935). " Muscular Force at Different Speeds of Shortening." *J. Physiol.*, **85**, 277.

GASSER, H. S. (1930). " Contractures of Skeletal Muscle." *Physiol. Rev.*, **10**, 35.

GASSER, H. S. & HILL, A. V. (1924). " Dynamics of Muscular Contraction." *Proc. Roy. Soc.*, *B*, **96**, 398.

GELFAN, S. (1930). " Studies of Single Muscle Fibres. I. The All-or-None Principle." *Amer. J. Physiol.*, **93**, 1.

GELFAN, S. & GERARD, R. W. (1930). " Studies of Single Muscle Fibres. II. Further Analysis of the Grading Mechanism." *Amer. J. Physiol.*, **95**, 412.

GILSON, A. S., SCHOEPFLE, G. M. & WALKER, S. M. (1947). " Time Course of Tension Development in the Muscle Response." *Ann. N.Y. Acad. Sci.*, **47**, 697.

GILSON, A. S., WALKER, S. M. & SCHOEPFLE, G. M. (1944). " The Forms of the Isometric Twitch and Isometric Tetanus Curves Recorded from the Frog's Sartorius Muscle." *J. cell. & comp. Physiol.*, **24**, 185.

HALL, C. E., JAKUS, M. A. & SCHMITT, F. O. (1946). " Cross Striations and Myosin Filaments in Muscle." *Biol. Bull.*, **90**, 32.

HARTREE, W. (1931). " Analysis of the Initial Heat Production of Muscle." *J. Physiol.*, **72**, 1.

HARTREE, W. (1932). " Analysis of the Delayed Heat Production of Muscle." *J. Physiol.*, **75**, 273.

HARTREE, W. & HILL, A. V. (1921). " Nature of the Isometric Twitch." *J. Physiol.*, **55**, 389.

HARTREE, W. & HILL, A. V. (1928). " Anaerobic Delayed Heat Production After a Tetanus." *Proc. Roy. Soc.*, B, **103**, 207.

HARTREE, W. & HILL, A. V. (1928). " Energy Liberated by an Isolated Muscle during the Performance of Work." *Proc. Roy. Soc.*, B, **104**, 1.

HILL, A. V. (1926). " Muscular Activity." Baltimore, Williams & Wilkins.

HILL, A. V. (1928). " Role of Oxidation in Maintaining the Dynamic Equilibrium of the Muscle Cell." *Proc. Roy. Soc.*, B, **103**, 138.

HILL, A. V. (1928). " Absence of Delayed Anaerobic Heat in a Series of Muscle Twitches." *loc. cit.*, p. 171.

HILL, A. V. (1928). " Recovery Heat Production in O_2 After a Series of Twitches." *loc. cit.*, p. 183.

HILL, A. V. (1938). " Heat of Shortening and Dynamic Constants of Muscle." *Proc. Roy. Soc.*, B, **126**, 136.

HILL, A. V. (1939). " Recovery Heat in Muscle." *Proc. Roy. Soc.*, B, **127**, 297.

HILL, A. V. (1939). " Mechanical Efficiency of Frog's Muscle." *loc. cit.*, p. 434.

HILL, A. V. (1940). " Dynamic Constants of Human Muscle." *Proc. Roy. Soc.*, B, **128**, 263.

HILL, A. V. (1949a). " Heat of Activation and Heat of Shortening in a Muscle Twitch." *Proc. Roy. Soc.*, B, **136**, 195.

HILL, A. V. (1949b). " Energetics of Relaxation in a Muscle Twitch." *loc. cit.*, p. 211.

HILL, A. V. (1949c). " Work and Heat in a Muscle Twitch." *loc. cit.*, p. 220.

HILL, A. V. (1949d). " The Onset of Contraction." *loc. cit.*, p. 242.

HILL, A. V. (1949e). " The Abrupt Transition from Rest to Activity in Muscle." *loc. cit.*, p. 399.

HILL, A. V. (1949 f). " Is Relaxation an Active Process ? " *loc. cit.*, p. 420.

HILL, A. V. (1950a). " A Challenge to Biochemists." *Biochim. Biophys. Acta*, **4**, 4.

HILL, A. V. (1950b). " Thermodynamics of the Active State of Muscle." *Biochem. J.*, **46**, xli.

HILL, A. V. (1950c). " Discussion on Muscular Contraction." *Proc. Roy. Soc.*, B, **137**, 40.

HILL, A. V. (1950d). " The Series Elastic Component of Muscle." *loc. cit.*, p. 273.

HILL, A. V. (1950e). " Development of the Active State of Muscle during the Latent Period." *loc. cit.*, p. 320.

HILL, A. V. (1950 f). " A Note on the Heat of Activation in a Muscle Twitch." *loc. cit.*, p. 330.

HILL, D. K. (1940). " Time Course of the O_2-Consumption of Stimulated Frog's Muscle." *J. Physiol.*, **98**, 207.

HILL, D. K. (1940). " Time Course of Evolution of Oxidation Recovery Heat of Frog's Muscle." *loc. cit.*, p. 454.

HØNCKE, P. (1947). " Investigations on the Structure and Function of Living Isolated Cross-Striated Muscle Fibres of Mammals." *Acta Physiol. Scand.*, **15**, Suppl. 48.

JORDAN, H. E. (1933). " Structural Changes in Striped Muscle during Contraction." *Physiol. Rev.*, **13**, 301.

KAHN, A. J. & SANDOW, A. (1950). " Effects of Excess K Followed by Ringer's Solution on Responses of Skeletal Muscle." *Fed. Proc.*, **9**, 68.

KATZ, B. (1936). " Neuromuscular Transmission in Crabs." *J. Physiol.*, **87**, 199.

KATZ, B. (1939). " Relation between Force and Speed in Muscular Contraction." *J. Physiol.*, **96**, 45.

KATZ, B. (1950). " Discussion on Muscular Contraction." *Proc. Roy. Soc.*, B, **137**, 40.

KUFFLER, S. W. (1946). " Relation of Electric Potential Changes to Contracture in Skeletal Muscle." *J. Neurophysiol.*, **9**, 367.

KUFFLER, S. W. (1947). " Membrane Changes during Excitation and Inhibition of the Contractile Mechanisms." *Ann. N.Y. Acad. Sci.*, **47**, 767.

KUFFLER, S. W. & KATZ, B. (1946). " Inhibition at the Nerve-Muscle Junction in Crustacea." *J. Neurophysiol.*, **9**, 337.

LEVIN, A. & WYMAN, J. (1927). " The Viscous Elastic Properties of Muscle." *Proc. Roy. Soc., B*, **101**, 218.

LONG, M. E. (1947). " Development of the Muscle-Tendon Attachment in the Rat." *Amer. J. Anat.*, **81**, 159.

MEYERHOF, O. (1947). " The Main Chemical Phases of the Recovery of Muscle." *Ann. N.Y. Acad. Sci.*, **47**, 815.

PANTIN, C. F. A. (1936). " On the Excitation of Crustacean Muscle. II. Neuromuscular Facilitation." *J. exp. Biol.*, **13**, 111.

PRATT, F. H. & EISENBERGER, J. P. (1919). " Quantal Phenomena in Muscle." *Amer. J. Physiol.*, **49**, 1.

RAMSEY, R. W. (1944). " Muscle Physics." Medical Physics. Ed. Glasser. Chicago, Year Book Publishers.

RAMSEY, R. W. (1947). " Dynamics of Single Muscle Fibres." *Ann. N.Y. Acad. Sci.*, **47**, 675.

RAMSEY, R. W. & STREET, S. F. (1940). " The Isometric Length-Tension Diagram of Isolated Skeletal Muscle Fibres of the Frog." *J. cell. & comp. Physiol.*, **15**, 11.

RAMSEY, R. W. & STREET, S. F. (1941). " Muscle Function as Studied in Single Muscle Fibres." *Biol. Symp.*, **3**, 9.

RAUH, F. (1922). " Die Latenzzeit des Muskelelements." *Z. Biol.*, **76**, 25.

REED, R. & RUDALL, K. M. (1948). " Electron Microscope Studies of Muscle Structure." *Biochim. Biophys. Acta*, **2**, 19.

ROOS, J. (1932). " The Latent Period of Skeletal Muscle." *J. Physiol.*, **74**, 17.

ROZSA, G., SZENT-GYÖRGYI, A. & WYCKOFF, R. W. G. (1950). " Fine Structure of Myofibrils." *Exp. Cell. Res.*, **1**, 194.

SANDOW, A. (1944). " General Properties of Latency-Relaxation." *J. cell. & comp. Physiol.*, **24**, 221.

SANDOW, A. (1945). " Effect of Activity on the Latent Period of Muscular Contraction." *Ann. N.Y. Acad. Sci.*, **46**, 153.

SANDOW, A. (1947). " Latency-Relaxation and a Theory of Muscular Mechano-Chemical Coupling." *Ann. N.Y. Acad. Sci.*, **47**, 895.

SANDOW, A. (1949). " Muscle." *Ann. Rev. Physiol.*, **11**, 297.

SANDOW, A. (1950). " Latent Period of Muscular Contraction." *Arch. phys. Med.*, **31**, 367.

SANDOW, A. & BRUST, M. (1946). " Effect of Activity on the Visco-Elasticity of Normal and Iodoacetate Muscles." *P.S.E.B.M.*, **63**, 462.

SANDOW, A. & KAHN, A. J. (1949). " Initial Effects of K on the Mechanical Responses of Skeletal Muscle." *Fed. Proc.*, **8**, 177.

SCHAEFER, H. & GÖPFERT, H. (1937). " Aktionstrom und Optisches Verhalten des Froschmuskels in Ihrer Zeitlichen Beziehung zur Zuckung." *Pflüg. Arch.*, **238**, 684.

SCHOEPFLE, G. M. & GILSON, A. S. (1945). " Configuration of the Free Loaded and After Loaded Twitch." *J. cell. & comp. Physiol.*, **26**, 119.

SCHOEPFLE, G. M. & GILSON, A. S. (1946). " Elasticity of Muscle in Relation to Actively Developed Twitch Tension." *J. cell. & comp. Physiol.*, **27**, 105.

SICHEL, F. J. M. (1941). " Relative Elasticity of the Sarcolemma and of the Entire Skeletal Muscle Fibre." *Amer. J. Physiol.*, **133**, 446P.

SNYDER, C. D. (1936). " The Latencies of Mechanical and Electrical Responses in Skeletal Muscle." *Amer. J. Physiol.*, **115**, 441.

STEIMAN, S. E. (1937). " Factors Determining the Type of Response in the Fibre of Striated Muscle." *Amer. J. Physiol.*, **118**, 492.

WILKIE, D. R. (1949). " Relation between Force and Velocity in Human Muscle." *J. Physiol.*, **110**, 249.

CHAPTER XVIII

STRUCTURE AND COMPOSITION OF MUSCLE IN RELATION TO FUNCTION

Microscopical Discontinuities

THE microscopical appearance of the striated muscle fibre, which shows it as a series of units or sarcomeres, is perplexing, since a satisfactory theory of muscular contraction demands a fundamental continuity in structure along the axis of the fibre. The *changes* in the microscopical appearance, which we must consider now, are likewise bewildering. According to the careful photographic measurements of Buchtal, Knappeis & Lindhard on the isolated fibres of the frog's semitendinosus, the normal height of the resting A-band is 1.37μ, whilst that of the I-band is 0.81μ ; on isometric contraction the A-band shortened by some 18 per cent., whilst the I-band *lengthened* by 28 per cent. Studies on isotonic contraction, *i.e.*, when the fibre as a whole was allowed to shorten, were unsatisfactory ; when the muscle was stretched, the A-band lengthened more than the I-band, and if the passively stretched band was made to contract isometrically the A-band shortened, whilst the I-band lengthened.

Contraction Bands. Qualitative results on the changes taking place

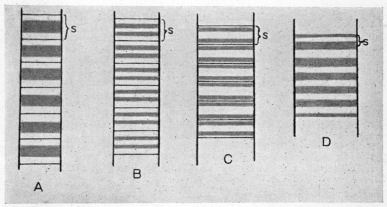

FIG. 240. Diagrams illustrating four successive stages in contraction of a striated muscle fibril. The dark stripes in A represent the Q- or A-discs ; in D the dark stripes are contraction bands. S represents one sarcomere unit. (Jordan. *Physiol. Rev.*)

during actual shortening have been described by numerous authors, and have been well summarised by Jordan ; the fundamental fact is that the fibre fattens as it shortens ; associated with this there are characteristic changes in the bands ; the first indication of contraction is the appearance of a light area bisecting the A-band, the H-band (Fig. 240) ; as contraction proceeds, the H-band widens, the opposite halves of the A-band apparently moving towards the Z-band in the I-region. As a result of this apparent movement of *A-material* through the I-band, we get the appearance of so-called *contraction bands*, consisting of the two halves of successive A-bands that have moved to meet at the Z-band (Fig. 240, D), the space between the contraction bands being now occupied by the H-bands, which have widened during the process of contraction ; the M-band or " membrane " now becomes easily visible bisecting the H-band. Thus,

on this microscopical basis, shortening of the fibre is associated with the removal of dark-staining " A-substance " from the A-band and its transfer to the I-band, contraction being, in effect, associated with a reversal of the relative positions of the dark and light material. As Jordan has emphasised, it would be quite wrong to deduce anything more from the microscopical appearances than this, *i.e.*, it would be wrong to conclude that there has been a radical alteration in the structures of the A- and I-regions, causing the I-region to become anisotropic and the A-region isotropic ; in fact it has never been shown that there is a reversal of isotropy during contraction, the only change definitely proved is an overall lowering of the birefringence, as we shall see. That the contraction bands are not artefacts has been shown by Speidel's studies on living muscle in the tail of the tadpole, viewed *in situ* under the microscope ; sometimes, especially under abnormal conditions, contraction was associated with the appearance of " nodes " (Fig. 241), localised regions in which the resting appearance of the striations had been replaced by contraction bands ; these nodes would frequently travel

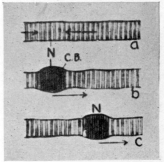

Fig. 241. Localised contraction nodes : *a* to *c*, stages in the formation and wave-like progression of a contraction node. (*a*) Relaxed fibre with resting cross-striæ, in which movement of muscle substance toward N is starting, as indicated by arrows ; *b*, a contraction node (N), comprising 12 sarcomeres, is formed, which then moves towards the right. The sarcomeres within the node have shortened sufficiently to form contraction bands (C.B.); *c*, as the node progresses, the sarcomeres in its path become contracted in succession, whilst those at the rear end of the node resume the relaxed condition. (Speidel. *Amer. J. Anat.*)

over the length of the fibre at a speed of some 70μ/sec. Sarcomeres in an uncontracted zone between two nodes exhibited a stretching of over 50 per cent. These results, whilst they are of interest in showing that contraction bands are formed *in vivo*, are also of value, in that they link up with the graded responses described by Gelfan (p. 487), and indicate the importance, from a mechanical viewpoint, of a properly synchronised contraction over the whole fibre since, when only one part is activated, contraction of this is associated with an extension of neighbouring parts.

Localisation of Substances in A- and I-Bands. Attempts at localising specific chemical substances in the striations date from 1905, when

Macallum treated a number of tissues with sodium cobaltinitrite and deduced from the concentration of precipitated material that the K^+ was localised in definite regions ; he concluded that, in the striated muscle fibre, K^+ was confined to the A-bands ; Scott incinerated fixed sections of muscle and found a high concentration of whitish ash in the A-bands, the I-bands being free of ash, except for the Z-bands ; Scott & Packer more recently have applied the freeze-drying technique of Gersh to the problem, and they also conclude that ash is mainly concentrated in the darkly staining A- and Z-regions, although a small amount of ash was found in the I-bands ; again, Draper & Hodge have incinerated muscle fibres in the electron-microscope by bombardment with high velocity electrons, a procedure which, they considered, would cause the volatilisation of K^+ ; as a result, the A, Z, and M-bands disappeared from the electron-micrograph, and they concluded that K^+ was localised in these regions, whilst Ca^{++} and Mg^{++} were concentrated in the I-bands. It must be appreciated that fixation of a tissue leads, in general, to a more or less complete loss of diffusible material, so that it is only residual material, presumably adsorbed to protein, that remains for examination.

The most satisfactory work on localisation in the muscle fibre is that of Caspersson & Thorell, who have applied their ultra-violet absorption technique to the problem (p. 3). In ultra-violet light a definite banding of the muscle fibres of *Drosophila* was observed, corresponding to regions of strong and low absorption of light at 2,600A, *i.e.*, by substances of the nucleotide type. To measure the degree of absorption it was necessary to fix the specimens, and various fixatives were tried, until one was obtained that produced no visible difference in the appearance of the fibre, before and after fixing, under the ultra-violet microscope.[1] The dark bands (regions of high ultra-violet absorption) were identified, by comparison with the polarisation-microscopical appearance, as the I-bands. Measurements of the ratio of the extinction coefficients at 2,650 and 2,850A gave values of 1·4–2·0 for the I-bands, and 0·96–1·42 for the A-bands. Pure adenylic acid gave a ratio of 2·3, whilst myosin gave one of 0·9, so that it is safe to say that the I-bands contained a high concentration of some nucleotide-like substance, possibly adenosine triphosphate (p. 501). In the fatigued muscle, banding was much less sharp, and longitudinal fine bands appeared suggesting a migration of I-substance down to the A-band. More recently Engstrom has combined Caspersson's ultra-violet absorption technique with micro-incineration, and there seems little doubt from his work that the ash remaining after incineration is in the I-bands rather than in the A-bands ; he points out, very pertinently, that a considerable contribution to the ash will be made by phosphate, so that it is not surprising, in view of the localisation of adenylic compounds in the I-bands, to find a high ash-content here also ; so great is the amount of ash, however, that he makes the plausible suggestion that creatine phosphate is also localised in this region. Of other studies of this nature we may mention that of Dempsey, Wislocki & Singer, who found very little phospholipid

---

[1] The fixative used was 25 per cent. acetic acid in absolute alcohol saturated with lanthanum acetate.

in the A-bands, by comparison with the I-bands, and a high phosphatase activity in the latter. These results, taken together, indicate an indisputable periodic chemical differentiation of the striated muscle fibre, although it would be unsafe to conclude, because of the limitations of most of the techniques, that a given substance is definitely localised in any region to the exclusion of others. In so far, however, as they emphasise discontinuities along the fibre-axis the results of such studies tend to obscure for us the fundamental process in contraction ; the underlying continuity, if it exists, must be sought by more refined methods. Let us therefore delve deeper into the ultra-structure of the muscle fibre.

The Muscle Proteins

The bulk of the solid matter of muscle is made up of protein which has been separated into a number of fractions ; summarising the position in 1939, Weber described them as follows :—

Myosin. A globulin-type of protein, first isolated and studied in detail by Edsall & Von Muralt in 1930 ; it was obtained by extracting the muscle with 1·2 M KCl at pH 8 and precipitation by dilution of the extract to 0·1–0·05 M KCl. It showed marked double-refraction of flow and formed thixotropic gels in concentrations of greater than 2 per cent., both properties indicating a marked asymmetry of its particles. On squirting a solution into distilled water, threads were formed which were used to study its X-ray diffraction spectrum.

Myogen and Globulin X. By pressing muscle, a juice was obtained containing these two proteins ; on dialysing the juice against a salt solution one component, *globulin X*, was precipitated, leaving behind another protein, *myogen*. Neither of these proteins exhibited double refraction of flow and they seemed to be of the corpuscular, as opposed to the fibrous, type.

Stroma Protein. This was the residue from extraction and included the structural elements of the sarcolemma and connective tissue.

The strong double refraction, and its characteristic of forming threads, pointed to myosin as the fundamental unit of the muscle fibre, the myogen and globulin, capable of existing in solution in high concentrations (myogen greater than 30 per cent., globulin greater than 5 per cent.) were obviously the constituents of the sarcoplasm. Nevertheless, Weber, from his quantitative studies of the double refraction of muscle and myosin, was inclined to consider that the myosin was concentrated only in the A-bands ; however, Astbury refused to be misled by such considerations and developed a theory of muscular contraction, based on the continuity of myosin chains, which we shall consider in due course.

Reviewing the position ten years later, Weber constructed the following table which describes the various fractions as they have been isolated, in apparently pure form, largely as a result of the discoveries of Weber, himself, and of Szent-Györgyi and his school in Szeged.

The most striking addition to our knowledge revealed by Table XXXV is the division of " myosin " into a number of fractions, and the appearance of tropomyosin ; thus Schramm & Weber in 1942 showed that " myosin "

TABLE XXXV

Protein Fractions of Muscle. (Weber, 1950.)

Protein	% of Total Protein	Names of Individual Proteins	Molecular Weight
Albumin	20	Myogen B (80 per cent.)	81,000
		Myogen A	151,000
Globulin X . . .	20		
Myosin	40	L-Myosin	840,000
		Actomyosin	14,000,000
		Actin F	
		Actin G	76,000
Stroma	20		
Protein of uncertain fraction .	6	Tropomyosin	90,500

could be fractionated into a rapidly sedimenting, high-molecular weight, compound—*S-myosin*—with a high and anomalous viscosity ; and a less rapidly sedimenting fraction, which they called L-myosin. It is the high-molecular weight substance, S-myosin, that is now called *actomyosin*, as a result of Szent-Györgyi's studies ; it results from the combination of *actin* with what we may now call true myosin. Actin itself was isolated by Straub and shown to exist in two forms, globular, or *G-actin*, with a molecular weight of 76,000 ; and a polymerised fibrous form, *F-actin* ; according to Jakus & Hall and Perry & Reed, F-actin is formed from G-actin by the linear aggregation of corpuscular particles. Only F-actin combines with myosin to give actomyosin.

Tropomyosin.   The   protein   *tropomyosin*,   recently   described by Bailey, is derived from muscle by treatment of the minced tissue with alcohol and subsequent extraction with molar KCl ; at the moment it is of more interest from the academic standpoint, of elucidating the way in which fibrous proteins of the *k-m-e-f* group are built up, than for its relationship to the actual contractile process. It has a relatively low molecular weight of 90,500 in salt solutions ; in water it aggregates, the fibres being some 200–300A thick and observable in the electron-microscope ; the aggregation is freely reversible (on addition of salt). In its homodisperse form it is markedly asymmetrical, showing birefringence of flow, and probably has an axial ratio of about 44 ; the formation of fibres therefore results in the end-to-end aggregation of already asymmetrical units. X-ray diffraction studies of orientated films reveal the typical α-configuration, convertible to the β-form by squeezing between plate-glass heated in steam. If pure myosin is treated in the same manner as muscle in the extraction of tropomyosin, little or none of this protein is obtained, so that it is argued that tropomyosin is not a breakdown product of myosin ; nevertheless its amino-acid composition reveals striking similarities ; and it may well be, as Bailey and Astbury have argued, that tropomyosin is a unit from which myosin is built, by end-to-end aggregation. According to the estimates of Astbury, Reed & Spark, the unit could be formed by a chain of 773 amino-acid residues folded double (or possibly treble), the chains being in the α-configuration.

Tropomyosin has the remarkable characteristic of forming regular crystals, a characteristic that is normally associated with the more globular type of protein, although it will be recalled that crystals of tobacco mosaic protein have been described. The crystals contain some 90 per cent. of water, so that, on the basis of a folded chain, the units in the crystal would be separated by some 40A of water. Further discussion of the characteristics of these proteins will be left till later ; it has become obvious that the myosin studied by Boehm, by Astbury, and by many others, was really a mixture of myosin with actomyosin, since the anomalous viscosity and thread-formation, considered to be characteristic of myosin, are properties exclusively belonging to actomyosin ; nevertheless the wide-angle X-ray study of both compounds reveals no striking difference, so that we may, without serious misgivings, proceed to consider the work of Astbury on the X-ray diffraction pattern of " myosin " and muscle.

X-Ray Diffraction Studies

It will be recalled that silk fibroin is a fibrous protein which gives the X-ray photo characteristic of bundles of polypeptide chains, lying with their long axes parallel to the axis of the fibre. The wide-angle fibre-period

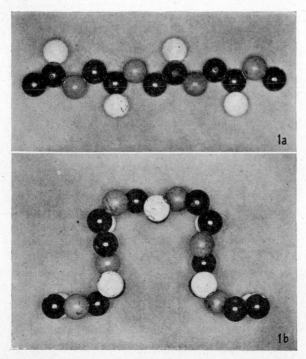

FIG. 242. Skeleton model of a polypeptide chain : (*a*) in the straight form, and (*b*) in a folded form. White balls represent side-chains. (Astbury. *Essays on Growth and Form.* Oxford.)

is 3·38A, and is due to the repetition of amino-acid residues along the polypeptide chain as in Fig. 44, p. 52 ; it is thought, moreover, that the chains or " grids " are packed together into tablet-shaped bodies, micelles or crystallites.   Keratin, the protein of hair, nail, and horn, gives a similar X-ray photo to that of silk fibroin, with the important difference that the meridional spacing, *i.e.*, the spacing along the fibre-axis, is not 3·38A, but 5·1A ; and it will be remembered that Astbury postulated a folding of the polypeptide chain, as in Fig. 242, to account for this repeat-period ; the remarkable long-range elasticity of keratin was explained on this basis, extension being the result of the unfolding of the chains to the fully extended β-configuration.

On allowing a pool of myosin sol to dry, a film remains, which may be studied by X-rays.   On passing the X-rays perpendicular to the surface of the film a simple ring photo is obtained, similar to that given by disorientated keratin in its natural state ; whilst, if the beam of X-rays is parallel to the surface, the picture is one of fibres lying roughly parallel to the surface of the film, but themselves randomly orientated in its plane. On stretching this film, however, the fibres tend to orientate themselves with their long axes in the direction of stretch, in the same way as the long molecules of rubber orientate themselves on stretching.   Under these conditions the wide-angle X-ray photo becomes almost indistinguishable from that given by keratin fibres, and similar, moreover, to the X-ray photo of the intact muscle fibre.   A stretched myosin film may thus be used to study the probable behaviour of the myosin fibrils in the intact muscle.   The analogy between myosin and keratin does not rest with the similarity in resting structure ; myosin, like keratin, when stretched further, also passes into the β-form, a change that likewise permits of a remarkable long-range reversible elasticity.   Thus, starting with an ordinary film, in which the molecules are not orientated with their axes parallel, an increase in length of some 57 per cent. is possible as a result of a simple orientation ; a further increase of 100 per cent. in length is then possible in virtue of the alpha-to-beta transformation.   In living muscle, however, it has been so far impossible to obtain X-ray evidence of the same transformation ; only when the muscle was washed and dried and then, after re-wetting, stretched ; in this case the transformation was incomplete before the muscle broke, so that it seems highly probable that there are certain chemical linkages holding the chains in the α-configuration more rigidly than in the case of keratin. However, the fundamental characteristic of muscle is not its power of stretching reversibly, but its power of *contracting*, and if this were the extent of the analogy between keratin and myosin it would not be very instructive.   Astbury has drawn attention, nevertheless, to the power of both keratin and myosin films to contract forcibly under appropriate conditions.   Thus, if wool is stretched slowly in 1 per cent. aqueous caustic soda by about 90 per cent., and then allowed to relax, it shortens to less than its original length ; on washing out the caustic soda and placing the fibre in water at about 80° C., still further shortening occurs, so that a supercontraction of about 20 per cent. is reached. With the fibre in this state, the X-ray picture is still essentially that given by the β-configuration, and yet such a high degree of contraction can best be interpreted as a folding of the polypeptide chains. Speakman has shown, moreover, that the first step in the induction of supercontraction is the breakdown of the disulphide side-chain linkages, such a breakdown being a necessary prerequisite to a folding of the chains. Myosin supercontracts spontaneously in water above about 40° C., *i.e.*, a far less drastic treatment is necessary, a fact which may be correlated with the presence of far fewer cystine residues in this fibrous protein. Neither in myosin nor in keratin is supercontraction associated with a significant change in the X-ray pattern ; this is, at first thought, surprising in view of the marked difference associated with the folding up from the β- to the α-configuration ; however, as Astbury has emphasised, the X-ray picture reveals only the structure of the best organised parts of the fibre ; in series with these crystalline parts there are probably regions in which this strict parallelism of the chains does not obtain, and it is just in these regions that we may expect folding to take place ; in the well organised regions the molecules will be so packed as to make it extremely difficult for any extensive folding. As the supercontraction increases in extent, for example, by placing the stretched fibres in steam, the X-ray photo reveals —not a change in fundamental spacing—but a progressive disorganisation of the fibre, the more crystalline regions being eventually dragged into the disorientation process. Studies with living and dead muscles, contracted to different extents, gave results consistent with the general hypothesis of a folding of myosin chains, in the sense that the X-ray photos of strongly contracted muscles showed remarkably little disorientation. To make this point clear we must appreciate that a structure, built up of long orientated units, can contract to some extent entirely in virtue of a loss of orientation ; a typical example of the elasticity due to this characteristic is shown by rubber which, in its resting state, consists of long molecules in a random arrangement ; on stretching rubber the long molecules become orientated in the direction of stretch and thus give a fibre-type of X-ray photo, the extra length obtained over the reversible region of elasticity being due, in great measure, to this lengthwise packing of the molecules. The force causing the rubber to contract from its stretched state is derived from the tendency of the molecules to re-assume their random orientation, *i.e.*, to increase their *entropy*. The contraction of keratin and myosin by the folding of chains is a different process; we are here dealing not with entropy changes, which refer only to the orientations of the molecules as a whole, but with changes in the *internal energy* of the molecules. It has been argued by Picken, from the thermo-elastic behaviour of rubber and muscle, that an important factor in muscular contraction is, indeed, a disorientation of previously orientated myosin molecules, muscular contraction being comparable with the changes found in rubber when released from stretch. Astbury has critically examined this hypothesis, and has shown, in the first place, that complete disorientation can only result in a contraction of 50 per cent. In a muscle caused to contract 58 per cent. by treatment with iodoacetate, however, there was little, or no evidence of a disorientation of myosin chains, as revealed by the X-ray photos ; moreover it is possible to calculate the contribution of entropy (*i.e.*, the tendency of the molecules to disorientate) to the tension developed in stretched wool or myosin, and it is easy to show that, in contrast with the state of affairs in rubber, its contribution is negligible.

The folding and unfolding of long chains, shown by myosin and keratin fibres, has some analogy with the changes occurring in the globular proteins on denaturation. The globular proteins must represent polypeptide chains folded in a specific manner, and it is profitable to regard this folding as a more advanced stage of the beta-to-alpha transformation. On denaturing a globular protein, linkages between side-chains, which normally held the chains in their folded configuration, are broken (Mirsky), and the liberated chains probably tend to aggregate together in a crude fibrous structure analogous to that obtained in highly supercontracted keratin or myosin. X-ray studies of these denatured proteins reveal the existence of the β-chains in a much disorientated form. As a useful working hypothesis, therefore, we may assume that myosin is capable of contracting reversibly in virtue of a release of certain bonds between the polypeptide chains, a release which permits them to assume a more folded configuration. Applying such a conception to the contraction of muscle, we may assume that the myosin in the relaxed state of the muscle is in the partially folded α-configuration ; as a result of a stimulus, certain bonds between the side-chains are reversibly loosened to permit a further folding of the chains ; each individual unit will therefore contract, causing a shrinkage of the fibril in the longitudinal direction, and a swelling in the transverse direction. We must remember, however, that the X-ray analysis only provides information regarding the well organised parts of any structure ; where there is no order in the arrangement of the atoms it is impossible to deduce anything, from X-ray analysis, of the changes taking place during contraction, so that considerable changes in normally disorientated regions of the fibril may occur during contraction without their becoming evident. The fact that contraction of muscle is not associated with significant changes in the X-ray picture suggests that the folding occurs in the badly orientated regions ; this is probable, as we have seen, on *a priori* grounds, but we must not allow this consideration to obscure the fact that so far no unequivocal evidence of chain-folding in the contracted state of muscle has been produced.

Electron-Microscopical Studies

The fundamental thesis of Astbury is that the long " myosin " chain is the essential contractile unit, a postulate that demands an underlying continuity throughout the sarcomeres of a muscle fibre. A striking confirmation of this attitude was provided by the electron-microscopical studies of Hall, Jakus & Schmitt on striated muscle fibres. The high resolution of the instrument made it possible to observe the individual filaments, some 50–250A thick, running continuously through the A- and I-bands. In the A-band they appeared to be relatively densely packed, sharply defined, and almost parallel in orientation, whereas in the I-band less orderly arrangement was suggested. In the contracted [1] fibre the filaments showed no signs of coiling ; and we must conclude that any shortening must be the result of changes on a scale not resolvable by the electron-microscope, *i.e.*, a folding of molecular chains as Astbury suggested.[2] The Z-membrane appeared to consist of interfibrillar material, possibly cementing the fibrils together in this region. A study of " myosin " fibrils obtained by extracting various muscles by the Edsall technique, and allowing a film of the extract to dry on the supporting film of the specimen grid, revealed a wide variation in the length of the particles, a finding that forced Hall, Jakus & Schmitt to conclude that the " myosin," prepared in this manner, was not a monodisperse system but consisted of long particles broken off by the extraction procedure from still longer units in the intact muscle ; the lengths varied greatly, although they were less than 15,000A, the length of a sarcomere ; thus the tendency for a whole fibre to break at the Z-bands into sarcomere units has its parallel in the rupture of the fibrillæ by KCl extraction. Average lengths and widths for several muscles are given in Table XXXVI :—

TABLE **XXXVI**

Average Dimensions of Muscle Fibrillæ. (*Hall, Jakus & Schmitt*, 1946.)

Muscle Source	Average Width	Average Length
Rabbit leg	120A	4,100A
Frog leg	140A	4,100A
Lobster abdomen . . .	140A	6,800A
Scallop adductor, striated . .	130A	5,000A
Clam (*Mya*) adductor, smooth .	150A	3,100A

Rozsa, Szent-Györgyi & Wyckoff, in a more recent study, arrived at essentially the same conclusions with respect to the structure of the myofibril ; they showed that the filaments were apparently overlaid with a

[1] One cannot emphasise too frequently that the electron-microscope can only show structure in the intensely dried, and generally fixed and stained tissue ; thus a contracted fibre is one that has been fixed whilst in the shortened condition, and it is difficult to say what may, or may not, have happened during fixation and subsequent preparation for electron-microscopical examination.

[2] Astbury concentrated his attention on the wide-angle diffraction pattern of muscle, *i.e.*, the short spacings ; recently Bear has investigated the larger spacings, which promise to yield more information regarding *differences* in structure than the short spacings and, moreover, provide a link between X-ray analysis and the electron-microscopic picture ; for example, a spacing along the collagen fibre of 640A was observed by X-ray analysis, and later identified as the typical banding of collagen in the electron-microscope (p. 102). In clam muscle (adductor, a smooth muscle), a period of 725A along the axis of the fibre was observed by X-ray diffraction methods, and in fibres stained with phosphotungstic acid a definite banding with an average periodicity of 360A, *i.e.*, about one-half the X-ray periodicity, was observed. The remarkable feature of this banding, however, was that it was quite unaffected by stretching the muscle to four times its normal length, whereas a similar banding in collagen was strongly affected by stretching, the period being increased from 640A to as much as 6,000A. The aggregations of dense electron-scattering material at periods along the smooth muscle fibre may represent, on a sub-microscopic scale, the larger, microscopical periodicity in striated muscle.

structureless material, the distribution of which determined the banded characteristics of the whole fibre. Again, Draper & Hodge have largely confirmed the earlier work of Hall, Jakus & Schmitt; they have emphasised the existence of a repeat-period along the myofibrils of some 250–400A, so that they may be represented as strings of beads.

Myosin and Actin

This brings us back to the consideration of the true nature of " myosin." According to Szent-Györgyi, myosin is normally present in muscle as a complex of actin and myosin, so that when " myosin " is obtained by extracting muscle with 0·5 M KCl for a few hours, what is really done is to split a large amount of the myosin from its combination, and also to extract a part of the actomyosin intact; this accounts for the fact, remarked on a long time ago, that although myosin is soluble in 0·1 M KCl, it is not possible to extract appreciable amounts from muscle with a solution of this strength, 0·5 M KCl being necessary. Not only is a definite concentration of salt necessary, but ATP (adenosine triphosphate) normally present in fresh muscle, contributes to the splitting; consequently, unless there is a suitable concentration of this substance in the muscle, extraction will not be very successful, the actomyosin being much less soluble than its components. This makes the early finding of Deuticke intelligible; Deuticke found that the amount of protein extractable from a muscle decreased greatly as this was fatigued or as rigor set in; parallel with this there was a decrease in the power of the muscle to form organic phosphates; since ATP is involved in the phosphorylation of organic compounds, Deuticke's results may be explained on the grounds that the concentration of ATP decreased in fatigue and so left larger proportions of the muscle proteins in the difficultly soluble actomyosin form. This finding also explains the observation of Needham and his group (Dainty *et al.*), that addition of ATP to " myosin " solutions caused a rapid decrease in the double refraction of flow (by 48 per cent.), and a smaller decrease in viscosity; the finding of Schramm & Weber, that the addition of ATP to the " heavy component of myosin," S-myosin, caused a reversible fall in the sedimentation constant to the value typical of their L-myosin, is also explained by Deuticke's results.

Action of ATP. Thus the active principle, from a contractile point of view, would appear to be actomyosin; and some support for this is given by the action of ATP on threads of actomyosin. The result is a rapid and reversible contraction of the thread; so striking is the phenomenon that Szent-Györgyi considered that here, *in vitro*, he was studying the fundamental process of muscular contraction. ATP, added to an actomyosin sol, caused a " superprecipitation," *i.e.*, a heavy flocculation of the protein; when added to gels these were vigorously contracted, or " syneresed," with the expulsion of a large proportion of their water. The view that the contraction of actomyosin threads had its parallel in muscular contraction was supported by a number of studies on washed muscle bundles; thus the psoas may be thoroughly washed with the ends of the fibres tied so as to prevent shrinkage during washing. On placing this " muscle " in Ringer solution, 0·001 M Mg and 0·02 per cent. ATP, the muscle shortened and, according to Szent-Györgyi, developed as much tension as it did *in vivo* on stimulation. Moreover, the effect was not confined to washed muscle fibres ; for example, Buchtal and his collaborators, in 1944, showed that isolated, electrically excitable, muscle went into a series of tetanus-like contractions when bathed in a Ringer solution containing minute concentrations of ATP (3·6–7·3.10⁻⁶ mole/ml.) ; in both the frog and the cat an injection into the artery supplying a muscle caused the prompt development of tetanus.[1]

Myosin and ATPase Activity. One further discovery, which provided the stimulus for all the recent work on the relation of ATP to muscular contraction, is that of the Russian workers, Engelhardt & Ljubimova, who found that the breakdown of ATP to ADP (adenosine diphosphate) and phosphate was apparently catalysed by " myosin " itself, *i.e.*, " myosin " had ATPase activity ; certainly myosin, crystallised several times, behaves as an ATPase, but whether this activity is due to the protein itself, or an associated enzyme, is still not certain ; although recent evidence favours the latter viewpoint. Thus Polis & Meyerhof were able, by fractional precipitation, to obtain myosin preparations with some three times the ATPase activity of the original material, whilst Kielley & Meyerhof have obtained an ATPase from muscle which is quite free from both myosin and actomyosin. Again, a number of other enzymatic activities have been found associated with myosin, for example a desaminase by Ferdmann, so that Szent-Györgyi considers myosin as a skeleton to which are attached various enzymes which he calls " protines." Whatever the real nature of the ATPase, it is significant that it is in such close connection with the contractile element of the muscle fibre, since it is thought that the breakdown of ATP to ADP is the energy-giving reaction most closely related to the actual contractile process ; as Szent-Györgyi has pointed out, this ATPase activity, associated with myosin, may provide a clue to the manner in which the muscle adjusts its rate of consumption of energy to the requirements of its mechanical task (p. 495).

Actomyosin and the Contraction of Muscle. Space will not permit us to follow Szent-Györgyi in his various speculations on the relationship between the actomyosin system, ATP, various ions such as Mg⁺⁺ and Ca⁺⁺, and the contractile process [2] ; we must content ourselves only with an examination of the likelihood that the contraction of an actomyosin thread is the true picture of the shortening of an actual muscle fibril.

Actin, in water at alkaline reaction, is in the corpuscular form ; on acidification, or addition of 0·1 M KCl, it is converted reversibly into a fibrous condition ; this conversion has been studied by Jakus & Hall and by Perry & Reid, in the electron-microscope, and by Astbury & Spark by X-ray diffraction. In the electron-microscope, actin appears as very fine filaments, perhaps 100A thick, which apparently result from an

---

[1] We may note that ADP was also effective as well as adenylic acid in the case of mammalian muscle ; it is possible that ATP is first synthesised from these compounds before acting. It may well be, however, that many of these phosphorus compounds exert their effects by depolarisation of the nerve or muscle membrane.

[2] These have been reviewed, competently and critically, by Barer and Sandow.

aggregation of the corpuscular units in an end-to-end fashion. Some confirmation of this is given by the X-ray diffraction photo of the fibres, which indicates a fibre-period which may be about 108A long ; and Astbury has pointed to a possible analogy between myosin and actin, on the one hand, and hair and feather keratin on the other. Thus feather keratin exhibits a fundamental difference from hair keratin, being built up of chains with a somewhat shortened β-configuration (3·1A compared with 3·4A), giving a long fibre-period of 95A. A long time ago, when discussing the structure of feather keratin, Astbury had suggested that it could be made up of the end-to-end aggregation of corpuscular units.

A mixture of actin with myosin (prepared according to the method of

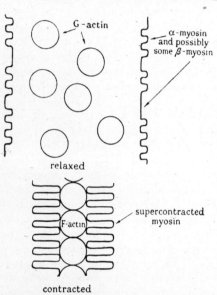

relaxed

contracted

FIG. 243. Diagrammatic representation of a possible mechanism of contraction by the formation of an actomyosin complex. (Astbury. *Proc. Roy. Soc.*)

Szent-Györgyi, and therefore presumably free from actin), gives rise to fibres which appear thicker than those of actin, so that Jakus & Hall suggest tentatively that the actomyosin fibre is an actin fibre with myosin molecules attached to it. The X-ray diffraction photo of actomyosin exhibits the characteristics of both myosin and actin, the wide-angle repeat of 5·1A being due to the myosin, whilst the small-angle repeat of 108A corresponds to actin.[1] A possible scheme of muscular contraction, based on a simultaneous aggregation [2] of G-actin to F-actin and a super-contraction of myosin chains, is illustrated in Fig. 243, from Astbury (1950).

Actomyosin gels, and their changes during the action of ATP, have been studied by Perry, Reed, Astbury & Spark ; the dried gel consists of a meshwork of interlacing fibrils. Figs. 244–246, Pl. XII, illustrate different stages in the syneresis following addition of ATP ; and it will be seen that the shrinkage of the gel, so typically observed, really consists in a coalescence of fibrils to form thick aggregates, which then apparently squeeze out the water originally contained within the fine actomyosin meshwork. No change in the X-ray diffraction picture was observed as a result of the transformation, the alpha 5·1A fibre-period remaining. The shrinkage of an actomyosin gel, or the contraction of an

---

[1] The small-angle repeat of 108A had been earlier discovered in dried muscle, but had been considered to be a large period in the myosin molecule.

[2] According to Laki, Bowen & Clark (1950), G-actin contains ATP ; if this is removed it fails to polymerise to F-actin. Straub (1949) had stated that the polymerisation is associated with the conversion of ATP to ADP, a claim that has been disputed by Dubuisson (1950, *d*).

PLATE XII

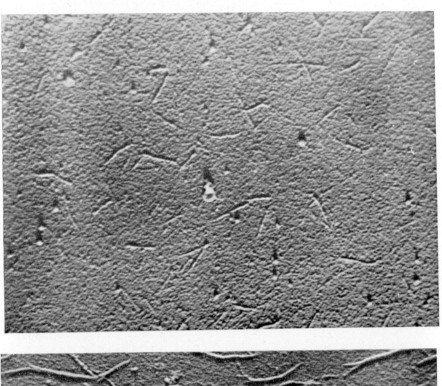

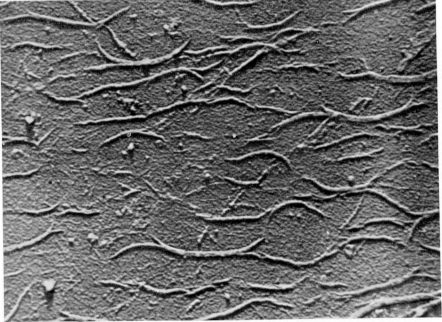

|_____| 1μ

FIGS. 244 and 245. Stages in syneresis of actomyosin suspension (Myosin-B) resulting from the addition of ATP. Chromium shadowed on collodion substrate. (Perry, Reed, Astbury & Spark. *Biochim. Biophys. Acta.*)

[*To face p.* 530.

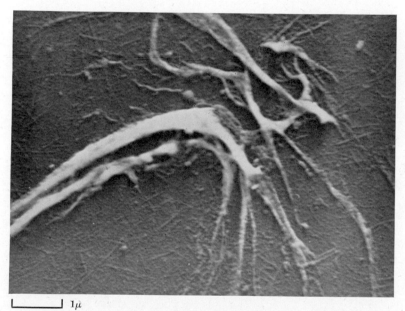

|_____| 1μ

Fig. 246. Late stage in syneresis of actomyosin suspension (Myosin-B) resulting from the addition of ATP. Chromium shadowed on collodion substrate. (Perry, Reed, Astbury & Spark. *Biochim. Biophys. Acta.*)

actomyosin thread, is thus something quite different from the folding of polypeptide chains envisaged by Astbury ; the latter is inclined to discount the significance of the actomyosin contraction, induced by ATP, as a factor in normal muscular contraction on this and other grounds. Before considering these other objections, let us try and form a picture of the processes taking place when ATP is added to actomyosin. According to the studies of Bailey & Perry, the linkage between actin and myosin is brought about by the SH-groups in the latter molecule ; moreover, the ATPase activity of myosin is also directly connected with these groups, any influence on the ATPase activity of myosin, by oxidation of its SH-groups, etc., being paralleled exactly by a similar influence on its ability to form a complex with actin. Thus ATP probably competes with actin for the same SH-groups in myosin, and because of its greater affinity for them it splits this linkage when added to actomyosin. The final effect of ATP will depend on the salt concentration ; if this is high (0·5 M), dissociation will be complete and actin and myosin will exist as separate entities in solution ; if the salt concentration is low, as in the gels and threads, the rupture of the SH-linkages is followed by aggregation of particles by way of other and less specific linkages, *e.g.*, ionic or hydrogen-bond types, linkages that are sensitive to the salt concentration of the medium.[1]

The objections raised to Szent-Györgyi's thesis are, first, that actomyosin fibres do not contract anisodiametrically like muscle fibres, *i.e.*, they do not fatten as they shorten, but merely shrink as a result of the expulsion of water. Secondly, Buchtal *et al.* (1947) observed that, whereas an unloaded actomyosin fibre shrank on treatment with ATP, a loaded fibre actually elongated. Both of these objections have been answered by Szent-Györgyi ; he points out that in a thread, the actomyosin molecules are quite unorientated, so that even if they did contract with an associated increase in thickness, this increase would not be observable ; if the thread is first stretched to bring the molecules parallel with the fibre-axis, ATP then causes shortening with widening. The behaviour of the loaded thread is explained by the action of ATP on the linkages between actomyosin molecules ; ATP loosens these, so that, if the contractile force generated by ATP is insufficient to allow the load to be lifted, the thread will extend because of this loosening. That the normal elasticity of muscle is related to its ATP content has been shown by Erdös and by Bate-Smith & Bendall, the post-mortem development of inelasticity, which culminates in rigor, being correlated with the disappearance of ATP.

At present, then, the most serious objections to Szent-Györgyi's thesis seem to have been met, nevertheless it would be as well to maintain a

[1] Whether the union of ATP with myosin leads to further change is still a matter of discussion ; according to Mommaerts and, more definitely, to Buchtal, Deutch, Knappeis & Munch-Petersen, myosin is actually phosphorylated after complex-formation, giving rise to a labile phosphorus group which is not connected with ATP, which in fact behaves as ADP. The last-mentioned authors have shown that myosin threads, *without ATPase activity*, are shortened by ATP. Fabry-Hamoir has given a brief discussion of the possible reactions of ATP and actomyosin—he concludes that a reaction with SH-groups is unlikely.

cautious attitude ; the extreme rapidity of contraction and relaxation in normal muscle makes it very unlikely that a far-reaching change in the structure of the fibrillar component is involved ; Astbury's notion of the folding of keratin-type chains is, from this viewpoint, the more attractive, although its experimental justification leaves a lot to be desired.

Before passing to a consideration of the changes in physical state of the muscle proteins during contraction, we may note that Snellman & Erdös have recently made an ultracentrifugal study of the combination of actin with myosin ; at a certain optimal ratio, namely one part of actin to three parts of myosin, only actomyosin is present ; if the proportion of myosin is increased, this protein appears as a definite entity in addition to actomyosin, *i.e.*, a more slowly sedimenting material is found to be present ; when the proportion of actin is increased, on the other hand, it appears that some free actin now remains. There is some evidence, therefore, of a stoichiometric relationship between myosin and actin.

Changes in Physical State of Proteins on Contraction

Some valuable contributions to our knowledge of the changes that take place in the state of the muscular proteins have been made by Dubuisson, who extracted the muscle at rest, and again when it was frozen in liquid air

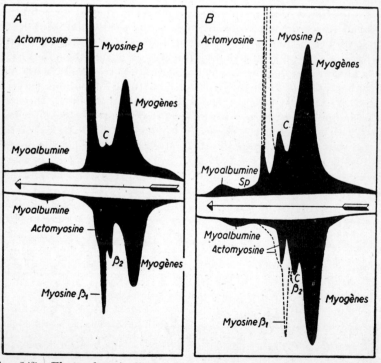

Fig. 247.   Electrophoresis diagrams of extracts from resting (A), and contracted muscle (B). Note more or less complete disappearance of the myosin and actomyosin fractions, together with the appearance of a new fraction, C. (Dubuisson. *Biochim. Biophys. Acta.*)

during contraction (or during bromacetate contracture), and studied the electrophoretic diagrams of the extracts. Fig. 247, A, illustrates the diagram obtained from resting muscle, with peaks corresponding to the *myogen group* [1] ; *myosin-β*—probably corresponding to the *crystalline myosin*, or *myosin w.s.*, of Szent-Györgyi and Jakus *et al.*, respectively ; *actomyosin* ; and a *myoalbumin*, described by Bate-Smith. The appearance of the extract from contracted muscle is shown in Fig. 247, B ; the significant changes, according to Dubuisson, are the more or less complete disappearance of the myosin and actomyosin fractions, associated with the appearance of what was considered to be a new fraction (C in the diagram) which has been called *contractin*, and which turns out to be the γ-myosin identified earlier as a normal constituent of muscle extracts ; moreover, a diffuse band, *sp*, appears, representing a mixture of proteins so far unidentified. Thus contraction is predominantly associated with an inextractibility of myosin, *i.e.*, it looks as though contraction results in a firmer binding of this protein than that pertaining during rest ; consequently the disappearance of actomyosin cannot be interpreted as a mere splitting of actin and myosin. It is of some interest that the reduced extractability of myosin following contraction is not related to a diminished concentration of ATP in the muscle, since Dubuisson has shown that adding ATP to the muscle does not influence the amount extracted. On the other hand salts such as KI and $K_4P_2O_7$, which are more vigorous extractives, are able to extract myosin and actomyosin from contracted muscle. Dubuisson's results indicate that the scheme of contraction of actomyosin, presented by Szent-Györgyi, is far too simple ; as Dubuisson says, in an excellent review of his work, the real problem confronting the worker in this field is the number of proteins that actually belong to the contractile structure of muscle and how their mode of combination is modified by the contractile process. It is possible that all the " myosins " are linked with other structural components of the fibre, and that the extraction procedures break down these linkages to a greater or less extent ; the diminished extractability during contraction could therefore be due to a more powerful binding of the various " myosins."

Birefringence and Contraction

The theories of muscular contraction, discussed above, have as their basis an essential continuity of contractile units along the length of the fibre ; the problem remains of reconciling this continuity with the microscopical discontinuities revealed by the various bands described earlier. The A-band is anisotropic, exhibiting the phenomenon of birefringence ; the anisotropy is due to two causes [2] ; first, the

---

[1] This group probably contains the myogen described by Weber, and various enzymes, such as glyceraldehyde dehydrogenase, phosphoglucomutase, etc. The application of different methods of study of the protein fractions in different laboratories has led to a complex terminology. At present it seems that β-myosin, " myosin proper," myosin-water soluble, Myosin-A and L-myosin are the same. α-myosin, actomyosin, S-myosin and myosin-B are likewise identical. The myosin-γ of Dubuisson, identifiable electrophoretically, has not been characterised further.

[2] The micellar birefringence is some 35 per cent. of the total. (Fischer, 1944.)

submicroscopic units are rod-shaped and lie with their axes more or less parallel with the axis of the fibre (form double refraction), and secondly, these units are themselves built up of molecules in an orderly or crystalline fashion (micellar, or *eigen*, double refraction). Both types of birefringence are positive, *i.e.*, they are due to particles arranged with their long axes parallel to the axis of the fibre, so that a fundamental structure, composed of long rod-shaped bundles of polypeptide chains is consistent with the birefringence of the A-bands. The I-bands have only 10 per cent. of the birefringence of the A-bands, and are generally described as isotropic ; this comparative isotropy could be due, either to a lack of order in the arrangement of the submicroscopic units in this region, or to the presence of some strongly negatively birefringent material which cancelled the positive birefringence of the contractile units.[1] The former hypothesis is ruled out by the electron-microscopic appearance of the muscle fibre, whilst the alternative has a fair amount of experimental support. Thus Matoltsy & Gerandas state that, on extraction of myosin and actin from muscle, the A-bands lose their birefringence whilst the I-bands become strongly negatively birefringent, and they claim to have isolated a protein, responsible for this negative birefringence, which they call *N-protein*, by extraction with a urea-salt solution. Solutions of this protein exhibited strong negative flow-birefringence ; if this were concentrated in the I-bands it would presumably cancel the positive birefringence of the actomyosin. Unfortunately, however, Dubuisson (1950a) has failed to confirm this work ; he finds that there are certainly unidentified proteins in muscle after removal of myosin and actomyosin, but they failed to exhibit birefringence. Other competitors for the negative birefringence are the lipids, said by Dempsey *et al.* to be concentrated in the I-bands, and possibly the nucleotide material which is unequivocally concentrated in this region (p. 520) ; that this material is a nucleic acid, however, seems very unlikely from the observation of Dempsey *et al.*, and also of Barer, that digestion of muscle with ribonuclease or desoxyribonuclease is without effect on the striations. It is of interest in this connection that Hamoir has isolated from fish muscles both a tropomyosin, which seemed to be identical with Bailey's preparation, and also a nucleoprotein which seemed to be a compound of tropomyosin and ribosenucleic acid, with a characteristic sedimentation constant, but an electrophoretic mobility identical with that of tropomyosin. Tropomyosin preparations containing less than 3 per cent. of nucleic acid behaved identically with tropomyosin as normally prepared ; when the content is increased (for example to 10 per cent.) a characteristic change in the shape and dimensions takes place, which is manifested in the altered sedimentation constant. It may well be, therefore, that the highly negatively birefringent material

[1] We may note, also, that stretching a striated muscle has little (Fischer, 1944) or no (Buchtal *et al.*, 1936) effect on its birefringence ; if the I-regions were regions of disorder we should expect stretching the fibre to reduce this disorder and so increase the birefringence of the whole fibre appreciably. That the anisotropy of the A-band is due, moreover, to the presence of a specific contractile material, not present elsewhere, is made very improbable by the observation that smooth muscle, whether derived from vertebrate or invertebrate sources (Fischer, 1944), has a higher birefringence than that of striated muscle ($2 \cdot 9$–$3 \cdot 3 . 10^{-3}$ compared with $2 \cdot 5$–$2 \cdot 6 . 10^{-3}$).

isolated from muscle is a breakdown product of nucleotropomyosin. According to Hamoir it is very unlikely that nucleotropomyosin is an artefact caused by the reaction of ATP with tropomyosin.

We may mention here an ingenious suggestion of Bernal, who argues for a reversed spiral arrangement of myosin chains as in Fig. 248 ; such an arrangement would produce regions in the fibril where the chains were parallel approximately to the fibre axis, and so give powerful positive

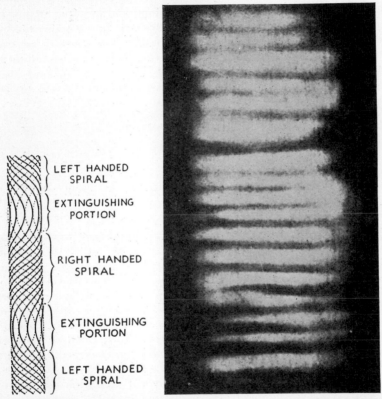

FIG. 248. Left: Diagram illustrating Bernal's tentative hypothesis to explain alternation of isotropy and anisotropy in a myofibril. Right : Photomicrograph, by Van Iterson, of a tobacco mosaic virus preparation in the polarisation microscope, showing the alternation of birefringence due to a reversed spiral arrangement of the sub-microscopic fibrillæ. (Bernal & Fankuchen. *J. gen. Physiol.*)

birefringence ; in other regions the rods would lie almost at right-angles to the axis, and so give very small birefringence. Such a reversed spiral arrangement should give a typical appearance in the polarisation microscope ; it has been observed by Van Iterson in solutions of cadmium glycerophosphate when placed in a narrow tube and agitated ; similar formations have been found with solutions of tobacco-mosaic virus (p. 67).

During contraction, the double refraction of the A-bands decreases markedly (see, for example, the work of Von Muralt), the change taking place contemporaneously with the development of tension. This is thought by Von Muralt, and also by Fischer, to be due to a loss of micellar double refraction and could be due to a disorientation of the polypeptide chains, *i.e.*, a disorientation only resolvable by X-ray analysis and beyond the resolution of the electron-microscope. Contraction is also associated with an apparent reversal of striation, the so-called contraction bands, an appearance that is most intelligibly interpreted as a diffusion of " I-substance " (*e.g.*, adenylic compounds) into the A-bands, with possibly a diffusion of A-substance (basophilic material and material that scatters electrons strongly) towards the I-bands. This last point is suggested by the observation of Hall, Jakus & Schmitt that, in the strongly contracted fibre, the dark material (electron scattering and with an affinity for phosphotungstic acid " stain ") has moved from the A-bands to the Z-region of the I-band. The changes have been summarised by D. M. Needham in the following scheme :—

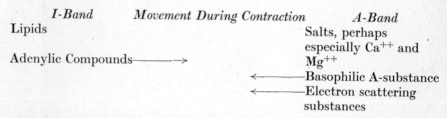

  I-Band   *Movement During Contraction*   *A-Band*
Lipids   Salts, perhaps
                   especially Ca^{++} and
Adenylic Compounds————$\rightarrow$ Mg^{++}
            $\leftarrow$————Basophilic A-substance
            $\leftarrow$————Electron scattering
                   substances

Tentatively we may assume that substances important for the metabolic needs of the muscle during contraction, *e.g.*, the adenylic compound, adenosine triphosphate (ATP), are not equally distributed throughout the fibre and that the metabolic events connected with contraction demand a movement of these substances. The idea that contraction is limited to the A-bands need not be seriously considered. It seems doubtful, moreover, whether the decreased birefringence of muscle on contraction is really the result of a change in the crystalline pattern ; thus Buchtal, Deutsch & Knappeis found that whereas ATP, applied to an electrically inexcitable muscle, causes no contraction, it does decrease the birefringence ; moreover, in the presence of iodoacetate, neither electrical excitation nor treatment with ATP changes the birefringence, although both treatments cause contraction.

Impedance and Transparency

Before concluding this description of muscular contraction, we may indicate two other changes that seem to be closely connected with the development of tension ; the impedance and transparency. We have seen that, in nerve, the passage of an action potential is associated with a transient decrease in impedance ; a similar decrease was observed by Dubuisson and Katz in muscle. This is followed, under isometric conditions, by an *increase*, taking place almost exactly at the moment when tension develops and lasting into the relaxation phase.[1] In Fig. 249, from D. K. Hill,

[1] The literature on this subject may be found confusing ; Dubuisson (1935) originally described two falls, an initial rapid one presumably associated with the action potential,

action potential, tension, and transparency are all recorded together, the time scale and amplification being adequate to reveal the latency relaxation of Sandow ; corresponding with the latter there is an increase in transparency which passes through a maximum as the tension begins to

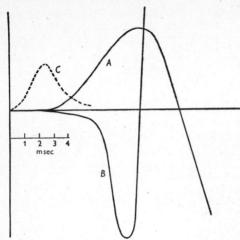

Fig. 249. Changes in opacity (A), and mechanical response (B), on stimulation of muscle. (C) shows course of action potential, not recorded, but as given by Katz. (D. K. Hill. *J. Physiol.*)

develop. A study of the characteristics of the early increase in transparency, and the later decrease, suggests that they have different origins, the former being probably due to a decreased absorption of light, whilst the latter is a scattering phenomenon. The changes described by D. K. Hill are to be distinguished from the more protracted change in transparency described by von Muralt.

and a slower one associated with contraction ; Bozler described only an increase in impedance and later Dubuisson (1937) showed that, under strictly isometric conditions, the initial fall is, indeed, followed by a rise. Katz observed a fall in the end-plate region associated with the end-plate and action potentials ; in his most recent review of the subject Dubuisson (1950) describes an initial fall—the a-wave—followed by two rises, b_1 and b_2. There seems no doubt that the initial fall in impedance is associated with passage of the excitation wave.

References

Astbury, W. T. (1947). " Structure of Biological Fibres and the Problem of Muscle." *Proc. Roy. Soc.*, B, **134**, 303.

Astbury, W. T. (1950). " Discussion on Muscular Contraction." *Proc. Roy. Soc.*, B, **137**, 40.

Astbury, W. T. & Dickinson, S. (1940). " X-Ray Studies of the Molecular Structure of Myosin." *Proc. Roy. Soc.*, B, **129**, 307.

Astbury, W. T., Reed, R. & Spark, L. C. (1948). " An X-Ray and Electron Microscope Study of Tropomyosin." *Biochem. J.*, **43**, 282.

Astbury, W. T. & Spark, L. C. (1947). " An Electron Microscope and X-Ray Study of Actin. II. X-Rays." *Biochim. Biophys. Acta*, **1**, 388.

Bailey, K. (1948). " Tropomyosin : a New Asymmetric Protein Component of the Muscle Fibre." *Biochem. J.*, **43**, 271.

BAILEY, K., GUTFREUND, H. & OGSTON, A. G. (1948). "Molecular Weight of Tropomyosin from Rabbit Muscle." *Biochem. J.*, 43, 279.

BAILEY, K. & PERRY, S. V. (1947). "The Role of Sulphydryl Groups in the Interaction of Myosin and Actin." *Biochim. Biophys. Acta*, 1, 506.

BARER, R. (1948). "Structure of the Striated Muscle Fibre." *Biol. Rev.*, 23, 159.

BATE-SMITH, E. C. (1937). "Native and Denatured Muscle Proteins." *Proc. Roy. Soc.*, B, 124, 136.

BATE-SMITH, E. C. & BENDALL, J. R. (1947). "Rigor Mortis and ATP." *J. Physiol.*, 106, 177.

BEAR, R. S. (1945). "Small Angle X-Ray Diffraction Studies on Muscle." *J.A.C.S.*, 67, 1625.

BORBIRO, M. & SZENT-GYÖRGYI, A. (1949). "Relation between Tension and ATP in Striated Muscle." *Biol. Bull.*, 96, 162.

BOZLER, E. (1935). "Change of a.c. Impedance of Muscle Produced by Contraction." *J. cell. & comp. Physiol.*, 6, 217.

BUCHTAL, F., DEUTSCH, A. & KNAPPEIS, G. G. (1944). "Release of Contraction and Changes in Birefringence Caused by ATP." *Acta Physiol. Scand.*, 8, 271.

BUCHTAL, F., DEUTSCH, A. & KNAPPEIS, G. G. (1946). "Effect of ATP and Related Phosphorus Compounds on Isolated Striated Muscles." *Acta Physiol. Scand.*, 11, 325.

BUCHTAL, F., DEUTSCH, A., KNAPPEIS, G. G. & MUNCH-PEDERSEN, A. (1949). "Phosphorylation and Adenine Nucleotide Uptake of Actomyosin and Actin-free Myosin." *Acta Physiol. Scand.*, 16, 326.

BUCHTAL, F., DEUTSCH, A. & MUNCH-PEDERSEN, A. (1947). "Effect of ATP on Myosin Threads." *Acta Physiol. Scand.*, 13, 167.

BUCHTAL, F. & FOLKOW, B. (1944). "Close Arterial Injection of ATP and Inorganic Triphosphate into Frog Muscle." *Acta Physiol. Scand.*, 8, 312.

BUCHTAL, F. & KAHLSON, G. (1944). "Action of ATP and Related Compounds on Mammalian Skeletal Muscle." *Acta Physiol. Scand.*, 8, 317.

BUCHTAL, F. & KAHLSON, G. (1944). "Motor Effect of ATP Compounds on Smooth Mammalian Muscle." *Acta Physiol. Scand.*, 8, 325.

BUCHTAL, F. & KAHLSON, G. (1946). "Effect of Acetylcholine and ATP on Denervated Muscle." *Acta Physiol. Scand.*, 11, 284.

BUCHTAL, F. & LINDHARD, J. (1939). "Physiology of the Striated Muscle Fibre." *Det Kgl. Danske Videnskabernes Selskab, Biologiske Meddelelser*, 14, 6.

CASPERSSON, T. & THORELL, B. (1942). "Localisation of Adenylic Acids in Striated Muscle Fibres." *Acta Physiol. Scand.*, 4, 97.

CREPAX, P., JACOB, J. & SELDESLACHTS, J. (1950). "Contribution à l'Étude des Protéinogrammes Électrophorétiques d'Extraits de Muscles Contracturés." *Biochim. Biophys. Acta*, 4, 410.

DAINTY, M., KLEINZELLER, A., LAWRENCE, A. S. C., MIALL, M., NEEDHAM, J., NEEDHAM, D. M. & SHEN, S. C. (1944). "Changes in Anomalous Viscosity and Flow-Birefringence of Myosin Solutions in Relation to ATP and Muscular Contraction." *J. gen. Physiol.*, 27, 355.

DEMPSEY, E. W., WISLOCKI, G. B. & SINGER, M. (1946). "Observations on the Chemical Cytology of Striated Muscle." *Anat. Rec.*, 96, 221.

DEUTICKE, H. J. (1930). "Kolloidzustandsänderungen der Muskelproteine beim Absterben und bei der Ermüdung." *Pflüg. Arch.*, 224, 1.

DRAPER, M. H. & HODGE, A. J. (1949). "Submicroscopic Localisation of Minerals in Skeletal Muscle by Internal 'Micro-Incineration' within the Electron Microscope." *Nature*, 163, 576.

DRAPER, M. H. & HODGE, A. J. (1949). "Studies on Muscle with the Electron Microscope." *Austr. J. Exp. Biol. & Med. Sci.*, 27, 465.

DUBUISSON, M. (1935). "L'Ionogramme de la Contraction Musculaire Étudié à l'Oscillographe Cathodique." *Arch. int. Physiol.*, 41, 177.

DUBUISSON, M. (1937). "Impedance Changes in Muscle during Contraction and Their Possible Relation to Chemical Processes." *J. Physiol.*, 89, 132.

DUBUISSON, M. (1950*a*). "Sur les Protéines de Structure des Muscles Striés." *Experientia*, 6, 102.

DUBUISSON, M. (1950*b*). "Influence de la Nature des Ions sur l'Extractibilité des Protéines de Muscles au Repos ou Contracturés." *Biochim. Biophys. Acta*, 5, 489.

DUBUISSON, M. (1950*c*). "Modifications dans la Structure Physico-Chimique de l'Édifice Contractile au Cours du Cycle de la Contraction Musculaire." *Biochim. Biophys. Acta*, 4, 25.

DUBUISSON, M. (1950*d*). "Sur la Polymerisation de la G-Actine." *Experientia*, 6, 103.

DUBUISSON, M. (1950e). "Sur les Protéines Extractibles du Muscle Strié, etc." *Experientia*, 6, 269.

DUBUISSON, M. (1950 f). "Discussion on Muscle." *Proc. Roy. Soc., B*, 137, 63.

DUBUISSON, M. (1950g). "Muscle Activity and Muscle Proteins." *Biol. Rev.*, 25, 46.

EDSALL, J. T. (1930). "Studies on the Physical Chemistry of Muscle Globulin." *J. biol. Chem.*, 89, 289, 315, 351.

ENGELHARDT, W. A. & LJUBIMOWA, M. N. (1939). "Myosine and ATPase." *Nature*, 144, 668.

ENGSTROM, A. (1944). "Localisation of Mineral Salts in Striated Muscle Fibres." *Acta Physiol. Scand.*, 8, 137.

FABRY-HAMOIR, C. (1950). "Contribution à L'Étude de la Combinaison Actomyosine-ATP." *Biochim. Biophys. Acta*, 4, 445.

FENN, W. O. (1945). "Muscles. " Chap. 33. Physical Chemistry of Cells and Tissues. Ed. Höber. London : J. & A. Churchill.

FISCHER, E. (1941). "Changes during Muscle Contraction as Related to the Crystalline Pattern." *Biol. Symp.*, 3, 211.

FISCHER, E. (1944). "Birefringence of Striated and Smooth Mammalian Muscles." *J. cell. & comp. Physiol.*, 23, 113.

FISCHER, E. (1947). "Birefringence and Ultrastructure of Muscle." *Ann. N.Y. Acad. Sci.*, 47, 783.

HALL, C. E., JAKUS, M. A. & SCHMITT, F. O. (1945). "Structure of Certain Muscle Fibrils as Revealed by the Use of Electron Stains." *J. app. Phys.*, 16, 459.

HALL, C. E., JAKUS, M. A. & SCHMITT, F. O. (1946). "An Investigation of Cross Striations and Myosin Filaments in Muscle." *Biol. Bull.*, 90, 32.

HAMOIR, G. (1951). "Fish Tropomyosin and Fish Nucleotropomyosin." *Biochem. J.*, 48, 146.

HILL, D. K. (1949). "Changes in Transparency of a Muscle during a Twitch." *J. Physiol.*, 108, 292.

JAKUS, M. A. & HALL, C. E. (1947). "Studies of Actin and Myosin." *J. biol. Chem.*, 167, 705.

JORDAN, H. E. (1933). "Structural Changes in Striped Muscle during Contraction." *Physiol. Rev.*, 13, 301.

KIELLEY, W. W. & MEYERHOF, O. (1948). "A New Mg-Activated ATPase in Muscle." *J. biol. Chem.*, 176, 591.

LAKI, K., BOWEN, W. J. & CLARK, A. (1950). "ATP and the Polymerisation of Actin." *J. gen. Physiol.*, 33, 437.

MACALLUM, A. B. (1905). "Distribution of K in Animal and Vegetable Cells." *J. Physiol.*, 32, 95.

MATOLTSY, A. G. & GERENDÁS, M. (1947). "Isotropy in the J-Striation of Striated Muscle." *Nature*, 159, 502.

MOMMAERTS, W. F. H. M. (1948). "Reactions between Actomyosin and ATP." *J. gen. Physiol.*, 31, 361.

MOMMAERTS, W. F. H. M. (1950). "Primary Reaction in Muscular Activity." *Biochim. Biophys. Acta*, 4, 50.

v. MURALT, A. (1932). "Über das Verhalten der Doppelbrechung des Quergestreiften Muskels Während der Kontraktion." *Pflüg. Arch.*, 230, 299.

v. MURALT, A. (1934). "Lichtdurchlässigkeit und Tätigkeitsstoffwechsel des Muskels." *Pflüg. Arch.*, 234, 233, 653.

NEEDHAM, D. M. (1950). "Myosin and ATP in Relation to Muscle Contraction." *Biochim. Biophys. Acta*, 4, 42.

PERRY, S. V. & REED, R. (1947). "An Electron Microscope and X-Ray Study of Actin. I. Electron Microscope." *Biochim. Biophys. Acta*, 1, 379.

PERRY, S. V., REED, R., ASTBURY, W. T. & SPARK, L. C. (1948). "An Electron Microscope Study of the Syneresis of Actomyosin." *Biochim. Biophys. Acta*, 2, 674.

PICKEN, L. E. R. (1940). "The Fine Structure of Biological Systems." *Biol. Rev.*, 15, 133.

POLIS, B. D. & MEYERHOF, O. (1947). "ATPase in Muscle. I. Concentration of the Enzyme in Myosin." *J. biol. Chem.*, 169, 389.

REED, R. & RUDALL, K. M. (1948). "Electron Microscope Studies of Muscle Structure." *Biochim. Biophys. Acta*, 2, 19.

ROZSA, G., SZENT-GYÖRGYI, A. & WYCKOFF, R. W. G. (1949). "The Electron Microscopy of F-Actin." *Biochim. Biophys. Acta*, 3, 561.

ROZSA, G., SZENT-GYÖRGYI, A. & WYCKOFF, R. W. G. (1950). "The Fine Structure of Myofibrils." *Exp. Cell Res.*, 1, 194.

SANDOW, A. (1949). "Muscle." *Ann. Rev. Physiol.*, 11, 297.

SCHMITT, F. O. (1944–5).   " Ultrastructure and the Problem of Cellular Organisation."
Harvey Lectures, **40**, 249.
SCHMITT, F. O. (1950).   " Morphology in Muscle and Nerve Physiology."   *Biochim.
Biophys. Acta*, **4**, 68.
SCHMITT, F. O., BEAR, R. S., HALL, C. E. & JAKUS, M. A. (1947).   " Electron Microscope
and X-Ray Diffraction Studies of Muscle Structure."   *Ann. N.Y. Acad. Sci.*, **47**, 799.
SCHRAMM, G. & WEBER, H. H. (1942).   " Uber Monodisperse Myosinlösungen."
Koll. Z., **100**, 242.
SCOTT, G. H. & PACKER, D. M. (1939).   " An Electron Microscope Study of Mg and Ca
in Striated Muscle."   *Anat. Rec.*, **74**, 31.
SNELLMAN, O. & ERDÖS, T. (1948).   " An Electron Microscope Study of Myosin, Actin
and Actomyosin."   *Biochim. Biophys. Acta*, **2**, 660.
SNELLMAN, O. & ERDÖS, T. (1948).   " Ultracentrifugal Analysis of Crystallised
Myosin."   *Biochim. Biophys. Acta*, **2**, 650.
SNELLMAN, O. & ERDÖS, T. (1949).   " Ultracentrifugal Studies of F-Actomyosin."
Biochim. Biophys. Acta, **3**, 523.
SPEIDEL, C. (1939).   " Histological Changes in Single Fibres of Striated Muscle during
Contraction and Clotting."   *Amer. J. Anat.*, **65**, 471.
SPIEGEL-ADOLF, M., HENNY, G. C. & ASHKENAZ, E. W. (1944).   " X-Ray Diffraction
Studies on Frog Muscles."   *J. gen. Physiol.*, **28**, 151.
STRAUB, F. B. (1949).   " On the Chemistry of Actin."   *Proc. 1st. Int. Congr. Biochem.*,
p. 127.
SZENT-GYÖRGYI, A. (1947).   " Chemistry of Muscular Contraction."   New York,
Academic Press.
SZENT-GYÖRGYI, A. (1949).   " Free Energy Relations and Contraction of Actomyosin."
Biol. Bull., **96**, 140.
SZENT-GYÖRGYI, A. (1950).   " Actomyosin and Muscular Contraction."   *Biochim.
Biophys. Acta*, **4**, 38.
WEBER, H. H. (1934).   " Die Muskeleiweisskörper und der Feinbau des Skeletmuskels."
Ergebn. d. Physiol., **36**, 109.
WEBER, H. H. (1950).   " Muskelproteine."   *Biochim. Biophys. Acta*, **4**, 12.
WEBER, H. H. (1950).   " Discussion on Muscular Contraction."   *Proc. Roy. Soc.*, B,
137, 40.

CHAPTER XIX

PHOTOSYNTHESIS AND PHOTODYNAMIC ACTION

LIGHT is the primary source of energy for green plants and certain coloured bacteria ; the energy so absorbed is used to build up organic compounds of high energy-content which may be subsequently used in the metabolism of the cell ; the process of absorption of energy is thus one of *photosynthesis*, and is described as *assimilation* in contrast to the process of *respiration* which involves the utilisation of the energy stored by photosynthesis.[1] In the green plants and algæ the photosynthetic reaction consists in the conversion of CO_2 and H_2O to carbohydrate, it being generally agreed that other organic compounds within the plant, such as fats and proteins, are formed as a result of secondary chemical reactions. Stoichiometrically it is easy enough to write down a reaction of CO_2 with H_2O to give a sugar, thus :—

$$6\ CO_2 + 6\ H_2O \rightarrow C_6H_{12}O_6 + 6\ O_2$$

As an overall description of photosynthesis it is probably correct, since it demands that for each volume of CO_2 absorbed, one volume of O_2 should be liberated, *i.e.*, that the *photosynthetic quotient*, $Q_P = \dfrac{\varDelta O_2}{-\varDelta CO_2}$, should be equal to unity. Numerous studies on green plants and algæ have shown that this quotient is, indeed, very close to unity. The reaction, as written above, appears simple ; nevertheless, the observation that photosynthesis cannot take place in damaged cells—nor yet in isolated chloroplasts—and a large variety of studies on the kinetics of photosynthesis, have revealed that it is extremely complex, taking place in many stages and probably requiring at each stage catalysts adapted to promote the successive intermediary reactions. Detailed knowledge of the various steps is lacking and only their broad nature can be surmised from studies on the kinetics of photosynthesis ; it is beyond the scope of this book to enter into a detailed analysis of these studies, nor yet to present in detail the recent conclusions of the prominent investigators in this field. It must suffice to present only a few of the main findings, and to indicate the general trend of opinion ; to understand these findings we must, however, have a clear picture of the mechanism of chemical reactions, of which photosynthesis is a special case.

THE MECHANISM OF CHEMICAL REACTIONS

Photosynthesis is a special case of a more general type of chemical process—the *photochemical reaction* ; and the understanding of the methods

---

[1] It will be remembered that certain bacteria utilise the energy of chemical reactions, such as the oxidation of sulphur, in order to synthesise organic chemical compounds from CO_2 ; here assimilation consists of *chemosynthesis*. In the higher organisms assimilation consists largely in the absorption of organic compounds of high energy-content, " ready-made."

and results of modern studies is only possible with some knowledge of the fundamentals of reaction kinetics. Let us consider briefly, therefore, some of the elementary principles of this branch of physical chemistry. We have seen, in the second section of this book, that chemical reactions involve a redistribution of energy, which is generally manifest in the absorption or liberation of heat. The first problem of reaction kinetics is why, under a given set of conditions, certain reactions take place and others do not. The failure of certain reactions to occur spontaneously, such as the decomposition of water :—

$$2 H_2O \rightarrow 2 H_2 + O_2 - 68 \cdot 3 \text{ Cal.}$$

may reasonably be attributed to the absence of the necessary energy, at ordinary temperatures, to make such an endothermic reaction proceed, the absorption of the $68 \cdot 3$ Calories for each mole of water vapour decomposed placing an impossible drain on the thermal capacity of the system. However, the failure to observe the opposite reaction :—

$$2 H_2 + O_2 \rightarrow 2 H_2O + 68 \cdot 3 \text{ Cal.}$$

at ordinary temperatures cannot possibly be due to this cause, so that it is not necessarily the exothermy or endothermy of a reaction that determines whether it will occur spontaneously at a measurable rate or not. If a flame is applied to a mixture of H_2 and O_2, the reaction proceeds violently, with the liberation of a great deal of energy as heat and light ; the reaction is set off by the transfer of a relatively small amount of energy, and it is this transfer that gives the clue to the mechanism of chemical reaction. The molecules of H_2 and O_2 are very stable, the atoms being linked by bonds of high energy-content. The first step in the reaction between H_2 and O_2 must be a weakening, or rupture, of the bonds that hold the atoms together ; and, because of the stability of these bonds, the energy required is high, 103 Calories in the case of H_2 and 117 Calories in the case of O_2. The final result of the reaction between H_2 and O_2 is to produce a compound with a smaller energy-content than that of the reactants, so that the excess energy is liberated as heat and light during the process, and the reaction is said to be exothermic ; however, a considerable amount of energy is first required to weaken the bonds in the H_2 and O_2 molecules, and it is this requirement that makes necessary some preliminary " detonating action." Once a given pair of molecules has reacted, the water molecule may pass its extra energy to other H_2 and O_2 molecules,[1] and allow them to react to give more energy ; and so the process goes on, gathering speed as a result of the liberation of energy until it may attain explosive proportions.

Activation Energy

An exothermic reaction will therefore proceed spontaneously at a measurable speed if there are a suitable number of molecules with the

---

[1] Actually the H_2O molecule *must* pass its energy on at the instant of formation, otherwise the atoms fly apart because of the high energy-content of the newly-formed molecule ; a *third body collision* is therefore a prerequisite for many reactions that are strongly exothermic.

necessary *activation energy* ; we may now ask what form does this activation energy take. The molecules of a gas may possess *kinetic*—or *translational*—energy, the average for a perfect gas being given by $\frac{1}{2}$ N m $\bar{c}^2$ per mole, which[1] is equal to 3/2 RT. In addition, a molecule may possess *internal energy* consisting of *rotations* about various axes, *vibrations* of the constituent atoms, and—finally—energy associated with the transition of the orbital electrons of the constituent atoms from one energy-state to another. Rotational and vibrational energy are associated with the emission or absorption of infra-red rays, whilst changes in electronic energy are accompanied by the emission or absorption of ultra-violet or visible light. We may thus speak of a variety of *energy-levels* of a given molecule, and, to be precise, we must indicate the state of the molecule in respect to these four types of energy—translational, rotational, vibrational and electronic. The last three types have a number of levels which are *quantised*, *i.e.*, their energies are given by : $nh\nu$, where n is an integer, h is Planck's constant $(6\cdot5.10^{-27}$ erg. sec.) and ν is the frequency of the vibration, the energy corresponding to the case where n equals unity is the *quantum*, and is the smallest amount of energy that can be acquired or emitted by an oscillator of a given frequency.

The energy of one molecule may be transmitted to another on collision ; and this interchange of energy is not confined to the translational variety, a molecule with high electronic energy being able to transfer high vibrational energy by collision with another ; moreover, the electronic energy of an excited molecule may be re-distributed into vibrational and rotational energies.

In an ideal gas, the number of collisions occurring per sec. in 1 ml. is given by kinetic theory as :—

$$z = 2\,n^2\sigma\,^2(\pi \mathrm{RT/M})^{\frac{1}{2}}$$

(n = no. of molecules/ml. σ = collision diameter. R = $8\cdot3.10^7$ ergs. deg.$^{-1}$ mole^{-1}) ; and the number of molecules having more than a minimum energy, E, is given by :—

$$\mathrm{N} = \mathrm{N}_o\,e^{-\mathrm{E/RT}}$$

By combining these equations one may compute the number of molecules colliding per sec. with more than this minimum energy, so that if E is the energy required for a collision to result in reaction, the rate of reaction would be given theoretically by :—

$$dx/dt = ze^{-\mathrm{E/RT}}$$

assuming that each collision with the necessary amount of energy did, indeed, result in reaction. The activation energy, *i.e.*, the energy required to induce the necessary instability in the reactants to permit the chemical change to occur, may be computed from the effect of temperature on the

---

[1] N is the number of molecules in one mole, *i.e.*, Avogadro's Number, $6\cdot023.10^{23}$; m is the weight of the molecule ; $\bar{c}^2$ is the " mean square velocity," *i.e.*, the mean of the squares of the velocities of the molecules ; R is the gas constant, $8\cdot314.10^7$ ergs/° C./mole, or $1\cdot987$ cal./° C./mole, or $0\cdot082$ litre-atm./° C./mole.

rate of reaction. The relationship between activation energy, reaction-rate, and temperature is given by the Arrhenius equation :—

$$k = Ce^{-E/RT}$$

where k is the velocity constant of the reaction, and, on the basis of the " collision theory " of reaction kinetics, the constant, C, may be equated to z. Thus, if log k is plotted against $1/T$, a straight line is generally obtained, the slope being equal to $-E/R$, whence E may be obtained. The differential form of the Arrhenius equation is :—

$$\frac{d \ln k}{dT} = \frac{E}{RT^2}$$

from which it is clear that the increase in k with temperature will be greater the higher the activation energy, E, *i.e.*, the temperature coefficient, Q_{10}, equal to the ratio of the reaction rates at T and T + 10, will be higher, the higher the activation energy of the process. For most reactions studied, the Q_{10} lies between 2 and 3.[1] A Q_{10} in the region of 3 means that raising the temperature 100° C. will increase the reaction rate about $3^{10} = 59,000$-fold ; and this striking effect of temperature serves to emphasise the significance of activation energies. Thus, raising the temperature increases both the *frequency* and *energy* of the collisions ; if all collisions resulted in reaction, the increased rate with a rise in temperature would be attributable only to the increased frequency of collision (which varies only as the square root of T). When, however, only a certain fraction of the collisions result in reaction, a fraction that is dependent on temperature, the reaction rate will increase on both counts : increased *frequency* of collision, and increased *average energy* of collision. Moreover, the higher the energy required (activation energy), the more will the process benefit on the second count, *i.e.*, the higher the activation energy the higher the Q_{10}. Finally, it will be obvious that the rate of reaction will vary inversely with the activation energy ; consequently, the more rapid the reaction, the lower will be its Q_{10} (that is, of course, provided that factors other than collision-energy are not significant).

Order and Molecularity of Reactions

The mechanism of a reaction is elucidated by a study of the way it proceeds with time, the equation describing this determining its " *order.*" Thus, if the reaction :—

$$A + B \rightarrow AB$$

requires that A and B collide with a minimal energy, the equation governing the reaction may take the form :—

$$\text{Rate} = \text{Constant} \times [A][B]$$

Such a reaction would be described as *bimolecular*, and its order of reaction would be the *second order*, because the equation takes the form :—

$$dx/dt = k(a-x)^2$$

where x is the amount of AB formed at time t, a is the original concentration of A and B, assumed equal, and k is the *velocity constant*.

---

[1] The Q_{10} is not an accurate method of indicating the effect of temperature, since it varies with the temperature.

First Order Reaction. A large number of reactions follow a simpler equation, of the form :—

$$dx/dt = k(a-x)$$

when they are called *first order reactions*, the rate of reaction at any time, t, being proportional to the number of unreacted molecules $(a-x)$. An example of this is the decomposition of nitrogen pentoxide :—

$$N_2O_5 \rightarrow N_2O_4 + \tfrac{1}{2}(O_2)$$

If the reaction depended simply on the collision of two molecules of N_2O_5, the decomposition taking place on collision, we should expect a second order reaction, the rate being dependent on the square of the concentration of N_2O_5. If, on the other hand, the molecule of N_2O_5 spontaneously disintegrated, *i.e.*, without acquiring activation energy from collision, the reaction would be expected to follow a first order type of equation, just as the spontaneous radioactive decay of a substance does, since here the rate, *i.e.*, the number of molecules decomposed in a given time, is simply determined by the amount of substance remaining at any moment $(a-x)$. It could be argued, therefore, that, because it was a first order reaction, the decomposition of N_2O_5 occurred spontaneously, without activation. However, a study of the temperature coefficient of the reaction, and of many other first order reactions of a similar type, has shown that the activation energy is high, often as high as 40–60 Calories per mole. To overcome this difficulty, Lindemann suggested that the reacting molecules do indeed obtain their activation energy by collision, but that the rate at which this activation occurs is rapid compared with the subsequent decomposition. Thus, whereas the rate of activation is dependent on the square of the concentration $(a-x)^2$, the actual rate of decomposition is determined, in ordinary circumstances, by the time required for the activated molecules to react ; consequently the number of molecules reacting in a given time is proportional to the number of molecules present, *i.e.*, the state of affairs is analogous to spontaneous decomposition. When the rate of activation is sufficiently decreased—by lowering the pressure of the gas—we may expect the reaction rate to become dependent on this factor and to change from first to second order, a state of affairs that is actually found. This point reveals the importance of an exact analysis of the mechanism of a chemical reaction ; a mere study of the overall kinetics suggested a non-activated type of reaction, similar to radioactive decay, whereas a further investigation revealed the existence of an activation process, the rate of which, however, was not *rate determining*. The first order reaction considered above is also *unimolecular*, in the sense that only one molecule decomposes at a time—*i.e.*, it is not necessary that two molecules of N_2O_5 should decompose simultaneously—so that the condition for activation is only that a collision should make *one* of the colliding molecules unstable, in contrast to the bimolecular reaction in which two molecules, A and B, had to react simultaneously on collision. A great many bimolecular reactions are first order for varying reasons ; for example, the hydrolysis of cane sugar involves the reaction of a water molecule with a sugar molecule, so that it is definitely bimolecular ;

however, the concentration of water remains effectively constant during the reaction ; hence the rate is determined by the product of a constant quantity with the concentration of sugar, *i.e.*, it is first order.[1] Many photochemical, and catalysed reactions, to be discussed later, are also first order, but for different reasons.[2]

Catalysed Reactions. Very many reactions take place at an interface, for instance on the surface of a solid, and are called *heterogeneous*, in contrast to the *homogeneous* reaction which takes place in a single phase ; these reactions exhibit a variety of orders, the exponent, n, in the kinetic equation :—

$$\text{Rate} = k\,(a-x)^n$$

being not necessarily an integer and sometimes zero. A zero-order reaction would be represented by :—

$$\text{Rate} = k\,(a-x)^o$$
$$= k$$

i.e., the reaction occurs at a constant rate until completed. The conditions for such a zero-order reaction would be the following. The reaction takes place at a limited surface only, the surface being fully occupied at any moment by the reacting molecules ; as soon as one molecule reacts and leaves the surface, another takes its place.[3] Thus, so long as the number of molecules on the surface is independent of the total concentration of the molecules, the rate of reaction will be independent of this concentration and hence of zero order. If, on the other hand, only a small area of the available surface is occupied at any moment, the rate may be determined by the rate at which the molecules from the bulk phase reach and leave the surface, in which case, if the reaction is unimolecular—as for example the decomposition of phosphine on glass—the equation will be of the first order. With intermediate conditions of surface saturation it is clear that intermediate exponents will be obtained. The heterogeneous reactions mentioned here are examples of catalysed reactions, in which the catalyst represents a separate phase from that in which the bulk of the reactants are distributed, in contrast to the catalysis of the hydrolysis of sugar by hydrogen ions, in which catalyst and reactants occupy the same phase. In homogeneous catalysis, the acceleration of the reaction is undoubtedly

---

[1] Thus $dx/dt = k.\,[\text{Sugar}]\,[\text{Water}]$
$$= k\,(a-x) \times \text{Constant}$$
$$= k'\,(a-x)$$
The reaction is described as *pseudo-monomolecular*.

[2] It is important that the difference between *molecularity* and *order* of a chemical reaction should be appreciated, especially by biologists. A large number of reactions are first order, but by no means unimolecular, yet only too frequently does one find in the biological literature claims that a certain process involves the splitting of one molecule into two because the kinetics of the process are first-order ; or, again, that a process such as the regeneration of visual purple involves the interaction of two molecules because the kinetics follow a second-order equation. The order of the reaction defines its kinetics, *i.e.*, how it proceeds with time, whilst the molecularity states how many molecules are involved in the actual reaction. The decomposition of N_2O_5 is unimolecular and first order, *i.e.*, although two molecules of N_2O_5 must collide to provide the activation energy, it is not necessary that both molecules decompose together.

[3] The surface is said to be saturated with the reacting molecules. An example of a heterogeneous zero-order reaction is the decomposition of gaseous HI at a gold surface.

brought about by the participation of the catalyst in the chemical reaction, a participation that permits the reaction to proceed in steps involving less activation energy than in its absence. Thus the conversion of SO_2 to SO_3 by O_2 :—

$$SO_2 + \tfrac{1}{2} O_2 \rightarrow SO_3$$

is catalysed by nitric oxide, NO. A simple explanation would be that NO undergoes oxidation first and is then reduced by SO_2 :—

$$NO + \tfrac{1}{2} O_2 \rightarrow NO_2$$
$$NO_2 + SO_2 \rightarrow NO + SO_3$$

the catalyst behaving as an intermediary ; although this may be too simple a view of the actual process, there is little doubt that NO permits the reaction to proceed along paths involving, at each stage, less activation energy than that involved in the simple reaction :—

$$SO_2 + \tfrac{1}{2} O_2 \rightarrow SO_3$$

Catalysis taking place at solid surfaces is often not very specific, a variety of different reactions being catalysed by the same solid, *e.g.*, glass. Presumably the acceleration in reaction-rate is effected by a decrease in stability of the reacting molecule, resulting from its adsorption on the surface ; in this unstable condition it may decompose directly, or as a result of a collision with another molecule, the collision-energy being smaller than that necessary under homogeneous conditions. Many catalytic processes are highly specific, a given surface promoting one type of reaction and not another ; if the catalyst behaves as an intermediary in the chemical reaction this is understandable, since it must be able to enter into chemical combination with at least one of the reactants ; where an adsorption process is concerned it may very well be that, even though a variety of substances can adsorb a reactant, it will be only the substance that has a particular molecular, or crystalline, configuration at its surface that can adsorb the reactant in such a way as to decrease its stability, in fact some substances may increase the stability of a reactant and thus behave as inhibitors, or *negative catalysts*.[1] The modern view of adsorption, moreover, regards it as frequently differing little, if at all, from true chemical combination, the linkage between adsorbent and adsorbate varying from covalent, ionic, hydrogen-bond to simple van der Waals forces of attraction. Consequently the difference between the heterogeneous catalyst and the homogeneous one tends to disappear, both permitting a reaction to proceed more readily by lowering the minimal activation energy necessary. In biological systems the catalyst is described as an *enzyme*, and is very frequently a protein. The enzymes are highly specific, in that they accelerate chemical reactions involving only certain specific groupings ; thus, although starch and cellulose are built up of glucose units, they are not hydrolysed by the same enzyme, the difference between

---

[1] Negative catalysts, however, are most frequently those that tend to break up a chain reaction, *i.e.*, they tend to inactivate active molecules or atoms resulting from a primary reaction, preventing them from handing on their energy to other reactants ; alternatively, they poison a catalyst already operating, by being themselves adsorbed on the active regions of the catalytic surface.

the maltose and cellobiose type of linkage being sufficient to require a difference in enzymes. This high degree of specificity can only be explained on the assumption that the enzyme possesses definite chemical groupings at its surface with which the substrate must unite in some way ; the union must be of such a character as to induce instability in the molecule, thereby permitting it to react. Thus, although the chemical groupings in the enzyme may allow union with a large variety of substrates, it is not difficult to envisage a state of affairs in which only one type of substrate molecule will be permitted to react. The poisoning of enzymes results, presumably, from the combination of the poison with the specific chemical groupings ; this is doubtless true of such poisonings as that of cholinesterase by eserine, the poison having a similar chemical grouping to that of the substrate, acetylcholine ; whether such non-specific poisons as the heavy metals and narcotics act in the same way is doubtful. The inactivation of enzymes by heat, for example, is probably due to a denaturation of the protein, and it may well be that the action of a heavy metal follows from a similar cause.

Photochemical Reactions

We have regarded activation as a loosening or breaking of bonds between the atoms of a molecule. The acquisition of this activation energy, in the cases so far presented, has resulted from thermal collisions, so that raising the temperature markedly accelerated the reaction-rate. Thermal energy of a molecule is manifest, as we have seen, not only in translatory motion, but also in rotation and vibration, such rotations and vibrations being reflected in the emission of infra-red radiation. As the temperature rises, a point is reached where the radiation becomes visible ; it can be calculated that the energy of a quantum of this visible light, $h\nu$, corresponds to transitions from one electronic energy-level to another. Since any molecule emitting energy of a given wavelength must be able to absorb it, it follows that activation energy can be supplied in the form of visible or ultra-violet light. Reactions activated in this way are called *photochemical reactions* ; the energy may be acquired directly by the reacting molecules, as in the decomposition of HI, or vicariously from some light-absorbing molecule ; in the latter case the reaction is said to be *photosensitised*, an example being the photographic emulsion sensitised to react to certain colours, or infra-red light, by the incorporation of dye-stuffs.

Quantum Efficiency and Fluorescence. Once the possibility of absorbed light-energy acting as activation energy is admitted, the general principles of the photochemical reaction are simple and straightforward. According to the Einstein equivalence law, a molecule will react each time it has absorbed a quantum of light, provided that the energy of the quantum is equal to, or greater than, the activation energy.[1] A simple interpretation

---

[1] The quantum is given by $h\nu$; ν, the frequency of the light, is related to the wavelength, λ, by : $\nu\lambda = c$, where c is the velocity of light, so that the quantum is : hc/λ. If each molecule must absorb one quantum the activation energy for one mole is : Nhc/λ, where N is Avogadro's number. N is $6\cdot023.10^{23}$, h is $6\cdot624.10^{-27}$ and c is $2\cdot9977.10^{10}$ cm./sec. The energy will be given in ergs, so that on dividing by $4\cdot184.10^{10}$, the result comes out in Calories.

Thus $E = 2\cdot859.10^{10}/\lambda$ Cal./mole

of the Einstein equivalence law would indicate that the *quantum efficiency*, *i.e.*, the number of molecules reacting per quantum absorbed, would be equal to unity ; actually very few reactions exhibit this efficiency ; some, such as the decomposition of HI by ultra-violet light, show an efficiency of 2, whilst many others have values of less than unity. The high efficiency in the decomposition of HI is due to the occurrence of secondary reactions following the primary reaction, which consists in the splitting of the molecule into two atoms :—

$$HI + h\nu \rightarrow H + I$$

Following this the atoms may react in a variety of ways, the principal ones being :—

$$H + HI \rightarrow H_2 + I$$
$$I + I \rightarrow I_2$$

Thus, one quantum causes the splitting of two molecules. A quantum efficiency of less than unity is given by *inelastic collisions* of the activated molecule with normal molecules, the absorbed light-energy being dissipated as heat ; alternatively, some of the light may be lost by *fluorescence*, the excited molecule retaining its energy for some 10^{-7} to 10^{-8} sec. and then re-emitting most of it at a longer wavelength.[1] The influence of inelastic collisions is well exemplified in the *quenching of fluorescence*, the activated molecule losing its energy by collision before it has time to fluoresce (the time between collisions in a gas at ordinary pressures and temperatures is of the order of 10^{-10} sec.) ; thus hydrogen is able to reduce the resonance fluorescence of mercury, the light-energy absorbed by the mercury being converted by inelastic collisions to heat. Studies of the quenching of fluorescence by various gases have shown, moreover, that the transfer of energy by these *collisions of the second kind* does not take place indiscriminately, since some molecules are able to quench more effectively than others. Fluorescence is a common feature of photosensitising substances, substances that absorb light-energy and pass it on to the reactants ; in the absence of these reactants fluorescence should be—and usually is—more pronounced, since the reactants can no longer quench it ; a study of the quenching of fluorescence in photosensitised reactions may therefore lead to conclusions regarding the identity of the participating molecules ; if a certain molecule does not quench fluorescence, it is unlikely to accept energy from the photosensitiser.

The photochemical reactions very frequently follow a first order equation; this is understandable since the rate of reaction will be determined by the rate of absorption of light and by the subsequent rate of reaction ; both of these quantities will frequently depend on the first power of the concentration, thus giving a first-order type of equation. We may expect, and do indeed find, that the effect of temperature is small, the Q_{10} of many photochemical reactions being about unity ; where, however, the

---

[1] If the same wavelength is emitted (*resonance fluorescence*) *all* of the absorbed energy is necessarily given out ; generally, however, some of the absorbed energy is retained as vibrational and rotational energy, consequently the quantum for re-emission is smaller, and the wavelength therefore longer, than that absorbed. Atoms, which cannot exhibit vibrational or rotational energy, give only resonance fluorescence.

photochemical process is only the first step in a series of reactions, it may well be that the overall reaction is considerably increased by a rise in temperature, since the subsequent steps may involve high activation energies.

Absorption Spectrum. The interpretation of the nature of the primary process in a photochemical reaction—for example, the decision as to whether a molecule on absorbing light immediately splits up into atoms, or remains only in an excited electronic state—is helped by a study of the *absorption spectra* of the reactants. Isolated atoms, *i.e.*, in the vapour state, emit light in limited regions of the visible and ultra-violet spectrum ; the light so emitted appears as discrete lines in the spectroscope ; the emission of this light is induced by transferring to the atoms the necessary energy which they re-emit ; *e.g.*, NaCl, heated in a Bunsen flame, emits its characteristic yellow light. The emission of light is due to the fact that during activation, *e.g.*, the application of a flame, the orbital electrons of the atom assume new energy-levels ; on returning to their lower, or *ground*, states they re-emit the energy, the frequency of the emitted light being given by the quantum expression :—

$$h\nu = E_1 - E_2$$

where E_1 and E_2 are two energy-levels.[1]

The spectrum of a molecule is not so simple as that of an atom, for the obvious reason that there are more possibilities of emission of energy (more *degrees of freedom*), since rotational and vibrational levels of energy are possible. By rotational levels of energy are meant the changes of energy associated with the rotation of the molecule about an axis ; by vibrational levels, the oscillation of the atoms about a mean position. As with the electronic levels, these are quantised.[2] On the basis of the quantum theory these energy-levels may be calculated, and hence the wavelengths with which they correspond ; rotational wavelengths are of the order of 2.10^6A and vibrational 1–23.10^4A, they thus represent radiation in the far infra-red. This does not explain, however, the fact that molecules show band spectra, consisting of many lines close together, in the ultra-violet and visible region. The explanation for this is that changes of electronic level in molecules also induce changes in the vibrational and rotational levels. Thus let us suppose that there is a certain electronic transition possible, corresponding to a frequency ν_2, so that the energy-change is equal to $h\nu_2$; if, now, the same amount of energy must be used to change the electronic level, and also to change the vibrational and rotational energies, it is clear that the electronic energy must be reduced, *i.e.*, it becomes $h\nu$, where ν is a new frequency, whilst the remaining energy is devoted to raising the vibrational and rotational energy-levels. The possible changes in these last-mentioned levels are numerous, and since

---

[1] If, during the activation process, the atoms ionise, the energy-levels are altered so that the wavelength of the emitted light alters ; the spectrum of the ionised atom is called the *spark spectrum* to distinguish it from the *flame* or *arc spectrum* of the normal atom.

[2] The rotational frequencies are given by : $\nu_r = \dfrac{h}{8\pi^2 K}(2n - 1)$, where K is the moment of inertia and n is the quantum number which must be an integer.

he quantum of energy must remain the same, this means that $h\nu$ must vary, becoming less as the vibrational and rotational energies increase. Thus the electronic levels can take a large number of values, and this corresponds to a large number of values of the wavelength of emission or absorption in the ultra-violet or visible, thereby giving rise to bands in the place of discrete lines.[1]

Finally, in solution, the molecules interact with each other to such an extent that a great many electronic levels are possible, and the bands are no longer resolvable into lines, they become continuous.

We may note that the transition from one electronic level to another usually involves the emission, or absorption, of energy in the ultra-violet region ; this is generally true of compounds in which the electrons are tightly bound in simple covalent bonds ; with such bonds as $C = C$, and $N = O$, certain electrons are more loosely held, so that transitions corresponding to lower energy-changes are possible, with the result that absorption or emission is at longer wavelengths.

A study of the absorption spectrum of a compound will often reveal the fate of the absorbed light-energy ; the first step is, of course, the raising of an electron to a higher energy-level, but whether the molecule so " excited " splits immediately (*i.e.*, within the vibration period of the atoms), or whether the molecule remains in this activated condition for sufficient time to enable it to react with another molecule, can often be decided from its absorption spectrum. Thus immediate splitting of a diatomic molecule means that the new electronic levels, associated with changed vibrational and rotational levels, do not appear, for the simple reason that atoms cannot exhibit this type of energy. The absorption spectrum in the ultra-violet region consequently exhibits a characteristic difference from that of a molecule which is not split into atoms on absorption in this region, but remains, instead, in an activated condition.

Beer's Law. Before passing to a consideration of the details of photosynthesis and other reactions involving light, we may briefly consider the experimental facts regarding the absorption of light. Beer's Law states that, if I_o is the intensity of the light incident on a solution, I, the intensity of the transmitted light, is given by :

$$I = I_o.10^{-\epsilon cd}$$

where c is the concentration of the solution in moles/l., d is the thickness through which the light is transmitted, and ϵ is called the *molar extinction coefficient* for the solute for a particular wavelength.[2] By plotting extinction coefficient against wavelength an absorption curve or *absorption*

---

[1] The possible frequencies corresponding to a change of electronic energy, $h\nu_2$, *i.e.*, a pure electronic energy-jump, are given by the equation :
$$\nu = \nu_1 + \nu_2 + \nu_o n^2 - \nu_o' (n \pm 1)^2$$
Where ν is the frequency emitted, ν_1 is the vibrational frequency, ν_o' is the new value of the rotational frequency caused by the change in electronic level, whilst ν_o is its original value. It is clear that ν can have a number of values.

[2] If the law is used in the form :
$$I = I_o e^{-\alpha cd}$$
α is called the *molar absorption coefficient* ; for a pure liquid the law takes the form :
$$I = I_o.10^{-kd}$$
where k is called the *extinction coefficient*.

spectrum is obtained, the regions of peak absorption being called *absorptio* *bands*.

DYNAMICS OF PHOTOSYNTHESIS

Light- and Dark-Reactions

The overall photochemical synthesis of green plants may be describe as :—

$$CO_2 + H_2O \xrightarrow{nh\nu} (CH_2O) + O_2 - 112 \text{ Cal.}$$

where the expression (CH_2O) is used to indicate a carbohydrate unit :—

$$H - \overset{|}{\underset{|}{C}} - OH$$

which may be built up successively to a sugar ; $nh\nu$ represents the numbe of quanta of light absorbed during the process. A simple experimen suffices to prove that photosynthesis can be broadly divided into " light-process " followed by a " dark-reaction." Thus if the absorptio of CO_2—or liberation of O_2—by a plant is measured with differen intensities of illumination, it is found that the rate increases up to point [1] ; above this level of illumination, further increases have no effec the system being *light-saturated*. This suggests strongly that with hig light-intensities a secondary, or dark-reaction, determines the speed of photosynthesis ; the supposition is confirmed, moreover, by th observation that with low intensities of illumination, where the light process presumably dominates the picture, photosynthesis is almos independent of temperature, as we should expect of a purely photochemica reaction ; at high light-intensities, on the other hand, temperatur coefficients of the order of magnitude found with non-photochemica reactions are observed.

Intermittent Light. The more precise separation of photosynthesis int a light- and a dark-reaction was made possible by Warburg, who studie the effects of intermittent light on the absorption of CO_2 by plants ; if th dark-reaction requires a measurable time, we may expect to be able to us light more efficiently by illuminating the plant intermittently, allowin time between the flashes for the dark-reaction to proceed.[2] This wa actually found by Warburg who, by using equal periods of light and dar and varying the frequency of alternation (the flash-frequency), was able t double the efficiency of photosynthesis, *i.e.*, a given amount of light energy presented at a flash-frequency of some 133 per sec., produced twic the amount of O_2 as the same amount of light-energy presented a continuous illumination. Warburg observed that certain concentration of cyanide—and other poisons that attacked enzymes containing th Fe-porphyrin type of catalyst, such as hydroxylamine, H_2S and azide—

---

[1] 20,000–40,000 lux for the alga *Chlorella*.
[2] Thus, if the result of the absorption of light were to produce a compound that mus subsequently react with another compound, or else revert to its former state, light wi be wasted if the newly-formed " light-product " has no compound to react with.

ad no effect on the rate of photosynthesis when the intensity of
lumination was low, *i.e.*, when the overall rate was determined by the
ght-reaction ; when the intensity was sufficiently high to produce
ght-saturation, on the other hand, the same concentration of cyanide, for
xample, markedly inhibited photosynthesis. It was concluded therefore
hat cyanide acted only on the slower dark-reaction and not on the initial,
apid, light-process. Emerson & Arnold developed the flash technique,
arying not only the rate of flashing, but also the relative periods of light
nd darkness ; by making the flashes very short (10^{-4} sec.) and the intervals
ng (0·01–0·1 sec.) they were able to effect a separation of the two main
omponents in photosynthesis.

Fig. 250 shows the effect of varying the length of the light-period, in

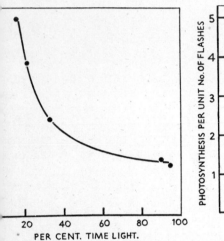

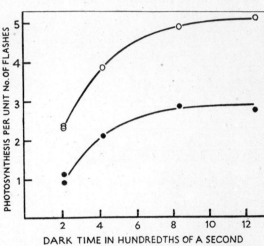

0. Variation in photosynthetic yield
g flash illumination with the bright
d in the cycle. Note how the yield
ases as the light-period decreases.
rson & Arnold. *J. gen. Physiol.*)

FIG. 251. Variation of photosynthetic yield per
flash with length of dark period between flashes
at 6° C. Open circles, CO_2 concentration of
$7·1.10^{-5}$ moles per l. Solid circles, CO_2 concentration of $4·1.10^{-6}$ moles per l. (Emerson &
Arnold. *J. gen. Physiol.*)

elation to the dark-period, from some 85 per cent. to 17 per cent. ; it is
een that, as the dark-period lengthens, the efficiency of photosynthesis
ncreases, so that a 400 per cent. improvement over the efficiency during
teady illumination is obtained with only 17 per cent. of the cycle light ;
he frequency of flashing was 50/sec. ; each light-period was therefore
·0034 sec. and the dark-period 0·0166. Fig. 251 shows the variation in
he photosynthetic yield-per-flash with the length of the dark-interval ;
is seen that the yield-per-flash falls off when the interval becomes
horter than about 0·1 to 0·08 sec., so that, if the separation of the
hotosynthetic process into a light- and dark-reaction is justified, the dark-
eaction probably takes place within some 0·1 to 0·08 sec. at 6° C. The
hape of the curve in Fig. 251 thus enables us to deduce the approximate
ength of the dark-, or *Blackman, period* as it is called, the length of the
ark-period at which the yield-per-flash begins to decline being a measure

of this ; thus the lower curve represents the same type of experiment wit
a much lower concentration of CO_2 ; it is seen that the yield-per-flas
falls off at about the same length of dark-period, a fact suggesting that th
availability of CO_2 is not a decisive factor for the speed of the dark
reaction. The observation that the actual *yields* are consistently lowe
with the low concentration of CO_2 indicates, on the other hand, that th
fast reaction, or primary photochemical process, is affected by th
availability of CO_2. Application of this form of analysis to the effects c
cyanide and narcotics, such as urethane, showed that the photochemica
process is apparently insensitive to cyanide whilst the dark-reaction is
narcotics, on the other hand, slowed the light-reaction, but not the dark
Emerson & Arnold pointed out, very justly, that the separation c
photosynthesis into a rapid, light-, and a slow dark-reaction may b
misleading, and they suggested a cyclical process as follows :—

$$CO_2 \nearrow \text{Chlorophyll} - CO_2$$

Free Chlorophyll   Chlorophyll – CO_2
                          (activated by light)

Blackman Reaction

The rapid reaction could thus be composite, involving the preliminar
fixation of CO_2 by chlorophyll, followed by the absorption of light to giv
an activated product ; the subsequent events, involving the reaction c
H_2O, and given the omnibus title of the " Blackman reaction," could b
slow. Emerson & Arnold showed that by increasing the intensity of th
flashes, an increase in yield-per-flash could be obtained—as one woul
expect—but that a maximum was reached, *flash saturation*, long before th
intensity had been raised to such a height that every chlorophyll molecul
was activated by each flash. On purely photochemical grounds we shoul
say that flash-saturation should be reached when every molecule c
chlorophyll received as many quanta of light, with each flash, as it require
to reduce one molecule of CO_2 ; the fact that saturation occurred whe
only one chlorophyll molecule in about 2,500 received a quantum show
that some factor, other than the mere absorption of light, determines th
rate of photosynthesis when the intensity of the light is high and th
flash-period is short.

This observation has given rise to a great deal of speculation, but is bes
interpreted in accordance with the assumption of Franck & Herzfeld tha
the product of the absorption of light—the primary photochemical produc
—is unstable and must be catalysed rapidly to a new product, otherwis
it loses its energy and reverts to its original state and becomes useless fc
photosynthesis. This catalyst is described as *Catalyst B.* If the number c
molecules of Catalyst B is small in comparison with the number c
chlorophyll molecules, say as 1 to 2,000, flash-saturation will be reached a
light-intensities such that only one chlorophyll molecule in about 2,000 i
activated with each flash. We may note that, with flashing light, th
efficiency of the light can be increased, *i.e.*, by allowing time for the dar
reaction to complete itself, so that the products of each flash of light ca

be most effectively utilised ; however, the *maximum rate of photosynthesis* is the same whether continuous or flashing illumination is used. Thus, on changing from continuous to flashing light of the same intensity, the mean amount of light falling on the system is reduced, and the observation that the efficiency can be increased by 400 per cent. indicates only that the same maximal rate can be achieved with the expenditure of a quarter of the light-energy. At light-saturation and at flash-saturation, therefore, the rates of synthesis are equal, a fact suggesting that the determining factor in the overall rate of synthesis is the dark-, or Blackman, series of reactions. The observation that the yield-per-flash, with cyanide present, could be made the same as that obtained in the absence of this poison—provided that the intervals between flashes were long enough—suggests, moreover, that it is one or more of the Blackman series of reactions that are susceptible to this poison. However, recent analyses of the effect of cyanide on the flash-saturation, carried out by Rieke & Gaffron and by Weller & Franck, have shown that this is not strictly true, cyanide inhibiting a reaction whose rate is not normally the limiting factor in photosynthesis. In the presence of cyanide this reaction now goes so slowly that it sets the pace for photosynthesis. It is thought that this cyanide-sensitive reaction is the binding of CO_2 by chlorophyll, *i.e.*, a reaction preceding the primary photochemical process ; normally it is sufficiently rapid to provide enough bound CO_2 for the reaction of each absorbed quantum of light ; so that the rate of photosynthesis is largely governed by the events subsequent to the primary photochemical change ; in the presence of cyanide, the binding of CO_2 becomes so slow as to become the determining factor.

Since the resolution of photosynthesis into two prime steps—the light-, or photochemical, and the dark-, or Blackman, reactions—a great deal of study and ingenuity have gone into elaborating the possible steps in the dark-reaction ; before entering further into this aspect we may look briefly into other photosynthetic processes, and see whether a common principle underlies them all.

Photosynthesis by Bacteria

The photosynthetic bacteria are divided roughly into three classes, although differences within a class may be as great as those between classes. The *green sulphur bacteria*, reducing CO_2 and oxidising H_2S as follows :—

$$CO_2 + 2\,H_2S \rightarrow CH_2O + H_2O + 2S$$

The *red sulphur bacteria* (*Thiorhodaceae*), which grow autotrophically in the presence of a number of inorganic sulphur compounds such as S, H_2S, Na_2SO_3, $Na_2S_2O_3$; they can also use organic compounds, and some species oxidise gaseous H_2 ; a typical reaction is :—

$$2CO_2 + H_2S + 2H_2O \rightarrow 2CH_2O + H_2SO_4$$

or, when H_2 is used in place of H_2S :—

$$CO_2 + 2H_2 \rightarrow CH_2O + H_2O$$

The *purple bacteria* (*Athiorhodaceae*) require organic material, *e.g.,* aliphatic acids, which are oxidised. A recent example of this type of reaction has been provided by Foster, who grew bacteria on a secondary alcohol, to give the reaction :— [1]

$$2 \, (CH_3)_2CHOH + CO_2 \rightarrow 2 \, (CH_3)_2CO + CH_2O + H_2O$$
(Isopropanol)   (Acetone)

Van Niel Hypothesis. As Van Niel pointed out, the reactions may be treated more generally as :—

$$CO_2 + 2 \, H_2A \rightarrow (CH_2O) + 2A + H_2O$$

the substance H_2A being, essentially, a reducing agent, or *hydrogen donor,* reducing CO_2 to CH_2O by the addition of hydrogen atoms, and being oxidised during the process to A and H_2O. The important point brought out by Van Niel is that the two processes, reduction of CO_2 and oxidation of substrate, are *linked reactions,* in the sense that the reduction of CO_2 necessarily demands the simultaneous oxidation of some substrate. Kluyver & Donker, in 1926, had suggested that H_2O may be considered as a reducing agent, or *hydrogen donor,* during the photosynthetic process, reducing CO_2 and becoming oxidised to O_2. Van Niel adopted this suggestion, and incorporated the photosynthesis of green plants into the general scheme by writing the equation :—

$$CO_2 + 2H_2O \rightarrow (CH_2O) + O_2 + H_2O$$

If the extra water molecule, introduced on each side of the equation, is to have any significance, this means that 4 atoms of hydrogen, derived from two molecules of H_2O, are really involved in the reduction of CO_2 to the carbohydrate level :

$$O = C = O + 4 \, H \rightarrow OH - \overset{\displaystyle OH}{\underset{\displaystyle H}{C}} - H \rightarrow OH - \overset{\displaystyle OH}{\underset{\displaystyle H}{C}} - H + H_2O$$

formaldehyde hydrate being a possible intermediary, although this is not a necessary consequence of the theory since the reduction of CO_2 could well take place when the latter is fixed, as in a COOH-grouping.[2] Thus for each molecule of CO_2 absorbed by the chlorophyll system, 4 H-atoms are involved ; a similar number are required for the bacterial photosyntheses but the unique feature of the plant photosynthesis is the utilisation of

---

[1] Generally the organic substance oxidised in the photosynthesis is completely used up, so that it is difficult to formulate the primary photosynthetic process, distinct from subsequent metabolic reactions ; in this case, however, acetone, formed from isopropanol, is not used by the bacteria. We may note that the presence of O_2 inhibits photosynthesis by the red (*Thiorhodaceae*) and purple (*Athiorhodaceae*) bacteria ; they are thus anaerobic organisms ; nevertheless many purple bacteria may be cultivated aerobically on suitable organic media ; photosynthesis is abandoned and the bacteria adopt a chemosynthetic metabolism.

[2] Rabinowitch considers that it is more probable that the H-atoms required for the reduction of CO_2 would be provided by 4 H_2O molecules, one from each, rather than two from two molecules. He therefore writes the overall photochemical process :—

$$CO_2 + 4 \, H_2O \rightarrow CH_2O + 3 \, H_2O + O_2$$

H_2O as a hydrogen donor, a utilisation which results in the evolution of gaseous O_2 (the most sensitive tests have failed to reveal any liberation of O_2 by the photosynthetic bacteria).

If Van Niel's hypothesis, regarding the essential similarity of all the photosynthetic reactions, is correct, we may postulate a common primary photochemical process, the differences in the overall reactions being due to the differing fates of the products of this primary reaction. Thus Van Niel suggests that the common process is the photochemical decomposition of water into a " reduced " and " oxidised " product ; the reduced product eventually reduces CO_2 to give carbohydrate, whilst the oxidised product reacts with its characteristic hydrogen donor, e.g., H_2S in the case of the green sulphur bacteria, fatty acid in the case of the *Athiorhodaceae*, and with H_2O in the case of the green plants ; in this last case producing H_2O_2 which finally gives gaseous O_2.

Quantum Efficiency. If 4 H-atoms must be removed from their normal linkages in H_2O molecules during the rearrangement leading to the reduction of CO_2, we may expect that at least 4 quanta of light must be absorbed for each molecule of CO_2 disappearing in photosynthesis. The earlier studies of quantum efficiency, carried out by Warburg & Negelein, did indeed indicate a number of 4 quanta (*i.e.*, a quantum efficiency of $1/4$) ; however, the more recent measurements by Emerson & Lewis (1939) on algæ suggest that some 12 quanta are involved in the transformation of one molecule of CO_2, although smaller numbers may be concerned in some of the syntheses of purple bacteria. These lower quantum efficiencies seem altogether more reasonable since, in a complex reaction involving probably many stages, we may expect considerable losses of energy by inactivation of molecules through thermal collisions.[1]

The Reduced State

Considerable support for the general thesis of Van Niel, regarding the fundamental unity underlying the diversity of photosyntheses, is provided by Gaffron's observation that green algæ, *e.g.*, *Scenedesmus*, after a preliminary 1–12 hour anaerobic period in the dark in an atmosphere of H_2, will, on illumination, absorb CO_2 rapidly without any evolution of O_2. The reaction taking place under these conditions conforms to the equation :—

$$CO_2 + 2H_2 \rightarrow CH_2O + H_2O$$

what Gaffron calls a " photoreduction." It is apparently identical with that carried out by some purple bacteria, *e.g.*, *Rhodovibrin*, in an atmosphere of H_2. Clearly, the photosynthetic reaction has been fundamentally changed by the anaerobic period, gaseous H_2 being used as the hydrogen donor in place of H_2O, *i.e.*, the green algæ, in this *reduced state*, seem to have reverted to a more primitive metabolism characteristic of some bacteria. The ability to utilise hydrogen from any molecule, be it H_2O,

[1] The subject is not yet closed, however. Warburg (1948) has repeated his experiments in the light of Emerson & Lewis' criticisms, but has once again found a quantum number of 4 for photosynthesis by *Chlorella*.

H_2S, or some organic compound such as glucose, depends, in biological systems, on the presence of a suitable enzyme, a *dehydrogenase* ; in the case of molecular H_2 we may term the enzyme a *hydrogenase*, its action consisting, presumably, in the modification of molecular H_2 to permit of its giving up H-atoms in a reaction with intermediate products of photochemical change. The development of the reduced state may thus be regarded as the emergence of a hydrogenase. Further studies of Gaffron have brought to light more details of this interesting transformation. During the development of the reduced state, H_2 is actually absorbed by the algæ ; moreover, if N_2 is used instead of H_2 to maintain the anaerobic conditions necessary for the adaptation, it is found that H_2 is actually released from the algæ. These results clearly point to the presence of a hydrogenase system capable of transferring hydrogen to organic compounds, when the partial pressure of H_2 is high, and of removing hydrogen when the partial pressure is low. The process of adaptation requires strict anaerobiosis, so that small amounts of O_2 in the atmosphere are sufficient to prevent it ; when adaptation is complete, however, comparatively high concentrations of O_2 are tolerated, the reaction :—

$$2\,H_2 + O_2 \rightarrow 2\,H_2O$$

taking place and serving to keep the O_2-concentration at a low level. O_2 thus inhibits the development of the hydrogenase, presumably by oxidising it as soon as it appears ; when it has fully developed, however, as in the completely adapted algæ, the hydrogenase is able to preserve itself from destruction by catalysing the oxidation of gaseous H_2.

The absorption of H_2 and CO_2 in the presence of light is described by Gaffron as *photoreduction*, in contrast to photosynthesis, by which is implied the absorption of CO_2 with a concomitant evolution of O_2, although it would seem that both fundamental reactions are concerned with the synthesis of carbohydrate, and that both have essentially similar quantum efficiencies. So long as the intensity of light is not too strong, the process of photoreduction continues at a steady rate [1] ; increasing the intensity of the light, however, causes a gradual transition to the orthodox photosynthetic process (reversion), with the evolution of O_2, the rate of change over increasing with the intensity of the light. A simple interpretation of this effect of light-intensity would be that O_2 is liberated by the light in so great an amount as to destroy the hydrogenase, but this view is probably too simple. It is thought that the evolution of O_2 in photosynthesis takes place in stages, a " photoperoxide " being formed which is subsequently decomposed by a catalase-type of enzyme— *Catalyst C* of Franck & Herzfeld. The accumulation of this peroxide is thought to be the factor responsible for inhibiting the hydrogenase, and bringing an end to photoreduction. Thus the liberation of O_2 may be prevented by metabolic poisons, such as hydroxylamine, nevertheless reversion takes place in its presence. In the absence of CO_2 the reduced state may be maintained indefinitely with high light-intensities, presumably because, now, the peroxides cannot be formed.

[1] That is, after an induction period.

Gaffron's Scheme of the Photosynthetic Process

A comprehensive study of the effects of metabolic poisons on the three aspects of photoreduction, namely the adaptation process, the reversion process, and the overall rate of photoreduction, has led Gaffron to develop a general scheme for the mechanism of photosynthesis. In this scheme photoreduction is considered as a special case, in which the formation of peroxides is kept to a minimum, the hydrogenase, appearing in the reduced state of the plant, actually preventing an accumulation by reacting with the precursors to the peroxides.

We may consider as the primary reaction, common to both photosynthesis and photoreduction, the following :—

$$CO_2.X.Y.HOH \rightarrow XHCO_2 + YOH$$

$CO_2.X.Y.HOH$ is considered to be a photosensitive complex of water, chlorophyll and CO_2 which gives rise to a *reduced product*, $XHCO_2$, which subsequently gives a carbohydrate unit, $HCOH$. The postulation of this complex begs, of course, a number of questions, such as the actual sequence of events in its formation, the extent to which it may be broken down before absorbing light, and so on. Essentially we may look on the above reaction as the result of the fixation of CO_2 by chlorophyll, and the photosensitised decomposition of H_2O, associated with the reduction of CO_2 by way of an intermediate, $HXCO_2$, the decomposition of water necessarily requiring the formation of an oxidised product, YOH. In normal photosynthesis by green plants, YOH is considered to be further transformed to a peroxide, ZH_2O_2, which is subsequently decomposed to give free O_2 by a catalase, Catalyst C :—

$$2Z . H_2O_2 + Fr \rightarrow FrO_2 + 2Z + 2H_2O \rightarrow Fr + O_2$$

However, when the adaptation process has enabled the hydrogenase to appear, the oxidised product, YOH, is converted to H_2O :—

$$YOH + HDo \rightarrow H_2O + Y + Do$$

The accumulation of peroxides, on the other hand, may convert the reduced hydrogenase, HDo, into an inactive form :—

$$Z(OH)_2 + HDo \rightarrow Z + H_2O + DoOH$$

The scheme, as Gaffron emphasises, is only a vague sketch of the processes taking place during photosynthetic activity ; its value lies in that, so far, the kinetic implications are not seriously contradicted by experimental observations, and in that it brings out, in a more detailed fashion, the fundamental unity underlying the diversity of bacterial and plant photosyntheses. Common to them all is the photochemical reaction consisting of the absorption of light quanta, which provide a liberal supply of energy with which water molecules may be activated and subsequently split up into reduced and oxidised products. This energy is supplied in large quantities, in spite of the fact that in many bacterial syntheses the overall energy requirements of the reaction may be negligible, a fact serving to emphasise that, at an early stage in photosynthesis, the activation of water is necessary, the later reactions being unable to contribute their energy to this fundamental step. The course of the reaction, after this fundamental photochemical process, is determined by the nature of the enzymes and substrates present in the cell. In the bacteria, the evolution of O_2 has never been observed, even by the most delicate tests ; the oxidised product, YOH, reacts with a substrate which may be H_2S, to give S and H_2O ; a carbon-containing compound, such as isopropanol, giving on oxidation acetone ; and so on, these various substrates being called *hydrogen donors*, since they provide the hydrogen which reduces the oxidised product. The two main reactions, reduction of CO_2 and oxidation of substrate are thus linked, in the sense that they either occur together or not at all. For example, the exact studies of Van Niel on the stoichiometric relationships in the reaction :—

$$2CO_2 + 2H_2O + H_2S \rightarrow 2\,CH_2O + H_2SO_4$$

have shown that absorption of CO_2 continues only so long as H_2S is present in the medium, incubation for twenty-one days after the complete oxidation of the H_2S causing no further absorption. The scheme proposed by Gaffron indicates why these reactions are linked, failure of the reduced product, XH, to combine with CO_2 causing a back-reaction,

$$XH + YOH \rightarrow H_2O + XY$$

leading to the re-formation of water.[1]

Fixation of CO_2

The fundamental scheme of Gaffron, a development of the schemes proposed by Van Niel, Franck & Herzfeld, Emerson, and others, demands the formation of an organic complex containing CO_2. That this molecule undergoes a preliminary incorporation in an organic molecule seems to have been well proven by the studies of Ruben and his colleagues with the aid of radioactive carbon, C^{11}. This isotope has a half-life of only 21·5 minutes, so that the effects of only brief exposures of algæ to $C^{11}O_2$ could be measured.[2] The results showed that exposure to $C^{11}O_2$ in the dark caused a distinct uptake of C^{11} which could be extracted as a water-soluble compound, the amount taken up being independent of the concentration of chlorophyll in the algæ. The C^{11}, moreover, was not found in the extracted pigment. A fairly exhaustive analysis of the aqueous extract of algæ, exposed to $C^{11}O_2$ in the dark, revealed the presence of the major part (if not all) of the C^{11} in COOH-groups. By ultra-centrifuging the extracts and measuring the sedimentation constants it could be estimated that the COOH-groups were incorporated in a substance of molecular weight about 1,000–1,600.

---

[1] The algæ, in their reduced state, in the absence of CO_2, do not dissipate all their absorbed light energy as heat ; instead, illumination results in an active evolution of H_2. In some way the metabolites of the cell are reduced by the hydrogenase ; presumably, in this case, the concentration of hydrogenase is sufficiently high to enable the reaction :
$$XH + XH \rightarrow H_2 + 2X$$
to proceed in spite of the tendency for XH to react with YOH ; the fate of the oxidised product, YOH, in these circumstances, has not been determined.

[2] Recently Livingston & Medes have reported briefly on the use of the long-lived C^{13} ; they showed that at least 66 per cent. of the $C^{13}O_2$ introduced into their photosynthesis chamber was fixed as starch by mature, starch-depleted leaves of *Phaseolus vulgaris*.

Ruben suggests, therefore, that the " dark-fixation " of CO$_2$ follows the equation :—

$$RH + CO_2 \rightleftharpoons RCOOH$$

thus pyrogallol and bicarbonate *in vitro* react in this way :—

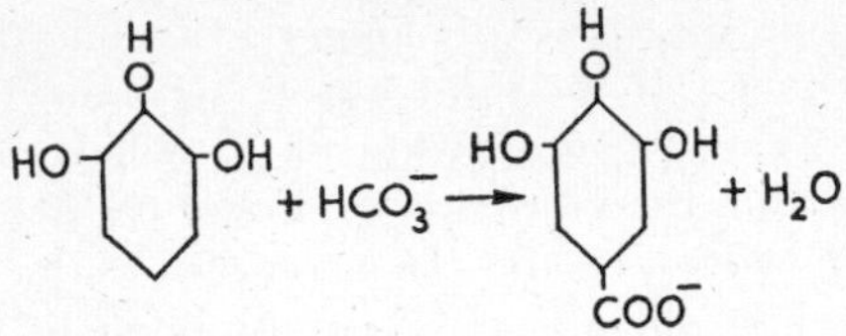

The subsequent photochemical reaction would be written :—

$$RCOOH + H_2O + nh\nu \rightarrow RCH_2OH + O_2$$

If, now, the compound RCH$_2$OH were to add a new CO$_2$ molecule to become :—

$$R \cdot CHOH$$
$$|$$
$$COOH$$

the same reaction would give :

$$R — CHOH$$
$$|$$
$$CH_2OH$$

and thus carbohydrate units could be built up on the large carrier molecule. Arnold observed that ultra-violet light inhibited photosynthesis, and concluded from the quantum mechanics of the process that the unit responsible for absorption of ultra-violet light was some 2,000 times the size of a chlorophyll molecule, *i.e.*, that it had a molecular weight of about 1,852,000. Ruben also observed that ultra-violet light inhibited the dark-conversion of CO$_2$ to COOH, so that it may well be that the organic group, R, is a protein of high molecular weight which splits off a much smaller group on extraction with water. When *Chlorella* was exposed to C^{11}O$_2$ in the light for a few minutes, fixation of C^{11} occurred, as we should expect ; a rather smaller amount was found in the form of − COOH, but it is interesting that no C^{11} was found in the extractable sugars. Formaldehyde has been suggested as an intermediate in the synthesis of carbohydrate, but no evidence of the presence of volatile aldehydes could be obtained. Finally, in this connection, we may recall that the kinetic studies on photosynthesis with flash-illumination led to the hypothesis of a thermal reaction taking place before the photochemical one, a reaction that was poisoned by cyanide (p. 553) ; the dark-fixation of CO$_2$, studied by Ruben, is poisoned by cyanide, consequently it is likely that it is essentially this reaction, catalysed by an iron-porphyrin type of enzyme—*Catalyst A* of Franck & Herzfeld's scheme—that is the preliminary to the photo-chemical one. One difficulty that remains to be resolved, however, is the apparent non-identity of the organic receptor for CO$_2$ with chlorophyll ; and whilst studies on fluorescence of chlorophyll in photosynthesising plants have not by any means given unequivocal results, they do suggest that it is chlorophyll that transfers absorbed light-energy to CO_2, as opposed to the transfer of the energy to H_2O and its subsequent reaction with CO_2 by a spatially separate process.

Fluorescence of Chlorophyll. Earlier it was remarked that a molecule that absorbed a quantum of light could re-emit most of the energy, so gained, as a quantum of light of longer wavelength, a phenomenon described as fluorescence. If the light-absorbing molecule is involved in a simple reaction, *e.g.*, the decomposition of I_2 which, on absorption of a quantum, rapidly (within the vibration period of the atoms) splits into two I-atoms, fluorescence will not occur. In a complex photosensitised reaction, on the other hand, where the absorbed energy must be passed on to other reactants, the chances of a re-emission are much greater, and it is not surprising that photosensitisers are, in general, fluorescent. Chlorophyll is no exception, either in the intact chloroplast, where it may be recognised by fluorescence-microscopy, or in extracts, the emitted light being red of about the wavelength corresponding to the maximal absorption. Under optimal conditions for photosynthesis, the loss of energy in this way is remarkably small, only one quantum in about a thousand being re-emitted. On *a priori* grounds we may expect fluorescence to increase under conditions unfavourable to photosynthesis, since unfavourable conditions suggest a deficiency of energy-accepting molecules in the neighbourhood of the chlorophyll, and thus favour " wastage " in the form of re-emitted radiation. Such an anti-parallelism has been observed by various workers, *e.g.*, Franck, French & Puck, especially under conditions of steady photosynthesis. Thus Kautsky observed that urethane, which inhibits the primary photochemical process, increases fluorescence, presumably by covering the active chlorophyll surface with a layer of molecules which prejudice the transfer of activation energy from the chlorophyll to the reactants. Again, cyanide and low temperature both increase the intensity of fluorescence ; these environmental influences are thought to affect the amount of CO_2-complex to which the light-energy must presumably be transferred at some stage in photosynthesis. At light-saturation, too, we may expect some increase in fluorescence, since now the whole photosynthetic apparatus is working at maximal capacity.[1]

Induction Period. After a period in the dark, illumination at high intensity is associated with an induction period, the rate of evolution of O_2 rising only slowly, over a period of several minutes, to its steady value. The induction period has been studied in great detail, and the facts are complex. It is thought that the period is due to the inactivation of an enzyme, Catalyst C, which catalyses the decomposition of peroxides to

---

[1] However, the state of affairs is not quite so simple, and its interpretation depends largely on the general theory of photosynthesis one adopts. At light-saturation the so-called Blackman reactions determine the steady rate, *i.e.*, the catalyst-B, which stabilises the initial photochemical products, which would otherwise revert back to their original form, becomes saturated ; consequently the initial photo-products do revert, and are therefore ready to absorb more light energy. Light-saturation *per se*, therefore, need not increase fluorescence, and this is what Wassink found with *Chlorella* ; in *Hydrangea* a definite increase occurs with light-saturation, and may be due to the overloading of catalyst A, the enzyme that provides the CO_2-complex which receives the energy.

give molecular O_2 ; in the dark, this is said to be partially inactivated, and is only re-activated during the exposure to light ; the time required for this build-up of Catalyst C represents the induction period. During the induction period, fluorescence exhibits a fair anti-parallelism with O_2-production ; it is thought that the accumulation of peroxides, and other intermediates, at the chlorophyll surface increases the number of non-energy-absorbing molecules in this region, thereby favouring fluorescence. The phenomena of fluorescence and induction are too complex for further discussion here ; the subjects are well worthy of mention, however, since they illustrate two further lines of investigation into the highly intricate process of photosynthesis. Any theory of the mechanism of photosynthesis must be able to account for the phenomena of fluorescence and induction, although the recent emphasis of Wassink on the variety of the fluorescence effects in different organisms and, in the same organism, under different conditions, suggests that no single generalisation will be able to cover the phenomena. Thus Wassink & Kersten point out that a *falling off* of photosynthetic yield, *without* large changes in fluorescence, can be observed in *Chlorella* at high light intensities or at low temperatures ; a *diminution* of photosynthetic yield with an *increase* in fluorescence may be observed, *i.e.*, anti-parallelism, in *Chlorella* with urethane and cyanide, and finally a *diminution* of photosynthetic yield may be associated with a *diminished* fluorescence in diatoms at light-saturation.

Before closing this discussion of the synthetic aspects of photochemical action we may remark on certain features common to the photo-synthetic and purely dark- or thermal reactions. The fixation of CO_2, *i.e.*, its incorporation in organic compounds, is by no means peculiar to photosynthesis. The autotrophic bacteria discussed earlier (p. 114) reduce CO_2 with the aid of energy derived from thermal chemical reactions, in other words, the reduction of CO_2 is *coupled* with an energy-supplying chemical reaction. Some bacteria make use of the energy derived from the " Knallgas " reaction :—

$$2H_2 + O_2 \rightarrow 2\,H_2O$$

to reduce CO_2. It will be remembered, moreover, that the adapted green algæ in an atmosphere of H_2, studied by Gaffron, convert O_2 in the dark to H_2O. The energy of this reaction is not wasted, since absorption of CO_2 takes place, apparently in accordance with the reaction :—

$$CO_2 + 2O_2 + 6H_2 \rightarrow (CH_2O) + 5\,H_2O$$

Here, then, is an example of the adaptation of a normally photosynthetic organism to a mode of synthesis employing chemical energy instead of light-energy. It is not difficult to envisage, as Gaffron has shown, the employment of the same system of enzymes to bring about both types of synthesis, the emergence of the hydrogenase during adaptation being the important factor.[1]

---

[1] The reaction is not, however, so simple as this general equation would indicate ; Gaffron's studies suggest that the reaction of H_2 with O_2 is rarely complete, and that the extent to which it goes depends on the concentration of CO_2 present, in other words, the presence of CO_2 governs the extent of the energy-giving reaction ; the reduction of CO_2 is thus truly coupled with the oxidation of H_2. The similarity between the dark- and

THE STRUCTURE OF THE PHOTOSYNTHETIC APPARATUS

The Chloroplast

CO_2 and H_2O, the main reactants in photosynthesis, are colourless substances and therefore do not absorb strongly in the visible spectrum ; the absorption of the necessary light-energy requires, therefore, a photosensitiser—*chlorophyll*—the green pigment of plants, algæ, diatoms and photosynthetic bacteria. In the higher plants and green algæ the chlorophyll (as well as other pigments, such as the carotenoids) is contained in cytoplasmic inclusion bodies, the *chloroplasts* ; in the bacteria and blue-green algæ the photosensitising pigment is not localised, but distributed throughout the cytoplasm.[1] Fig. 252 illustrates a section

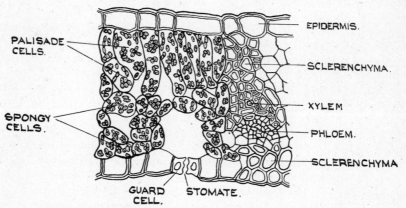

FIG. 252.   Section through leaf of higher plant.   Schematic.

through a leaf of a higher plant ; and it will be seen that the chloroplasts are contained mainly in the palisade and spongy cells. They are disk-shaped or flat ellipsoids, about 5μ across ; under the high power of the microscope they appear composite, being made up of dark *grana* some $0{\cdot}3{-}2\mu$ across, more or less uniformly distributed through a lighter coloured stroma. Chloroplasts have been isolated by Menke from spinach leaves [2] by the ultracentrifugal methods employed in the separation of inclusion bodies described earlier (p. 29) ; besides pigments, they contain mainly protein and lipids ; and the observation that the grana tend to disappear

light-reduction of CO_2 by H_2 is evident if we consider that the fundamental effect of light is to force $H + OH$ into a CO_2-chlorophyll complex to give $XHCO_2$ and YOH ; a similar result is obtained by the dark reaction :—

$$XYCO_2 + O_2 + 2HDo \longrightarrow 2XCO_2 + 2\,YOH + 2\,Do$$
$$XCO_2 + HDo \longrightarrow XHCO_2 + Do$$

[1] The term *chromoplast* is often used as a more general word covering the chloroplasts of the green plants and the homologous bodies in the red and brown algæ.

[2] When the leaves are macerated in distilled water the chloroplasts escape from the cells, but soon swell up and appear to become granular ; in $0{\cdot}5$ M sucrose, however, they retain their integrity, so that it is possible that they possess a limiting membrane, permeable to water, but not to sucrose.

PLATE XIII

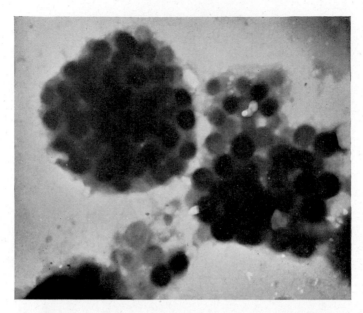

FIG. 254. Spinach chloroplasts showing dense grana embedded in paler matrix material. × 7,800. Electron-micrograph. (Granick & Porter. *Amer. J. Bot.*)

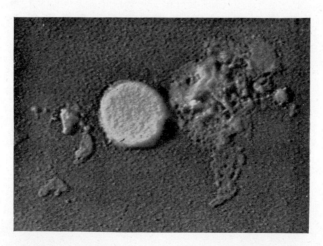

FIG. 255. Isolated granum from spinach chloroplast. Electron-micrograph. Gold shadowed. × 25,000. (Granick & Porter. *Amer. J. Bot.*)

[*To face p.* 565.

on extraction with fat solvents, and to be preferentially stained by fat-soluble dye-stuffs such as Rhodamine-B and Sudan Red III, suggests that the lipids are concentrated in these regions. There is some doubt as to whether the chlorophyll is entirely concentrated in the grana, or distributed through the stroma as well. The birefringence of the chloroplasts has been studied by Menke, and, more recently, by Frey-Wyssling ; both workers concluded that the chloroplast is built up of layers perpendicular to the optic axis, thus giving rise to a negative form birefringence, the optic axis being at right-angles to the surface. When this form birefringence was neutralised by a suitable solvent, a weak positive micellar birefringence was observed, presumably due to a radial arrangement of lipoid molecules. The picture derived from the birefringence of the chloroplast is therefore very similar to that of the nerve myelin sheath, namely layers of lipid separated by leaflets of protein (Fig. 165, p. 378). Support for a laminar structure is given by direct photomicrographs in ultra-violet light ; and it would appear that the grana are simply denser aggregates of matter distributed regularly along the laminæ, as in Fig. 253. The strong absorption of ultra-violet light, which made possible this photomicrography, suggests the presence of nucleoproteins ; the fact that

Fig. 253. Laminar structure of a grana-carrying chloroplast. (Rabinowitch, after Menke. *Photosynthesis and Related Processes.* Interscience. N.Y.)

the chloroplasts are apparently self-reproductive would also suggest the presence of this type of protein. Recent studies of chloroplasts with the electron-microscope have confirmed the existence of grana as definite entities ; Fig. 254, Pl. XIII, taken from a paper by Granick & Porter, shows the grana as discrete bodies, there being about 40–60 in each chloroplast ; in any given chloroplast their shape and size are remarkably constant, the diameter being about 6,000A and the thickness about 800A. The studies of Granick & Porter led them to the belief that the grana were embedded in a matrix ; no conclusive evidence was brought forward as to whether the chlorophyll was completely aggregated in the grana, although extraction of these bodies with methanol (in which the lipids and chlorophyll are soluble) certainly reduced their density. An electron-micrograph of an isolated granum is shown in Fig. 255, Pl. XIII. That photosynthesis probably takes place at the surface of the laminæ is suggested by the observation of Menke & Koydl that the laminæ, in thin slices of chloroplasts, are actually pushed apart by the presence of accumulated material.

Chemical analysis of isolated chloroplasts has not been extensive ; Menke found in dried chloroplasts the relative amounts of protein, lipids and ash shown in Table XXXVII.

TABLE XXXVII

Percentages of Protein, Lipid and Ash in Dried Chloroplasts. (Menke, 1938.)

Protein . . 47·7
Lipids (Ether sol.) 37·4
Ash . . . 7·8
Residue . . 7·1

Only 0·02–0·06 per cent. of the ether-soluble material was phosphorus, so that the phospholipids only amounted to 0·5–1·5 per cent. of the dried material. Mommaerts, from his studies of the chloroplasts, concluded that chlorophyll and protein were present in definite proportions, equivalent to one molecule of chlorophyll to one Svedberg-unit of 17,500. Menke showed, however, that Mommaerts' preparation was probably a mixture of cytoplasm and protoplasts ; according to Menke the ratio of protein to chlorophyll is nearer 100 : 17·2, *i.e.*, about 3 chlorophyll molecules, of weight 926, to 1 Svedberg-unit.

The Pigments

Photosynthetic organisms and tissues have a variety of colours; red, yellow, green, purple, brown, etc. Common to all the pigment systems associated with photosynthesis is the green pigment, chlorophyll, the actual colour of the organism being determined by the absolute amount of this substance and the amounts, in relation to this, of a variety of accessory pigments. Thus the various shades of the green leaf, commonly observed, are due to varying mixtures of yellow *carotenoids* [1] ; the red colour, especially obvious in growing shoots, is due to the presence of water-soluble *flavones*, present in the vacuoles of the cells, which may be converted into red *anthocyanins*. The blue-green, red, purple and brown algæ contain *phycobilins*, [2] besides carotenoids, and it is the strong absorption by these substances in the green and yellow that robs the organism of the green colour due to chlorophyll, and leaves it red, purple, or blue.

The chlorophyll of green plants is a mixture of two closely related compounds, *chlorophyll-a* and *chlorophyll-b*, consisting of structures built up of four pyrrole nuclei co-ordinated with an atom of Mg. They are esters of dibasic acids, the *chlorophyllins*, the esterifying alcohols being methyl alcohol and *phytol* ($C_{20}H_{39}OH$), so that the chlorophylls may be described as *methyl-phytyl-chlorophyllides*. Leaves contain an enzyme which splits the alcohol groups from the molecule ; and with its aid a number of artificial

---

[1] Carotene is one of the yellow pigments found in green leaves ; the remaining pigments are sometimes referred to as xanthophylls ; they are generally oxidation products of carotene, containing OH- or CO-groups in the ring structure, and may best be described as carotenols ; thus luteol, the most abundant of the xanthophylls in green leaves, is $C_{40}H_{54}(OH)_2$. *Fucoxanthol* is found in brown algæ and diatoms, but not in higher plants ; other carotenoids peculiar to algæ are *myxoxanthone* and *myxoxanthophyll* of blue-green algæ. Purple bacteria contain *violascin, rhodopin, rhodopurpurin,* etc.

[2] Phycobilins are chromoproteins of high molecular weight ; thus the red *phycoerythrin* and the blue *phycocyanin* have molecular weights in the region of 280,000, some 2 per cent. of the weight being due to the prosthetic pigment group and the remainder to a globulin type of protein. The prosthetic groups are built up of pyrrole units.

chlorophyllides may be prepared. *Bacteriochlorophyll*, extracted from photosynthetic bacteria, is classified by Fischer as a relation of chlorophyll-*a*; Fischer considers bacteriochlorophyll as the most primitive of the photosynthetic pigments and indicates how, by a process of hydrogenation and subsequent splitting off of water, chlorophyll-*a* may be derived from it.

Chlorophyll-*a*

Chlorophyll-*b*, he considers, was developed later. Hæmin, the prosthetic group of the respiratory pigments, is built up on the same pyrrole basis and could, according to Fischer, give rise to bacteriochlorophyll.

Chlorophyll of the *a*-type (bacteriochlorophyll) was considered, up till recently, to be the only green pigment of bacteria, algæ and diatoms, although it had been suggested that a substance, *chlorofucin* (also called chlorophyll-*γ*, or chlorophyll-*c* [1]), found in diatoms and brown algæ in addition to chlorophyll-*a*, was also a photosynthetically active pigment. Wilstätter & Page concluded that it was an artificial post-mortem product, but in 1942 Strain & Manning isolated chlorofucin by partition chromatography from extracts of diatoms (*Nitzschia closterium*), and showed that its absorption spectrum differed from those of both chlorophyll-*a* and -*b* ; these authors suggested the term *chlorophyll-c* for the compound and emphasised the importance of this substance in the carbohydrate economy of the earth, since diatoms are the most abundant autotrophic organisms over much of the earth's surface.

Absorption and Action Spectra. Chlorophyll is soluble in alcohol, acetone, etc., and may be extracted from leaves by vigorous shaking with these solvents ; it shows two regions of strong absorption (Fig. 256), one in the red at about 6,800 A and the other in the blue-violet at about 4,400 A, whilst very little of the intermediate wavelengths are absorbed ; this accounts for the green colour. We may expect, therefore, that irradiation of leaves or algæ with red light would be far more efficient than irradiation with, say, green light which is barely absorbed ; by plotting the amount of photosynthesis, resulting from the supply of a given number of quanta of light-energy, against the wavelength of the light, we should obtain what is called an *action spectrum*, the region of maximal activity corresponding

[1] Not to be confused with the chlorophyll-*c* alleged to be present in the higher plants, the claim regarding which was subsequently withdrawn, it having been shown to be a mixture of chlorophyll-*a* and pheophytin-*a*, *i.e.*, of chlorophyll and the product obtained by removing Mg from the molecule.

to the region of maximal absorption by the photosynthetic pigment. The two curves, action spectrum and absorption spectrum, will only be similar in outline provided that (*a*), one quantum of absorbed light is just as effective whatever its wavelength, and (*b*), either that the only pigment present is chlorophyll or that other absorbing pigments, such as the carotenoids, contribute their absorbed light-energy just as efficiently to photosynthesis as does chlorophyll. This last assumption has not been sustained by experiment, the action spectrum for photosynthesis being different from the absorption spectrum of chlorophyll. The similarity in

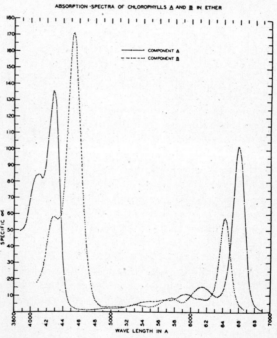

ABSORPTION ·SPECTRA OF CHLOROPHYLLS A AND B IN ETHER

COMPONENT A
COMPONENT B

Fig. 256. Absorption spectra of chlorophylls *a* and *b* in ether. (Zscheile. *Bot. Gaz.*)

certain regions, however, *e.g.*, in the red, indicates that chlorophyll exercises a dominant role in photosynthesis.

Thus Fig. 257, taken from a paper of Rabideau, French & Holt, shows the action spectrum for photosynthesis by leaves, measured by Hoover, and it is compared with the absorption spectra of leaves [1] of *Phaseolus*, of *Chlorella*, of isolated chloroplasts, and of fragments of chloroplasts obtained by treating an aqueous extract with ultrasonic vibrations. The shapes of the curves are, of course, influenced by the carotenoid pigments, but the maxima in the blue and red (particularly the red at ca. 6,800A), indicate

[1] The measurement of the absorption of light at different wavelengths by intact leaves is fraught with difficulties which have been specially investigated and amply discussed by Mestre (1935), and by Rabideau, French & Holt (1946), among others.

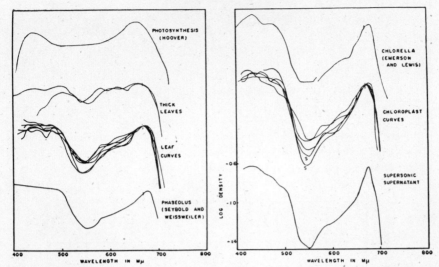

FIG. 257. Action spectrum for photosynthesis (top left-hand curve) compared with absorption spectra for leaves, *Chlorella*, and chloroplast preparations. (Rabideau, French & Holt. *Amer. J. Bot.*)

the role of chlorophyll in photosynthesis. Recent work along these lines has been devoted to ascertaining whether the auxiliary pigments contribute to photosynthesis, or whether light absorbed by them is " wasted energy." That photosynthesis may be carried out without the aid of the auxiliary pigments was shown by Warburg & Negelein, who demonstrated photosynthesis in red light, which is not absorbed by carotenoids. French, in 1937, studied the action spectrum of purple bacteria, and compared this with the absorption of light by the green bacteriochlorophyll and the red

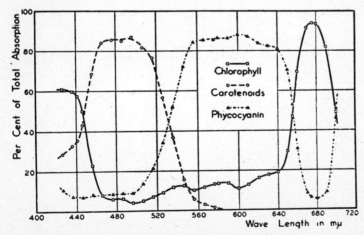

FIG. 258. Computed percentage absorption of the different wavelengths of visible light by the chlorophyll, carotenoids and phycocyanin of *Chröococcus*. Note that in the red region absorption is due predominantly to chlorophyll, whilst in the orange and yellow it is mainly due to phycocyanin. (Emerson & Lewis. *J. gen. Physiol.*)

mixture of carotenoids of these bacteria. He concluded that the accessory
pigments contributed nothing to photosynthesis. More recently Emerson
& Lewis have tackled the same problem in the blue-green alga, *Chröococcus*.
From the absorption spectra of the separately extracted pigments—
chlorophyll, carotenoids and phycocyanin—it was possible to compute,
with fair accuracy, the percentage of the total incident light absorbed by a
given pigment. Computed curves of this sort are shown in Fig. 258 ;
they indicate that in the red region, at 6,800A, most of the absorption
is due to chlorophyll, whereas a little further off, in the orange and yellow,
absorption is predominantly by the blue pigment, phycocyanin. Clearly,
if the light absorbed by phycocyanin is useless for photosynthesis, a
given number of quanta of yellow light at 6,000A should be far less

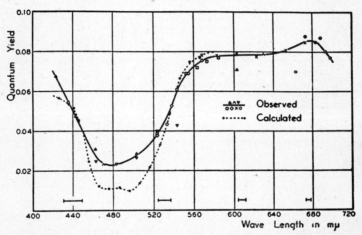

FIG. 259. The quantum yield of *Chröococcus* photosynthesis. The solid
line is drawn through the experimental points. The dotted curve shows
the expected dependence of the quantum yield on wavelength, on the
assumption that the yield for light absorbed by chlorophyll and phycocyanin is 0·08 at all wavelengths, and that the light absorbed by the
carotenoids is not available for photosynthesis. (Emerson & Lewis.
J. gen. Physiol.)

efficient than the same number of red quanta. The quantum yield should
therefore fall precipitately on passing from 6,760 to 6,000A. Fig. 259
shows the quantum yield plotted against wavelength ; it will be seen that
it is nearly constant over the range 6,900–5,700A, a result which can only
be explained on the assumption that both phycocyanin and chlorophyll
are photosynthetically active and, also, are equally efficient, *i.e.*, have a
quantum yield of 0·08. The sudden fall in quantum yield beyond 5,700A
is clearly associated with absorption of light by the carotenoids ; this
suggests that they are not photosynthetically active. However, the dotted
curve in Fig. 259 has been computed on this assumption, and it will be
seen that it deviates considerably (well beyond the experimental errors)
from the observed yields in the region of maximal carotenoid absorption.
If it is assumed that the carotenoids are photosynthetically active, but
with a quantum efficiency only one-fifth that of chlorophyll, the calculated

and experimental curves can be made to fit, so that we may conclude from this study of Emerson & Lewis first, that chlorophyll and phycocyanin are equally effective in photosynthesis, and secondly, that there is a possibility that the carotenoids are active, but with a much smaller efficiency. A similar conclusion regarding carotenoids, particularly fucoxanthin, was reached by Dutton & Manning from studies of the diatom *Nitzchia closterium*.[1] As Engelmann pointed out, such results lend significance to the wide variety of pigments in photosynthetic organisms ; thus sunlight, or diffuse daylight, falling on terrestrial plants, contains sufficient energy in the red and blue wavelengths to provide an adequate amount for photosynthesis. On passing through water, on the other hand, the light becomes depleted of its red, infra-red and violet wavelengths, the light turning bluish ; and it would, therefore, not be surprising if marine algæ developed pigments capable of utilising the blue and green wavelengths more efficiently than chlorophyll, as for example the brown algæ which absorb in the green. Thus green algæ (*Chlorophysaceæ*) are found in shallow water, whilst the red (*Floridæ*) are found in deep water, and the brown algæ occupy an intermediate position. Oltmanns emphasised, however, that the *intensity* of the light, as well as quality, also plays a part in the development of pigments, the total concentration of pigment tending to increase with depth of habitat as well as the proportion of phycoerythrin to chlorophyll (in the red algæ). In land plants chromatic adaptation is not so evident for the reason given above ; nevertheless the adaptation to differences in the intensity of the prevailing illumination is very real, it being customary by botanists to classify plants as *ombrophilic* and *heliophilic*, the ombrophilic being characterised by their high density of chlorophyll (*e.g.*, *Aspidistra elatior*) [2] ; moreover, the relative proportions of chlorophyll-*a* to chlorophyll-*b* show striking changes, the relative amount of -*b* increasing with increasing ombrophilia. The absorption spectrum of chlorophyll-*b* differs from that of -*a* in that there is stronger absorption between 4,500 and 4,800A, *i.e.*, in the blue region, and this promotes the more efficient use of the light in shady regions, which has an abundance of the blue wavelengths.

[1] Emerson & Lewis have carried out a similar study on the green alga, *Chlorella*. They find excellent agreement between the absorption and action spectra in the red, with a maximum at about 6,800A ; with wavelengths beyond 6,850A—the region of maximal fluorescence of chlorophyll—there is a steep fall in quantum efficiency. Emerson & Lewis doubt, in fact, whether wavelengths beyond 7,600 are effective in photosynthesis, *i.e.*, whether the energy corresponding to a quantum of light in the infra-red is large enough. The importance of the " accessory " pigments has recently (1950) been emphasised by the work of Haxo & Blinks on a number of algæ. Thus, in the red algæ, photosynthesis was minimal in the regions of 4,350 and 6,750A, regions corresponding to the absorption maxima of chlorophyll ; photosynthesis was maximal in the region of greatest absorption of the phycobilin pigments. With the green algæ, *Ulva* and *Monostroma*, the action and absorption spectra coincided ; since the algæ contained carotenoids which must have absorbed light, this suggests that these substances are also active in photosynthesis. Arnold & Oppenheimer have suggested that the energy absorbed by the " accessory pigment," *e.g.*, phycoerythrin in the case of *Chröococcus*, is handed on to chlorophyll by a process analogous to that of *internal conversion* in radioactivity.

[2] Thus *Theobroma cacao*, an ombrophilic species, has a chlorophyll content of 0·79 per cent. of the fresh weight, compared with 0·11 per cent. for *Pinus sylvestris*, a typical heliophilic tree.

Chlorophyll-Protein Complex. It has been suspected for some time that pure chlorophyll, obtained by extracting green leaves with alcohol or acetone, has a different absorption spectrum from that of chlorophyll, *in situ*, the absorption maxima apparently being some 100–200A closer to the red end of the spectrum in the intact plant. It has consequently been suggested that chlorophyll, in the cell, is linked with a protein as one or more prosthetic groups, extraction with organic solvents being sufficient to split this linkage. Numerous studies, especially on bacteria, have confirmed the difference in absorption spectra in the intact and isolated conditions. If, instead of extracting with an organic solvent, the leaves, or unicellular organisms, are ground up with water and filtered, fairly stable colloidal solutions of chlorophyll are obtained, which exhibit absorption maxima corresponding to those in the intact cells ; as with isolated chloroplasts, these extracts are devoid of photosynthetic activity. Fishman & Moyer purified the complex by precipitation with $(NH_4)_2SO_4$ and found isoelectric points, by electrophoresis, of 3·9 and 4·7 for *Aspidistra* and *Phaseolus* ; on shaking the extracts with ether the complex was split, the chlorophyll going into solution in the ether. Smith studied the aqueous extracts in the ultra-centrifuge ; he showed that they were not true colloidal solutions, in the sense that there was no uniformity in the size of the particles ; on clarifying the suspension with digitonin or bile salts, he found units of molecular weight 265,000, the order of size of other plant proteins such as phycoerythrin, phycocyanin, and seed globulin. A clarifying agent, such as digitonin, splits the chlorophyll from the protein which, together with the carotenoids, sediments separately. French found absorption maxima in live purple bacteria, presumably due to bacteriochlorophyll, at 4,200, 5,900 and 8,800A, whilst in methyl alcohol the maxima were at 4,100, 6,050 and 7,700A. In a study of many species and varieties of purple bacteria, Wassink and his collaborators showed that the absorption spectra of the alcoholic extracts had identical maxima at 7,740A, whilst in the intact organisms there was considerable variation, due presumably to different complexes with protein.

Development of Chlorophyll. It is a common observation that a seedling, allowed to develop in the absence of light, is very pale and deficient in chlorophyll (it is said to be *ætiolated*) ; on exposure to light it becomes green. Clearly the chlorophyll is formed directly by the photochemical reaction of a precursor. Pringsheim, in 1874, first recognised this precursor by its absorption bands at 6,200–6,400A in an extract of ætiolated leaves, and he called it *ætiolin*, whilst Monteverde, in 1893, called it *protochlorophyll* ; Scharfnagel, in 1931, recognised the characteristic absorption bands in ætiolated *Zea* seedlings. Fischer identified the substance as chlorophyll-*a*, minus two H-atoms in the 7–8 positions, but the question as to whether it was a true precursor, or a breakdown product, of chlorophyll remained open until Frank measured the action spectrum for the conversion of protochlorophyll into chlorophyll, *i.e.*, she determined the number of quanta of energy in different parts of the spectrum necessary to produce the same amount of chlorophyll in ætiolated *Zea* seedlings. The action spectrum revealed peaks at 6,450 and 4,450A, with minor ones at 5,750 and 5,450A, comparing with the peaks of the absorption spectrum of chlorophyll at 6,750 and 4,450A in aqueous extracts. If chlorophyll is formed by the absorption of light by the precursor, protochlorophyll, it is very likely that the latter substance has an absorption spectrum similar to the action spectrum, *i.e.*, with maxima in the blue and orange (4,450 and 6,450A) ; it is of interest that Noack & Kiessling obtained maxima at 6,200–6,290, 5,600–5,760, 5,230–5,270 and 5,960–6,020A in extracts from the seed coats of pumpkins ; if we allow for a certain shift of the absorption spectra of the pigment that occurs with extraction in organic solvents, it is possible that the absorption spectrum and action spectrum will coincide, although it is noteworthy that Noack & Kiessling found no significant absorption in the blue, whereas the action spectrum indicated strong absorption in this region. Frank observed that the effectiveness of blue light was not influenced by the carotenoids in the tissue ; thus they were either located so as not to screen the protochlorophyll or, alternatively, the light absorbed by the carotenoids may be utilised in the conversion of protochlorophyll to chlorophyll.

The isolation of the chemical and photochemical components in the formation of chlorophyll was made by Yocum, who showed that 0·001 M cyanide inhibited the O_2-uptake of leaves from dark-grown bean seedlings by about 66 per cent., whilst there was no effect on the rate of formation of chlorophyll during the first hour, during which time, however, the concentration of protochlorophyll fell continuously. After this induction period, cyanide completely blocked the formation of chlorophyll. Thus cyanide apparently inhibits the synthesis of protochlorophyll, which is a thermal reaction, but has no effect on the photochemical conversion of protochlorophyll to chlorophyll.

Evolution of O_2 by Isolated Chloroplasts

Dried leaves, or freshly isolated chloroplast suspensions, do not exhibit photosynthesis, nor yet do they evolve O_2 consistently on exposure to light ; that there is *some* evolution of O_2 associated with the illumination of these systems seems, however, to be generally proved, *e.g.*, by Molisch, but the methods necessary to demonstrate this evolution have had to be very sensitive,[1] and it was considered by Inman that it probably represented the decomposition of some easily reduced compound in the dried leaf or chloroplast. In 1939 R. Hill showed, with the aid of a spectroscopic test,[2] that O_2 was indeed evolved consistently by isolated chloroplasts, provided that aqueous extracts of acetone-extracted leaves, or yeast extracts, were added ; the efficiency of the yeast extracts seemed to be related to the presence of ferric salts (although the leaf extracts

[1] Luminous bacteria (p. 602) were employed ; they will luminesce in a concentration of O_2 corresponding to a partial pressure of 0·0007 mm. Hg ; Beijerinck, in 1899, was the first to use this test on illuminated emulsions of clover-leaf chloroplasts.

[2] The conversion of added hæmoglobin to oxyhæmoglobin was the first test used ; Holt & French, in following up this work, made use of the fact that the reaction results in the liberation of hydrogen ions, adding dilute alkali to the medium at a rate required to keep the pH constant ; the same authors have also followed the reaction by the reduction of the dye, 2-6-dichlorophenol-indophenol.

contained none), and it was found that potassium ferric oxalate could replace these extracts, the evolution of O_2 following the stoichiometric equation :—

$$4 K_3Fe(C_2O_4)_3 + 2 H_2O + 4 K^+ \rightarrow 4 K_4Fe(C_2O_4)_3 + 4 H^+ + O_2$$

The activity, in terms of output of O_2 per gramme of chlorophyll, was, however, only about one-tenth that of the intact leaf. Later, Hill & Scarisbrick showed that the liberation of O_2 was more vigorous, and comparable in extent with that taking place in the intact leaf, if potassium ferricyanide was also added, the ferricyanide oxidising the ferrous oxalate back to the ferric form and thus preventing the evolved O_2 from doing so. In effect, therefore, the Hill-reaction consists of the decomposition of H_2O :—

$$2 H_2O \rightarrow O_2 + 4 H$$

or, as it is written :—

$$2 H_2O \rightarrow O_2 + 4 H^+ + 4 e$$

the electrons being given to the ferric oxalate to convert it to the ferrous form :—

$$4 Fe^{+++} + 4 e \rightarrow 4 Fe^{++}$$

Essentially it is the presence of the electron-acceptor (oxidising agent) that permits the reaction to proceed. CO_2 is unnecessary for the reaction, so that the Hill-reaction permits an artificial resolution of the photosynthetic process into two stages. In the absence of any electron-acceptor, the decomposition of H_2O to O_2 and H_2 is immediately reversed, and a measurable evolution of O_2 is not observed ; in the presence of ferric oxalate, on the other hand, the reduced product, whatever it is, may be oxidised and hence the recombination with O_2 may be prevented. In the intact plant CO_2 is presumably the electron-acceptor, but it can only act if all the necessary enzymes are present, a mere suspension of chloroplasts being inadequate for photosynthesis. Thus the concept of H_2O as the source of O_2, already made use of in the earlier description of photosynthesis, fits in well with this scheme, and it is therefore of great interest that Ruben and his colleagues have shown, with the aid of O^{18}, that the O_2 evolved in photosynthesis does, indeed, come from H_2O, the proportion of O^{18} in the evolved gas being the same as that in the isotopic H_2O employed.

A study of the quantum efficiency of the Hill-reaction by French & Rabideau gave very variable values, ranging from 0·013–0·080, with a mean of 0·04, which may be compared with efficiencies of 0·01 for photo-oxidation in leaves (p. 575) and 0·09 for true photosynthesis ; the great variability suggests that enzymes are necessary for the Hill-reaction and that variations in the mode of preparation of the chloroplast suspensions cause fluctuations in the amount and activity of these catalysts. Support for this viewpoint is given by the studies of Kumm & French, who have shown that the activity of a chloroplast suspension increases greatly with preliminary illumination of the plant from which it was obtained ; it is possible that an intermediate substance, important for photosynthesis, is built up in the light.

PHOTO-OXIDATION AND PHOTODYNAMIC ACTION

Solarisation

It has been recognised by botanists for a long time that excessive light may injure a green plant, the word " solarisation " being used to describe this deleterious influence. A more particular investigation into the phenomenon has shown that it may be regarded as the result of a transition from one predominant type of photochemical reaction to another. The damage is more easily produced in an atmosphere deficient in CO_2, and it is observed that during the excessive illumination the evolution of O_2 ceases and gives place to an *absorption* of this gas. The amount of O_2 taken up depends on the partial pressure of O_2 in the atmosphere ; and an essentially similar photo-oxidation is observed in plants killed by boiling, or in plant juices. The fact that the concentration of CO_2 is critical in determining the ability of a given light-intensity to cause solarisation suggests that, in the absence of suitable concentrations of substrate, the light-energy, absorbed by chlorophyll, is used in a less specific manner to oxidise the constituents of the cell ; if this oxidation proceeds unchecked, the structural components of the leaf—protein and carbohydrate—will become involved and the damage will be irreparable. According to Franck & French, the non-specific photo-oxidation normally runs parallel with photosynthesis, a certain amount of the intermediate products of photosynthesis in the plant being thereby wasted, but not sufficient to prejudice the normal metabolism ; during CO_2-deficiency, however, the concentration of intermediates is reduced, and the photo-oxidative process becomes dangerous, attacking the vital structures. With a normal concentration of CO_2, very high intensities of light must be used to cause solarisation ; under these conditions, presumably, catalyst A (p. 561) is saturated, *i.e.*, the enzyme responsible for fixing the CO_2 is loaded to maximal capacity so that light-energy, normally passed on to the CO_2-complex, is used in the non-specific oxidation.

Photodynamic Action

This non-specific photo-sensitised oxidation is not peculiar to the photosynthetic system ; for many years a variety of phenomena have been classed together under the name of *photodynamic action* ; and it would seem that they have the fundamental characteristic in common of being photosensitised oxidations. Thus a variety of unicellular organisms and viruses may be killed by treating them with a dye-stuff, *e.g.*, eosin, and subsequently exposing them to light. A frog muscle, treated in the same way, exhibits a series of twitches and eventually goes into a contracture ; enzymes, such as invertase, peroxidase and catalase, may be inactivated ; the proteins of plasma may be oxidised and denatured so that the fibrinogen, for example, fails to clot on the addition of thrombin ; red blood cells may be made to hæmolyse, and so on. In all the cases examined, the effect may be completely prevented by the removal of O_2 from the system, either by anaerobiosis or by the addition of reducing agents such as sulphite ; consequently photodynamic action may be described as photo-oxidation. The dye-stuffs most commonly employed in studying photodynamic phenomena belong to the fluorescein series, *e.g.*, eosin, rose Bengal, erythrosine, but many other pigments, such as chlorophyll and hæmatoporphyrin, are effective. Photodynamic dyes are more or less fluorescent in visible light, and this is symptomatic of their suitability as photosensitisers, since a fluorescent substance is one that can hold its quantum of absorbed energy for about 10^{-7} to 10^{-8} sec., in contrast to non-fluorescent substances which lose their absorbed energy by collision much more rapidly ; the excited molecule has thus sufficient time to pass its quantum on to energy-absorbing reactants.

The general problems presented by photodynamic action are the nature of the oxidised substance, *i.e.*, whether it is protein, carbohydrate or fat, and the nature of the activated molecule, *i.e.*, whether O_2 is activated and subsequently oxidises substrate, or whether the substrate is activated, and reacts with normal O_2. The former hypothesis has been supported by Kautsky, who suggested that O_2 is activated to the $^1\Sigma$ state with a relatively long life of 10^{-3} to 10^{-2} sec. The energy of this state, however, requires a wavelength of less than 7,623A, whereas photo-oxidation with a wavelength as long as 8,000A has been observed. Studies of the quenching of fluorescence by substrates, moreover, indicate that O_2 need not necessarily be the energy-acceptor, and now opinion favours the activation of the oxidisable substrate as the primary process :—

$$\text{Dye} + h\nu \rightarrow \text{Dye}*$$
$$\text{Dye}* + \text{X} \rightarrow \text{X}* + \text{Dye}$$
$$\text{X}* + O_2 \rightarrow \text{XO}_2$$

where the asterisk denotes the activated condition.

With regard to the nature of the oxidisable substrate, protein is favoured by most workers ; thus blood plasma, treated with hæmatoporphyrin and irradiated with visible light, exhibits a rapid consumption of O_2 ; Smetana has shown that this O_2-consumption is due predominantly to the proteins albumin and globulin ; fats, glucose, and urea being responsible for only a negligible proportion.[1] Again, Howell has shown that the clotting of plasma can be inhibited by photodynamic action, the effect being to alter the fibrinogen molecule, which no longer coagulates with heat. Thus where photodynamic action is manifested in cell damage, there is little reason to doubt that structural proteins are attacked ; that other molecules may be involved is *a priori* reasonable, as, for example, the oxidation of intermediates in photosynthesis in solarisation.[2]

Photodynamic Hæmolysis. One of the most exhaustively studied cases

---

[1] Uric acid seems to be photodynamically oxidised in urine.

[2] Ascorbic acid in milk is photodynamically oxidised, lactoflavine being, presumably, the photosensitiser ; a bottle of milk left in the sunshine for half-an-hour loses half its ascorbic acid content.

of photodynamic action is hæmolysis—*photo-dynamic hæmolysis.* Suspension of red cells in saline containing a low concentration (say 1.10^{-6} M) of rose Bengal, for example, and exposure of this suspension to light from a 100-watt lamp, causes hæmolysis after an induction period (Fig. 260). According to the concentration of the dye, and the intensity of the light, the induction period varies from a matter of seconds to many minutes. If the light is switched off before hæmolysis is complete, the latter does not immediately cease, but continues for some time in the dark, the final degree of hæmolysis attained being determined by the amount that had

Rose Bengal

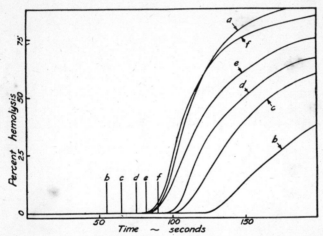

Fig. 260. Photodynamic hæmolysis. Percentage hæmolysis is plotted against time after illumination began. Curve *a* was obtained when light was continuous throughout the run ; in curves *b* to *f* the light was discontinued after the point on the time abscissæ indicated by the vertical line bearing the corresponding letter. (Blum & Morgan. *J. cell. & comp. Physiol.*)

taken place before extinguishing the light. Photodynamic hæmolysis consists, therefore, of a primary damage to the cells, followed by a dark or " after-light " hæmolytic process.[1] Blum showed that the dye is adsorbed on to the surface of the cell; consequently a prime factor in the relative efficacies of different dyes is the extent to which they are adsorbed ; thus, from a $2–10.10^{-5}$ M solution, 80 per cent. of the rose Bengal is taken up by the cells, whilst only 30 per cent. of erythrosine is adsorbed. In terms of the actual concentrations of dyes required to cause a given degree of

[1] Photodynamic dyes are generally hæmolytic in the absence of light, but in much higher concentration than that required to cause photodynamic hæmolysis ; such hæmolysis is described as *dark hæmolysis*, so that the process succeeding irradiation must be given another name ; Davson & Ponder have used the term *after-light hæmolysis* to describe this phase.

hæmolysis, rose Bengal is the more effective agent ; on the basis of the amounts actually on the cell surface, however, the two dyes are equally effective. Moreover, Blum found that the number of quanta of light required to hæmolyse a single cell was approximately 1.10^{10}, independently of the dye or its concentration. There is therefore little doubt that the first step in hæmolysis is the photosensitised destruction of a constituent of the cell membrane. The presence of reducing agents completely inhibits the light-hæmolysis ; consequently this destructive action is oxidative. The hæmolysis taking place after irradiation, the after-light hæmolysis, was investigated by Davson & Ponder ; they showed that it was not due

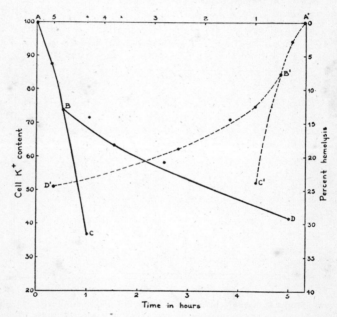

Fig. 261. Illustrating the escape of potassium from the erythrocyte accompanying photodynamic hæmolysis. Curve ABC shows the escape of K during illumination ; curve BD shows escape of K continuing after cutting off illumination at B. Curves A′B′C′ and A′B′D′ represent the concomitant hæmolysis. (Davson & Ponder. *J. cell. & comp. Physiol.*)

merely to a continuation of the oxidative process initiated in the light, since it was quite unaffected by reducing agents ; furthermore, it was not due to the presence of lytic substances formed during the light-phase, since dilution of a suspension of irradiated cells with isotonic NaCl had no effect on the course of the after-light hæmolysis. It was shown that, before any hæmolysis occurred, the cells lost K^+ (Fig. 261) and that, as hæmolysis proceeded, the remaining cells continuously lost this ion. This escape of K^+ continued during the after-light period, and it was concluded that the after-light hæmolysis was due, essentially, to the cation permeability induced during the light-phase, *i.e.*, that the cells, during the light-phase, had been made permeable to both Na^+ and K^+, a state of affairs that gives rise to the so-called colloid-osmotic hæmolysis described by Davson & Danielli (p. 246). Hence the persistence of the hæmolytic process after irradiation is due to secondary changes—colloid osmotic swelling—resulting from the primary oxidative damage to the cell membrane.

From the study of this type of hæmolysis we may conclude that photodynamic action results from the transfer of light-energy, by an adsorbed molecule of dye, to the structural proteins ; as a result of this activation, they combine with molecular O_2. That the damage is not due to the formation of toxic substances in solution, which then damage the cell, is made very probable by the studies of Blum on the red cell, and is confirmed by the neat experiment of Rask & Howell in which two turtle hearts " in tandem " were perfused with a Ringer solution containing hæmatoporphyrin. Irradiation of the first heart (when the second was in darkness) caused irregularity in the beat and eventual stoppage, whilst the second heart was quite unaffected.

On the assumption that the dye must be adsorbed to the cell, we can explain the inhibiting action of plasma on hæmolysis ; addition of quite small quantities of plasma reduces, or completely inhibits, the photodynamic action, which now requires a much higher concentration of dye to produce the same effect ; the active molecule in the plasma is the albumin, and it would seem that the plasma prevents the dye from adsorbing to the cell surface mainly because the dye is adsorbed to the plasma albumin.[1] The most commonly studied photodynamic dyes do not penetrate cells, so that their peripheral action is understandable ; Hyman & Howland have studied the effect of injection of eosin and rose Bengal directly into the cytoplasm of *Amœba*, followed by irradiation. The result is a series of changes leading to the eventual bursting of the cell, changes that can probably be attributed to a greatly increased fluidity of the cytoplasm, associated with a marked increase in permeability to water, with the result that the contractile vacuole is over-worked. Internally, therefore, the photodynamic action is significant ; and since a dye applied externally tends to destroy the cell membrane, it must favour its own penetration ; the photodynamic lysis of protozoa, *e.g.*, *Paramœcium*, is most probably due to combined internal and external action.[2]

Photodynamic Action in Living Animals. Since visible light cannot penetrate to any great depth of tissue, we may expect photodynamic action, resulting from the injection of a dye and subsequent irradiation of an animal, to be confined to the surface structures. This appears to be the case, white rats and mice so treated exhibiting symptoms attributable to a generalised stimulation of the sensory nerve endings in the skin. Later, necrotic lesions develop with loss of hair. The phenomena are by no means confined to experimental studies ; it has been known for

[1] This effect is not peculiar to photodynamic hæmolysis ; saponin and many other lysins are inhibited by plasma.

[2] Giese has described the photodynamic killing of a protozoan, *Blepharisma*, the photosensitiser being the red pigment normally present in the cytoplasm. A similar action with other pigmented cells has not been described.

a long time [1] that cattle and sheep develop skin diseases as a result of eating certain weeds, and that these diseases attack a white animal in preference to a coloured one.   Thus St. John's wort (*Hypericum*) is a weed that may become a serious menace to sheep in some parts of the world ; that the disease is due to a photodynamically active pigment in the plant is made probable by a number of investigations ; for example Horsley has extracted a fluorescent pigment, *hypericin*, from the whole plant ; injection of the product into white rats produces typical photodynamic lesions.   The disease of geeldikkop (yellow thick head) in sheep has the characteristic signs of photodynamic action, and is also apparently due to the eating of certain plants, such as *Lippia* sp., *Tribulus*, sp., etc.   The toxic principle in the plant, in this case, is, however, not photodynamically active ; it damages the liver and causes various breakdown products of chlorophyll (which are normally excreted in the bile) to appear in the bloodstream ; and it is one of these products, *phylloerythrin*, that is photodynamically active.   So long as the animal does not eat chlorophyll the signs do not occur.   Finally we may mention the sensitisation of animals to buckwheat (*Fagopyrum esculentum*), the condition of " fagopyrism " ;   Chick & Ellinger have shown that the flower and husk of the seed cause an inflammatory condition in albino rats when they are exposed to light in the range 5,400–6,100A ; these authors extracted an active principle with acetic acid and methyl alcohol which gave a reddish fluorescence.

In humans the effects of sensitisation to hæmatoporphyrin, for example, are very similar to those of sun-burn ; in the latter case the signs result from a direct action of ultra-violet light, the absorption by proteins in this region of the spectrum being very characteristic.   The two effects thus differ, in that the one is photosensitised and the other is the result of a direct photochemical reaction ; they differ, furthermore, in that the effects of ultra-violet light are apparently not oxidation reactions, the hæmolysis, stimulation of muscle, destruction of bacteria, etc., being unaffected by anaerobiosis.   In this connection we may remember that the study of cell structure was greatly facilitated by the characteristic absorption of the nucleic acids in the region of 2,600A, whilst proteins absorbed most strongly at the longer wavelength region of about 2,800A ; the strong absorption of nucleic acids in the ultra-violet might suggest that the lethal action of ultra-violet rays is due to nuclear damage.   The careful and systematic studies of Hollaender and his colleagues on this subject have revealed, however, that, where cells are concerned, the light is most probably absorbed by the proteins of the cytoplasm ; with bacteria, yeasts, and dermatophytes, on the other hand, absorption by the nucleoproteins seems to be the decisive factor.   Thus Giese found that ultra-violet light

---

[1] Blum quotes probably the earliest recorded case of a photodynamic disease in cattle from an article by J. Lambert in the Philosophical Transaction of the Royal Society, 1776, **66**, 493.   " I shall now inform you of a very extraordinary and singular effect of lightning on a bullock in this neighbourhood, which happened about a fortnight since. The bullock is pyed, white and red.   The lightning, as supposed, stripped off all the white hair from his back, but left the red hair without the least injury. . . ."   Doubtless the loss of hair was due to photodynamic action, since only the white parts were affected.

of 2,804A was more effective in suppressing division of *Paramœcium* than light of 2,654A ; both radiations caused injury, however, and it is of interest that recovery from the longer wavelength was more rapid than from the shorter ; this is understandable if the shorter wavelength causes nuclear damage, whilst the longer wavelength only cytoplasmic injury.

References

ARNOLD, W. (1933). " The Effect of Ultraviolet Light on Photosynthesis." *J. gen. Physiol.*, **17**, 135.

ARNOLD, W. & KOHN, H. I. (1934). " The Chlorophyll Unit in Photosynthesis." *J. gen. Physiol.*, **18**, 109.

ARNOLD, W. & OPPENHEIMER, J. R. (1950). " Internal Conversion in the Photosynthetic Mechanism of Blue-green Algæ." *J. gen. Physiol.*, **33**, 423.

BLUM, H. F. (1937). " Photodynamic Hæmolysis. II. Modes of Inhibition." *J. cell. & comp. Physiol.*, **9**, 229.

BLUM, H. F. (1941). " Photodynamic Action and Diseases Caused by Light." New York, Reinhold.

BLUM, H. F. (1950). " Photophysiology and Photopathology." *Medical Physics*. Ed. O. Glasser. Chicago, Year Book Publishing Co.

BLUM, H. F. & HYMAN, C. (1939). " Effect of Concentration of Dye on Photodynamic Hæmolysis Time." *J. cell. & comp. Physiol.*, **13**, 287.

BLUM, H. F. & MORGAN, J. L. (1939). " Photodynamic Hæmolysis. III." *J. cell. & comp. Physiol.*, **13**, 269.

BLUM, H. F. & PRICE, J. P. (1950). " Delay of Cleavage of the *Arbacia* Egg by Ultraviolet Radiation." *J. gen. Physiol.*, **33**, 285.

CHICK, H. & ELLINGER, P. (1941). " The Photo-sensitising Action of Buckwheat (*Fagopyrum esculentum*)." *J. Physiol.*, **100**, 212.

DAVSON, H. & PONDER, E. (1940). " Photodynamically Induced Cation Permeability and its Relation to Hæmolysis." *J. cell. & comp. Physiol.*, **15**, 67.

DUTTON, H. J. & MANNING, W. M. (1941). " Evidence for Carotenoid-sensitised Photosynthesis in the Diatom *Nitzschia closterium*." *Amer. J. Bot.*, **28**, 516.

EMERSON, R. & ARNOLD, W. (1932). " A Separation of the Reactions in Photosynthesis by Means of Intermittent Light." *J. gen. Physiol.*, **15**, 391.

EMERSON, R. & ARNOLD, W. (1932). " Photochemical Reactions in Photosynthesis." *J. gen. Physiol.*, **16**, 191.

EMERSON, R. & LEWIS, C. M. (1939). " Factors Influencing the Efficiency of Photosynthesis." *Amer. J. Bot.*, **26**, 808.

EMERSON, R. & LEWIS, C. M. (1942). " The Photosynthetic Efficiency of Phycocyanin in *Chröococcus*, and the Problem of Carotenoid Participation in Photosynthesis." *J. gen. Physiol.*, **25**, 579.

EMERSON, R. & LEWIS, C. M. (1943). " The Dependence of the Quantum Yield of *Chlorella* Photosynthesis on Wavelength of Light." *Amer. J. Bot.*, **30**, 165.

EMMONS, C. W. & HOLLAENDER, A. (1939). " The Action of Ultraviolet Radiation on Dermatophytes." *Amer. J. Bot.*, **26**, 467.

ENGELMANN, T. W. (1883 ; 1884). *Bot. Z.*, **41**, 18 ; **42**, 81, 97. (Quoted by Rabinowitch.)

FISCHER, H., LAMBRECHT, R. & MITTENZWEI, H. (1938). " Uber Bacterio-chlorophyll." *Z. physiol. Chem.*, **253**, 1.

FISHMAN, M. & MOYER, L. S. (1942). " The Chlorophyll-Protein Complex. I. Electrophoretic Properties and Isoelectric Point." *J. gen. Physiol.*, **25**, 755.

FOSTER, J. W. (1940). " Role of Organic Substrates in Photosynthesis of Purple Bacteria." *J. gen. Physiol.*, **24**, 123.

FRANCK, J. & FRENCH, C. S. (1941). " Photo-oxidation Processes in Plants." *J. gen. Physiol.*, **25**, 309.

FRANCK, J., FRENCH, C. S. & PUCK, T. T. (1941). " The Fluorescence of Chlorophyll and Photosynthesis." *J. phys. Chem.*, **45**, 1268.

FRANCK, J. & GAFFRON, H. (1941). " Photosynthesis : Facts and Interpretations." *Adv. in Enzym.*, **1**, 199.

FRANCK, J. & HERZFELD, K. F. (1941). " Contribution to the Theory of Photosynthesis." *J. Phys. Chem.*, **45**, 978.

FRANK, S. R. (1946). " The Effectiveness of the Spectrum in Chlorophyll Formation." *J. gen. Physiol.*, **29**, 157.

FRENCH, C. S. (1937). " The Rate of CO_2 Assimilation by Purple Bacteria at Various Wavelengths of Light." *J. gen. Physiol.*, **21**, 71.

FRENCH, C. S. (1940). " The Pigment-protein compound in Photosynthetic Bacteria. I. The Extraction and Properties of Photosynthin. II. The Absorption Curves of Photosynthin from Several Species of Bacteria." *J. gen. Physiol.*, **23**, 469, 483.

FRENCH, C. S. & HOLT, A. S. (1946). " Evolution of O_2 with the Simultaneous Reduction of a Dye by Illuminated Suspensions of Chloroplasts." *Amer. J. Bot.*, **33**, 835.

FRENCH, C. S., HOLT, A. S., POWELL, R. D. & ANSON, M. L. (1946). " The Evolution of O_2 from Illuminated Suspensions of Frozen, Dried and Homogenised Chloroplasts." *Science*, **103**, 505.

FRENCH, C. S. & RABIDEAU, G. S. (1945). " Quantum Yield of O_2-production by Chloroplasts Suspended in Solutions containing Ferric Oxalate." *J. gen. Physiol.*, **28**, 329.

FREY-WYSSLING, A. & STEINMANN, E. (1948). " Die Schichtendoppelbrechung grosser Chloroplasten." *Biochim. Biophys. Acta*, **2**, 254.

GAFFRON, H. (1936). " Metastabiler Sauerstoff und Kohlensäure-Assimilation." *Biochem. Z.*, **287**, 130.

GAFFRON, H. (1940). " CO_2 Reduction with Molecular H_2 in Green Algæ." *Amer. J. Bot.*, **27**, 273.

GAFFRON, H. (1942). " The Effect of Specific Poisons upon Photo-reduction with Hydrogen in Green Algæ." *J. gen. Physiol.*, **26**, 195.

GAFFRON, H. (1942). " Reduction of CO_2 Coupled with the Oxyhydrogen Reaction in Algæ." *J. gen. Physiol.*, **26**, 241.

GAFFRON, H. (1944). " Photosynthesis, Photoreduction and Dark Reduction of CO_2 in Certain Algæ." *Biol. Rev.*, **19**, 1.

GAFFRON, H. & RUBIN, J. (1942). " Fermentative and Photochemical Production of Hydrogen in Algæ." *J. gen. Physiol.*, **26**, 219.

GIESE, A. C. (1939). " Effects of 2654 and 2804 A on *Paramœcium caudatum*." *J. cell. & comp. Physiol.*, **13**, 139.

GIESE, A. C. (1945). " The Ultraviolet Action Spectrum for Retardation of Division of *Paramœcium*." *J. cell. & comp. Physiol.*, **26**, 47.

GIESE, A. C. (1946). " An Intracellular Photodynamic Sensitiser in *Blepharisma*." *J. cell. & comp. Physiol.*, **28**, 119.

GRANICK, S. & PORTER, K. R. (1947). " The Structure of the Spinach Chloroplast as Interpreted with the Electron Microscope." *Amer. J. Bot.*, **34**, 545.

HARRIS, D. T. (1926). " Photo-oxidation of Plasma." *Biochem. J.*, **20**, 240.

HAXO, F. T. & BLINKS, L. R. (1946). " Photosynthetic Action Spectra in Red Algæ." *Amer. J. Bot.*, **33**, 836.

HAXO, F. T. & BLINKS, L. R. (1950). " Photosynthetic Action Spectra of Marine Algæ." *J. gen. Physiol.*, **33**, 389.

HILL, R. (1939). " O_2 Produced by Isolated Chloroplasts." *Proc. Roy. Soc.*, B, **127**, 192.

HILL, R. & SCARISBRICK, R. (1940). " Production of O_2 by Illuminated Chloroplasts." *Nature*, **146**, 61.

HILL, R. & SCARISBRICK, R. (1940). " The Reduction of Ferric Oxalate by Isolated Chloroplasts." *Proc. Roy. Soc.*, B, **129**, 238.

HOLLAENDER, A. & EMMONS, C. W. (1939). " The Action of Ultraviolet Radiation on Dermatophytes." *J. cell. & comp. Physiol.*, **13**, 391.

HOLT, A. S. & FRENCH, C. S. (1946). " Evolution of O_2 by Isolated Chloroplasts Immersed in Solutions of Various Oxidising Agents." *Amer. J. Bot.*, **33**, 836.

HOLT, A. S. & FRENCH, C. S. (1946). " Photochemical Production of O_2 and H^+ by Isolated Chloroplasts." *Arch. Biochem.*, **9**, 25.

HORSLEY, C. H. (1934). " Investigation into the Action of St. Johns Wort." *J. Pharm.*, **50**, 310.

HOWELL, W. H. (1921). " L'Action Photodynamique de l'Hématoporphyrine sur le Fibrinogène." *Arch. int. Physiol.*, **18**, 269.

HYMAN, C. & HOWLAND, R. B. (1940). " Intracellular Photodynamic Action." *J. cell. & comp. Physiol.*, **16**, 207.

INMAN, O. L. (1935). " The Evolution of O_2 in the Process of Photosynthesis." *C.S.H. Symp.*, **3**, 184.

JOHNSTON, E. S. & MYERS, J. E. (1943). " Photosynthesis." *Ann. Rev. Biochem.*, **12**, 473.

KATZ, E. & WASSINK, E. C. (1939). " Infrared Absorption of Chlorophyllous Pigments in Living Cells and in Extracellular States." *Enzym.*, **7**, 97.

KAUTSKY, H. (1936). " Chlorophyllfluoreszenz und Kohlensäuseassimilation." *Biochem. Z.*, **284**, 412.

KAUTSKY, H., DE BRUIJN, H., NEUWIRTH, R. & BAUMEISTER, W. (1933). " Photosensibilierte Oxydation als Wirkung eines aktiven metastabilen Zustandes des Sauerstoff-moleküls." *Ber.*, **66**, 1588.

KISTIAKOWSKY, G. H. (1928). " Photochemical Processes." N.Y., Reinhold.

KISTIAKOWSKY, G. H. (1935). " Photochemical Formulations of Reactions of Radicals and Atoms." *C.S.H. Symp.*, **3**, 44.

KLUYVER, A. J. & DONKER, H. J. L. (1926). *Chem. Zelle Gewebe*, **13**, 134. (Quoted by Van Niel.)

KOHN, H. I. (1936). " Number of Chlorophyll Molecules Acting as an Absorbing Unit in Photosynthesis." *Nature*, **137**, 706.

KON, S. K. & WATSON, M. B. (1936). " The Effect of Light on the Vitamin C of Milk." *Biochem. J.*, **30**, 2273.

KOSMAN, A. J. & LILLIE, R. S. (1936). " Photodynamically Induced Oxygen Consumption in Muscle and Nerve." *J. cell. & comp. Physiol.*, **6**, 505.

KUMM, J. & FRENCH, C. S. (1945). " Evolution of O_2 from Suspensions of Chloroplasts : Activity of Various Species and Effects of Previous Illumination." *Amer. J. Bot.*, **32**, 291.

LILLIE, R. S., HINRICHS, M. A. & KOSMAN, A. J. (1936). " The Influence of Neutral Salts on the Photodynamic Stimulation of Muscle." *J. cell. & comp. Physiol.*, **6**, 487.

LIPPAY, F. (1929). " Uber Wirkungen des Lichtes auf den quergestreiften Muskel I–IV." *Pflüg. Arch.*, **222**, 616 ; **224**, 587, 600 ; **226**, 473.

LIVINGSTON, L. G. & MEDES, G. (1946). " Biosynthesis of C^{13} Compounds." *Amer. J. Bot.*, **33**, 838.

MENKE, W. (1938). " Uber den Feinbau der Chloroplasten." *Koll. Z.*, **85**, 256.

MENKE, W. (1938). " Isolierung von Chloroplasten aus Spinatblättern." *Z. physiol. Chem.*, **257**, 43.

MENKE, W. (1940). " Uber den Zustand der Carotenoide in den Plastiden." *Naturwiss.*, **28**, 31.

MENKE, W. (1940). " Der Chlorophyllgehalt der Chloroplasten aus Spinatblätter." *Z. physiol. Chem.*, **263**, 100.

MENKE, W. & KOYDL, E. (1939). " Direkter Nachweis des lamellaren Feinbaues der Chloroplasten." *Naturwiss.*, **27**, 29.

MESTRE, H. (1935). " The Absorption of Radiation by Leaves and Algæ." *C.S.H. Symp.*, **3**, 191.

MEYER, S. J. & BURR, G. O. (1940). " Some Effects of Light of High Intensity on Chlorella." *J. gen. Physiol.*, **24**, 45.

MOLISCH, H. (1925). " Uber Kohlensäure-Assimilation toter Blätter." *Z. Bot.*, **17**, 577.

MOMMAERTS, W. F. H. M. (1938). " Some Chemical Properties of the Plastid-Granum." *Proc. K. Akad. Wetensch.*, **41**, 896.

NOACK, K. & KIESSLING, W. (1929). " Zur Entstehung des Chlorophylls und seiner Beziehung zum Blutfarbstoff." *Z. physiol. Chem.*, **182**, 13.

OLTMANNS, F. (1893). *Jahb. f. wiss. Bot.*, **16**, 1. (Quoted by Rabinowitch.)

PACE, N. (1942). " The Ætiology of Hypericism, a Photosensitivity Produced by St. Johns Wort." *Amer. J. Physiol.*, **136**, 650.

RABIDEAU, G. S., FRENCH, C. S. & HOLT, A. S. (1946). " Absorption and Reflection Spectra of Leaves, Chloroplast Suspensions and Chloroplast Fragments as Measured in an Ulbricht Sphere." *Amer. J. Bot.*, **33**, 769.

RABINOWITCH, E. I. (1945). " Photosynthesis and Related Processes." N.Y., Interscience.

RASK, E. N. & HOWELL, W. H. (1928). " The Photodynamic Action of Hematoporphyrine." *Amer. J. Physiol.*, **84**, 363.

RIEKE, F. F. & GAFFRON, H. (1943). " Flash Saturation and Reaction Periods in Photosynthesis." *J. phys. Chem.*, **47**, 299.

ROBERTS, E. A. (1946). " Electron Microscopic Studies of Plant Cells and their Contents." *Amer. J. Bot.*, **33**, 231.

ROLLEFSON, G. K. (1935). " The Theory of Photoactivation and the Properties of Photoactivated Molecules." *C.S.H. Symp.*, **3**, 19.

RUBEN, S., HASSID, W. Z. & KAMEN, M. D. (1939). " Radioactive Carbon in the Study of Photosynthesis." *J.A.C.S.*, **61**, 661.

RUBEN, S. & KAMEN, M. D. (1940). " VI. Molecular Weight of the Intermediate Products and a Tentative Theory of Photosynthesis." *J.A.C.S.*, **62**, p. 3451.

RUBEN, S., KAMEN, M. D. & HASSID, W. Z. (1940). " Photosynthesis with Radioactive Carbon. II. Chemical Properties of the Intermediates." *Loc. cit.*, p. 3443.

RUBEN, S., KAMEN, M. D. & PERRY, L. H. (1940). " III. Ultracentrifugation of Intermediate Products." *Loc. cit.*, p. 3450.

RUBEN, S., RANDALL, M., KAMEN, M. & HYDE, J. L. (1941). " Heavy Oxygen (O^{18}) as a Tracer in the Study of Photosynthesis." *J.A.C.S.*, **63**, 877.

SMETANA, H. (1938). " Photo-oxidation of Body Fluids." *J. biol. Chem.*, **124**, 667.

SMITH, E. L. (1941). " The Chlorophyll-protein Compound of the Green Leaf." *J. gen. Physiol.*, **24**, 565.

SMITH, E. L. (1941). " The Action of Na Dodecyl Sulphate on the Chlorophyll-protein Compound of the Spinach Leaf." *J. gen. Physiol.*, **24**, 583.

SMITH, E. L. & PICKELS, E. G. (1941). " The Effect of Detergents on the Chlorophyll-protein Compound of Spinach as studied in the Ultracentrifuge." *J. gen. Physiol.*, **24**, 753.

STRAIN, H. H. & MANNING, W. M. (1942). " Chlorofucine (Chlorophyll-γ), a Green Pigment of Diatoms and Brown Algæ." *J. biol. Chem.*, **144**, 625.

STUTZ, R. E. & BURRIS, R. H. (1948). " Distribution of C^{14} among Organic Acids of Higher Plants Fixing $C^{14}O_2$." *Amer. J. Bot.*, **35**, 813.

TSENG, C. K. & SWEENY, B. M. (1946). " Physiological Studies of *Gelidium cartilagineum*. I. Photosynthesis with Special Reference to the CO_2 Factor." *Amer. J. Bot.*, **33**, 706.

VAN NIEL, C. B. (1941). " The Bacterial Photosyntheses and their Importance for the General Problem of Photosynthesis." *Adv. in Enzym.*, **1**, 263.

WARBURG, O. (1928). " U. d. katalytischen Wirkungen der lebendigen Substanz." Berlin, Springer. (Quoted by Franck & Gaffron.)

WARBURG, O. (1948). " Assimilatory Quotient and Photochemical Yield." *Amer. J. Bot.*, **35**, 194.

WARBURG, O., BURK, D. & SCHOCKEN, V. (1950). " The Quantum Efficiency of Photosynthesis." *Biochim. Biophys. Acta*, **4**, 335.

WARBURG, O. & NEGELEIN, E. (1923). " U. d. Einfluss der Wellenlänge auf den Energie-umsatz bei der Kohlensäureassimilation." *Z. physik. Chem.*, **106**, 191.

WASSINK, E. C. (1948). " Photosynthesis." *Ann. Rev. Biochem.*, **17**, 559.

WASSINK, E. C., KATZ, E. & DORRESTEIN, R. (1939). " Infrared Absorption Spectra of Various Strains of Purple Bacteria." *Enzym.*, **7**, 113.

WASSINK, E. C. & KERSTEN, J. A. H. (1943/5). " Observations sur la Photosynthèse et la Fluorescence Chlorophyllienne des Diatomées." *Enzym.*, **11**, 282.

WELLER, S. & FRANCK, J. (1941). " Photosynthesis in Flashing Light." *J. Phys. Chem.*, **45**, 1359.

YOCUM, C. S. (1946). " Relation between Respiration and Chlorophyll Formation." *Amer. J. Bot.*, **33**, 828.

ZSCHEILE, F. P. (1935). " Towards a More Quantitative Photochemical Study of the Plant Cell's Photosynthetic System." *C.S.H. Symp.*, **3**, 108.

ZSCHEILE, F. P. & COMAR, C. L. (1941). " Influence of Preparative Procedure on the Purity of Chlorophyll Components as shown by Absorption Spectra." *Bot. Gazette*, **102**, 463.

PLATE XIV

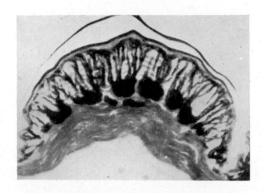

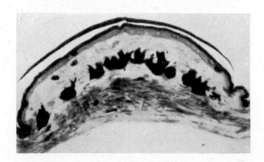

FIG. 263. Upper : Disposition of melanophores in lizard in brown state. The *stratum corneum* has been displaced during sectioning. Branches of melanophores extend to *stratum germinativum*. Lower : Green condition. Pigment concentrated. (Kleinholtz. *J. exp. Biol.*)

[*To face p*. 587.

xanthophores appear to play only a passive role in this chromatic response (Fig. 263, Pl. XIV).

Mechanism of Dispersion and Concentration

How, may we ask, is this change in distribution of pigment brought about ; do the cells invariably change their shape, as might be deduced from Schmidt's diagrams of *Hyla*, or does the form of the cell remain constant while the pigment diffuses from the centre outwards, during dispersion, and back again during the concentration phase? Because of their dominant position, and because of the greater ease of observing them, the melanophores of vertebrates and cephalopods, and the erythrophores of crustacea, have been studied almost exclusively, with the result that what knowledge we have of the concentrating and dispersing mechanisms is confined to these varieties of chromatophore.

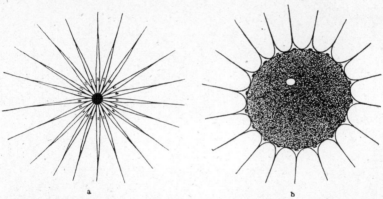

FIG. 264. Chromatophore, with attached muscle cells, of the squid, *Loligo.* (*a*) Muscle fibres are relaxed and the pigment is concentrated, giving the light condition. (*b*) The muscle fibres are maximally contracted, giving dispersion of pigment. (Bozler. *Z. vgl. Physiol.*)

Cephalopoda. In the cephalopod, *e.g.*, the squid or octopus, we find indisputable evidence for a change in shape of the melanophore, brought about by the contraction of radially disposed muscle fibres. The phenomenon has been studied by Bozler in some detail, and Fig. 264 illustrates his conception of the expansion and contraction of the pigment. The melanophore, in its relaxed condition, is a small spherical cell, so that if all the melanophores in the skin are in this *concentrated* condition the animal is pale ; the muscle fibres pull radially and, when contracted, draw the sphere out into a large thin disc ; in this condition the pigment is said to be *dispersed*, and the animal is dark.

Vertebrates. In vertebrates the melanophores are cells with many branching processes ; Fig. 265, from Hogben & Slome, illustrates various conditions of the melanophores of the horned toad, *Xenopus*, the different states being characterised by the varying degrees of dispersion of the pigment along the fine ramifying processes. It is very difficult to determine whether the changes in apparent shape of the melanophore, such as those

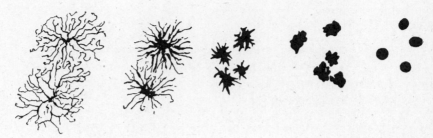

Fig. 265.   Different degrees of dispersion and concentration of pigment in the melanophores of the horned toad, *Xenopus*. (Hogben & Slome. *Proc. Roy. Soc.*)

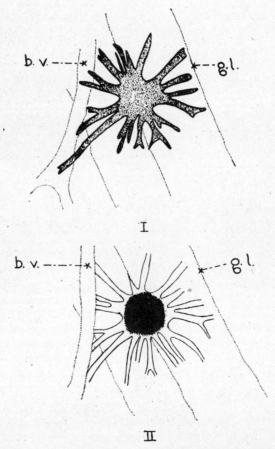

I

II

Fig. 266.   *Camera lucida* drawings of a melanophore from a scale of *Fundulus heteroclitus*, mounted in culture-medium two and one-half days previously. × 400.   I. In atropine sulphate ; pigment expanded.   II. In adrenaline ; pigment contracted.   The processes are still visible for varying distances from the cell body.   *b.v.*, blood vessel ; *g.l.*, growth line of scale. (Matthews. *J. exp. Zool.*)

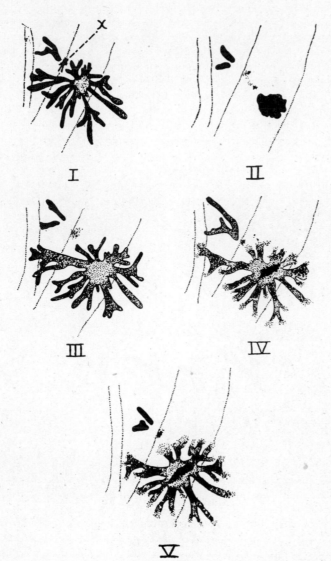

FIG. 267. *Camera lucida* outlines of a melanophore of *Fundulus heteroclitus* in tissue-culture. × 400. I. A process of the cell was injured at *x*. II. Medium has been changed to KCl; pigment peripheral to injury clumped in centre of isolated process. III. Medium has been changed back to NaCl; pigment of isolated process is partially expanded whilst that of the cell is maximally expanded. IV. Atropine added; pigment in process maximally expanded. Fifteen minutes before this drawing was made, the cell body had been destroyed with micro-needles, and its pigment does not respond to atropine. V. In adrenaline. Pigment in process is contracted, but there is no change in the cell body. (Matthews. *J. exp. Zool.*)

depicted in Fig. 265, are due to the migration of pigment in amœboid contractions and expansions of the cell, since the limiting regions of the cell are only differentiated from the surroundings by the pigment ; thus an alternative to this formation of pseudopods could be that the pigment actually diffused into optically empty ramifications of a cell which retained its branched shape permanently. The observation that a given melanophore retains its identical shape, on concentration and subsequent dispersion of its pigment, strongly favours the view that the pigment diffuses into processes with fixed boundaries. Conclusive proof of this is provided by Matthews' studies of the migration of pigment in cultured cells ; grown in tissue culture, the outlines of melanophores remain visible even when the pigment is in the concentrated state. By treating the cells with adrenaline the pigment was concentrated, and the outline remained the same ; on treatment with atropine the pigment migrated peripherally to re-fill the contours (Fig. 266). The melanophores illustrated in Fig. 266 were not isolated, but formed part of a tissue-culture, so that it was

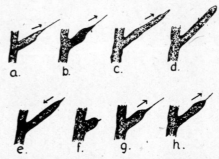

FIG. 268.   A series of stages in the movement of pigment into and out of a chromatophore branch of *Palæmonetes*.   The walls of the chromatophore adhere closely to the contained pigment. (Perkins & Snook. *J. exp. Zool.*)

possible that the processes were really channels in the surrounding interstitial matrix. This was excluded, however, by the observation that nuclei, obviously belonging to the melanophore, were often localised within the processes. How the migration of the granules is brought about remains a mystery ; Matthews has shown that the tendency of the pigment to concentrate is a property of the protoplasm, independent of the organisation of the cell as a whole ; thus a process, separated from the main body by micro-dissection, exhibited a concentration of pigment into the centre of the process on treatment with a concentrating agent (KCl) ; replacement of KCl with NaCl caused a subsequent dispersion in both the isolated process and the remaining cell (Fig. 267). That a change in protoplasmic structure is associated with the migration of pigment, is shown by Matthews' observation that, in the concentrated condition, the cell was brittle and not easily distorted, in marked contrast to the expanded state. That concentration is not simply a driving of the granules in front of a wave of gelating protoplasm, is shown by the fact that isolated granules may be left behind the main body and then continue to move ;

sometimes following the general trend, but sometimes moving in the opposite direction.

Arthropoda. With respect to the red chromatophores of the shrimp, *Palæmonetes*, Perkins & Snook have arrived at generally similar conclusions to those of Matthews, in that the processes are a part of the cell and not pre-existing intercellular spaces. Their microscopical observations, however, led them to believe that the dispersion of pigment was a filling up of collapsed tubes, as illustrated in Fig. 268. If this is true, dispersion must be accompanied by a considerable increase in cell volume, presumably brought about by osmosis from outside.[1]

THE CONTROL OF PIGMENT MIGRATION

Changes in pigment distribution result most frequently, but not invariably, from a change in the conditions of illumination of the animal ; thus a frog placed in darkness becomes black, and in a bright environment becomes pale ; the shrimp, *Palæmonetes*, becomes pale in darkness and dark in daylight ; the flat fishes not only adapt themselves to the colour of their background, but also to the pattern, as Mast has shown. In some instances, however, stimuli, other than light, play an important role ; for example, the frog, *Rana temporaria*, is very sensitive to humidity and temperature, becoming dark at low temperature and high humidity, and pale under the reverse conditions. Again, the fiddler crab, *Uca*, exhibits a definite 24-hourly rhythm of lightness and darkness, becoming pale at night and dark during the day ; Brown & Sandeen have shown that keeping this crab in darkness for weeks fails to modify the rhythm, which is thus inherent. Finally, the amphipod *Hyperia* becomes whitish whenever it attaches itself to a jellyfish, but when free is a dark reddish brown. Apart from these, and a few other instances, however, the light-stimulus is undoubtedly the most important.

Responses to Light

In general we may distinguish three types of response to light, as follows : (*a*) the *primary response* which is a direct reaction to illumination of the skin and occurs in the blinded animal ; it is generally manifest as a dispersion of the pigment in those chromatophores that principally determine the colour of the animal.[2] The primary response is seen in its most pronounced form in the chameleon ; thus Zoond & Eyre state that, if a letter Y is cut out of a piece of copper sheet and placed on the skin of a chameleon in bright sunlight, an exact reproduction is obtained on the skin like a photographic negative. (*b*) *The black-background response.* This is a dispersion of the pigment cells when the animal is placed in a

---

[1] True amœboid movements of pigment cells are found in the Culicidæ, of which *Corethra* has been studied by Martini & Achundow ; thus larvæ, if kept on a white background, become thoroughly transparent ; and on a black background become black, a colour change brought about by the rapid movement of the black pigment cells on the air-sacs.

[2] The *Natantia*, e.g., the shrimp, are said, by Hogben, to prove an exception to this rule.

light environment on a light-absorbing background. (*c*) *The white-background response*. This is a concentration of pigment when the animal is placed in a light environment on a light-scattering background.

Since the response to light is complex, it is important always to specify the exact conditions under which an animal is maintained. The various possibilities may be tabulated as follows for normal and blinded animals (Table XXXVIII) :

TABLE XXXVIII

Four possible types of pigmentary response. (*After Hogben*, 1942.)

Illumination (from above)	Dim		Bright	
Surroundings	Black background	White background	Black background	White background
Normal . . .	D	C	$D_1 + D_2$	$D_1 + C$
Blind	O	O	D_1	D_1

Here C represents a tendency to concentration of pigment ; and D_1 and D_2 tendencies to dispersion, due to the direct and black-background responses respectively. When the overhead illumination is dim, the primary response is not elicited ; with a high intensity of overhead illumination, on the other hand, the primary response may become significant and either contribute to the black-background response or antagonise that of the white background.

That the black-background response is not merely due to a diminished illumination of the eye, *per se*, was shown by Hogben & Slome, who found that a blinded South African clawed toad, *Xenopus*, adopted an intermediate colour between the extreme pallor obtained in white surroundings and the dark colour when placed on a black background; the same was true if normal animals were kept in the dark for a long time, their colour being that of blind animals. Hence an animal in daylight, but on a black background, shows the most intense dispersion of its pigment. The same state of affairs was found with the isopod crustacean, *Ligia oceanica*, by H. G. Smith. Hogben & Slome concluded that the eye must be broadly differentiated into two regions, so far as the pigmentary response is concerned. Thus, with an aquatic vertebrate, on a black background, a limited ventral region of the retina will be illuminated, since only rays within a cone, whose half-angle is the critical angle for an air-water interface, can enter the eye. On the black background, only this region is stimulated, and the result is a maximal expansion of the melanophores. On a white background the whole retina is illuminated ; if stimulation of the dorsal region of the retina causes concentration of pigment, and if this region is prepotent over the ventral region, the white-background response can be explained. On this basis the blind animal is not so dark as the black-background animal because the important ventral region is unstimulated, nor yet is it so pale as the white-background animal because the dorsal region is unstimulated.

Evidence for such a differentiation in the gillyfish, *Fundulus heteroclitus*, has been provided by the histological and physiological studies of Butcher ; the upper (dorsal) region of the retina contained rods and single and double cones, whilst the lower region, some 30 per cent. of the whole area, only contained rods and double cones ; moreover, there was a specialised " crescentic ridge " in the lower retina. By putting a " blinker " over the fish's eye in such a way as to cut off different regions of the retina from illumination, Butcher showed that stimulation of the upper portion of the retina caused paleness, and that this area was prepotent over the lower region which caused, by itself, darkening. Further confirmation was obtained by making incisions through the eye to sever different regions of the retina from their central connections. Essentially the same state of affairs was found by H. G. Smith in the crustacean, *Ligia* ; in this (compound) eye, it was the latero-ventral group of ommatidia that were concerned with the white-background response, whilst the dorsal group controlled the black-background response.

The secondary responses are thus mediated by the eyes ; we have yet to discuss the manner in which the effects of these visual stimuli are transmitted to the effectors, the chromatophores. In the cephalopods, nervous control over the pigmentory system is well established ; the muscle fibres, causing the expansion of the melanophores, are activated by nerve fibres ; cutting a mantle nerve in the squid leads to a blanching of the area innervated, a finding that suggests that the muscle fibres are maintained in a tonically contracted state. The detailed mechanism of the control is not understood ; there seems no doubt that there are a number of chromatic centres in the ganglia, and that certain drugs may act on these centres, whilst others act more peripherally ; of the latter group, adrenaline causes an expansion of the chromatophores, *i.e.*, a contraction of the muscle fibres, whilst acetylcholine has the opposite effect.

Pituitary Hormones. The colour changes effected by the cephalopods are extremely rapid ; moreover, the expansion of the melanophores depends only on a muscular contraction, so that a predominantly nervous control is not surprising. In amphibians, on the other hand, the very sluggish responses (hours are required for the development of colour changes in frogs) suggest that the activation of the melanophores requires the release of a hormone into the blood.[1] The early work of Smelt in 1916, among others, showed that the pituitary gland was important, and this was confirmed by Hogben & Winton, who showed that an extract of beef pituitary caused a rapid blackening of a pale frog ; removal of the pituitary made the animals pale. The intermediate lobe of the pituitary seems to be the region responsible for this activity, producing a hormone called *intermedin*, or *substance B* ; Hogben & Slome consider that, at least for

---

[1] The hormone, once secreted into the blood, may act quickly, but unless it is rapidly removed a change in colour will take a long time, since what is required is a significant change in its concentration in the blood. As Hogben points out, however, we cannot immediately deduce from the sluggishness of the responses that the control is humoral ; the effectors themselves may have a very long latent period. Thus the reaction time in some teleosts is less than one minute, whilst in *Xenopus* it is 100 minutes.

the toad *Xenopus*, the antagonistic actions of the ventral and dorsal regions of the retina are mediated by separate principles derived from different regions of the pituitary, the *pars tuberalis* liberating a *W-substance*, responsible for blanching, whilst the intermediate lobe is responsible for darkening. The evidence in favour of this assumption is largely based on studies of the kinetics of colour changes in amphibia, these being such as to indicate that a given change is brought about by the removal of one hormone from the blood and the secretion of its antagonist. It has frequently been denied that the melanophores of amphibians are innervated ; recently, however, both histological and physiological evidence has been provided by Stoppani and by Vilter, among others, in favour of an active concentration of pigment by nervous means. Thus Stoppani cut the sciatic nerve of the toad, *Bufo arenarum*, and found that the leg darkened a little ; on stimulation of the peripheral end, blanching occurred. Certainly the injection of adrenaline (*e.g.*, 1 ml. of 1 : 10,000) causes a blanching which begins in about ten minutes and lasts for hours ; consequently Vilter's hypothesis that the sympathetic is antagonistic to the pituitary has some support.

Eye-Stalk Hormones. In crustaceans it is generally agreed that there is no innervation of the chromatophores ; Perkins, in 1928, was the first to exhibit a hormonal control in this order. Within an hour after injection of an extract of the eye-stalk of a pale shrimp, *Palæmonetes*, into a blinded animal, whose chromatophores were expanded, the pigment had contracted. So far as the shrimp is concerned, therefore, the active hormone tends to concentrate the pigment. The eye-stalk is a complex structure containing, besides the eye and its associated nervous structures, a *sinus gland* and an organ described as the *X-organ* ; these are thought to be the regions responsible for liberating the hormone ; certainly the sinus gland is important, but the function of the X-organ is not clear (*vide* Hanström). The hormonal control of the migration of crustacean pigment is complicated by the fact that the same extract will cause dispersion in one group and contraction in others. Thus the extract from the eye-stalk of the shrimp induces concentration of the red and yellow chromatophores in this species, but causes the black and red pigments of crabs, *e.g.*, *Uca*, to expand. This variability in behaviour of the extract is reflected in a similar variability in the response to blinding, *i.e.*, removal of the eye-stalks. For instance, blinded *Palæmonetes* have their dark pigment cells expanded, whilst the brachyuran crab, *Uca*, has them contracted. The presence of more than one active principle has been postulated by many workers in this field, and extracts from the central nervous system have been described having an opposite action to that of the sinus gland. In crustacea the problem is highly complex, owing to the relatively large number of chromatophores of different types that contribute materially to the colour changes ; as an example of this we may reproduce a table of Abramowitz (1935), showing the changes in the white, black, red and yellow chromatophores of the crab *Portunus* when placed on different backgrounds.

TABLE **XXXIX**

Responses of Chromatophores of Crab to Different Backgrounds (D = Dispersion ; C = Contraction ; I = Intermediate State).

Background	White	Black	Red	Yellow
White	D	C	C	C
Black	C	D	D	D
Blue	C	D	D	C
Red	C	D	D	D
Yellow. . . .	I	C	C	D
Green	D	D	I	C
Darkness . . .	C	D	D	C

It will be seen that all four types react independently, although the responses of the red and black chromatophores are usually the same. We have therefore to decide whether separate principles are elaborated to react on each type, or whether a single hormone acts on each type differently. The latter hypothesis is unlikely from Abramowitz' work.

Before leaving the crustaceans we may mention that the diurnal rhythm, so prominent in *Uca*, is dependent on the integrity of the eye-stalks (Brown & Sandeen) ; Brown & Webb have shown that it is possible to set the rhythm out of phase by cooling the crab to around 0° C. for several hours ; on re-warming, the changes of colour take place every 24 hours, as before, but they are out of phase by the number of hours the crab was kept cold. Some evidence for the existence of two hormonal principles was provided by a study of the effects of sinus extracts at different phases ; Brown & Scudamore found that weak extracts were effective in dispersing black pigment during the day, but had no effect by night, *i.e.*, they were unable to antagonise the paling at night which occurs rhythmically.

Caudal Bands. The most thorough study of the control of the migration of pigment has been made on fishes by Parker and his school ; it will be sufficient to confine attention here to the teleosts, of which the gillyfish, *Fundulus*, and the cat-fish, *Ameiurus*, have been studied most intensively. The responses of teleost fishes are frequently very rapid, the dispersion of the melanophores in *Fundulus* requiring only forty-five seconds. Such rapid changes demand a direct nervous action on the effectors. This innervation is best proven by the formation of *caudal bands* ; thus, by a localised incision in the tail of *Fundulus*, the nerve supply to a limited region can be severed without interference with the blood supply to the same region. The first effect of denervation is a dark band, appearing within about half a minute and taking five minutes to attain its maximum density. Within six hours it has begun to fade, and after two to three days it is indistinguishable from the rest of the animal. When this has happened, the region is still functionally different from the rest since, on placing the fish on a black background, the caudal band appears bright against the darkened animal. If the animal is maintained for a day or two on the black background, however, the caudal band eventually darkens. Thus the caudal band is distinguished by a very much delayed response to visual stimuli, a fact suggesting that slow-acting humoral mechanisms come into play over long periods. Certainly fishes, like amphibia, respond to pituitary extracts by darkening, and Kleinholz has shown that injection of intermedin into a *Fundulus* with a blanched caudal band causes the latter to darken. However, this does not explain the blanching of the caudal band when the animal is maintained on a white background for some time. According to Parker, the phenomena associated with the production and disappearance of caudal bands may best be explained on the basis of a double innervation of the melanophores, an adrenergic—pigment-concentrating—and a cholinergic—pigment-dispersing—innervation. The effect of an incision is thought not to be due to the cutting off of tonic concentrating impulses but, on the contrary, to an irritative excitation of the cut nerve, the dispersing fibres being more sensitive to the irritation than the concentrating fibres. Evidence for this rather unusual effect of nerve section is the following : if a fish with a caudal band is kept in a white vessel, as we have seen, the dark band fades. On making a new incision, distal to the original cut, a second dark band appears within the region where the first band was. Regeneration of the nerve fibres cannot be invoked to explain this finding, since experiments have shown that this takes many days. It would seem, therefore, that the cut fibres, which had subsided into quiescence, were re-excited by the new cut. Support for this view is given by the effects of cold blocks applied distally to the cut ; if one is applied before the second incision, the new band extends only as far as the block ; if the second cut has already been made, a cold block causes the new band to fade distally to the block. Electrical excitation of the nerves of a fish has long been known to cause a blanching of the region supplied, so that, if there really are dispersing and concentrating fibres, they differ radically in their responses to electrical excitation and cutting ; thus the concentrating fibres are activated by electrical stimulation whilst the dispersing fibres by section. This rather *ad hoc* proposal is not easy to accept, but recent studies by Parker & Rosenblueth on the cat-fish have shown that high-frequency stimulation causes concentration of pigment whilst low-frequency stimulation of the same nerve, with pulses of long duration, causes dispersion. That the two antagonistic nervous mechanisms are equivalent to the sympathetic and parasympathetic systems of warm-blooded animals is suggested by the action of adrenalin, which blanches, and of acetylcholine which darkens, an eserinised cat-fish. The gradual blanching of a dark caudal band on a fish kept on a white background, and the gradual darkening of a pale band of a fish on a dark background, have been explained by Mills and by Parker as being due to the slow diffusion of adrenaline or of acetylcholine, liberated at the nerve endings in the adjacent innervated regions. Thus Mills observed that the fading of a band did not occur evenly, but progressively from without inwards, as though the fading depended on the diffusion of some principle. Parker showed, further, that the time required for fading or darkening of a band depended on the width, as the following table shows :—

TABLE XL

Times Required for Caudal Bands and Body of Fish to Change Colour Under Different Conditions. (Parker, 1934.)

Loss of Initial stripe	1 mm. stripe	30	hour
	2 mm. ,,	78	,,
Change from Light to Dark. . .	Body	1·8	,,
	1 mm. ,,	20·5	,,
	2 mm. ,,	37	,,
Change from Dark to Light. . .	Body	4·6	,,
	1 mm. ,,	26·4	,,
	2 mm. ,,	51·6	,,

On this basis, then, the paling of a caudal band is due to the slow diffusion of adrenaline, liberated in neighbouring regions of the pale fish, whilst the darkening of a pale band is due to diffusion of acetylcholine, liberated by the active dispersing fibres of the dark fish. The diffusion, according to Parker, is trans-cellular, similar to that which must occur in the nutritive processes of coelenterates where the more superficial ectodermal elements receive their nutriment by diffusion of material from the gastrovascular cavity.

Hormonal Control in Teleosts. Teleosts possess, besides a nervous, a humoral control over their melanophores, although the latter is generally subservient to the former. Injection of extracts of mammalian or fish pituitary causes pigment dispersion in the cat-fish, *Ameiurus,* for example ; in *Fundulus* it seems doubtful whether pituitary extract has much influence on the innervated melanophores.[1] In the cat-fish the importance of hormonal control is well brought out by a study of Osborn, who showed that a hypophysectomised fish fails to exhibit the maximal contraction of melanophores obtained in normal animals ; in this fish, therefore, both hormonal and nervous factors are involved in dispersion.

Primary Response. The primary response to light, obtainable in blinded animals, has been briefly mentioned ; it is seen in its most characteristic form in lizards, such as the chameleon, the " horned toad," *Phrynosoma,* and *Anolis.* The control of chromatic behaviour of *Anolis* has been well worked out by Kleinholz, who has shown that a direct nervous influence on the melanophores is most probably not present in this species, denervated areas responding to changes in background in exactly the same way as normal areas. The pituitary plays a dominant, if not exclusive, role in chromatic reactions in *Anolis,* a hypophysectomised animal becoming light green and showing no response to background. Not only does the hypophysectomised *Anolis* fail to respond to backgrounds, but it also loses its primary response to light, remaining a pale green in sunlight, whilst a normal, but blinded, animal goes brown under the same conditions.

[1] As indicated earlier (p. 596), when the melanophores are released from nervous control, the extract causes pigment dispersion.

Clearly, the primary response is not a simple effect of light on the chromatophores, but apparently depends on the presence of dermal photoreceptors which reflexly transmit impulses to the pituitary. We may note, however, that Kleinholz' conclusions have been questioned by Parker, as also those of Zoond & Eyre on the chameleon ; these workers denervated one side of an eviscerated chameleon by a longitudinal incision beside the spinal cord ; they found that the denervated side failed to respond directly to changes in illumination, but remained permanently dark. The control of the melanophores of the chameleon is largely nervous (in contrast to that of *Anolis*), so that Zoond & Eyre postulated a local reflex mechanism, mediated by nervous paths, in this primary response. Hogben has questioned the likelihood of such an accurate reflex response, and is inclined to agree with Parker that the melanophores are, indeed, directly susceptible to light. Certainly the highly localised primary responses cannot be easily interpreted on the basis of a reflex activation of the pituitary, as it is difficult to see how, on this basis, the response could be confined to a definite region ; Kleinholz' finding, that hypophysectomised animals fail to show a direct response, is best interpreted on the assumption that the primary response is more effective when there is some intermedin in the blood.

This short review of the main findings concerned with the mechanisms of chromatic responses has revealed an unexpected degree of complexity, even when attention is concentrated only on those chromatophores that contribute most to the colour changes, namely the melanophores ; when it is realised that colour changes are rarely effected by only one type of chromatophore, and that the different types may sometimes respond in the same way, and sometimes differently, to the same stimulus, it is not surprising that, in spite of some 1,200 papers published on the subject within the past thirty-seven years, we are still far from a complete elucidation of the processes involved in any one organism. The value of these studies, interesting as they are as steps towards the elucidation of problems that are fascinating in themselves, extends beyond the immediate phenomena of chromatic behaviour, since their understanding demands an extension of our still limited knowledge of the nervous and humoral mechanisms in cold-blooded vertebrates and invertebrates.

References

ABRAMOWITZ, A. A. (1935). " Colour Changes in Cancroid Crabs of Bermuda." *Proc. Nat. Acad. Sci., Wash.* 21, 677.

ABRAMOWITZ, A. A. (1936). " Physiology of the Melanophore System in the Catfish, *Ameiurus*." *Biol. Bull.*, 71, 259.

ABRAMOWITZ, A. A. (1937). " Role of the Hypophyseal Melanophore Hormone in the Chromatic Physiology of *Fundulus*." *Biol. Bull.*, 73, 134.

BOZLER, E. (1928 ; 1931). " Die Chromatophoren der Cephalopoden." *Z. vgl. Physiol.*, 1928, 7, 379 ; 1931, 13, 762.

BROWN, F. A. & SANDEEN, M. I. (1948). " Responses of the Chromatophores of the Fiddler Crab, *Uca*, to Light and Temperature." *Physiol. Zool.*, 21, 361.

BROWN, F. A. & SCUDAMORE, H. H. (1940). " Differentiation of Two Principles from the Crustacean Sinus Gland." *J. cell. & comp. Physiol.*, 15, 103.

BROWN, F. A. & WEBB, H. M. (1948). "Temperature Relations of an Endogenous Rhythmicity in the Fiddler Crab, *Uca*." *Physiol. Zool.*, **21**, 371.

BUTCHER, E. O. (1938). "Structure of the Retina of *Fundulus heteroclitus* and the Regions of the Retina Associated with the Different Chromatophoric Responses." *J. exp. Zool.*, **79**, 275.

CARLSON, S. P. (1935). "Colour Changes in *Uca pugilator*." *Proc. Nat. Acad. Sci.*, **21**, 549.

HANSTRÖM, B. (1939). "Hormones in Invertebrates." Oxford, O.U.P.

HOGBEN, L. (1942). "Chromatic Behaviour." Croonian Lecture. *Proc. Roy. Soc.*, *B*, **131**, 111.

HOGBEN, L. & KIRK, R. L. (1944). "Relation of Colour Change to Surface Absorption of Radiation." *Proc. Roy. Soc.*, *B*, **132**, 68.

HOGBEN, L. & LANDGREEBE, F. (1940). "Receptor Fields of the Teleostean Visual Response." *Proc. Roy. Soc.*, *B*, **128**, 317.

HOGBEN, L. & SLOME, D. (1931). "Dual Character of Endocrine Co-ordination in Amphibian Colour Change." *Proc. Roy. Soc.*, *B*, **108**, 10.

HOGBEN, L. & SLOME, D. (1936). "Dual Receptive Mechanism of the Amphibian Background Response." *Proc. Roy. Soc.*, *B*, **120**, 158.

HOGBEN, L. & WINTON, F. R. (1922). "The Melanophore Stimulant in Posterior Lobe Extracts." *Biochem. J.*, **16**, 619.

KLEINHOLZ, L. H. (1935). "The Melanophore Dispersing Principle in the Hypophysis of *Fundulus heteroclitus*." *Biol. Bull.*, **69**, 379.

KLEINHOLZ, L. H. (1938). "Pituitary and Adrenal Glands in the Regulation of the Melanophores of *Anolis corolinensis*." *J. exp. Biol.*, **15**, 474.

KLEINHOLZ, L. H. (1938). "Control of the Light Phase and Behaviour of Isolated Skin." *J. exp. Biol.*, **15**, 492.

KROPP, B. (1929). "The Melanophore Activator of the Eye." *Proc. Nat. Acad. Sci.*, **15**, 693.

MARTINI, E. & ACHUNDOW, I. (1929). "Versuche über Farbenanpassung bei Culiciden." *Zool. Anz.*, **81**, 25.

MATTHEWS, S. A. (1931). "Pigment Migration within the Fish Melanophore." *J. exp. Zool.*, **58**, 471.

MILLS, S. M. (1932). "Evidence for a Neurohumoral Control of Fish Melanophores." *J. exp. Zool.*, **64**, 245.

OSBORN, C. M. (1938). "The Role of the Melanophore Dispersing Principle of the Pituitary in the Colour Change of the Catfish." *Biol. Bull.*, **79**, 309.

OSBORN, C. M. (1939). "The Physiology of Colour Changes in Flatfishes." *J. exp. Zool.*, **81**, 479.

PARKER, G. H. (1934). "Cellular Transfer of Substances, especially Neurohumours." *J. exp. Biol.*, **11**, 81.

PARKER, G. H. (1948). "Animal Colour Changes and their Neurohumours." Cambridge, C.U.P.

PARKER, G. H. & ROSENBLUETH, A. (1941). "Electric Stimulation of the Concentrating and Dispersing Nerve Fibres of the Melanophores of the Catfish." *Proc. Nat. Acad. Sci.*, **27**, 198.

PERKINS, E. B. (1928). "Colour Changes in Crustaceans, especially in *Palæmonetes*." *J. exp. Zool.*, **50**, 71.

PERKINS, E. B. & SNOOK, T. (1932). "Movement of Pigment within the Chromatophores of *Palæmonetes*." *J. exp. Zool.*, **61**, 115.

SCHMIDT, W. J. (1920). "U. d. Verhalten der verschiedenartigen Chromatophoren beim Farbwechsel des Laubfrosches." *Arch. Mikr. Anat.*, **93**, 414.

SMITH, H. G. (1938). "Receptor Mechanism of the Background Response in Chromatic Behaviour of Crustacea." *Proc. Roy. Soc.*, *B*, **125**, 249.

STEGGERDA, F. R. & SODENWALL, A. L. (1939). "Relationship of the *pars tuberalis* to Melanophore Response in Amphibia." *J. cell. & comp. Physiol.*, **13**, 31.

STOPPANI, A. O. M. (1942). "Neuroendocrine Mechanism of Colour Change in *Bufo-arenarum*." *Endocrinology*, **30**, 782.

VILTER, V. Quoted by Parker (1948).

WARING, H. (1940). "Chromatic Behaviour of the Eel." *Proc. Roy. Soc.*, *B*, **128**, 343.

ZOOND, A. & EYRE, J. (1934). "Studies on Reptilian Colour Response." *Phil. Trans.*, **223**, 27.

CHAPTER XXI

BIOLUMINESCENCE

In photosynthesis, absorbed light drives a reaction which, in the green plants at least, would not proceed in the absence of this supply of energy, first, because the activation energy of at least one step is too high to permit the reaction to proceed at a measurable speed at ordinary temperatures, and secondly, because the reaction is strongly endothermic. Just as an electric motor, driven in reverse, can produce electricity, so we may expect that certain exothermic chemical reactions can give up their energy of reaction as light. The emission of light during a chemical reaction is, of course, a familiar phenomenon, and represents the return of excited atoms and molecules to their ground states of energy ; but most frequently such emission of light is associated with a high temperature of the reactants, for example the light of a flame from coal gas. In other words, the emission of electronic energy is associated with the liberation of large amounts of vibrational, rotational and kinetic energy. Such luminous reactions take place in the gaseous phase, since the activated molecules must emit their energy before they lose it by inelastic collisions ; and, in solution, this takes place very rapidly. If, however, an activated molecule can keep its energy for a sufficient time without losing it by inelastic collisions, it may give it up as light ; and if the great majority of the activated molecules possess this immunity from loss by collision, the liberation of energy need not be accompanied by any great production of heat, and, moreover, can take place in solution. We have seen that molecules that can retain their activated state for appreciable periods (of the order of 10^{-8} sec.) are fluorescent ; we may therefore expect to find this liberation of " cold light " by molecules that react to form fluorescent compounds.

Chemiluminescence

The existence of chemiluminescence has been recognised for a long time ; thus the " phosphorescence " of phosphorus [1] is due to its slow oxidation ; and a cold flame below room temperature can be obtained by boiling a solution of phosphorus in chloroform under reduced pressure and mixing

---

[1] Phosphorescence, correctly defined, is a delayed fluorescence, the light emitted persisting for some time after the exciting radiation has been cut off (a matter of seconds or more). Many fluorescent compounds can be made to phosphoresce by taking steps to reduce the de-activating collisions, e.g., by dissolving in glycerol and cooling to form a rigid glass. A study of this type of phosphorescence exhibits the presence of two bands ; one, characteristic of the normal fluorescence (the *a-phosphorescence*) and another, of longer wavelength, which is apparently due to the activated molecule having passed to a new activated state of lower energy (the P or *phosphorescent state*) ; on returning to its ground level it emits the longer-wavelength *β-phosphorescence* ; alternatively, if it receives activation energy by collision, it may return to its F, or *fluorescent state* before going to its ground level, in which case the phosphorescence has the shorter wavelength.

the vapour with air. A very large number of organic compounds luminesce on slow oxidation in solution ; we need only mention here the Grignard-reagents which, on oxidation in ethereal solution, may be brightly luminescent ; luminol, aminophthalylhydrazide, on oxidation gives a brilliant luminescence, visible light being detectable at dilutions of the reagent as low as one part in a hundred-million, whilst the quaternary salts of dimethyldiacridylium luminesce in a dilution a hundred times greater than this (1 in 10^{10}). Kautsky showed that siloxene :—

can be made to chemiluminesce with permanganate in solution ; moreover, on addition of a fluorescent dye-stuff to the medium, *e.g.*, rhodamine, the spectral characteristics of the emitted light were identical with those of the fluorescence-spectrum of the dye ; the emission of light by the dye, however, was not a simple fluorescence, resulting from the absorption of light previously emitted by siloxene, but was due to a direct activation of the dye-stuff molecules by the siloxene molecules.[1] Thus, the chemiluminescence of siloxene alone is equivalent to a reversed photo-chemical reaction whilst the *induced* chemiluminescence of the rhodamine is equivalent to a reversed photosensitised reaction.

Luminescent Organisms

The emission of light by living organisms has excited the interest of investigators since the time of Aristotle ; the " phosphorescence " of the sea, the light of the glow-worm, and the flash of the firefly are familiar terms but, to the untravelled town-dweller in England, as remote from his experience as the aurora borealis or tropical storms. Luminescence, however, is a widespread phenomenon, quite apart from these three instances ; it may be observed on a rotting tree-trunk in many woods in consequence of the growth of luminous fungi ; on recently dead fishes on the beach ; on meat,[2] and on many aquatic animals, of which the jelly-fish may be taken as an example. That O_2 was necessary for luminescence was shown by Boyle, as long ago as 1667, in his experiments with the vacuum, but the association of luminosity with microscopical organisms is largely the result of the work of Pflüger, who actually cultured luminous bacteria scraped from dead fish. Altogether, luminescence in some form or other has been described in species belonging to some forty

---

[1] Or rather by the activated oxidation product of siloxene.
[2] Dahlgren refers to reports of glowing sausages hanging up in butchers' shops ; the meat had presumably been preserved with sea-salt containing luminous bacteria.

orders, so that a comprehensive description of the living phenomena is out of the question here ; instead, we may consider some typical examples : the bacteria, a protozoon, a medusa, the much studied ostracod *Cypridina*, the firefly, and several types of fish.

Bacteria. The luminescence of many living marine forms is due to the presence of luminous bacteria, either on their surface or in their blood and tissues[1] ; moreover, the luminesce of dead fish, so commonly observed, is due to saprophytic organisms. The luminous bacteria do not form a definite taxonomic group of their own, but may be found under such diverse classifications as micrococcus, bacillus, pseudomonas, microspira, etc. Most are more or less elongated, exhibiting rapid motion in virtue of their flagella ; they are most commonly found on dead fish, cast on the beach, in which decay has begun a short time before ; in the laboratory many types can be cultured in 1·5 per cent. agar jelly in sea-water containing 2 per cent. peptone, 1 per cent. glycerol and powdered $CaCO_3$, the last being necessary to maintain the pH constant, otherwise the acids formed by metabolism eventually inhibit luminescence. Grown under these conditions, and with a suitable supply of O_2, the emission of light is continuous, the chemical reaction, leading to this, doubtless taking place within the organisms since filtrates from actively luminescent bacteria fail to luminesce. It is of interest to record that Beijerinck, towards the end of the last century, exploited the O_2 requirements of luminous bacteria to establish the liberation of this gas by illuminated chloroplasts ; thus he mixed luminous bacteria with an emulsion of clover chloroplasts in the dark ; when all the O_2 had been used up, the bacteria were extinguished, but immediately started to luminesce again after exposure of the system to light.[2]

Noctiluca Miliaris. The " phosphorescence " of the sea is not ordinarily due to bacteria but to protozoa, of which the cytoflagellate, *Noctiluca miliaris*, is the most widely distributed. Although unicellular, it is about 0·5-1 mm. in diameter. According to the detailed microscopical study of Pratje, the cytoplasm contains numerous droplets which, being soluble in alcohol and staining with Sudan III, are probably lipoid. Quatrefages, in 1850, observed that, under the microscope, the glowing of the organism was generally confined to certain regions ; on increasing the magnification of the microscope he observed that the glow was not uniform but consisted of a large number of discrete bright points ; if the glow or " blush " moved over the surface, this was due to the lighting up of new points and the extinguishing of others in a progressive fashion. *Noctiluca* does not emit light unless stimulated, *e.g.*, by disturbing the sea-water ; and, as with the bacteria, the luminescence is intracellular in that filtrates show no luminescence.

---

[1] Thus the amphipod crustacean, *Talitrus*, glows when it is infected with luminous bacteria ; the infection can be passed from one individual to another, and apparently from one species of crustacean to another. On culturing in an artificial medium the organisms multiply, but do not glow ; on transferring the cultured bacteria to a *Talitrus*, however, they at once glow.

[2] Harvey used the same test to demonstrate the *absence* of evolution of O_2 by illuminated photosynthetic sulphur bacteria. The minimum tension of O_2 for luminescence of bacteria is of the order of 0·005 mm. Hg.

PLATE XV

Fig. 269. *Pelagia noctiluca.* (Dahlgren. *J. Franklin Inst.*)

Fig. 273. Photograph of *Porichthys notatus* to show relative size and distribution of the photophores visible from the ventral view. (Greene & Greene. *Amer. J. Physiol.*)

Pelagia Noctiluca. The most typical luminous coelenterate is the jelly-fish, *Pelagia noctiluca,* common on the shores of the Mediterranean (Fig. 269, Pl. XV). It has the typical jelly-fish form and swims by a series of rhythmic contractions of its umbrella. For the emission of light, a definite stimulus is necessary ; for example, a slight touch with a glass rod produces at first a local glow which spreads by the same nervous influences as those that are responsible for the rhythmic contractions. Increasing the strength of the stimulus increases the area of the luminous region ; and, with a sufficiently strong excitation, the whole animal glows brightly. In contrast to the forms so far studied, the luminescence is induced by the secretion of material on to the surface, so that touching with the finger causes the latter to glow. Fig. 270 illustrates a portion of a section through

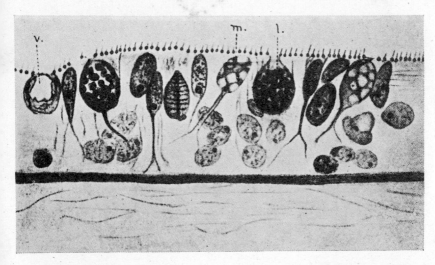

Fig. 270. Portion of a section of the ex-umbrella surface of *Pelagia noctiluca,* showing several kinds of cell. *l,* luminous cells ; *m,* mucin-secreting cells ; *v,* empty cells from which the luciferin has been discharged. (Dahlgren. *J. Franklin Inst.*)

the umbrella surface ; as with all coelenterates, the epithelium consists of a variety of cells with different functions ; it is thought that the highly granular cells, *l,* secrete the material which subsequently luminesces on the surface. *Pelagia* exhibits a diurnal rhythm in its sensitivity to stimuli, responding in the early evening but not during the day ; it would appear, therefore, that light acts as an inhibiting stimulus. The studies of Heymans & Moore on the effects of varying the salt content of the medium bring out the importance of the nervous mechanism in the control of luminescence ; thus, the omission of Ca^{++} or K^+ from the sea-water confined the effects of a stimulus to a local glow, whilst the omission of Mg^{++} caused hyperirritability both in respect to contraction of the umbrella and to luminescence, flashes appearing spontaneously and the smallest stimulus causing the whole body to break into light.

Cypridina. Of the crustaceans, this ostracod may be singled out since, owing to its abundance, its luminous secretion has been very thoroughly studied, from the biochemical viewpoint. It is only one-eighth of an inch long, covered by a hinged chitinous shell which almost hides its swimming legs ; the luminous organ may be likened to a gland which opens on to the surface of the body near the mouth by way of several ducts. According to Okada the gland of *Cypridina hilgendorfii* contains four types of cells, each group opening into a different duct. One type, common to all ostracods, contains large yellow granules some 10μ in diameter ; there are two other types of granular cell—the granules being very much smaller—and mucous cells. The gland or organ is invested with muscle fibres which, on contraction, apparently extrude the cellular secretions. According to Dahlgren, the luminous organ of the related ostracod, *Pyrocypris*, consists of an invaginated reservoir, opening through the

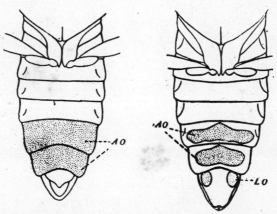

Fig. 271. Illustrating positions of light-organs in the firefly. Left : Adult male, ventral view of abdomen. *AO*, adult light-organ, located on the sixth and seventh abdominal segments. Right : Adult female taken immediately after emergence, ventral view of abdomen. *AO*, adult light-organ ; *LO*, larval light-organ. (Hess. *J. Morph.*)

upper lip by several ducts, whilst the gland proper, made up of two types of cell, secretes into this reservoir, the muscle expelling the secretion out of the reservoir along the ducts. Luminescence takes place when the secretion is mixed with sea-water.

The Firefly. The firefly is an example of an organism containing a definite *light-organ* which may be activated by nervous influences to emit a bright flash of light, the luminescence being intracellular. In the male, the organ occupies the whole ventral surface of the 6th and 7th segments, whilst in the female only about two-thirds of these segments are occupied (Fig. 271). The structure of the organ is shown in Fig. 272 ; essentially it consists of two layers, reflecting and photogenic. The cells of the former contain crystals of some urate which give the layer a reflecting property, whilst the latter is made up of large cells filled with yellow granules. An adequate supply of O_2 is ensured by the numerous tracheæ which penetrate both layers and branch profusely in the photogenic layer ; each branch ends in a *tracheal cell* which gives rise to tracheal capillaries, or *tracheoles*, which enter the cells. The photogenic layer is overlaid on the ventral side by a layer of hypodermal cells which secrete a non-pigmented cuticle.

The control of the emission of light seems to be exercised by regulation of the supply of O_2 to the photogenic cells through the tracheoles. Thus Snell examined the luminescence under low partial pressures of O_2 ; if flies are maintained at about 4 mm. Hg, the O_2-regulating mechanism seems to fail and the flies become continuously luminescent. Suddenly

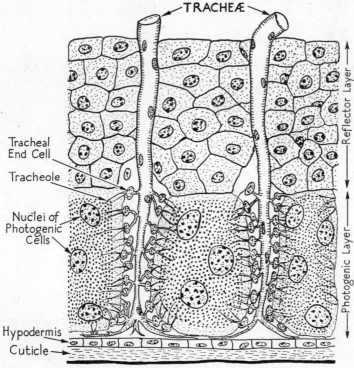

FIG. 272. Structure of firefly light-organ.
(After Hess. *J. Morph.*)

raising the O_2-tension causes a very brilliant flash, whilst decreasing the pressure below 4 mm. Hg extinguishes the glow. If the flies, under water, are subjected to a reduced pressure, followed by a return to normal, the tracheal system is filled with water ; in consequence, no glow takes place at low O_2-tensions, and there is no sudden flash on raising this tension. It was suggested by Dahlgren that the tracheal end-cells were contractile and actively pumped air into the terminal tracheoles ; certainly the nerve fibres seem to end at these cells.

The significance of the flashing of the firefly, *Photinus pyralis*, has been elucidated by the studies of Buck, among others. The female is wingless,[1]

---

[1] The glow-worm is a wingless female or a larva.

and in the evening perches on a blade of grass whilst the males, who during the day remain quiescent, fly about emitting flashes. The female never flashes spontaneously, but only in response to the flash of a male within some 3–4 metres ; if the female makes this response, the male immediately turns directly towards her and flashes again ; the female flashes in response, and after about five of these exchanges the insects mate. The ability of the male fly to distinguish a flash, emitted by a female, from one emitted by a male is not due to any difference in the spectral quality of the light emitted by the two sexes, but depends entirely on the interval elapsing between his own flash and the answering one. If this is precisely two seconds, the male responds to it, whereas he ignores any flashes not occurring at other intervals after his own ; thus Buck was able to attract males to a torch by flashing it exactly two seconds after the appearance of a flash, or alternatively, by squeezing a male (which makes him emit a flash) just two seconds after seeing a flash. The diurnal rhythm of the firefly was also investigated by Buck ; as indicated above, the flies only become active in twilight ; about 9 p.m., with the onset of darkness, they become quiescent again till the next evening. In the laboratory, a change from bright light to darkness induced flashing ; also, the change from dim light to darkness caused a temporary increase in frequency of flashing ; these effects of sudden changes of illumination could be produced at any time of the day. Fireflies maintained in continuous dim light flashed spontaneously when the sum of the time spent in dim light and that previously spent in darkness was 24 hours ; moreover, a change from darkness to dim illumination induced flashing provided the firefly had previously been in darkness for 24, 48, 72, or 96 hours, but not for 12, 36, 60, and 84 hours. The exact interpretation of these results is difficult, but it is clear that there is an inherent periodicity, manifested in phases of flashing which recur at 24-hourly intervals ; superimposed on this, however, there seems to be a response to sudden changes of illumination.

Fishes. The Californian singing fish,[1] *Porichthys notatus*, is an example of a luminous vertebrate, its ventral surface containing some 840 small organs, *photophores*, which emit light to produce a definite pattern on the body (Fig. 273, Pl. XV). The luminescence takes place within the photophores, a section through one being illustrated in Fig. 274. The epidermis of the fish has no scales and is well supplied with mucous cells ; the dermis is a thick vascularised layer of connective tissue in which the organ is embedded. From within outwards it consists of a *reflector*, a *gland*, and a *lens*. The reflector is made up of connective tissue, the matrix of which is modified into fine spicules which reflect light strongly ; blood vessels pass through on their way to the gland which is a shallow cup of granular cells ; the lens is avascular. Thus the photophore exhibits the main features of an eye, but its function is to emit, instead of to receive, light. Histological study failed to reveal any definite nerve supply to the organ, and Greene concluded that it was controlled by a humoral

---

[1] This animal makes a noise by compressing its air-sac, the diaphragm separating its two compartments being set in vibration by the unequal pressures generated.

mechanism. Mechanical stimulation does not usually cause luminescence ; with powerful electrical stimulation, on the other hand, all the photophores light up and, if the fish is held some ten to twelve inches from the face in complete darkness, the features of the person holding it may be recognised. Since, with a 2 sec. tetanic stimulus, the latent period is about 8–10 sec., it is possible that the nervous discharge liberates a hormone which subsequently acts on the photophores ; Greene found that a subcutaneous injection of adrenaline was followed by luminescence, the number of

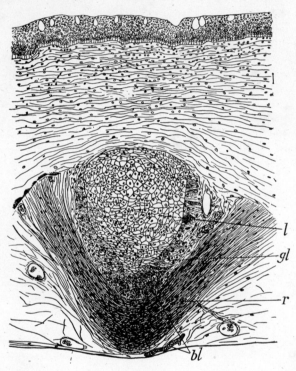

Fig. 274. Section through photophore of *Porichthys notatus*. *l*, lens ; *gl*, gland ; *r*, reflector ; *bl*, blood vessels. (Greene. *J. Morph.*)

activated photophores increasing progressively until, in about ten minutes, the whole animal was alight and remained thus for longer than an hour.

A perfect example of symbiosis is provided by the East Indian fishes *Photoblepharon palpebratus* and *Anomalops katoptron* ; these have a large white organ just under each eye which may be concealed at will either by drawing a fold of black tissue over it, in the case of *Photoblepharon*, or by turning the whole organ over and downwards into a groove so that the white surface is not exposed. The organ consists of rows of tubes, well supplied with capillaries ; the tubes are filled with a mass of bacteria which luminesce continuously so long as they are adequately supplied with O_2 ; these organisms may be grown in an artificial medium but fail to luminesce under these conditions. Unlike the majority of luminous fishes, *Photoblepharon* and *Anomalops* frequent shallow water, consequently their luminous organs are of value only at night and are presumably of use in recognition.

The Significance of Luminescence

The value of luminescence to the organism is sometimes obvious from its behaviour and habitat, but sometimes obscure. The amount of light penetrating to depths greater than about 300 fathoms is insufficient to stimulate the human eye ; nevertheless, a great many deep-sea fishes have well-developed eyes, so that it is very probable that luminescence plays an important role in the recognition of the sexes, in attracting prey, or blinding an enemy, at these depths. In nocturnal animals and insects the same functions are apparent in shallow water or on land ; thus the value of luminescence as a mating signal in the firefly has already been described ; in the marine worm, *Odontosyllis enopia*, the sexual function is again well illustrated ; the female suddenly becomes acutely phosphorescent, and swims rapidly through the water in small luminous circles ; around this circle is a halo of luminescence, probably due to luminous eggs. If the male does not appear, the illumination ceases after some 10–20 sec., but the performance is repeated several times. The male appears as a delicate glint of light about 10–15 ft. from the luminous female, and when he has located her they rotate together in spirals, scattering sperm and eggs in the water. The luminosity of the polynoid worm, *Achola astericola*, is under control, and is used as a sacrificial lure ; if the worm is cut in two parts, for example by a crab, the posterior part lights up and wriggles, whilst the anterior part remains dark and seeks concealment. The use of light for protection, much as the squid uses its ink, is illustrated by the organ of the fish *Malæocephalus lævis*, studied by Hickley ; the gland consists of an invagination of the surface epithelium, and it opens around the anus ; muscle fibres, on contraction, squeeze out the secretion which, in contact with sea-water, luminesces brightly for a long time. Hickley thinks that the fish uses its light to blind an attacking fish. Finally, an apparently useless luminescence is exhibited by the annelid worm, *Chætopterus*. It lives in the sand and mud, between low water and 5 fathoms, in a tough parchment-like U-shaped tube secreted by its own integument ; the ends of the tube project into the water, and a current—the respiratory stream—is forced through the tube by means of three flat paddles in its middle. It is one of the most luminescent of animals but, as it never comes out of its tube, it is very difficult to see why it should luminesce.

Biochemistry of Luminescence

Luciferin-Luciferase System. We may now pass to the biochemical aspects of luminescence, studied intensively by Newton Harvey and his school at Princeton, and Kluyver & Schouwenburg in Holland, over many years ; as we shall see, however, the exact nature of the chemical reaction leading to luminescence remains a baffling secret. Biochemical studies have been largely confined to the extract obtainable from the osctracod, *Cypridina*, although a fair amount of work has also been done on the luminous bacteria. As long ago as 1885 Dubois postulated that the essential feature of luminescence was the oxidation of a substance, *luciferin* —the constituent of the coloured granules of photogenic cells—by means of an enzyme, *luciferase*. Thus on boiling a luminous organ, and then adding fresh organ to it, the boiled organ was able to luminesce, the enzyme, luciferase, being destroyed by the boiling whilst the luciferin was not. More recent work has confirmed in general outlines this resolution of the reactants into an enzyme, of a protein nature—and therefore purified by prolonged dialysis in a collodion sac—and a substrate, luciferin, a substance of comparatively low molecular weight which is separated from the enzyme during dialysis. The fact that the secretions of *Cypridina*, and of many other organs, only luminesce when extruded into sea-water, and the fact that extracts always require the presence of O_2 to produce luminescence,[1] suggest that luciferin and luciferase are secreted as granules, their subsequent dissolution in water permitting the oxidative reaction. That the breakdown of the granules is an important element in luminescence is shown by the fact that many cytolytic agents, such as saponin, increase luminescence ; for example, the luminous slime from *Pholas*, allowed to stand until its light disappears, lights again on the addition of saponin which liberates luciferin from the remaining granules, the enzyme luciferase being still present. The observations of Hickley on the secretion of the fish *Malæocephalus lævis* are of some interest in this connection. Histological studies have shown that the secreting cells accumulate granules, and that secretion is accompanied by the complete breakdown of the cells, in marked contrast to the behaviour of secreting cells in other glands. The secretion is thus a mass of granules, but these are clumped together in globes some 30–40μ in diameter and apparently covered with a cytoplasmic sheath. In sea-water these globes break up rapidly to give granules about 1–2μ long, with a greenish fluorescence. It is a common observation that in distilled water the photogenic secretions are not luminous ; and Hickley observed that, in the case of *M. lævis*, the globes failed to break up in this medium ; the envelopes disintegrated, but the granules remained clumped. If sea-water was added immediately, the luminescence appeared, but only if less than three minutes elapsed ; it would seem that the deleterious effect of distilled water is due to its stabilisation of the granular clumps, in much the same way that salt-free solutions cause the agglutination of many cells.

It is clearly impossible to generalise widely on the mechanism of luminescence, even supposing that a luciferin-luciferase system is involved in all examples ; with some glands it seems certain that the enzyme and substrate are secreted by separate types of cell, only the combined secretions

[1] An exception to this rule is provided by extracts of the luminous ctenophore (comb-jelly) *Mnemiopsis Leidyi* ; Harvey showed that the extract was luminous in the presence of nascent H_2, and concluded from his experiments that some " bound O_2 " was present, which was liberated by the appropriate stimulus. The inhibitory action of light, observed in this organism, could then be due to photodynamic oxidation ; the fact that light-exposed ctenophores cannot regain the power to luminesce in the absence of O_2 certainly indicates that storage of O_2, probably as a loosely bound complex similar to oxyhæmoglobin, is a characteristic feature of this luminous secretion.

possessing the potentiality for luminescence ; in others it may well be that both are secreted by the same cell, in which case the dissolution of the granules, and the aerobic conditions in sea-water, allow the luminescence to proceed. With intracellular luminescence, as in bacteria and photophores both enzyme and substrate must be present in the same cell ; the bacteria luminesce continuously, but in the case of the photophore we must seek some mechanism which prevents the reaction from proceeding.

Purification of Luciferin. The purification of luciferin was first undertaken in 1935 by Anderson, who extracted *Cypridina* with methyl alcohol in the absence of O_2 and submitted the extract to repeated benzoylation and hydrolysis. In this way a product some 2,000 times as active (per gramme of dry weight) as the original material was obtained. It is a yellow material but is apparently not a carotenoid. It behaves as a compound of relatively low molecular weight, and the fact that it could be prepared by benzoylation suggested to Anderson that it was a polyhydroxybenzene derivative.[1] Later Chakravorty & Ballentine established the presence of a ketohydroxy side-chain : $R.CO.CH_2OH$, and a hydroquinone ring, probably either anthraquinone or naphthaquinone. Various other suggestions have been made regarding the chemical structure of luciferin, for example the Dutch workers Eymers and Van Schouwenburg, from their analyses of the energy-distribution of the emitted light, have suggested that luciferin may be a flavine derivative, *i.e.*, related to vitamin B_1 (fireflies certainly contain large amounts of riboflavine), whilst Kluyver suggests that it is 1-4-dihydroxynaphthyl-2-hydroxymethyl ketone. However, Harvey and his colleagues have added this substance, and a large number of closely related substances, to *Cypridina* luciferase and have failed to observe luminescence.

The enzyme luciferase is apparently a protein ; it is non-dialysable, is destroyed by trypsin and can produce antibodies when injected into a rabbit.

The Activated Molecule. The importance of the enzyme in the *luminescence* is exhibited by the finding that luciferin may be oxidised by a variety of oxidising agents, or even by atmospheric O_2, without producing any light. For example, the addition of ferricyanide to a luciferin-luciferase system immediately quenches the light, because the luciferin is now oxidised by this reagent ; addition of hydrosulphite causes the reappearance of luminescence, proving that this oxidation is reversible. Thus, as Harvey suggested, the light-emitting molecule may very well be the luciferase itself, in accordance with the hypothetical reaction :—

$$\text{Luciferin} + \tfrac{1}{2}O_2 \rightarrow \text{Oxyluciferin} * + H_2O$$
$$\text{Luciferin} * + \text{Luciferase} \rightarrow \text{Luciferin} + \text{Luciferase} *$$
$$\text{Luciferase} * \rightarrow \text{Luciferase} + h\nu$$

or, even more simply :—

$$\text{Luciferin} + \text{Luciferase} + O_2 \rightarrow \text{Oxyluciferin} + \text{Luciferase} *$$
$$\text{Luciferase} * \rightarrow \text{Luciferase} + h\nu$$

[1] Chase & Gregg have recently shown that nitrogen is a constituent of the preparation purified according to Anderson's procedure ; there is as much as 8 per cent. present.

the energy liberated by the oxidation of luciferin being transferred to the catalyst at the moment of reaction.

We may therefore distinguish two general possibilities for the mechanism of luminescence ; first, that the emitting molecule is an activated oxidation product of luciferin (a view favoured by the Dutch workers), and second, that the enzyme, luciferase, is the emitting molecule. Evidence bearing on this point is provided by some work of Harvey on the colours of different luminescences. To the naked eye, the colours of the light emitted by different organisms are often easily distinguishable ; for example, the yellowish flash of the firefly, *Photuris*, is recognisably different from the more reddish signal of *Photinus* ; these differences are revealed by the curves showing the spectral distribution of energy in the luminescences, *i.e.*, the curve obtained by plotting the relative energies in the different wavelengths against the respective wavelengths. The early work of Ives showed that the light of *Photinus* extended from 5,100 to 6,700A, *i.e.*, from the blue-green to the red, whilst Coblentz' analysis of the light of *Photuris* indicated a more limited range, from 5,100 to 5,900A. Harvey (1924) studied the effects of different combinations of luciferin and luciferase from two different species of *Cypridina* ; the Japanese ostracod, *Cypridina hilgendorfii*, gives a bluish light, whilst the Jamaican species gives a yellow light ; the results of these different combinations are shown in Table XLI.

TABLE **XLI**

Effects of Different Combinations of Luciferin and Luciferase
(Harvey, 1924).

Luciferase	Luciferin	Colour
Japanese	Japanese	Bluish
Japanese	Jamaican	Bluish
Jamaican	Jamaican	Yellowish
Jamaican	Japanese	Yellowish

Clearly, the colour of the luminescence is determined by the luciferase ; if the enzyme consisted of a protein carrier with a chromophore group, the different luciferases could then be due to differing chromophore groups. The observation that the spectral quality of the luminescence may change according to the conditions of growth of luminous bacteria, *e.g.*, by Dubois, could be interpreted on the assumption that there are at least two types of luciferase in the same bacteria, and that the relative amounts change ; Harvey's finding (1924) that a rise in temperature tends to lengthen the wavelength of the emitted radiation could also be explained on this basis, the rise in temperature changing the relative contributions of the two or more luciferases. The same facts could, however, be explained in accordance with the other viewpoint, the different colours being due to varying chemical reactions undergone by the same luciferin, the different luciferases catalysing different reactions.

Strehler & McElroy, however, sound a warning note on these cross-reactions ; it may well be that the luciferase of the one species contains an appreciable amount of luciferin of the same species (as an impurity) ; in the absence of ATP this combination would fail to luminesce (p. 616). The luciferin preparation of the other species would certainly contain ATP, and thus cause luminescence independently of its luciferin content. If this is true, the luminescence need not be characteristic of the luciferase.

Spectral Distribution of Energy. Eymers and Van Schouwenburg have analysed the spectral distribution of energy in the light emitted by *Photobacterium phosphoreum* ; by plotting their curve on a frequency, as opposed to a wavelength, basis, they claim that it can be resolved into two components with " fundamental frequencies " of 18,200 and 20,300 cm.$^{-1}$, corresponding to wavelengths of 5,550 and 4,950A. From an analysis of the published results on the emissions of a number of firefly organs, they conclude, furthermore, that there is a " fundamental

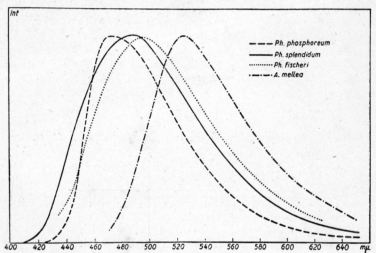

Fig. 275. Emission spectra of luminous bacteria. Ordinates : Relative energy. Abscissæ : Wavelength. (Van der Burg. *Biochim. Biophys. Acta.*)

frequency " common to them all, namely 17,600 cm.$^{-1}$. This analysis, as the authors themselves point out, is difficult to justify theoretically,[1] and Van der Burg has dismissed it as being entirely unsound ; some energy distribution curves for a number of species of luminous bacteria, determined by Van der Burg, are shown in Fig. 275.

Non-Luminescent Oxidation of Luciferin. The observation of Harvey

[1] The prime assumption is that the light emitted is due to an electronic transition uncomplicated by vibrational-rotational changes, the broadening of the emission line being due to the influence of the solvent, an effect which would be symmetrical. We may note that the fundamental frequencies are expressed in *wave-numbers*, $\bar{\nu}$, related to the true frequencies, ν, by the equation : $\bar{\ } = \dfrac{\nu}{c}$, where c is the velocity of light (2·9977.10^{10} cm./sec.) ; λ, the wavelength, is given by : $c = \nu\lambda$, whence $\bar{\nu} = 1/\lambda$, *i.e.*, its units are cm.$^{-1}$.

that *Cypridina* extracts, which had finished luminescing, could be made to luminesce again after the addition of a reducing agent suggested that the chemiluminescent reaction was reversible; however, Anderson showed that it is only the non-luminous form of oxidation that produces a reversible oxidation product, the true luminescent reaction being irreversible; the fact that *Cypridina* extracts become luminescent on addition of reducing agents means simply that, in ordinary circumstances, a part of the luciferin is always oxidised reversibly, *i.e.*, without emission of light. Treating *Cypridina* luciferin with steadily rising concentrations of ferricyanide progressively modifies the response on mixing with luciferase. Without ferricyanide treatment, the emission rapidly develops

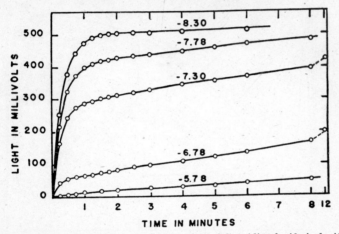

Fig. 276. Course of the luminescent reaction of *Cypridina* luciferin-luciferase system, after preliminary exposure of the luciferin to various concentrations of ferricyanide before adding the luciferase. The logarithms of the ferricyanide concentrations are shown on the curves. With the lowest concentration, practically all the light is emitted during the first 1·5 min., with almost no ensuing dim light emission. With the highest concentration, no rapidly emitted light occurs, but only slow, dim luminescence. The rapid, bright type of luminescence is due to the luciferin that has not combined with ferricyanide. (Chase. *J. cell. & comp. Physiol.*)

its maximum intensity and then falls; but, as the concentration of ferricyanide is raised, the rapid emission becomes smaller whilst a slower emission follows. Thus, in Fig. 276, from the more recent work of Chase (1949), the total light emitted (determined by a rapidly recording photoelectric device) is plotted against time; with the lowest concentration of ferricyanide, practically all the light was emitted in the first 1·5 min., whilst with the highest concentration there was only a slow emission. Presumably the slow emission is determined by the time taken for the reversibly oxidised luciferin to be reduced by the bacteria, in which condition it can be oxidised by the irreversible luciferin-luciferase reaction with the emission of light.[1]

[1] Chase utilised this reaction to make a rough approximation to the molecular weight of luciferin; assuming that 1 mole of ferricyanide reacted with 1 mole of luciferin, from his finding that $1·3.10^{-6}$ g. of the former were required to oxidise $1·8.10^{-6}$ g. of the latter,

Kinetics of the Flash. The elucidation of the mechanism of bioluminescence must clearly await the preparation, and chemical identification, of luciferin and its oxidation products ; nevertheless, as with photosynthesis, some progress has been made with the aid of a study of the kinetics of the process, *i.e.*, of the development and decay of the luminescent flash obtained, either by mixing *Cypridina* luciferin with luciferase in the presence of O_2, or by admitting O_2 to a suspension of bacteria maintained under anaerobic conditions. Variations in the kinetics induced by changes of temperature, addition of narcotics or cyanide, alterations in the O_2-tension or the substrate of bacteria, and of many other factors have been studied by both the American and Dutch

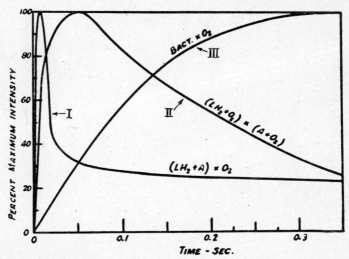

F<small>IG</small>. 277. Development of luminescence by *Cypridina* luciferin-luciferase system (I and II) and by a bacterial suspension (III). Intensities are adjusted to give the same peak values. I. Effect of admitting O_2 to a luciferin-luciferase mixture. II. Effect of mixing oxygenated luciferin with oxygenated luciferase. III. Effect of admitting O_2 to a bacterial suspension—the *bacterial flash*. (Chance, Harvey, Johnson & Millikan. *J. cell. & comp. Physiol.*)

schools ; space will not permit anything more than a brief description of the results of just one or two of these studies. If a mixture of luciferin and luciferase is suddenly oxygenated, the development and decay of luminescence follow the curve shown in Fig. 277 (Curve I), taken from the work of Chance, Harvey, Johnson & Millikan ; the peak intensity is reached in 8 msec., and the decay is at first rapid, slowing down later. If, on the other hand, oxygenated luciferin and luciferase solutions are mixed, the Curve II of Fig. 277 is obtained, the rise in intensity being only about a third as fast, and the decay being continuous. Variations in the

he computed a molecular weight of 450 ; since the luciferin was doubtless not pure, the molecular weight was less than this. According to Chase (1940, 1943), the changes in the absorption spectrum of luciferin during the luminescent and non-luminescent reactions are the same ; the luminescent reaction is some 100 times faster than the reversible oxidation.

luciferase concentration had no effect on the development of the flash, but diminishing the concentration decreased the rate of decay ; changes in luciferin concentration had no effect on the rate of rise. Within a wide range of O_2-tension the kinetics were unaffected by variation of this factor. According to Chance and his colleagues, the minimal number of steps in the luminescent process, which must be postulated to explain these phenomena, are four, as follows :—

(1) $LH_2 + A \rightarrow A.LH_2$ (Luciferin + luciferase to give complex).
(2) $A.LH_2 + \frac{1}{2} O_2 \rightarrow A.LH_2O$.
(3) $A.LH_2.O \rightarrow A^* + L + H_2O$.
(4) $A^* \rightarrow A + h\nu$.

Thus the finding that preliminary mixing of luciferin and luciferase, before the admission of O_2, greatly accelerates the development of light demands that reaction (1) should be relatively slow ; the independence of

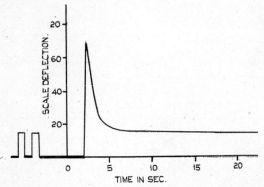

Fig. 278. Photoelectric record of the flash obtained by admitting O_2 to a bacterial suspension. Deflections at left show the initial light intensity of the suspension. (After Johnson, Van Schouwenburg & Van der Burg. *Enzymologia*.)

O_2-tension demands that (2) should be virtually instantaneous, but the observation that the development of light requires a measurable time, even when LH_2 and A have been mixed, suggests the existence of a two-stage breakdown process of $A.LH_2O$ to give reactions (3) and (4). Results of experiments on the bacterium, *Achromobacter fisheri* carried out at the same time, and subsequent studies by Schoepfle, could be interpreted on the same scheme ; as Curve III of Fig. 277 shows, however, the whole process is much slower, the time to reach the peak being about 1/3 sec.

Van Schouwenburg studied luminous bacteria exclusively ; if these are maintained under poorly aerated conditions the luminescence begins to fail ; admission of O_2 then produces a " flash "— an increase in the luminescence which attains an intensity several times greater than that of the normal continuous glow under well aerated conditions (Fig. 278). Presumably, under the anaerobic conditions, luciferin has accumulated in a higher than normal concentration ; after the flash, as Fig. 278 shows, the luminescence settles down to its steady value. Harvey was the first to study the bacterial flash, and he stated that its intensity was independent of the duration of the preliminary period of anaerobiosis ; however, Johnson, Van Schouwenburg & Van der Burg showed that, if this period is extended beyond about twenty minutes, the intensity of the flash decreases ; if, on the other hand, glucose is added to the medium, this loss of intensity does not occur except when very long periods of anaerobiosis are concerned. Glucose seems thus to be important for the accumulation of luciferin, if it is assumed that this is the cause of the flash. Studies of the effects of other substrates showed that so long as the substance could be utilised in the absence of O_2, *e.g.*, pyruvate, it increased the intensity of the flash. These results, and the effects of various enzyme inhibitors, such as carbon monoxide, cyanide, urethane, etc., led Johnson and Van Schouwenburg to the following scheme for the chemiluminescent reaction :—

(1) $L + XH_2 \rightleftharpoons LH_2 + X.$

(2) $A + LH_2 \rightleftharpoons ALH_2.$

(3) $A.LH_2 + \frac{1}{2}O_2 \rightarrow A + L + H_2O + h\nu.$

(4) $A \rightleftharpoons nB.$

XH_2 is a hydrogen-donor, *e.g.*, glucose, necessary to convert the reversibly oxidised luciferin to the reduced form, LH_2, which is capable of reacting with luciferase to give luminescence. The final reaction is introduced to account for an apparent breakdown of the catalyst. The advantage of this scheme is that it takes into account the fact that luciferin (LH_2) is always oxidised to some extent by the reversible, non-luminous, reaction to give an oxidised product, L ; thus the amount of LH_2 (reduced luciferin) present in bacteria depends on the rapidity with which reaction (1) goes to the right. It would be idle to follow these speculations further at the present time ; as indicated above, real progress can only be made on the basis of a knowledge of the chemical structure of luciferin and a decision as to which is the emitting molecule, luciferase or an oxidation product of luciferin.[1]

Involvement of ATP in Luminescence

McElroy and his colleagues have studied the firefly luciferin-luciferase system and done much to clarify the reactions ; they have confirmed the existence of a non-dialysable component in the lantern of this organism, the enzyme luciferase. They have shown, however, that the dialysable material, hitherto given the name luciferin and considered to be a single entity, consists of at least three components : ATP ; a bivalent ion such as Mg^{++}, Mn^{++}, or Co^{++} ; and a compound which may be called luciferin ; this was purified by chromatography (Strehler & McElroy) and gave a yellow-green fluorescence at pH greater than $7 \cdot 0$. The importance of this

---

[1] Those who wish to pursue this aspect of the subject further can most profitably read a paper by Johnson, Eyring, Steblay, Chaplin, Huber & Gherardi (1945) in which a complex subject is handled by authors competent in the modern theory of absolute reaction rates ; with some reason these authors abandon the notion that luciferase is the excited molecule, mainly as a result of Chase's study of the absorption spectrum of purified extracts (1943).

discovery can hardly be over-estimated, firstly because it may require a re-evaluation of a great deal of work involving the addition of a " luciferin solution " to a luciferase preparation, since the " luciferin solution " may have contained varying amounts of the three components necessary for luminescence. Secondly, the establishment of the necessity for ATP in the luminescent reaction immediately brings the latter into relation with the carbohydrate metabolism of the organism (p. 501). Thus McElroy & Ballentine have shown that the luciferin preparation contains organic phosphate and that the luminescent reaction is associated with the release of inorganic phosphate. They suggest that the luciferin molecule undergoes the following series of reactions :—

$$R.CO.CH_2OH \rightarrow R.CO.CHO + 2\,H$$
$$R.CO.CHO + H_2O \rightarrow R.CO.COOH + 2\,H$$
$$R.CO.COOH \rightarrow R.CHO + CO_2$$
$$R.CHO + H_2O \rightarrow R.COOH + 2\,H$$

i.e., essentially the reverse of those postulated by Ruben for photosynthesis. It is considered that the energy liberated by the reactions may be stored as " phosphate-bond energy."

Quantum Efficiency. The quantum efficiency of the luminescence of bacteria is of some interest. The most recent estimate is that of Eymers & Van Schouwenburg ; from a study of the inhibition of respiration of *Photobacterium phosphoreum* they conclude that only 18 per cent. of the total O_2-consumption is concerned in the light-emitting reaction ; making use of this figure, they compute that at $16°$ C. some 450 molecules of O_2 are consumed per quantum of light emitted. These authors conclude that this light-emitting reaction is insensitive to cyanide, the inhibition of luminescence by this poison being attributable to its effects on the general vegetative metabolism of the bacteria, effects which influence the amount of luciferin present ; they suggest, in consequence, that the enzyme concerned in bacterial luminescence is of the flavine type, a substance whose fluorescence has characteristics in common with the bacterial luminescence.

Inhibition by Light

The effects of light on the luciferin-luciferase system have come in for study, since at one time it was thought that many types of luminescence were inhibited by irradiation of the intact organism. Harvey's early studies indicated that light of wavelengths between 4,600 and 3,800A, *i.e.*, between the blue and near ultra-violet, inactivated luciferin in the presence of O_2 ; longer wavelengths could be made active in the presence of a dye such as methylene blue ; the action was thus typical of the photodynamic action discussed earlier, the coloured impurities being responsible for absorption of light in the absence of a dye. Chase & Giese worked on purified preparations and showed that luciferin can only be inactivated by wavelengths less than 2,800A ; inhibition could only be effected with visible light on addition of photosensitising dyes such as eosin or riboflavine [1] or by adding crude *Cypridina* extracts. Luciferase was even less sensitive, only the far ultra-violet being active, and photo-dynamic action not being observed. The inactivation of luciferin is apparently due to a reversible oxidation of the type described by Anderson (p. 613), since partial inactivation by light resulted in the dual type of luminescence—an initial bright flash due to the remaining luciferin, and a longer glow associated with the gradual reversal of the oxidised to the reduced form.

[1] Chase suggests that purification of luciferase by dialysis leads to the loss of riboflavine ; thus the dialysate has maximal absorption at 3,600 and 4,500A, probably due to free flavine.

References

ANDERSON, R. S. (1933). " Quantitative Determination of Luciferin." *J. cell. & comp. Physiol.*, **3**, 45.

ANDERSON, R. S. (1935). " The Partial Purification of *Cypridina* Luciferin." *J. gen. Physiol.*, **19**, 301.

ANDERSON, R. S. (1936). " The Reversible Reaction of *Cypridina* Luciferin ; its Relation to the Luminescent Reaction." *J. cell. & comp. Physiol.*, **8**, 261.

BUCK, J. B. (1937). " The Effect of Light and other Agents on Flashing in *Photinus pyralis*, with Special Reference to Periodicity and Diurnal Rhythm." *Physiol. Zool.*, **10**, 45.

BUCK, J. B. (1937). " Signal System and Colour Vision in *Photinus pyralis*." *Physiol. Zool.*, **10**, 412.

CHAKROVORTY, P. N. & BALLENTINE, R. (1941). " On the Luminescent Oxidation of Luciferin." *J.A.C.S.*, **63**, 2030.

CHANCE, B., HARVEY, E. N., JOHNSON, F. & MILLIKAN, G. (1940). " Kinetics of Bioluminescent Flashes." *J. cell. & comp. Physiol.*, **15**, 195.

CHASE, A. M. (1940). " Riboflavin and the Photochemical Oxidation of *Cypridina* Luciferin." *Amer. J. Physiol.*, **129**, 332.

CHASE, A. M. (1940). " Changes in the Absorption Spectrum of *Cypridina* Luciferin Solutions during Oxidation." *J. cell. & comp. Physiol.*, **15**, 159.

CHASE, A. M. (1943). " The Absorption Spectrum of Luciferin and Oxidised Luciferin." *J. Biol. Chem.*, **150**, 433.

CHASE, A. M. (1948). " Effects of pH, etc., on Luminescence of *Cypridina* Luciferin-Luciferase Reaction." *J. cell. & comp. Physiol.*, **31**, 175.

CHASE, A. M. (1949). " Effect of Ferricyanide on the Reaction of *Cypridina* Luciferin and Luciferase, and the Combining Weight of Luciferin." *J. cell. & comp. Physiol.*, **33**, 113.

CHASE, A. M. & GIESE, A. G. (1940). "Effects of Ultra-violet Radiation on *Cypridina* Luciferin and Luciferase." *J. cell. & comp. Physiol.*, **16**, 323.

CHASE, A. M. & GREGG, J. H. (1949). " Analysis of *Cypridina* Luciferin for Nitrogen." *J. cell. & comp. Physiol.*, **33**, 67.

DAHLGREN, U. (1915–17). " The Production of Light by Animals." *J. Franklin Inst.*, **180**, 513, 711 ; **181**, 109, 243, 377, 525, 658, 805 ; **183**, 79, 211, 323, 593, 735.

EYMERS, J. G. & VAN SCHOUWENBURG, K. L. (1936). " A Quantitative Study of the Spectrum of the Light Emitted by *Photobacterium phosphoreum* and by some Chemiluminescent Reactions." *Enzym.*, **1**, 107.

EYMERS, J. G. & VAN SCHOUWENBURG, K. L. (1937). " Determination of O_2 Consumed in the Light-emitting Process of *Photobacterium phosphoreum*." *Enzym.*, **1**, 328.

EYMERS, J. G. & VAN SCHOUWENBURG, K. L. (1937). " Further Quantitative Data Regarding Spectra Connected with Bioluminescence." *Enzym.*, **3**, 235.

GIESE, A. C. & CHASE, A. M. (1940). " The Effect of Cyanide on *Cypridina* Luciferin." *J. cell. & comp. Physiol.*, **16**, 237.

GREENE, C. W. (1899). " The Phosphorescent Organ in the Toad Fish, *Porichthys notatus*." *J. Morph.*, **15**, 684.

GREENE, C. W. & GREENE, H. H. (1924). " Phosphorescence of *Porichthys notatus*, the Californian Singing Fish." *Amer. J. Physiol.*, **70**, 500.

HARVEY, E. N. (1920). "The Nature of Animal Light." Philadelphia, Lippincott.

HARVEY, E. N. (1924). "What Determines the Colour of the Light of Luminous Animals ? " *Amer. J. Physiol.*, **70**, 619.

HARVEY, E. N. (1926). "Inhibition of *Cypridina* Luminescence by Light with some Observations on Methylene Blue." *J. gen. Physiol.*, **10**, 103.

HARVEY, E. N. (1927). "On the Quanta of Light Produced and the Molecules of O_2 Utilised during *Cypridina* Luminescence." *J. gen. Physiol.*, **10**, 875.

HARVEY, E. N. (1940). "Living Light." Princeton, University Press.

HARVEY, E. N. & KERR, I. M. (1938). "Luminescence in Absence of Oxygen in the Ctenophore, *Mnemiopsis Leidyi.*" *J. cell. & comp. Physiol.*, **12**, 319.

HESS, W. N. (1922). "Origin and Development of the Light Organs of *Photurus Pennsylvanica.*" *J. Morph.*, **36**, 245.

HEYMANS, C. & MOORE, A. R. (1924). "Bioluminescence in *Pelagia noctiluca.*" *J. gen. Physiol.*, **6**, 273.

HICKLEY, C. F. (1924 ; 1926). "A New Type of Luminescence in Fishes." *J. Mar. Biol. Assn.*, **13**, 914 ; **14**, 495.

JOHNSON, F. H. (1939). "Total Luminescence of Bacterial Suspensions in Relation to the Reactions Concerned in Luminescence." *Enzym.*, **7**, 72.

JOHNSON, F. H. (1947). "Bacterial Luminescence." *Adv. in Enzym.*, **7**, 215.

JOHNSON, F. H., EYRING, H., STEBLAY, R., CHAPLIN, H., HUBER, C. & GHERARDI, G. (1945). "Nature and Control of Reactions in Bioluminescence." *J. gen. Physiol.*, **28**, 463.

JOHNSON, F. H. & HARVEY, E. N. (1937). "Osmotic and Surface Properties of Marine Luminous Bacteria." *J. cell. & comp. Physiol.*, **9**, 363.

JOHNSON, F. H., REXFORD, D. & HARVEY, E. N. (1949). "The Hypothetical Structure of Luciferin." *J. cell. & comp. Physiol.*, **33**, 133.

JOHNSON, F. H., VAN SCHOUWENBURG, K. L. & VAN DER BURG, A. (1939). "The Flash of Luminescence following Anaerobiosis of Luminous Bacteria." *Enzym.*, **7**, 195.

KAUTSKY, H. & NEITZKE, O. (1923). "Spektren emmissionsfähiger Stoffe bei Erregung durch Licht und durch chemische Reaktionen." *Z. Physik.*, **31**, 60.

KAUTSKY, H. & ZOCHER, H. (1923). "U. d. Wesen der Chemilumineszenz." *Z. Elektrochem.*, **29**, 308.

KLUYVER, A. J., VAN DER KERK, G. J. M. & VAN DER BURG, A. (1942). "Effect of Radiation on Light Emission by Luminous Bacteria." *Proc. K. Akad. Wetensch.*, **45**, 886, 962.

McELROY, W. D. (1947). "The Energy Source for Bioluminescence in an Isolated System." *Proc. Nat. Acad. Sci.*, **33**, 342.

McELROY, W. D. & BALLENTINE, R. (1944). "The Mechanism of Bioluminescence." *Proc. Nat. Acad. Sci. Wash.*, **30**, 377.

McELROY, W. D. & HARVEY, E. N. (1951). "Differences Among Species in the Response of Firefly Extracts to ATP." *J. cell. & comp. Physiol.*, **37**, 83.

McELROY, W. D. & STREHLER, B. L. (1949). "Factors Influencing the Response of the Bioluminescent Reaction to ATP." *Arch. Biochem.*, **22**, 420.

OKADA, Y. K. (1926). "Luminescence et Organe Photogène des Ostracodes." *Bull. Soc. Zool. de France*, **51**, 478.

PRATJE, A. (1921). "*Noctiluca miliaris.* Morphologie und Physiologie." *Archiv. f. Protistenk.*, **42**, 1.

SCHOEPFLE, G. M. (1940). "Kinetics of Luminescent Flashes in the Bacterium, *Achromobacter fischeri*, at Different Temperatures." *J. cell. & comp. Physiol.*, **16**, 341.

SNELL, P. A. (1932). "Control of Luminescence in the Male Lampyrid Firefly, *Photurus Pennsylvanica*, with Special Reference to the Effect of O_2-tension on Flashing." *J. cell. & comp. Physiol.*, **1**, 37.

STREHLER, B. L. & McELROY, W. D. (1949). "Purification of Firefly Luciferin." *J. cell. & comp. Physiol.*, **34**, 457.

VAN DER BURG, A. S. (1950). "Emission Spectra of Luminous Bacteria." *Biochim. Biophys. Acta*, **5**, 175.

VAN SCHOUWENBURG, K. L. & EYMERS, J. G. (1936). "Quantitative Relationship of the Light-emitting Process of Luminous Bacteria." *Nature*, **138**, 245.

CHAPTER XXII

PHOTOCHEMICAL ASPECTS OF VISION

Light as a Stimulus

IN an earlier chapter we have seen how the energy of light may be trapped for the purpose of photosynthesis, the prime source of energy in the living world ; in the present chapter we shall be concerned with the use of light-energy in another type of photochemical reaction, the *light-stimulus*. In the higher organisms this takes place in highly differentiated organs— eyes—which are essentially aggregates of light-sensitive cells with some form of dioptric apparatus to permit an exact localisation of the stimulus. The receptors make nervous connections with the brain so that the light-stimulus may govern or modify the motor activity of the animal. In lower forms, such as the earthworm, the light cells may be scattered in the superficial parts of the body, but their close relationship with the nervous system permits motor responses to these local light-stimuli.[1]

Action Spectra. It is reasonable to assume that the fundamental process

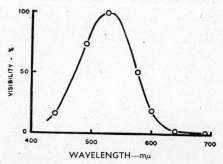

FIG. 279. The reciprocal of the energy, necessary to evoke a discharge of fixed magnitude from a single visual cell of *Limulus*, has been plotted against the wavelength of the stimulating light to give an action spectrum. (Hartline. *J. Opt. Soc. Amer.*)

involved in the response of an organism to light is a photochemical reaction taking place in the light-sensitive receptors. We can conclude, therefore, that these receptors contain a photosensitive substance, or at any rate a light-absorbing substance. We have already seen that the nature of a photochemically active substance may be inferred from the *action spectrum* of the tissue in which the reaction takes place, the argument being that, if the reaction depends on the absorption of light, the most efficient

[1] The unicellular organism, *Amœba*, responds to a source of light by moving away from it—it is *negatively phototropic*. The mechanism of this response has been elucidated by Mast ; the whole surface of *Amœba* is probably uniformly sensitive to light, in that irradiation of any part favours gelation ; since locomotion is achieved by the extension of a pseudopod, the tendency for one side of the organism to gelate will be reflected in movement *away* from this side, because the pseudopod will be formed in a region favouring solation (p. 11).

wavelength of the spectrum will be that which is absorbed most strongly. (It may be recalled that a comparison of the action spectrum with the absorption spectrum revealed the importance of accessory pigments in photosynthesis by certain algæ, p. 570.) The action spectra of a number of invertebrates have been studied, use being made of some phototropic response—as in the case of the clam, *Mya*, studied exhaustively by Hecht— or, alternatively, by measuring the action potentials in the optic nerve, as Hartline has done with the horse-shoe crab, *Limulus polyphemus*. Thus, if the intensities of different coloured lights, required to produce the same frequency of discharge in the optic nerve, are plotted against the

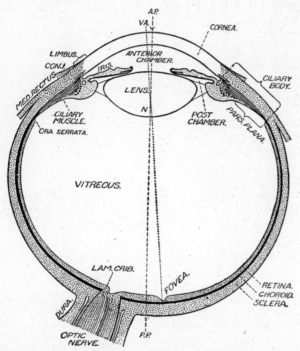

FIG. 280. Horizontal section of the eye. *P.P.*, posterior pole ; *A.P.*, anterior pole ; *V.A.*, visual axis. (Wolff. *Anatomy of the Eye and Orbit.* H. K. Lewis.)

wavelength, as in Fig. 279, a typical visual action spectrum, or *spectral sensitivity curve*, is obtained ; a maximum in the region of 5,300A being found with this eye. In the clam, *Mya*, Hecht found that a blue-green light of about 5,000A was the most effective ; and, in general, action spectra seem to fall into one of two classes, showing maxima at about 5,000A and 5,300–5,500A. These action spectra should conform to the absorption spectra of the photosensitive pigments in the respective light-sensitive organs ; the most exact correlation between the two has been established for the human eye, but before going into this in detail we must consider the nature of vision in man.

The Eye. Fig. 280 is a diagrammatic representation of a section through

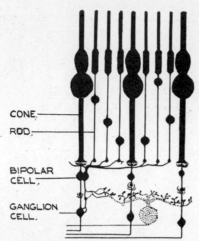

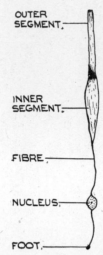

FIG. 281. Diagrammatic illustration of the essential structure of the retina as a series of nerve cells.

FIG. 282. Diagrammatic illustration of a rod.

the human eye, and Fig. 281 illustrates the structure of the retina, which consists essentially of three layers of cells—the receptors, the bipolar cells, and ganglion cells ; the receptors of the human eye (as with most vertebrates) are of two types, long thin *rods* and more robust *cones* ; these make synaptic connections with the *bipolar cells*, whilst the latter connect with *ganglion cells* with axons leading out of the eye as the *optic nerve*.

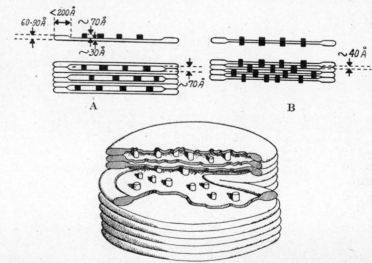

FIG. 284. Above : Two possibilities for the arrangement of the unit discs in the rod outer segment. A, Unit discs arranged in pairs. B, Unit discs arranged with uniform spacing throughout the segment. Below : Perspective scheme of the arrangement of the unit discs corresponding to alternative A, above. (Sjöstrand. *J. cell. & comp. Physiol.*)

PLATE XVI

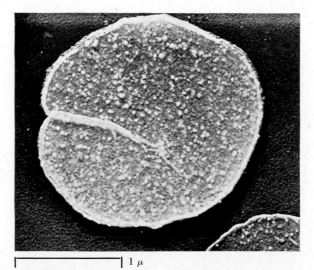

FIG. 283.   Electron-micrograph of disc, fragmented by ultra-sonic radiation,
from outer segment of guinea-pig's retinal rod. (Sjöstrand. *J. cell.
& comp. Physiol.*)

The rods are the receptors with which we shall be concerned here ; one is illustrated in Fig. 282 ; it consists of a cylindrical part, the *rod proper*, a conducting fibre and a nucleus, or *rod body*. The rod proper is the site of the chemical reactions concerned with vision ; it is divided into an *outer* and *inner segment* ; the outer segment probably contains the photo-sensitive substance, whilst the inner segment seems to be concerned with the restitutive processes taking place during and after a stimulus. The outer segments may be separated mechanically from the rest of the retina and have been studied by polarisation-optical and electron-microscopical techniques. According to W. J. Schmidt, the outer segment is built up of alternate protein and lipoid layers, *i.e.*, the structure along the length of the rod is similar to that along the radius of the axon sheath (p. 378). Sjöstrand treated the segments with sonic radiations, which broke them into discs some 70–80A thick at the edge (Fig. 283, Pl. XVI) ; with a length of about 17μ ; this means that the outer segment contains some 2,000 of these units tightly packed together. The discs have incisions, and it is possible that they are held together by a fibre running the length of the segment. Fig. 284 is a schematic representation of the possible structure.

Duplicity Theory of Vision

Action and Absorption Spectra. The fovea contains only cones, so that if the two types of receptor subserve different visual functions we may expect an essential difference according as an object is directly viewed, in which case its image is formed on the fovea, or indirectly, when a more peripheral part of the retina, containing both rods and cones, is used. Such, indeed, is the case, a finding that represents the main factual basis for the *duplicity theory of vision*, which postulates that the rods are concerned with night vision and the cones with day vision. The main facts of night vision may be briefly enumerated. On placing a subject in a dark room, at first the visual threshold is high, a light-stimulus of relatively high intensity being required to stimulate the " light sense " ;. as he remains in the dark the threshold falls progressively, so that by the end of half-an-hour, when he is said to be fully dark-adapted, the sensitivity to light may be a thousand times greater than before. Vision under these conditions is peripheral, the test stimulus being perceived only when its image falls off the fovea ; moreover, it is achromatic, in the sense that different wavelengths produce only a sensation of light and not of colour.[1] This does not mean, however, that a series of stimuli of different wavelength, but the same energy-content, will produce the same sensation of brightness ; on the contrary, under these conditions the different wavelengths appear differently bright, but not coloured. The action spectrum for the human dark-adapted eye, *i.e.*, for the rods, may be obtained, therefore, by plotting the number of quanta of the different wavelengths, required to stimulate the light-sense, against the wavelength.

[1] On raising the intensity of a coloured stimulus a point is reached when a sensation of colour is obtained, *i.e.*, the *chromatic threshold* has been crossed ; at about this level of intensity the cones are being stimulated.

In general, the reciprocal of this number of quanta is plotted, so that the *efficiencies of the different wavelengths in threshold stimulation* are shown, as in Fig. 285. It will be seen that the most effective wavelength is in the blue-green, at 5,000A, whilst red and violet lights are much less efficient. It is fair to deduce from this curve that the photo-pigment in the human rods has an absorption maximum at 5,000A. Extraction of the vertebrate eye with aqueous digitonin gives a magenta-coloured solution containing a light-sensitive pigment, called by Kühne *visual purple* or *rhodopsin* ; the relative amounts of this substance obtainable from different eyes correlated fairly well with the relative numbers of rods (*e.g.*, the guinea-pig retina is almost a pure rod retina whilst that of the chicken has mainly cones ; very little visual purple is extractable from the latter type of retina). The absorption spectrum of a purified solution of visual purple has been studied by a number of workers, with excellent

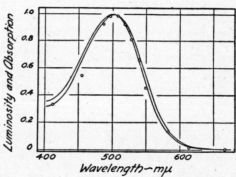

FIG. 285. Action spectrum for the human dark-adapted eye. The *plotted points* are the reciprocals of the number of quanta required to stimulate vision for the different wavelengths, the value for 5,000A being put equal to unity. The points have been corrected for variations in the transmission of light by the ocular media with different wavelengths. The *curves* are the percentage absorption spectra of visual purple for two different concentrations of the pigment. (Hecht, Shlaer & Pirenne. *J. gen. Physiol.*)

agreement, the maximum occurring at 5,000A. (In Fig. 285 both rod-sensitivity and visual purple-absorption have been plotted together, the points being those for rod sensitivity, and the actual lines representing the absorption of light by two different concentrations of visual purple.) The evidence that visual purple is directly concerned with rod vision is therefore very strong.

Chemical Reactions of Visual Purple

The nature of the reactions that visual purple undergoes in the rods is not clearly understood. Kühne, in 1878, observed that, on exposure to light, visual purple solutions went first yellow and then white ; more recently the stages in this conversion of visual purple to colourless products have been analysed by Wald and Bliss in America, and by Lythgoe in England. Lythgoe & Quilliam showed that the first product to be formed on exposure of visual purple solutions to light was a substance, *transient orange,* which was rapidly transformed in the dark to a yellow substance, *indicator yellow,* which was given this name because, in alkaline solution, it was pale yellow but changed to a deep chrome yellow in acid solution ; in the latter medium (*e.g.,* pH 4·9), indicator yellow is unstable and is transformed to colourless products. According to Lythgoe's results, light is necessary to form transient orange, all other products resulting from thermal or dark-reactions. Wald extracted retinæ at different stages of exposure to light ; he found that, after exposure just long enough to produce a yellow colour, a substance which he called *retinene,* and which he identified as a carotenoid related to vitamin A, could be extracted with mild reagents like petroleum ether ; if exposure to light was continued, however, the amount of extractable retinene decreased whilst vitamin A made its appearance, and there was little doubt that retinene was being converted to this substance. Moreover, regeneration of visual purple from vitamin A took place in the retina on maintaining it in the dark. If the retina was not exposed to light at all, *i.e.,* if it was extracted in the dark-adapted state, no retinene was obtainable with petroleum ether, although a more vigorous extractive, such as chloroform, was effective. Wald therefore suggested that the action of light was to loosen retinene in the visual purple molecule (or possibly to break it off), thereby allowing its extraction with petroleum ether. Continued exposure to light—by preventing the regeneration of visual purple from retinene that would otherwise occur—allowed a further thermal process to proceed, namely the conversion of retinene to vitamin A. These results form the basis of what has come to be called the *Wald cycle.*

How are we to relate Wald's and Lythgoe's findings ? Visual purple is a protein, presumably fairly strongly attached to the rods, since digitonin must be used to extract it ; Hecht & Pickels have estimated its molecular weight to be 270,000 ; and from a study of the optical density of a solution containing a known amount by weight, Broda, Goodeve & Lythgoe computed a " molecular weight per chromophore," or " carrier weight," of about 26,500 or less. Thus, if we accept Hecht & Pickels' figure of 270,000, this means a large protein molecule containing some ten chromophore groups responsible for the absorption of visible light.[1] The most likely relationship between the various coloured and colourless products is that suggested by Bliss as follows :—

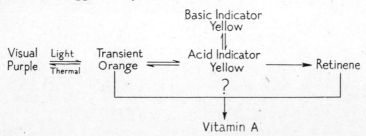

[1] Recently Weale has drawn attention to the fact that the molecular weight of a substance may be computed from an equation derived by Houston, relating the wavelength of maximal absorption with a number of experimentally determined variables and universal constants. Using this equation, Weale arrives at a value of 45,600, much

According to Bliss's results, retinene may be obtained from acid indicator yellow in a bleached solution of visual purple by the addition of methanol and subsequent extraction with petroleum ether ; after about ten hours the solution at pH 3·9 contains very little indicator yellow, whilst large amounts of retinene are still extractable. Bliss showed, moreover, that transient orange does not give retinene.

We may therefore regard the photochemical events in the light-stimulus as the absorption of a quantum of light by visual purple ; this rapidly produces transient orange which itself is rapidly transformed to indicator yellow, both changes involving reactions in the chromophore group, but not such as to split this group from the protein carrier. Presumably the energy liberated in one or other of these chemical events is transmitted to the rod to initiate the visual stimulus. Retinene and vitamin A are both substances of low molecular weight and thus represent products of fission of the visual purple molecule ; they are probably not connected directly with the primary stimulating action of light. The retinæ of diurnal animals are, however, subjected for long periods to bright illumination, so that it is very likely that most of the visual purple is, under these conditions, in the bleached condition, the chromophore group having been split off and converted to vitamin A.

Significance of Dark-Adaptation.   Visual purple is photosensitive ; it not only absorbs light in the process leading to excitation of the rod, but undergoes chemical change.[1] The phenomena of dark-adaptation are therefore mainly, if not completely, explicable on the basis of the necessity for the regeneration of the visual purple, bleached during previous exposure of the eye to light. Thus, if the sensitivity of the rods is a direct function of the concentration of visual purple in them, the rods, immediately after a period of light-adaptation, are insensitive to light, the threshold in these circumstances being determined, in a mixed retina, by the cones. As the period in the dark increases, the amount of visual purple extractable from the retina rises (this was found by Tansley, and later by Peskin, in the frog) and the sensitivity of the rods runs a parallel course, so that, in the completely dark-adapted eye, sensitivity and concentration of visual purple are at their maxima. If this is true, dark-adaptation may be described as a *peripheral* phenomenon ; it is determined by events in the receptors, rather than in the central nervous system. An excellent confirmation of this viewpoint is provided by the studies of Hartline & McDonald on the action potentials in single fibres of the optic nerve of *Limulus*, the horseshoe crab. In Fig. 286, the logarithm of the stimulus, necessary to evoke a discharge of fixed

---

smaller than that of Hecht & Pickels. As Weale points out, the Svedberg sedimentation method, employed by Hecht & Pickels, may give large errors in the presence of digitonin (required to extract the visual purple), since this substance can form polymers of very high molecular weight or, alternatively, may aggregate individual visual purple molecules into larger units. If Weale is right, there will be only two chromophore groups per molecule, a number at which Collins & Morton have arrived by an independent argument.

[1] It is worth noting that the photochemical reaction in which visual purple participates is *not* an example of photodynamic action, since it is unaffected by anaerobiosis (Chase & Hagan, 1943).

magnitude, has been plotted against time in the dark after the eye had been light-adapted ; and it will be seen that a nearly thousand-fold increase in sensitivity results from 100 minutes of dark-adaptation. The purely photochemical interpretation of adaptation has been developed by Hecht, who considered that the sensitivity of the eye was determined by the steady state in the reaction :—

$$\text{Visual Purple} \underset{\text{Dark}}{\overset{\text{Light}}{\rightleftharpoons}} \text{Bleached Products}$$

the visual purple bleached by light being regenerated by a thermal reaction.

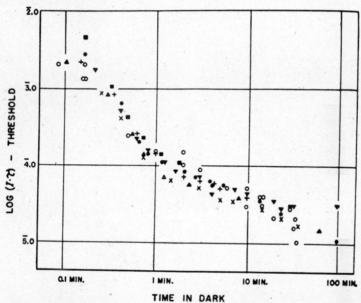

FIG. 286. Dark-adaptation of a single receptor in the eye of *Limulus*. The ordinates are the energies necessary to evoke a response of fixed magnitude in a single fibre of the optic nerve ; the abscissæ are the times after a light-adapting exposure of the eye. Note that the energy necessary to evoke the response decreases with time in the dark, *i.e.*, the receptor becomes more sensitive. (Hartline & McDonald. *J. cell. & comp. Physiol.*)

An effective light-stimulus, according to this view, was one that caused the decomposition of a definite amount of visual purple, *i.e.*, pushed the equilibrium over to the right. On the basis of simple reaction kinetics Hecht was able to show that changes in sensitivity at different levels of brightness were in general accord with this scheme. The most recent studies of dark-adaptation, following various preliminary periods of light-adaptation, have cast some doubt on the validity of this simple mechanism, however ; and it would seem that nervous influences cannot be entirely excluded from dark-adaptation phenomena.

Minimal Effective Stimulus

According to Dartnall, Goodeve & Lythgoe, visual purple solutions are bleached with a quantum efficiency of unity ; and the suggestion naturally arises that the minimum number of quanta required to excite a rod is also unity. Hecht, Shlaer & Pirenne were the first to estimate this minimum : they found that, in a dark-adapted human, the minimum amount of energy contained in a flash, such that it could be perceived six times out of ten presentations, was some 54 to 148 quanta. They computed that some 4 per cent. of the incident light was reflected from the cornea, some 50 per cent. absorbed by the ocular media, and at least 80 per cent. of the

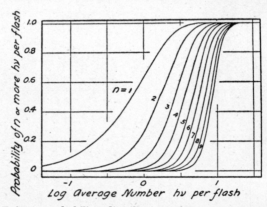

FIG. 287. Poisson probability distributions. For any average number of quanta (*hv*) per flash, the ordinates give the probabilities that the flash will deliver to the retina *n* or more quanta, depending on the value assumed for *n*. (Hecht, Shlaer & Pirenne. *J. gen. Physiol.*)

remainder passed through the retina without being absorbed by the rods. The range of useful light was therefore some 5–14 quanta. The flashes fell on an area containing some 500 rods, so that the probability that more than one rod received a quantum was negligible ; consequently, some 5–14 rods had to receive a single quantum in order to evoke the sensation of light. This implied a process of synaptic summation, the stimulated rods converging to the same bipolar cell, excitation of the latter occurring only when a certain number of discharges (5–14) from the separate rods reached it.[1] Energy corresponding to five quanta is an extremely small amount, so small that fluctuations in the number of quanta in a flash, imposed by the uncertainty principle, become significant. Thus, in the region of the threshold, a flash that is presented once and recognised, is not necessarily seen at the next presentation ; this variability in the threshold had been recognised for a long time, and ascribed to a variation in the physiological factors ; Hecht, Shlaer & Pirenne, however, pointed out that the variability could be explained by fluctuations in the stimulus, since the number of quanta in a given flash could only be expressed as a

---

[1] That such a summation can occur is beyond doubt, both on histological and physiological grounds.

probability, not a certainty. By making use of this variability, these authors were able to estimate, by an independent method, the minimum number of quanta required to excite vision. For instance, let us suppose that n quanta are necessary ; the chance of seeing a flash depends, therefore, on the chance that this flash has n or more quanta in it. This probability can be calculated from the Poisson distribution :—

$$\mathbf{P}_n = a^n/e^a n$$

where $\mathbf{P}_n$ is the probability that the flash will yield n quanta, and a is the *average* number of quanta in a flash, *i.e.*, the number that all flashes would have if there were no quantum fluctuations. In Fig. 287 the probability that there will be n or more quanta in a flash has been plotted against the average number of quanta per flash ; it will be seen that the curves are characteristically different according as n varies. If, now, the

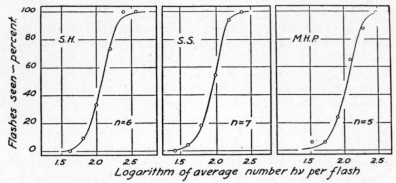

Fig. 288. Relationship between the average energy-content of a flash of light (in number of quanta) and the frequency with which it is seen by three observers. Each point represents 50 flashes, except for S.H. where the number is 35. The curves are the Poisson distributions of Fig. 287 for values of n equal to 5, 6, and 7. (Hecht, Shlaer & Pirenne. *J. gen. Physiol.*)

probability of seeing a flash depends only on the probability that this flash has a certain number, n, or more, quanta in it, the curve obtained by plotting the *probability of seeing* against the average number of quanta per flash, a, should have the same general form, and its exact shape will be given by the *actual* number of quanta necessary. For example, if only one is necessary the rise in the curve will be gradual, whilst if n is 9 the rise will be very steep. In Fig. 288 these frequency-of-seeing curves have been plotted for three observers, the points being frequencies-of-seeing whilst the lines have been computed from the Poisson equation as in Fig. 287 ; it will be seen that, according to the subject, a number of 5–7 quanta represents the minimum.

The same statistical approach can be made to a number of other visual phenomena ; thus, if both the intensity and time of a flash are varied, the threshold stimulus may be expressed as a function of these two variables (*e.g.*, over a certain range the product $I \times t$ is constant) ; the nature of this function may be computed independently, on the basis of quantum theory, on the assumption of a minimum number of quanta for the effective stimulus. Bouman & Van der Velden, on this basis, found that the best fit of their data could be obtained with a minimum number of two, which had to be absorbed within a definite time-interval of 0·02 sec.

Further Chemical Aspects

Retinene-Reductase. Before passing to a brief consideration of cone vision, we may return to the subject of the chemistry of the photo-pigment, visual purple. According to the studies of Morton and his school, retinene is vitamin A-aldehyde and may be prepared by oxidation of vitamin A. Retinene, so prepared, easily forms coloured complexes with proteins and amino-acids; these complexes are yellow and have indicator properties, consequently the conversion of indicator yellow to retinene is likely to be a reversible process.[1] The conversion of retinene to vitamin A has been shown by Bliss to require an enzyme; thus extracts of visual purple from alum-treated retinæ failed to yield vitamin A, but addition of an extract of fresh retinæ allowed all the retinene present to be converted to vitamin A. Recently Wald & Hubbard have investigated this transformation in detail. They have shown that the conversion of retinene to vitamin A does not take place in the isolated rod outer segments (which contain the visual purple); thus the outer segments could be separated mechanically from the rest of the retina, and exposure of a suspension of these outer segments to light converted the visual purple to retinene, but no vitamin A was formed. A suspension of crushed retinæ, added to the outer segments, immediately allowed the production of vitamin A to proceed. Clearly, the isolated outer segment lacks some factor necessary for the reduction of retinene; this water-soluble factor was shown to be stable after boiling and was therefore unlikely to be a protein; Wald & Hubbard supposed it to be a co-enzyme, capable of giving up hydrogen in the reduction process and acting in conjunction with a more specific enzyme, *retinene-reductase*, located in the outer segment. Such a co-enzyme could be *reduced cozymase*—$DPN.H_2$—an important element in the complex series of reactions resulting in the conversion of glycogen to lactic acid; and it was shown that this substance, added to a light-exposed suspension of rod outer segments, allowed the conversion of retinene to vitamin A. The reaction may therefore be written :—

$$\underset{\text{(retinene)}}{C_{19}H_{27}CHO} + \underset{\text{(reduced cozymase)}}{DPN.H_2} \xrightarrow{\overset{\text{retinene}}{\text{reductase}}} \underset{\text{(vitamin A)}}{C_{19}H_{27}CH_2OH} + \underset{\text{(cozymase)}}{DPN}$$

Presumably the DPN (diphosphopyridine nucleotide) is reduced back to $DPN.H_2$ by reaction with a derivative of fructose diphosphate, as in muscle. The reduction of retinene to vitamin A, described by Wald & Hubbard, was irreversible; Bliss (1949) has investigated the trans-formation further, and has shown that a reversible reduction can be

[1] Morton considered indicator yellow to be an adventitious product in the visual cycle, formed from retinene and a protein in the retina; this view has been opposed by Dartnall, who favours the view that indicator yellow, in an activated condition, transmits energy to the rod. More recently Morton (Collins & Morton, 1950) has come round to this point of view.

brought about by the DPN-specific alcohol dehydrogenase from liver. The demonstration of the reversibility of the retinene-vitamin A transformation therefore suggests that the regeneration of visual purple from vitamin A need not go in a closed cycle, as indicated earlier ; instead, the vitamin A may be reduced to retinene which then may react with protein to form visual purple.

Porphyropsin. Visual purple has been extracted from all the vertebrate eyes examined ; in fresh-water fishes, however, the absorption of the " visual purple " has a maximum at 5,220A. Wald therefore uses visual purple as a generic name to include *rhodopsin*, the pigment with an absorption maximum at 5,000A found in marine fishes, mammals, etc., and *porphyropsin*, the pigment with a maximum at 5,220A. Porphyropsin goes through a similar visual cycle to that of rhodopsin, but the retinene and vitamin A extracted from the bleached retina are different, their absorption maxima being correspondingly shifted by 200 to 230A towards the red ; they are called retinene$_2$ and vitamin A$_2$. Euryhaline fishes have mixtures of both rhodopsin and porphyropsin in their retinæ, and their retinenes and vitamins A are correspondingly mixed.

Cephalopsin. Studies on invertebrate photo-pigments have been few, but have brought to light a most interesting characteristic. Bliss extracted a pigment from the squid eye and found an absorption spectrum very similar to that of vertebrate visual purple, the maximum being at 4,950A. Similar pigments were found in the eyes of the blue crab and the horse-shoe crab. The remarkable feature of these photo-pigments was their stability in light ; vertebrate visual purple, as we have seen, is decomposed by light, whereas the squid visual purple gives only a very small amount of bleached products—retinene and vitamin A—on illumination. If, however, the extracts are treated with protein denaturants, such as formaldehyde, they become photosensitive, releasing large amounts of indicator yellow, retinene, and vitamin A after exposure to light. Thus the invertebrate visual purple, to which Bliss has given the name *cephalopsin*, appears to play the role of *photosensitiser* in the visual process, in contrast to the vertebrate visual purple which *participates* in the visual chemical reactions, and is converted to new products after the absorption of light. We must remember, however, that the invertebrate *Limulus* eye exhibits the phenomenon of dark-adaptation (Fig. 286) in just the same manner as the vertebrate eye ; consequently, until more is known about adaptation, it would be unsafe to say that the invertebrate photo-pigment is unchanged after irradiation, otherwise it would be ready for reaction immediately after a light-stimulus, and the phenomenon of dark-adaptation would not be manifest in this type of eye.

Photopic Vision

Vision in most vertebrates is *duplex* in nature, mediated by rods and cones ; the latter are the less sensitive,[1] consequently studies on the

---

[1] Baumgardt has recently argued that rods and cones have about equal sensitivity, the low threshold in scotopic vision being due to the much larger numbers of rods in synaptic relation with a single bipolar cell, resulting in greater possibilities of spatial summation, than is the case with the cones.

absolute threshold are studies of rod vision. At levels of brightness corresponding to about full moonlight we have a transition zone in which both rods and cones are functional; and, beyond this, the rods are thought to be non-functional because their visual purple has been completely bleached. Vision at high levels of brightness is thus presumed to be a function of the cones; and this type of vision is characterised, moreover, by the ability to discriminate the different wavelength bands as colour sensations. Space will not permit a study of the phenomena of colour vision, bedevilled as the subject is with conflicting theories. From the photochemical viewpoint we need only emphasise that the discrimination of two stimuli, in virtue of both differences in intensity and differences in colour (*i.e.*, wavelength), requires the simultaneous excitation of receptors of several sorts. It is reasonable to assume that these hypothetical receptors have different photosensitive pigments, and therefore different action spectra. The presence of well-defined photosensitive pigments in the cones has never yet been established, and, until this is done, the interpretation of colour vision must remain on a speculative basis.

We may note, however, that Wald has prepared extracts of the predominantly cone retina of the chicken; the absorption spectra indicated the presence of a pigment, *iodopsin*. If Dartnall is right, the difficulty in establishing the presence of cone pigments in retinæ, and the low sensitivity of the cones to light, are due to the same cause, namely the very small quantities of the pigments in the cones by comparison with the quantity of visual purple in the rods. It is of great interest that Dartnall has obtained evidence for the presence of two new pigments (besides porphyropsin) in the tench's retina; he calls them provisionally *visual yellow 2* and *visual red*.

References

BALL, S., COLLINS, F. D., DALVI, P. D. & MORTON, R. A. (1949). "Reactions of Retinene with Amino Compounds." *Biochem. J.*, **45**, 304.

BALL, S., COLLINS, F. D. & MORTON, R. A. (1948). "Chemistry of Visual Processes." *Nature*, **161**, 424.

BALL, S., GOODWIN, T. W. & MORTON, R. A. (1948). "Preparation of Retinene$_1$— Vitamin A Aldehyde." *Biochem. J.*, **42**, 516.

BALL, S. & MORTON, R. A. (1949). "Vitamin A and Retinene in Relation to Photopic Vision." *Biochem. J.*, **45**, 298.

BLISS, A. F. (1943). "Derived Photosensitive Pigments from Invertebrate Eyes." *J. gen. Physiol.*, **26**, 361.

BLISS, A. F. (1946). "Chemistry of Daylight Vision." *J. gen. Physiol.*, **29**, 277.

BLISS, A. F. (1946). "Photolytic Lipids from Visual Pigments." *J. gen. Physiol.*, **29**, 299.

BLISS, A. F. (1948). "Retinene and Indicator Yellow." *Nature*, **162**, 661.

BLISS, A. F. (1948). "Mechanism of Retinal Vitamin A Formation." *J. biol. Chem.*, **172**, 165.

BLISS, A. F. (1948). "Absorption Spectra of Visual Purple of the Squid and its Bleaching Products." *J. biol. Chem.*, **176**, 563.

BLISS, A. F. (1949). "Reversible Enzymic Reduction of Retinene to Vitamin A." *Biol. Bull.*, **97**, 221.

BLISS, A. F. (1950). "Pigment Layer Factor in Visual Purple Regeneration." *Fed. Proc.*, **9**, 12.

BOUMAN, M. A. & VAN DER VELDEN, H. A. (1947). "The Two-quanta Explanation of the Dependence of the Threshold Values and Visual Acuity on the Visual Angle and the Time of Observation." *J. Opt. Soc. Amer.*, **37**, 908.

BRODA, E. E., GOODEVE, C. F. & LYTHGOE, R. J. (1940). "The Weight of the Chromophore Carrier in the Visual Purple Molecule." *J. Physiol.*, **98**, 397.

CHASE, A. M. & HOGAN, W. H. (1943). "Photochemical and Thermal Reactions of Visual Purple in Absence of Oxygen." *J. cell. & comp. Physiol.*, **21**, 65.

COLLINS, F. D. & MORTON, R. A. (1950). "Studies on Rhodopsin. 1. Methods of Extraction and the Absorption Spectrum." *Biochem. J.*, **47**, 3.

COLLINS, F. D. & MORTON, R. A. (1950). "Studies on Rhodopsin. 2. Indicator Yellow." *Biochem. J.*, **47**, 10.

COLLINS, F. D. & MORTON, R. A. (1950). "Studies on Rhodopsin. 3. Rhodopsin and Transient Orange." *Biochem. J.*, **47**, 18.

DARTNALL, H. J. A. (1948). "Visual Purple and the Photopic Luminosity Curve." *Brit. J. Ophthal.*, **32**, 793.

DARTNALL, H. J. A. (1948). "Indicator Yellow and Retinene." *Nature*, **162**, 222.

DARTNALL, H. J. A. (1950). "New Photosensitive Pigments from the Tench Retina." *Nature*, **166**, 207.

DARTNALL, H. J. A., GOODEVE, C. F. & LYTHGOE, R. J. (1936). "Quantitative Analysis of the Photochemical Bleaching of Visual Purple Solutions in Monochromatic Light." *Proc. Roy. Soc.*, *A*, **156**, 158.

DAVSON, H. (1949). "Physiology of the Eye." London, Churchill.

GLOVER, J., GOODWIN, T. W. & MORTON, R.A. (1948). "Conversion *in vivo* of Vitamin A Aldehyde (Retinene) to Vitamin A." *Biochem. J.*, **43**, 109.

HARTLINE, H. K. (1940). "Nerve Messages in the Fibres of the Visual Pathway." *J. Opt. Soc. Amer.*, **30**, 239.

HARTLINE, H. K. & MCDONALD, P. R. (1947). "Light and Dark Adaptation of Single Photoreceptor Elements in the Eye of *Limulus*." *J. cell. & comp. Physiol.*, **30**, 225.

HECHT, S. (1921). "Relation Between the Wavelength of Light and its Effect on the Photosensory Process." *J. gen. Physiol.*, **3**, 375.

HECHT, S. (1924). "Intensity Discrimination and the Stationary State." *J. gen. Physiol.*, **6**, 355.

HECHT, S. (1924). "Visual Discrimination of Intensity and the Weber-Fechner Law." *J. gen. Physiol.*, **7**, 235.

HECHT, S. (1942). "The Chemistry of Visual Substances." *Ann. Rev. Biochem.*, **11**, 465.

HECHT, S. & PICKELS, E. G. (1938). "Sedimentation Constant of Visual Purple." *Proc. Nat. Acad. Sci. Wash.*, **24**, 172.

HECHT, S., SHLAER, S. & PIRENNE, M. H. (1942). "Energy, Quanta, and Vision." *J. gen. Physiol.*, **25**, 819.

LAURENS, H. & HOOKER, H. D. (1920). "Sensibility of *Volvox* to Wavelengths of Equal Energy Content." *J. exp. Zool.*, **30**, 345.

LYTHGOE, R. J. (1937). "Absorption Spectra of Visual Purple and of Indicator Yellow." *J. Physiol.*, **89**, 331.

LYTHGOE, R. J. & QUILLIAM, J. P. (1938). "Thermal Decomposition of Visual Purple." *J. Physiol.*, **93**, 24.

LYTHGOE, R. J. & QUILLIAM, J. P. (1938). "Relation of Transient Orange to Visual Purple and Indicator Yellow." *J. Physiol.*, **94**, 399.

MAST, S. O. (1938). "Factors Involved in the Process of Orientation of Lower Organisms in Light." *Biol. Rev.*, **13**, 186.

MORTON, R. A. & GOODWIN, T. W. (1944). "Preparation of Retinene *in vitro*." *Nature*, **153**, 405.

PESKIN, J. C. (1942). "Regeneration of Visual Purple in the Living Animal." *J. gen. Physiol.*, **26**, 27.

SCHNEIDER, E. E., GOODEVE, C. F. & LYTHGOE, R. J. (1939). "The Spectral Variation of the Photosensitivity of Visual Purple." *Proc. Roy. Soc.*, *A*, **170**, 102.

SJÖSTRAND, F. S. (1949). "An Electron Microscope Study of the Retinal Rods of the Guinea Pig Eye." *J. cell. & comp. Physiol.*, **33**, 383.

TANSLEY, K. (1931). "Regeneration of Visual Purple : the Relation to Dark Adaptation and Night Blindness." *J. Physiol.*, **71**, 442.

VISSCHER, J. P. & LUCE, R. H. (1928). "Reactions of the Cyprid Larvæ of Barnacles to Light with Special Reference to Spectral Colours." *Biol. Bull.*, **54**, 336.

WALD, G. (1935). "Carotenoids and the Visual Cycle." *J. gen. Physiol.*, **19**, 351.

WALD, G. (1937). "Visual Purple System in Fresh-water Fishes." *Nature*, **139**, 1017.

WALD, G. (1937). "Photolabile Pigments of the Chicken Retina." *Nature*, **140**, 545.

WALD, G. (1938). "On Rhodopsin in Solution." *J. gen. Physiol.*, **21**, 795.

WALD, G. (1939). "The Porphyropsin Visual System." *J. gen. Physiol.*, **22**, 775.

WALD, G. (1941).   " Vitamin A in Invertebrate Eyes."   *Amer. J. Physiol.*, **133**, 479.
WALD, G. (1945/46).   " The Chemical Evolution of Vision."   *Harvey Lectures*, **41**, 117.
WALD, G. (1948).   " Synthesis from Vitamin-A_1 of Retinene$_1$, etc."   *J. gen. Physiol.*,
     31, 489.
WALD, G. (1950).   " The Interconversion of the Retinenes and Vitamins A *in vitro*."
     Biochim. Biophys. Acta, **4**, 215.
WALD, G. & HUBBARD, R.   " The Reduction of Retinene to Vitamin-A *in vitro*."
     J. gen. Physiol., **32**, 367.
WEALE, R. (1949).   " Absorption Spectra, Molecular Weights, and Visual Purple."
     Nature, **163**, 916 ; **164**, 959.
WHITE, G. M. (1924).   " Reactions of the Larvæ of the Shrimp and Squid to Mono-
     chromatic Light."   *Biol. Bull.*, **47**, 265.

INDEX

PRINTED IN GREAT BRITAIN BY THE WHITEFRIARS PRESS LTD.
LONDON AND TONBRIDGE